PREFACE

Rightly known as the 'bible' of the pumping industry, the PUMPING MANUAL is a tome of practical information and data on the selection, installation, operation and maintenance of industrial pumps for most applications. The Contents follow a logical sequence of pump evolution, performance and characteristics, pump types, pumping practice and operation, pump ancillaries, duties, services and applications, finishing with a comprehensive editorial index. Nowhere else can be found in one reference work so much fundamental, essential and useful reference material. It is an indispensable part of the bookshelf for any engineer or technician whose responsibilities encompass a pumping process, whether it be water supply, irrigation, drainage, chemical and refining, oil and gas, electrical power, nuclear power, pulp and paper, food and beverage, sewage and sludge, slurry, fire or the like.

This eighth edition has been completely, reworked, updated and extended to incorporate the latest technological developments and new chapters include: calculations, area ratio, statistical analysis, cavitation and recirculation, progressing cavity pumps, hydraulic drive downhole pumps, positive displacement pumps, canned motor pumps, plastic pumps, mechanical face seals, bellow seals, prime movers, *etc.* Within the Section on Applications, new chapters have been added on: chemical process and refinery pumps, power generation pumps and flue gas desulphurisation.

The Trade & Technical Press Limited are also the Publishers of the monthly technical journal, 'World Pumps' which, as its title indicates, is subscribed to by pump users and buyers throughout the world.

The Publishers

ACKNOWLEDGMENTS

American Petroleum Institute
H.H.Anderson
M.V.Bevan
BPMA
British Standards Institute
D.Burgoyne
CAT Pumps
A.W.Chesterton Inc
A.Coombs
John Crane International
Dresser Industries
E.I.Dupont de Nemours
Duriron Co
Europump
Flexibox International
Dr.D.F.Florjancic
Flygt Pumps
Franklin Electric
W.H.Fraser
D.Fussele
Graco Inc
Hayward-Tyler
IHC Holland
Ingersoll Rnad
I.J.Karassik
Kinder Janes Engineers
Klein, Shanzlin & Becker
McGraw Edison Co
O.J.Mizera
Mono Pumps
E.Müller
National Engineering Laboratory
J.Nicholls
Patterson Pump Co
Plenty Mirrlees
E.Potts
Rheinhütte
E.G. & G.Sealol Ltd
Siemens AG
P.Spamer
SPP Group plc
Sulzer Brothers Ltd
VDMA
N.Wallace
Warman International
R.H.Warring
Weir Pumps plc
Wirth GmbH
Worthington Group

CONTENTS

ACKNOWLEDGMENTS – ILLUSTRATIONS AND TABLES

Page Number	Company
6,top	Worthington Pumps
7	Klein Schanzlin & Becker (KSB)
8	Weir Pumps Ltd
12,13,25	I.J.Karassik
15 to 20	BPMA
29	Weir Pumps Ltd
33	Mono Pumps Ltd
41,43	Sulzer Brothers Ltd
44	Hydraulic Institute, 14th Ed,1983
45	Albany Engineering Ltd
73 to 76	Demco Div,Cooper Industries
129	Sulzer Brothers Ltd
133	Pompes Guinard
136	Worthington Pumps
138	Lowara Pump Ltd
142,top	Chadburn Engineering Ltd
142,bottom	Ritz Pumpenfabrik
144,table	Tonka Flo Pumps Osmonics Inc
147	Rheinhütte
148	Sundstrand Fluid Handling
150,top	Tangie Engineering Ltd
150,bottom	Duijvelaar Pompen
153	Friedrich Köstner GmbH
154,top	Balcke-Durr
154,bottom	Andritz
156	Balcke-Durr
157,top	Mono Pumps
157,bottom	Allis Chalmers
162	Bombas Ideal
167,top	Reiss Engineering Co Ltd
167,bottom	Kamat Pumpen GmbH
172	Gasco Pumps Inc
175	Ajax Pumps
176	Gasco Pumps Inc
177	Kamat Pumpen
178	CAT Pumps
185	Kecol Pumps Ltd
186	Blagdon Pumps
187	Charles S.Madan

Page Number	Company
188	Wickham & Co Ltd
189	Graco UK Ltd
190	Depa (UK) Ltd
194,right	William R.Selwood Ltd
195	Kecol Pumps Ltd
196,top	Blagdon Pumps
196,bottom	Flotronic Controls Ltd
201	Lederle GmbH
206	Viking Pumps – Houdaille Inc
207	Worthington Pumps
208,211	Viking Pumps – Houdaille Inc
214	SSP Pumps Ltd
219	ITT Jabsco
220,top	Evro Johnson Pumps
220,bottom	SSP Pumps Ltd
222	SSP Pumps Ltd
235	Robbins Myers
236	Lederle GmbH
237 to 239	Mono Pumps Ltd
241	Eco Pump Corp
247	Albany Engineering Co Ltd
249,top	Micropump Corp
249,bottom	Totton Pump Ltd
250	Viking Pumps – Houdaille Inc
254,256	Foster Interspace Corp
259,260	Plenty Mirrlees Pumps
263 to 265	ITT Jabsco
268,269	Bredel BV
272,top	C.P.Instruments Co Ltd
272,bottom	Verder Vleuten BV
274,centre	Autoclude Ltd
276,bottom	Bredel BV
279	Tecstream OMG Ltd
280	Totton Pumps Ltd
282	Dia-Meter Pumm p Ltd
282,top	Pulsafeeder
282,bottom	Bran & Lüebe Ltd
285	Gorman-Rupp Industries
286	Metering Pumps Ltd

Page Number	Company
287	Graco Inc
290	Varisco Pompe
291,bottom	The Duriron Co Inc
293,top	MSP Ltd/Cospet
293,bottom	Finsbury Pumps Aqua Corp Ltd
296	Worthington Pumps
299	Hermetic Pumpen GmbH
300	Durco/Hayward Tyler
302	Fristam Pumps
304	Kestner Engineering Co
305	March/May, Fluid Transfer Systems
306	Sihi Ryaland Pumps
307 to 309	Hayward Tyler
310,top	Wilo Salmson Pumps
310,bottom	Lewa
311	Hermetic Pumpen GmbH
313	Nash Engineering
316	Fristam Ltd
319	Edwards High Vacuum Int
320	Nash Engineering
321	Balzers
323	Lederle GmbH
324	Elmira Machine Industries Inc
327	Pompes Guinard
330	Flygt Pumps
331	Deming Pumps
334,335,337	Weir Pumps Ltd
345	Duijvelaar Pompen
347	Sulzer Brothers Ltd
349,350	Appareils & Evaporateurs Kestner
352	Durco (Duriron Co Inc)
353	Shunk & EBE GmbH
356	Durco (Duriron Co Inc)
357,360	Vanton Pumps Ltd
361,left	Chem-Resist
361,right	Vanton Pumps Ltd
371	Mono Pumps
375,377	Sulzer Brothers Ltd
378,379,380	The Johnson Rubber Co
381	Adams & Co
390	Industrial & Marine Packings Ltd
391	Latty International
402	Flexibox International
403	John Crane International
406,bottom	Flexibox International
408,bottom	John Crane International
409,bottom	John Crane International
413,top	Borg Warner
414,415,416	Flexibox International
417,418	John Crane International
419	Flexibox International
420,top	John Crane International
420,bottom	E.G. & G.Sealol Ltd
425,top	John Crane International
426,left	Oy Safematic Ltd
426,right	Flexibox International
428,429,430,431	John Crane International
433	BW/IP International
435	E.G. & G.Sealol Ltd
436	Feodor Burgmann
439	E.G. & G.Sealol Ltd
440	John Crane International
449	Durco (Duriron Co Inc)
453	Sulzer Brothers Ltd

Page Number	Company
464	Scanpump
469,top	Optalign/Pruftechnik
469,bottom	Girdlestone Pumps Ltd
470,471	SSP Ltd
475	Henry Sykes & Hatz
493 to 497	Sulzer Brothers Ltd
502	George Meller Ltd
510,bottom	Hawker Siddeley Electric Motors Ltd
517	Hawker Siddeley Electric Motors Ltd
521,top	Perkins Engines
521,bottom	Finsbury Pumps
523	Volvo Penta
527	Combidrive Ltd
530	Sulzer Brothers Ltd
531,532	TASC Drives Ltd
533,left	Combidrive Ltd
533,right	Posiva
534	Posiva
537	Optalign/Pruftechnik
540,top	Plenty Pumps
542,Fig 4	S.J.Electro Systems Inc
543	Base Ten Systems Ltd
556,560	Grundfos Pumps Ltd
557,Fig 2	Sulzer Brothers Ltd
579,Fig 4	Sulzer Brothers Ltd
594,top	Selwood Pumps
594,bottom, left	Selwood Pumps
594,bottom, right	Sykes Pumps Ltd
595	Geho-Holthuis BV
599	Hayward-Tyler
603	Rheinhütte
605	Hayward Tyler
607	Tangie Engineering Ltd
610	Chemie & Filter
613 to 616	Chemie & Filter
617	Wallace & Tiernan
626	Sulzer Brothers Ltd
627	Mouvex Pompes
628,631	Stothert & Pitt Ltd
632,633	Sulzer Brothers Ltd
634	Rheinhütte/Siemens AG
635	Sulzer Brothers Ltd
636	Weir Pump Ltd
640,left	Hayward Tyler
640,Fig 4	Sulzer Brothers Ltd
642,top	Sulzer Brothers Ltd
642,bottom	Hayward Tyler
643	Hayward Tyler
650,Fig 4	Westinghouse Electric Corp
653	Sulzer Brothers Ltd
658	Midland Dairy Machines Ltd
659	Alpha Technical Services
663	Bredell BV
667	Campden Food Preservation Research Association
668,left	Totton Pumps Ltd
668,rigbht	ITT Jabsco
671,Fig 1	Graco Inc
671,Fig 2	Flux-Gerate GmbH
673	Girdlestone Pumps Ltd
674	Mouvex/Pompes

Page Number	Company
705	Putzmeister
707,left	Mono Pumps Ltd
707,right	The Haigh Engineering Co Ltd
710 to 722, all figs	Warman International Ltd
726	SPP Pumps Ltd
727	Godiva Fire Pumps Ltd
728	Duijvelaar Pompen
732	Peroni & CSpA
734,735	CAT Pumps Inc
736	CEW

Page Number	Company
680	VP Balco Pumps
683,Fig 3	IHC-Holland
6874	IHC-Holland
685,686	Holthuis BV
687,table 4	Geho Pumps/Holthuis BV
687,bottom	Wirth GmbH
688	Holthuis BV
689	Geho Pumps Holthuis BV
691	Putzmeister
694	Ritz Pumpenfabrik GmbH
704	Weir Pumps Ltd

Why not the best
in sealing technology?
Mechanical seals,
packings and
gaskets from
BURGMANN.
The No. 1.

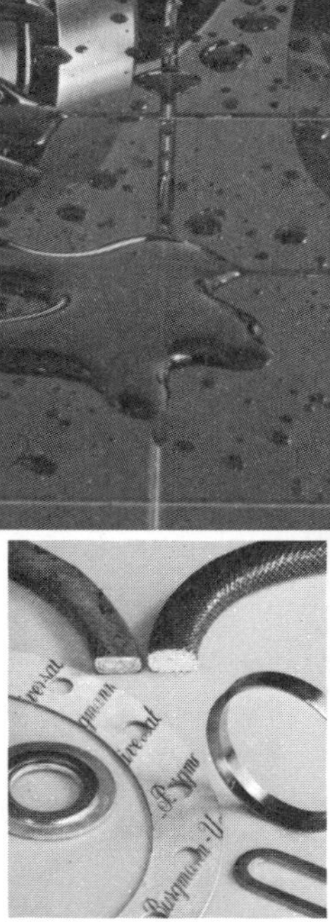

SECTION 1

Introduction

S.I. UNITS
PUMP EVOLUTION
PUMP TYPES (GENERAL)
FUTURE TRENDS

S.I. Units

THIS HANDBOOK is written for the benefit of all who have a practical interest and involvement with pumps and pumping applications.

The publishers have chosen to use both imperial measure and S.I. system of units due to the fact that in spite of intensive official efforts to popularise the use of the metric system, pure S.I. units on occasions do not lend themselves to the scale of figures encountered in the industrial process. The figures given in the Handbook are, therefore, neither exclusively metric nor imperial. Where possible every effort has been made to list the metric data first followed by the imperial equivalent in brackets.

The S.I. system of units are embodied in the pump specifications of the International Organization for Standardization (ISO) the International Electro Technical Commission, the British Standards Institution and the DIN.

S.I. is considered the official abbreviation of the French title 'Le Système International d'Unités' given to a coherent system of units selected from the metric system.

It is hoped that by adopting the use of both metric and imperial units, this Handbook will find greater application throughout the world and help to eliminate some of the ambiguity that has arisen over the adoption of S.I. units.

Typical examples here relate to the standard S.I. unit of pressure, the Pascal which corresponds to 0·000145 lb/in^2 which is not a satisfactory unit when used for centrifugal pumps. As a result the unit of bar often preferred (1 bar = 10^5) because the value is close to both metric atmosphere (1 kgf/cm^2 = 98066·50 Pa) and standard atmosphere (101325·0 Pa). However, it is not equal to either.

Other areas where confusion arises are in units of pressure, total head (performance) capacity and horsepower.

As a result, a list of 'Preferred Terms' to be used in the pumping industry is presented which, it is hoped, will be adopted by pump users, specifiers and manufacturers.

PUMP INDUSTRY PREFERRED TERMS

	Pump Industry Preferred Units				Pure S.I. Units	
Description	**Unit**	**Symbol**	**Dimension**	**Remarks**	**Unit**	**Symbol**
Length dimension (L)	metre	m	(L)	mm if necessary	metre	m
Area (A)	square metre	m^2	(L^2)	mm^2 if necessary	square metre	m^2
Velocity (v)	metre/second	m/s	($L \times T x^{-1}$)		metre/second	m/s
Volume (V)	cubic metre	m^3	(L^3)	litre optional if appropriate	cubic metre	m^3
Flow rate (Q)	cubic metre/hour	m^3/h	(L^3T^{-1})	litre/second if appropriate	cubic metre/second	m^3/s
Pressure (p)	bar	bar	($M \times L^{-1}T^{-2}$)	1 bar = 0·1 MPa	pascal	Pa
Stress (σ)	kilonewton/metre^2	kN/m^2	($m \times L^{-1}T^{-2}$)	bar is often used 1 bar = 100 kN/m^2	newton/m^2	N/m^2
Head (H), NPSH	metre	m	(L)		metre	m
Specific speed	$\frac{r/min \sqrt{m^3/h}}{H^{3/4}}$	n_s	($L^{3/4}T^{-3/2}$)	multiply pure S.I. unit by 3175 to arrive at industry preferred unit	$\frac{rad/s \sqrt{m^3/s}}{(g \times H)^{3/4}}$	n_s
Force	newton	N	($M \times L \times T^{-2}$)		newton	N
Power (P)	kilowatt	kW	($M \times L^2 \times T^{-3}$)	1 BHP = 0·746 kW	watt	W

Dynamic viscosity (μ)	centipoise	cP	$(M \times T^{-1}L^{-1})$	1 cP = 10^{-2} Ns/m^2	newton sec/m^2	Ns/m^2
Kinematic (v)	centistoke	cSt	(L^2T^{-1})	1 cSt = 10^{-6} m^2/s	metre^2/second	m^2/s
Vacuum	millibar	mbar	$(M \times L^{-1}T^{-2})$	1 bar = 750 mm Hg 1 mb = 100 pascal	pascal	Pa
Density (ρ)	kg/m^3		$(M \times L^{-3})$	tonne/m^3	kg/m^3	
Concentration	%	%		volume/total volume		
	%	%		mass/total mass		
					milligram/litre	mg/l
Temperature (Θ)	degree Celsius	°C	pure number		degree Celsius	°C
Efficiency (η)	%	%	pure number		%	
Speed (n)	revolutions/minute	r/min	(T^{-1})	rad/s = 9·55 r/min	radians/second	rad/s
Torque	newton metre	Nm	$(M \times L^2T^{-2})$		newton metre	Nm
Moment of inertia Mk^2	kilogram metre^2	kg m^2	$(M \times L^2)$	M = mass k = radius of gyration	kilogram metre^2	kg m^2

Pump Evolution

THE PUMP is probably the earliest form of machine and today is the second most common dynamic machine in use, the first being the electric motor.

The forerunner of all pumps is the Shadoof or cup-shaped pot mounted on the end of a counter weighted arm. Invented by the Egyptians somewhere around 2000 BC, it is still in use today in remote parts of the world, with an oil drum or petrol can replacing the original clay pot.

A definite step forward in the mechanization of pumping was the development of a lifting wheel carrying on the rim a number of buckets which dipped into a river and raised the water to an irrigation channel, the wheel being propelled by primitive gearing which, in turn, was driven by animal or human power. This bucket-lift principle was developed into multi-bucket systems and the paddle wheel configuration with diameters up to 10 metres or more to retain the required lift. The former proved the better 'mechanical' system since the turning wheel could be of small diameter, mounted as high as necessary, with no limit to the length of endless rope carrying the series of buckets.

Around 1000 BC, or slightly later, the Archimedean screw form of pump appeared – actually developed in Egypt again, not invented by Archimedes himself – with the spiral made from leather wrapped around a wooden spindle. The concept is exactly the same as the modern Archimedean screw pump, except that it appears mainly to have been used in fully-enclosed form with a circular surrounding casing constructed of wood.

During Roman times (250 to 0 BC) the first reciprocating pumps appeared and remained the main pump type in use for several centuries, operated by hand, animal, water or wind power. Mechanical skill developed and metals came more into use, but the limiting factor with all early pumps was the relatively low power available to operate them. The highest powers developed by windmills or waterwheels were in the order of 10 horsepower. There was also the fact to be faced that the reciprocating pump, which relied on suction could at best, only lift water some 10 metres and more often less. Bucket-type pumps thus continued to be the choice for 'high' lifts.

It was experimental work on suction and the production of a vacuum which lead to a form of steam driven vacuum generator or pump for water raising which was

XVI century drawing of Archimedian screw.

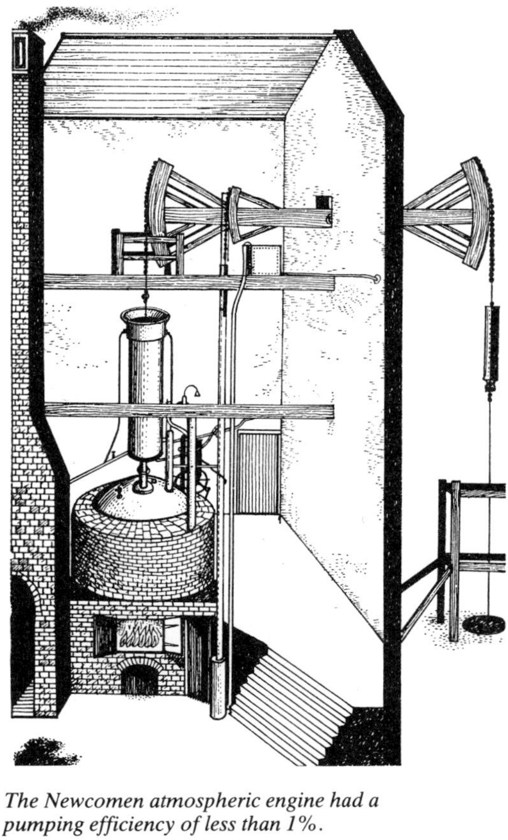

The Newcomen atmospheric engine had a pumping efficiency of less than 1%.

in fact an atmospheric engine or elementary form of steam engine. The practical steam engine itself evolved from this – and the era of large scale pumping emerged.

Right up until the latter part of the last century the reciprocating pump dominated the field, simply because there were no real alternatives. It was developed in increasing sizes and increasing efficiencies. The first driven by beam engines and then later at higher speeds by much more efficient reciprocating steam engines. More than 100 years ago 1000 horsepower installations were commonplace in water works, with pumps achieving efficiencies of 90%.

The latter part of the 19th century proved particularly significant with the development of the steam turbine as a high speed, high power source and the first turbine or centrifugal pump, built by Osborne Reynolds in 1875. The two went together. The centrifugal pump was more compact with only rotary rather than reciprocating motion involved. As a consequence, it could readily be driven faster than a reciprocating pump. No longer was it necessary to build a bigger pump at a faster speed, although for some time the efficiency of a turbine driven centrifugal pump remained less than that of a reciprocating pump. Also it had to be designed for a particular delivery end head with efficiency falling off markedly if operated at other than its design point. Nevertheless, appearance of the centrifugal pump and subsequently mixed flow and axial flow derivatives, sounded the death knell of the reciprocating pump where large volumes of water had to be dealt with. Then the appearance of the electric motor as an alternative source of pump power the centrifugal pump really came into its own in an even wider range of sizes and designs for a variety of different duties.

The modern centrifugal pump now dominates the world pump market, particularly where large deliveries are required. From the 1000 horsepower practical limit of reciprocating pumps of a century ago, some of the centrifugal giants of to-day are of 150 000 horsepower or more.

On the other hand, the reciprocating pump did fight back to some extent with the direct acting duplex and triplex pumps, also where quantities required are small and pressures required are high, the reciprocating pump is far superior to the centrifugal. Thus it retains its status in quite different fields of application.

In the meantime various other types of rotary or rotating pumps had been designed, tried and (mostly) failed to find any real practical application. The basic principle of the centrifugal pump itself, in fact, was first tried out as hand-cranked models in the latter part of the 17th century and through into the 19th century – but all the inventors appeared to try to make the pump work the wrong way round – *ie* by sucking water in instead of pushing it out. They also failed from sheer lack of power to drive this form of pump at a suitable speed.

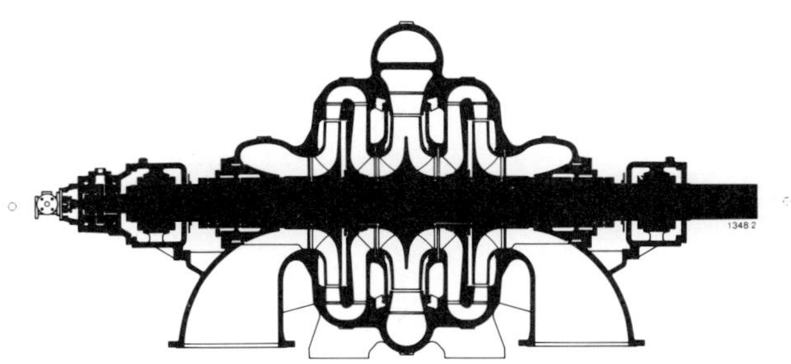

Modern diffuser casing pump.

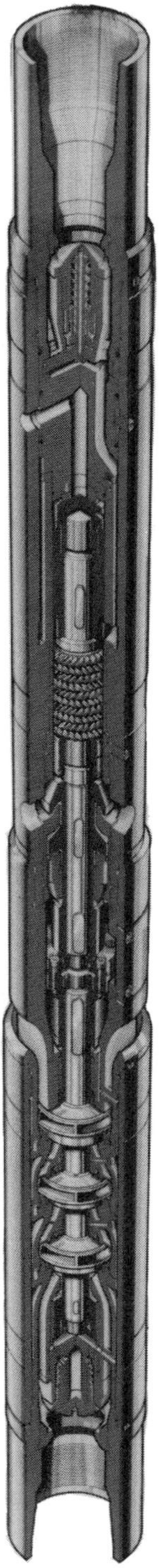

Hydraulic turbine drive downhole pump operates at speeds up to 15 000 r/min.

The Weir pump incorporated two steam chests mounted one on top of the other.

Others subsequently developed as successful configurations, also appeared surprisingly early. The sliding vane pump was invented around 1580 by Ramelli; and the gear pump by Serviere in 1593. Both are now standard types of rotary pumps with positive displacement characteristics (unlike the 'rotating' centrifugal pump). The other main type, the screw pump, appeared much later. It was invented by Revillion in 1830. The eccentric screw pump, or original 'mono' pump took a further century to appear.

Other types of pumps followed through logical development, together with new or original principles being exploited. The liquid ring pump developed from the vane pump. The Roots pump evolved as a compressor from the gearpump principle, but with clearance between the rotors. This idea was further extended in the lobe rotor pump for handling all types of liquid. The peristaltic pump originated as a laboratory device – and was dependant on the appearance of modern plastic tube materials. By contrast the appearance of the diaphragm pump is somewhat obscure. Certainly it seems to have been produced in a somewhat crude form with a leather diaphragm, but only became an accepted type with the availability of rubber in sheet form. In its modern form it now dominates the field of metering and proportioning duties.

The likelihood of any radical new type of pump being developed appears remote. It would need to employ quite new principles (at present unknown) to compete with the performance and efficiencies achieved by present-day pump designs. That is not to say there will be no new designs of pumps, most certainly there will, but their success will be judged by the cost-effectiveness. Equally the performance of known types of pumps continues to be improved upon, and in particular cases their range of applications extended. When the peristaltic pump first appeared, for example, few people would have visualized its successful development into a hose pump for handling slurries of high specific gravity on a cost effective basis. Also as a final comment the first 'real' mechanical pump, the Archimedean screw has developed into giant sizes for water-raising duties. It has also quite recently appeared in miniature size, the screw being a helix wound from wire operating in a plastic tube. This is proving to be one of the most effective pumps available for pumping out old oil from internal combustion engine crank cases, and small enough to be inserted down the dipstick tube. Unlike most other small pumps used for such a duty, it is equally effective lifting cold oil as it is for warm oil.

Pump Types (General)

THE TWO main categories of pump as defined by their basic principle of operation are positive displacement pumps and centrifugal pumps. Lesser known and/or used type are ejectors, pulsators, gas lift pumps, hydraulic elevators and various miscellaneous types difficult to categorise.

Both positive displacement (PD) and centrifugal are broad descriptions. Positive displacement pumps sub-divide into reciprocating (piston pumps and rotary pumps), the latter appearing in a variety of forms. In a case of a rotary pump, the essential working element is a rotor which may be of impeller, vane or screw form *etc*. Pumps with impeller-type rotors may in fact even be referred to as impeller pumps although this is confusing since the description 'impeller' is more generally reserved for the rotating elements of a turbo machine. Positive displacement pumps also embrace many other individual types outside reciprocating and rotary machines, *eg* bucket, scoop, wheel, *etc*; ejectors, pulsators *etc*. Some types are neither positive displacement nor turbo machine in characteristics, sub-classification in such cases is thus largely of academic rather than practical interest.

In contrast to displacement pumps which generate pressure hydrostatically, energy is converted in centrifugal pumps by hydrodynamic means. Accordingly, all pumps can be divided into dynamic or displacement categories as shown in Tables 1 and 2.

Centrifugal pumps

Centrifugal pump is the general description for machines with impellers which displace fluid by momentum rather than positive mechanical travel. As a consequence through-flow has interdependancy of head and delivery so that performance is not readily predictable from first principles. Correctly, they are best termed turbo machines since they include machines with different impeller forms and which displace the liquid flow through the pump in different ways. The alternative description is roto-dynamic pumps although this is not generally acceptable. Turbo-pompes (France) and Krieselpumpen (Germany) are descriptions widely used in Continental Europe. The latter literally means centrifugal pump, although this is in fact only one class of turbo machine.

TABLE 1 – CLASSIFICATION OF DYNAMIC PUMPS

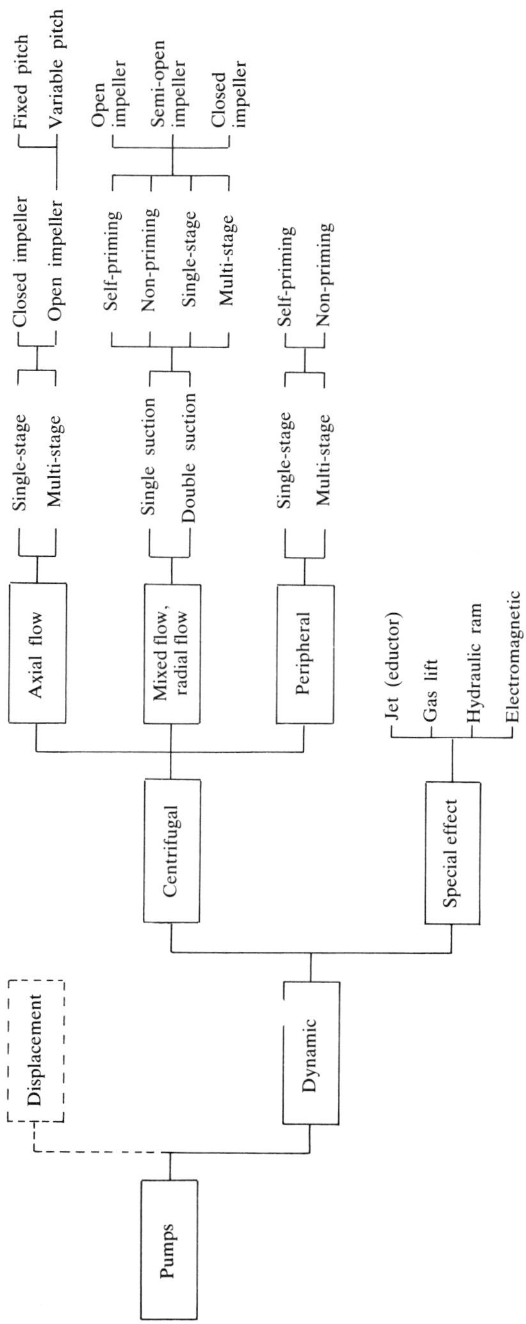

TABLE 2 – CLASSIFICATION OF DISPLACEMENT PUMPS

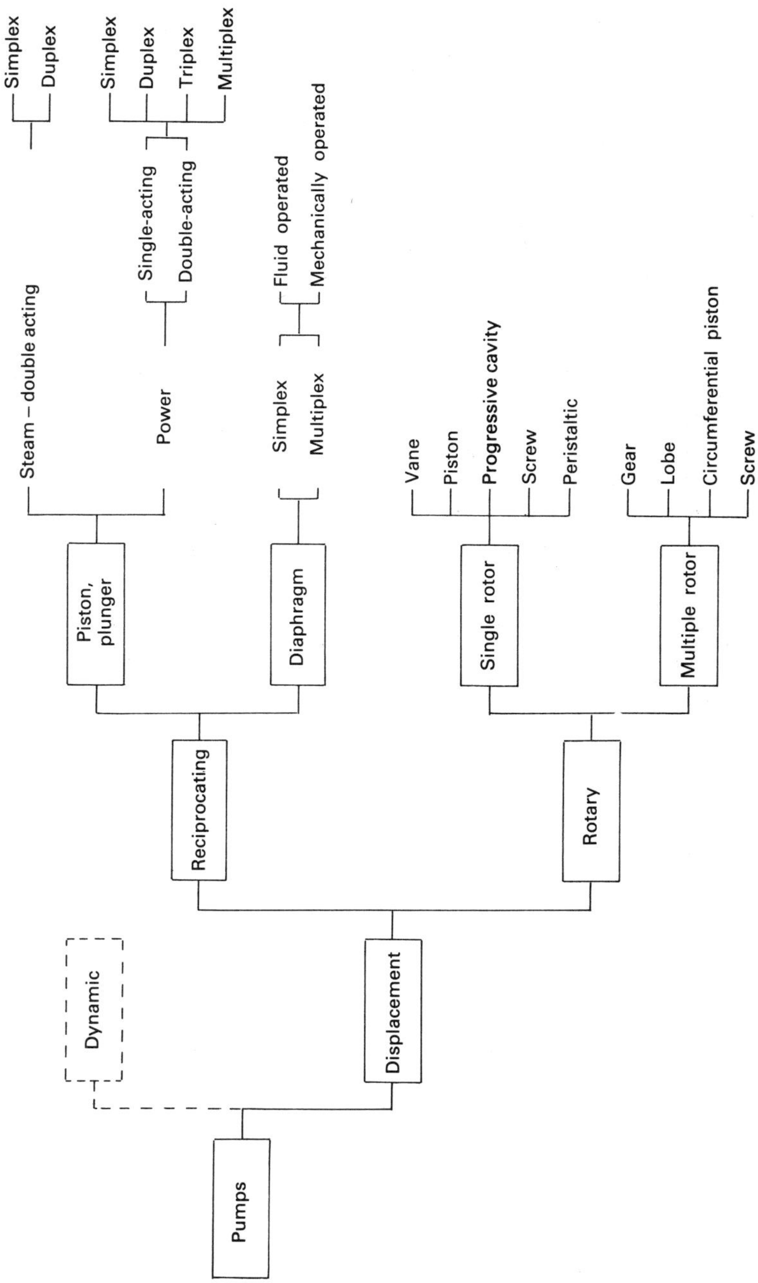

The main sub-classifications of turbo machines are centrifugal pumps, mixed flow pumps, axial flow pumps and channel pumps. These all have different impeller forms and the descriptions refer to the manner in which the fluid is displaced, thus the impeller of a true centrifugal pump displaces the fluid radially; that of an axial flow pump axially and that of a mixed flow pump in a direction with both radial and axial velocity components. A channel pump employs an impeller with turbine-like blades mounted on the periphery running in an annular channel (or channels) surrounding the periphery of the wheel. This can be further sub-classified according to the number of channels employed or the form of channel.

Classification by geometry
This is a common form of classification of turbo machines, and centrifugal pumps in particular, based on the shape of the casing.

Classification by inlet geometry
This is commonly applied to turbo machines and to a lesser extent rotary pumps. It describes the basic geometry of the section entry to the pump.

Classification by layout
This refers to the design (or possible) position of the pump shaft access, *eg* horizontal, vertical, or inclined. This indicates the mounting requirements (and likely floor space required) in the case of turbo machines. A further classification which applies with turbo machines (particularly) is how the casing halves divide for disassembly where applicable.

Classification by mounting
This is generally descriptive of the design method of mounting the pump and is applicable but not necessarily always specified for all types of pumps.

Classification by operation
This basically describes the design duty of the pump, *eg* main pump, source pump, standby pump, auxiliary pump, *etc*. It does not necessarily follow that the use of such a pump is restricted to the specified operation.

Classification by liquid handled
This is a specific classification indicating that the pump is able to handle a particular type or types of fluid or product.

Classification by material
This describes the materials from which the pump or the wetted part are constructed and thus its likely suitability for handling chemically active or corrosive fluids.

Classification by drive
This specifies the method of drive intended for the pump, *eg* electric motor, integral (electric) motor, manual, manually driven, turbo driven, shaft driven *etc*.

Submersible pumps
Pumps of this type are of sufficient importance to warrant a classification of their own representing the type of pump with integral electric motor which can be immersed in the product being handled. They can be sub-divided into various categories according to intended duty, *eg* deep well, borehole *etc* and by the form of canned motor.

Comprehensive data on all types of centrifugal pumps and submersible pumps are covered in greater detail within the various sections of this handbook. For further reference see *Centrifugal Pumps* by H.H.Anderson and *Submersible Pumps and their Applications* by H.H.Anderson, both published by The Trade & Technical Press Ltd

PUMP TYPES

Hand pump

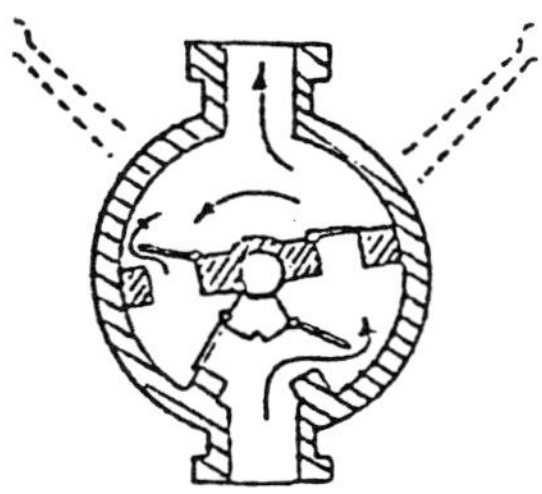

Figure illustrates a semi-rotary hand pump, but all hand pumps are included.

Reciprocating pump

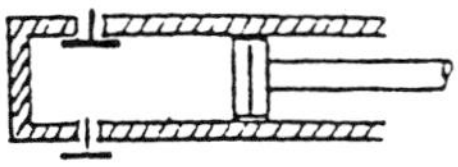

Piston pump

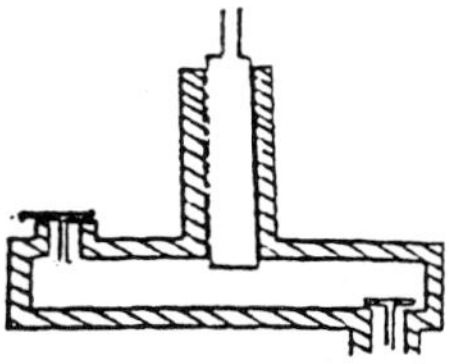

Plunger pump

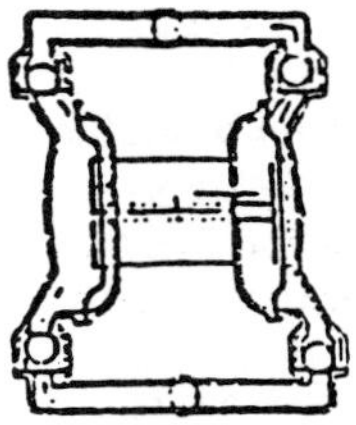

Diaphragm pump

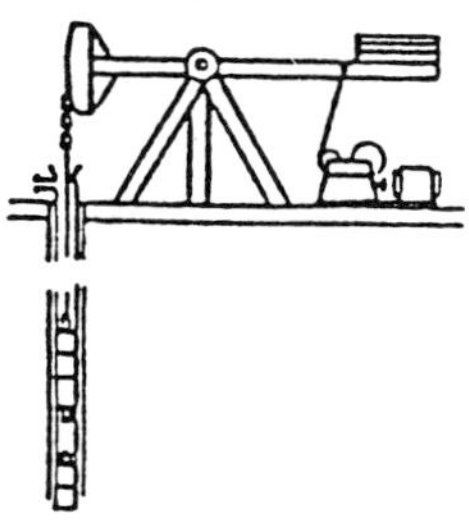

"Nodding Donkey" (Beam pump)
This is a borehole reciprocating pump

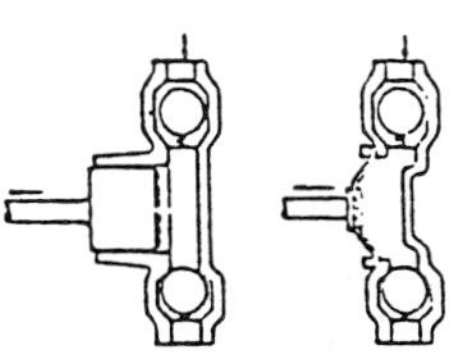

Proportioning and dosing

contd....

PUMP TYPES (contd.)

Rotary

Gear pump
Both internal and external pumps are included.

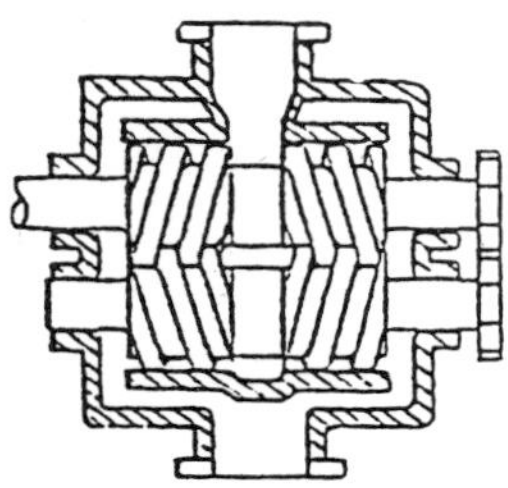

Screw pump
Includes two or three screw pumps, but excludes Archimedian screw.

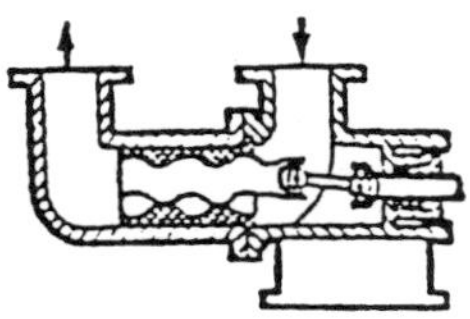

Helical rotor pump
Also termed progressive cavity and eccentric screw. Included under this heading is the helical vane pump.

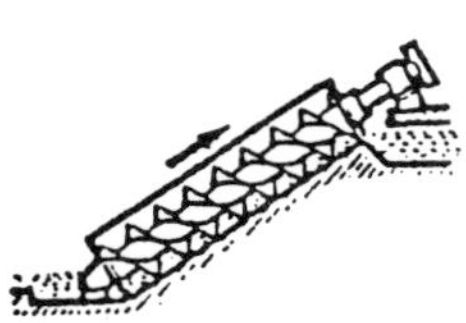

Other rotary pumps
This category includes the archimedian screw.

Vane pump
This category includes roller vane, sliding vane, and flexible vane.

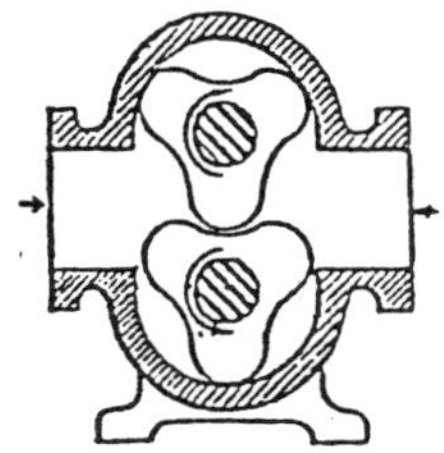

Lobe pump
Figure shows a single lobe pump.

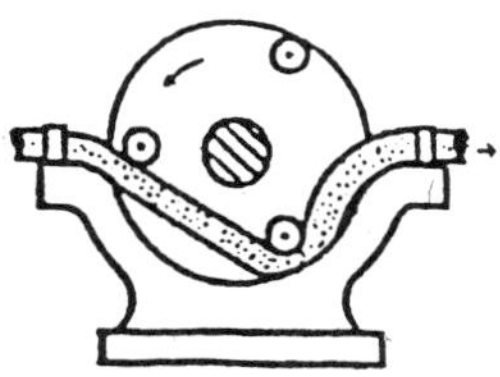

Peristaltic
Includes all types and sizes.

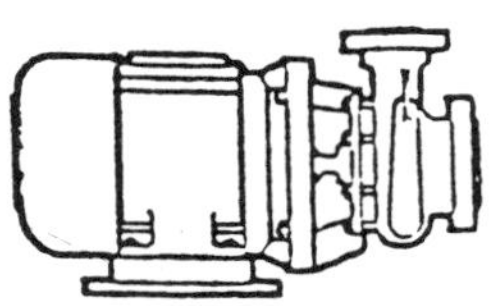

Single-stage single-entry close coupled pump
Generic figure to cover all discharge diameter sizes sometimes referred to as radial flow or rotodynamic. There is no distinction on other design features such as volutes and mounting or whether they are horizontal or vertical.

contd....

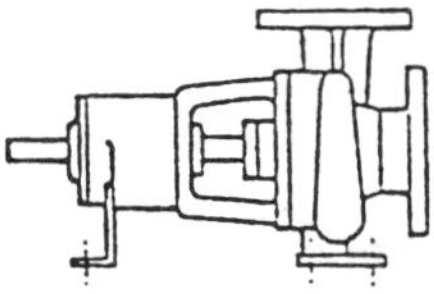

Single-stage single-entry coupled pump
Generic figure to cover all sizes including back pull out and API and ISO standard pumps.

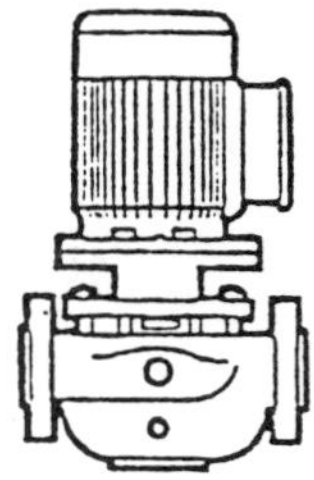

In-line pumps
Covers centrifugal pumps with branches in the same axis.

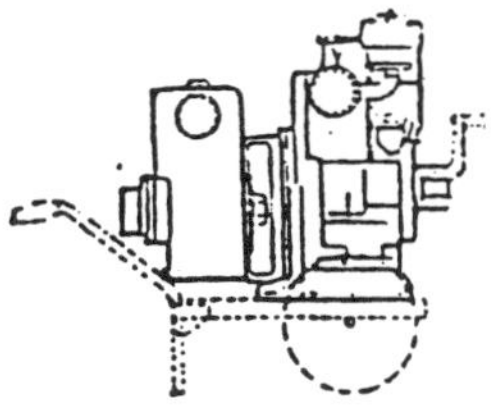

Single- and multi-stage
Self-priming close coupled pump
A category that covers both single and multiple stage including contractor type pumps.

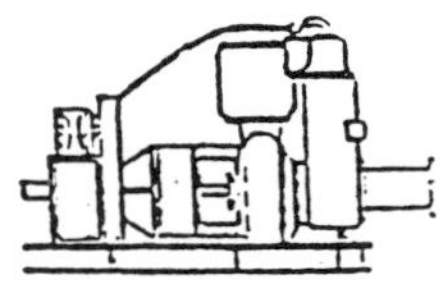

Single- and multi-stage self-priming coupled pump.

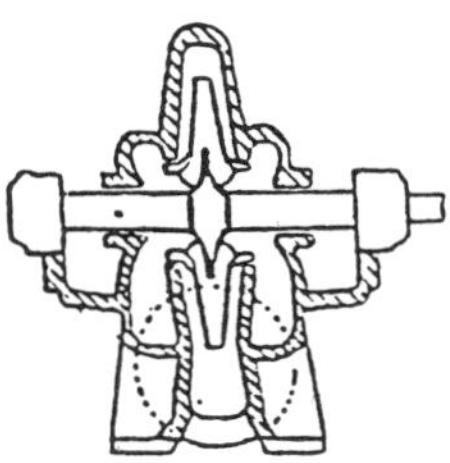

Single-stage double entry pump
Generally splitcase pump.

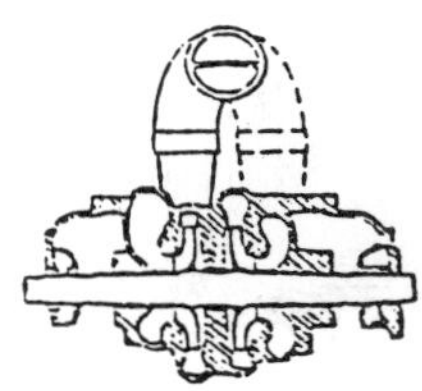

Multi-stage single entry split pump
Figure illustrates a two-stage example.

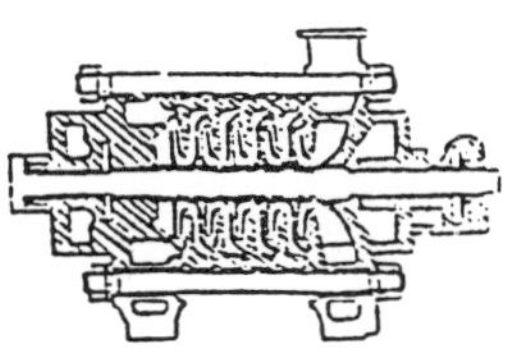

Multi-stage single-entry pump
This has two or more impellers arranged in series and can be vertical or horizontal. Figure shows a ring section. Caisson pumps are also included in this category.

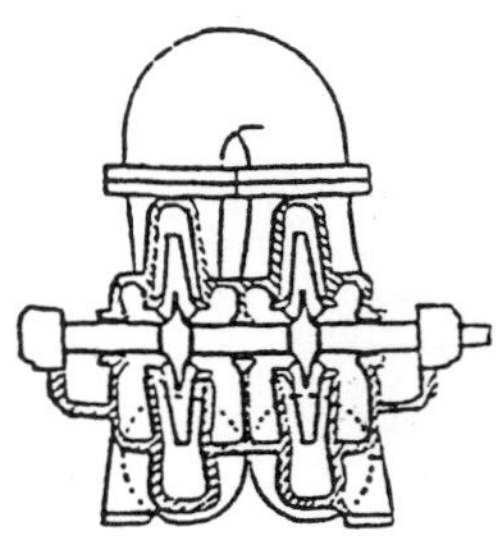

Multi-stage double-entry pump
Generally a split case pump.

contd....

PUMP TYPES (contd.)

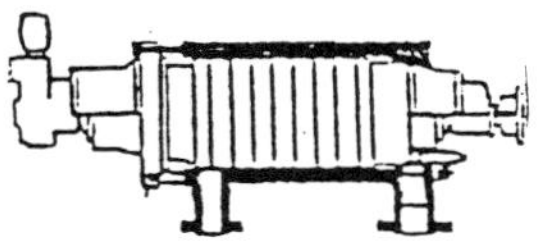

Multi-stage barrel insert pump
Generally of ring section design.

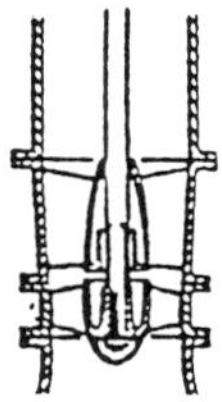

Axial flow pump
Includes all variants of this type.

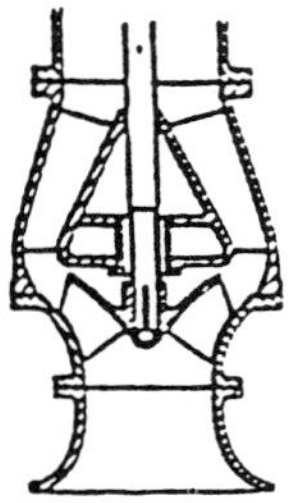

Mixed flow pump
Includes all variants of this type whether vertical or horizontal.

Borehole shaft driven
All sizes are included in one heading.

Regenerative pump
Also called peripheral.

Side channel pump.

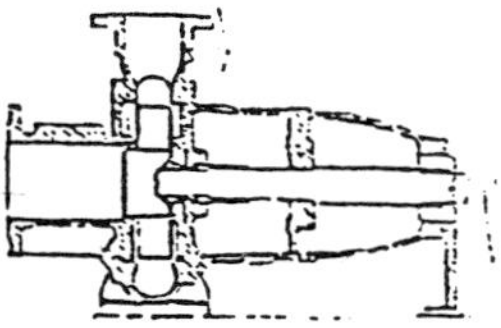

Channel impeller pump
Single-stage shown in figure.
All types included in this heading.

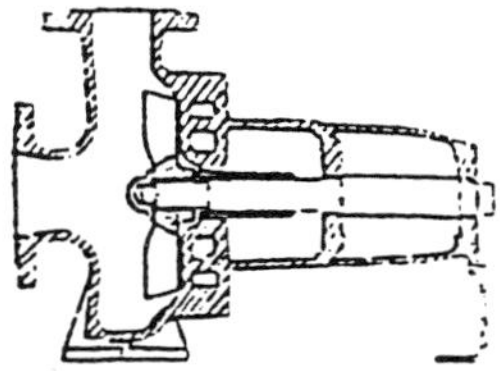

Torque flow pump
Specialist pump using disc impeller with ribs to impart momentum to the liquid through turbulence.

contd....

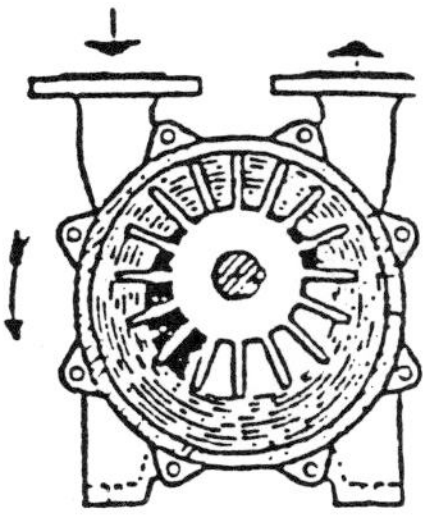

Liquid ring pump
All types irrespective of liquid used as rotating ring are included (0703).

Submersible borehole pump
This includes both electric and hydraulic drives and the motor in every case is included.

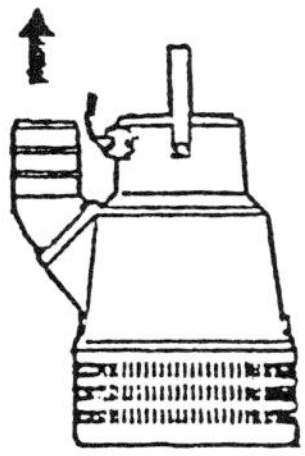

Submersible contractors pump
These are single-stage submersible pumps in which the motor is included in the BSO return.
Majority of drainage types would be included in this heading (3005).

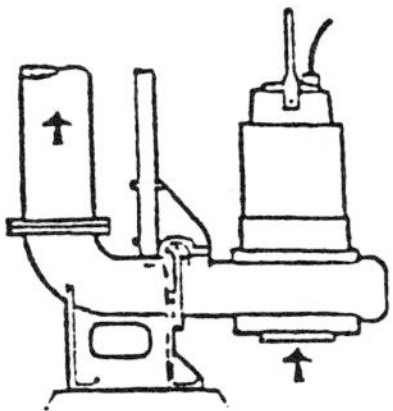

Submersible sewage pump
These are usually single-stage pumps in which the motor is included.

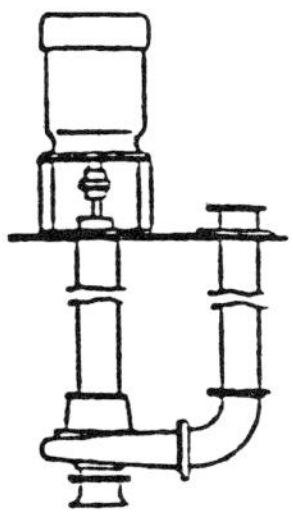

Submerged pump
This is a generic name for pumps generally vertical in which the motor is mounted in a dry environment and the pump head is immersed in the liquid sump pump, suspended, wet sump, deepwell, are some of the names in use for this type.

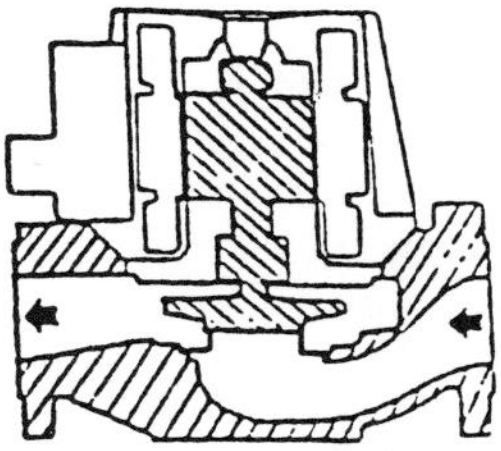

Glandless domestic circulator
A stationary circulation pump for heating and hot water service systems with a rated input not exceeding 300 W.
N.B. Motors to be included as circulators are close-coupled.

contd....

PUMP TYPES (contd.)

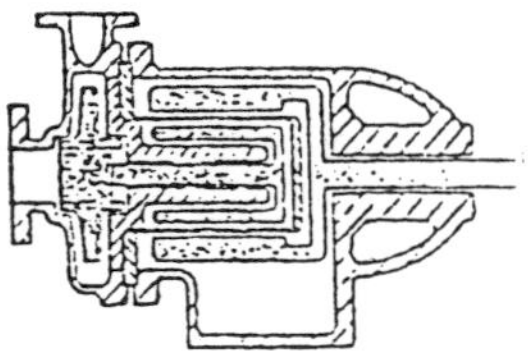

Glandless magnetic drive pump

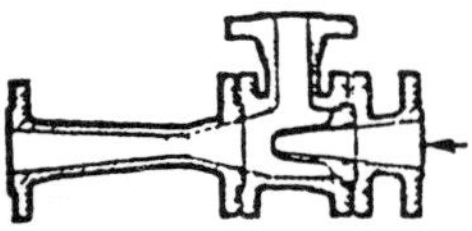

Jet pump.

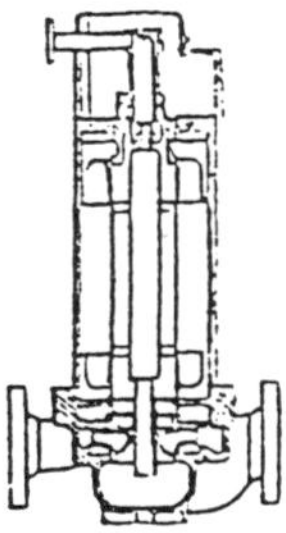

Glandless canned motor
This heading includes 'dry' type where the stator is sealed from the rotor by a cam or wet stator.

Reciprocating pumps

Reciprocating pumps have positive action and will deliver a certain volume of water against a pressure determined by the system to which the pump is attached. Reciprocating pumps are used for small quantity high pressure duties where their efficiency can exceed that of a centrifugal pump. For example, 10 l/s 100 bar would be an entirely practicable duty for a centrifugal pump as far as mechanical operation is concerned, and advantages of low costs, smooth delivery, easy regulation, small space and foundations would accrue, but a centrifugal pump efficiency of about 45% would take almost twice the power of a reciprocating pump at 80% efficiency. This difference of power maintains the position of the reciprocating pump within its sphere.

In general the choice between centrifugal and reciprocating types is determined by physical limitations of peripheral speeds, erosion, metal strengths, and the physical size of units from the aspect of manufacture, transport to site and erection.

Choice of type is also largely determined by economic aspects and by the range of duty and the cost of power. For example, a modest duty of 10 l/s at 30 m can be produced by a cheap single stage pump with an efficiency of 52%. Where power is cheap or where the operating hours represent a small proportion of the day, such a pump may be entirely economic. On the other hand, where power is expensive and where a pump is running for a large proportion of the day, the multi-stage design, working on a more favourable type number, that is within improved impeller proportions as a result of a lower head per stage, would perform the duty mentioned previously with an efficiency of 70%. A reciprocating pump on this duty would give an even higher efficiency, but would be uneconomic on cost of installation. For the highest pressure duties the reciprocating pump has a very much stronger appeal, but even there the disadvantages of vibration, physical dimension and uneven flow severely limits its applications.

TABLE 3 – SUB-CLASSIFICATIONS OF CENTRIFUGAL PUMPS AND TURBO MACHINES

Name, classification or type	Description	Remarks
Turbo machines (roto-dynamic)	1.Centrifugal 2.Mixed flow (a) Helical (b) Diagonal 3.Axial flow 4.Channel (a) Side channel (b) Peripheral	General classification.
Single-stage	Head developed in a single-stage.	Usually descriptive of centrifugal pumps only.
Two-stage	Two impellers in series.	
Multi-stage	Several impellers in series.	
Low-pressure	Single-stage pump with low discharge pressure.	Nominal classification by discharge pressure developed.
High-pressure	Pump with high discharge	
Super-pressure	Pump with very high discharge pressure.	
Single-entry	Single suction entry to impeller(s).	Classification by inlet (suction) geometry; the same classification can apply to other pump types, *eg* rotary pumps.
Double-entry	Entry may be single (single suction) to a double-entry impeller or two single-entry impellers in parallel; or split into two suction branches (double suction).	
Axial inlet (end suction)	Axial inlet.	
Side inlet (side suction)	Radial or tangential inlet.	
Top inlet (top suction)	Horizontal pump with inlet on the top.	
Bottom inlet (bottom suction)	Horizontal pump with inlet on the bottom.	
Horizontal	Roto-dynamic pump with horizontal shaft.	Classification of turbo machines by basic layout; the same classification can apply to other pump types.
Vertical		
Inclined	Axial flow pump with inclined shaft.	
Volute	Centrifugal pump with spiral discharge casing.	Classification based on shape of casing; other descriptions may also apply.
Double-volute	Centrifugal pump with two volute casings at 180°, delivering through a single discharge.	
Diffuser	Centrifugal pump with fixed diffuser vanes following the impeller	
Annular (casing)	Centrifugal pump with constant cross section circular discharge casing.	
Bowl	Diagonal sub-type mixed flow pump with bowl shaped casing.	
Tubular	Axial flow pump with straight tube casing.	
Angle	Axial flow pump with curved tube casing.	
Barrel	Multi-stage centrifugal pump with stages assembled in a shaped outer casing.	
Overhung	Centrifugal pump with impeller mounted outside the bearings.	

cont...

TABLE 3 – SUB-CLASSIFICATIONS OF CENTRIFUGAL PUMPS AND TURBO MACHINES ...continued

Name, classification or type	Description.	Remarks
Split casing	1.Axially split (horizontally split) – casing divides in the plane of the shaft (thus *horizontally split* in the case of a horizontal pump). 2.Radially split (vertically split) – casing divides in a plane at right angles to the sahft (thus *vertically split* in case of a horizontal pump). 3.Diagonally split – casing divided in a plane diagonal to the shaft.	Classification by division of casing halves (where applicable).
Foot mounted	Mounting feet incorporated pump body.	
Frame mounted	Vertical pump (usually) mounted on frame to transfer weight of top mounted motor to foundations.	
Lantern mounted	Lantern form mounting fitted to, or integral with, the pump casing; the lantern may be in the form of a skirt (skirt mounted).	Descriptive of method of mounting the pump; the same classifications can apply to other types of pumps.
Pedestal mounted	Horizontal pump with casing mounted on a pedestal or headstock.	
Flange mounted	Overhung pump flange-mounted to driver.	
Wall mounted (bulkhead mounted)	Casing designed for mounting on a wall or bulkhead.	
Tank mounted	Pump designed for suspended mounting on a tank flange.	
Pipeline mounted (in-line pump)	Pump which is designed to mounted direclty, and unsupported, in a pipeline.	
Direct mounted	Pump mounted directly on an extension of its shaft.	
Integral	Pump incorporated as a part of an integral machine; also known as a built-in pump.	
Wet sump pump	Usually a vertical centrifugal pump of a suitable design to be immersed.	
Dry sump pump	Usually a vertical pump with enclosed suction, or suction inlet installed in a dry chamber.	
Canned motor pump	Glandless pump set or submersible pump with sealed electric motor.	
Wet motor pump	Glandless pump set or submersible pump with stator windings in contact with fluid being pumped.	
Submersible pump	Pump set capable of operation immersed in fluid being pumped.	
Immersible pump	Pump set capable of operation partially immersed in fluid being pumped.	

cont...

Sub-classifications of centrifugal pumps are given in Table 3.

Advantages of centrifugal pumps

When compared with a reciprocating pump, the centrifugal pump offers the following advantages:

(i) Higher speed resulting in lower size and cost.

(ii) Continuous delivery free from pressure fluctuations.

(iii) Having known characteristics a centrifugal pump can:

- (a) operate on minimum flow without exceeding a predetermined pressure.
- (b) operate on maximum flow without exceeding a predetermined power demand.
- (c) be designed to meet several duties, thus in many (but not all) cases, matching the pump characteristic to the site requirement.

(iv) Applicable to direct drive in almost every case.

(v) Absence of vibration and simpler foundation.

(vi) When handling liquids containing solids, *eg* paper, pulp *etc*, a centrifugal pump tends to deliver a constant weight of solid matter irrespective of variation of consistency. The heavier consistencies cause a greater friction loss, thus reducing flow and compensating in some measure for consistency changes.

Advantages of reciprocating pumps

(i) Within their field higher efficiencies than centrifugal pumps.

(ii) Applicable to variable pressures without adjustment of speed – a useful factor where the head is uncertain.

(iii) Self-priming and therefore able to handle a certain amount of air or other vapour without failing to pump.

(iv) Capable of utilizing kinetic energy or rotation to give peak pressures, and as a result often able to clear accidental obstructions in the delivery main.

Reciprocating pumps are, therefore, refined to duties where quantity is low and pressure high, for example quantities up to 10 l/s and pressures up to 2000 bar.

Rotary pumps

Rotary pumps are positive displacement machines but differ from reciprocating pumps in that delivery is continuous and thus smoother, although internal losses are normally somewhat higher through slip (internal leak-back). Slip increases with increasing pressure, thus rotary pumps are less suited to developing high pressures than reciprocating pumps. Compared with centrifugal pumps they are much more restricted in practical sizes and thus deliveries.

Basic types of rotary pump are summarised in Table 4. These are restricted to pump types employing an impeller or rotor form providing a 'suck' and 'squeeze' action. Screw pumps can be regarded as a special case since single screw pumps provide only a 'lifting' action unless running in a close-fitting elastomeric stator. Twin and multiple rigid screw pumps, on the other hand, provide 'squeeze'. There are numerous variations in rotary pump operating principles as shown in Table 5.

TABLE 4 – MAIN TYPES OF ROTARY PUMP

Single impeller types	Rotor-form types	Screw-form
Gear 1.External 2.Internal Vane 1.Sliding vane 2.Swinging vane 3.Scraper 4.Cam-vane Flexible impeller (flexible vane) Liquid ring	Lobe rotor (numerous forms)	Screw 1.Single screw† 2.Twin screw 3.Multiple screw

†**Note**: The Archimedean screw is not generally classified as a rotary pump.

TABLE 5 – SUB-TYPES AND CHARACTERISTICS OF ROTARY PUMPS

Basic type	Sub-types	Remarks
Gear pump	External gear	Good efficiency; generates high-frequency pressure 'ripple'.
	Internal gear	Gentler pumping action than external gear pump.
Vane pump	Sliding vane	Good efficiency; lower-frequency frequency pressure 'ripple' than gear pump.
	Swinging vane	Low speed; heavy duty types for handling slurries, *etc*.
	Rolling vane	Generally excellent performance as high-pressure water pump.
	Cam vane	Reduced friction and wear; particularly used as a vacuum pump.
	Flexible stator	Versatile but limited in pressure capabilities and size.
Lobe rotor	Numerous	Wide variety of rotor forms employed.
	Roots pump	Based on two 8-shaped rotors; mostly used as an air blower.
	Waukesha	Extension of lobe rotor principle giving 'external circumferential piston' pump with absence of pressure and 'ripple'.
Screw pumps	Single screw	
	Eccentric screw	Single rigid screw rotating in an elastomeric stator. Twin and multiple screw
	Goodyear	Special form of screw rotor allied to a wiper wheel.
	Other variants	Other combinations of single screw and matchiing stator.
Rotary piston		
Shuttle block		
Semi-rotary		

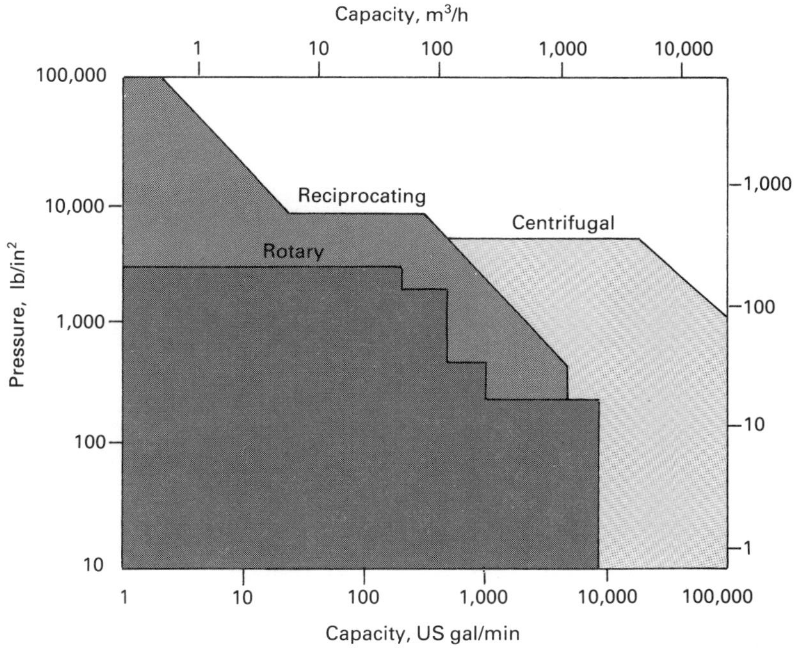

Figure 1
Approximate upper limit of pressure and capacity by pump class.

Rotary pumps are a particularly useful type since they are suitable for handling a wide variety of fluids from the very lowest to the very highest viscosities (with suitable modification of design where very high fluid viscosities are concerned). As a general rule, however, they are suitable only for handling fluids free from solid contaminants which could jam in the small clearance spaces involved or produce high wear. Their main application is for the handling of clean fluids from light oils upwards, although many are equally suitable for water and some types are eminently suitable for handling gases. Figure 1 shows the approximate upper limits of pressure and capacity currently available commercially throughout the free world for centrifugal, reciprocating and rotary pumps.

Future Trends

IT WOULD appear unlikely that any new principle will be discovered to challenge the supremacy of the centrifugal pump for bulk fluid handling, at least in numbers used. At the same time it appears equally unlikely that there will be any major developments in the field of positive displacement pumps other than detail improvements and possible extension of certain types to further applications. An example here is the development of the eccentric helical screw/elastomeric stator pump to suit a far wider range of applications than was originally visualized, including water raising. This is not to say that there will be no significant development in pumps and pumping techniques during the next decade.

Major parameters to consider at the present time are cost effectiveness of pumping and energy saving, the two going hand-in-hand to a large extent because of the high cost of buying energy and the (periodically threatened at least) run down in the availability of fossil fuels. To this can be added the possibility of further materials being developed to improve pump component life, particularly under arduous or corrosive duty applications. Only the latter seems truly competitive in the sense that materials development, particularly in the case of ceramics, continues unabated and there is still much to discover and learn. Pump design, on the other hand, whichever type of pump is considered, has largely reached a plateau of efficiency beyond which any further improvements in efficiency may not be cost effective. That is to say in the absence of any technological breakthrough the cost of achieving higher efficiencies outweigh any economical gain. A new development here is in the vaneless laminar flow design described in Section 3.

Technological breakthroughs too tend to have quite different and often contrasting effects. To quote two examples from the immediate past, the development and application of mechanical seals has solved many problems. The formed bellows seal is a particularly outstanding example. At the same time it is no complete answer nor has it rendered the packed gland obsolete, in fact the demand for, and production of, soft packings has actually increased rather than decreased. Much of this can be due to another technological development in the materials used for soft packings more expensive initial cost but very much more cost effective in the long term.

Centrifugal pumps

As far as pumps themselves are concerned the centrifugal pump seems the main target for further development, although reaching a nominal plateau of efficiency some time ago. Already, during recent years, there has been a better understanding and practical application of hydraulic design which is a critical fact as far as the efficiency of such pumps is concerned. This, together with computer-aided design and computer-aided engineering indicates that the practical optimum design of a centrifugal pump for whatever service condition needs to be met, is now within reach.

Two aspects of the possible changes in fluid machines over the next 20 years are the increase of power, speed, pressure and temperature of existing designs and the emergence of entirely new designs and materials.

The third millennium is nearer to us than the mid-thirties when the usual turbo alternator was 20 megawatts. The increase in the next 15 years to 2000 megawatts and above will involve 50 megawatt turbine driven feedpumps at at 6000 to 9000 r/min. Refineries, chemical plants, steelworks, desalination plants, paper mills and waterworks will similarly increase their liquid pump demands, but present designs and metallurgy can cope with such anticipated increases. New and untried processes and nuclear, space travel, gas turbine and sea developments are certain to require pumps but the problems to be met are more difficult to foresee. H.H.Anderson, who is one of the world's leading authorities and designers of centrifugal pumps, has a dream of a rotating tube to produce pressure without the need for liquid to enter and leave a vane system. This has not yet been fulfilled. The aim of this device would be to eliminate losses and cavitation so that efficiency would be almost 100% and the generation of head be almost unlimited. It would, therefore, appear that the vaned impeller will always be with us, and that progress will depend on high speeds and improved metallurgy. The basic principles of the pumps that we now know remaining unchanged. Volute pumps replaced diffuser pumps for modest duties nearly 70 years ago and a further development to vaneless diffusers may occur in pumps as in turbo blowers.

More immediate and obvious trends include the production of higher heads per stage and higher running speeds. Higher heads per stage mean that a single-stage pump could be suitable for a duty previously requiring a multi-stage machine or the number of stages required to achieve the required total head could be reduced. In either case the result is a smaller more compact pump with a shorter shaft and better rigidity. Immediate limits realizable would appear to be about 1000 metres head per stage corresponding to impeller tip speeds of the order of 140 to 150 m/sec. It is to be anticipated that more and more single-stage centrifugal pumps will approach this plateau. In fact 2000 metres stage head is normal today on light hydrocarbon liquids.

Higher heads

Higher heads per stage are directly linked to higher operating speeds. With direct drive from two-pole electric motors, operation is tied to synchronous speeds of 3550 and 2950 r/min for 60 Hz and 50 Hz a.c. supplies, respectively. Higher directly coupled speeds are obtainable from steam turbines or gas turbines. Equally, there is an increasing use of geared up drives from electric motors. The general trend which is to be expected to continue is towards the use of higher and higher operating speeds for centrifugal pumps. The plateau in this respect can only be guessed at, some current pumps already operate at speeds in excess of 24 000 r/min.

Frequency converters

Equally significant in this particular sphere is the increasing awareness of the benefits obtainable from frequency converters, readily enabling higher synchronous speeds to be obtained from a.c. motors. Very efficient solid state frequency converters have already taken over from bulky relatively inefficient motor generator sets and will undoubtedly continue to appear in ever increasing sizes. A further advantage with the solid state frequency converter is that it can also provide for variable speed drive.

Hydraulic design

The field of hydraulic design in centrifugal pumps is a broad one, ranging from optimizing impeller design from the point of view of efficiency with a particular product to be handled to the prevention of cavitation and the reduction or elimination of hydraulic pulsations, resulting from the interaction of the impeller vanes and the collector. Thus, further developments can be expected in the design of impellers as well solutions to hydraulic stability problems. The most fruitful field of potential development at the present time appears to be in the employment of inducers.

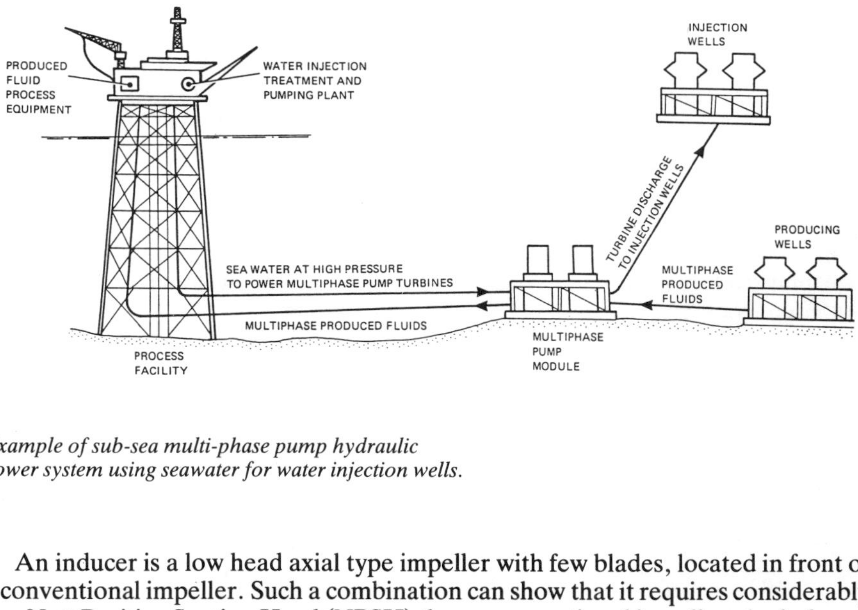

Example of sub-sea multi-phase pump hydraulic power system using seawater for water injection wells.

An inducer is a low head axial type impeller with few blades, located in front of a conventional impeller. Such a combination can show that it requires considerably less Nett Positive Suction Head (NPSH) than a conventional impeller. An inducer, therefore, can reduce NPSH requirements of a pump or permit the pump to be operated at a higher speed with a given NPSH. The principle, it should be noted, was first patented in 1926 but it is only in recent years that the inducer has come into broad commercial application, especially on duties close to best efficiency flow.

Drivers

The ultimate future of drivers themselves also appears reasonably clear accepting fossil fuels as exhaustible (which is debatable in the medium- long-term) with no likely cost effective alternative *eg* from other natural sources or synthetics; and ruling out wind and wave powers as equally unlikely to be consistent enough or cost effective; whatever form the future development of energy transformation takes, the most cost effective end source produced will be electrical energy. This as well as the electric motor being the main driver for pumps at present it should continue to be so in the foreseeable future. Looking more deeply into the future, the only likely alternative seems to be some direct method of transforming internal energy within a fluid itself into pressure energy. This could dispense with both drivers and pumps.

In the meantime, there is an interesting 'competitor' to the electric motor – the hydrostatic drive. Again this needs a pump and driver (to generate pressure on an hydraulic fluid), but the hydraulic pump set can be remotely located from the pump itself driven by a directly-coupled hydraulic motor. A particular application is to submersible pumps, but hydrostatic drive may well be used more in the immediate future where there are operating advantages in separating driver and pump as well as for 'normal' pump drives. In the case of the latter, there will be some loss of efficiency compared with an electric motor drive (since an hydraulic pump and motor combination cannot be 100% efficient), but against that a hydrostatic drive does offer the advantage that it can be at variable speed with no set maximum speed limit.

Knowledgeable users

Cost effectiveness has been mentioned several times, and more and more users are necessarily giving considerable study to this subject. The days of the 'simple' solution where the user passed the pump problem to the manufacturer completely, accepted the particular result and worked from there on any further problems have largely past. More and more users are becoming knowledgeable about pumps themselves and can assess, rather than accept, what is being offered.

Parameters to consider

With knowledge and experience, pump assembly drawings are an invaluable guide since potential design weaknesses can be detected before purchase. Areas of paramount concern are the bearings and seals, as these account for at least 70% of all pump failures. Users often specify bearings with a B-10 life of 40 000 plus hours of operation. More sophisticated pump users know that the specification by itself means very little. Some 40 000 hours, about four-and-a-half years without bearing changes, is more the exception than the rule.

Load capacity at operation is not the only consideration when studying the bearings. Advanced design calls for:

(i) Labyrinth or face seals to protect the bearings. Commonly used lip seals last only about 2000 hours at 1750 r/min or moisture and dirt get into the bearing chamber. They can reduce bearing life by as much as 80%.

(ii) Thrust loads at off-design operation. A well designed pump will tolerate significant off-design operations.

(iii) Breather design. A filtered or closed system is superior to a simple open port which allows moisture and dirt to enter.

(iv) A method of permitting users to monitor easily the condition of oil inside the chamber.

In the sealing area review, check the stuffing box, particular if a mechanical seal is used. The traditional stuffing box design does not consider mechanical seals.

Indicative of mechanical sealing designs are:

(i) Tapped piped connections on the suction and discharge flanges. These permit increases and decreases of pressure on the seal.
(ii) Flush connection within a very close distance from the mating location of seal faces. This improves substantially the cleaning capability. A lantern ring inlet there is virtually useless.
(iii) Box radial cross-section is larger than that provided for packing to minimize clogging and cool more efficiently.
(iv) To minimize vibration, the stuffing box should be close to a bearing support.

Redesign of popular models has been accomplished by some pump manufacturers to reduce energy use, however, despite rising concern about energy costs, it is still largely left to pump users to solve the problem. Among the ingenious responses to energy losses caused by improperly designed fluid handling systems, initial selection of pumps and poor performance after installation a broad sampling is indicated here:

(i) Use of variable speed drives only in applications in which energy, process and maintenance savings justify increased costs.
(ii) Selection of control valves to minimize pressure drop.
(iii) Substitution of smaller pumps for oversized units. Cost of requirement for high pressure energy throughout the system is reduced by using smaller booster pumps to supply necessary higher pressure on one line.
(iv) With larger pumps, installation of a by pass and elimination of a fixed orifice. The orifice continuously recirculates flow from pump discharge to suction.
(v) Avoidance of oversized pumps. Perhaps the largest single cause of energy waste is operation at higher than required flows.
(vi) Avoidance of gas entrainment in pumps.
(vii) Process changes in design stage to reduce pumping requirements difficult to justify economically. Changes have included reducing wear, temperature across heat exchangers and cooling water pumping requirements, heating process fluids before pumping to minimize pressure drops and reduced viscosity.
(viii) Use of centrifugal pumps running backwards as an hydraulic turbine, this permits recovery of previously lost energy due to reduced pressures on water or process fluids.
(ix) Selection of pump motors and drives with requirements matching those of the system. More efficient operation of smaller sized motors at capacity will result, rather than oversized motors at half load.
(x) Selection of balanced mechanical seals. Seals control leakage more efficiently than mechanical packing and can extend service life.
(xi) Proper pump maintenance. This includes replacement of worn parts and impellers before excessive clearance occurs. Impellers in oversized centrifugal pumps can be trimmed to achieve head reduction of 10 to 50%.

Energy efficiency numbers in the form of pump curves mean little unless a proper definition is offered on how they were achieved. If efficiency is to have meaning – and it should be demanded to make pump selection more intelligent – answers to several questions must be known. These include:

(i) Was any back-filling of the vanes done?
(ii) How many test points were taken?
(iii) What was the water temperature during the test?
(vi) What are the clearances between the impeller and volute for open and enclosed impellers?

The village pump of the future

Right at the other end of the scale there is a vast potential in the third world for the village level operation and management of maintenance pump, VLOM pump as defined by a World Bank/United Nations panel. Intended for use in areas where there is no power, it has to be a hand pump. At the same time it has to be maintainable by villagers with no mechanical skills. Also, because a hand pump can only serve a small number of outlets a large number of such pumps are required in any community development programme. With minimal funds available to subsidise water supply developments, the VLOM pump also has to be cheap and backed up by the availability of low cost spare parts.

On the face of it robust run-of-the-mill hand pumps should really provide the answer. But they do not. Although many thousands of such pumps are already used in the less-developed countries for local water supplies, surveys have shown that a surprisingly high proportion (often over 70%) are out of order at any one time awaiting maintenance crews to install such simple spares as cup seals. Over 80% have failed within the first year of installation.

The third world has been waiting a long time for the VLOM pump. One agency has estimated that over 20 million such pumps will be needed by the end of the 20th century.

At last, it would appear that a hand operated pump, inexpensive to maintain requiring the minimum of skills (only one maintenance tool) backed-up by readily available, low cost spare parts has been developed.

The Aquadev hand pump is a development of Kenya's Afridev pump that has been designed according to the VLOM principle and for local manufacture. Low cost maintenance is the key to the development of the pump and plastic wear components have been used wherever possible to minimise corrosion. These include the foot valve and plunger, fulcrum and hanger bearings, combined coupling and centraliser, and rising main.

The use of plastic materials has enabled the cost of spare parts to be kept to an absolute minimum and the simple design means that routine annual maintenance can be carried out in less than two hours using only eight spare parts.

It is now possible for aid agencies to purchase and install true VLOM hand pumps that go a long way to overcoming the problems which have beset ground water development programmes.

The right to clean water and adequate sanitation is unquestionable, yet only half of the world's population have access to potable water supplies. The introduction of a hand pump specially designed to withstand arduous environmental conditions with the ability to be maintained cheaply and effectively on a local village basis is

Encapsulating all the design parameters established in the Afridev concept, the Aquadev handpump is designed specifically for village level operation and management of maintenance.

not a magic solution to the problems facing the drought-ridden third world. It is however, a pump capable of being integrated into the local community allowing people to manage and maintain their own water supplies, thereby providing a firm and reliable base from which to tackle what is clearly a long-term problem.

SECTION 2

Pump Performance and Characteristics

Fluid Characteristics

MAJOR FLUID parameters affecting both the performance of pumps and the choice of pumps are:

(i) Fluid density or specific gravity which broadly speaking affects the pumping power required and is also temperature dependant.

(ii) Fluid viscosity affecting pump performance and the ability of certain pumps to handle products with high viscosity.

(iii) Vapour pressure affecting the suction performance of a pump.

(iv) Specific heat and thermal conductivity governing the degree of heat generated during pumping (especially noticeable in high pressure pumps off-loaded by bypassing).

(v) Type of fluid – *eg* clean, contaminated, chemically active *etc*, which can affect choice of pump type detail design of the pump and material used. See Table 1.

Density, specific gravity and specific weight

Density is defined as mass per unit volume, with the 'engineering' equivalent specific weight as weight per unit volume (*eg* kg/l or lb/ft^3 or lb/gal). Specific gravity is dimensionless and is simply the density or specific weight of the fluid relative to the density or specific weight respectively, of water. It is a particularly useful factor for converting 'water' performance to that for fluids of other densities.

The specific weight of clean cold water is 1·0 kg/l (62·3 lb/ft^3) at normal ambient temperature.

Thus specific gravity of any fluid =

$$\text{specific weight in kg/l}$$

$$\frac{\text{specific weight in lb/ft}^3}{62{\cdot}3}$$

various other empirical 'gravity' scales are used by specific industries, based on hydrometer measurement – *eg* Baumé degrees, Twadell degrees, *etc*. Such readings can be corrected to specific gravity when necessary, examples are given in Table 2.

TABLE 1 – GENERAL CLASSIFICATION OF FLUIDS

Fluid Type	Parameters Affecting Pump Performance
Water (and aqueous solutions)	No specific problems.
Oils	Wide viscosity range, and change of viscosity with temperature.
Chemically active fluids	Corrosive fluids require selection of pump materials to suit and may also necessitate a controlled-leakage or zero-leakage pump (*eg* mechanical seals).
Solids in suspension	Can present clogging problems, also abrasive wear.
Slurries and pastes	May degrade water performance of pumps and require modified or special types of impellers or pumps.
Volatile liquids	Can present special problems in handling due to low vapour pressure, and in sealing.
Viscous and plastico-viscous fluids	May present special problems in power requirements, feed rates attainable, avoidance of channelling, excessive heating or degradation of the product.
Shear-sensitive fluids	Such as thixotropic and other non-Newtonian fluids where the basic product is subject to shear breakdown and consequent change in properties.
Hazardous fluids	Classified as fluids and/or their vapours which are flammable, toxic or chemically reactive.
Special fluids	May range from liquid gases to molten metals; this category also includes fluids (such as concrete) which are difficult to handle.

TABLE 2 – ARBITRARY HYDROMETER SCALES

Scale (and symbol where appropriate)		Standard Temperature	Specific Gravity Equivalent	
			Liquids heavier than water	Liquids lighter than water
Barkometer	N	–	$1000 + \frac{N}{1000}$	–
Baumé (original)	°Baumé	150°C	$\frac{146.3}{146.3 - °\text{Baumé}}$	$\frac{146.3}{146.3 + °\text{Baumé}}$
Baumé (American)	°Baumé	60°F	$\frac{145}{145 - °\text{Baumé}}$	$\frac{145}{145 + °\text{Baumé}}$
Baumé (German)	°Baumé	150°C	$\frac{144.3}{144.3 - °\text{Baumé}}$	$\frac{144.3}{144.3 + °\text{Baumé}}$
Twaddell	°Twaddell	–	$1000 + \frac{°\text{Twaddell}}{1000}$	–
Beck	N	125°C	$\frac{170}{170 - N}$	$\frac{170}{170 + N}$
Brix	N	–	–	$\frac{400}{400 - N}$
Gay-Lussac	N	–	–	$\frac{100}{100 - N}$

Other hydrometers may be designed to read fluid proportions directly and the Richter and Sikes hydrometers (alcoholmeters) are calibrated to read percentage of alcohol by weight in water directly.

Density and fluid volume

Changes of density with temperature may be significant in affecting the volume of liquid in a closed circuit or closed container, or the ullage required for drum filling. Where necessary, volume changes can be calculated directly from the coefficient of thermal expansion for the fluid over the appropriate temperature range as shown in Table 3. The expansion coefficient is applied in the formula:

$$V_2 = V_1 (1 + \alpha t)$$

where:

V_1 = volume at initial (or standard) temperature

V_2 = volume at new temperature

t = temperature difference deg C

α = coefficient of volumetric expansion (for given values or range of temperature)

TABLE 3 – MEAN COEFFICIENTS OF VOLUMETRIC EXPANSION
(circa 20 °C)

Fluid	Coefficient $\alpha \times 10^{-5}$
Acetic acid	107.00
Alcohol, amyl	93.00
Alcohol, ethyl	110.00
Alcohol, methyl	122.00
Aniline	85.00
Benzene	124.00
Carbon disulphide	121.00
Chloroform	126.00
Ethyl ether	163.00
Ethyl bromide	137,00
Glycerine	53.00
Mercury	18.18
Methyl iodide	121.00
Olive oil	70.00
Paraffin	90.00 (110 for 20 - 199°C)
Pentane	159.00
Sulphuric acid (100%)	57.00
Toluene	109.00
Turpentine	94.00
Xylol	101.00
Water, 5 - 10°	5.30
Water, 10 - 20°	15.00
Water, 20 - 40°	30.20
Water, 40 - 60°	45.80
Water, 60 - 80°	58.70

In the case of water and aqueous fluids the maximum density change between freezing point and boiling point is of the order of 4% and volume and density changes are generally ignored. In the case of petroleum products, petrochemicals and solvents, maximum density change over a similar temperature range may be as high as 8%. Thus, where large volumes of relatively expensive petroleum products may be involved, more accurate determination is required of the volume changes caused by variations in temperature. Such data are available in ASTM/IP tables, but can also be derived from volume correction coefficients applicable over a limited temperature range (usually 10 °C). Results are less accurate if the same correction factors are applied over wider temperature ranges. Volume correction coefficients are given in Table 4. The expansion (or contraction) factor is given directly by multiplying the appropriate volume correction coefficient by the difference in temperature. This factor can be applied to the original volume to find the actual expansion (or contraction) involved; or be multiplied by 100 to be rendered as a percentage change in volume.

TABLE 4 – VOLUME CORRECTION COEFFICIENTS FOR OILS

Specific Gravity 60/60° F	k_v per °F	k_v per °C	Specific Gravity 60/60° F	k_v per °F	k_v per °C
0.5994 – 0.6022	0.00096	0.00173	0.7367 – 0.7417	0.00062	0.00112
0.6023 – 0.6053	0.00095	0.00171	0.7418 – 0.7471	0.00061	0.00110
0.6054 – 0.6082	0.00094	0.00169	0.7472 – 0.7523	0.00060	0.00108
0.6083 – 0.6112	0.00093	0.00167	0.7524 – 0.7574	0.00059	0.00106
0.6113 – 0.6144	0.00092	0.00166	0.7575 – 0.7621	0.00058	0.00104
0.6145 – 0.6176	0.00091	0.00164	0.7622 – 0.7672	0.00057	0.00103
0.6177 – 0.6211	0.00090	0.00162	0.7673 – 0.7725	0.00056	0.00101
0.6212 – 0.6239	0.00089	0.00160	0.7726 – 0.7777	0.00055	0.00099
0.6240 – 0.6269	0.00088	0.00159	0.7778 – 0.7833	0.00054	0.00097
0.6270 – 0.6299	0.00087	0.00157	0.7834 – 0.7894	0.00053	0.00095
0.6300 – 0.6336	0.00086	0.00155	0.7895 – 0.7949	0.00052	0.00094
0.6337 – 0.6368	0.00085	0.00153	0.7950 – 0.8006	0.00051	0.00092
0.6369 – 0.6401	0.00084	0.00151	0.8007 – 0.8074	0.00050	0.00090
0.6402 – 0.6433	0.00083	0.00149	0.8075 – 0.8158	0.00049	0.00088
0.6434 – 0.6466	0.00082	0.00148	0.8159 – 0.8244	0.00048	0.00086
0.6467 – 0.6506	0.00081	0.00146	0.8245 – 0.8329	0.00047	0.00085
0.6507 – 0.6539	0.00080	0.00144	0.8330 – 0.8424	0.00046	0.00083
0.6540 – 0.6582	0.00079	0.00142	0.8425 – 0.8519	0.00045	0.00081
0.6583 – 0.6634	0.00078	0.00140	0.8520 – 0.8626	0.00044	0.00079
0.6635 – 0.6677	0.00077	0.00139	0.8627 – 0.8748	0.00043	0.00077
0.6678 – 0.6719	0.00076	0.00137	0.8749 – 0.8909	0.00042	0.00076
0.6720 – 0.6765	0.00075	0.00135	0.8910 – 0.9079	0.00041	0.00074
0.6766 – 0.6810	0.00074	0.00133	0.9080 – 0.9305	0.00040	0.00072
0.6811 – 0.6849	0.00073	0.00131	0.9306 – 0.9523	0.00039	0.00070
0.6850 – 0.6902	0.00072	0.00130	0.9524 – 0.9755	0.00038	0.00068
0.6903 – 0.6958	0.00071	0.00128	0.9756 – 1.0000	0.00037	0.00067
0.6959 – 0.7007	0.00070	0.00126	1.0001 – 1.0184	0.00036	0.00065
0.7008 – 0.7054	0.00069	0.00124	1.0185 – 1.0375	0.00035	0.00063
0.7055 – 0.7108	0.00068	0.00122	1.0376 – 1.0552	0.00034	0.00061
0.7109 – 0.7161	0.00067	0.00121	1.0553 – 1.0759	0.00033	0.00059
0.7162 – 0.7212	0.00066	0.00119	1.0760 – 1.1249	0.00032	0.00058
0.7213 – 0.7262	0.00065	0.00117			
0.7263 – 0.7315	0.00064	0.00115			
0.7316 – 0.7366	0.00063	0.00113			

Viscosity

The viscosity of a fluid governs its flow characteristics and specifically functional losses when the fluid is in motion. Viscosity also controls slippage and internal leakage and thus has a direct bearing on pump efficiency. The viscosity of a fluid may demand the use of a specific type of pump if it is to be handled efficiently. Fluid viscosity is normally measured in arbitrary empirical scales *eg* Redwood No 1 or Redwood No 2 (UK practice) Engler degrees or Engler seconds (continental Europe) Saybolt Universal Seconds (SUS) or Saybolt Furol (SSF) (American practice) Ford Cup 113 or 114 (American practice).

Viscosity definitions

If a plate is moved at constant speed c_O over a viscous medium (Figure 1), the medium adheres to the underside of the plate and is entrained at the speed c_O. The internal friction of the liquid causes the speed to vary at right angles to the direction of flow between the fixed and moving plates.

$$F = \eta A \times dc/dy$$

related to the friction surface of the underside:

$$\tau = \eta\, dc/dy$$

The proportionality factor η is called *dynamic viscosity,* with the dimension mass (length x time).

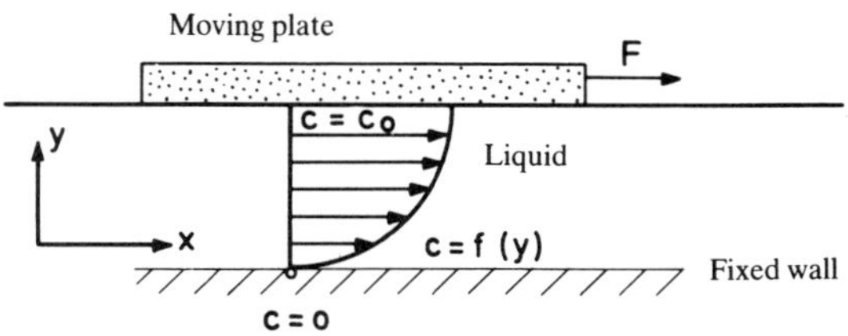

$$F = \eta \times A \times \frac{dc}{dy} \rightarrow \tau = \eta \frac{dc}{dy}$$

where:

F	=	frictional force
η	=	dynamic viscosity
A	=	friction surface
τ	=	shear stress

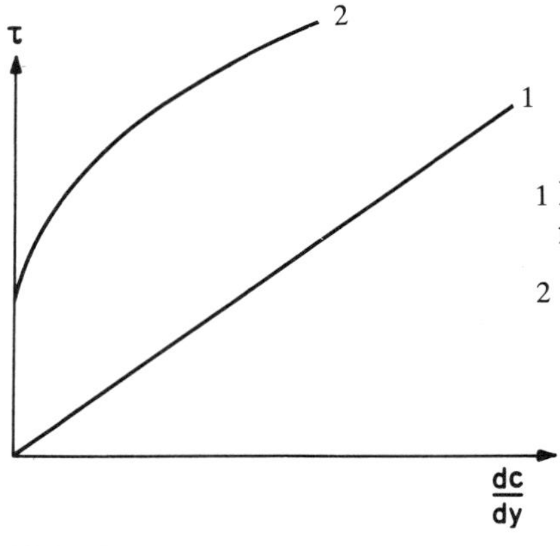

1 Newtonian fluid

2 Non-Newtonian fluid (e.g. carbon black in boiled oil, effluent sludge)

Figure 1

The international units recommended are:

$$1\,\text{Pa s} = 1 \quad \frac{\text{kg}}{\text{sm}}$$

Previously the unit poise (P) was used as viscosity unit:

$$1\,\text{cP} = 10^{-2} \times \text{P} = 10^{-3}\ \frac{\text{kg}}{\text{m s}} = 10^{-3}\,\text{Pa s} = 10^{-2} \quad \frac{\text{g}}{\text{cm} \times \text{s}}$$

Liquids whose frictional behaviour conforms to this equation are called Newtonian fluids. Viscosity depends on temperature and pressure, though the influence of the latter is negligible compared with that of temperature. With liquids viscosity diminishes with rising temperature.

For hydrodynamic purposes it is convenient to relate dynamic viscosity η to density ρ. This gives us the *kinematic viscosity.*

$$\nu = \frac{\eta}{\rho} \text{ with the dimension «length}^2\text{/time»}$$

The following units are introduced by DIN 1301 and 1342:

$$1 \quad \frac{\text{mm}^2}{\text{s}} = 10^{-6} \quad \frac{\text{m}^2}{\text{s}}$$

Previously the unit stoke (St) was customary:

$$1\,\text{cSt} = 10^{-2} \quad \text{St} = \frac{\text{mm}^2}{\text{s}} = 10^{-6}\ \frac{\text{m}^2}{\text{s}}$$

Degrees Engler (E): The degree Engler expresses the ratio between the efflux time of 200 cm³ distilled water at 20 °C and of the same amount of test liquid at 20 °C (DIN 51560).

The following equation is used for conversion:

$$\nu = {}^{\circ}\text{E} \times 7{\cdot}6\,(1 - 1/{}^{\circ}\text{E}^3) \qquad \left(10^{-6} \times \frac{\text{m}^2}{\text{s}}\right)$$

Saybolt viscosity: Saybolt Seconds Universal (SSU). This unit is customary in the USA and defines the efflux time for a given quantity of liquid from a defined viscosimeter.

Viscosity also depends to a considerable extent on the amount of gas dissolved in the liquid. Crude oil containing a lot of gas is less viscous than the same oil with little gas.

Pumping viscous liquids

By virtue of their good delivery properties (no pulsation, no safety valve needed as with positive displacement pumps, simple delivery control) the use of centrifugal pumps is being extended increasingly in the chemical industry and refineries to high-viscosity media (up to about 100×10^{-6} m²/s), although an efficiency loss must be taken into account compared with positive displacement pumps with the same service data.

The economical duty limit for centrifugal pumps is about 150×10^{-6} m²/s. Use of a centrifugal pump is possible up to about 500×10^{-6} m²/s (but a higher NPSH must be made available for this higher viscosity. Channel impeller and torque flow pumps allow higher values (800 to 1000 x 10^{-6} m^2/s), depending on size and type.

Reciprocating or rotary positive displacement pumps are employed for still higher viscosities (Figure 2).

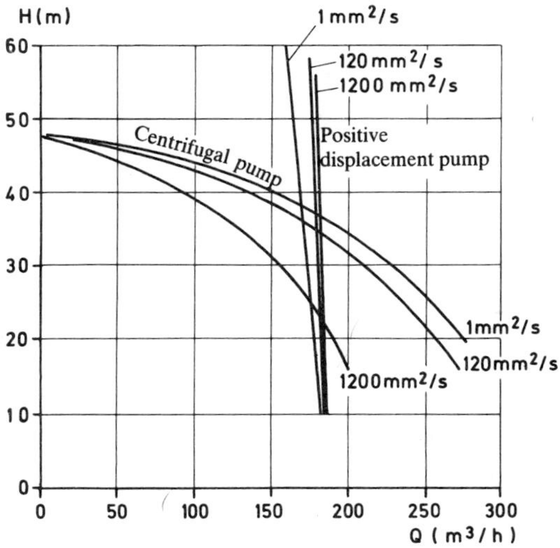

Figure 2
Comparision of characteristics for reciprocating and centrifugal pumps at constant speed and different viscosities.

The pressure losses in the impeller and diffuser channels of centrifugal pumps, the impeller friction and internal leakage losses, depend to a large extent on the viscosity of the pumping liquid. Consequently, the characteristics ascertained for water use their validity when pumping liquids or other viscosity such as oil.

The higher the viscosity of a liquid compared to water, the greater is the loss of delivery capacity and head for a given power input. Consequently, the best efficiency point of the pump moves towards lower flow rates and efficiency. The power input shifts up parallel to that for water. The head against closed valve is generally retained. For converting the water characteristic to a liquid with a defined viscosity, the correction values laid down in the Standards of Hydraulic Institute, New York, USA, 14th edition 1983 are employed internationally (Table 5). The correction values are based on tests with single-stage pumps in oil (DN 50 to 200 mm with relatively low specific speeds). The corrections are mean values from various measurements.

The Hydraulic Institute correction values are valid only as follows:

(i) For non-Newtonian fluids, accepting solid mixtures, paper stock or other non-homogeneous liquids;

(ii) For open or closed radial hydraulics (not for mixed flow or axial flow hydraulics or side channel hydraulics);

(iii) Where there is adequate NPSH available;

(iv) Within the diagram liits of Table 5.

TABLE 5 – CORRECTION VALUES FOR PUMP CHARACTERISTICS WHEN PUMPING VISCOUS LIQUIDS

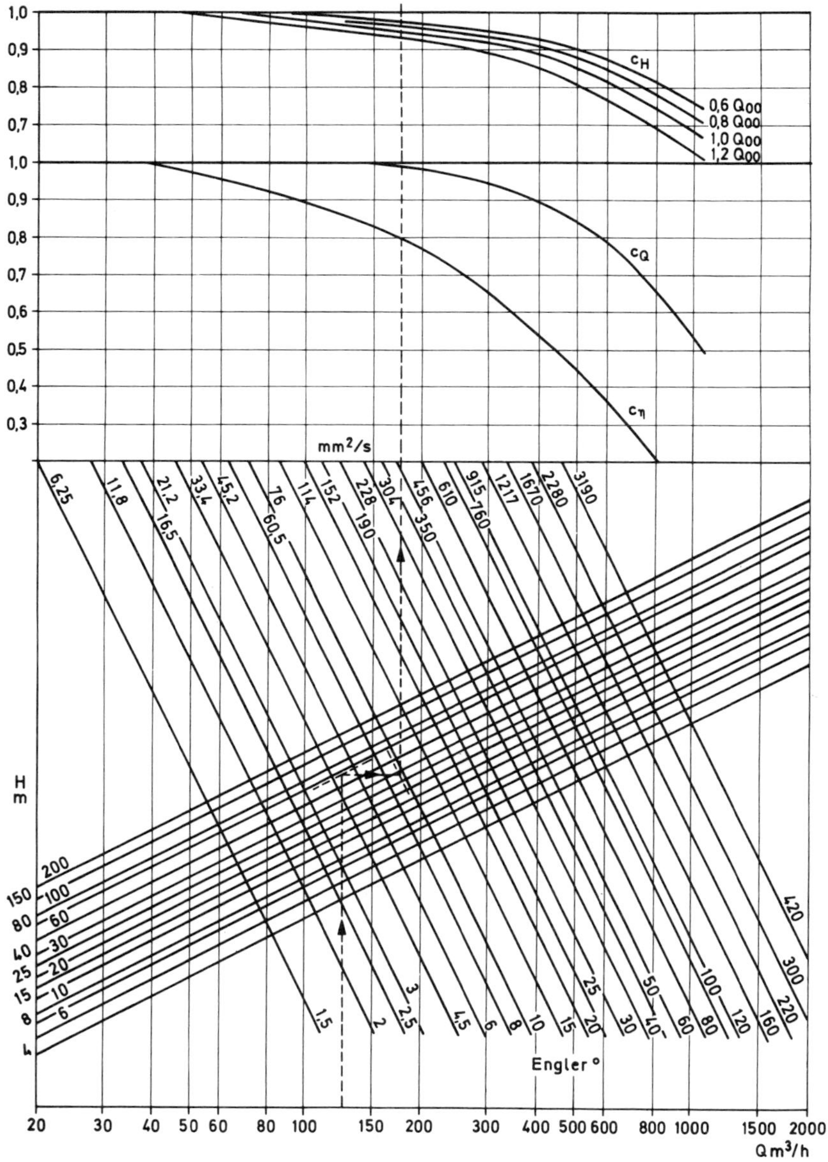

It should be noted that with multi-stage pumps only the stage head is taken and with double entry pumps only half the flow rate. If the characteristic for pumping water is known, that for the viscous liquid can be determined by multiplying the water values by the appropriate correction factors.

Pump with 14 inch branches in stainless steel for pumping high viscosity polymers up to 1 000 000 Redwood No 1.

Viscosity is quite independent of the density or specific gravity of a fluid. Thus, water and many aqueous solutions have a viscosity of approximately 1 centistoke at normal ambient temperatures. Petroleum products with specific gravity less than that of water have viscosities ranging from less than that of water, *eg* petrol to hundreds of times greater, *eg* heavy lubricating oils.

Viscosity and temperature

The viscosity of any given fluid is also considerably influenced by temperature. In general the viscosity of all liquids decreases with increasing temperature and increases with decreasing temperature. The opposite if generally true of gases. The rate of change, however, can vary widely with different liquids and can be referred to in terms of viscosity index. The higher the viscosity index, the less the change of viscosity with change of temperature and *vice versa*.

Compared with most other types of fluid, water is unusual in having both a low viscosity and a high viscosity index. Variations of viscosity are, therefore, seldom significant where pump design and performance are concerned. Oil fluids, without additives, generally have a viscosity index of 140 down to 100 or less, the figure tending to decrease with increasing 'weight' or actual viscosity. Over extremes of temperature, this may represent a change in viscosity of hundreds, or even thousands, of centistokes.

The kinematic viscosity of water is 1 centistoke (4 seconds Redwood No 1) at around 20 °C. A figure commonly adopted for water performance calculation, however, and also for aqueous solutions which have substantially the same flow characteristics as water, is 4 centistokes (equivalent to 30 seconds Redwood No 1).

Characteristic viscosity figures for other fluids are normally quoted for specific temperatures. Lacking further data, a close approximation of viscosity/ temperature characteristics can be made by plotting the 2 or 3 figures available on a log-log, log-scale graph (ASTM chart) and joining them by a straight line. This is not an exact method but for most fluids the viscosity temperature relationship is linear with such scales. More complete data are usually available for fluids where viscosity/temperature variations may be critical, either in tabular form or plotted in the form of an ASTM graph, as shown in Figure 3.

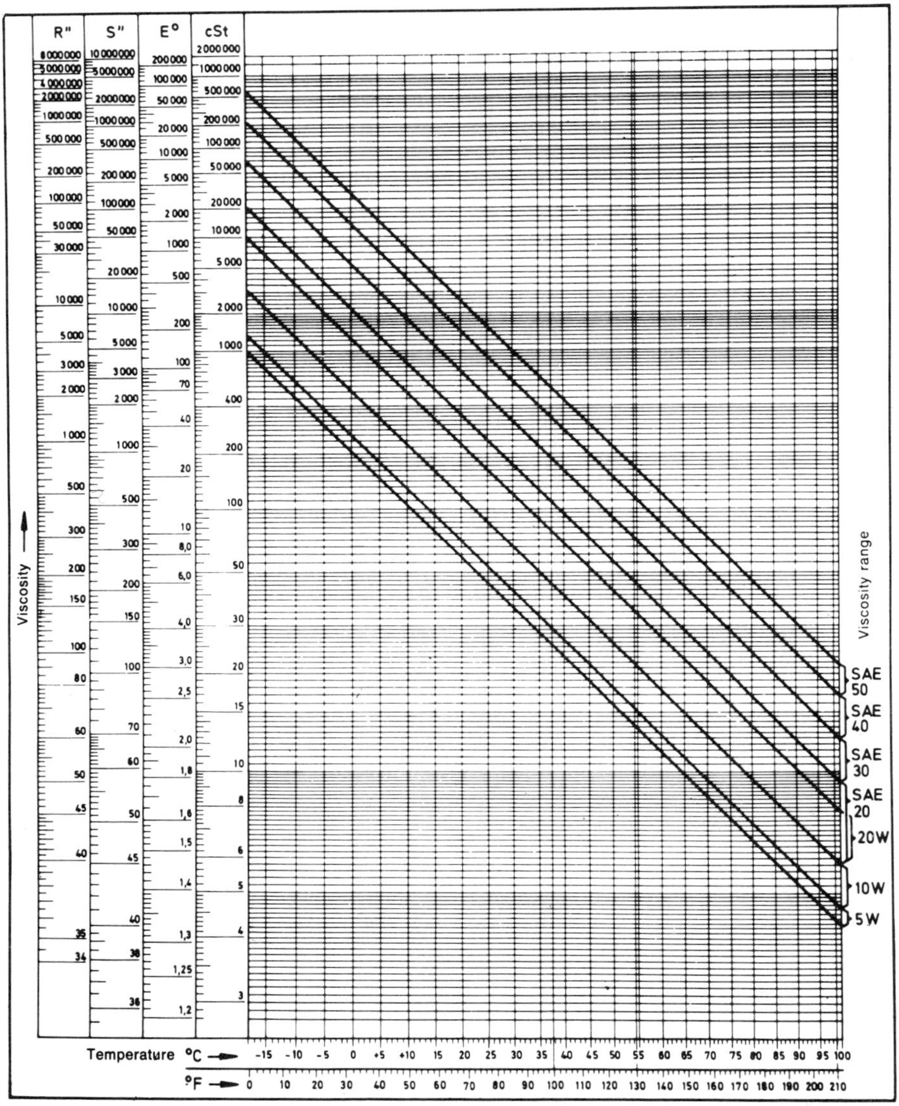

Figure 3
Viscosity–temperature chart.

Viscous behaviour of fluids
Fluids where the viscosity remains constant with agitation or shear rate (viscosity is only affected by temperature changes) are known as Newtonian fluids. Typical

fluids of this type are water, aqueous solutions, mineral oils, hydrocarbons, syrups and some resins.

Other types include:

(i) Dilatant fluids – where viscosity increases where agitation or shear rate is increased. Fluids of this type include clays and some slurries.

(ii) Rheopectic fluids – where viscosity increases with increasing agitation or shear rate up to a maximum value up to any constant rate of agitation.

(iii) Plastic and pseudoplastic fluids – where viscosity decreases with increasing shear rate, but initial viscosity may be so high as to prevent start of flow in a normal pumping system.

These are also known as Bingham fluids. Fluids of this type include latex, paints and gels. Generalised viscosity characteristics of these fluids are shown in Figure 4.

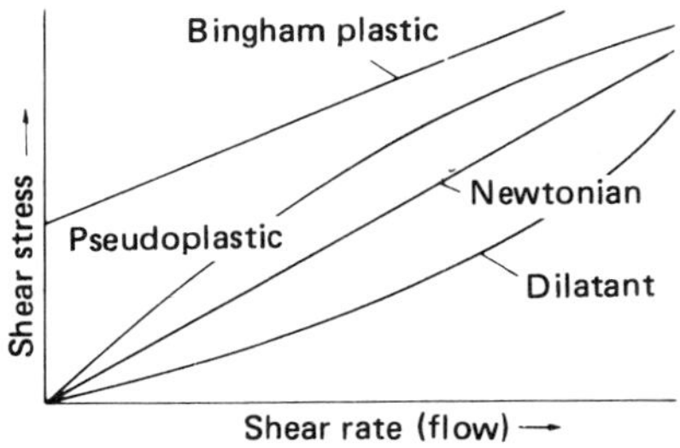

Figure 4
General viscosity characteristics of dilatant, rheopectic and plastic and pseudo-plastic fluids.

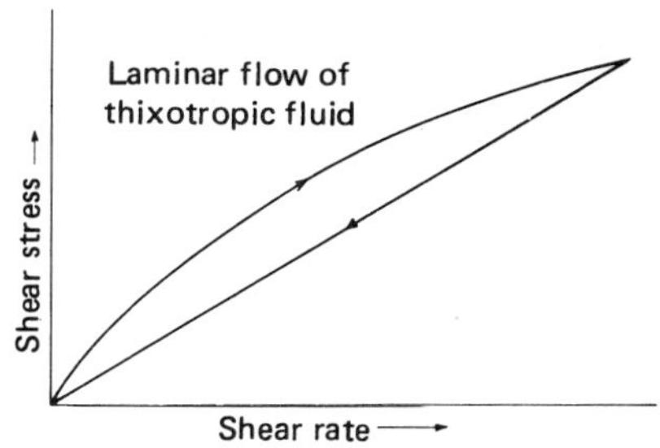

Figure 5
Typical rheogram for a thixotropic fluid under laminar flow.

Thixotropic fluids

These are a further type with distinct characteristics. In this case viscosity decreases as agitation or shear rate is increased. Thixotropic fluids exhibit a hysteresis effect in that there apparent or instantaneous viscosity is dependent on the previous history of the fluid. Figure 5 is a typical rheogram for a thixotropic fluid under laminar flow. Turbulent flow will tend to change the structure of the fluid, which will recover if left standing for a sufficient time. Fluids of this type include greases, soaps, starches, vegetable oils, varnishes, some resins, tar, asphalts, glues and some inks. In a similar vein, colloidal fluids behave like thixotropic fluids, but will not recover their original viscosity when agitation is stopped. Fluids of this type include colloidal solutions of soaps in water and oils, lotions, shampoos and gelatinous compounds.

Solids in suspension

Fluids containing solids in suspension, generally known as slurries, exhibit an increase in specific gravity. Such fluids are, however, non-Newtonian and the viscosity figure under any conditions is an apparent rather than a true one. The degree of suspension, and thus the consistency of the fluid, may also depend on the flow rate. This may be generally related to a full velocity or the minimum flow rate necessary to maintain the solids in suspension and prevent them from settling out. This, in turn, depends on the size of the solids and also their concentration.

The handling of fluids containing solids sets particular problems as far as pump design is concerned. Thus, the pump must have internal clearances sufficient to pass the solids without jamming or clogging, and usually also requires hardened surfaces or hard facings to resist their abraiding action. Other contaminants may include stringy and fibrous solids, calling for further modification or comminuting device preceding the pump to reduce the size of the fibrous material before it enters the pump.

A further class of suspended solids is one where the solids content is delicate and may be damaged by normal pumping *eg* fruit, fish. Where this has to be avoided *ie* the solids content is an important part of the product being handled – the pump type may have to be selected to avoid damage to the product.

Homogeneous mixtures
Homogeneous mixtures of solids and liquids may range in character from thin pastes to thick pulps and stock, with flow characteristics varying accordingly. In general, with such mixtures, gravitational flow characteristics remain similar to those of normal fluids up to a particular consistency. With higher consistencies gravitational flow separates into droplets, the size of the droplets increasing with increasing consistency until they take the form of large slugs. These flow characteristics can affect the design of pumps suitable for handling particular mixtures, especially as regards flow on the intake side.

Vapour pressure
Vapour pressure is a constant for a given liquid at a given temperature and represents a positive quantity to be taken into account when determining the maximum suction lift available. The net positive suction head available is in fact equal to the barametric pressure less the sum of fluid vapour pressure, suction losses and static head (positive or negative). High values of vapour pressure can, therefore, lead to serious reductions in net positive suction head which, if less than the value required, can lead to the fluid vaporising and the pump cavitating. The greater the vapour pressure to start with *ie* the more volatile the liquid, and also the higher the liquid temperature, the more the problem is aggravated. The vapour pressure of water is given in Table 6. Typical values for vapour pressure of miscellaneous fluids are given in Table 7.

Volatile fluids can represent a particular problem in that the vapour pressure of a fluid has a significant effect on the maximum suction lift available from the pump to achieve a required net positive suction head (NPSH).

Hazardous fluids
Fluids are described as hazardous if they or their vapours are flammable, toxic or chemically reactive. This applies particularly to fluid which has escaped by leakage, or vapours of that fluid. Hazards can be divided into three separate categories:

(i) Danger to health.

(ii) Flammability.

(iii) Reactivity and radioactivity.

A classification of some hazardous fluids on this basis is given in Table 8. Fluids which are inflammable or create explosive atmospheres normally require particular care in handling to conform with such national regulations as may apply *eg* National Fire Protection Association (USA), HM Factory Inspectorate (Great Britain), VDE Specifications and PTB Approved Controls (Germany and other European Countries), SEV Test Certificates (Switzerland).

TABLE 6 – VAPOUR PRESSURE OF WATER

Temp °C	Vapour pressure mm mercury	Temp °C	Vapour pressure mm mercury
0	4·579		
1	4·926	50	92·51
2	5·294	51	97·20
3	5·655	52	102·09
4	6·101	53	107·20
5	6·543	54	112·51
6	7·013	55	118·04
7	7·513	56	123·80
8	8·045	57	129·82
9	8·609	58	136·08
10	9·209	59	142·60
11	9·844	60	149·38
12	10·518	61	156·43
13	11·231	62	163·77
14	11·987	63	171·38
15	12·788	64	179·31
16	13·634	65	187·54
17	14·530	66	196·09
18	15·477	67	204·96
19	16·477	68	214·17
20	17·535	69	223·73
21	18·650	70	233·7
22	19·827	71	243·9
23	21·068	72	254.6
24	22·377	73	265·7
25	23·756	74	277·2
26	25·209	75	289·1
27	26·739	76	301·4
28	28·349	77	314·1
29	30·043	78	327·3
30	31·824	79	341·0
31	33·695	80	355·1
32	35·663	81	369·7
33	37·729	82	384·9
34	39·898	83	400·6
35	42·175	84	416·8
36	44·563	85	433·6
37	47·067	86	450·9
38	49·692	87	468·7
39	52·442	88	487·1
40	55·324	89	506·1
41	58·34	90	525·8
42	61·50	91	546·1
43	64·80	92	567·0
44	68·26	93	588·6
45	71·88	94	610·9
46	75·65	95	633·9
47	79·60	96	657·6
48	83·71	97	682·1
49	88·02	98	707·3
		99	733·2

TABLE 7 – SPECIFIC GRAVITY AND VAPOUR PRESSURE OF INDUSTRIAL SOLVENTS

Fluid	Specific gravity 20/20 °C	Vapour pressure mm Hg at 20 °C
Acetone	0·791 to 0·793	184·00
Amyl acetate	0·860 to 0·870	5·20
sec-Amyl acetate	0·856 to 0·866	5·60
Amyl alcohol	0·810 to 0·820	4·80
sec-Amyl alcohol	0·810 to 0·816	5·00
iso-Butyl acetate	0·868 to 0·873	16·40
n-Butyl acetate	0·874 to 0·884	10·00
iso-Butyl alcohol	0·803	8·00
n-Butyl alcohol	0·808 to 0·812	4·40
sec-Butyl alcohol	0·807 to 0·809	12·10
tert-Butyl alcohol	0·781 to 0·784	7·00
Butyl carbitol	0·953 to 0·958	0·02
Butyl cellosolve	0·900 to 0·905	0·60
Carbon disulphide	1·267	295·00
Carbon tetrachloride	1·596	91·00
Cyclohexanol	0·950 to 0·954	1·00
Diacetone alcohol	0·938 to 0·941	0·80
Diisobutyl ketone	0·808 to 0·815	1·70
Dioxitol (carbitol)	1·024 to 1·030	0·20
Ethyl acetate	0·900 to 0·903	72·80
Ethyl alcohol	0·790	43·60
Ethly lactate	1·020 to 1·036	1·80
Ethyl ether	0·715	442·00
Hexylene glycol	0·922 to 0·924	0·02
Methyl oxide	0·858 to 0·860	8·00
Methyl acetate	0·930 to 0·940	166·00
Methyl alcohol	0·792 to 0·793	96·00
Methyl dioxitol	1·016 to 1·026	0·20
Methyl ethyl ketone	0·805 to 0·807	71·70
Methyul isobutyl ketone	0·800 to 0·804	15·20
Methyl isobutyl carbinol	0·807 to 0·809	2·20
Methyl oxitol	0·963 to 0·967	8·00
Methyl oxitol acetate	1·003 to 1·008	3·30
Oxitol (cellosolve)	0·928 to 0·933	3·80
Oxitol acetate	0·971 to 0·976	1·20
iso-Propyl acetate	0·870 to 0·873	48·00
iso-Propyl alcohol	0·785 to 0·787	31·20
iso-Propyl ether	0·725 to 0·727	119·40
Trichlorethylene	1·466	56·00

TABLE 8 – HAZARDOUS FLUIDS

Group name according to BS 229 1957 and BS 2474		Spontaneous ignition temp		Hazard identification†		
		°C	°F	Health	Flamm-ability	Reactiv-ity
(i)	Methane	538	999	1	4	0
(ii)	Blast furnace gas	–	–	2	4	0
	Carbon monoxide	610	1128	2	4	0
	Propane	466	871	1	4	0
	Butane	405	761	1	4	0
	Pentane	308	588	1	4	0
	Hexane	261	502	1	3	0
	Heptane	222	433	1	3	0
	iso-Octane	220	428	0	3	0
	Decane	208	406	0	2	0
	Benzene	564	1044	2	3	0
	Xylene	464	867	2	3	0
	Cyclohexane	260	500	1	3	0
	Acetone	538	1000	1	3	0
	Ethyl methyl ketone (MEK)	516	900	1	3	0
	Methyl acetate	502	935	1	3	0
	Ethyl acetate	427	800	1	3	0
	n-Propyl acetate	450	842	1	3	0
	n-Butyl acetate	422	790	1	3	0
	Amyl acetate	–	–	1	3	0
	Chloroethylene (vinyl chloride)	472	882	2	4	2
	Methanol (methyl alcohol)	464	867	1	3	0
	Ethanol (ethyl alcohol)	423	793	0	3	0
	i-Butyl alcohol	427	800	1	3	0
	n-Butanol (butyl alcohol)	365	689	1	3	0
	Amyul alcohol	300	572	1	3	0
	Ethyl nitrite	90	194	2	4	4
	Butadiene 1:3	428	804	2	4	2
(iii[a])	Ethylene	450	842	1	4	2
	Diethyl ether (ethyl ether)	180	356	2	4	–
	Ethylene oxide	428	804	2	4	3
(iii[b])	Coal gas (town gas)	–	–	2	4	0
	Coke oven gas	–	–	2	4	0
(iv)	Acetylene	294	571	1	4	4
	Carbon disulphide	199	212	2	3	0
	Ethyl nitrate	–	–	–	3	4
	Hydrogen	580	1085	0	4	–
	Water gas	–	–	2	4	0

†Degree of hazard from 0 = non-existent to 4 = very hazardous.

Pump Performance

THE THEORETICAL maximum suction lift obtainable by a pump is that corresponding to a pump reducing the absolute pressure to zero at the pump inlet, or mathematically atmospheric temperature divided by fluid density. In the case of clean cold water this theoretical head is 10·33 metres (33·9 ft) whereas for any liquid:

$$\text{Theoretical maximum lift} = \frac{10{\cdot}33}{SG}\ \text{metres} \quad \text{or} \quad \frac{33{\cdot}9}{SG}\ \text{feet}$$

where SG is the specific gravity of the fluid.

It also follows that this lift is directly proportional to prevailing atmospheric pressure *ie* decreasing with increasing altitude; and also varies with temperature (which affects fluid density and thus SG).

The practical maximum suction lift available (MSLA) is also modified *ie,* reduced by:

(i) Friction losses involved in the suction piping system and velocity head:

$$\frac{V^2}{2g}$$

(ii) The effect of the vapour pressure of the fluid at the temperature at which it is being pumped.

Dynamic losses are:

(a) Entry losses in the suction pipe;

(b) Frictional losses produced by flow through the pipe;

(c) Losses at any fittings in the inlet system;

(d) Possible losses at the pump inlet.

These four figures are often combined, their sum being expressed as the effective loss of head.

Similarly, the vapour pressure of the fluid represents an effective loss of ambient pressure. Thus, maximum suction lift available (MSLA) from a pump under dynamic conditions (see Figure 1) is given by:

$$\mathbf{MSLA} = P_A - h_f \pm h_s - P_V + P_g - V^2/2g$$

where:

h_f = the sum of all dynamic friction losses

h_s = static head, either negative if below the pump or positive if above the pump

P_V = vapour pressure of fluid

P_g = gauge pressure on the surface of the liquid (gauge pressure being the measured pressure above atmospheric)

P_A = absolute atmospheric pressure

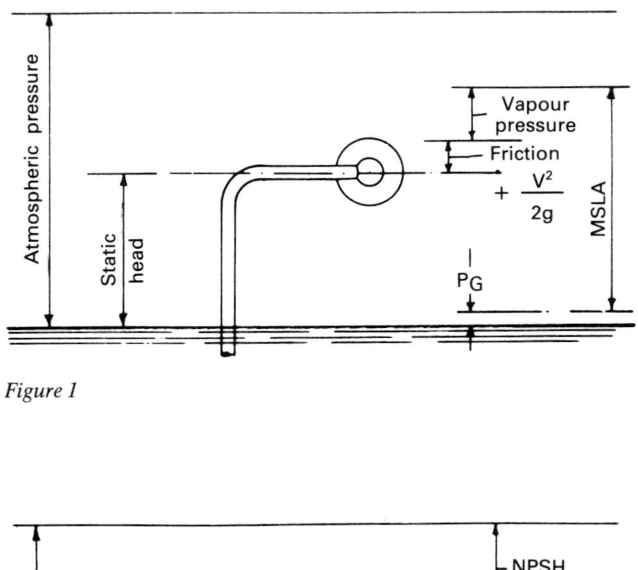

Figure 1

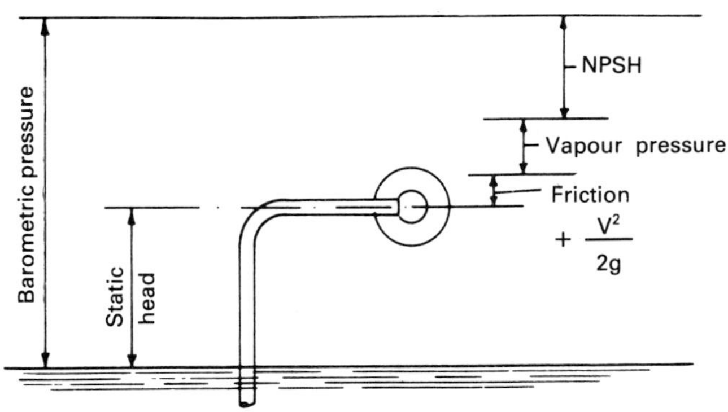

Figure 2

Net positive suction head (NPSH)

Actual suction performance – the net positive suction head (NPSH) – is the total suction head in metres (feet) of liquid absolute determined at the suction nozzle referred to datum less the vapour pressure of the liquid in metres (feet) absolute.

Actual suction performance is normally described in terms of net positive suction head (NPSH), representing the difference between the theoretical figure and sum of the static suction lift, suction friction head and vapour pressure as shown in Figure 2. Basically, this implies that under given operating conditions the absolute pressure at the pump inlet must not be less than the vapour pressure of the liquid being pumped, otherwise it will flash into vapour and suction head will break down or cause cavitation in the pump.

Expressed in terms of heads:

NPSH = atmospheric pressure – MSLA

This implies that under any given operating conditions involving actual atmospheric pressure static lift and dynamic losses, the absolute pressure at the pump intake must be greater than the vapour pressure of the liquid being pumped, otherwise the fluid will flash into vapour and the suction flow will break down causing the pump to cavitate.

In simple terms, the required NPSH of a pump is the 'allowance' necessary to cover head losses within the pump. Part of these losses will be reduced by friction and viscous drag, part by internal leakage (in the case of positive displacement pumps), and part by any dynamic depression head generated within the pump *eg* with rotor dynamic pumps.

Given a required NPSH for a pump to operate at rated capacity, the allowable suction lift can be determined by deducting suction friction head and vapour pressure from the theoretical suction lift available (suitably corrected for atmospheric pressure or altitude and temperature). If the sum to be deducted from the theoretical suction lift is the greater, then the difference is the positive static head necessary to ensure satisfactory operation

NPSH required

The required NPSH of a pump is a manufacturer's figure and specifically related to speed and capacity in the case of roto-dynamic pumps. It also varies widely with different types of pump, *eg* from virtually zero in the case of reciprocating pumps to a higher proportion of the theoretical suction head with axial flow pump (which are normally operated on flooded suction). Figures may be quoted against water temperature or against capacity and in the latter case they are often allied to the suction lift possible at such capacities. It is a general rule with all rotor dynamic pumps that as the available NPSH decreases the capacity also decreases. Thus forgiven operating conditions the higher the suction lift required the lower the capacity of a given size of pump and *vice versa.* Excessive suction lifts or insufficient NPSH generally lead to cavitation. This condition (or more exactly a reduction in available NPSH) can result in a rise in fluid temperature increasing the vapour pressure.

In the case of reciprocating pumps even more care may be needed in the design of the pump inlet system because of the pulsating nature of the flow. If sufficient NPSH cannot be provided, a booster pump will have to be used mounted close to the tank to provide maximum NPSH and to minimize the pulsating effect of the main pump. However, as a general rule, suction conditions on roto-dynamic pumps are usually far more critical than in positive displacement pumps (basically because the NPSH required by this class of pump is inherently higher). Thus, larger roto-dynamic pump installations are seldom finalized without a detailed study and analysis of the pump suction piping, entry conditions and other factors affecting the overall operating conditions, in order to ensure that the NPSH requirement is properly – and consistently – met.

The required NPSH can be represented diagrammatically as shown in Figure 3 which illustrates the importance of vapour pressure considerations. Vapour pressure is constant for a given liquid at a given temperature, the required NPSH is a function of the pump design and so, since all other factors are known, using such a diagram, the permissible suction lift can be calculated. Working over a greater lift than this would almost certainly cause problems by fluid vapourization.

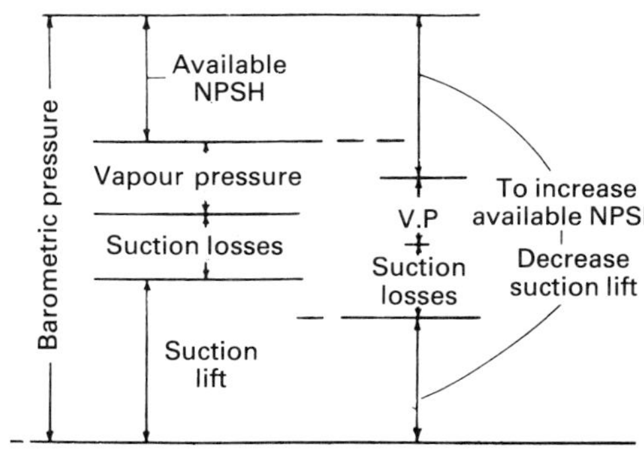

Figure 3

Where the suction supply is from a closed tank or sealed reservoir, tank pressure is substituted for atmospheric temperature, and converted to equivalent head to be in constant units. NPSH, in fact represents the pressure head required or available to force a given flow rate of specified fluid through the suction piping into the pump, but where it is given on pump characteristic curves it is normally presented as a head figure and corrected to the centre line of the pump. Basically, therefore, the NPSH depends on the suction system which may be categorised under four headings:

(i) Liquid level under atmospheric pressure (Figure 4)

NPSH available (metric units) $= \dfrac{10{\cdot}2}{SG}(P_A - P_v) \pm h_s - h_f$

NPSH available (English units) $= \dfrac{1{\cdot}3}{SG}(P_A - 2{\cdot}04\,P_v) \pm h_s - h_f$

where P_A = atmospheric pressure

In the case of pump:

(1) use $+ h_s$

(2) use $- h_s$

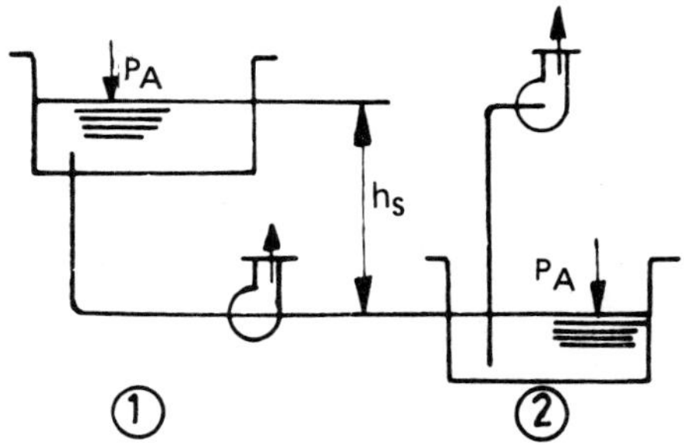

Figure 4
Liquid level under atmospheric pressure.

(ii) Liquid level exposed to pressure (Figure 5)

NPSH available (metric units) $= \frac{10{\cdot}2}{SG}(P_1 + P_A - P_v) \pm h_s - h_f$

NPSH available (English units) $= \frac{2{\cdot}31}{SG}(P_1 + 0{\cdot}49\,P_A - P_v) \pm h_s - h_f$

In the case of pump:

(1) use + h

(2) use – h

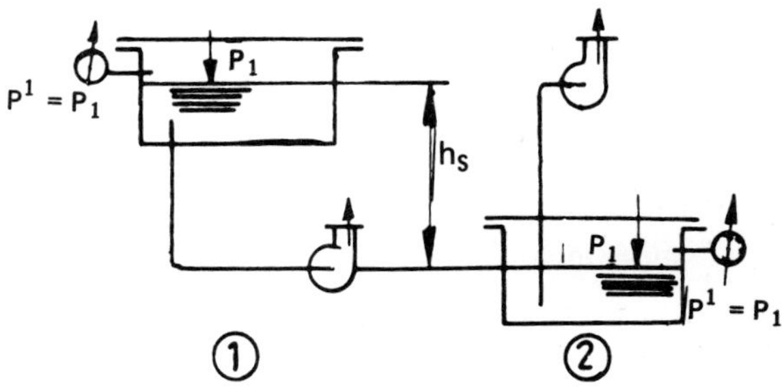

Figure 5
Liquid level exposed to a pressure.

(iii) Liquid level under vapour pressure of fluid (Figure 6)

NPSH available $= h - h_f$
(metric units)

In the case of pump (1):

$P^1 = P_V - P_A$

$= P_V - 0{\cdot}00134P_A$

In the case of pump (2):

$v^1 = P_A - 760\ P_V$

$= 1000\ (P_A - P_V)$

NPSH available = $h - h_f$
(English units)
In the case of pump:
(1) $P^1 = P_V - 0{\cdot}49\,P_A$
(2) $v^1 = P_A - 2{\cdot}04\,P_V$

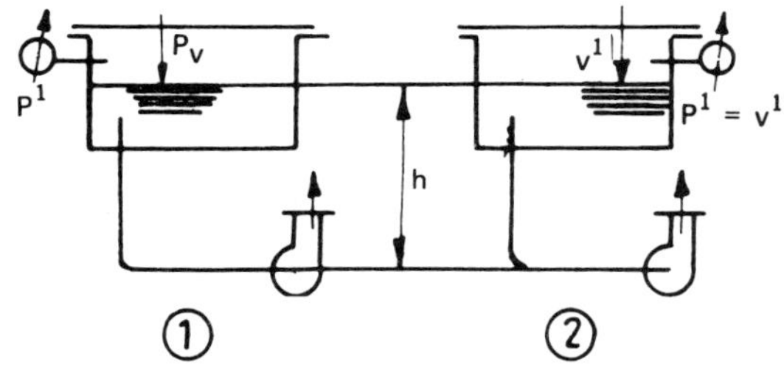

Figure 6
Liquid level under vapour pressure of liquid.

(iv) Liquid level exposed to a vacuum (Figure 7)

NPSH available (metric units) $= \dfrac{10{\cdot}2}{SG}\left(P_A - \dfrac{v^1}{1000} - P_V\right) \pm h - h_f$

In the case of pump:
(1) use + h
(2) use − h

Symbols and units used in these formulas are as follows:

NPSH available (English units) $= \dfrac{1{\cdot}13}{SG}(P_A - v^1 - 2{\cdot}04\,P_V) \pm h - h_f$

In the case of pump:
(1) use + h
(2) use − h

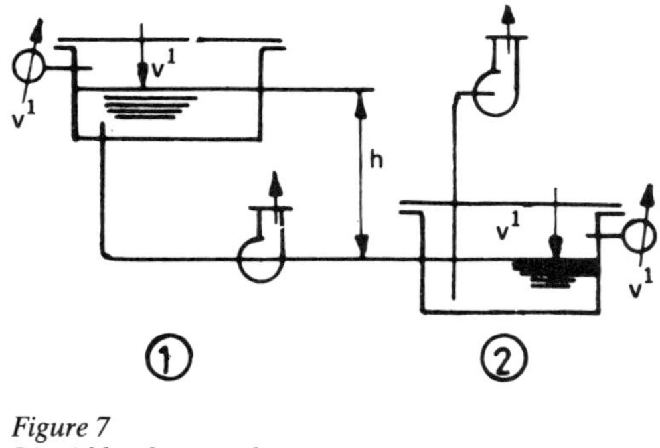

Figure 7
Liquid level exposed to a vacuum.

Symbols and units used in these formulas are as follows:

Symbol	Meaning	Metric Unit	English Unit
NPSH		metres	feet
P_A	barometric pressure	1.013 bar 760 mm Hg	29.92 in Hg
P_1	pressure on liquid level	bar g	lb/in^2 g
P_V	vapour pressure	bar g	lb/in^2 g
v^1	vacuum on liquid level*	millibar	in Hg
p^1	pressure*	bar g	lb/in^2 g
SG	specific gravity of fluid		
h	static level difference	metres	feet
h_f	friction loss in suction line	metres	feet

* = critical pressure

Effect of pump type

The NPSH required by a pump is a function of the pump design and type. Figure 8 gives the NPSH required for a centrifugal pump versus a screw pump with both units operating on a medium with a viscosity identical to water. Figure 9 shows the NPSH required by a centrifugal pump and a screw pump selected for the same duty, but then used on different media with an increasing viscosity scale. From this it can be clearly seen that as a liquid becomes more viscous, the NPSH required by a centrifugal pump causes difficulty in most commercial applications whereas the screw pump can readily carry on pumping. It is normal to decrease as viscosity increases, this being for overall efficiency as well as 'NPSH required' problems.

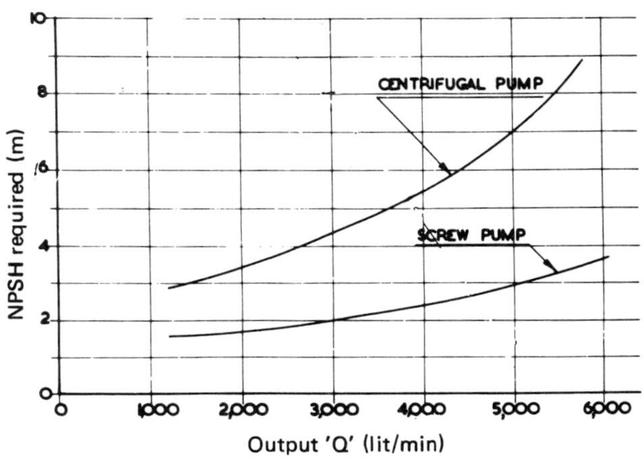

Figure 8
Output = 3500 l/min.
Head = 35 m.

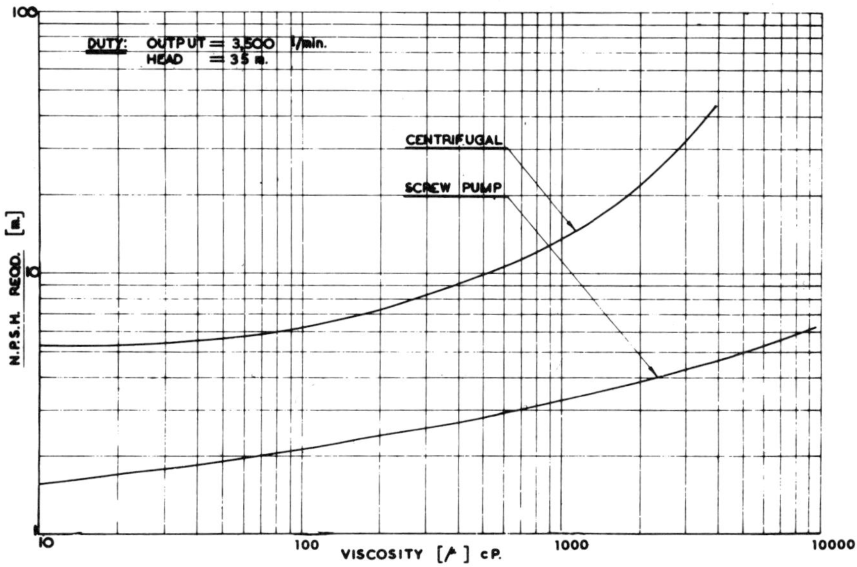

Figure 9
Output = 3500 l/min.
Head = 35 m.

TABLE 1 – SUCTION CHARACTERISTICS OF PUMPS

Pump Type	Maximum Suction Lift		Likely Practical Maximum Suction Lift		Remarks
	Feet	Metres	Feet	Metres	
Centrifugal, small					Not self-priming – usually worked with flooded suction.
Centrifugal, single-stage	27	8.25	20	6.0	Not self-priming
Centrifugal, two-stage	27	8.25	15	4.5	Not self-priming
Centrifugal, multi-stage	27	8.25	15	4.5	Not self-priming
Centrifugal : self-priming	27	8.25	15	4.5	
Centrifugal : regenerative	27	8.25	15	4.5	Self-priming
Centrifugal : mixed flow	15	4.50	5–10	1.5–3	Not self-priming
Centrifugal : axial flow					Not self-priming – usually operated on low head or flooded suction
Borehole : immersible			Nil	Nil	Flooded suction
Submersible			Nil	Nil	Flooded suction
Reciprocating : direct-acting	27	8.25	22	6.7	Self-priming
Reciprocating : plunger	27	8.25	22	6.7	Self-priming
Reciprocating : piston	27	8.25	22	6.7	Self-priming
Radial piston	27	8.25	22	6.7	Self-priming
Gear			5	1.5	Usually operated with flooded suction
Vane			6	1.8	Can self-prime at high speeds – usually operated with flooded suction

Practical suction lifts

Maximum suction lift available for any pump depends both on the NPSH required by the pump and the suction conditions. The NPSH figure will vary with the type of pump. Certain types of pump are inherently unsuitable for developing any appreciable suction lift (*ie* are relatively ineffective at reducing the absolute pressure at the pump intake), or are restricted to low working values. Also some types of pump which are capable of high suction lift are not self-priming and may in fact have to be worked with flooded suction to overcome this limitation, or be fitted with a self-priming device. Thus, small centrifugal pumps are often designed as immersible units. Larger non self-priming pumps may more readily operate auxiliary priming or a self-priming device to enable them to be operated with good suction lift characteristics. Table 1 summarises the suction lift characteristics of the main types of pump.

Head and pressure

Pressure can be measured in terms of the height of a column of liquid exerting that pressure on the horizontal liquid surface at the bottom of the column. It is independent of the cross section of the column and can thus be expressed as a single linear quantity *eg* metres or feet.

The relationship between pressure (P) and head (H) thus follows as:

$$P = wH$$

where:
w is the specific weight of the fluid

Or in engineering units:

$$\text{Pressure (bar)} = \frac{\text{density (gm/cm}^3\text{) x H (metres)}}{10} = \frac{\text{SG x H (metres)}}{10}$$

$$\text{Pressure (lb/in}^2\text{)} = \frac{\text{specific weight (lb/ft}^3\text{) x H (feet)}}{144} = \frac{\text{SG x H (feet)}}{2{\cdot}25}$$

$$\text{Head (metres)} = \frac{\text{10 x P (bar)}}{\text{density (gm/cm}^3\text{)}} = \frac{\text{10 x P (bar)}}{\text{SG}}$$

$$\text{Head (feet)} = \frac{\text{144 x P (lb/in}^2\text{)}}{\text{specific weight (lb/ft}^3\text{)}} = \frac{2{\cdot}25\text{ P (lb/in}^2\text{)}}{\text{SG}}$$

Requirements from the pump

To meet a specific pumping duty, a pump must meet the suction conditions prevailing and develop a sufficient delivery head. In practical terms the total head developed must take into account:

(i) Any difference between liquid levels on inlet and outlet sides.

(ii) Any diference between vacuum and/or pressure on the inlet and outlet side liquid free surfaces.

(iii) Frictional resistance, *ie* head required to overcome resistance to flow through pipes and fittings.

(iv) The velocity head at point of final discharge.

Static head conditions

Static head conditions are readily defined from the geometry of the layout. Thus, on the suciton side there are three possibilities:

(i) Suction lift – where the pump is called upon to raise the fluid from a lower level.

(ii) Suction head – where the pump operates on flooded suction and the fluid intake is effectively 'pressurised' by a positive head.

(iii) Zero head – where the pump operates on flooded suction but no appreciable head is involved.

On the delivery side the possibilities are:

(i) Positive delivery head – where the fluid is eventually discharged at a higher level than the pump.

(ii) Zero head – where the pump run is horizontal and no raising of fluid level is involved.

Dynamic heads must be considered separately and their contribution can vary considerably with different installations. On the suction side dynamic losses should be reduced to a practical minimum consistent with any suction lift involved in order to ensure favourable operating conditions for the pump.

On the discharge side the total system head which governs the working point of the pump in the case of centrifugal pumps, or the 'pressure loading' in the case of positive displacement pumps.

Position head and velocity head

Position head refers to the height of a specific point in a system above a datum line – *eg* in Figure 10 two position heads are involved. The difference between the two representing a pressure head.

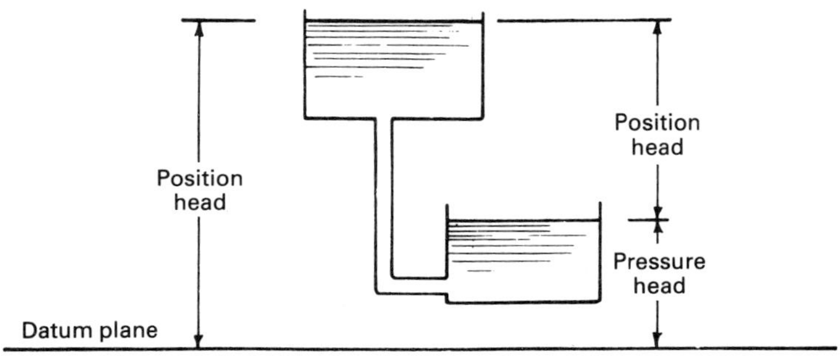

Figure 10

Velocity head is a measure of the energy related to dynamic flow conditions or specifically flow velocity. The fact that flow is present implies that energy has been expended to achieve that velocity and changes in energy will occur within the system if the flow velocity is modified. Velocity head is specifically defined as the height through which the fluid would have to fall to attain that specific velocity. For example:

$$H_V = \frac{V^2}{2g}$$

or H_V (metres) = $0{\cdot}05\ V^2$ (where V is in metres/sec)
or H_V (feet) = $0{\cdot}0155\ V^2$ (where V is in feet/sec)

Hydraulic gradient

Pressure heads and energy levels throughout a system can also be represented by a hydraulic grade line and energy grade line. The description hydraulic gradient is given to the slope of the hydraulic grade line. Basically, this is equivalent to the head load per unit length. Specifically, in Figure 11 the vertical distance between the energy grade line and the velocity grade line at any point represents the velocity head. Both lines drop in the direction of flow and for constant pipe sections this slope is constant and equal to the head loss due to friction.

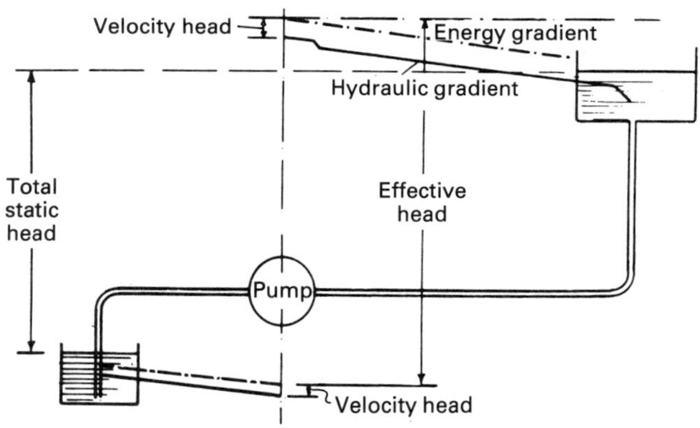

Figure 11

Static head and total system head

In a typical system a pump has to raise liquid from a lower level to a higher level. The vertical lift between the lower and the pumps is known as the static suction head and the vertical lift between the pump and the final delivery point is known as the static discharge (or delivery) head. This is shown in Figure 12. The total static head is then the algebraic sum of these two heads (*Note:* if the pump is working with positive static suction head the total static head is represented by the difference between the static delivery head and the static suction head).

To avoid confusion it is best to define the total static head as the difference between the initial and final point of free delivery of liquid in the system. A distinction between positive and negative suction heads can be made by describing them as static suction lift when the level is below the pump and static suction head (or positive suction head) when the level is above the centre line of the pump.

Under dynamic conditions when the fluid is being moved the head (or equivalent pressure) represents a resistance to flow which has to be overcome by the pump. In addition there will be further resistance to flow introduced by the friction of the

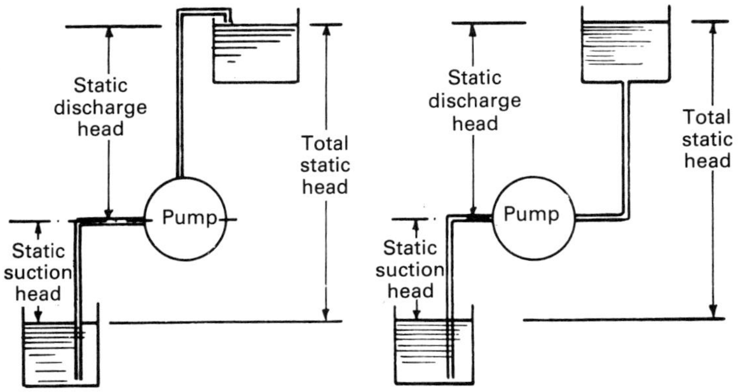

Figure 12

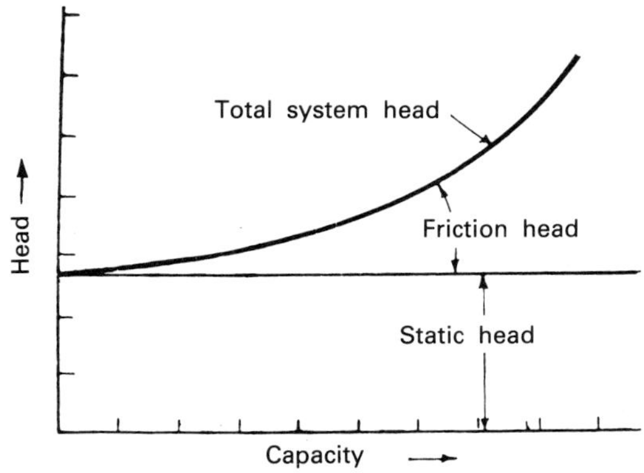

Figure 13

fluid passing through the pipes, valves and fittings in the piping system. This can be illustrated by an additional head (or pressure) representing the system friction. The total head to be overcome or system head is thus represented by the sum of the total static head and the system friction head as illustrated in Figure 13. The true system head curve must also take into account any pressure differences which may exist in the system.

Static head figures will be independent of flow rate and so will be constant for a given system provided no changes in head conditions are involved – *eg* a change in suction head as the level is lowered. With a variable head system, calculations can be made for both 'low' and 'high' liquid levels (or maximum and minimum total static head levels), to assess the likely differences in performance. Alternatively, a 'maximum' or 'mean' head figure can be adopted.

Specific points to bear in mind when making pump performance calculations are:

(i) Pump performance is specified in terms of delivery Q and head H (or pressure).

(ii) In the case of roto-dynamic pumps delivery Q is variable with head H, the characteristic of a particular pump being defined by its H-Q curve. Pumps of this type have a design operating point on the H-Q curve, at which maximum efficiency is achieved and they should normally be operated at this point.

(iii) In the case of positive displacement pumps, delivery Q is normally independent of head (except where modified by slip) and for a given size of pump is normally proportional to pump speed. There may well be optimum operating points (*ie* speed and delivery) for maximum efficiency, dependent also on fluid viscosity.

(iv) Pump performance may also be modified by suction conditions.

(v) Dynamic losses (*ie* frictional losses in pipework *etc*) can be determined as described in the Chapter on Pipework Calculations.

Rotary pumps

Positive displacement rotary pump characteristics are different from turbo machines and a given size of pump will have a range of capacity proportional to speed. There will be a nominal limit to speed (and thus maximum capacity), although this will be dependent on fluid viscosity. Maximum speed (and thus capacity) can be exceeded by increasing the speed for low viscosity fluids. The actual capacity will also be dependent on the system head as this affects the amount of slip. Consequently, actual capacity and speed are not simply related, *eg* operating at half speed does not necessarily give half the capacity. True working points can only be established from the characteristic curves of a particular pump, although capacity may be adjusted from zero to maximum (true) capacity by varying the speed. Unless the pump is matched to operate at or maximum rated capacity for the system and fluid concerned, however, there will normally be a loss of efficiency.

Basically, therefore, a suitable rotary pump size can be selected on a nominal capacity related to the head required, and from this the operating speed and power required. Speed may be modified by fluid viscosity requirements which will derate capacity and thus call for a larger size of pump to maintain the required capacity. Performance at reduced speed will be specific to the design of pump, as noted previously. Alternatively, where a constant speed pump is concerned, *eg* driven by an electric motor, capacity ratings and corresponding brake horsepower (bhp) input required may be given for different heads or pressures. Where such data are given in tabular form for specific heads (or pressures), capacities and bhp figures for intermediate values can be interpolated. Extrapolation, however, may give inaccurate results. The figure for pressure, rather than head, is often used for rotary pumps when system head requirements must be rendered in terms of equivalent pressure.

It should also be appreciated that with positive displacement rotary pumps the possible variations between extremes of speed, pressure (or head) and the fluid viscosity can be virtually infinite. A specific duty can usually be performed by several pumps of different size, and the choice of the best may be far from obvious. In such cases the pump manufacturers are in the best position to recommend a particular model but can only do this with complete knowledge of the system characteristics and service required.

System head calculations

In pumping systems the term 'static head' is used to describe the height of the column of liquid acting on the suction and discharge side as previously described. The suction head may be negative *ie* suction lift, if the liquid level is below the pump, and positive if above. In either case, total static head is the algebraic sum of the two heads. Only vertical heights are considered in determining the static heads, regardless of the actual configuration of the pipework and measurement is normally made to the centre line of the pump. The head is then expressed directly in metres or feet and represents the pressure loading on the pump under static conditions.

Confusion often arises from different descriptions of the term 'head' and in particular from failure to distinguish from actual total head or system head and total static head; confusion is often increased moreover by differences in terminology. The distinction is that system head refers to the sum of the total static head together with any extra resistence by way of frictional effects and energy loss.

Discharge characteristics

The discharge side of the circuit involves a static discharge head or 'standing' head representing the pressure against which the liquid must be forced, together with frictional losses through the pipeline and fittings. A further energy loss is likely at the delivery end of the pipe *ie* an exit loss.

Friction and energy losses through the piping and fittings are dependent on flow velocity and will increase with increasing capacity. Calculations may be based on a specific flow rate responding to required capacity, or computed over a range of capacities – see Figure 14. The former yields a design working point for the system from which a suitable size of pump may be selected and is generally suitable for positive displacement pumps. The latter is more useful for roto-dynamic pumps since it enables the effect of a change in the working point of the pump to be analysed and shows its effect on pump efficiency.

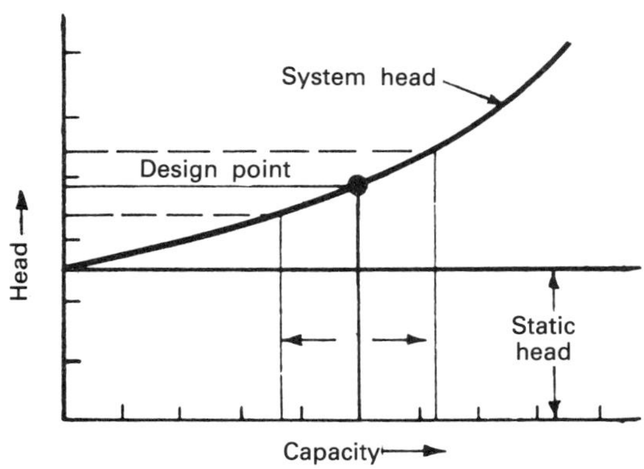

Figure 14

Cost of pumping

The direct cost of pumping can be expressed arithmetically as

$$\text{Cost per unit volume pumped} = \frac{\text{head x cost per hp input x SG of fluid}}{\text{K x }\eta}$$

where:
K is an empirical constant depending on the units involved and
η is the efficiency of the pump

It follows that the significant parameters are:

(i) Head – a reduction in head requirements reducing the direct cost of pumping calling for optimum pipe sizing *etc* for minimum frictional losses.
(ii) HP input – needing consideration of pump/driver characteristics.
(iii) Pump deficiency – an increasing significantly parameter as the capacity or demand increases.

In a large system, a difference in efficiency of only 1% may well exceed the initial cost of pump and driver in a period considerably less than that of the life of the pump and the service involved. In the case of a process or chemical pump working under very arduous conditions it can be a matter of months only.

Typical life for other types of process pumps and general purpose pumps may be one, two, five, ten, fifteen or even more years.

The true pumping cost is represented by the direct pumping costs plus the further items listed a to f allocated over a period of working. All are likely to be variable, but some of them are controllable by planned routine and preventative maintenance.

(a) Net depreciation of capital investment in:
  (i)pump;
  (ii) driver;
  (iii) system.
(b) Interest on capital borrowed.
(c) Maintenance costs of:
  (i) pump;
  (ii) driver;
  (iii) system.
(d) Loss of performance through:
  (i) wear on pump or driver;
  (ii) system corrosion.
(e) Loss of production through shutdown time.
(f) Offset figures representing a recovery of intial costs which are not accounted for in the computation of direct costs.

In the case of fixed capacity demand the type of pump may be more or less predetermined by the delivery required or the type of fluid being handled. Initially, the system head (and particularly the friction head) may be regarded as variable quantities. Any saving which can be realised here will be a direct power saving since:

$$\text{Input power required} = \frac{Q \times \text{SG of fluid}}{\gamma}$$

where Q is the delivery

Where pipelines are short, and the head is mostly static head pipe sizing is relatively unimportant, except for necessary considerations of flow velocity. The economics of the system are then more or less directly related to pump efficiency and the efficiency of the driver to a fuel converter. The two together represent the overall efficiency of the pump and driver. Data plotted in this way may well indicate the most favourable pump type/driver combination at the hydraulic output power level required, see Figure 15. Alternatively, individual combinations may be investigated and compared on the basis of overall efficiency at the specific capacity and head required, provided it is feasible to use alternative drivers. In a majority of cases an electric motor is a more or less automatic selection for the driver, both as regards suitability and on account of low initial cost. The efficiency achieved with electric motors is also substantially higher than with prime movers.

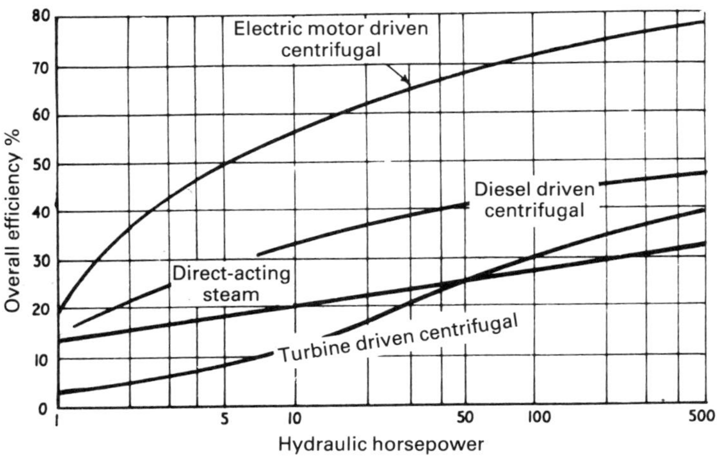

Figure 15

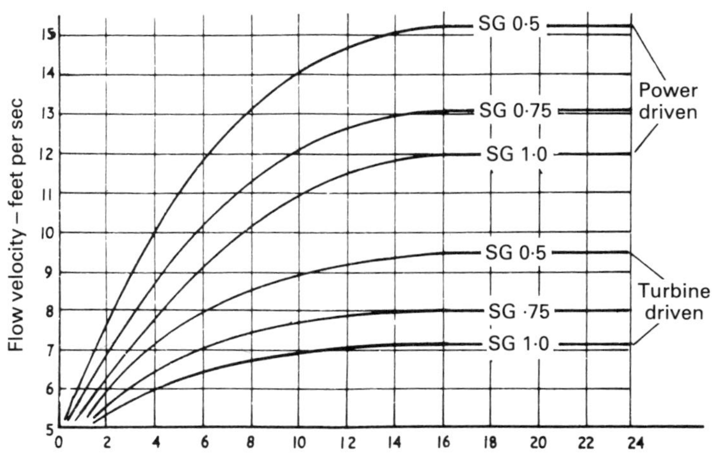

Figure 16

Some authorities advocate pipe sizing relative to the speed of the pump and specific gravity of the fluid. This is based on achieving economic flow velocities inversely proportional to pump speed and specific gravity. Such recommendations may differ from arbitrary pipe sizing on flow velocity considered with respect to friction head. Some typical data are summarised in Figure 16. It should be noted that these apply to the delivery line of centrifugal pumps only. Further, any such data based on power costs are subject to variation with changing charges or fuel costs.

Determination of optimum pipe sizing on a flow rate and friction head basis does not necessarily result in optimum system design where long lengths of piping are involved (*ie* relatively large friction heads), since this ignores the cost of the pipework. Although this is basically an initial cost, true pumping cost items are also involved over a period of service. The system designer should always concentrate on possible savings in static head and friction head where large quantities of fluid are to be handled by the pump.

Possible savings in static head are intimately concerned with the specific system projected and depend mainly on the routing of the pipework which may be dictated largely by factors outside the system designers control (although there are almost invariably alternatives to consider). A typical example is where an obstruction such as a rise in the ground level has to be negotiated. Carrying the pipeline over the obstruction will increase the static head of the system, burying the pipe through the obstruction would increase the cost of the installation. This increase in cost will, however, be offset by:

(i) a direct power input saving which can be calculated directly from the static head saved;

and

(ii) a smaller saving in actual pipe length reducing pipe cost and friction head, although these savings may be negligible by comparison with (i).

The total degree of offset is calculable although the possibility of other factors affecting the issue should not be overlooked.

In many cases involving bulk flow handling, questions such as the aforementioned may have a further factor such as a definite limit on the head available from the most suitable type of pump *eg* an axial flow pump. Alternative schemes in such cases might be to split the duty between two or more pumps to provide 'lift' to a high tank or reservoir from one pump and bulk flow over substantially flat terrain from another pump; the use of a vertical multi-stage pump or an axial flow pump. Pipe sizing may also have to be adjusted for the hydraulic gradients involved, *eg* if a pump is used in a pipeline containing downward sloping runs, pipe friction needs to be high enough to ensure that the line remains full at all likely flow rates.

The larger the scale of the project in fact the more it becomes apparent that there is no 'exact' solution. Any solution must be a compromise to some extent and admits a number of possible alternatives which may involve the use of different types of pump as well as different system layouts. Given the same problem it would be anticipated that individual designers would come up with different solutions based on their individual experience and judgement. Logically the best scheme would be the one giving the lowest overall cost per m^3 litre (gallon) of produce pumped, but although overall costs can be estimated, this is not necessarily a constant figure.

Optimum pipeline costing

Instead of friction head, and thus total system head, being determined for a single pipeline size, or a specific combination of sizes as indicated by optimum flow conditions, it can be instructive to calculate the friction head at the flow rate required for a variety of alternative pipe sizes – spot calculations only being necessary. The corresponding input powers required can then be plotted against pipe size or more realistically the cost of the power plotted against pipe size as shown in Figure 17.

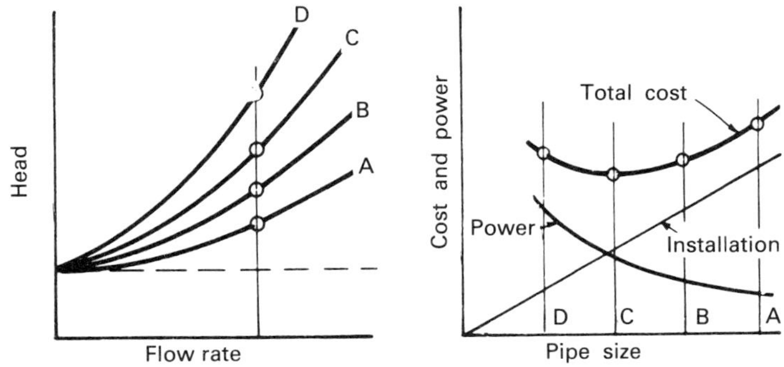

Figure 17

A further set of data is then tabulated relating pipe size to cost of pipe work *ie* material costs plus installation costs. Material costs will be approximately proportional to diameter, although actual figures are readily obtainable and should always be used. Material costs include the cost of both pipes and fittings. Installation costs will probably not vary much over the diameter range investigated and can be taken as constant if actual figures are lacking. A curve showing total installation cost against pipe size can then be plotted on the same graph as shown in Figure 18.

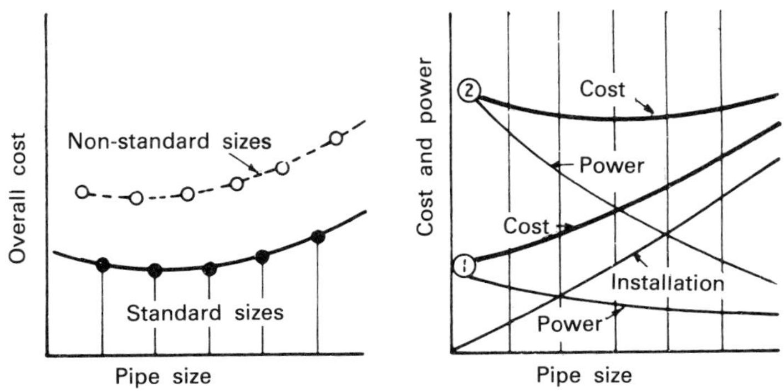

Figure 18

Pumping costs should be estimated as direct cost based on a nominal total gallonage selected so as to arrive at cost figures of the same order as total installation costs or based on a specific period of working.

Loss of performance

Pump wear will inevitably result in a loss of performance, increase in the direct cost of pumping. In some systems the loss of performance may not be noticed at all as the pump is still apparently working satisfactorily. In other cases it may affect the whole process involved.

Loss of performance is likely to be noticed in the case of centrifugal pumps since the working point can be shifted considerably with a substantial reduction in capacity and efficiency, see Figure 19. Such a shift will tend to occur between maintenance periods when worn parts are replaced and the greater the life of the pump the more difficult it may become to recover the original working point after necessary replacement parts are fitted.

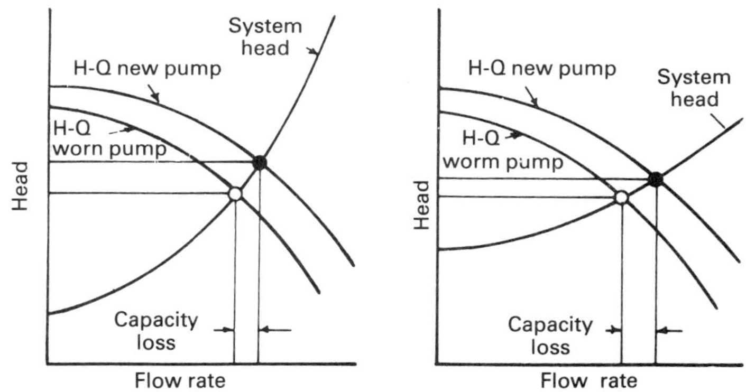

Figure 19

Loss of pump efficiency represents a higher cost of pumping and hence an increase in gradient of the total cost curve for that pump compared with its original performance on a gross discharge basis. This can be compared with the total cost curve for a new pump (inevitably with a higher initial cost) to establish a break-even point when the new pump becomes more economic. This is an over-simplification of the problem since it assumes that the efficiencies of the old and the new pump remain constant up to break even point. In practice the old pump is likely to suffer a greater loss of efficiency than the new pump, so the break even point will occur at a lower future gross discharge figure although this could be offset by a further rise in the initial cost of the new pump in that period. It does, however, illustrate a basic method of estimating when it can become more economic to replace an existing pump with a more efficient one.

Systems with variable demand

Variable demand represents a shift in the working point of the pump, which apart from the mechanical control involved, can seriously affect the efficiency of a centrifugal pump. This may favour the choice of a pump which has variable delivery at more or less constant efficiency or, if the capacity required is outside the normal range of such pumps, the use of two or more pumps in parallel or a roto-dynamic pump with more favourable characteristics.

Many systems for which a centrifugal pump is otherwise suitable may, however, have a variable demand in which case, a certain loss of efficiency may have to be accepted from part of the head or part of the capacity used for control purposes, using either discharge throttling or bypass control. Both methods will inevitably result in power loss, so if economic regulation is of primary importance, discharge regulation by speed control should be investigated first since this is less wasteful of power and there is usually a considerably smaller loss of pump efficiency. Speed control is now a particularly attractive proposition with the increasing availability of variable frequency power units.

The effect of discharge throttling on the working point of the pump is shown in Figure 20. In this case a head loss is accepted to provide capacity control, the cost being directly determinable by the head loss in the throttling valve. The actual loss need not be all that high; a head drop acros the control valve of 30 to 40% of the frictional head loss at the working point generally provides good control. The steeper the H-Q curve the greater the power loss to achieve tghe same degree of throttling and *vice versa.* If the full throttling range required can be achieved with the working point still remaining within the specified working envelope of the pump, then perfectly satisfactory working can be assumed. If not, then the pump should be sized so that the majority of its working time yields a working point within the pump envelope.

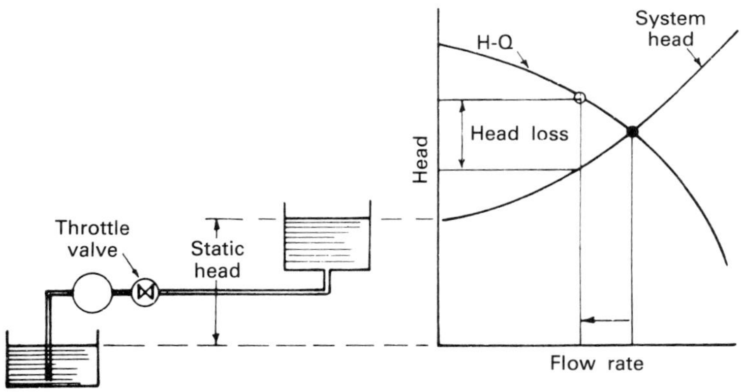

Figure 20

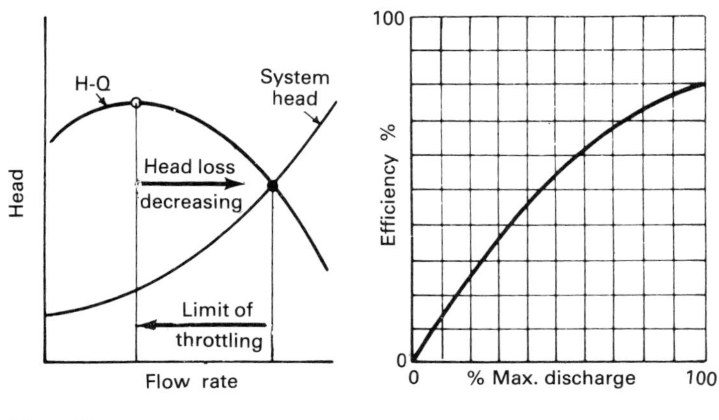

Figure 21

In the case of the pump with an unstable H-Q curve discharge throttling can have a stablising effect, provided the head loss across the control valve always decreases as the valve is opened, see Figure 21. Under such conditions the valve will provide both stabilisation and effective capacity control. This effect is only likely to be realised, however, where the system head curve is quite steep *ie* there is a high friction head and relatively low static head.

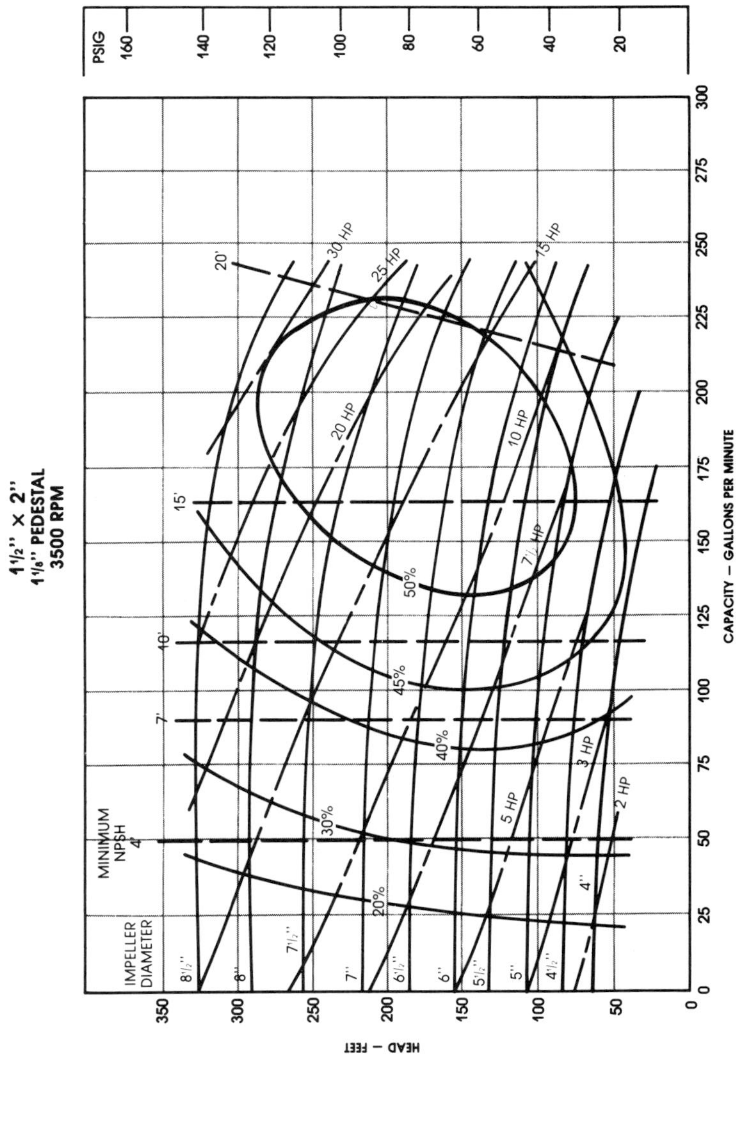

Curves show performance with clear water @ 85 °F. If specific gravity is other than 1·0, hp must be corrected. Operate in maximum efficiency range for optimum performance.

Typical examples of performance curves.

cont...

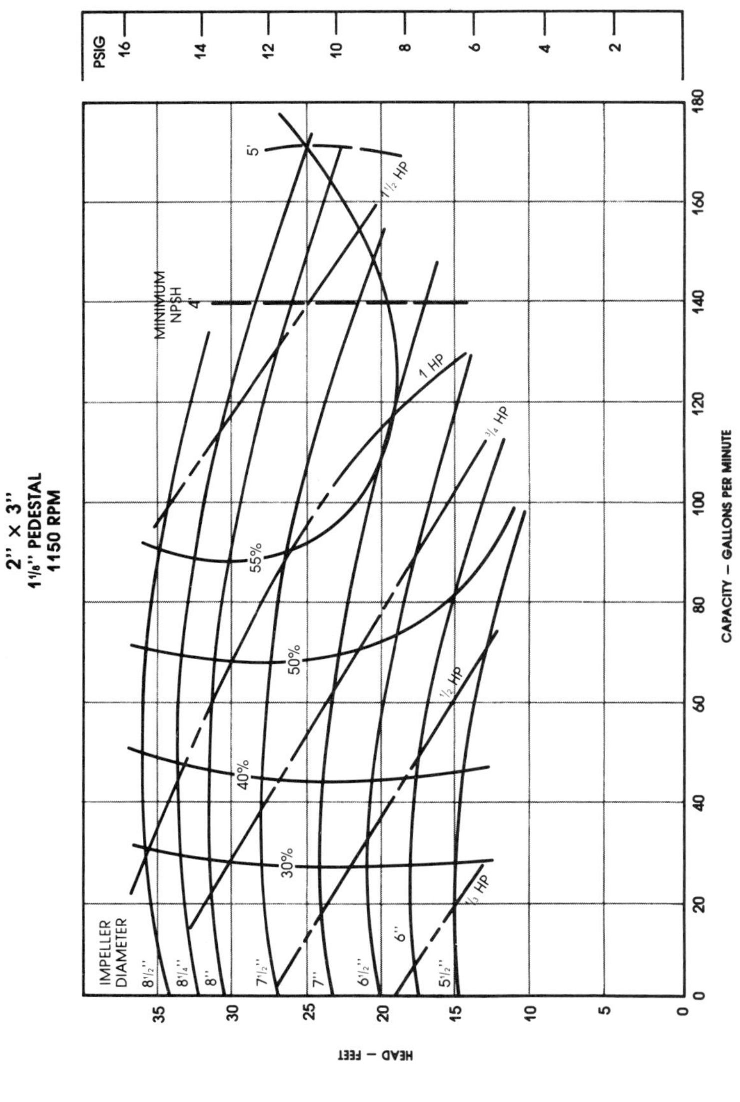
2" × 3"
1 1/8" PEDESTAL
1150 RPM
IMPELLER DIAMETER
8 1/2"
8 1/4"
8"
7 1/2"
7"
6 1/2"
6"
5 1/2"
30%
40%
50%
55%
1/3 HP
1/2 HP
3/4 HP
1 HP
1 1/2 HP
MINIMUM NPSH
4'
5'
PSIG
HEAD — FEET
CAPACITY — GALLONS PER MINUTE

cont...

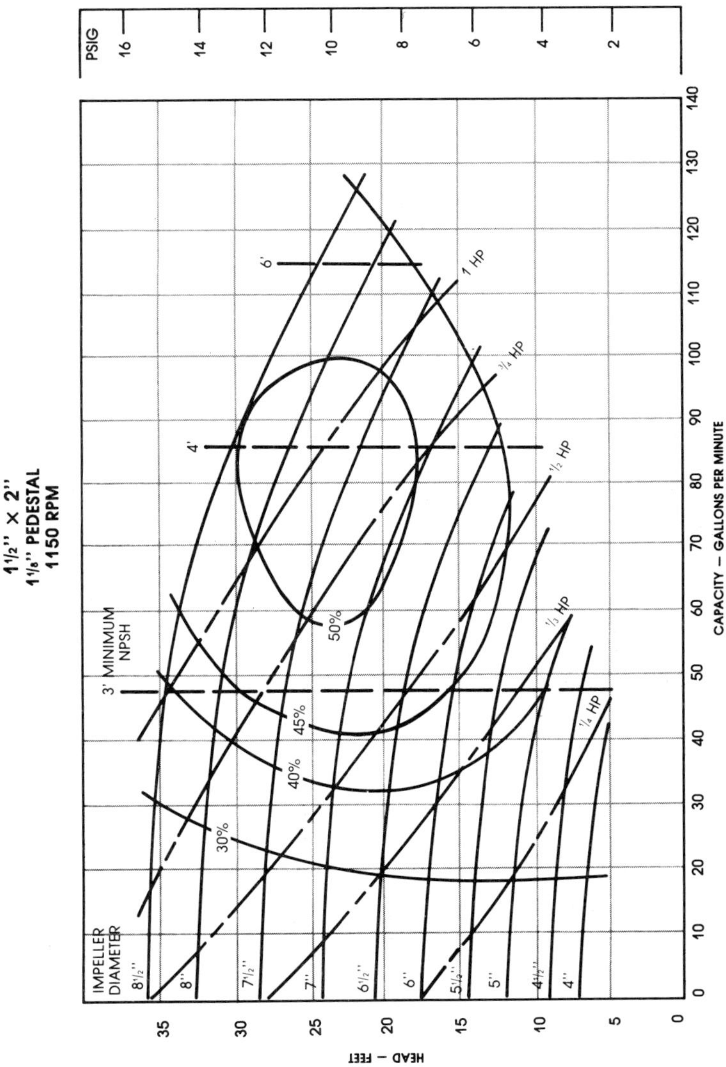

Curves show performance with clear water @ 85 °F. If specific gravity is other than 1·0, hp must be corrected. Operate in maximum efficiency range for optimum performance.

Typical examples of performance curves (contd.)

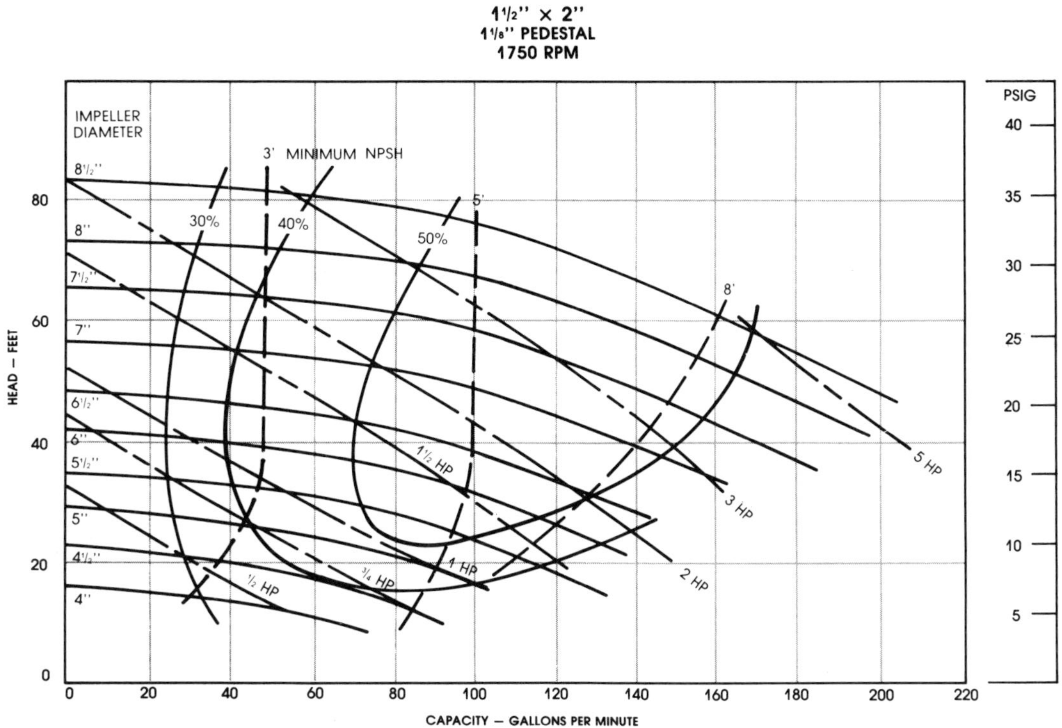

Curves show performance with clear water @ 85 °F. If specific gravity is other than 1·0, hp must be corrected. Operate in maximum efficiency range for optimum performance.

Typical examples of performance curves (contd.)

The effect of bypass regulation is shown in Figure 22. Here control is obtained by using or 'bypassing' part of the capacity, that is the pump in effect has two feeds. Rather than shifting the working point of the pump along the H-Q curve the effective H-Q curve is modified as far as the main supply is concerned. Bypass regulation is mostly used on boiler feed pumps where the demand tends to vary over wide limits, and on higher specific speed rotor dynamic pumps with steep H-Q curves.

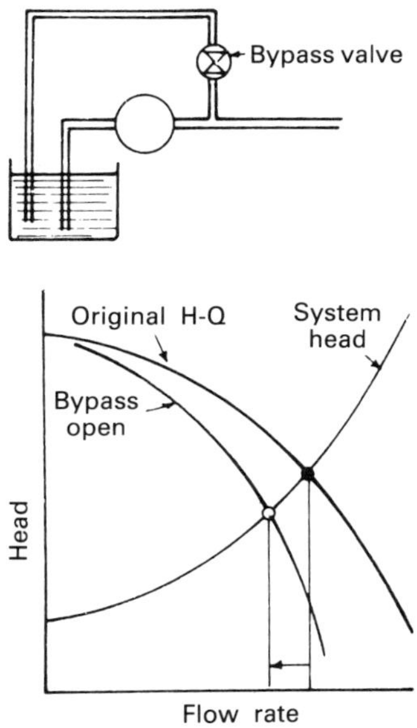

Figure 22

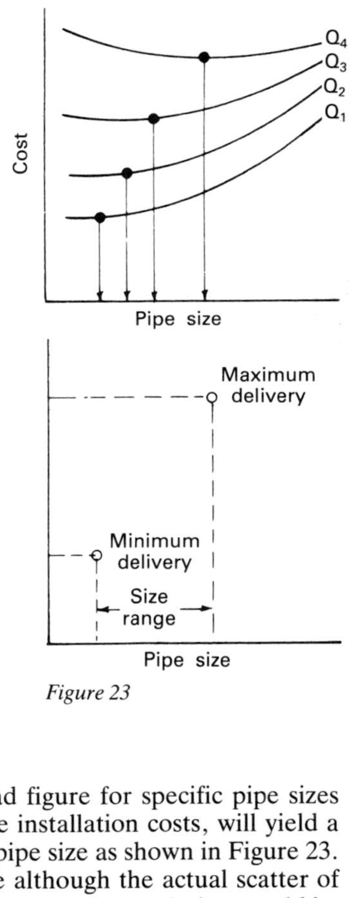

Figure 23

Variable demand and economic pipe sizing

Each discharge rate will yield its own system head figure for specific pipe sizes which, calculated as power costs and added to the installation costs, will yield a series of total curves for total cost plotted against pipe size as shown in Figure 23. Each delivery rate will have its optimum pipe size although the actual scatter of optimum pipe sizes may be relatively small. In general the best solution would be to adopt the optimum pipe size indicated by the largest flow rate (nearest standard size) or the largest pipe size indicated, if this is different. Adjustment of pipe size to favour a particular throttle rate may however be better practice when the demand for this particular rate predominates, as this will enable some of the cost of throttling to be recovered. This analysis is more likely to be of academic rather than practical interest, however, since the main requirements with regulated flow are:

(i) To achieve the required variation in delivery to meet demand variations.

(ii) To realise good pumping efficiency at all demand levels.

Changes in demand

Possible future changes in system demand are also an important consideration in system economics. The most likely change is an increase in demand. This is likely to have a more significant effect on pipe line sizing than pump sizing and may well favour the adoption of apparently oversize piping. Part of the additional initial cost will then be immediately recoverable in power savings resulting from the lower frictional head.

As far as the pump is concerned, a small increase in demand could very likely be met by increasing the speed of the pump and a large increase by the addition of another pump, with the system characteristics still remaining favourable. A solution, which may appeal in certain cases where a substantial increase in demand is anticipated within a relatively short period, is to install a larger pump run at a lower speed, and subsequently increase the speed and uprate the pump performance to meet rising demand. This may provide a much cheaper overall solution than the purchase of a second pump.

Calculations – Type Number and Efficiency

HYDRAULICS HAS been defined as a subject having only one mathematical principle; that is to say Bernoulli's theorem and a mass of empirical formulas.

The design of centrifugal pumps naturally suffers in some measure from the certainties of cast surfaces and from the vagaries of water flow. Considerable progress in improvement of efficiencies is resulting in a combination of careful statistical analysis of all tests and the application of Newton's Laws and Bernoulli's theorem. Work on turbulence and boundary layer has been invaluable in giving that last bit of improvement so essential today.

Since the generation of head is directly affected by the efficiency of the pump, consideration should be given to pump efficiency.

Efficiency and type number

The efficiency of a centrifugal pump depends upon size, speed and type number. Type number (previously referred to as specific speed) is a shape number differentiating (with respect to efficiency and to head and to quantity coefficients) between narrow impellers, small volute throat areas (low type number) and wide impellers, large volute throat areas (high type number). As a pure number the actual value is of little importance, provided it is used consistently in empirical charts of efficiency and of head and quantity coefficients. The simple expression:

Type number N_S is equal to:

$$\frac{\text{r/min}\sqrt{\text{l/s}}}{\text{Head in m}^{3/4}}$$

(avoiding uneccesary coefficients and assuming the constant gravity of these charts) is in line with standard specifications and is used in this book.

The type number of a pump indicates the shape of the pump and is sometimes defined as the speed at which the pump would run if reduced geometrically to give:

(i) l/s at 1 m head

as this is rather difficult to visualise, the following explanation is suggested.

The type number is regarded as a ratio defining the shape of the pump, colloquially described as long and thin or short and fat. For a certain design of pump, the ratio of the diameter of the casing throat to the diameter of the impeller will be obtained as follows. The head is proportional to peripheral velocity squared: velocity^2 squared which is proportional to impeller diameter squared: diameter^2 x rotational speed^2. For a given head we can, therefore, say impeller diameter is proportional to the square root of head divided by the speed.

The absolute velocity leaving the impeller is regarded as the volute throat velocity or diffuser velocity, which in turn is proportional to the impeller peripheral velocity, that is to say, it is proportional to the square root of head.

The volute throat is the largest section of the scroll preceding the expansion cone to the delivery branch.

The quantity pumped is equal to the throat velocity multiplied by the area of the throat and therefore is proportional to:

$$\sqrt{\text{head}} \times \text{the area of the throat}$$

Hence, the area of the throat is proportional to Q divided by the square root of H where Q is quantity, and the diameter of the throat is proportional to the square root of Q divided by H to the power of one-quarter.

Therefore, the diameter of the throat to the diameter of the impeller is proportional to:

$$\frac{\sqrt{Q}}{H^{1/4}} \bigg/ \frac{\sqrt{H}}{\text{r/min}}$$

This, in turn, is proportional to:

$$\frac{\text{r/min} \times \sqrt{Q}}{H^{3/4}}$$

that is to say, is proportional to the type number.

It is, therefore, possible to indicate the change of type of pump by the varying ratio of throat diameter to the impeller diameter. From the aforementioned it can be seen that this ratio is dimensionless and is identified with the type number.

Small quantity high head pumps will have a relatively large impeller diameter with narrow outlet to give small flow areas and small quantity. Efficiency will, therefore, be prejudiced by excessive loss due to disc friction. This is because the large impeller will have a large disc friction compared with the small liquid power consequent upon the small quantity pumped.

This machine will have a low type number and a comparatively low efficiency. At the other end of the range, a pump for a large quantity and a low head will have a wide impeller and a relatively small diameter, so that although the disc friction is not great, there will be prejudice to efficiency by the lack of guidance in the short impeller passages. This pump will have a high type number. Between these limits, the efficiency will reach an optimum.

It is, therefore, possible to plot the effect of type number on efficiency thereby determining the optimum type number and consequently the running speed for a given duty. Compromise may be necessary to suit the driver, *ie* 50 cycle frequency in UK. Furthermore, for certain duties it may be necessary to pump against very high heads. Some sacrifice of efficiency may therefore be necessary to obtain a reasonable number of stages or to avoid the running of two pumps in series.

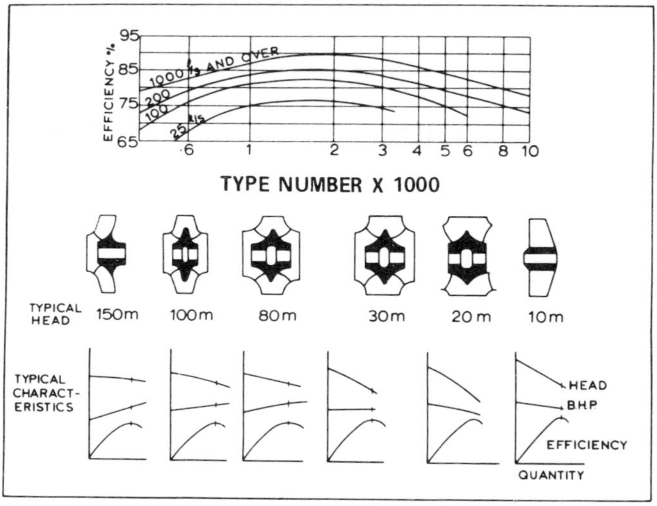

Figure 1
Speed and efficiency characteristics.

Figure 1 illustrates the efficiency of centrifugal pumps plotted against type number as abscissae with lines representing various quantities in litres per second. The chart also shows the shape of impeller for the various type numbers and the type of head volume, power and efficiency characteristics expected. It will be seen that low type number pumps at the left hand of the chart have a head characteristic which does not rise very greatly from best efficiency point and zero flow, whilst the high type numbers at the right hand end of the chart have a head characteristic which rises very steeply from best efficiency flow to zero flow. The reason for this change of characteristic is due to the change of area ratio consequent upon change of type number. An explanation of area ratio is discussed in detail within this Section.

Variation of efficiency with size and speed

In addition to illustrating efficiency variation with type number, Figure 1 illustrates how an increase of size results in an increase of efficiency. The efficiency improvement consequent upon increase of size is dependent upon the Reynolds number. More specifically it can be said that a pump is a dynamic device for producing head which depends on velocity^2, but it suffers from losses depending, according to Reynolds number, velocity to a power in the neighbourhood of 1·7 to 1·8.

Increase of size and speed will, therefore, increase efficiency since the dynamic head, depending upon velocity, increases at a greater rate than with losses which are varying in the ratio of velocity to the neighbourhood of 1·7 or 1·8.

It has been found over the years by analysing the true Reynolds number for the various passages within the pump and the direct flow quantity, that the latter is a sufficiently accurate arbiter for the efficiency of a group of pumps. It is, therefore, possible to plot efficiency directly against flow quantity at best efficiency point for a series of various type numbers thus obtaining in effect a group of tests of various flows and type numbers from which Figure 1 can be constructed. This in effect means that efficiency of a small pump at high speed can be the same as a large pump at low speed, provided the type number and the flow are kept the same. This is the reason why Figures 1 and 2 can in general show efficiency against quantity and type number only without reference to physical size or operating speed. Where pumps operate against very high heads, the large shaft diameter and run dry clearances considerably reduce the efficiency below this chart.

Efficiency step up formulas

Having considered the variation of efficiency with size and type number, consideration will now be given to efficiency step up formulas, the effect of surface roughness on efficiency and the value of efficiency.

Efficiency formulas for variation of size

The efficiency charts illustrated in Figures 1 and 2 based on many years test experience incorporate the aggregate performance of several thousand pumps. Flow measurements varying between 2 l/s and 3000 l/s were taken on eight different instruments, any two of which could run in series to provide a check of accuracy.

The resulting curve of efficiency against quantity for any given type number was found to be consistent and also could be correlated to the investigation on how pipe friction varies with change of Reynolds number. The pump losses could be separated into constant losses, *eg* bearings, glands, disc friction and flow passage losses, which were analogous to pipe friction losses.

The passage losses could be further split into a constant portion and a portion varying as a Reynolds number which, from the efficiency aspect, could be regarded as varying according to the quantity pumped. The pump maker, therefore, could produce a formula covering the whole range of pumps from the smallest to the largest. This gradual formula containing constant losses can, therefore, never reach 100% efficiency, experience suggesting efficiency of infinitely large pumps would be in the order of 94%.

This suggested that the losses for an infinitely large pump would only be 6%, unfortunately, the most accurate flow measurement would still show a permissible error according to Standard Specifications of the order of 1½% to 2% which is a large variation in the remaining 6% between 94% and 100%.

Surface finish

On the curve of efficiency compared with quantity, the small quantity losses are largely skin friction whilst the large quantity losses are almost entirely eddy friction. When comparing a group of pumps from say 50 mm branch to 750 mm branch, it is assumed that the whole group will have a uniform surface finish for example, bronze, cast iron or mild steel dressed smooth. Here the size of any surface error can be considered as uniform throughout the group, as for example a CLA surface of four microns.

This roughness has quite a large friction effect on a 50 mm pump, but a negligible effect on a 750 mm pump, the consequent change of efficiency due to Reynolds number between these two sizes being shown in Figure 1, all other aspects being equal or eliminated by appropriate corrections.

Departures from uniformity of surface such as may be caused by mad matching of casing halves *etc* or by noduling consequent upon handling corrosive waters, may reduce the efficiency of the pump below the value shown in the chart by as much as 5 to 10% or even more.

On the other hand, by adopting the superior finishes of vitreous linings, by manufacturing the pump parts of plastics *etc* or by the physical polishing of the water passages, a small quantity pump may be given a small absolute value of surface roughness with respect to diameter. Such a pump would have a slightly higher efficiency, perhaps 2% or more.

It is, therefore, important to ensure that the states of surface smoothness of model and full size pumps are alike before any general step-up formula, such as mentioned previously, can be applied.

Value of efficiency

Very roughly, it may be said that 1% increase of efficiency is comparable to the price of the whole pump. Certain contracts now include moneytary penalties and bonuses to ensure that efficiency guarantees are met on site.

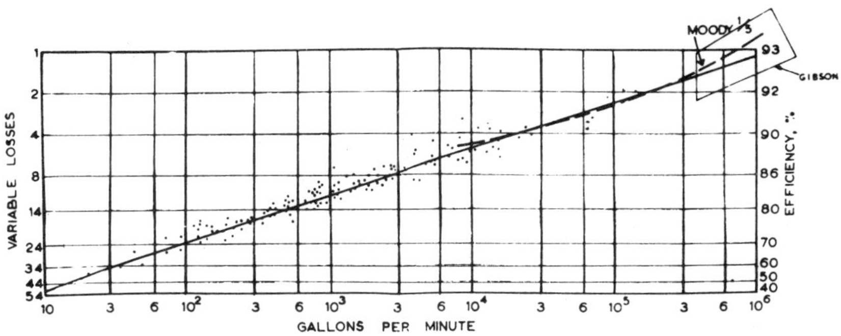

Figure 2
Original chart of efficiency at optimum specific speed.

Efficiency, quantity chart

Figure 2 shows the original chart of efficiency of pumps at optimum type number plotted against quantity in gallons/minute. Each of the many test points were corrected to the efficiency it would give at optimum type number according to Figure 1 so that type number is eliminated as a variable from this chart.

Initially, the gal/min efficiency curve was plotted and its mathematical formula evaluated. It was then re-plotted as a straight line on logarithmic paper by separating the constant and the variable losses as in Figure 2.

To the right of Figure 2 a scale of efficiency appears, but the true logarithmic scale of Figure 2 is the variable loss scale on the left, 4% variable loss corresponding to 90% efficiency, 14% variable loss corresponding to 80% efficiency and so on. Each point on Figure 2 is the average of all the pumps made of that particular size and number, the chart representing a record of several thousand pumps.

Efficiency, quantity formula

The curve of Figure 2 is similar to the variable portion of Reynolds number pipe friction curve. The solution of the gal/min – efficiency curve can be mathematically expressed as follows:

$$1{\cdot}0 \text{ minus efficiency} = (\text{gal/min})^{-0{\cdot}32} + 0{\cdot}06$$

or

$$0{\cdot}94 \text{ minus efficiency} = (\text{gal/min})^{-0{\cdot}32}$$

By plotting (0·94 – efficiency) against gal/min, a straight line graph can be obtained as in Figure 2. This suggested that 0·06 or 6% of losses are constant, independently of gal/min or of Reynolds number. This equation can be transposed to:

1·0 efficiency = total losses = 0·03 fixed losses (disc friction glands, bearings and leakage)

+ 0·03 constant friction head loss

+ $(\text{gal/min})^{-0{\cdot}32}$ variable friction head loss

The last two terms:

$$0{\cdot}03 + (\text{gal/min})^{-0{\cdot}32}$$

covering the pipe friction portion of the loss are of similar form to the expression for Reynolds pipe friction curve.

$$\frac{f}{2} = 0{\cdot}0009 + 0{\cdot}0765\,(\text{Reynolds number})^{-0{\cdot}35}$$

where f is the friction coefficient for smooth pipe flow.

The various losses in the pump have been separated, the major loss being passage friction (*ie* pipe friction).

Scatter of test points

Figure 2 represents a sufficient number of tests to eliminate measurement error and to show only variation of pump performance. The spread of test points at any given flow is seen to be proportional to the variable losses which is to be expected. Comparison may be made to BS 2613 For Electrical Machines, which allows an efficiency tolerance of 10% of (100% – efficiency) *ie* 10% of losses. In contrast ISO 3555 Pump Test Code allows an efficiency tolerance of 2½% of the actual efficiency specified which is intended to cover errors of test observation and not scatter of pump performance. ISO 3555 tolerance, therefore, is comparable to pump performance scatter on the largest sizes, but is only a small proportion of pump scatter on the smallest sizes.

Variations of geometry, single-stage, multi-stage, single entry, double entry, single volute, double volute or diffuser give negligible efficiency change.

Efficiency majoration formula for fluid machines

Expressions for variation of efficiency with size are essentially empirical, with guidance as to the general form of the expression from theoretical sources. Since statistical data are the main basis here it follows that the greater the number and range of machines in the survey, the more accurate will the formula become.

Figure 3 shows a record of some 15 000 pump tests and several hundred turbine tests covering flows from 0·4 l/s to 400 m^3/s and provides an expression for efficiency which is relatively simple. The distribution is gaussian with scatter proportional to variable losses, 75% of points within one-sixth, 95% of points within one-third of variable losses the flow range is from 1 to 1 million.

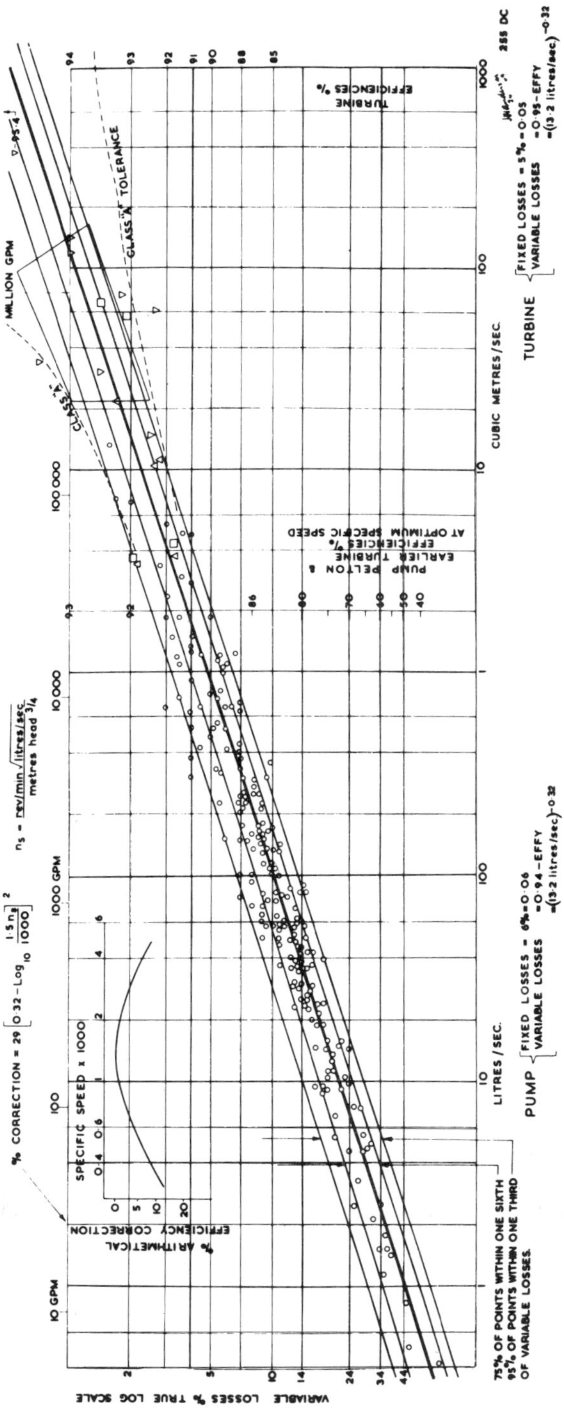

Figure 3
Pump and water turbine efficiencies.

Pump and turbine formulas

The average efficiency η of the 15 000 centrifugal pumps of pelton turbines and of earlier turbines is given by the expression:

$$0{\cdot}94 - \eta = (13{\cdot}2\ \text{l/s})^{-0{\cdot}32}$$

The average efficiency of 670 of the latest turbines is given by:

$$0{\cdot}95 - \eta = (13{\cdot}2\ \text{l/s})^{-0{\cdot}32}$$

This is 1% higher than the pump formula since a turbine handles a greater liquid power for the same losses as a pump of the same geometry.

Majoration formulas

Pump and pelton turbines

$$\frac{0{\cdot}94-\eta_a}{0{\cdot}94-\eta_b} = \left[\frac{\text{Flow}_b}{\text{Flow}_a}\right]^{0{\cdot}32}$$

Water turbines

$$\frac{0{\cdot}95-\eta_a}{0{\cdot}95-\eta_b} = \left[\frac{\text{Flow}_b}{\text{Flow}_a}\right]^{0{\cdot}32}$$

Pump data

Each of the 200 plus circles on the chart of Figure 3 represent the average efficiency of all pumps of that size and duty. The number of pumps for each circle varying from a few to several hundred according to the number made and tested of that particular size and duty. Speeds generally are normal for the duty.

Type number (N_S)

The pump efficiencies are corrected to optimum type number by the following formula:

$$\text{Efficiency correction} = 0{\cdot}29 \left[\log_{10} \frac{1400}{N_S}\right]^2$$

Losses to the left of the optimum of the N_S efficiency curve are due to disc friction and losses to the right are due to the lowering value of the head coefficient. This leads to a rational dimensionless formula for efficiency and type number with a roughness function and a through flow function.

Reversible pump turbines

Compared to normal machines a fall of 1% efficiency occurs here due when pumping to the presence of gates and when turbining to the relatively larger runner diameter than that of a small turbine. A 1% efficiency increase is therefore allowed here before plotting.

Use of model with superior finish

A highly polished surface on a model will result in a higher efficiency than the chart value since this model becomes a geometric replica of a large machine which has the normal finish of the machines on the chart. For example, the efficiency of a full size machine, having a surface finish comparable to 4 microns and a duty of 20 000 l/s is forecast by the test of a one-tenth model or 200 l/s having a surface finish comparable to 2 microns. This model is, therefore, a geometric replica of a twice size machine which has the normal finish of 4 microns and a duty of 2^2 x 200 l/s or 800 l/s.

The efficiency of the full size machine is, therefore, given by stepping from 800 l/s to 20 000 l/s (instead of from 200 l/s) in order to allow for superior model finish.

The efficiency relationship now becomes:

$$\frac{94 - \eta \text{ full size}}{94 - \eta \text{ model}} = \left[\frac{800}{20\,000}\right]^{0\cdot32}$$

This correction for finish has been fully confirmed by tests of homologous pumps of 200, 300, 500, 1000 and 3000 mm branches with various surface finishes.

Examples of use of chart

Plotting of tests

At the actual test speed, the best efficiency in litres per second, the corresponding efficiency and the type number are determined. The efficiency correction from actual type number to optimum type number as shown on the chart is added arithmetically to the test efficiency and the resulting efficiency is plotted at the litres per second involved.

Example:

300 l/s 700 type number, 84·2% efficiency on test.
Correction for 700 type number is 2·6%.
Total 84·2% plus 2·6% equals 86·8 efficiency which is plotted at 300 l/s.

Determination of efficiency from the chart

Example:

1000 l/s is 2700 type number.
Efficiency from chart at 1000 l/s equals 89·2%.
Correction for 2700 type number is 2·3%.
Efficiency at 1000 l/s 2700 type number, is 89·2% minus 2·3% equals 86·9%.

Area Ratio – The Effect of Pump Geometry on Pump Performance

Inlet conditions

THE INLET portion of a pump comprises the path of the liquid from suction branch to the point at which it is flowing through the passages of the impeller. Between these two points a pressure drop occurs due to friction and increase of velocity of flow. This pressure drop increases as the quantity pumped increases.

The liquid entering the suction branch will have a pressure which is greater by a certain margin than its saturation pressure for the particular temperature. If the pressure drop between inlet branch and impeller passages becomes as great as the margin above saturation, then saturation conditions will obtain in the impeller and the liquid will tend to vaporize with consequent loss of pressure and risk of erosion of the impeller. The reason for this loss of pressure is as follows:

> The head generated by a centrifugal pump is expressed as the height to which a liquid of given specific gravity would be raised. Consequently, if the specific gravity of the fluid is reduced by passing from liquid to vapour, the pressure generated will be reduced similarly, although the head expressed as feet of fluid will remain unaltered.
>
> It is therefore the function of the inlet of the pump to feed the impeller with an adequate supply of liquid without risk of vaporization. To this end, the inlet vanes should be designed to give minimum shock at the required duty. A typical inlet diagram for radial entry is shown in Figure 1. The velocities concerned are the peripheral velocity of the inlet tips, the relative velocity through the impeller passages and the radial entry velocity. It will be seen that the diagram is a right angled triangle.

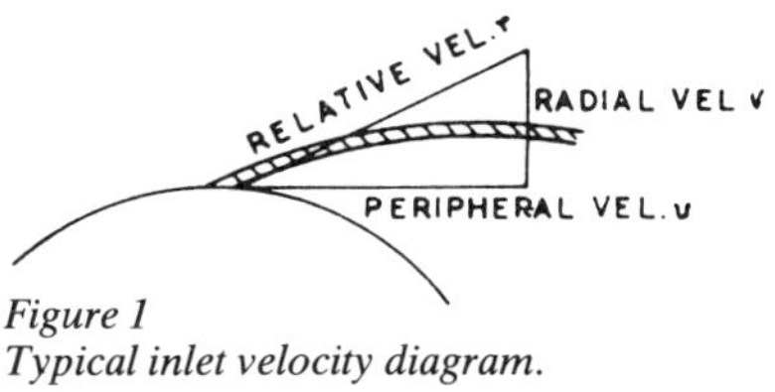

Figure 1
Typical inlet velocity diagram.

Outlet conditions

An outlet velocity diagram is shown in Figure 2. The triangles of velocities comprise the peripheral velocity of the impeller, the relative velocity of flow through the outlet passages of the impeller and the absolute velocity of the liquid when leaving the impeller. The diagram also indicates the radial and the whirl, or tangential, velocity of the liquid. These two velocities are combined in the absolute leaving velocity.

Assuming that in the theoretical pump, the absolute leaving velocity of the liquid coincides with the velocity and angle of flow in the diffuser, or volute collecting chamber, this would, in theory, indicate that no shock occurs at exit from the impeller. The quantity of liquid passing through the pump at this velocity is the designed quantity of the pump and at this point in the ideal pump gives the maximum hydraulic efficiency.

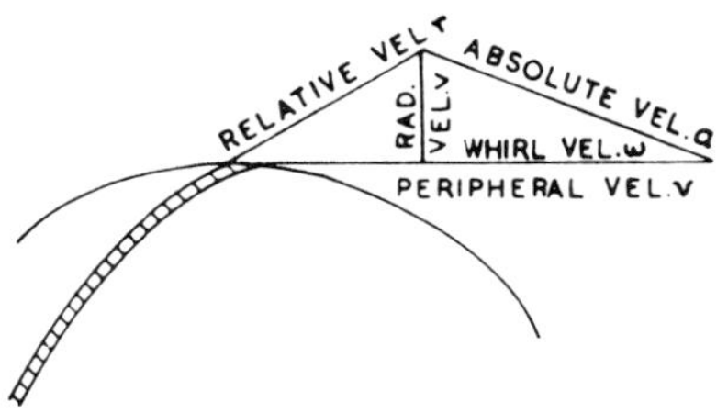

Figure 2
Typical outlet velocity diagram.

Symbols

Let the peripheral velocity of the impeller be	u	m/sec
Radial velocity	v	m/sec
Relative velocity	r	m/sec
Absolute velocity	a	m/sec
Diffuser or volute velocity	t	m/sec
Whirl velocity	w	m/sec
Acceleration due to gravity	g	m/s^2
Quantity of liquid at maximum hydraulic efficiency be	Q	m/sec

For maximum hydraulic efficiency $a = t$

Let the ratio:

$$\frac{\text{Outlet area between vanes of impeller}}{\text{Diffuser area}} = Y$$

Then since impeller and diffuser or volute are running full, the velocities in these parts will be inversely as the areas:

$$\frac{t}{r} = Y$$

Torque equation

The generated head, based upon the relation between torque and angular momentum, is given by the equation:

$$\text{head} = \frac{uw}{g}$$

Head characteristics

$$\text{Head generated by impeller} = \frac{uw}{g} \quad \text{metres}$$

From the two right angled triangles in Figure 2 when a = t

$v^2 = r^2 - (u - w)^2$
$w^2 = t^2 - v^2 = t^2 - r^2 + (u - w)^2$
$w^2 = t^2 - r^2 + u^2 - 2\,uw + w^2$
$2\,uw^2 = t^2 - r^2 + u^2$ thus:

$$\frac{uw}{g} = \frac{t^2 - r^2 + u^2}{2g}$$

$$r^2 = \frac{t^2}{Y^2}$$

$$\therefore \quad \frac{uw}{g} = \frac{t^2\,(1 - \frac{1}{Y^2}) + u^2}{2g} = \text{head generated}$$

If Y = 1 *ie*, Impeller area = diffuser area then head generated

$$= \frac{u^2}{2g} \quad m$$

If Y is less than 1 *eg* ½

$$\text{Head} = \frac{u^2}{2g} - \frac{3t^2}{2g}$$

If Y is greater than 1, *eg* 2

$$\text{Head} = \frac{u^2}{2g} + \frac{\tfrac{3}{4}t^2}{2g}$$

Thus, if the area of the impeller is greater than the diffuser area the head generated at maximum hydraulic efficiency will exceed:

$$\frac{u^2}{2g}$$

If the impeller area is less than the diffuser area the head generated will be less than:

$$\frac{u^2}{2g}$$

In Figure 3, A, B, C represent the triangle of velocities at maximum hydraulic efficiency quantity Q.

At quantities less than this, a typical diagram will be AFC where relative velocity is AF, the whirl is CJ and the absolute velocity CF, the peripheral velocity u remaining constant.

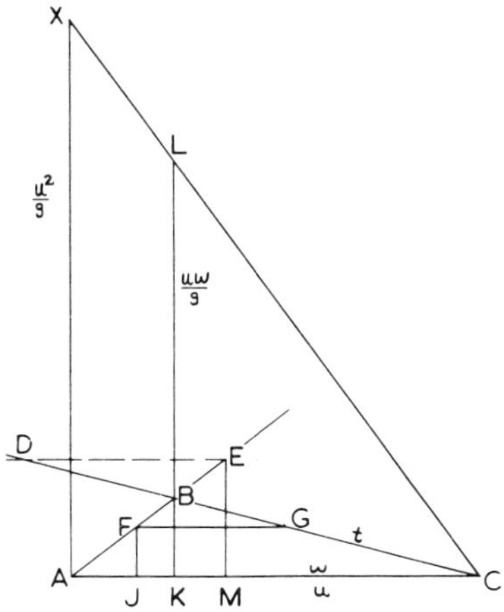

Figure 3
Velocity triangle at outlet.

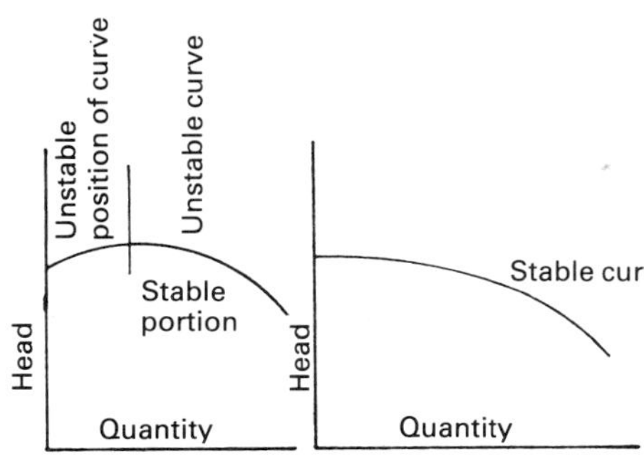

Figure 4
Stable and unstable head curves.

A line parallel to AC will cut off CG

$$\frac{\text{Diffuser velocity CF}}{\text{Relative impeller velocity AF}}$$

$$= \frac{CB}{AB} = \frac{t}{r} = \frac{\text{Impeller area}}{\text{Diffuser area}}$$

Similarly for quantities greater than Q:

$$\frac{CD}{AE} = \frac{CB}{AB} = \frac{t}{r} = \frac{\text{Impeller area}}{\text{Diffuser area}}$$

The absolute velocity CF is reduced by shock to the diffuser velocity CG. There are several ways of interpreting this shock loss. If the pressure remains unaltered the loss in energy will be given by the algebraic difference of the squares of the velocities. There is, however, a definite changing of the angle of the flow, and therefore it is proposed to assume, for the purpose of these pages, that the energy loss is given by the line FG which is the closing line in the velocity diagram AFGC. This completing line FG connects the peripheral velocity AC, the relative AF and the final diffuser velocity CG.

Figure 3 also indicates the values of $\frac{uw}{g}$ in the triangle AXC

Since AX $= \frac{u^2}{g}$ and

CK = whirl, then a perpendicular KL represents:

$$\frac{\text{whirl velocity}}{\text{peripheral velocity}} \times \frac{u^2}{g} \text{ from similar triangles } = \frac{wu}{g}$$

It is convenient to regard the maximum efficiency Q as zero on the chart of characteristics quantities less than Q being indicated by negative values and quantities greater than Q being indicated by positive values.

For example, in Figure 6 the origin represents a quantity Q. The point marked –1 represents zero quantity and +1 represents 2Q quantity.

Basing the curve in terms of Q and:

$$\frac{u^2}{2g}$$

it can be stated that:

$$Q = 1 \quad \text{and} \quad \frac{u^2}{2g} = 1 \text{ for the sake of simplicity}$$

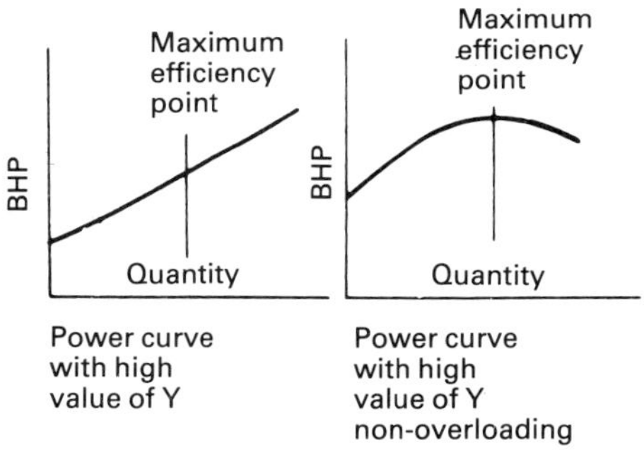

Figure 5
Power curves.

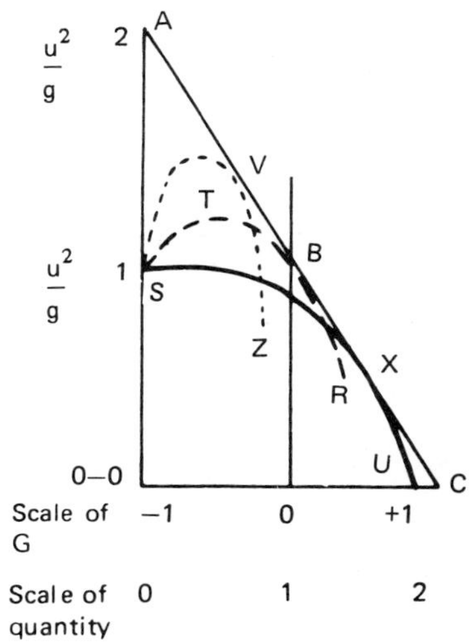

Figure 6
Estimated head-flow characteristics.

A distance G on the curve will represent G + 1 quantity where G may be positive or negative. When G = –1 quantity G + 1 = 0, quantity is 1

Consider the special case where:

$$Y = 1 \text{ and Head} = \frac{u^2}{2g}$$

The curve:

$$\text{Head} = \frac{uw}{g}$$

is indicated on the graph as the straight line ABC, since head at zero quantity is:

$$\frac{u^2}{g}$$

when w = u and head at quantity Q is:

$$\frac{u^2}{2g}$$

The equation to ABC is:

$$\text{Head} = (1-G) \frac{u^2}{2g}$$

where (1 + G), Q is quantity flowing.

$$\text{The velocity FG} = \frac{FB}{AB} \times AC \text{ (Figure 3).}$$

$$= \frac{AB - AF}{AB} AC$$

$$= \frac{\text{Rel vel at Q} - \text{Rel vel at quantity } (G+1)Q}{\text{Relative velocity at quantity Q}} \times u$$

$$= \left[\frac{r-(G+1)r}{r}\right] u = \left[1-G-1\right] u = -Gu$$

$$\text{Energy lost} = \frac{G^2 u^2}{2g}$$

Similarly the velocity DE can be equated to Gu. Subtract this loss from the expression:

$$\text{Head} = (1-G) \frac{u^2}{2g} \text{ to obtain head} = (1-G-G^2) \frac{u^2}{2g}$$

The curve is indicated by STBR, this loss occurring for quantities greater and less than Q.

Where quantity:

$$\frac{G^2u^2}{2g}$$

is subtracted from ABC note that whether G is negative or positive, G^2 is positive, and therefore subtracted in each case.

The theoretical curve from a centrifugal pump for given values of Y can now be considered. For other values of Y the head at Q is:

$$\frac{t^2\left[1-\frac{1}{Y^2}\right]+u^2}{2g}=\frac{uw}{g}$$

Now quantity flowing as a ratio of Q is (1 + G), and actual diffuser velocity as a ratio of diffuser velocity at Q is 1 + G.

$$\text{Then head} = \frac{(1-G-G^2)\,u^2+(1+G)\,(1-\frac{1}{Y^2})t^2}{2g}$$

If quantity is zero 1 + G is zero and head is:

$\frac{u^2}{2g}$ irrespective of value of Y

Hence all pumps whatever the area ratio Y will give:

$$\text{Head} = \frac{u^2}{2g} \text{ at zero quantity.}$$

If Y is greater than 1 the curve will rise, then fall as shown in SVZ, Figure 6 (this may be unstable).

If Y is equal to 1 the curve is STBR as already shown.

If Y is less than 1 the curve will fall more steeply and will be in the stable region as shown SXU.

In order to draw the curves to illustrate the stable and unstable characteristics it is necessary to move the origin O to points corresponding to X and V respectively, the zero quantity remaining at –1 as before and the scale being altered to suit.

Power and efficiency characteristics

Since the relation $\frac{uw}{g}$ = head

is based upon torque on shaft it follows that the torque taken by an ideal pump with no losses will be proportional to uw x quantity.

The work done per kilogramme of liquid, based on torque on shaft is $\frac{uw}{g}$

Hence work done /kg x quantity/second x constant will represent the power taken by the pump assuming no losses.

The quantity will be proportional to u – w since this represents the projection AJ of the relative velocity AF on the line AC (Figure 3). It can thus be said that the power is:

$$(u-w)\,\frac{(uw)}{g}\times\text{constant}$$

where w varies between zero and u.

Differentiating with respect to $\frac{w}{u}$ and equating to zero we obtain the value

$w = \frac{u}{2}$ for maximum power.

The power curve is therefore a parabola whose value at zero quantity is zero. At quantity to give head equal to $\frac{u^2}{2g}$ the power is maximum and at double this quantity the power is zero. Hence for all pumps the maximum power occurs when the head generated is $\frac{u^2}{2g}$

If, due to the varying value of Y, the quantity Q for maximum hydraulic efficiency is greater or less than quantity to give:

$$\frac{uw}{g} = \frac{u^2}{2g}$$

then the power curve will fall or rise after maximum efficiency power. This is the determining factor of non-overloading power characteristics. (Figure 7).

The value of Y determines the position of maximum hydraullic efficiency, but the maximum power will always occur at:

$$\text{head} = \frac{u^2}{2g}$$

When Y = 1, maximum power occurs at maximum hydraulic efficiency quantity.

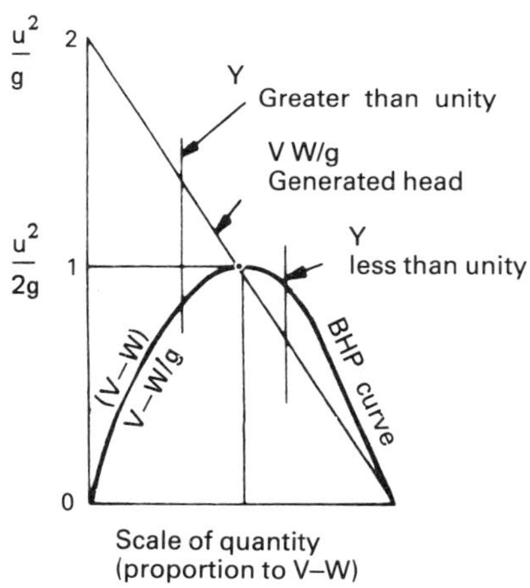

Figure 7
Power characteristics.

Efficiency

In order to determine overall efficiency including losses, values must be assigned to these losses. When differentiating to obtain maximum efficiency it is not always possible to give a general form to the efficiency, including losses, of a pump where Y is not equal to 1, since the actual diffuser velocity t is required; therefore only cases where Y = 1 will be considered.

Efficiency taking into account shock losses only
The following relations have already been obtained:

$$\text{Head} = (1 - G - G^2)\ \frac{u^2}{2g}$$

$$\text{Power} = (u - w)\ \frac{uw}{g} \text{ x constant}$$

(neglecting mechanical losses and friction losses in the pump)

$$= (1 + G)(1 - G) \text{ x constant}$$

$$= (1 - G^2) \text{ x constant}$$

$$\text{Quantity} = (1 + G) \text{ x constant}$$

$$\text{Efficiency} = \frac{\text{Liquid Power}}{\text{Input Power}} = \frac{\text{Head x Quantity}}{\text{Input Power}}$$

$$= \frac{(1 - G - G^2) \text{ x } (1 + G)}{(1 - G^2)}$$

$$= \frac{1 - G - G^2}{1 - G} = 1 - \frac{G^2}{1 - G}$$

The hydraulic efficiency has its maximum at the designed quantity, is 50% at no flow and zero at 1·62 x the designed quantity.

Other losses
A further hydraulic loss is the friction loss through the passages of the pump. This loss generally varies as the square of the quantity passing through the pump.

Mechanical losses comprise disc friction, bearing and windage losses, gland friction. Leakage losses through glands and neckrings, *etc,* also must be taken into account. Mechanical and leakage losses are roughly constant.

In order to obtain some idea of the shape of the efficiency curve it is necessary to assess these losses. For any given pump it is possible to estimate the losses from data based on actual tests. It will be assumed that the friction loss, varying as the square of the quantity, is equal to 5% of the generated head at theoretical maximum efficiency quantity and also that the constant losses represent an increase of input power from 100% to 110% of the power taken at the theoretical maximum efficiency quantity. This power curve will be given by a constant x $(1 - G^2) + \frac{1}{10}$

One can now plot the head, power and efficiency curves of an ideal pump and subtract the head losses, and add the power losses to obtain the corresponding three curves for an actual pump. It will be noted that the friction loss through the pump makes the head curve fall more steeply. The addition of power losses to the input power curve reduces the pump efficiency at zero quantity from 50% to zero. At the same time the portion of the pump efficiency curve between zero quantity and maximum efficiency becomes 'fuller' in shape, giving the contours corresponding to actual tests.

One particular discrepancy between the calculated curves on Figure 8 and the test curves of a typical pump is the shape of the power curve for very small quantities. The calculated power at zero quantity is $\frac{10}{110}$ of maximum power, that is, approximately 9%. In an actual pump this ratio is nearer 30%. It would appear that in addition to the losses already mentioned, a further loss occurs on very small quantities. It is probable that this further loss is due to wasteful circulation and eddies.

This additional loss apparently disappears beyond about 50% of maximum efficiency quantity, so that it will affect the portions of the curve which are of less consequence in average pumping problems.

In drawing the curves an indication is made of additional power loss but it is not possible to calculate what this loss would be, the curves in full lines and dotted lines indicating only 5% head loss and the 10% power loss.

It is therefore found that the maximum overall efficiency of the pump with Y = 1 and losses as selected, would occur approximately at 90% of the quantity Q. The value of this efficiency would be 86% and the maximum input power would occur at 100/90% x maximum efficiency quantity. This maximum power would exceed the maximum efficiency power by 2%. The characteristics of such a pump are shown on a percentage basis in Figure 8.

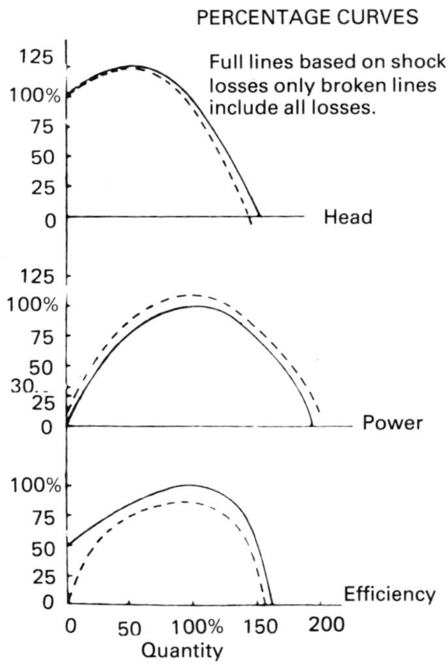

Figure 8
Percentage curves.

Type number

It is evident that the shape of characteristic is dependent primarily on area ratios of impeller and casing. Therefore, one should expect to obtain any desired shape characteristic, whatever the type number of the pump, by adopting a suitable area ratio.

This fact is borne out in practice by the following examples:

(i) 8% and 30% pressure rise from maximum efficiency to zero quantity obtained from two different pumps at 700 type number.

(ii) 10% and 30% pressure rise obtained from two different pumps at 1200 type number.

(Note on type number)

$$N_S = \text{type number} = \text{r/min}\ \frac{\sqrt{\text{flow}}}{(\text{Head})^{3/4}}$$

The type number of a pump indicates the shape of the pump and is sometimes defined as the speed at which a pump would run if reduced geometrically to give 1 l/s at 1 m head. As this is rather difficult to visualize the following may be considered:

(i) The term 'type number' could be discarded and the type number called instead 'type quantity'. This ratio would then be regarded as the quantity handled by a pump when reduced geometrically to give 1 m head at 1 r/min. The impellers shown in Figure 9 have the same diameter and are all designed to give the same head at the same r/min. The alteration in shape to give increased quantity is evident, the width and eye diameter of the impeller and the diameter of the volute throat progressively increasing as the type number increases, whilst the impeller outlet diameter remains unaltered. It should be noted that if the term 'type quantity' is adopted the present values of type numbers should be squared to give the true quantity ratios, since type number is a function of the square root of the quantity.

(ii) For a certain design of pumps; *eg* a range of pumps where Y = Y, the ratio diameter of volute throat/diameter of impeller is obtained as follows:

head = u^2 x constant = dia^2 x $(\text{r/min})^2$ x constant

diameter = $\sqrt{h}$/r/min x constant

Absolute velocity leaving impeller = volute throat velocity = constant x u, *ie* is proportional to $\sqrt{h}$

Quantity pumped = throat velocity x area of throat, therefore is proportional to $\sqrt{h}$ x area of throat

Hence, area of throat is proportional to:

$$\frac{Q}{\sqrt{H}}$$

and diameter of throat is proportional to:

$$\frac{\sqrt{Q}}{H^{1/4}}$$

Therefore, diameter of throat/diameter of impeller is proportional to:

$$\frac{\sqrt{Q}}{H^{1/4}} \Bigg/ \frac{\sqrt{H}}{\text{r/min}} = \frac{\text{r/min}\sqrt{Q}}{H^{3/4}} \text{ x constant}$$

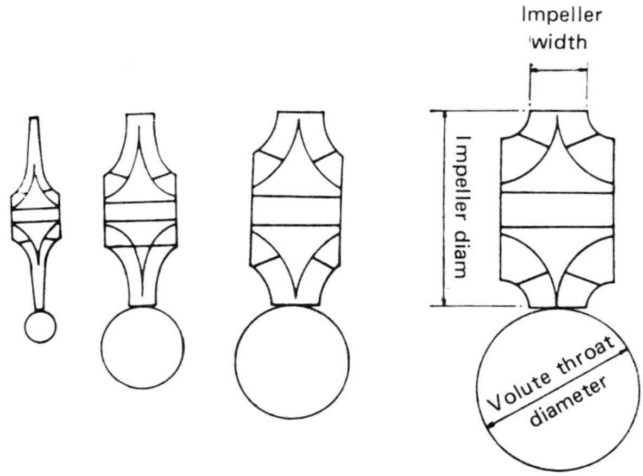

Figure 9
Change of type.

It is therefore possible to indicate the change of type of pumps shown in Figure 9 by the varying ratio-throat diameter/impeller diameter. From the aforementioned it is seen that this ratio is identified with the type number. In practice, it is found that the shorter length of vane of the larger eye impellers modifies the relation between type number and diameter ratio on larger values of type number.

Type number based on the best efficiency duty of the pump is a relationship which defines the pump shape at Constant $N_{S}y$, *eg* the 45° lines on Figure 10.

It should, however, be noted that a range of pumps at constant type number can have various shapes and characteristics according to the area ratio, *ie* a vertical line on Figure 10.

Assumptions

It has been necessary to make the following assumptions to prepare this analysis. Although these are only assumptions and cannot be proved mathematically, there is no doubt that they explain the particular contours of centrifugal pump characteristics and indicate the variation of these contours for various designs of pumps.

(i) The loss of energy due to shock at impeller outlet in a centrifugal pump is represented as a function of the side completing the velocity polygon whose other sides are relative impeller outlet velocity, peripheral impeller velocity and absolute diffuser or volute throat velocity.

(ii) It is necessary to assume that the loss of head due to friction through the pump varies as the square of the quantity, and that the power losses (other than hydraulic) are approximately constant.

(iii) It is necessary to assume some value for the volumetric efficiency of the pump.

The two latter assumptions are based upon actual test results.

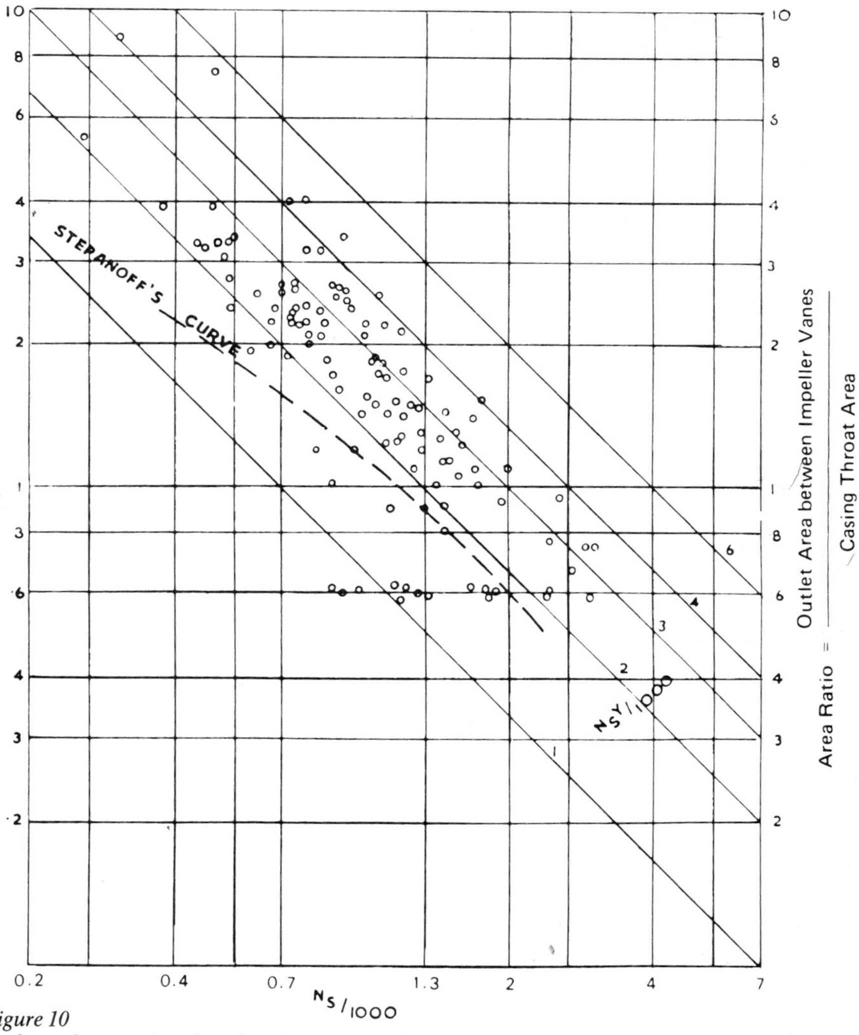

Figure 10
A chart of area ratios plotted against type number.

Conclusions

Head, Power and Efficiency

In an ideal pump, *ie*, taking into account shock losses only, the head generated is represented by:

$$H = \frac{u^2(1-G-G^2)+(1+G)\left[1-\frac{1}{Y^2}\right]t}{2g}$$

where t is a constant, being the velocity in the diffusers at the maximum efficiency quantity. In the particular case where Y = 1

$$H = (1-G-G^2)\,\frac{u^2}{2g}$$

The power absorbed by the pump is given by:

Input power = constant x $(1 - G^2)$

$$\text{Efficiency} = 1 - \frac{G^2}{1-G}$$

If Y is greater than 1 the head curve will tend to be unstable and the power curve will continue to rise as the quantities exceed maximum efficiency quantity. If Y is less than 1 the head curve will be in the stable region, and the power curve will fall beyond maximum efficiency quantity, *ie,* the pump will be non-overloading.

Type number over the whole characteristic from zero flow to zero head varies from zero to infinity, but type number is always determined from flow, head and speed at best efficiency point and is a useful arbiter of efficiency and of guidance in design.

Actual tests of pumps

Comparing the actual tests with the calculated curves it is found that it is necessary to make one further correction, namely, that the impeller and passages must be assumed to run partly empty. The value of the friction losses through the pump cannot be calculated nor can the volumetric efficiency or degree of fulness of the passages. When comparing the test results with calculations, values must be assumed for these unknown factors, hence it is not claimed that this analyusis gives absolute values. Nevertheless, it will be seen from Figures 11 and 12 that the shape of the characteristic given by test agrees very closely with the shape given by calculation according to the preceding analysis.

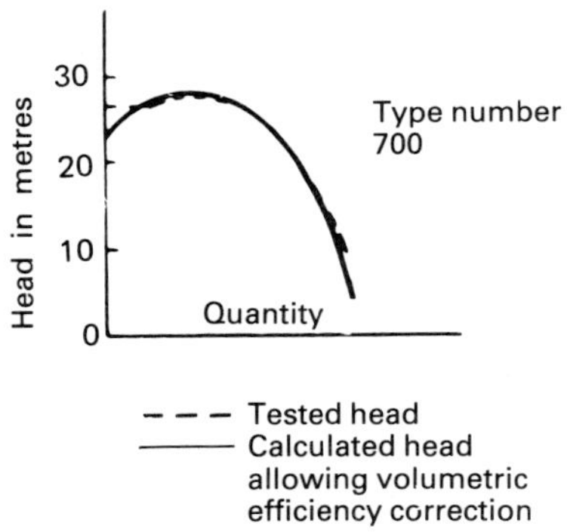

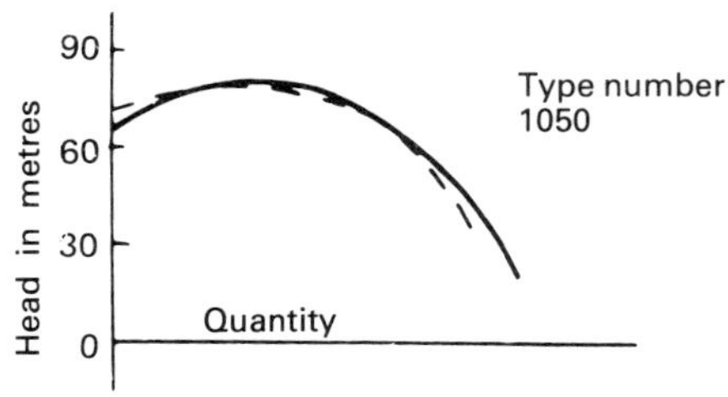

Figures 11 and 12
Comparison of test and calculated head curves to demonstrate shape of characteristics.

For all pumps the maximum input power will occur at a quantity such that the theoretical generated head equals $u^2/2g$.

In an actual pump

In the analysis one exmaple based on assumed losses is indicated.

The test characteristics of two actual pumps are shown in comparison with estimated characateristics in Figures 11 and 12.

Pipework Calculations

LIQUIDS PUMPED or discharged through pipes are assumed to fill the pipe section where flowrate (Q) and flow velocity (V) are directly related viz:

$$Q = 0{\cdot}7854\ d^2 \times V$$

where:

d = pipe bore

V = flow velocity

Arbitrary pipe sizing is based on recommended flow velocities established by practice as providing a reasonable compromise between good flowrates for a given pipe size together with low friction losses in delivery line and suitable hydraulic conditions in suction lines. A suitable pipe size then follows from:

$$d = k\sqrt{\frac{Q}{V_r}}$$

where:

k is a constant depending on units employed

V_r is the recommended flow velocity

TABLE 1 – RECOMMENDED SUCTION FLOW VELOCITIES

Pipe Bore		Water		Light Oils		Boiling Liquids		Viscous Liquids	
inches	mm	ft/sec	m/sec	ft/sec	m/sec	ft/sec	m/sec	ft/sec	m/sec
1	25	1.5	0.50	1.5	0.50	1.0	0.300	1.0	0.300
2	50	1.6	0.50	1.5	0.50	1.0	0.300	1.1	0.330
3	75	1.7	0.50	1.6	0.50	1.0	0.300	1.2	0.375
4	100	1.8	0.55	1.8	0.55	1.0	0.300	1.3	0.400
6	150	2.0	0.60	2.0	0.60	1.1	0.350	1.4	0.425
8	200	2.5	0.75	2.3	0.70	1.2	0.375	1.5	0.450
10	250	3.0	0.90	3.0	0.90	1.5	0.450	1.7	0.500
12	300	4.5	1.40	3.0	0.90	1.5	0.450	1.7	0.500
over 12*		5.0	1.50						

* General formula : pipe diameter (inches) = $\sqrt{\frac{\text{gal/min}}{10}}$

TABLE 2 – RECOMMENDED DELIVERY FLOW VELOCITIES

Pipe Bore mm	inches	Water m/sec	ft/sec	Light Oils m/sec	ft/sec	Boiling Liquids m/sec	ft/sec	Viscous Liquids m/sec	ft/sec
25	1	1.00	3.5	1.00	3.5	1.00	3.5	1.00	3.5
50	2	1.10	3.6	1.10	3.6	1.10	3.6	1.10	3.6
75	3	1.15	3.8	1.15	3.8	1.15	3.8	1.10	3.7
100	4	1.25	4.0	1.25	4.0	1.25	4.0	1.15	3.8
150	6	1.50	4.7	1.50	4.7	1.50	4.7	1.20	3.9
200	8	1.75	5.5	1.75	5.5	1.75	5.5	1.20	4.0
250	10	2.00	6.5	2.00	6.5	2.00	6.5	1.30	4.5
300	12	2.65	8.5	2.00	6.5	2.00	6.5	1.40	4.5
	over 12*	3.00	10.0						

*General formula: pipe diameter (inches) = $\sqrt{\dfrac{\text{gal/min}}{20}}$

TABLE 3 – COMMON FLOW VELOCITIES IN COMMERCIAL PRACTICE

Medium	Piping		Velocity m/sec	Remarks
Water	Piston pumps	suction	0·5 to 1·5	
		delivery	1·0 to 2·0	
	Feed pumps of steam boilers	suction	0·3 to 0·5	The piping is selected
		delivery	2·0 to 2·5	according to its length. A lower
	Piping for condensate and sludge	suction	0·3 to 0·5	velocity is chosen with long
	Gravel, sand and other drifted			piping, a higher velocity for
	substances	delivery	0·5 to 2·0	short piping (does not apply to
	Piping for cold water	delivery	1·0 to 3·0	delivery of liquids containing
	Piping for cold water	suction		solid particles)
	up to 50 mm diameter	maximum	1·0	
	up to 100 mm diameter	maximum	1·3	
	up to 200 mm diameter	maximum	1·7	
	above 200 mm diameter		2·0	
	Piping for cooling water	suction	0·7 to 1·5	
		delivery	1·0 to 2·0	
	Pressure water		15·0 to 30·0	In special cases up to 5 m/sec
	Delivery piping in mines		1·0 to 1·5	
	Supply to water turbines		3·0	Low head
			3·0 to 7·0	High head
	Municipal water mains, main		1·0 to 2·0	
	feed pipings municipal water system		0·5 to 1·2	Normally 0·6 to 0·7 m/sec
Petrol Oils	Benzole, gas oil		1·0 to 2·0	
	Heavy		0·5 to 2·0	According to viscosity
Hydro-carbons		suction	0·3 to 0·8	
Air	Low-pressure piping		12 to 15	
	High-pressure piping		20 to 25	
Steam	For steam lines up to 4 MPa		20 to 40	Velocities must be chosen
	High-pressure steam		30 to 60	economically according to
	Super-heated stean		39 to 80	the length of the piping
	Low-pressure heating system		10 to 15	
	Exhaust steam		15 to 40	

Recommended flow velocities differ for suction lines and delivery lines and also with the nature of the fluid handled. Specific recommendations are given in Tables 1, 2 and 3 the classification 'viscous liquids' is somewhat arbitrary since with certain fluids of this type flow velocities may have to be reduced in order to avoid channelling or overheating.

Simplified values

For water services the following flow velocity limits are commonly adopted:

General services – V_{max} = 1·2 to 3 m/sec (4 to 10 ft/sec) †

Water supplies – Vmax = 2 m/sec (7 ft/sec)

Boiler feed – V_{max} = 2·5 to 4·5 m/sec (8 to 15 ft/sec) †

†The higher figures for largest pipe sizes.

A general formula may also be used for calculating pipe bore size directly viz:

$$\text{Pipe bore (mm)} = \sqrt{\frac{\text{l/min}}{0{\cdot}145}}$$

$$\text{Pipe bore (in)} = \sqrt{\frac{\text{gal/min}}{20}}$$

In the case of centrifugal pumps optimum flow velocities are commonly determined relative to the fluid specific gravity and the type of driver, as shown in Table 4.

TABLE 4 – RECOMMENDED FLOW VELOCITIES BASED ON FLUIDS SG

Pipe dia.		Power driven pumps						Turbine driven pumps					
		SG = 1·0		SG = 0·75		SG = 0·5		SG = 1·0		SG = 0·75		SG = 0·5	
in	mm	ft/sec	m/sec	ft/sec	m/sec	ft/sec	m/sec	ft/sec	m/sec	ft/sec	m/sec	ft/sec	m/sec
2	50	6·00	1·80	7·00	2·10	7·5	2·30	5·00	1·50	5·50	1·70	6·00	1·80
3	75	7·00	2·10	8·00	2·40	8·5	2·60	5·50	1·70	6·00	1·80	6·50	2·00
4	100	8·00	2·40	9·00	10·0	3·00	6·00	1·80	6·50	2·00	7·00	2·15	
6	150	9·00	2·75	10·00	3·0	12·0	3·65	6·50	2·00	7·00	2·15	8·00	2·40
8	200	10·00	3·00	11·25	3·40	13·0	4·00	6·75	2·10	7·50	2.30	8·50	2·60
10	250	11·00	3·32	12·00	3·65	14·0	4·20	7·00	2·15	7·75	2·35	9·00	2·75
12	300	11·50	3·50	12·50	3·80	14·5	4·40	7·00	2·15	8·00	2·40	9·25	2·80
14	350	11·75	3·60	13·00	4·00	15·0	4·50	7·00	2·15	8·00	2·40	9·50	2·90
16 and over	400	12·00	3·65	13·00	4·00	15·0	4·60	7·00	2·15	8·00	2·40	9·50	2·90

Critical flow velocity

Flow velocity is not a critical factor where clean liquids are concerned (except that it is the major parameter affecting friction losses). Where the liquid contains solids, however, flow velocity can determine whether the flow is homogeneous (*ie* the solids are transported in suspension in the fluid), or heterogeneous (*ie* the solids tend to settle out and form a sliding layer over a settled bed). To produce homogeneous flow the flow velocity must be greater than the full velocity of the solids; the latter thus represents a critical flow velocity or minimum flow velocity necessary for maintaining the solids in suspension. Critical flow velocities are related to the size and type of solid and range from 1 to 1·5 m/s (3 to 5 ft/s) for slurry fines up to 3·25 to 4·25 m/s (11 to 14 ft/s) for sludges.

Pipe velocity feet per second – 1 inch steel pipe

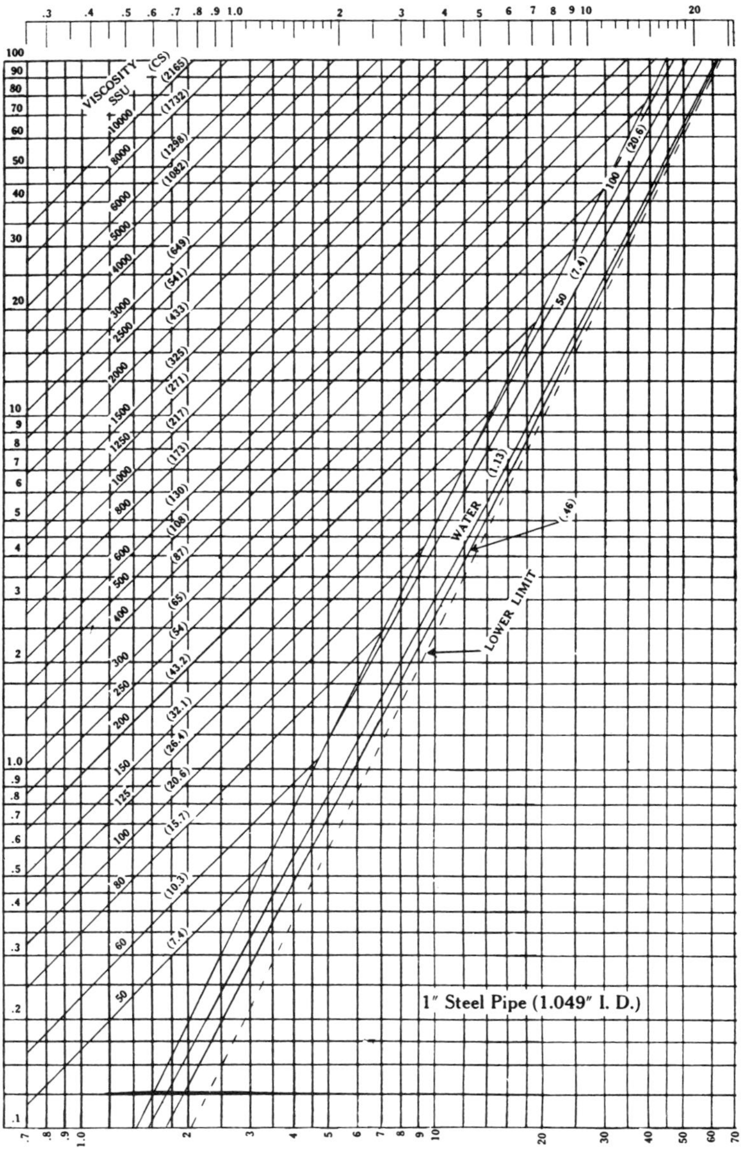

Gallons per minute

Pressure drop given on left-hand vertical scale is water. For pressure drop with other fluids multiply by specific gravity of fluid.

Pipe velocity feet per second – 1¼ inch steel pipe

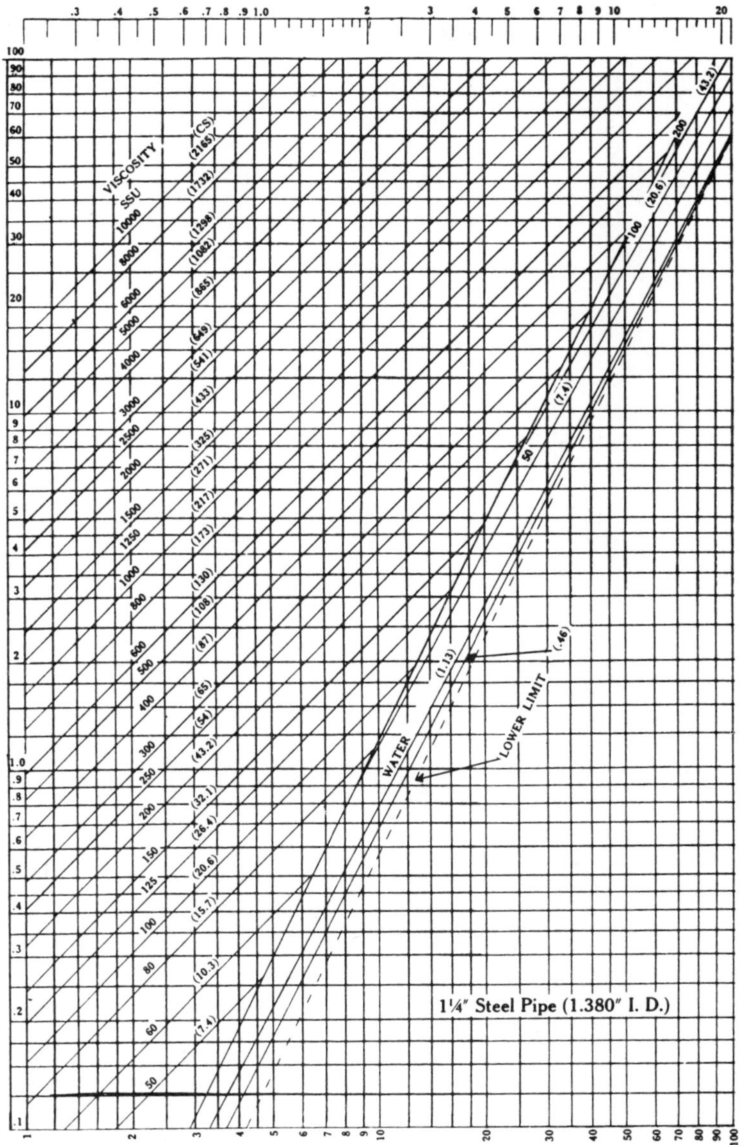

Gallons per minute

Pressure drop given on left-hand vertical scale is water. For pressure drop with other fluids multiply by specific gravity of fluid.

Pipe velocity feet per second – 1½ inch steel pipe

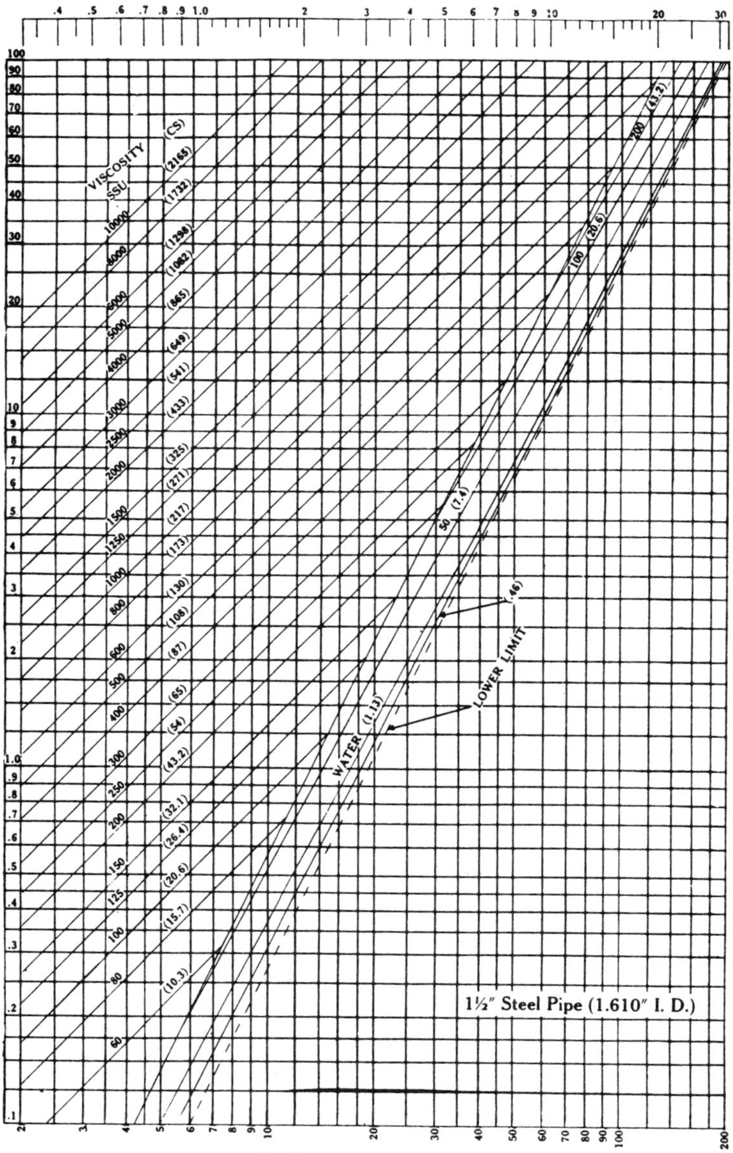

Gallons per minute

Pressure drop given on left-hand vertical scale is water. For pressure drop with other fluids multiply by specific gravity of fluid.

Pipe velocity feet per second – 2 inch steel pipe

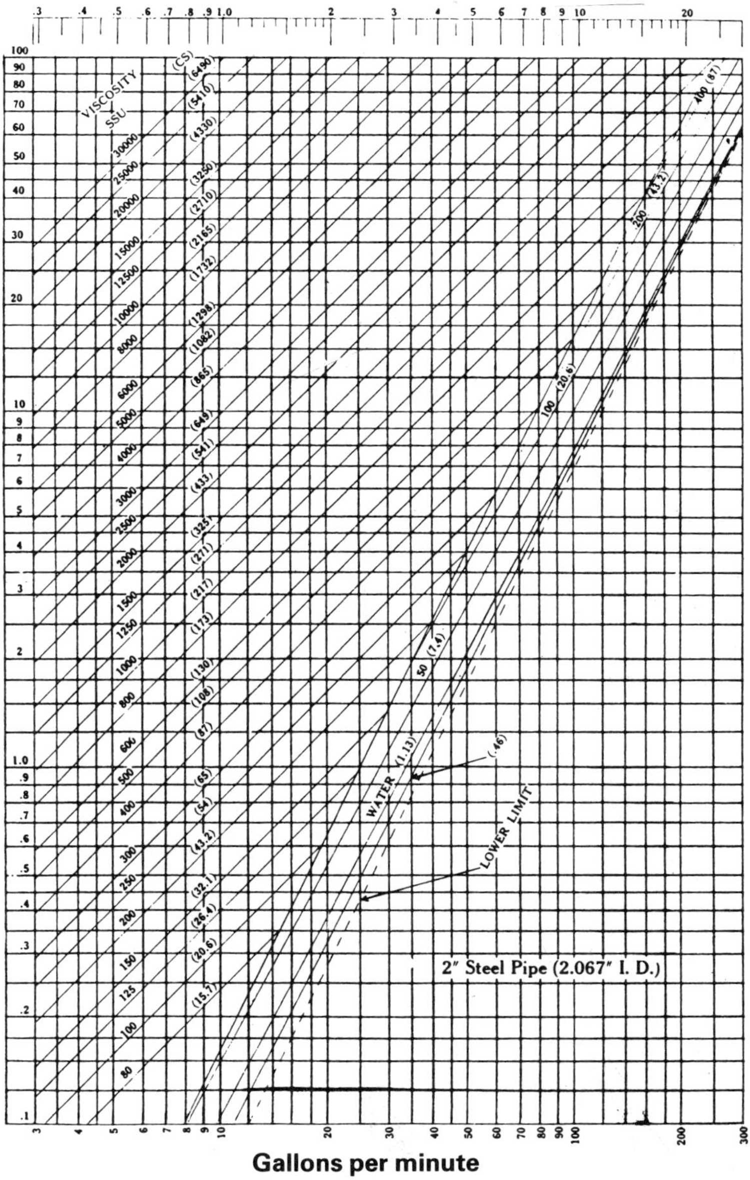

Pressure drop given on left-hand vertical scale is water. For pressure drop with other fluids multiply by specific gravity of fluid.

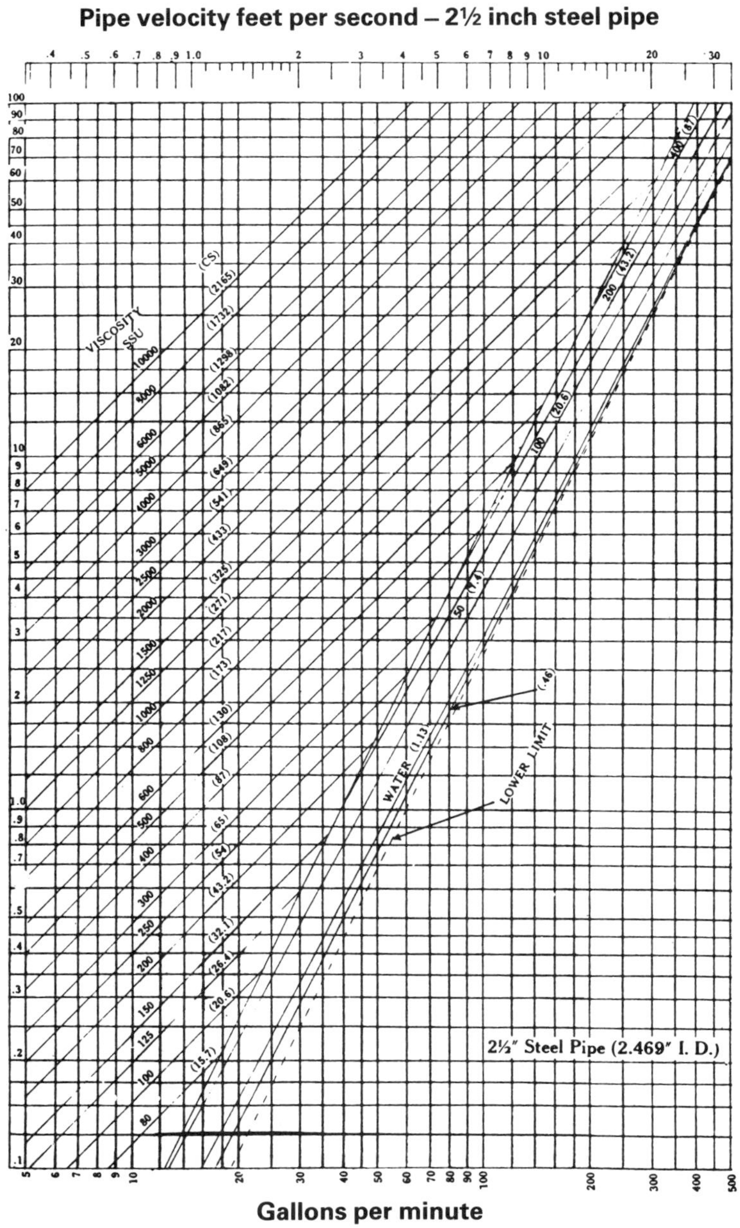

Pressure drop given on left-hand vertical scale is water
For pressure drop with other fluids multiply by specific gravity of fluid.

Pipe velocity feet per second – 3 inch steel pipe

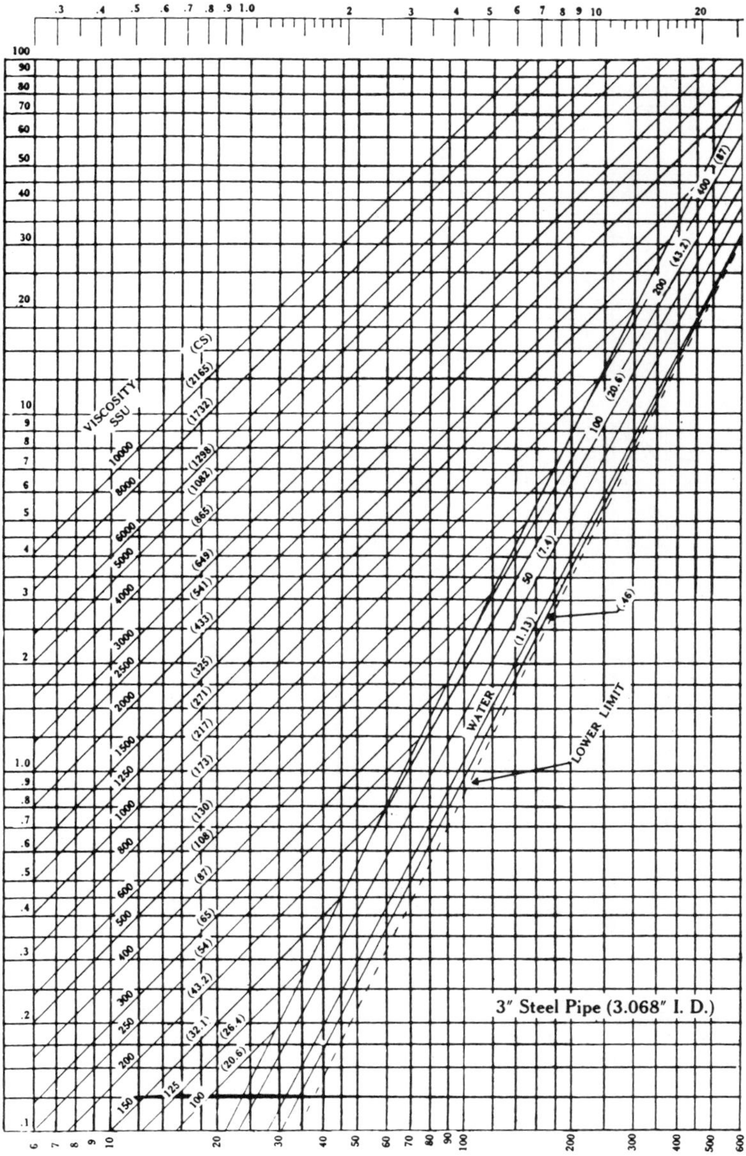

Pressure drop given on left-hand vertical scale is water. For pressure drop with other fluids multiply by specific gravity of fluid.

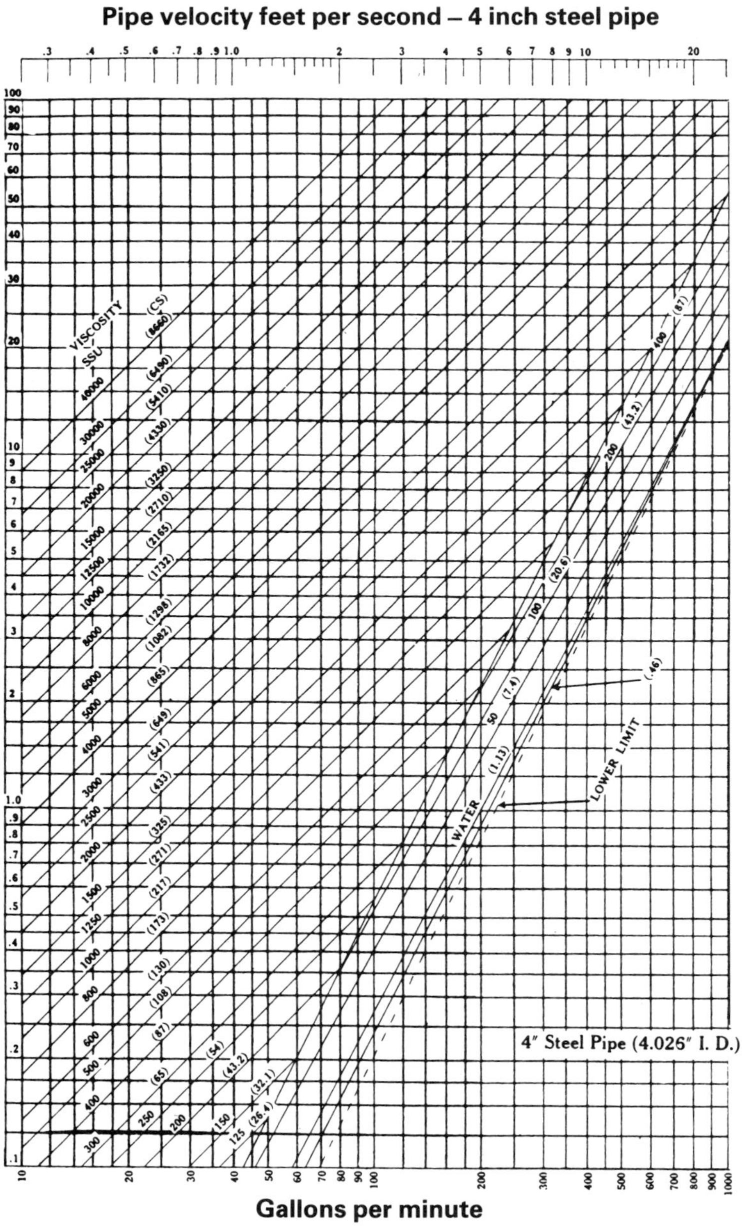

Pressure drop given on left-hand vertical scale is water.
For pressure drop with other fluids multiply by specific gravity of fluid.

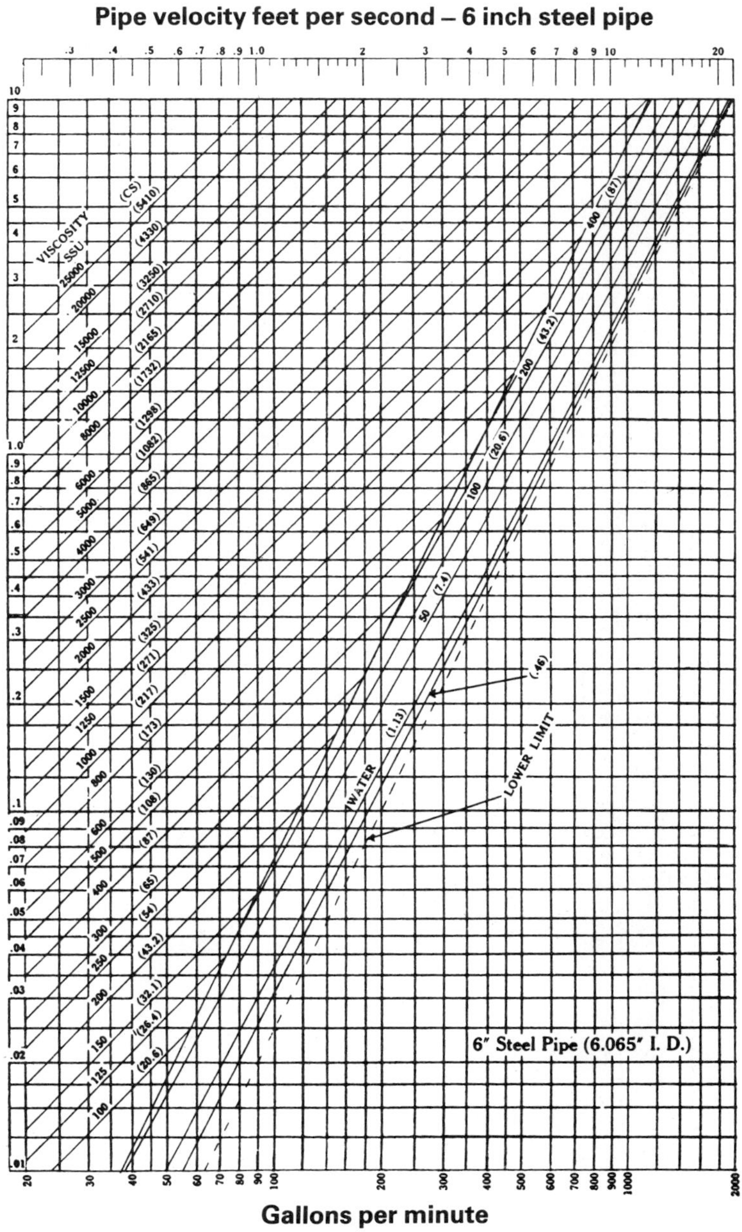

Pressure drop given on left-hand vertical scale is water. For pressure drop with other fluids multiply by specific gravity of fluid.

Pipe velocity feet per second – 8 inch steel pipe

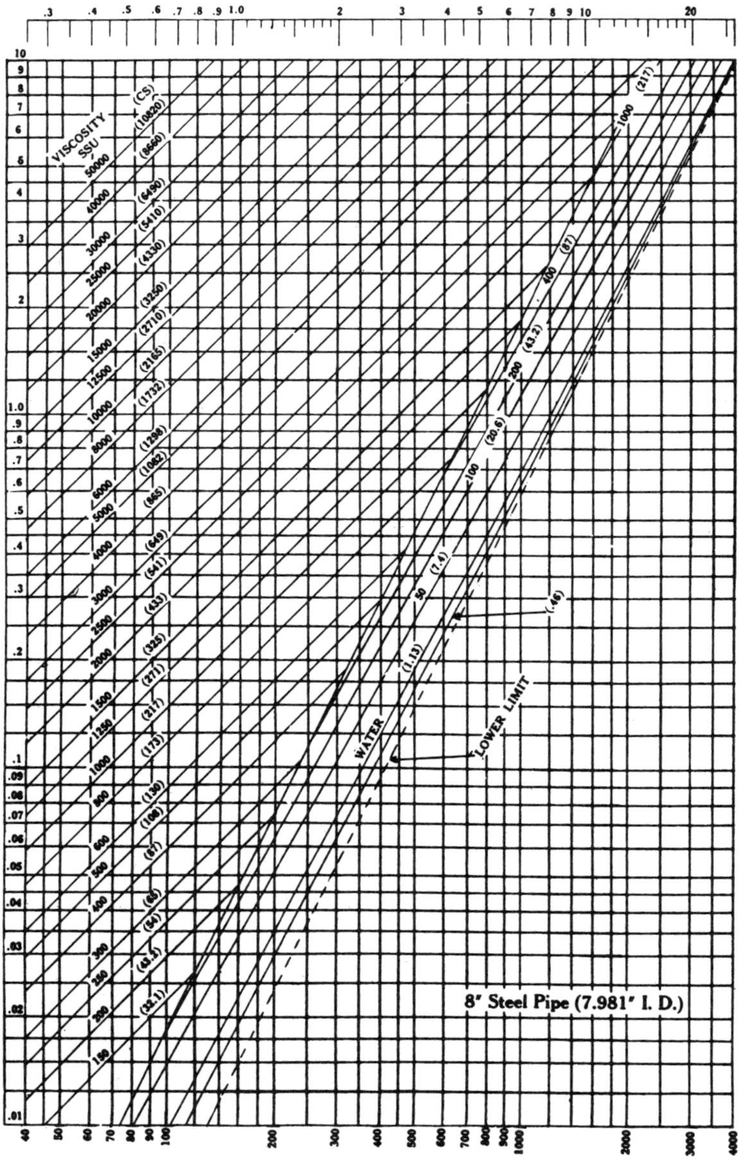

Gallons per minute

Pressure drop given on left-hand vertical scale is water. For pressure drop with other fluids multiply by specific gravity of fluid.

Pipe velocity feet per second – 10 inch steel pipe

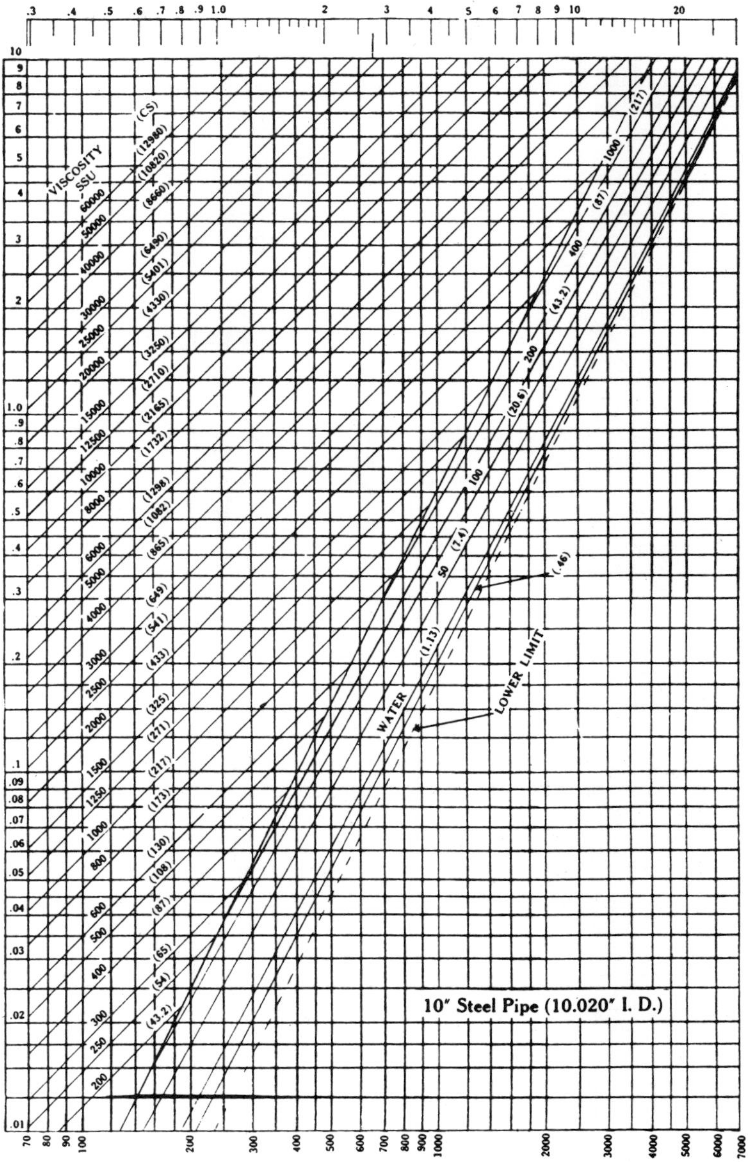

Gallons per minute

Pressure drop given on left-hand vertical scale is water. For pressure drop with other fluids multiply by specific gravity of fluid.

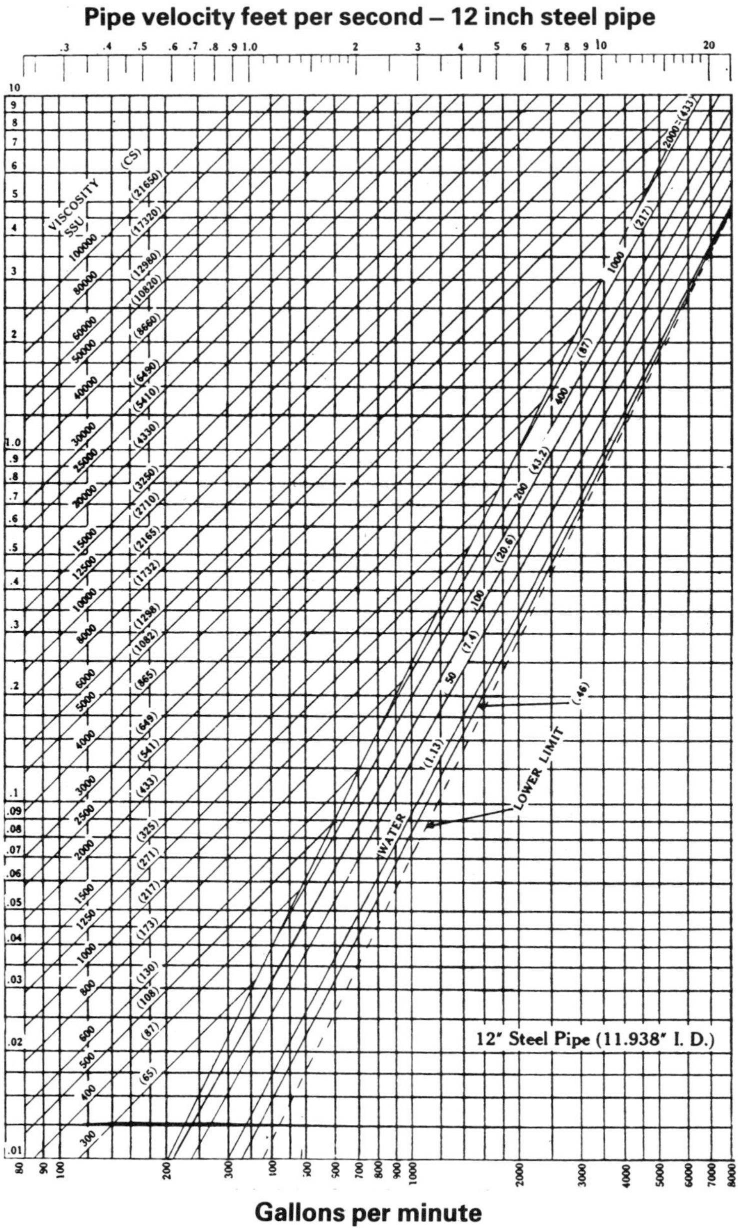

Pressure drop given on left-hand vertical scale is water. For pressure drop with other fluids multiply by specific gravity of fluid.

Pipe velocity feet per second – 14 inch steel pipe

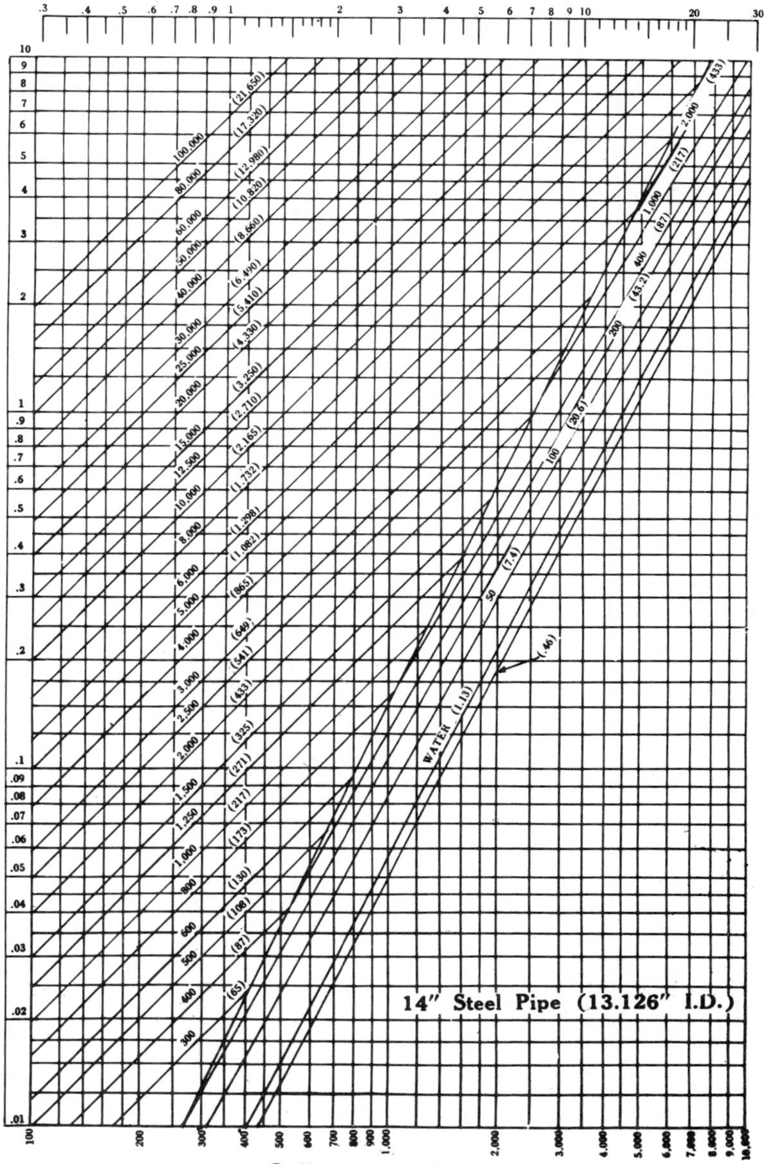

Gallons per minute

Pressure drop given on left-hand vertical scale is water. For pressure drop with other fluids multiply by specific gravity of fluid.

Pipe velocity feet per second – 16 inch steel pipe

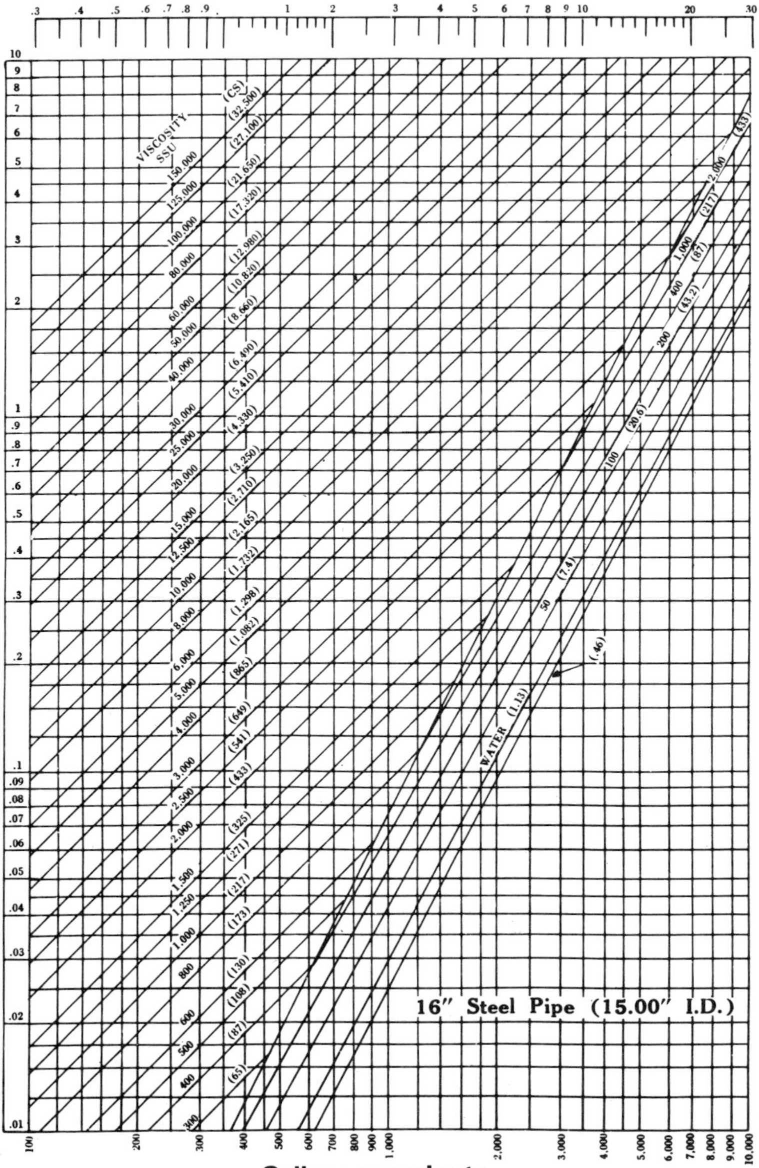

Gallons per minute

Pressure drop given on left-hand vertical scale is water. For pressure drop with other fluids multiply by specific gravity of fluid.

Determination of friction losses

Friction losses in pipes and fittings need to be determined at total head required for a particular pumping duty. Equally, since friction losses are directly related to pipe size and velocity, one method of controlling (or adjusting) friction losses is to adjust the pipe size (which for a given delivery will have the effect of modifying the flow velocity.

Frictional losses for flow in straight pipes can be calculated in terms of pressure drop or head from the following general formulas:

$$\text{Pressure drop } \triangle P = k_1 \, x \, f \, x \, \frac{L \rho Q^2}{d^x}$$

$$\text{Head loss } \triangle H = k_2 \, x \, f \, x \, \frac{L Q^2}{d^x}$$

where:

Q is the flow rate

f is a friction factor

d is the pipe bore

L is the pipe length involved

ρ is the fluid density

k_1 and k_2 are constants depending on the units employed (see Table 5)

x is an exponential of the order of 5·0 (but specifically often taken as 4·87)

TABLE 5 – VALUES FOR k_1 AND k_2 IN FRICTION LOSS FORMULAS (Note: For engineering calculations, take exponential x = 5)

L	ρ	Q	d	ΔP	k_1	ΔH	k_2
m	tonnes/m^3	lit/min	mm	bar	0.1613	metres	641270
ft	lb/ft^3	gal/min	in	lb/in^2	0.0018	feet	0.026
ft	lb/ft^3	US gal/min	in	lb/in^2	0.000216	feet	0.0311
ft	lb/hr	barrels/bar	in	lb/in^2	0.0001058	feet	0.01524

The friction factor f is dependant on the flow condition. For laminar flow (Reynolds number of flow beyond 2000), f = 64/R_e. For turbulent flow (R_e above 3000), friction factor varies in a more complex manner, depending both on flow Reynolds number and relative roughness of the pipe bore. It is most commonly read from a chart – see Figure 1. In the case of the rough bore pipes, roughness is defined in terms of e/d where e is the absolute roughness or effective height of bore irregularities in the same units as the pipe bore d, see Figure 2.

Note: The Reynolds numbers quoted are for English units (see under Reynolds number).

It will be appreciated that the relative roughness of pipe can vary with age and/or build-up of slime deposits, *etc*, and so age corrections may sometimes be applicable.

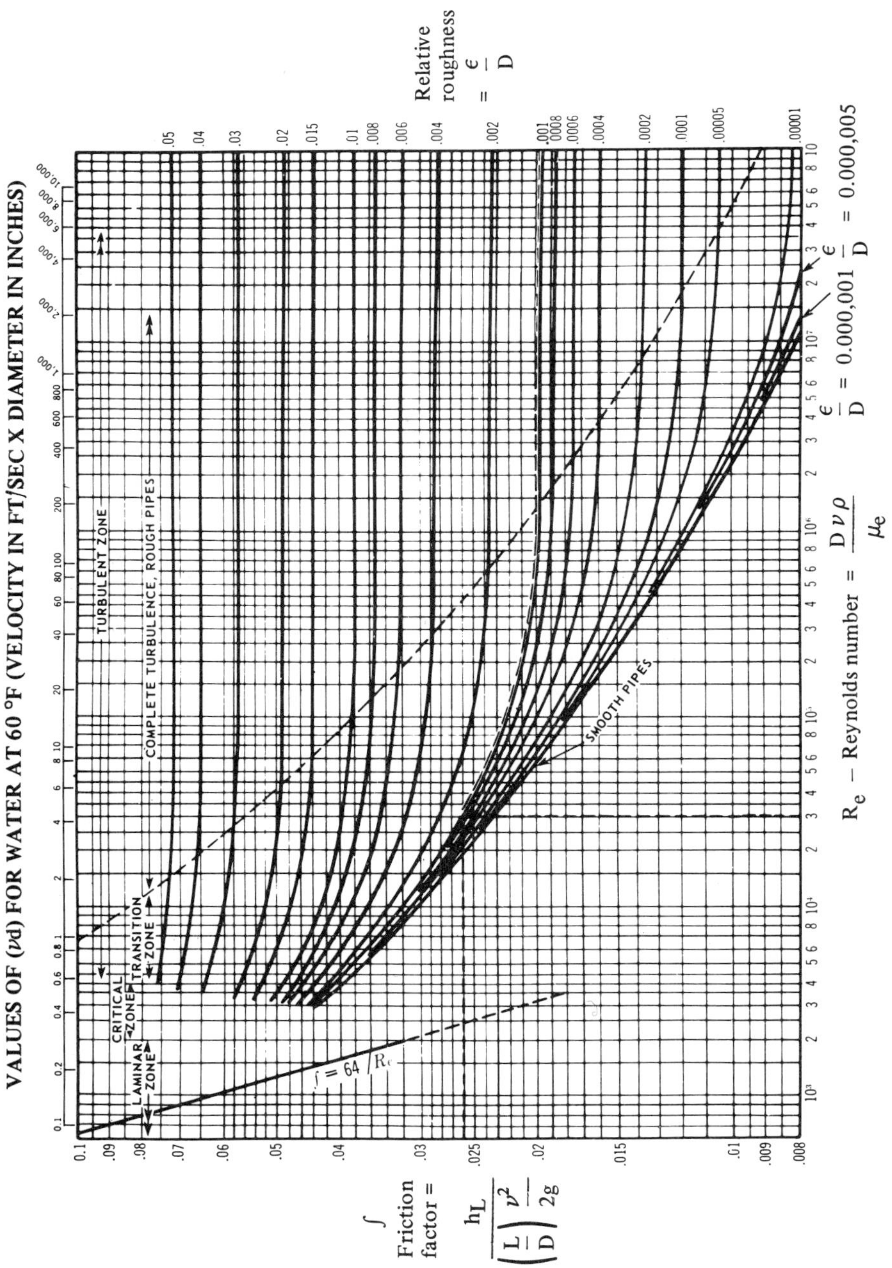

Figure 1
Friction factors for pipes.
Example: Friction factor for pipe with relative roughness 0.001 at flow Reynolds number of 30 000 = 0.026

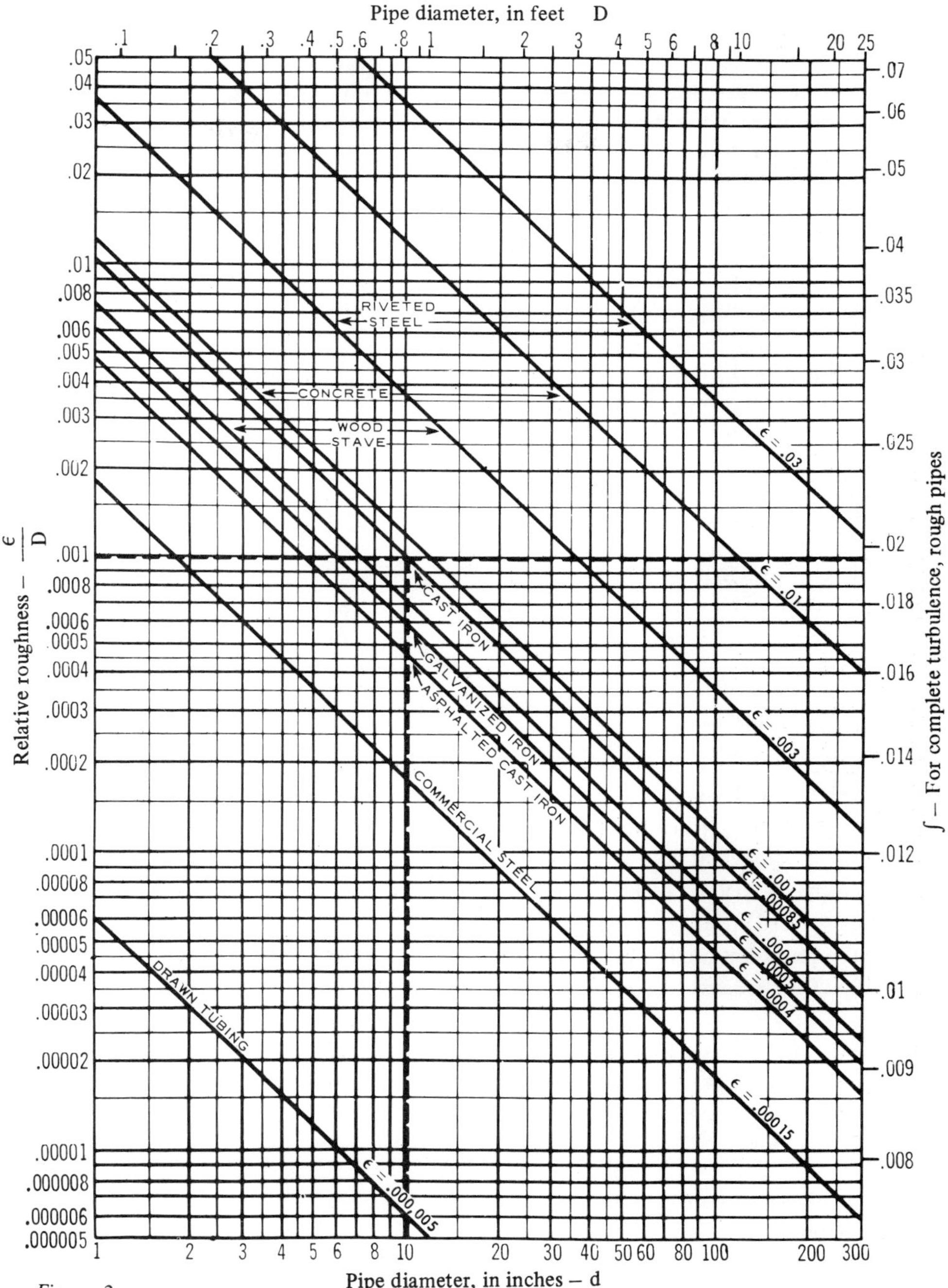

Figure 2
Friction factors and relative roughness for commercial pipes with fully turbulent flow (based on ASME data originated by L.F.Moody).
Example: For 10 in diameter cast iron pipe, relative roughness (E/D) = 0.00085.
Friction factor = 0.0196

Friction losses are commonly determined from charts or tables (mostly based on the Hazen Williams' formula) but the data presented are not always fully accurate. It is the most convenient form of data to use, however, particularly as it is normally related to standard pipe sizes. Note, however, that it refers to standard bore sizes, actual bore sizes may differ sufficiently to seriously modify the actual loss. If the dimensional difference is marked, a correction can be made by multiplying the quoted friction loss by:

$$\frac{d_n}{d_a}$$

where:

d_n is the standard (nominal) bore size and

d_a is the actual bore size

Note also that friction factors cannot be determined accurately from chart or tabular data for flow losses without reference to the actual Reynolds number involved.

Reynolds number (R_e)

The Reynolds number is a dimensionless quantity determined as:

$$R_e = \frac{kdV}{\nu}$$

where:

d = pipe bore

V = flow velocity

ν = kinetic viscosity of the fluid

k is a constant depending on units employed

For d in centimetres, V in m/sec and ν in centistokes, k = 10 000

For d in inches, V in ft/sec and ν in centistokes, k = 7740

In the case of clear cold water:

R_e = 10 000 dV for d in centimetres and V in m/sec

R_e = 7740 dV for d in inches and V in ft/sec

In the case of non-circular pipes, the equivalent hydraulic diameter or 4 x cross-sectional flow area/wetted perimeter is substituted for the pipe diameter d.

Pipe sizing by pressure drop

Pipe sizing can be determined directly from pressure drop, working pressure drop calculations directly as a solution for pipe bore. This method is widely used in high pressure systems when it is necessary to establish an acceptable level of pipe friction.

Typical pressure drop recommendations for pipe sizing are as follows:

Suction lines – pressure drop per 100 m 0·0115 to 0·23 bar (0·05 to 1 lb/in^2 per 100 ft) depending on the available NPSH.

Delivery lines – 0·115 to 1·38 bar per 100 m (0·5 to 6 lb/in^2 per 100 ft) depending on the flow rate, viz:

(a) 0·46 to 1·4 bar per 100 m for flow rates up to 450 l/min
(2 to 6 lb/in^2 per 100 ft for flow rates up to 100 gal/min)

(b) 0·33 to 1·15 bar per 100 m for flow rates from 450 to 900 l/min
(1·5 to 5 lb/in^2 per 100 ft for flow rates from 100 to 200 gal/min)

(c) 0·23 to 0·982 bar per 100 m for flow rates from 900 to 2250 l/min
(1 to 4 lb/in per 100 ft for flow rates from 200 to 500 gal/min)

(d) 0·11 to 0·46 bar per 100 m for flow rate above 2250 l/min
(0·5 to 2 lb/in^2 per 100 ft for flow rates above 500 gal/min)

Bends and fittings

Pressure drop or head loss produced by heads and individual components in the pipeline can be expressed as:

(i) Equivalent length of straight pipe
(ii) A resistant coefficient (K)
(iii) A flow co-efficient (v)

Of these, the equivalent straight length is the most convenient and the most usual system adopted for bends, tees, elbows *etc*, and such data is also available for valves as shown in Tables 6 and 7. The fact that equivalent lengths quoted for a range of sizes is largely superfluous. The value of the equivalent L/d should be a constant for the same flow conditions and valid for all sizes of that particular component (*ie* differing only if there are deficiencies in local geometry in different sizes).

Where resistance coefficients (K) is given this gives a direct conversion of velocity head loss into head loss or pressure drop viz:

$$\triangle H = K x \quad \frac{V^2}{2g}$$

$$\triangle P = K x \quad \frac{V^2 w}{2g}$$

where:
w = specific weight of fluid

It also follows that:

K = f x L/d

where:

f is the friction factor involved at the measured flow condition.

TABLE 6 – EQUIVALENT STRAIGHT LENGTHS OF FITTINGS
(Note: Equivalent length = table factor x pipe diameter in same length unit as diameter)

Flush sharp-edged entry	20–25
Slightly rounded entry	10–12
Flush bellmouth entry	4
Sharp entry projecting into liquid	35
Bellmouth entry projecting into liquid	10
Footvalve with strainer	100
Round elbow	45
Short radius bend	30–35
Medium radius bend	15
Close return bend	100
Tee: straight through	10
side outlet, sharp angled	50–55
side outlet, radiused (swept tee	20–25
Branch piece, straight through	10
Branch piece, flow to branch	45
Branch piece, flow from branch	22
Bellmouth outlet	9
Sudden enlargement	45
Taper, divergence angle above 60°	45
Taper increases or reduces with less than 15° divergence angle.	22
	1

TABLE 7 – EQUIVALENT STRAIGHT LENGTH OF VALVES
(Note: Equivalent length = table factor x pipe diameter in same length unit as diameter)

Type of Valve	Factor
Screwdown valve, straight	100
Screwdown valve, angled	50
Gate valve	7
Gate valve, half closed	15
Gate valve, three-quarters closed	60–65
Globe valve	250–450
Swing check valve	60–70
Reflux (non-return) valve	45

Flow co-efficient

For valves (and particularly control valves) it is generally more accurate to express the flow rate and flow characteristics in terms of a flow coefficient (C_V), defined as the flow of water at 60 °F in US gallons/minute at a pressure drop of 1 lb/in^2 across the valve; or the metric equivalent flow factor (K_V) defined as the number of cubic metres per hour of water at 20 °C which will flow with a pressure drop of 1 bar. These give slightly different values for the same flow conditions, viz:

$K_V = 0{\cdot}883\ C_V$

$C_V = 1{\cdot}16\ K_V$

The flow through valves handling liquids with a viscosity similar to that of water is then given by:

$$Q = C_V\sqrt{\frac{\Delta P}{SG}}$$

and the pressure drop from:

$$\Delta P = \left(\frac{Q^2}{C_V}\right) \text{x SG of fluid}$$

Flow co-efficients for various types of valves are given in Table 8.

TABLE 8 – TYPICAL C_V VALUES FOR VALVES
(For valves fully open)

Valve Type	NOMINAL DIAMETER in (mm)								
	½ (12.5)	1 (25)	2 (50)	3 (75)	4 (100)	6 (150	8 (200)	10 (250)	12 (300)
Ball	26	94	480	1300	2300	5400	10000	16000	24000
Butterfly	–	–	85	260	475	1125	2100	3400	4800
Diaphragm (straight through)	–	30–40	100–140	300–350	500–600	1500–1800	2000–2500	3500–4000	5000–6000
Diaphragm (Weir type)	–	15	80	180	320	600	1200	2000	2500

Total friction loss

Total friction loss is determined as follows:

(i) Breakdown the system into individual sections, starting with the suction entry, suction pipe, through to the end of the delivery pipe.

(ii) Add together the straight lengths of pipe.

Note that different diameters of pipe must be considered as separate items for calculation.

Then either:

(iii) Render bends, fittings, *etc*, in terms of equivalent lengths of pipe and add to (ii) to arrive at a total effective length of pipe (or lengths of different diameters). Total head loss can then be computed for this length (or the aggregate of separate lengths of different diameters).

or

(iv) Render straight lengths of pipe in terms of head loss. Calculate head loss for individual fittings, *etc*, based on resistance coefficients and add together to find total head loss.

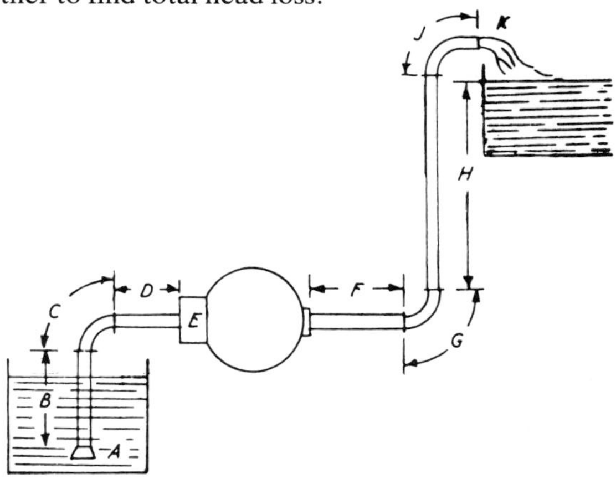

Figure 3

As an example, consider the system shown in Figure 3. Breaking it down into individual components the losses to be evaluated are:

A – inlet loss at foot valve or entry to suction pipe.

B & D – straight runs expressed as a total length.

C – bend expressed in equivalent straight length.

B, D and the equivalent straight length C are then totalled and the frictional loss for this length is computed.

E – pressure drop through filter is evaluated in terms of head.

Total dynamic losses on the inlet side thus = A + (B + D + equivalent straight length of C) x head loss per foot for that size of pipe at required flow rates (capacity) + E.

Similarly, on the delivery side the equivalent straight length of pipe is equal to F + H + equivalent straight length of J. This total length multiplied by the head loss per foot for the delivery pipe size at the required flowrate gives the frictional loss in the outlet pipe. To this must be added the energy loss at the point of delivery K.

TABLE 9 – PIPE FRICITON LOSS COEFFICIENTS λ

Laminar flow	Turbulent flow		
	Hydraulically smooth pipes	Hydraulically rough pipes	Pipes in transient range
	Limits: $R_e \cdot \frac{k}{d_i} < 65$	Limits: $R_e \cdot \frac{k}{d_i} > 1300$	Limits: $65 < R_e \cdot \frac{k}{d_i} < 1300$
Formula for λ $\lambda = \frac{64}{R_e}$ $\lambda = \frac{64 \cdot \nu}{c \cdot d_i}$	Formula for λ: a) Blasius formula for the range $2320 < R_e < 10^5$ $\lambda = 0.3164 \cdot R_e^{-0.25}$ b) Nikuradse formula for the range $10^5 < R_e < 5 \cdot 10^6$ $\lambda = 0.0032 + 0.221 \cdot R_e^{-0.237}$ c) Prandtl and von Kármán formula for the range $R_e > 10^6$ $\frac{1}{\sqrt{\lambda}} = 2 \lg (R_e \cdot \sqrt{\lambda}) - 0.8$	Formula for λ: Nikuradse formula $\frac{1}{\sqrt{\lambda}} = 2 \lg \frac{d_i}{k} + 1.14$	Formula for λ: Prandtl-Colebrook formula $\frac{1}{\sqrt{\lambda}} = -2 \lg \left[\frac{2.51}{R_e \sqrt{\lambda}} + \frac{k}{d_i} \cdot 0.269\right]$

TABLE 10 – PIPE BEND, RESISTANCE LOSS COEFFICIENT ζ

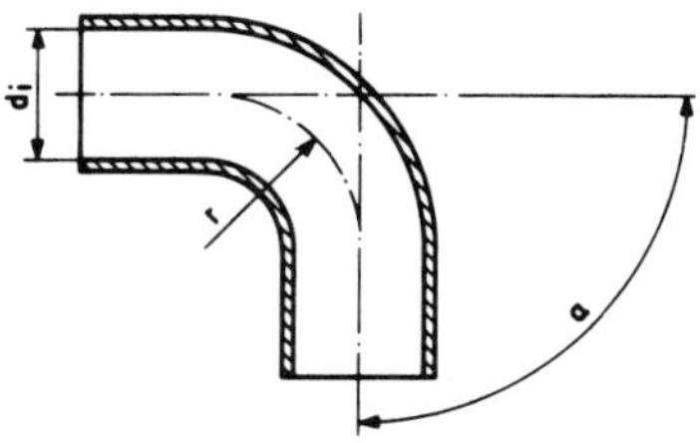

α \ $\frac{r}{d_i}$	1	1,5	2	4	6	
15°	0.03	0.03	0.03	0.03	0.03	
30°	0.07	0.07	0.07	0.07	0.07	Interior
45°	0.14	0.11	0.09	0.08	0.075	pipe wall
60°	0.19	0.16	0.12	0.10	0.09	*smooth*
90°	0.21	0.18	0.14	0.11	0.09	
15°	0.10	0.08	0.06	0.05	0.04	
30°	0.23	0.19	0.14	0.11	0.08	Interior
45°	0.34	0.27	0.20	0.15	0.12	pipe wall
60°	0.41	0.33	0.24	0.19	0.15	*rough*
90°	0.51	0.41	0.30	0.23	0.18	

The total system head is then found by adding the total of the frictional and energy losses to the total static head of the system.

This will give a single head figure for a specific capacity, or if frictional and energy losses are computed over a range of capacities, a curve of system head against capacity – Figure 4. H-Q curves for a pump superimposed on this diagram will then indicate suitable pump size. The system head curve is more informative since the intersection of system head with the individual H-Q curves indicates the working points of the pumps they represent. Ideally, the operating point should correspond with the point of maximum efficiency of the pump, but in practice there will be a certain range over which efficiency will be high and an operating point within this range is usually satisfactory, with pump size chosen accordingly.

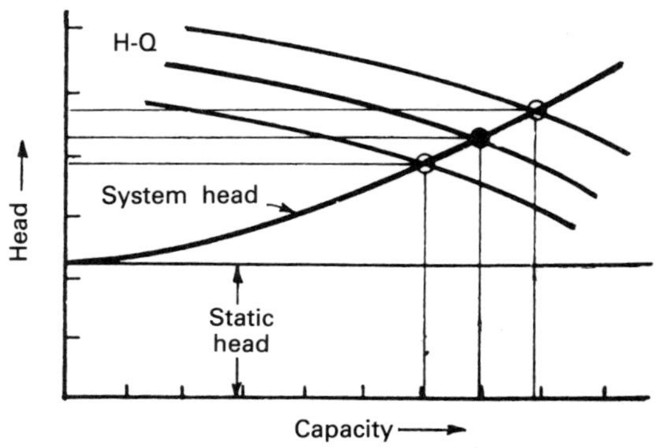

Figure 4

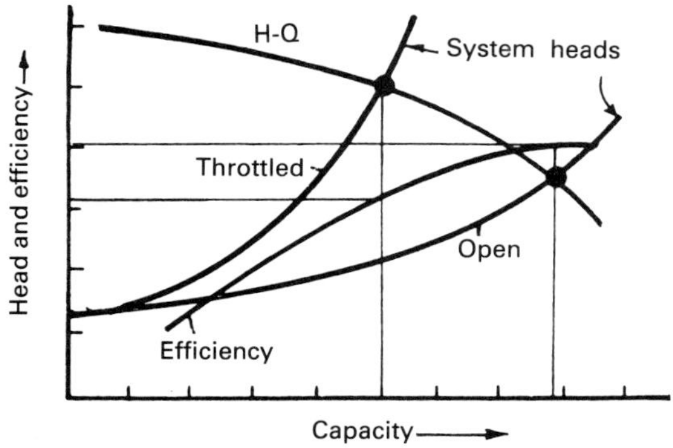

Figure 5

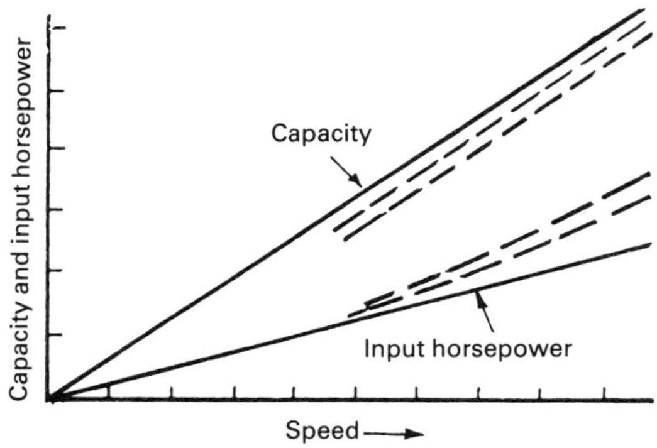

Figure 6

In the case of constant speed roto-dynamic pumps, a larger size than necessary is uneconomic since the flow will have to be throttled in order to achieve the required capacity, at which point the pump may be operating at an appreciably lower efficiency, see Figure 5. Alternatively, if it is not possible to throttle the flow *eg* if the fluid contains abrasive solids, a higher flow velocity and capacity will result which may produce severe erosion problems as well as being expensive in power to accommodate the higher frictional losses. A common fault is choosing an oversized pump, largely because excessive safety factors are often added to system demand requirements. For maximum economy accurate analysis of system requirements is necessary in order to arrive at the best pump size. Provided the working point or its range falls within a normal envelope, variations in head or capacity demands can then be met by differences in input power if necessary, see Figure 6.

Acceleration head

In the case of piston or plunger (reciprocating) pumps, a certain amount of energy is required to accelerate the fluid in the suction line. This is referred to as acceleration head. Sufficient head must, therefore, be available on the suction side to overcome both suction system friction losses and acceleration head. Provided the suction line is relatively short the acceleration head required can be determined from the following formula:

$$H_a = \frac{LVNC}{gK}$$

where:

H_a = head in feet of liquid pumped to produce the required acceleration
L = actual length of suction pipe in feet
V = mean velocity of flow in the suciton line in ft/sec
N = pump r/min
C = a factor for the type pump:
C = 0·040 for quintuplex single-acting
C = 0·055 for sextuplex
C = 0·066 for triplex single- or double-acting
C = 0·115 for duplex double-acting
C = 0·200 for duplex single-acting
C = 0·200 for simplex double-acting
g = 32·2 ft/sec^2
K = a factor depending on the fluid:
K = 1·4 for de-aerated hot water
K = 1·5 for water, amine, glycol
K = 2·0 for most hydrocarbons
K = 2·5 for relatively compressible liquids such as hot oil, ethane

Note also the following:

(i) V increases as pump speed is increased.
H_a, therefore, varies with the square of pump speed.

(ii) H_a is greatest for liquids of relatively low compressibility such as water.

(iii) H_a varies directly with L.

SECTION 3

Pump Types

CENTRIFUGAL PUMPS
AXIAL AND MIXED FLOW PUMPS
RECIPROCATING PUMPS
POSITIVE DISPLACEMENTS
DIAPHRAGM PUMPS
ROTARY PUMPS
ROTARY LOBE PUMPS
SCREW PUMPS
PROGRESSING CAVITY PUMPS
GEAR PUMPS
VANE PUMPS
FLEXIBLE IMPELLER PUMPS
PERISTALTIC PUMPS
METERING AND PROPORTIONING PUMPS
SELF-PRIMING PUMPS
CANNED MOTOR PUMPS
GLANDLESS PUMPS
LIQUID RING PUMPS
VACUUM PUMPS
SUBMERSIBLE PUMPS
HYDRAULIC DRIVE DOWNHOLE PUMPS

Centrifugal Pumps

THE DESCRIPTION centrifugal pump is applied generally to all types of pumps with an impeller having fixed blades housed in a suitable shaped casing, so that when the impeller rotates momentum is applied to liquid in the pump casing transposing it from the inlet to the outlet side. To achieve this it follows that the pump casing has to be full of liquid (*ie* a basic pump of this type is not self-priming).

Generally speaking then a centrifugal pump comprises an impeller and a casing together with a driving shaft. The point at which the shaft enters the casing requires a stuffing box with gland and mechanical seal or packing. Sleeves, neck rings, wearing rings *etc* are provided at points where stationary and rotating parts are close together. The shaft will require journal and thrust bearings and a coupling from the driving unit.

Multi-stage centrifugal pump mounted on skid complete with power train.

Pump performance and efficiency depends on the area ratio of the impeller and casing flow passages and on the specific speed defined as:

$$N_S = \frac{(\text{volumetric flow})^{0\cdot 5}}{(\text{head})^{0\cdot 75}} \times \text{r/min} = \frac{Q^{0\cdot 5}}{H^{0\cdot 75}} \times \text{r/min}$$

or

$$N_S = \frac{N\sqrt{Q}}{H^{0\cdot 75}}$$

Values of specific speed devised for any pump depend on the units employed. Preferred units are:

$$N_S\,(\text{metric}) = \frac{(\text{l/s})^{0\cdot5}}{\text{m}^{0\cdot75}} \times \text{r/min}$$

$$N_S\,(\text{Imperial}) = \frac{(\text{Imp gal/min})}{\text{feet}^{0\cdot75}} \times \text{r/min}$$

$$N_S\,(\text{US}) = \frac{(\text{US gal/min})^{0\cdot5}}{\text{feet}^{0\cdot75}} \times \text{r/min}$$

Equivalents are:

N_S(Imperial) = N_S (US) x 0·913
N_S (US) = N_S (Imperial) x 1·097
N_S (metric) = N_S (Imperial) x 0·67
N_S (Imperial) = N_S (metric) x 1·50

ISO 2548 gives the type number or specific speed as:

$$N_S = \frac{\text{Rad/s}\ \sqrt{\text{m}^3/\text{s}}}{\left[\frac{\text{Nm}}{\text{Kg}}\right]^{0\cdot75}}$$

Near the broad peak of the specific speed and efficiency chart, the ISO SI specific speed is unity. Here the Imperial specific speed is 2500 and the metric specific speed 1670.

The efficiency of the first class pump with no limitation of design will be such as is implied in the greater clearances of API 610 refinery pumps and is given by the expression:

$$0\cdot94 - \eta = [13\cdot2\ \text{l/s}]^{-0\cdot32}$$

Correction Factor

The pump efficiencies are reduced for other than optimum type numbers by a negative correction *ie*:

$$\text{Efficiency correction} = -0\cdot29 \left[\log_{10} \times \frac{1400}{N_S}\right]^2$$

With multi-rotor pumps, the specific speed should define the performance of each rotor when the rotors are working within the same casing and are carried on the same shaft. The correct value for Q is thus the total flow divided by the number of rotors.

With multi-stage pumps the correct value for Q is again the total flow. But since the rotors are working in series, the true head is defined as the total head divided by the number of stages.

Effect on impeller form

The optimum form of impeller profile and ratio of the throat to impeller diameter are directly influenced by specific speed. Both this latter ratio and the impeller diameter will effect the head produced. For high heads the impeller diameter needs to be large and the pump casing thin with a relatively narrow outlet restricting the capacity available. Because of the relatively large impeller disc area involved allied to smaller flow, efficiency will tend to be low. Characteristically, such pumps will have a low specific speed.

To provide higher capacities it becomes necessary to widen the impeller and reduce diameter with a corresponding increase in the throat/impeller diameter ratio and a consequent reduction in head obtainable such configurations will have both higher specific speed and higher efficiency until a point where mixed flow rather than radial (pure centrifugal) flow results. Efficiency will then start to fall again, narrowly due to lack of guidance in the shortened impeller passages.

With increasing specific speed the optimum impeller form is that which produces increasingly predominant axial flow, finally ending up with a true form for pure axial flow.

This relationship is illustrated in Table 1 which is also the basis of a sub-classification of rotor dynamic pumps into centrifugal, mixed flow and axial flow pumps. There are no clear cut divisions, merely broad ranges over which a particular type is most efficient.

TABLE 1

Pump type	Specific speed range for maximum efficiency N^s (metric)	N_s (Imperial)	N_s (US)
Centrifugal	333 to 1670	500 to 2500	680 to 3300
Mixed flow	1670 to 2500	2500 to 7000	3300 to 9000
Axial flow	2500 to 5250	7500 to 15000	9500 to 20000

From this it will be seen that centrifugal pumps can be expected to have a competitive efficiency over the specific speed range of 333 to 1670 (metric) or 500 to 2500 (Imperial) only.

Since specific speed effects impeller design the form of the head capacity curve is also related to specific speed as in the power input curve (which may have rising or falling characteristics). The difference in efficiency for different capacities (pump size or pump speed) may be quite marked. Thus, in some cases, it may be necessary to sacrifice efficiency to attain a desired output performance – *eg* to achieve a higher head by selecting a pump with lower specific speed.

In general, centrifugal pumps are suitable for both low and high heads. The basic design lends itself to generating heads up to about 2000 metres (6600 ft) in a single-stage, but a more usual categorisation is:

low head types – maximum total head up to 30 metres (100 ft);

medium head types – maximum total head 150 to 600 metres (500 to 2000 ft);

high head types – maximum total head over 600 metres (over 2000 ft).

Where higher heads are required two or more stages can be combined in series in a multi-stage pump. Single-stage space rocket pumps reach 3047 metres (10 000 ft) on short life.

Quite high suction lifts are also possible with centrifugal pumps (once primed) provided the specific speed is kept below about 2500.

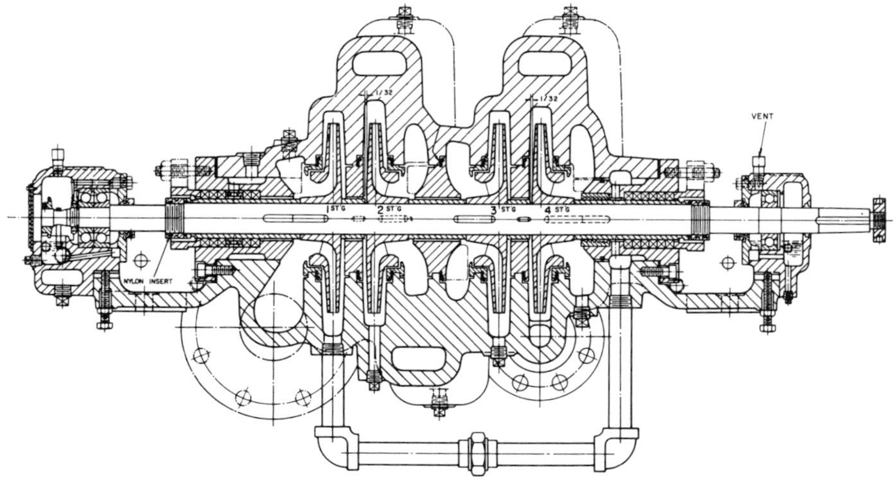

Four-stage centrifugal pump for water services especially boiler feed duties.

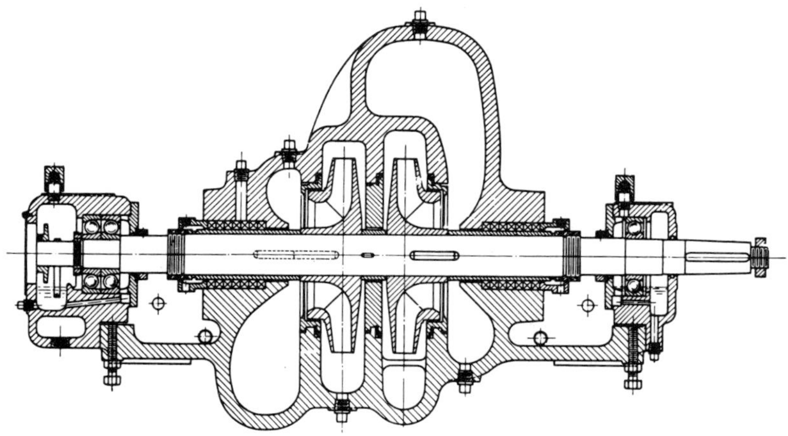

Two-stage axially split case pump.

Basic geometry

The impeller may be single-entry (with hydraulic or mechanical balancing devices) or double-entry. Single-entry impellers are generally fitted to casings which are split on a plane normal to the shaft axis. Double-entry impellers are generally fitted to casings split on the horizontal centre line *ie* in the plane containing the shaft axis. The latter arrangement permits the placing of the branches below the centre line so that the pump can be examined without disturbing pipes when the upper half casing is removed. The discharge from the impeller is collected in the volute or spiral portion of the casing and lead into the delivery branch.

The volute pump has a simple expanding spiral casing designed to provide recuperation of energy by conversion of velocity head into pressure head. This may also be provided by the introduction of stationary guide vanes surrounding the impeller as in diffuser pumps. Diffusers may provide more effective energy recovery than volutes at low specific speeds. Volutes may, however, also be followed by a straight diffuser, and the efficiency of a volute pump may be higher than that of a diffuser type without the disadvantage of increased bulk, weight and cost.

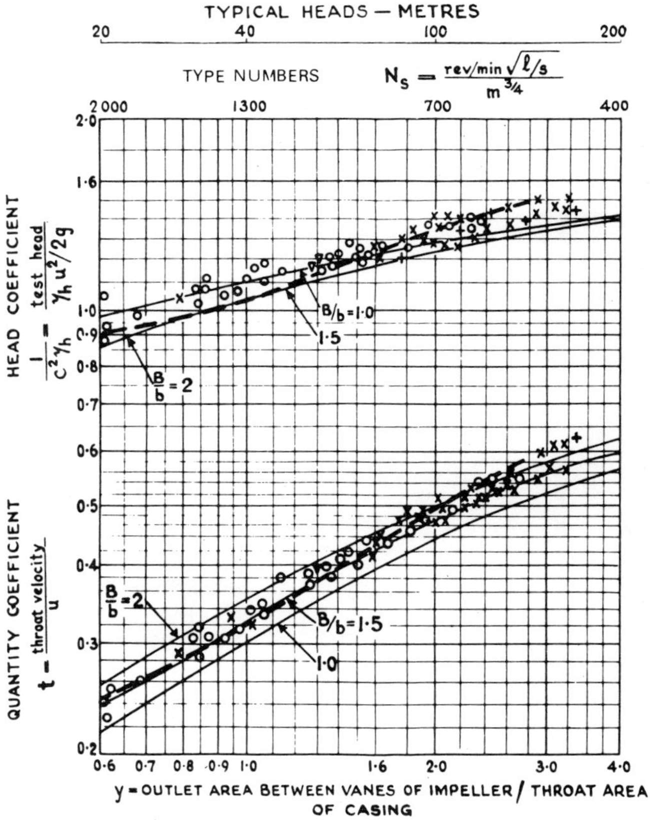

——————— WORSTER
- - - - - - - - - STEPANOFF
TEST POINTS. . . ANDERSON

Multi Bowl x
Single Entry Volute small . . + large . . Δ
De-volute . . . . . . O

Figure 1
Correlation of dimensions and head – flow quantity performance.

The ratio of the outlet area between impeller vanes to the casing or diffuser area is the abscissae of the figure from which the head and flow coefficients are determined. The loss, *ie* 100% – efficiency is split into one-fifth mechanical and one-fifth hydraulics so that for example at 80% efficiency, the hydraulic efficiency, used in the head determination, is 80/96 = 83·3%. u in the formula is the peripheral velocity of the impeller.

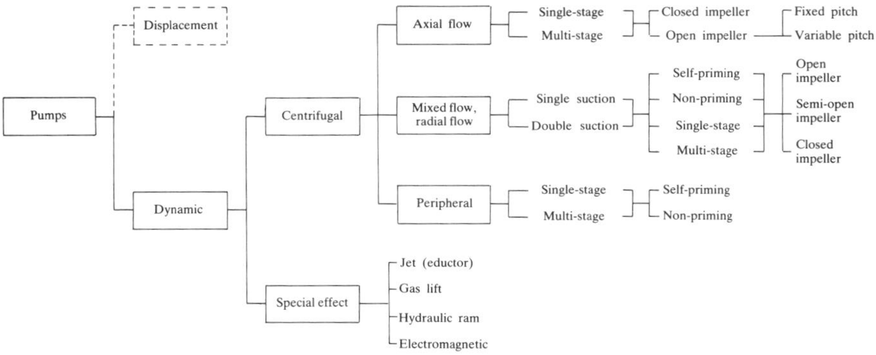

Classification of dynamic pumps.

Stainless steel hot water centrifugal pump.

Working characteristics

The working characteristics of a centrifugal pump are determined by the interdependent relationship between head and capacity which can be conveniently expressed in the form of an H-Q curve. The shape of H-Q curve is primarily dependent on the specific speed but further related to the form and number of blades on the impeller and the form of the casing and recuperators employed.

In the case of centrifugal pumps the H-Q curve may be stable (Figure 2) or unstable (Figure 3). With stable characteristics maximum head is achieved at zero discharge. The value of H then decreases as the discharge increases. With unstable characteristics the value of H at first increases from the value at zero discharge, as the discharge increases, and then falls with further increase in discharge.

Stability in either case is related to the power loading of the pump. With a stable H-Q curve the input power required rises to a peak at or near the design operating point and then falls again – Figure 4. With an unstable H-Q curve the input power required continues to rise after the pump reaches the design operating point – Figure 5.

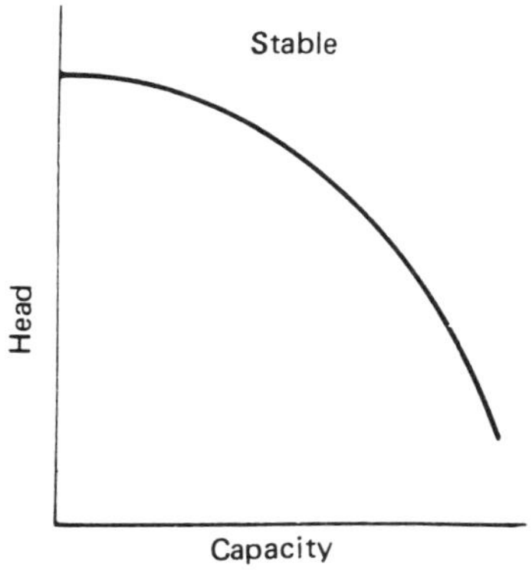

Figure 2

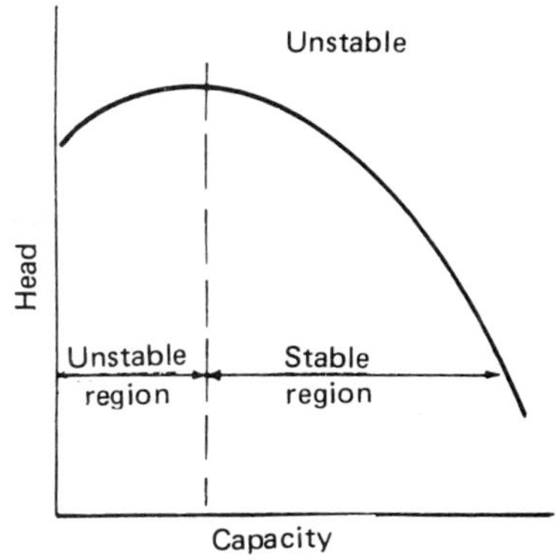

Figure 3

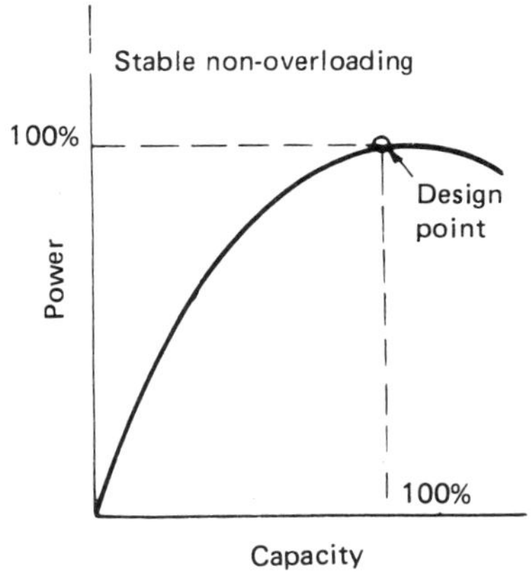

Figure 4

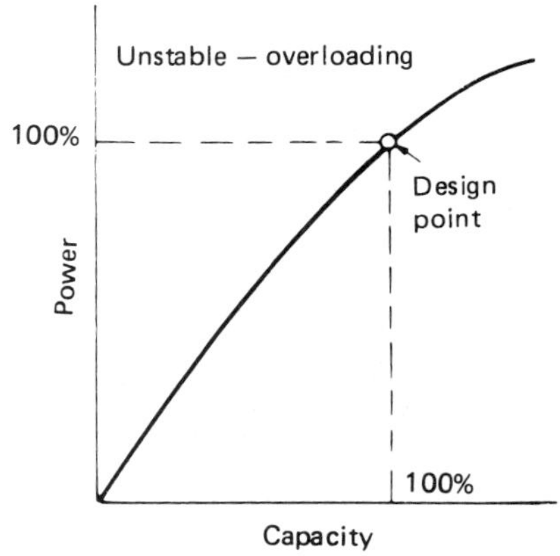

Figure 5

The significant difference is that with a stable H-Q curve, any fall in head below the design operating point cannot overload the pump drive *ie* characteristics are non-overloading. With an unstable H-Q curve a fall in head can occur which will either overload the driver or allow it to deliver higher power (if the driver has a reserve of power). The characteristics are thus overloading.

Working point

The optimum or design operating point of a centrifugal pump is that point on the H-Q curve corresponding to maximum efficiency as shown in Figure 6. The steeper the slope of H-Q curve the more significant the effect of any change in head on the working point.

For example, a pump with a steep H-Q curve will show a small change in delivery, but a large change in head with a shift in working point, whilst a pump with a flat H-Q curve show a large change in capacity but a small change in head with a shift in working point. Thus, the former would be preferable for duties which involve variations in head but require a reasonably constant discharge. The latter would be preferable when the demand is variable, but a substantially constant head is required.

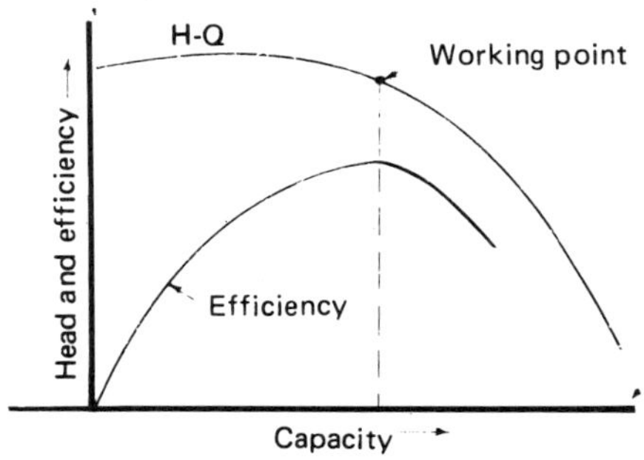

Figure 6

The H-Q curves for centrifugal pumps may be almost flat, with maximum efficiency tending to occur just after mid capacity. Power demand increases steadily up to and possibly beyond the operating design operating point. The H-Q curve of a mixed flow pump is steep with the point of maximum efficiency displaced towards maximum delivery. The power input curve is substantially horizontal so that power demand will vary little regardless of the working point. The H-Q curve for an axial flow pump is still steeper with maximum power demand at zero delivery and a falling power curve. It follows that any reduction in capacity introduces overload of a driver designed to meet the demand at the design operating point. This can be countered either by providing increased power or by unloading the pump when the head rises to a predetermined figure.

Working range

Although maximum efficiency is achieved only at a specific working point, the potential working range can be extended in either direction along the H-Q curve – theoretically over the full length of the curve to the cut-off point – if efficiency of operation is not important. With pumps having unstable H-Q characteristics, however, the practical operating ranges should not be considered to extend the capacities lower than the H-Q curve peak.

The working range may be further limited by liquid temperature rise. At reduced deliveries power may be dissipated in the form of fluid heating which could eventually lead to flashing and the pump becoming vapour bound. To avoid this a minimum safe flow may be specified determined by the allowable temperature rise. Similar limitations may be set by the flow pattern established at reduced deliveries – *eg* to avoid high unbalanced forces being generated by irregular flow patterns.

The potential working range may also be extended by increasing or decreasing pump speed resulting in displacement of the H-Q curve upwards or downwards respectively. Practical limits in this case are set by minimum efficiency acceptable and upper and lower limits for the speed variation (or speed change) see Figure 7. For an extended working range, it is desirable that the impeller designs should give as flat an efficiency curve as possible.

The pump designer's task is largely to provide a pump based on an optimum specific speed for the duties involved. For a specific size of pump this will determine the running speed for a given duty. Some adjustment may be necessary in order to accomodate a standard driver speed (*eg* an electric motor).

It is also common practice to fit different diameter impellers in a single casing, giving a range of characteristics from a particular model. Each impeller will then

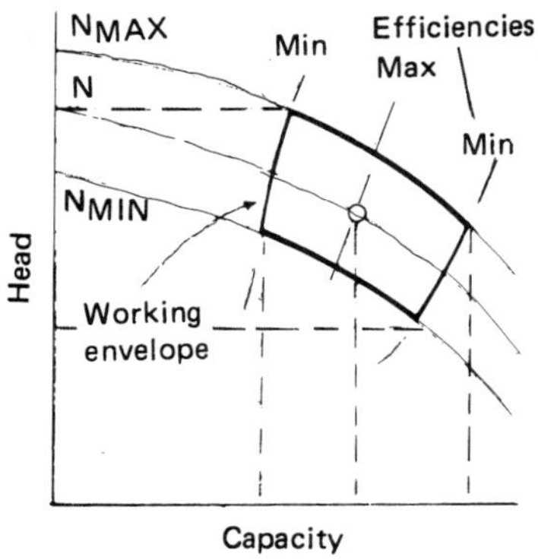

Figure 7

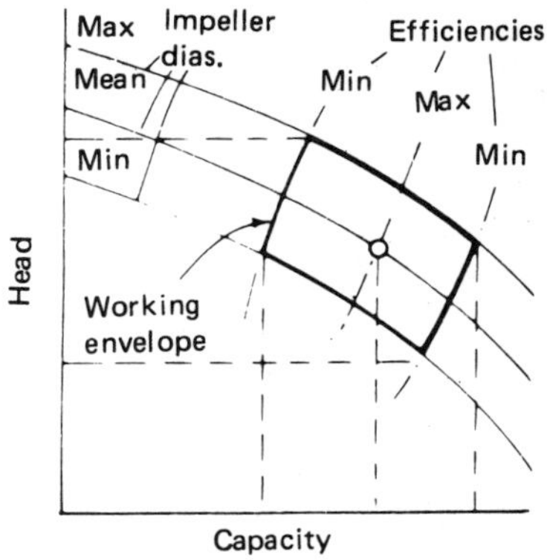

Figure 8

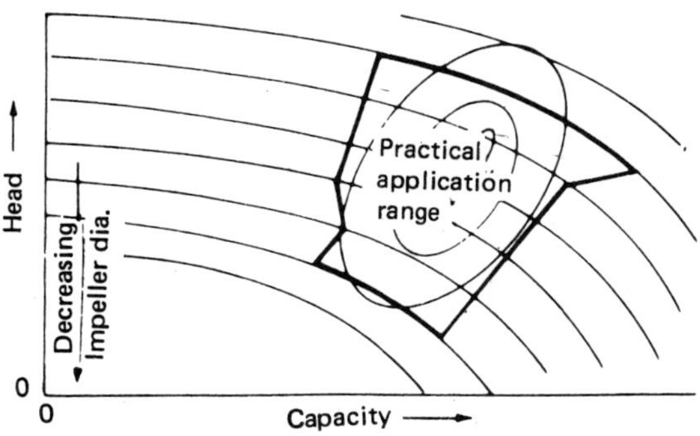

Figure 9

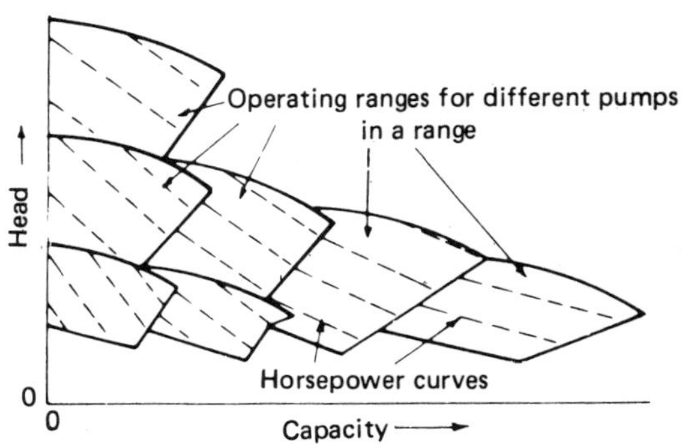

Figure 10

generate its own H-Q curve see Figure 8. The effect is to create a similar working envelope to that produced by changes in pump speed. The practical working envelope in either case is determined from ISO efficiency curves superimposed on the diagram in Figure 9.

Where a series or range of pumps is involved, these are normally designed with overlapping performance; for practical purposes each is allocated a specific working area which is calculated as described previously. A complete chart covering the pumps then shows a series of boxes or enclosed areas delineating the head/capacity range of each particular pump as shown in Figure 10. The only additional data usually given are the hp input curves for each box. Such a chart then provides complete information for the selection of a suitable size of pump based on capacity, head and motor horsepower. For detailed information (particularly efficiency values) it is then necessary to refer to the specific head/capacity curves for that pump with different impellers and superimposed ISO efficiency lines.

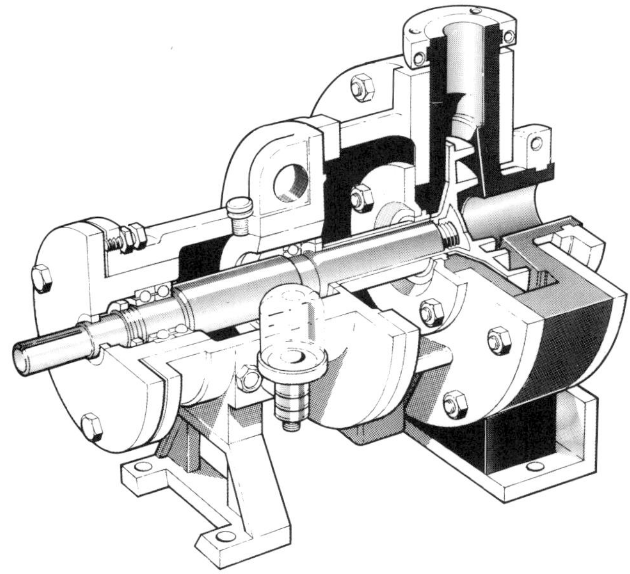

Cutaway view of modern centrifugal pump.

Cutaway of horizontal close-coupled pump.

Such a geographical analysis is to be preferred to selection from rating tables since it gives a better overall picture of the pump characteristics at the same time it may be necessary to investigate other characteristics in detail depending on the application, or even to compare the performance against other types of pump which might be suitable. In the selection of centrifugal pumps or comparison with alternative types, the important thing is to appreciate properly the variable nature of their characteristics and the importance of establishing an optimum design operating point. Figure 11 shows typical characteristics for a centrifugal pump.

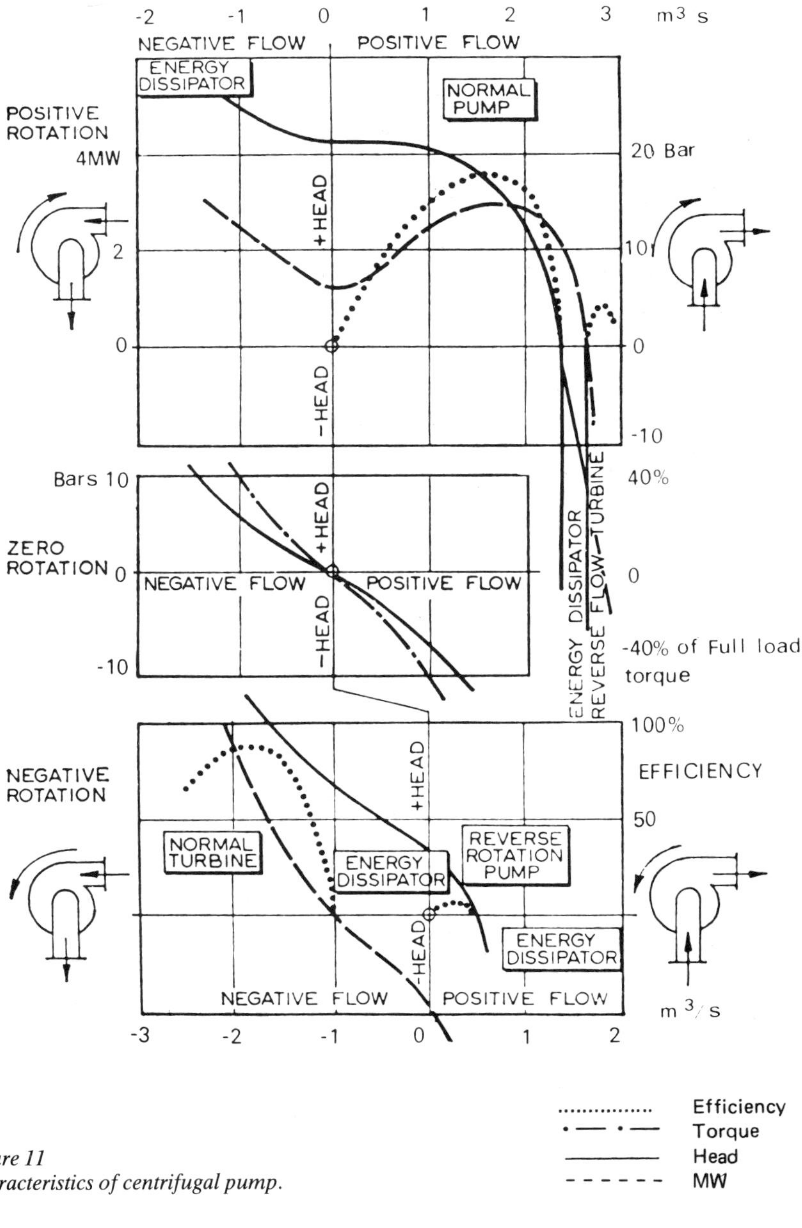

Figure 11
Characteristics of centrifugal pump.

TABLE 2 – PRESSURE AND CAPACITY CONVERSION

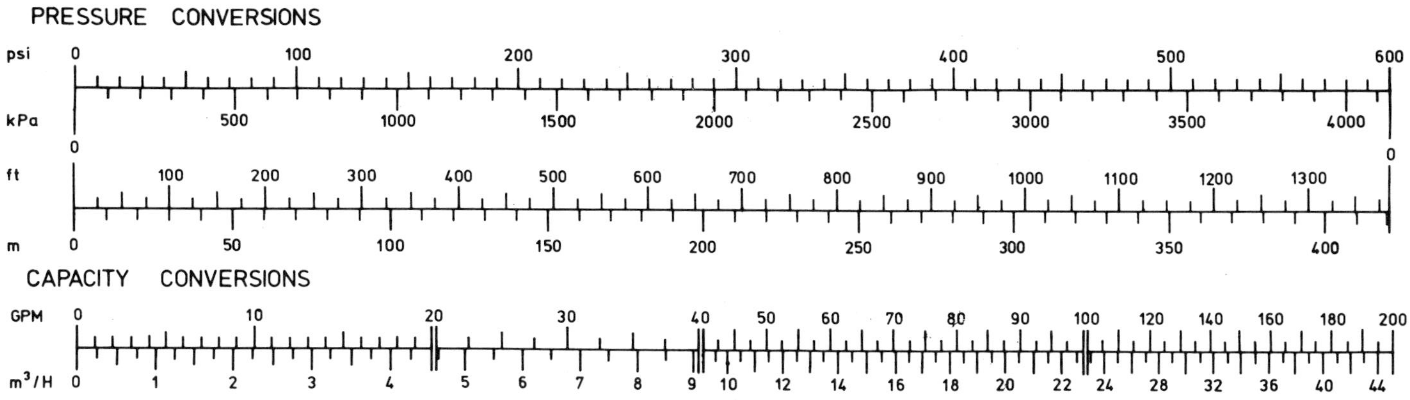

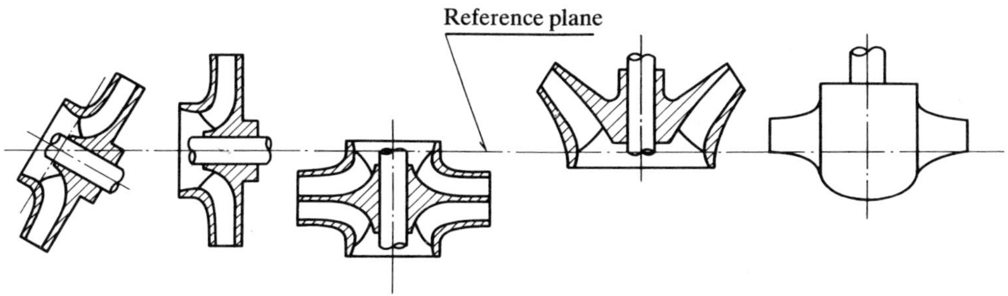

Figure 12
Reference plane for NPSH value according to ISO.

Cavitation factor

The H-Q curve extends only to a point where cavitation is fully developed and delivery ceases in consequence. This is known as the cut-off point. The cut-off point may be quite distinct in the case of centrifugal pumps with flat H-Q curves. With steeper H-Q curves the slope may be more gradual to the cut-off point and in the case of axial flow pumps no cut-off point may be apparent. The cut-off point can also be effected by speed and suction lift.

Analysis of cavitation characteristics

Cavitation aspects determine the running speed which in turn determines the basic dimensions of the pump. Between the inlet branch and the eye of the impeller a pressure drop occurs due to increase of flow velocity and to friction.

This pressure drop is referred to NPSH (net positive suction head) and is the difference between the input head (including the velocity head in the inlet pump) and the saturation pressure of the liquid handled.

NPSH has two values:

(i) the lower value when cavitation occurs;

(ii) the upper value which contains a margin of pressure to ensure operation sufficiently free from cavitation so that efficiency is not prejudice.

DIN 24260 defines total suction head H_H as:

$$H_H = \frac{p_{ges} - p_D}{\rho \times g}$$

If the suction head is referred to the centre line of a horizontal pump, it is identical to the actual NPSH value. For vertical shaft or slanting pumps the reference plane as defined by the ISO as shown in Figure 12. The NPSH value determines the cavitation condition of the pump. Data on NPSH, suction head or cavitation coefficiency of a pump must, therefore, always be related to the corresponding cavitation criterion (*eg* on set of cavitation bubbles, inception of head drop, 3% drop in head). The NPSH value for a pump is defined as:

$$NPSH = \frac{p_{sabs} - p_D}{\rho \times g} + \frac{c_s^2}{2g} = \frac{p_b + p_s - p_D}{\rho \times g} + \frac{c_s^2}{2g}$$

where:

p_{sabs} = absolute pressure in the suction pipe, related to the pump centreline $= p_b + p_s$

p_s = positive gauge pressure (negative figure for negative pressure)

p_b = atmospheric pressure

p_D = absolute vapour pressure at the fluid temperature

c_s = flow velocity in the suction nozzle

The NPSH value of the pump defines the total pressure at the suction nozzle necessary for the pump to operate under defined cavitation conditions (*eg* with 1% head drop). The NPSH value for a particular pump depends on the flowrate for a given speed and fluid.

The approximate NPSH value for 3% head drop can be determined from Figure 13 with pumps for overhung impellers and from Figure 14 for pumps with impellers between bearings.

The NPSH values given apply to the point of optimum efficiency.

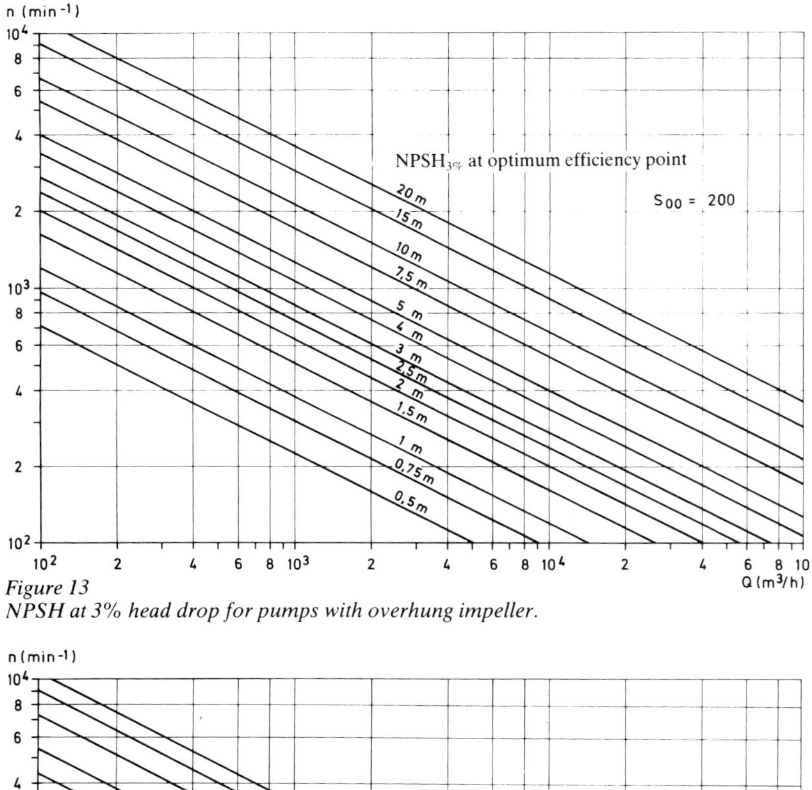

Figure 13
NPSH at 3% head drop for pumps with overhung impeller.

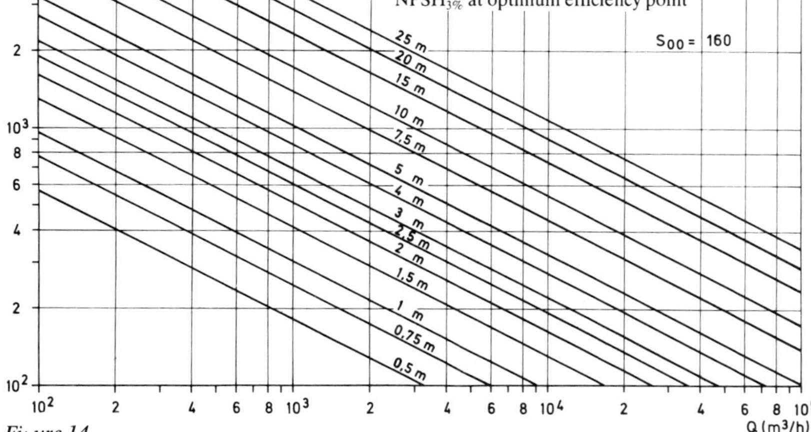

Figure 14
NPSH at 3% head drop for pumps with impellers between bearings.

Various examples of centrifugal pumps.

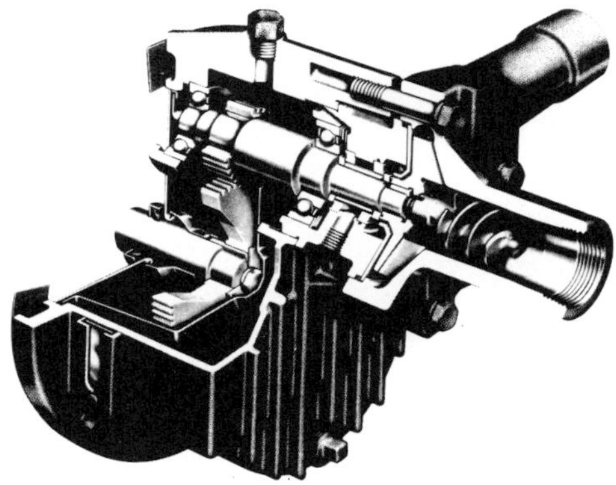

High pressure centrifugal pump.

Available plant NPSH

The NPSH value of the plant defines the total pressure at the pump suction nozzle for given fluid characteristics at a certain flowrate (the dependency on flowrate is limited to the pipeline losses). The NPSH value of the plant, also known as available NPSH is independent of the pump itself and is defined as:

$$NPSH_{avail} = \frac{p_{eabs} - p_D}{\rho \times g} + Z_e - Z_s + \frac{c_2^2}{2g} - H_{vs}$$

where:

p_{eabs} = absolute pressure on the fluid surface at the intake

c_c = mean flow velocity in the intake vessel (or generally in the suction tank, usually very small)

When the pump is operating in the suction mode (water level below the impeller inlet), Z_e is negative. The term $(Z_e + Z_s)$ is then defined as the geodetic suction head.

If boiling fluid is being pumped, the pressure above the water level is the vapour pressure ($p_{e\ abs} = p_D$); the pump can then only be operated with positive suction head (*ie* Z_e is $> Z_s$). NPSH figures stated for a pump without defining the corresponding cavitation criterior usually refer to the critical suction head at 3% head drop. For the majority of applications, the available plant NPSH for continuous operation must exceed that at 3% head drop by an adequate safety margin in order to avoid cavitation erosion.

The required safety margin:

(i) increase rapidly with rising peripheral speed at the impeller inlet;

(ii) is reduced if cavitation-resistant materials are used;

(iii) rises with increasing corrosive media;

(iv) depends on the operating conditions of the pump and the type and temperature of the medium being pumped.

For pumps with high stage heads stroboscopic observations of cavitation bubble zones are often employed to establish the available plant NPSH necessary to avoid cavitation erosion. In such cases the required positive suction head is usually provided by a booster pump.

$$S_A = \frac{\text{NPSH-plant}}{\text{NPSH}_{3\%} \text{ at optimum efficiency point}}$$

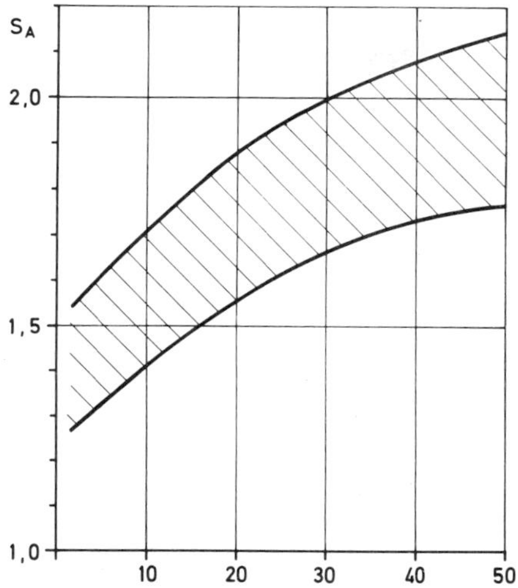

Figure 15
Approximate values for selecting available plant NPSH.

Figure 15 shows approximate values for selecting plant NPSH as a function of the NPSH at 3% head drop. Depending on the application deviation can be made from this curve; with seawater, for example slightly higher margins are employed and for hydrocarbons lower values can be used.

Methods of improving suction performance

In a great number of cases the highest permissible speed and thus the size and cost of a pump is determined by its suction performance or the required or available NPSH. For given flow, head and available plant, NPSH values permissible speed can be increased by the following measures:

(i) using special suction impeller of various shapes;

(ii) installing a double-entry first-stage impeller;

(iii) installing an inducer;

(iv) using a booster pump;

Inducers and suction impellers must be designed so that no pulsations which could endanger the plant occur during part load operation. Suction performance increases slightly with rising water temperature.

Cavitation erosion

When cavitation bubbles implode at the impeller or other pump components, very high local pressures are generated and these may exceed the fatigue strength, yield point, or compression strength of the material. If this takes place, pitting of the material known as cavitation erosion may result after varying operating periods.

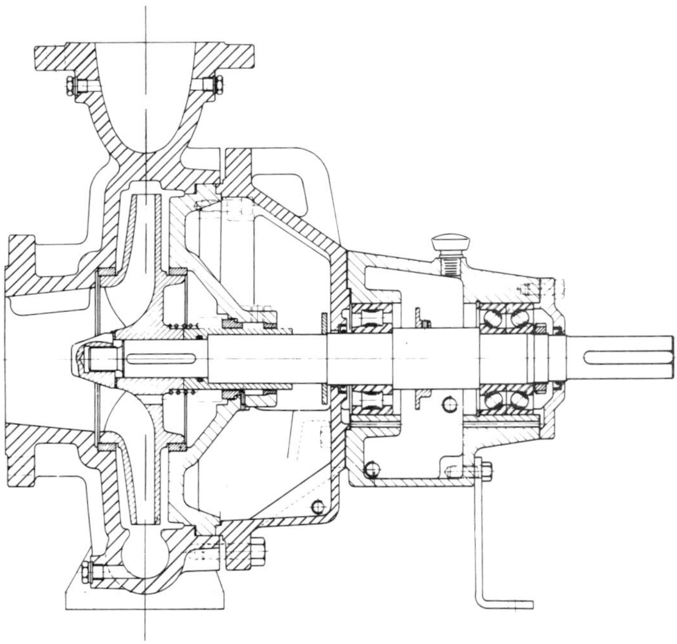

Cross-section of end suction pump.

Vertical multi-stage centrifugal pump.

Erosion of material

(i) increases with increasing implosion energy the intensity of erosion is approximately proportional to $(NPSH)^3$;
(ii) decreases with increasing tensile strength or hardness of the material;
(iii) increases with increasing cavitation bubble zones, assuming that the bubbles implode on the surface of the material and not in the liquid;
(iv) decreases with rising water temperature;
(v) decreases with increasing gas content in the fluid since non-condensable gases reduce implosion pressures;
(vi) increases with more corrosive media;
(vii) is usually considerably greater at part load than when pumping in the region of optimum efficiency. Cavitation erosion hardly ever occurs when pumping hydrocarbon media.

Pump rotation

Suction and discharge nozzle locations are effected by pump rotation. It is, therefore, very important to understand how the direction of rotation is defined.

Rotation is defined as clockwise or counter-clockwise by looking at the driven end of a horizontal pump or looking down on a vertical pump, although some manufacturers still designate rotation of a horizontal pump from its outboard end. To avoid misunderstanding clockwise or counter-clockwise rotation should always be qualified by including the direction from which one looks at the pump.

The term inboard end – the end closest to the driver – and outboard end – the end farthest away, are used only with horizontal pumps. The terms lose their significance with dual-driven pumps. Any centrifugal pump casing pattern may be arranged for either clockwise or counter-clockwise rotation, except for end suction pumps which have integral heads on one side. These require separate directional patterns. For more detailed information regarding the design and application of centrifugal pumps refer to CENTRIFUGAL PUMPS by H H Anderson ISBN 85461 776 6 published by The Trade & Technical Press Ltd also PUMP HANDBOOK 2nd edition by Igor J Karassik ISBN 0-07-033302-5 published by McGraw-Hill Book Company.

Axial and Mixed Flow Pumps

AXIAL AND mixed flow pumps are the normal choice for high volume, low pressure pumping duties, particularly for large scale primary water supplies, flood control, irrigation and drainage. Such types are available in a wide range of sizes and capacities. Typical bowl sizes range from 0·3 to 2·1 metres (12 to 84 inches). Capacities range from about 9000 l/min (2000 gal/min) to over 9 000 000 l/min (200 000 gal/min). Heads generated may range from about 1·5 metres (5 ft) to 22 metres (75 ft).

It is a general characteristic of such pumps that the power input curve is much flatter than that of a centrifugal pump, thus input power demand does not vary very much with the working point. Hydraulic performance, however, differs appreciably. Axial flow pumps generate head pressure through an axial motion developed by a combination of propeller and internal vane design. The combination induces fluids to travel strictly along the axis of the pump drive shaft.

The world's largest horizontal submersible axial flow pump.

Axial flow pump.

Mixed flow pump.

The mixed flow pump on the other hand employs a chamber/impeller/vane design to impart both an axial and radial motion to fluids travelling downstream. This powerful motion is created by lifting fluids with an impeller, whilst simultaneously forcing fluids out against the bowl like impeller chamber. The outward movement of the fluids generates a radial motion, further accenuated by an internal vane arrangement, known as an upper diffuser section. By combining axial and centrifugal motion, the mixed flow pump generates greater head pressure to downstream fluids than is possible with a single motion axial flow pump. These differences are noted in the generated comparative H-Q curves as shown in Figure 1. In the case of a mixed flow pump, the H-Q curve tends to be steep with the point of maximum efficiency displaced towards maximum capacity.

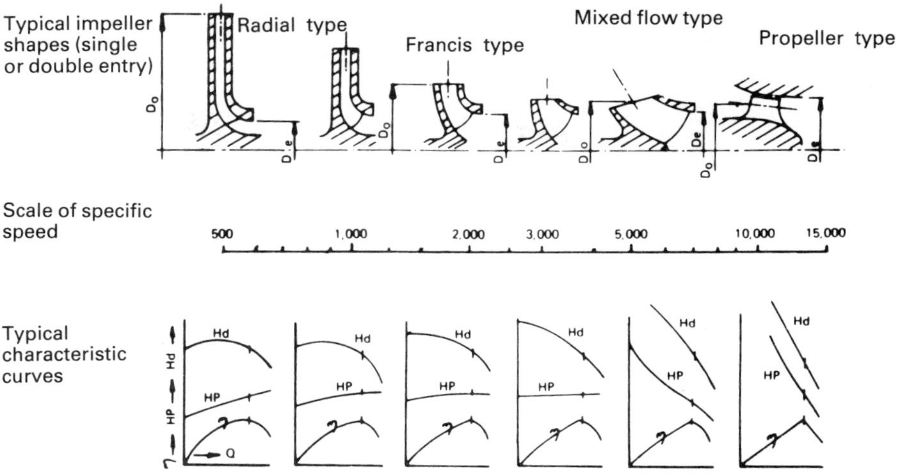

Figure 1
Typical impeller shapes and effect on performance for various speeds.

The H-Q curve of an axial flow pump has substantial linear falling characteristics, although the actual head obtainable is much lower. Efficiency is higher over a greater percentage range of head than for a centrifugal pump. The power input curve substantially follows the form of the H-Q curve up to the design working point. Maximum power demand occurs at zero delivery.

Typical generalised H-Q curves for mixed flow, axial flow and regenerative pumps are given in Figure 2. In the case of a mixed flow pump, the H-Q curve tends to be steep with the point of maximum efficiency displaced towards maximum capacity. The power input curve is much flatter than that of a centrifugal pump, so that input power demand does not vary much with the working point as shown in Figure 3.

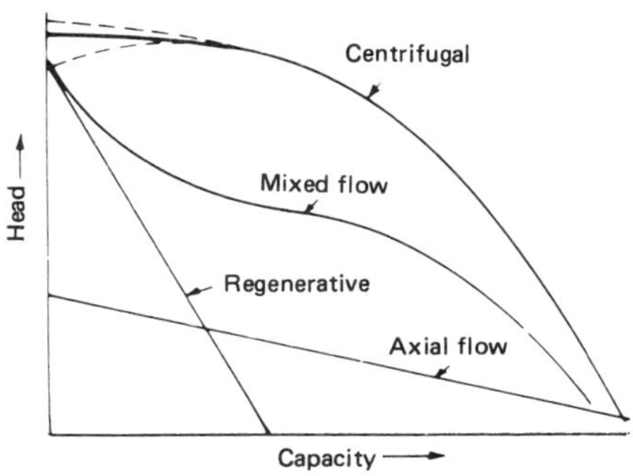

Figure 2

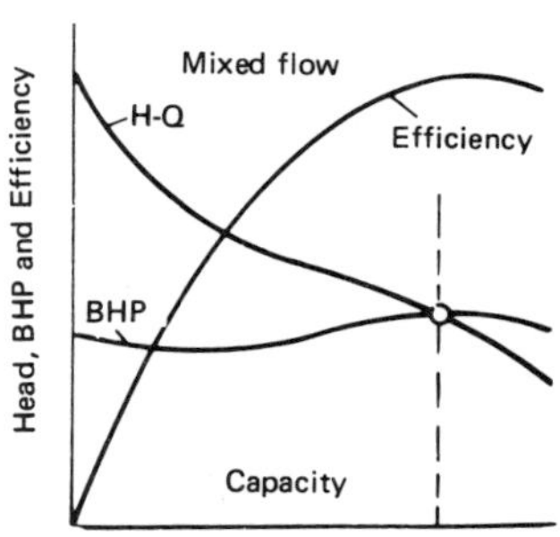

Figure 3

Axial flow pump with impeller located in pipe bend.

Regenerative pumps have an even steeper H-Q curve – substantially straight with a steep gradient as shown in Figure 2. Pressure developed tends to rise sharply with decreasing capacity making this type unsuitable for discharge regulation by throttling. Power output falls with increasing capacity.

Axial flow impellers have no shrouds, and the axial thrust is created strictly by the difference in pressure on the two faces of the impeller vanes. In addition, there may be a difference in pressure acting on the two shaft hub ends, one generally subject to discharge pressure and the other to suction pressure.

With mixed flow impellers, axial thrust is a combination of forces caused by the action of the vanes on the liquid and those arising from the difference in the pressures acting on the various surfaces. Wearing rings often provided on the back of mixed flow impellers, with either balancing holes through the impeller hub or an internal balancing pipe leading back to the suction. Except for very large units and in certain special applications, the maximum axial thrust developed by mixed flow and axial flow impellers, is not significant because the operating heads of these pumps are relatively low. Ths thrust is carried by thrust bearings with the necessary low capacity.

Volute pumps.

Axial flow pumping systems installed at the Jerzani pumping station on the River Tigris.

General form

Axial and mixed flow pumps are commonly mounted vertically directly over a sump (Figure 4) this is most often the case when the source of water is a river or reservoir. Fluids enter through a flared suction bell that has been reinforced by heavy vanes. The vanes, in addition to lending support to the suction bell, act to direct the liquid flow parallel to the drive shaft as it travels upstream. Once passed the suction bell, fluids encounter either an axial propeller or a mixed flow impeller. While differing in design, both are always dynamically balanced, one piece casting, mounted on a stainless steel pump shaft. The drive shaft may be encased in a tube or open, with supports properly spaced for intermediate shaft bearings, positive drive is provided by a heavy duty drive key and thrust collar.

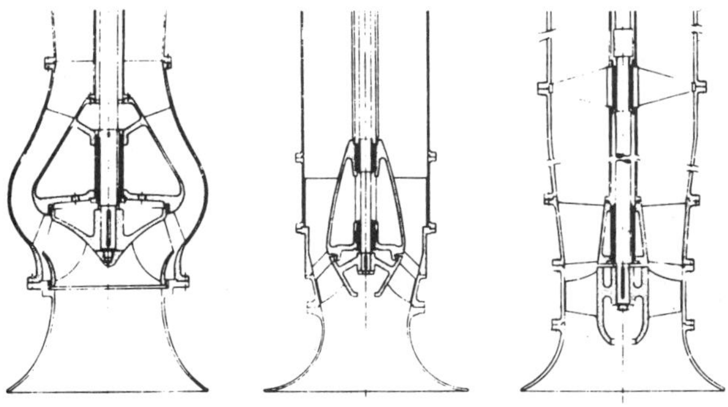

Mixed flow unit with diffuser and closed impeller: for higher head applications

Mixed flow model with open impeller

Axial flow design: for highest capacity requirements

Figure 4
Vertical wet-pit pumps.

The rotating element is mounted in an individual housing which is usually replaceable and situated just above the suction bell, close to the pump inlet. The housing may be bronze, stainless steel or any other material similar to the impeller. After emerging from the housing, fluid travels past an upper diffuser chamber and out through the guide case. The guide case consisting of a column pipe and discharge elbow is of welded steel plate or cast iron. Sections are flanged or bolted together. A registered fit is used to maintain proper alignment on all mated parts. Elbows commonly terminate in either an ANSI standard flange or a plane end to accommodate a 'Dresser' type coupling. Depending upon the installation, engineering considerations will dictate whether the discharge elbow is positioned above or below the main flow.

Various installations for mixed flow and axial pumps are shown in Figures 5, 6, 7, 8 and 9. Since axial and mixed flow pumps use column, discharge elbows and lubrication systems similar to large single stage turbine pumps, it might be expected that field problems would also be similar. Whilst this is theoretically correct, the slower rotating speeds of the axial and mixed flow pumps eliminate many of the problems especially those associated with resonant motor and discharge elbow vibration.

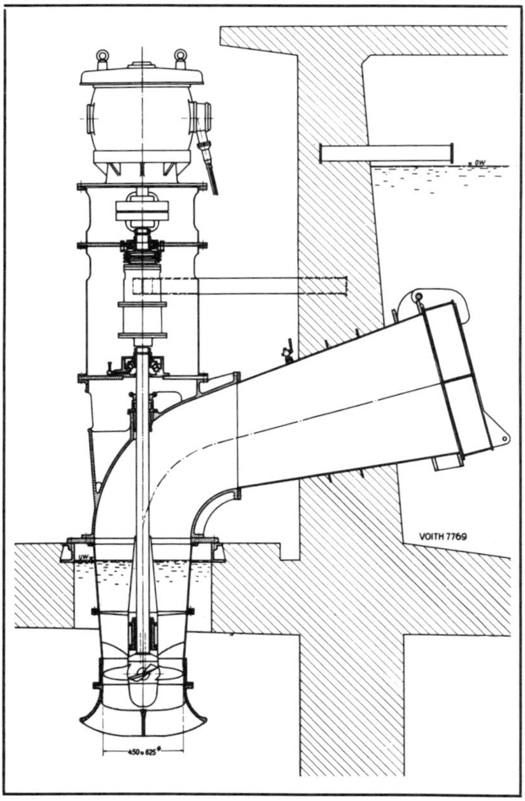

Figure 5

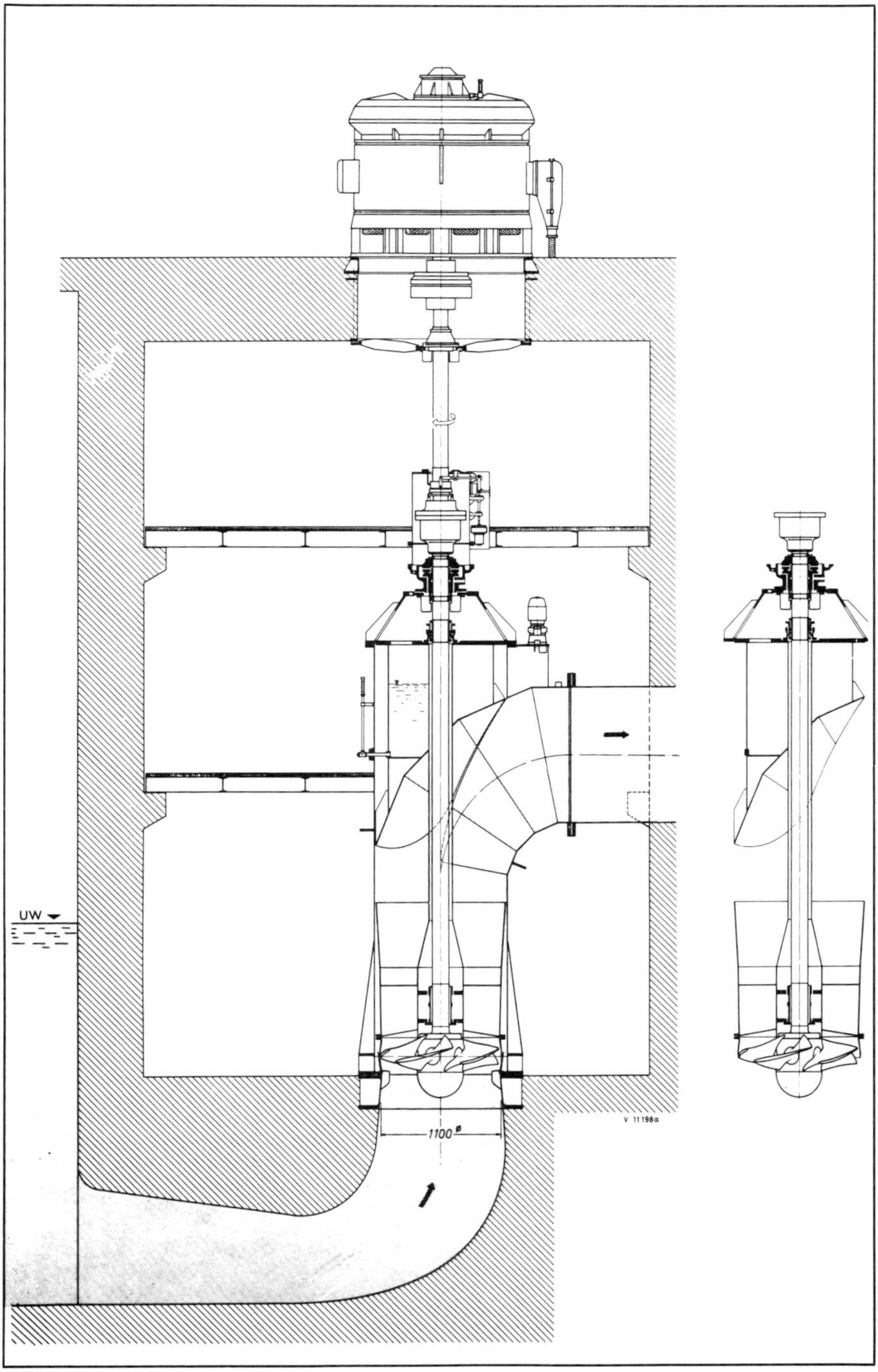

Figure 6

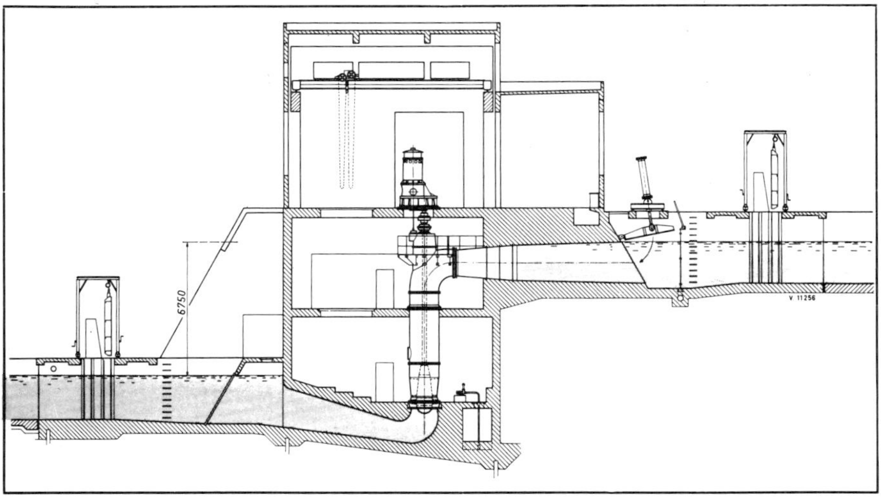

Figure 7

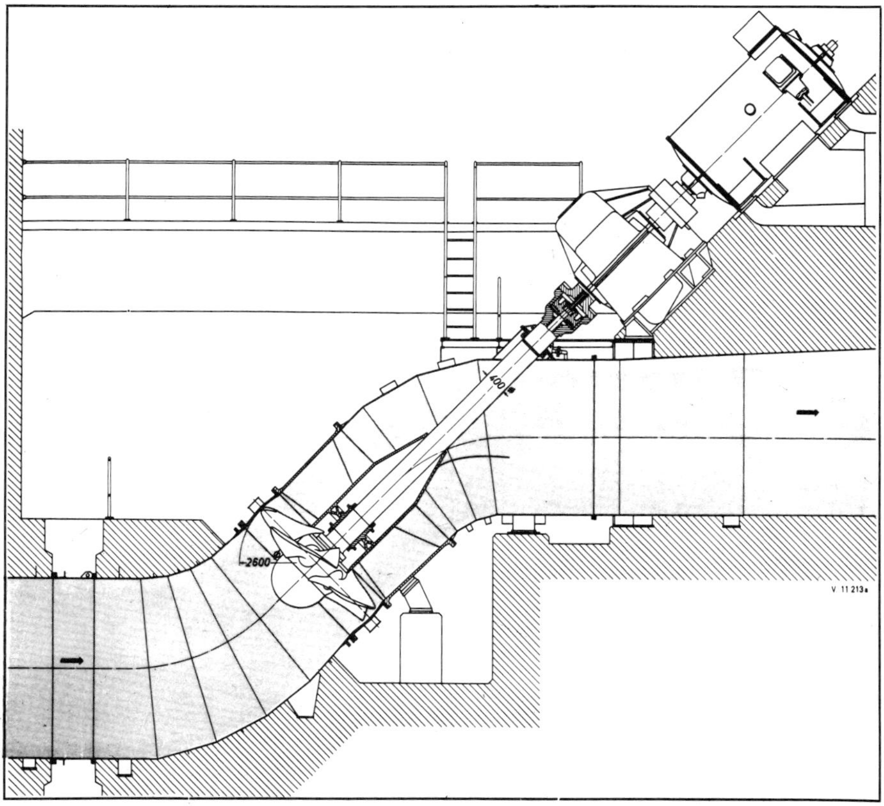

Figure 8

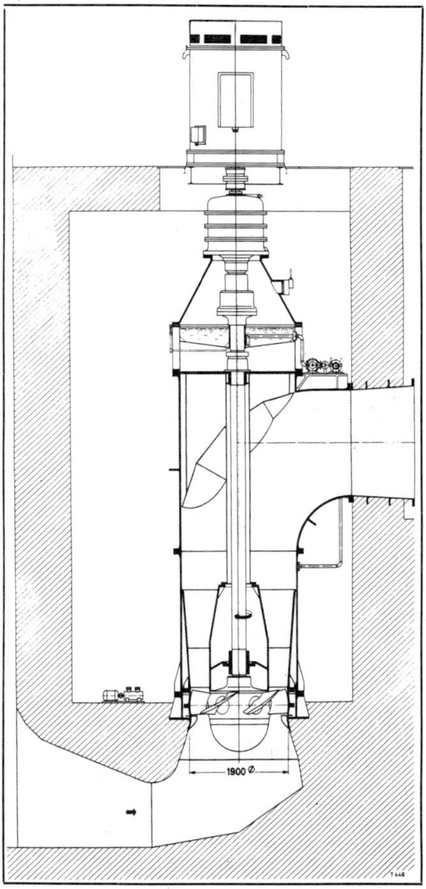

Figure 9

A pump running with a partially clogged suction strainer may experience a higher than anticipated total head caused by the additional loss at the intake. While this is suction head, it adds to the total; thus, required power will be more than anticipated. When the clogging is severe enough, the pump may exhibit cavitation noise as well. If a pump station must handle debris of this magnitude, a rack and screen should be used. Small debris such as leaves, plastics and weeds tend to hang up on the leading edges of impeller vanes. In an axial pump especially, the effect is to reduce efficiency and increase total head with a consequent increase in the power required. The distinctive feature of this problem is that power at start up is normal. It then increases as a function of time over a period ranging from a few minutes to several hours. When the pump is shut off, backflushed and restarted, the initial steady state power is again normal, then the process is repeated.

The cause of this phenomenon in axial flow pumps has been attributed to increased head due to the formation of an air core in the pump column, which in turn has been caused by pumping aerated water. While this may be true in some

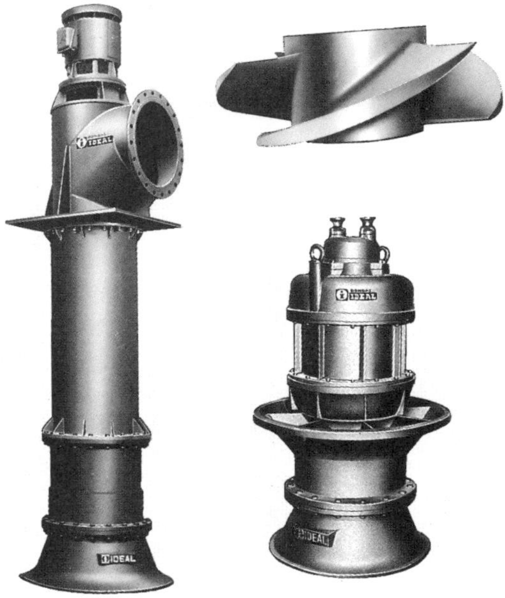

Helical axial flow pump designed for large water flows to low heads. Capacities to 20 000 m^3/h, heads to 18 m.

Helicoidal axial flow pump for large flows, but to medium heads. Lifting river water, draining lakes and land, electricity cooling water installations and handling sea water.

cases, the problem also occurs when pumping non-aerated water, and almost without exception when the water is carrying debris of some kind or another. In a number of instances the power will eventually stabilise; thus the installation of a larger motor will keep the system operating. If the debris cannot be disposed of in some other manner, use of a mixed flow bowl assembly, usually at slower rotating speed, is the best answer.

'Pull-out options'

Pull-out options which make for easier maintenance and inspection are a common feature of axial and mixed flow pumps. The best designs permit removal of the entire bowl assembly (including all rotating parts, diffuser, impeller housing and suction bell) through the outer shell without disturbing either discharge or floor plate connections. Axial and mixed flow pumps are generally used for slant mount installations with column lengths being 30 metres (100 ft) or less. Special attention should be paid to lubrication because of the side load on the bearings. The bowl bearings are grease lubricated through lines from the motor base. Drive shaft bearings are drip oil lubricated from a conventional base-mounted oil reservoir. Shaft enclosing tubes are supported in the column sections at 3 metres (10 ft) intervals by steel guides or spiders.

Selection

There are frequent situations when it is known in advance that abrasives or solids handling problems are going to exist. The following is a general guide to the selection of axial and mixed flow pumps.

Leaves, moss, weeds, plastic materials and similar debris tend to hang on the leading edges of impeller vanes, inhibiting the pumping action and reducing flow area. The reduction in area increases the internal pump head, but if system head is constant, pump total head also increases. In the case of axial flow pumps this causes an increase in required horsepower. Also, since the pumping action is similar to an airfoil, lift capability is impaired and efficiency suffers. The reaction of a mixed flow pump is less severe, because the H-Q curve does not rise as steeply with increasing head and the pumping action has a radial component, making it less sensitive to change of vane shape. Whenever possible, a mixed flow pump is a better choice for these requirements.

Where from sand, salt crystals, mill scale or other uniformally sized material gradually increases the appearance between impeller and bowl seat or seal rings, first at a rapid rate, then decreasing as the clearance width approaches the size of the largest particle. If the particle sizes are known, anticipated clearance can be estimated and pump selection made for a relatively higher capacity. Abrasion resisting materials are also required.

Renewable bowl liners for semi-open impellers and propellers, or dual seal rings for enclosed impellers, will reduce the eventual cost of repairs. If they are made of abrasion-resisting materials, the life between repairs will also be extended.

Impellers made of hardened material, when used with compatible bowl liners or sealing ring material will also extend pump life.

Since the wear rate increases with flow velocity and rotating speed, larger, slower pumps will have longer life in both abrasive and corrosive service.

Additional submergence over the minimum required is good insurance and it reduces the chance of random surface vortex formations that might draw floating debris into the pump suction intake, causing wear and eventual clogging.

Vertical diffusion vane pumps are not suitable for pumping raw sewage. Other applications in the sewage treatment cycle that can be handled by propeller and mixed flow pumps include settled sewage, various effluents and activated sludge. Pumps should be fitted with labyrinth seal rings on both sides of the impeller to prevent stringy material from building up on the pump shaft.

Channel impeller pumps

A channel impeller pump employs an impeller with turbine type blades mounted on the periphery running in an annular channel (or channels) surrounding the periphery of the wheel. Basically, this can be subclassified according to the number of channels employed *eg* single channel, double channel or three channel.

In practice only two main sub-types emerge known generally as the peripheral pump and side channel pump respectively. The main difference is in the form of positioning the channels. The peripheral pump has a double-sided channel in which the liquid circulates. This channel being located partly in the cylindrical part of the casing and partly in the side plates. The side channel has two channels cut in the side plates only, adjacent to each side of the impeller blades. Characteristics are quite different, *eg* the side channel pump is self-priming and can develop a much higher

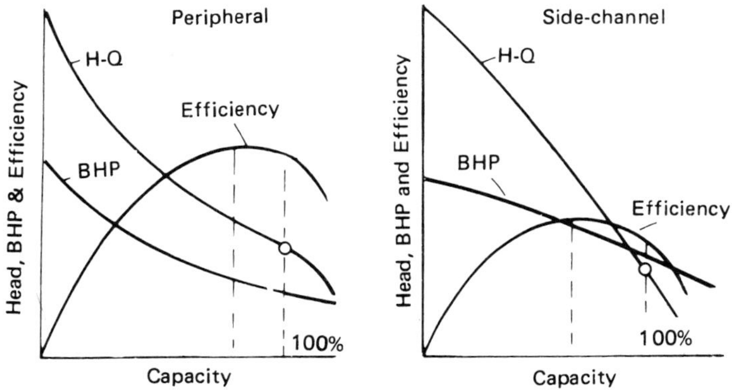

Figure 10

head although its efficiency is lower, hence the two are distinct types (see also Figure 10). The peripheral pump is also known as a regenerative pump.

See *Vertical Turbine, Mixed Flow and Propeller Pumps* by J.L.Dicmas and *Pump Handbook* by Igor J.Karassik, both published by McGraw Hill Book Company.

Reciprocating Pumps

A RECIPROCATING pump works on the principle of a reversing piston motion within a cylinder drawing in fluid on the ingoing stroke and delivering it under pressure on the outgoing stroke. To do this it requires one way valves (or equivalent piston-swept ports) on both the suction and delivery side. A variety of configurations is possible dependant on the mechanical system used to derive the reciprocating piston motion; the number and arrangement of cylinders; the valving system; *etc*. A distinction is also drawn between a reciprocating pump with a conventional piston/conrod arrangement and one where the piston component is equal to the cylinder bore over the whole of its length (known as a plunger or ram pump). Diaphragm pumps are also a type of reciprocating pump normally regarded as being in a separate category.

The general characteristics of a reciprocating piston pump are that it is a true positive displacement pump with delivery directly proportional to swept volume and speed of reciprocation. The head capacity (H-Q) characteristics are defined by vertical lines. In practice the H-Q curves are contained within a rectangular envelope, the boundaries of which are established by the maximum design working pressure and the maximum speed. The maximum design working pressure is established by the strength of the pump components subjected to internal pressure. Maximum speed is determined by such considerations as acceptable limits for piston speed, satisfactory valve operation, and adequate time for the suction side of the pump to fill completely with a charge of fluid.

Piston speed limitations may indirectly affect capacity. Thus, for higher operating speeds it may be desireable to reduce the stroke of the pump which may result in a lower capacity machine. Suction considerations can also introduce a variable factor. With increasing fluid viscosity, more time *ie* a lower speed, may be necessary to ensure satisfactory filling without 'channelling' or flow breakdown. Figure 1 shows the classification of reciprocating pumps.

Working characteristics

The working characteristics of a reciprocating pump are further modified by slippage, which will tend to increase with increasing head. Thus the H-Q lines will tend to depart somewhat from a true vertical, as shown in Figure 2. Working within the 'upper corner' of the envelope is also likely to be empirical – see Figure 3.

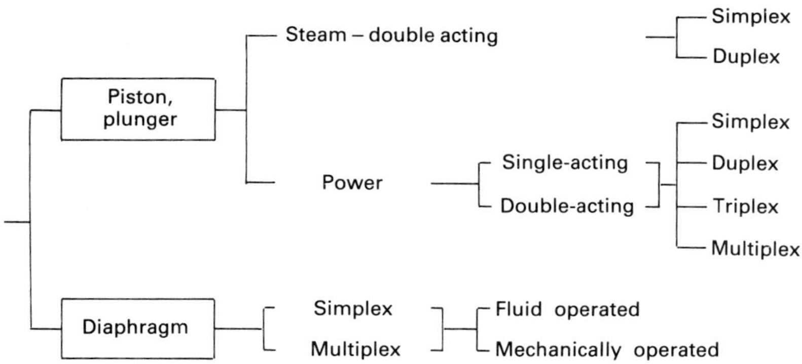

Figure 1
Classification of reciprocating pumps.

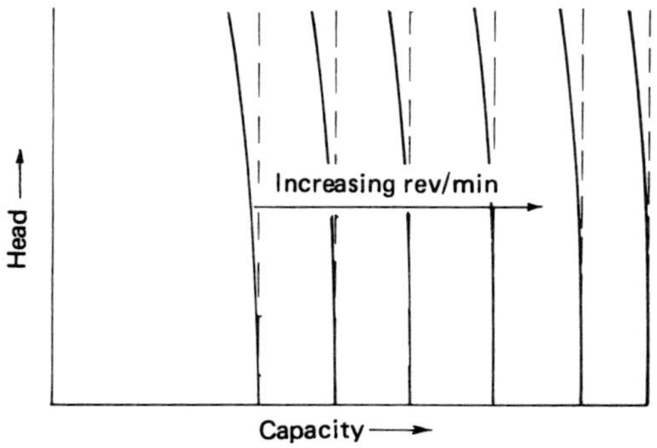

Figure 2

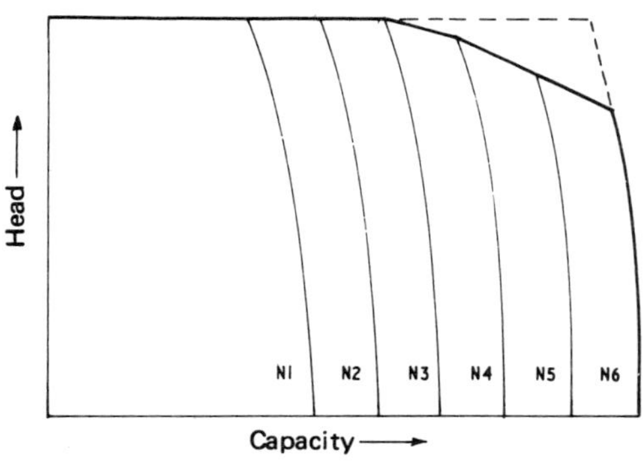

Figure 3

Theoretically at least, the working point of a reciprocating pump can lie anywhere within the envelope set by maximum design working pressure and maximum speed. The size of the pump is largely nominal since the capacity is determined by size x speed. Thus a capacity rating would be specific only to a particular operating speed. The actual working point used, however, may be modified by considerations of power input, efficiency, and fluid handling.

Power output is directly proportional to head x delivery. Thus for a given operating speed (constant delivery) input power is equal to efficiency x head. Efficiency at first rises rapidly with increasing head and then remains substantially constant. For maximum efficiency, a reciprocating pump should be worked at head figures corresponding to the flat portion of the efficiency curve. Efficiency will not vary greatly if the pump is operated over a range of heads or over a range of deliveries (*ie* different speeds).

Triplex positive ram displacement pump with electric motor and reduction box.

High pressure plunger pump.

Power requirements

Since input power is directly proportional to head, a reciprocating pump can be overloaded. With excess power available, dangerously high internal pressures can build up. Protection can be provided by a relief valve. It also follows that control of delivery by discharge throttling is impracticable. Variable delivery can only be obtained by altering the speed of the pump or the displacement of the machine. The latter method is usually based on varying the stroke, although other methods employed include the variation of valve timing and the use of by pass devices.

Increasing fluid viscosity represents a higher head requirement and consequently increased power input. A considerable proportion of this power input can be dissipated as head resulting in an appreciable rise in temperature. This is self compensating in the sense that increasing the temperature of a fluid reduces its viscosity to maintain efficient working with more viscous fluids and limit the temperature rise to an acceptable degree, it is usual to decrease the pumping speed (derate the capacity of the pump).

Delivery

A reciprocating pump delivers fluid in a cyclic flow pattern and this generates pressure pulsations. Theoretically, the peak-to-peak pressure pulsation ($\triangle P$) is given by:

$\triangle P = W \times C \times \delta V$ (in consistent units)

where:

W is the mass density of the fluid

C is the speed of sound through the fluid

δV is the instantaneous change in flow velocity

The latter parameter (δV) depends upon, amongst other things, the point at which the valve opens during the sinusoidal motion of the plunger. If it opens at the very beginning of the pressure stroke, at bottom dead centre, the velocity change is at a maximum.

Working parameters involved (see also Figure 4) are:

X'_O = linear displacement of the plunger from bottom dead centre when the discharge valve starts to open

C_V = number of plunger displacements in trapped volume

S = pump stroke

P_O = discharge pressure

K = bulk modulus of elasticity of liquid handles

These are related in the following way:

$$X'_O = (1 + C_V) S \times \frac{P_O}{K}$$

Since P varies in a similar fashion to X'_O (although not in strict proportion), it follows that:

(i) The greater the 'clearance volume' in the pump, the higher the pulsation level.

(ii) The longer the stroke, the higher the pulsation level.

(iii) The higher the discharge pressure, the higher the pulsation head.

This formula also implies that the greater the bulk modulus of the fluid, the lower the pulsation level. However, this is more than offset by the fact that the speed of sound through the fluid (C) in the original formula is directly proportional to bulk modulus. Thus, in fact, more 'elastic' fluids will tend to generate lower pulsation levels when pumped. Equally the actual form of delivery flow/time curve will depart from the theoretical sine wave form.

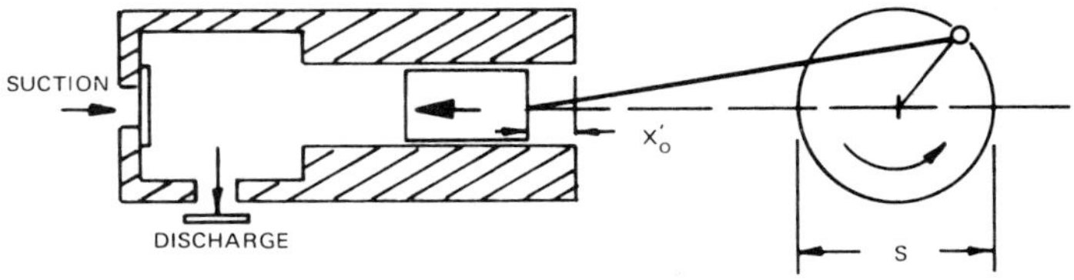

Figure 4
Displacement of piston = S on discharge stroke.

Suction and discharge
A reciprocating pump works on a two stroke principle. On the outgoing (suction) stroke the suction valve opens and the cylinder is filled with fluid (Figure 5). On the ingoing (delivery) stroke the suction valve closes and the discharge valve opens to deliver fluid (Figure 6). The theoretical flow/time curve for a single cylinder reciprocating pump is shown in Figure 7.

In the case of a single-acting power driven pump, discharge flow remains zero during the suction stroke, exaggerating the pulsating nature of the flow while a double-acting pump flow is momentarily zero at each end of the stroke, but again with sinusoidal characteristics as shown in Figure 8.

Figure 5
Suction.

Figure 6
Discharge.

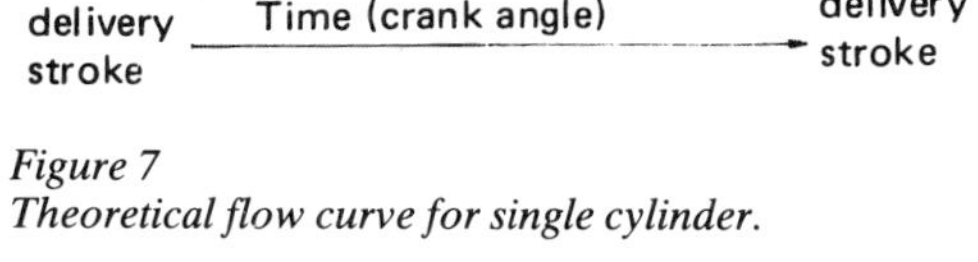

Figure 7
Theoretical flow curve for single cylinder.

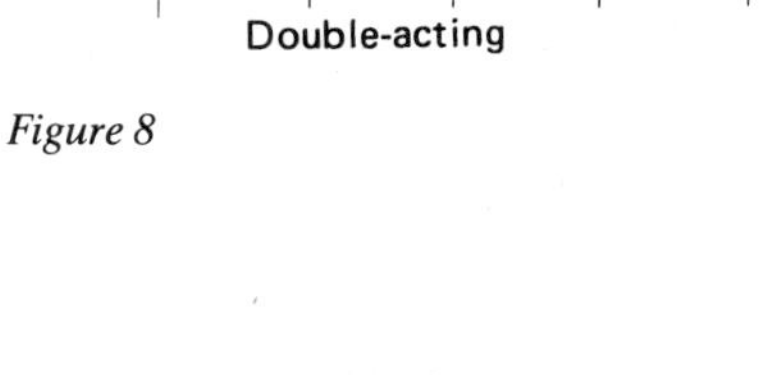

Figure 8

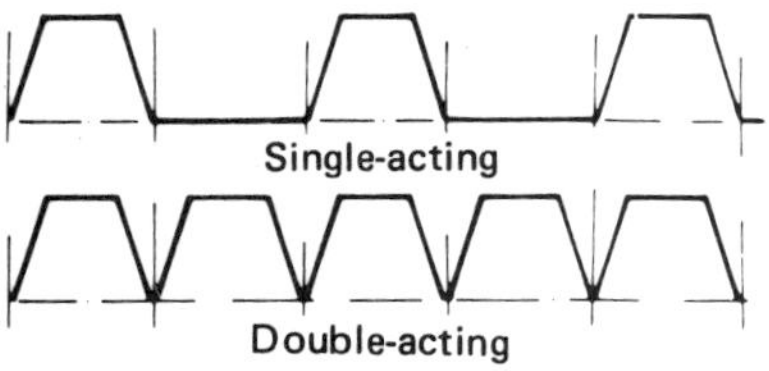

Figure 9

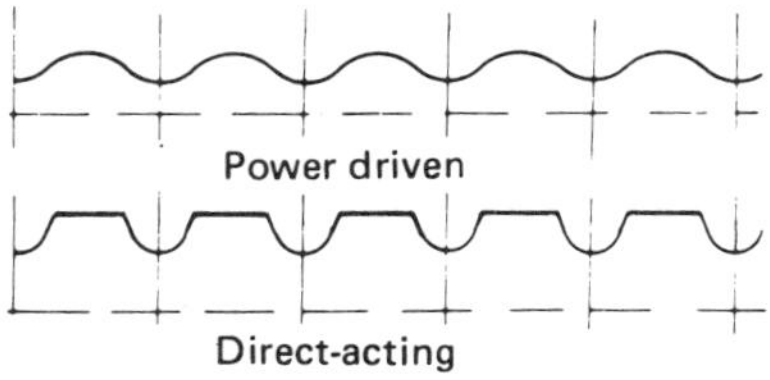

Figure 10

With a *direct-acting* reciprocating pump the discharge is again pulsating but with the flow basically steady over the majority of the stroke, see Figure 9. Thus, a direct-acting pump produces a smoother flow than a power driven pump.

A simple method of smoothing the flow with a double-acting pump is to introduce a cushion chamber into which a proportion of the flow is forced under pressure and ejected when the pressure falls off. The effect is to provide a loop-over of sustained flow during the period at the end of the stroke and the beginning of the next, smoothing out pulsations – Figure 10. This is commonly adopted with single cylinder double acting (simplex) pumps.

An alternative method of approach is to employ two or more cylinders working out a phase. Thus, with a two cylinder or duplex pump, flow variations are appreciably reduced even without cushioning. With a triplex pump the flow is smoother again, and by the time the quintuplex operation is reached, the flow is usually within plus or minus a few per cent of the mean flow even without cushioning and the ripple effect can generally be disregarded. This compares with the 60% above and 100% (zero) below the mean flow characteristics of a simplex pump without cushioning.

Capacity is directly proportional to speed (strokes per minute) for any particular size of pump with a fixed stroke. Speed may be expressed directly in strokes per minute in the case of a direct-acting pump or r/min in the case of a power driven pump. With a crank driven pump this is the same as the speed of the driver, but not necessarily so with other forms of power transmission. Figure 11 shows the variation in flow for duplex, triplex and quintuplex acting pumps. They are approximate and representative of pumps with a connecting rod length equal to five times the crank flow. Figure 12 shows speed-torque curves for typical triplex and quintuplex power pumps.

The facility for operating a quintuplex pump without flow cushioning and pulsation dampening is of particular importance in high pressure plunger pumps. This is especially true if the flow from a high pressure pump is to be carried through rigid pipework when, to avoid serious damage to both the installation and the pump, it is absolutely essential to install a pulsation dampener unless the flowrate is extremely low. These are very costly items and at pressures above 35 bar, can cost as much as one and a half times the cost of the pump. Cheaper pulsation dampeners can be obtained but these invariably contain moving parts which are subject to wear.

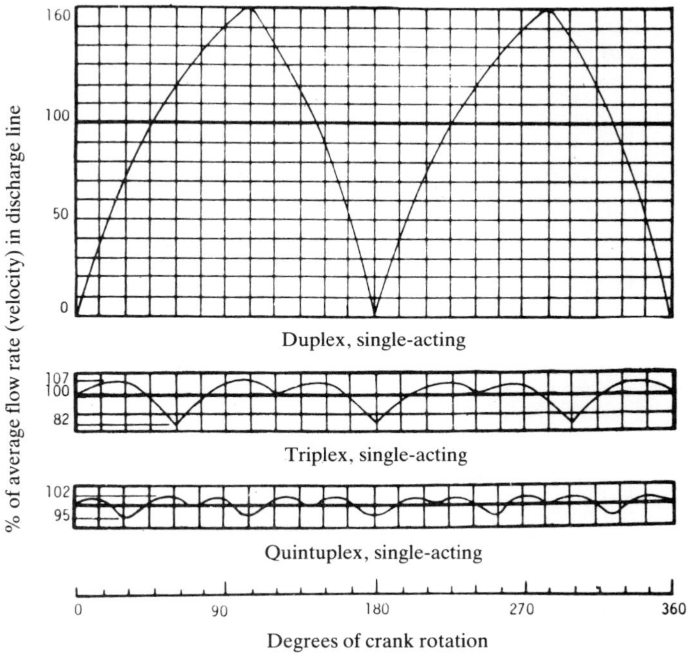

Note:
The above curves are approximate and represent pumps with a connecting rod length equal to five times the crank throw.

Figure 11
Reciprocating power pump comparative flow curves.

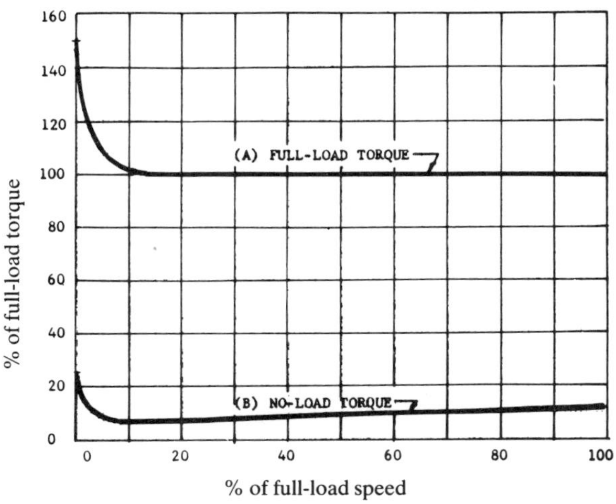

(A) Full-load torque – for pump start-up against design discharge pressure.
(B) No-load torque – for pump start-up on a bypass open to pump suction.

Figure 12
Triplex and quintuplex power pump speed – torque curves.

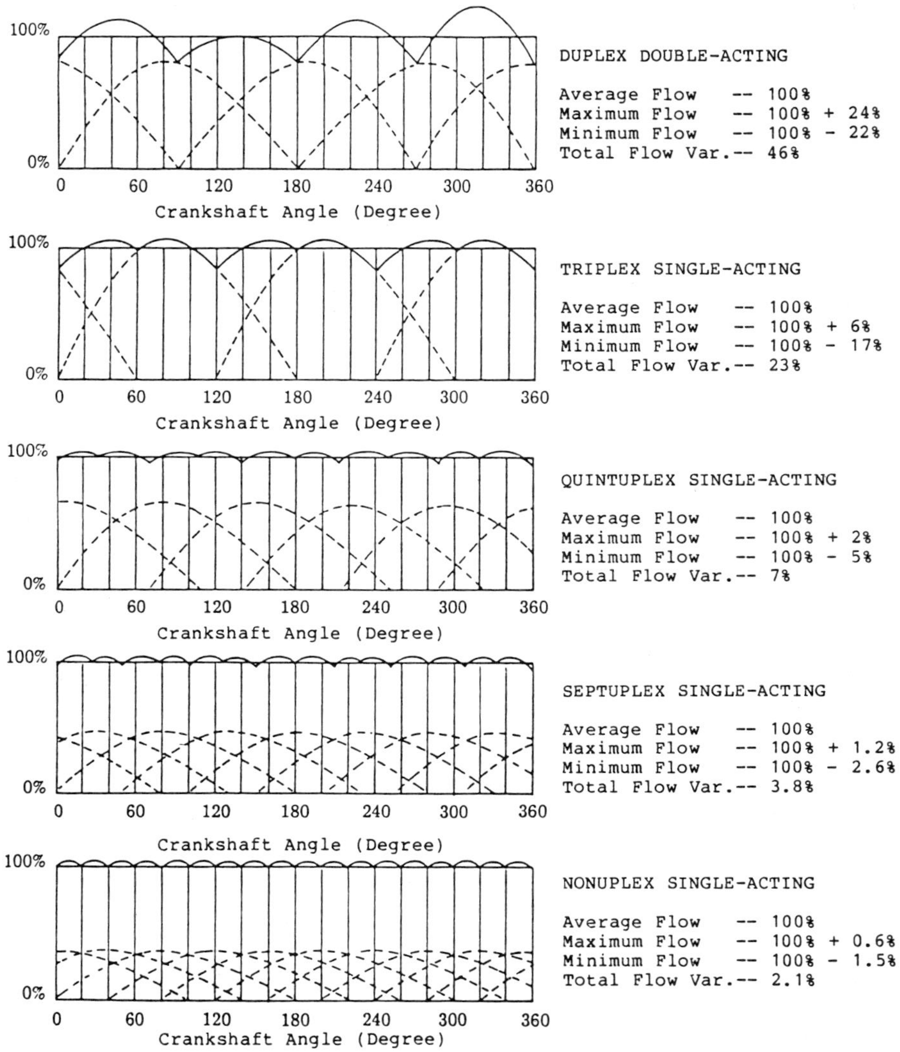

Reciprocating pumps flow characteristics

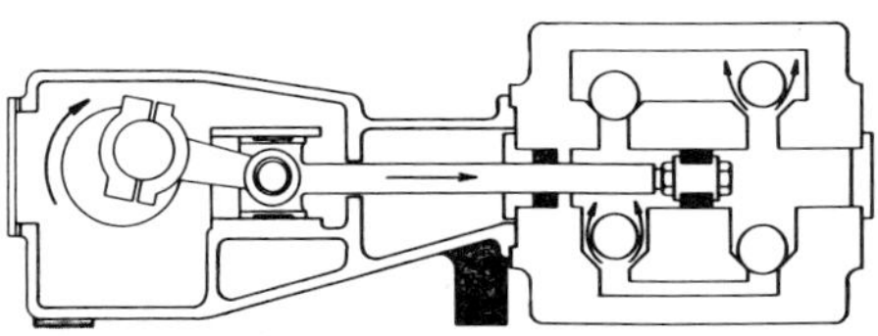

Horizontal double-acting piston power pump.

Cause of pressure pulsations

The basic cause of pressure pulsations is related both to the compressibility of the fluid and the geometry of the pump. Specifically, the piston in any reciprocating pump has to travel some distance from the beginning of the discharge stroke before sufficient pressure is built up to open the discharge valve. This results in compression of the fluid in the cylinder as shown in Figure 13. As soon as the valve opens, fluid suddenly escapes from the cylinder simultaneously relieving itself of compression – *ie* generating an instantaneous rise in pressure above the discharge pressure as shown in Figure 14.

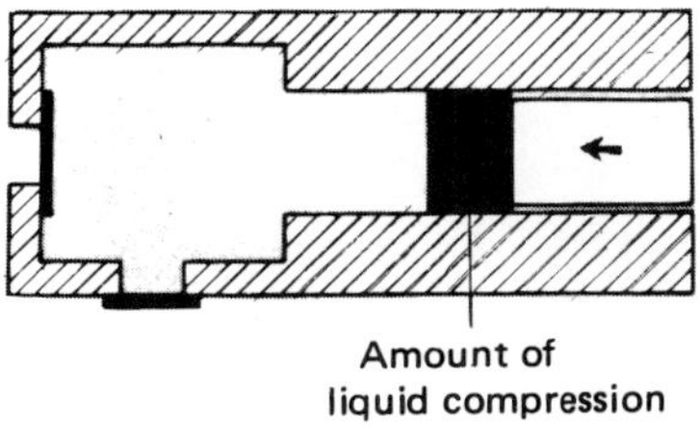

Figure 13
Liquid compression in pump.

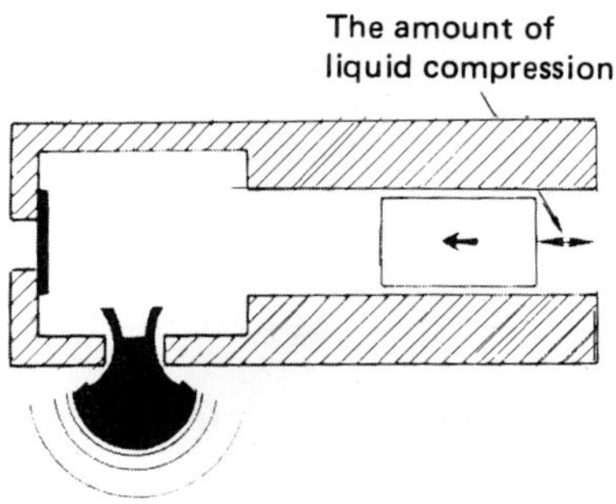

Figure 14
Pressure pulsation as valve opens.

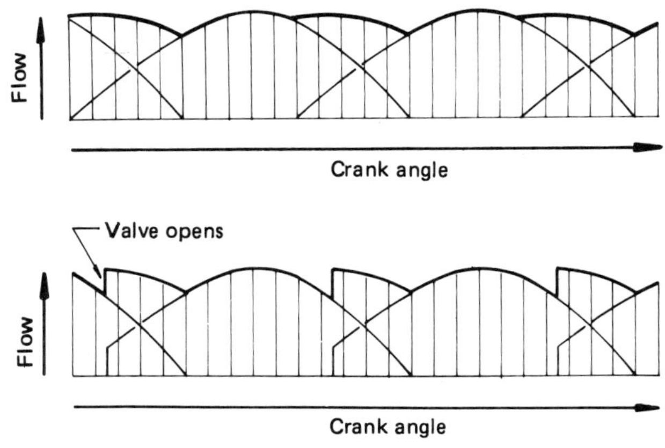

Figure 15
Theoretical flow/time characteristics of a triplex pump with (below) actual/time characteristics.

In terms of the flow/time curve this creates a 'step' in the theoretical curve each time the discharge valve opens. Figure 15 shows this effect on the practical performance of a triplex pump compared with the theoretical curve.

Reducing pressure pulsations

The greater the number of cylinders involved working out of phase, the lower the level of pump ripple. However, in all cases, the higher the delivery pressure the more important – or even necessary – it becomes to incorporate some form of cushioning in the design, or to fit a pulsation dampener. This is especially true if the flow is carried through rigid pipes. Pulsation dampeners in particular can reduce pulsation levels to a relatively insignificant level. However, it should be borne in mind that as previously stated pulsation dampeners can cost more than the pump. Figure 16 shows an oscilloscope trace of undampened pressure pulsation and dampened pressure pulsation.

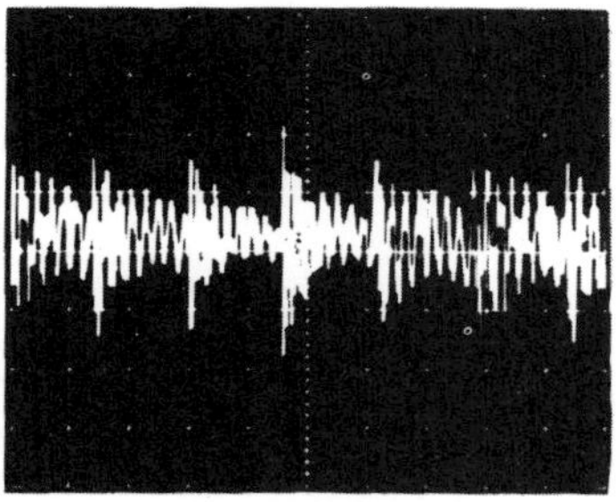

Oscilloscope trace of undampened pressure pulsation

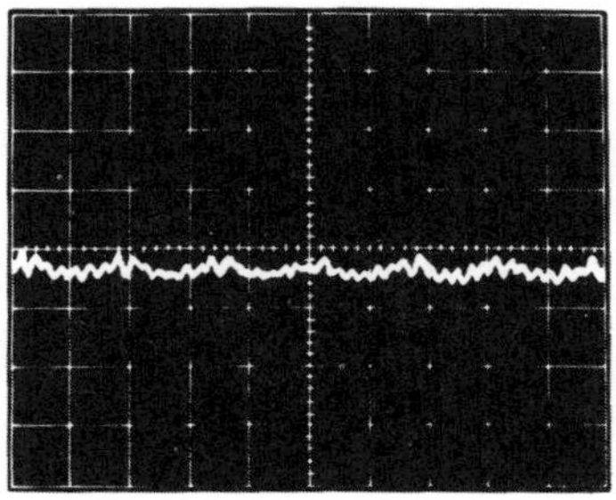

Oscilloscope trace of dampened pressure pulsation

Figure 16

High pressure pumps

Basically, the pressure rating of a reciprocating pump is governed by the type(s) of valves which can be employed with a particular design. As a general rule, the highest pressure can only be achieved with seated valves (*eg* poppet valves). Simple porting or slilding or rotary valves tend to have inherent pressure limitations. Fine clearances and long leakage paths are also necessary features of a high pressure pump.

Multi-cylinder pumps are normally used for high pressures and large deliveries, particularly for handling oil fluids. High speed pumps of this type may be rated for continuous running at 1500 r/min. They are usually in-line configuration of either horizontal or vertical layout. Larger units are normally designed for speed of 100 to 600 r/min. These are normally of horizontal configuration. Volumetric efficiencies can be as high as 97% at up to 1000 bar (15000 lb/in^2).

Pump layout

In-line pumps are particularly suitable for pressure duties, handling fluids with low lubricity. If necessary, bearings (and other parts) may be lubricated from a separate pressure lubricant system. Radial piston pumps are generally preferred for high pressure handling of oil fluids (*eg* hydraulic oils) and provide a more compact unit for similar performance. Radial piston configuration also lends itself readily to extension to variable delivery.

The self-oiling piston pump is a heavy-duty, robust, reliable pump suitable for pumping long-distances and against high heads.

Radial piston pumps

Radial piston pumps are grouped broadly into:

(i) true radial configuration with fixed cylinders, where the pistons are driven by a rotating inclined cam plate or similar mechanism.

(ii) rotary configuration with fixed inclined cam plate and rotating cylinder block.

In both cases variable delivery can be achieved by making the inclination of the cam plate adjustable.

The rotary pump is more limited in the maximum pressure it can develop because porting has to be employed, and speed is limited by the mass of rotating cylinder block. Maximum pressure achieved with pumps of this type is usually limited to about 350 bar (5000 lb/in^2).

Axial piston pumps

In the axial piston pump the cylinders are disposed parallel to the crankshaft *ie* axially, and the pistons reciprocated by an inclined swash plate on the pump spindle. Again, the spindle (and swash plate) may rotate, with cylinder block fixed; or the cylinder block rotate around a fixed spindle (and swash plate). The former is more usually produced as a fixed displacement pump and the latter as a variable displacement pump.

Other designs based on the same principle of working include the bent axis or tilted body pump where the swash plate is mounted square on the shaft, and the cylinder block at an angle to it. In this case again, however, seating type valves cannot be employed and this limits the pressure such pumps can achieve. They can be run at higher speeds than a rotary pump, however, they are readily adapted for variable delivery.

Piston and plunger pumps for slurry service

Reciprocating pumps are used to handle slurries for in-plant processes and pipeline applications. As pipeline systems grow in length and capacity, they require higher pressures. This is advantageous for a reciprocating pump which has the desirable characteristic of maintaining high effficiency at any desired flowrate and pressure. The type used, be it piston or plunger, single- or double-acting, will depend on the particular application. Developed pressures range up to 206 bar (3000 lb/in^2) with overall efficiencies of 80 to 90%.

Basic construction may or may not be the same as for clear fluid application. The differences may be in types of valves, addition of surge chambers, or fluid injection into the lower portion of the stuffing box.

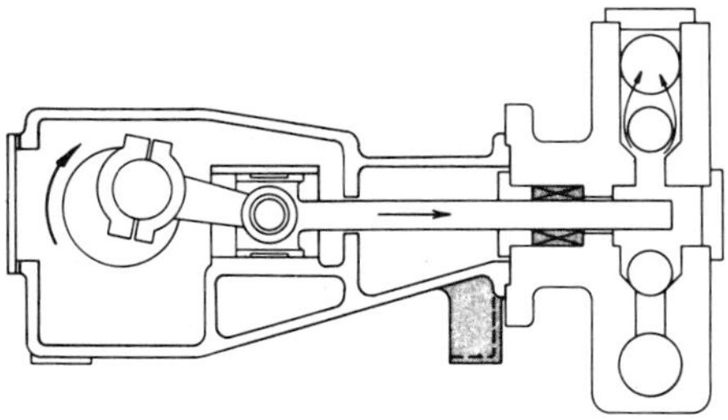

Horizontal single-acting plunger power pump.

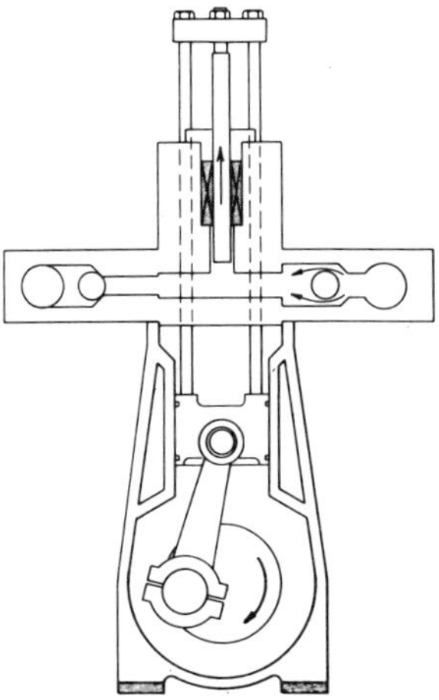

Vertical single-acting plunger power pump.

Reciprocating slurry pumps are so designed that the fluid end parts, which are subject to deteriorating effects of slurries, can be easily and quickly replaced without dismantling any other major pump component. These parts are usually replaced in accordance with a preventative maintenance programme. The scheduled replacement time is based on the user's experience with the slurry

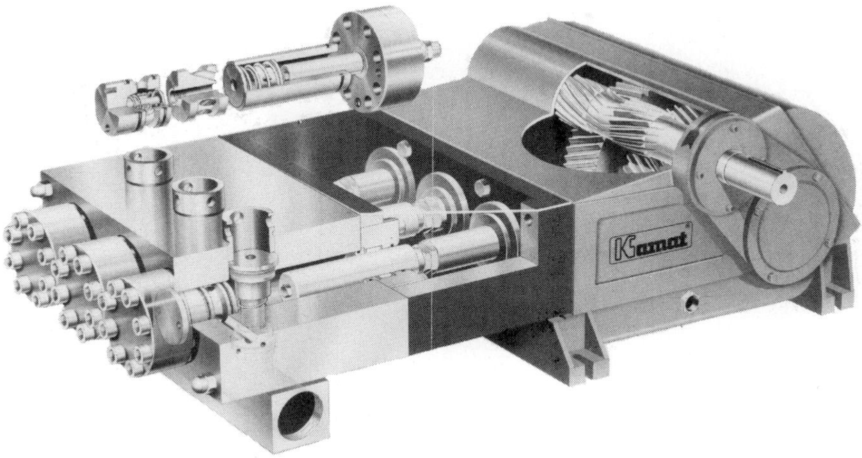

Cutaway of triplex plunger pump.

pumped. Replacement timing should be such that the part will still be performing adequately and will not have worn to the point of causing failure of other parts of the machine.

Hydraulic passages should be sized so that the lowest velocity of the fluid will be above the critical carrying velocity (4 to 6 ft/s as an average). The highest velocity should be below that which causes excessive erosion. Typical average operating velocities through a reciprocating slurry pump passages are 6 to 12 ft/s.

Lubrication and flushing of packing are extremely important. Metered clear, external injection, which is timed to the position of the plunger during its stroke, or continuous flow injection is employed to achieve this. The mode of flushing will depend on whether dilution of fluid pumped from flushing fluid can be tolerated.

To protect the main stuffing box packing, clear fluid is usually injected into the stuffing box between the bottom of the throat bushing and the packing. The injection lines are selected to withstand full working pressure and have a safety check valve located between the stuffing box and the injection fluid source to prevent accidental backflow of slurry into the clear fluid system.

Valves for use in slurry service are designed for velocities between 6 to 12 ft/s to reduce erosion and abrasion of the valve seat and other valve components. Valve construction usually has replaceable valve inserts that are made of an elastomer or polymer. Metal-to-metal ball valves may be used depending on the slurry, material, carrier fluid and temperature.

Special considerations must be given to the slurry abrasion, attrition, particle size and concentration. Slurry particle size has an influence on the valve lift and the ability of an elastomer valve to seat when used. Experience to date shows that slurry concentrations of up to 65% by weight can be handled successfully.

Suction pressure on a pump handling a slurry is usually higher than when handling clear fluid. This is to take into account the acceleration head of the solids and gases entrained with the fluid. Likewise pulsation dampeners are usually larger on the suction and discharge size of the pump for the same reasons.

Triplex pumps

To facilitate starting or stopping a slurry pump it should be fitted with adequate connections so the fluid end passages can be flushed of the slurry with clear fluid. This is especially true when there are to be extended periods when the pump will be shut down.

Rod and plunger packing requires special considerations when dealing with abrasive materials. In a piston pump, the piston runs in a renewable metal cylinder or liner. The liners are made of abrasion- and corrosion-resistant metals to resist wear for each specific slurry. Piston rods and plungers are also coated to resist wear. Where the abrasion of the slurry is not great and the pressures are below 137 bar (2000 lb/in^2), large volume piston pumps are more suitable. Transportation of coal slurry will fall into this class of service.

Positive Displacement Pumps

WHEN RUNNING at a constant speed, pumps of this type positively displace a liquid volume at almost a fixed rate, irrespective of the resistance the flow of liquid encounters. The two main types are:

(i) reciprocating

(ii) rotary

Table 1 shows the classification of positive displacement pumps

TABLE 1

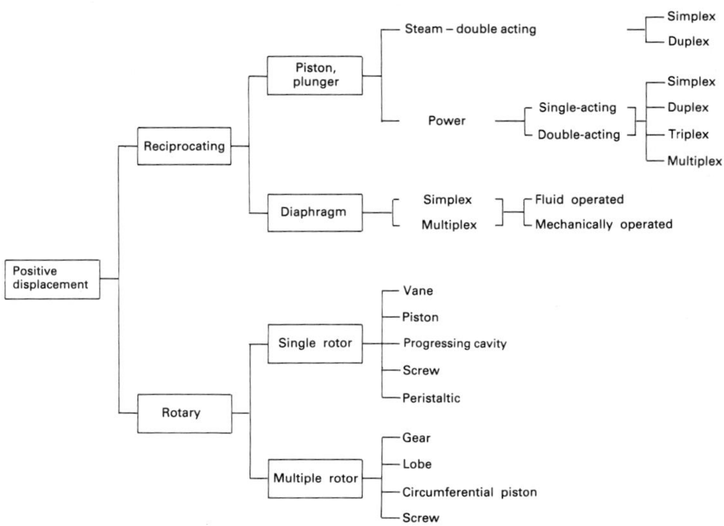

A typical reciprocating pump has a ram, plunger, piston or other cylindrical element working backwards and forwards within a cylinder or pump barrel. This motion is usually derived from a crank revolving at uniform speed, and a connecting rod. Automatic valves control the flow of liquids into the cylinder and out again.

The pump's capacity fluctuates with the number of plungers or pistons. In general, the higher the number, the less capacity variation at a given r/min. Reciprocating pumps are designed for specific speed, pressure, capacity and horsepower. Pumps are built in both horizontal and vertical construction. Horizontal is used on plunger pumps up to 149 kW (200 hp). This construction is usually below waist level and permits ease of assembly and maintenance. Large Horizontal pumps are built with 3 or 5 plungers and rated to 2235 kW (3000 hp) and usually have 2 or 3 pistons which are single- or double-acting. Vertical construction is used on plunger pumps up to 1118 kW (1500 hp) with the fluid end above the power end. This construction eliminates the plunger weights on the bushings, packing and cross-head and aligns the plunger with the packing. A special seal arrangement is required to prevent the liquid of the fluid end from mixing with the oil of the power end. There can be 3 to 9 plungers.

Applications

Typical applications for reciprocating pumps include, ammonia service, carbonate service, chemicals, crude oil pipeline, cryogenic service, fertilizer plants, high pressure water cutting, hydro-forming, hydrostatic testing, liquid petroleum gas, liquid pipeline, power oil, power press, soft water injection for water flood, slurry pipeline (70% by weight) slush ash service, steel mill descaling, water blast service.

A positive rotary pump usually has one or more closely fitting elements that revolve continuously within a fixed casing. It has no valves and the liquid flows through the passages in a nearly uniform stream.

The rotary motion of these pumps distinguishes them from reciprocating positive displacement pumps in which the main motion of moving elements is reciprocating. The positive displacement nature of the pumping action of rotary pumps distinguishes them from the general class of centrifugal pumps in which liquid displacement and pumping action depend to a large part on developed liquid velocity.

It is a characteristic of rotary pumps, as positive displacement pumps, that the amount of liquid displaced by each revolution is independant of speed. Also it is characteristic of rotary pumps that a time-continuous liquid seal of sorts is maintained between the inlet and outlet ports by the action and position of the pumping elements and the close running clearances of the pump. Hence, rotary pumps generally do not require inlet and outlet valve arrangements as reciprocating pumps do.

Rotary pumps are useful in handling both fluids and liquids where fluid is a general term that includes liquids, gases, vapours and mixtures thereof, and sometimes solids in suspension and where liquid is a more specific term that is limited to true liquids which are relatively incompressible and relatively free of gases, vapours and solids.

Performance laws

Positive displacement pumps displace a volume of liquid which changes pro-rata, with the speed. Due to internal leakage, varying with the pressure and viscosity of the fluid, the output of the pump is reduced by this amount. Thus, at various speed the positive pump has head discharge characteristics parallel to each other and almost vertical to the capacity (discharge) ordinate, (see Figure 1).

Usually the rotary pump has a greater internal leakage than the reciprocating pump and, therefore, the head discharge characteristic will depart more from the vertical for an identical viscosity.

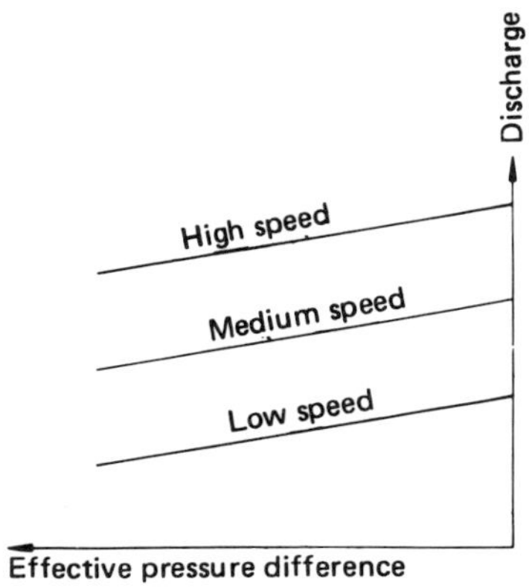

Figure 1

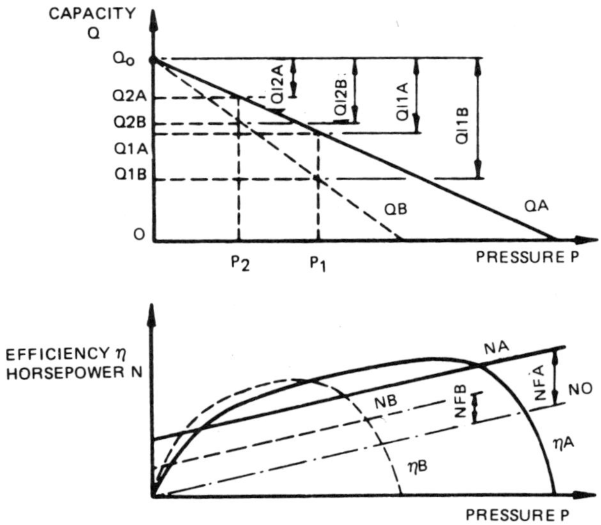

Indices

1	High pressure
2	Low pressure
A	High viscosity
B	Low viscosity
k	High speed
L	Low speed

Symbols

Q_o	Displacement capacity
Q	Pump capacity (output)
Q_L	Leakage capacity
N_o	Hydraulic horsepower
N	Total horsepower
N_F	Friction horsepower
n	Speed
P	Pressure
ν	Viscosity
η	Efficiency

Equations

$$QL1A = QL2B \frac{P_1}{P_2} \times \left(\frac{\nu_B}{\nu_A}\right)^x$$

$$N_{FKA} = N_{FLB} \left(\frac{\nu_A}{\nu_B}\right)^\gamma \times \left(\frac{n_k}{n_L}\right)^z$$

$$N_o = \frac{Q_o \cdot P}{1428} \qquad Q_o \text{ gal/min}, \; P \text{ lb/in}^2$$

$$Q = Q_o - QL$$

$$N = N_o + N_F$$

x = Viscosity factor (leakage) $\frac{1}{2}$ to $\frac{1}{3}$

γ = Viscosity factor (friction) $\frac{1}{2}$ to $\frac{1}{3}$

z = Friction factor (speed) 2 to 3

Figure 2
Performance graph of positive displacement pump at variation of speed, pressure and viscosity.

Pump characteristic and performance
A typical performace graph of a positive displacement pump is shown in Figure 2 which also gives typical formula necessary for the various versions for variation of speed, pressure, viscosity *etc.*

Range charts for positive displacement pumps
Range charts for positive displacement pumps are normally prepared for varying viscosities. They are shown on a logarithmic scale and as their head discharge characteristic is a straight line (the inclination of which depends on the viscosity), they have a configuration as shown in Figure 3. Since the displacement is proportionate to speed, range charts are made for the most likely commercial speeds which decrease with increasing size of pump.

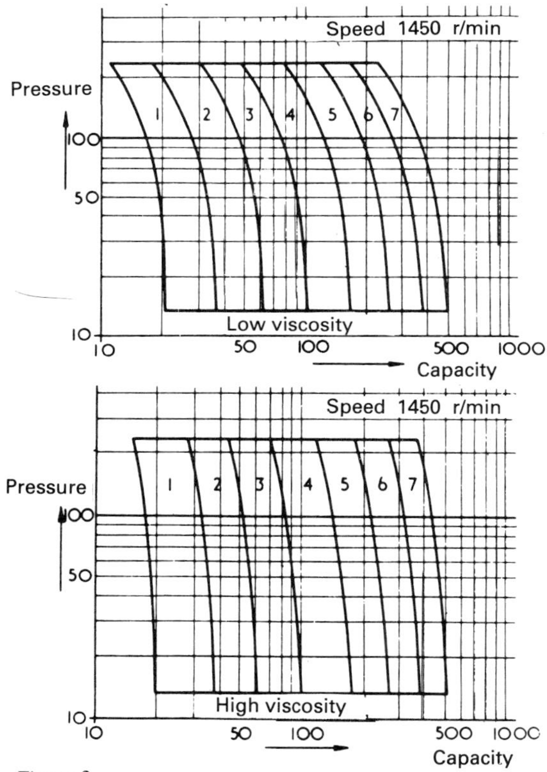

Figure 3
Typical positive displacement pump range chart at constant speed and for low and high viscosity.

Flow control
Whenever positive displacement pumps are installed in series some variable capacity capability is essential. Otherwise, any variation in capacity between series pumps or series groups of pumps would result in disastrous inter-station pressures.

The flow is determined by the first pump in the line. Subsequent pumps should be equipped with capacity controls responsive to their inlet pressures. The preferred control is a continuous modulation type such as variable speed, unless large reservoir capacity is available between pumps.

Recirculation from discharge to suction through throttling bypass valves may be used at the expense of energy, to match the delivery from downstream to upstream pumps. Excessive bypass flow in relation to through flow can result in significant temperature rise of the liquid. When downstream pump capacity is less than the upstream delivery, the interpump pressure will rise, indicating a need for increased capacity. When the downstream pump capacity exceeds the upstream delivery, the downstream pump will 'draw down' the interpump pressure to the point where net positive inlet pressure difficulties are ensured.

Reservoir accumulation between pumps permit a limited degree of mismatch in capacities, allowing the use of incremental capacity controls such as suction valve unloading and intermittant pump bypass.

In any event, effective discharge dampeners on the upstream pump and suction stabilizers on the downstream pump are necessary to prevent an inherent pressure pulsations and control modulation variances from adversely affecting operation.

Since the capacity of positive displacement pumps is virtually independent of head, there is no problem from the head capacity characteristics in parallel operation – even for pumps of different sizes.

Particular attention to suction acceleration head requirements is necessary when more than one pump is taking suction from a common suction pipe. Since it cannot be assured that two pumps will not, at some point, have simultaneous suction strokes, the acceleration requirements of each pump must be added for that portion of the suction line that furnishes the total flow. This suggests extra large suction lines, individual ones, from the liquid source, or suction stabilizers sized for total flow with individual outlet connections for each pump.

Diaphragm Pumps

A DIAPHRAGM pump is a reciprocating pump where the pumping element is a flexible diaphragm. Capacity is directly proportional to diaphragm diameter and stroke and rate of reciprocation. Since practical strokes achievable are necessarily limited (*ie* to considerably less than the 'bore' or pump diameter), it follows that maximum capacity for any size of diaphragm is determined by the maximum permissible reciprocating speed which is usually low.

The particular advantage offered by diaphragm pumps is that only the diaphragm and suction and discharge passages are wetted by the fluid being handled and are thus true zero leakage pumps. Valves are required, but these can be a simple design since the flow pattern is straightforward and relatively open port areas can be utilized. Simple ball valves or cone valves are generally used, although disc or flap valves may be preferred for larger sizes. They also readily lend themselves to variable delivery designs either by varying the diaphragm movement (stroke) with constant speed or by varying of the speed.

Double diaphragm pump for widest range of applications.

Diaphragm pumps are self-priming and can run dry without damage. Where necessary, double diaphragms may be incorporated so that in the event of failure of one diaphragm the fluid being handled can be contained without leakage.

Basic diaphragm pumps comprise:

(i) mechanically driven diaphragm – where the diaphragm is linked to a crank motion or similar mechanism to produce oscillatory movement

(ii) hydraulically driven diaphragm – where the diaphragm movement is derived from pressure fluctuations generated in a fluid chamber. These pressure pulsations are normally produced by a reciprocating piston, hence the type is commonly called a piston diaphragm pump.

(iii) air driven diaphragm – where the diaphragm is automatically reciprocated by compressed air applied alternately to opposite ends of a diaphragm chamber.

(iv) electromagnetically driven diaphragm – where the diaphragm movement is generated by the plunger of an electromagnet, the coil of which is energised by pulses of electrical current. Such designs are basically limited to small sizes and particularly used as metering, proportioning or dosing pumps, in conjunction with digital electronic controllers.

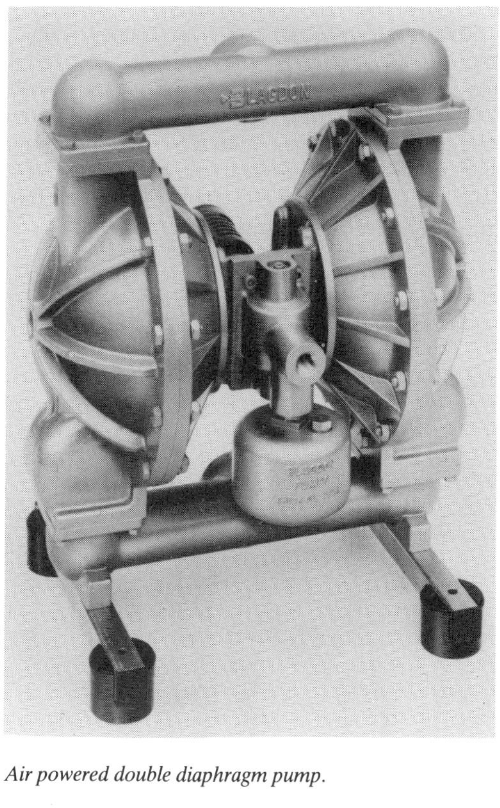

Air powered double diaphragm pump.

Air operated diaphragm pump with inter changeable ball or cone non-return valves for all fluid transfer applications.

Characteristics of diaphragm pumps

Being a positive displacement pump the head capacity curve is substantially vertical, with cut-off at maximum rated pressure which is of the order of 3 to 3·5 bar for mechanically driven diaphragm pumps and 7 to 10 bar for hydraulically operated diaphragm pumps as shown in Figure 1.

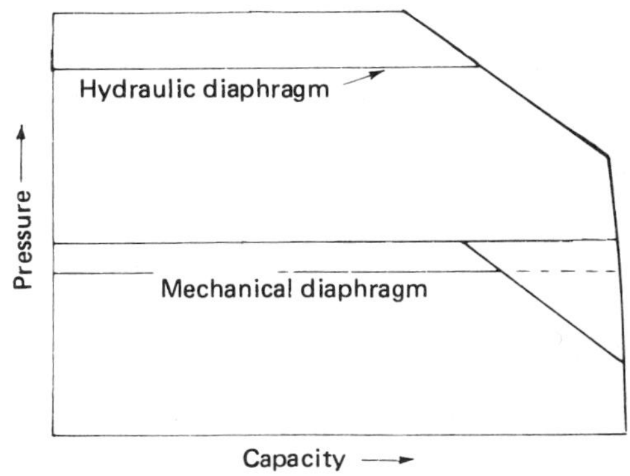

Figure 1

The working envelope thus takes the form shown in Figure 2(a), with rounding off around maximum head (pressure). Actual delivery can be varied by altering the speed, in which case the lower the speed the less the rounding off effect as shown in Figure 2(b).

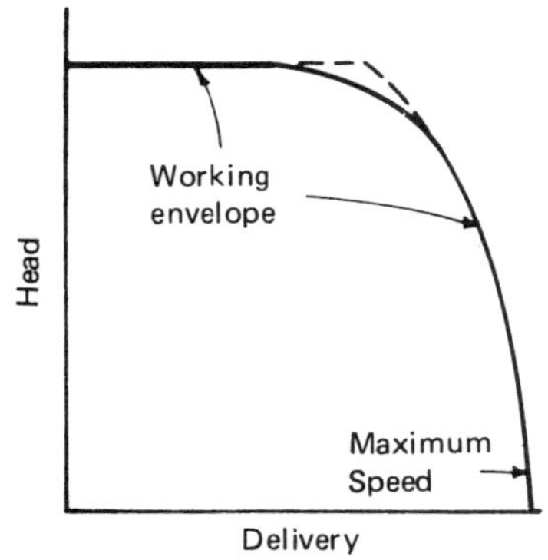

Figure 2(a)

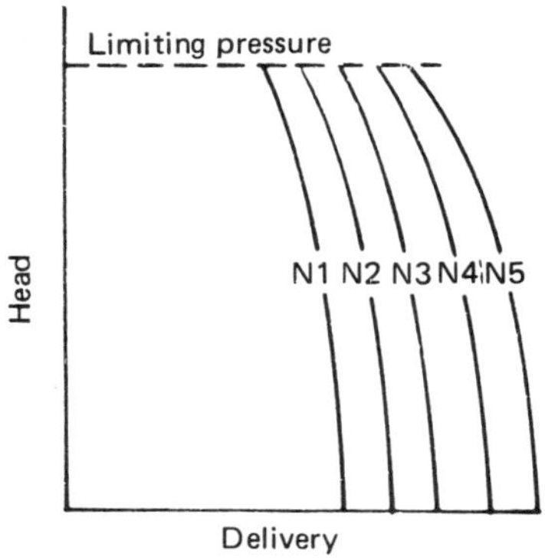

Figure 2(b)

Choice of a suitable size of pump must take into account the head involved as, if the pump is worked near its maximum permissible pressure, its effective capacity may be substantially reduced, depending on the detailed design of the pump. Efficiency figures are never quoted for diaphragm pumps, but in the case of mechanically driven diaphragm pumps are usually low and of the order of only 10 to 25%.

Diaphragm pumps produce a pulsating delivery, but this can be cushioned if necessary by incorporating an air chamber on the delivery side – *eg* if the pump is to be specifically employed to develop a constant pressure output such as for spraying.

Diaphragm pumps normally have good suction lift characteristics and are strongly self-priming; although in practice priming may be necessary for operating

A 3 inch diaphragm pump for use with diesel or petrol engine and electric motors. Maximum output is 19 m^3/h (4200 gal/h).

a suction lift in excess of about 5 metres (15 ft). The preferred mode of operation is on suction lift rather than flooded suction. Diaphragm pumps can operate as vacuum pumps as well as pressure pumps.

Materials

The diaphragm material is usually an elastomer chosen for compatibility with fluid being handled. They are customarily made of fabric-reinforced synthetic rubber and many combinations of pump and diaphragm materials are possible to cover a wide range of pumped products. For some solvents and agressive acids or alkalis, Teflon* diaphragms can be used either directly or as an overlay on the conventional diaphragm.

Since many diaphragm pumps are used to pump abrasive slurries, the valves usually have elastomeric faces or are elastomeric balls. Large ball check valves may have metal cores covered by a thick wall of synthetic rubber, or they may be of solid rubber. Other materials include glass and ebonite.

Pump materials include cast iron, aluminium, stainless steel, Carpenter 20, Hastelloy C, and plastics reinforced with glassfibre.

Double diaphragm pumps

Pumps with double diaphragms are employed where zero-leakage characteristics have to be maintained in the event of diaphragm failure. This involves the use of two diaphragms separated by a small chamber filled with an inert or buffer fluid, and is mostly applicable to piston diaphragm designs used in metering the proportioning pumps.

Double diaphragm pumps feed solvents, extenders and bases, with pigment dosing being carried out by fast-flow pumps, in a paint production process.

*Teflon, Du Pont's registered trademark.

TABLE 1 – SOME APPLICATIONS FOR AIR OPERATED DOUBLE DIAPHRAGM PUMPS

Liquids, from water to pastes, also shear-sensitive, thixotropic, abrasive and corrosive; liquid-gas-mixtures:	
Chemical industry	acids, solvents, basic liquors, colours, resins, pigments, latex, tar emulsions, wastes, adhesives
Cosmetics	toothpaste, creams
Refineries, petrochemical	oil, sludge, tank roof cleaning
Ceramic, china	ceramic and porcelain slurry, glaze, slip, enamel, ceramic colours
Food industry	marmalade, chocolate, blood, dairy produce, animal food, cottage cheese, ketchup, fruit yoghurt
Breweries, wineries	yeast, diatomaceous earth
Marine, shipyards	tank- and bilge-washing, ship cleaning
Construction	sump and pit emptying, clay-slurries, concrete mud, asbestos-cement mud, sand and stone slurries, sealing compound
Mining	dewatering, coal and stone slurries, muds, mortar
Fire brigade, municipal services	dewatering, sump emptying, sewage sludge
Mechanical engineering	grinding emulsions, polioshing muds and pastes
Metallurgy, foundries	metal slurries, hydroxide and carbide mud, black wash
Textile industry	latex, carpet backing
Paper industry	pulp and paper stock, slurries
Environmental protection	additives, thin muds, lime slurry, hazardous products, filterpress feeding
Medicine	blood plasma
Nuclear	contaminated liquids
Aerospace technology	satellite refuelling
Bio-technology	sterile products
Semi-contactor industry	ultra-pure liquids
Aviation	helicopter refuelling, tank emptying
Powders in low density and micron-size: smooth transportation, very economical and dust-free:	
	fumed silica, talc, activated carbon, carbon black salicylic acid
	diatomaceous earthy fly dust, filter dust, several plastic powders
	flour, aluminium oxide, fire fighting powder, some herbicides

Pump heads

Diaphragm pump heads are relatively compact units and two or more can be connected in series or parallel, with a common driver to provide higher pressures or capacities, respectively. With parallel operation, two diaphragms may be combined in a single head assembly to give a double-acting pump. Single- or double-acting pumps can also be connected for duplex work. Larger pumps of this type may give capacities up to or exceeding 1600 l/min (350 gal/min), hydraulic operation being used in such cases with an electric motor driver for the reciprocating piston.

Mechanically driven diaphragm pumps

Direct or mechanically driven diaphragm pumps are simple in design and construction, particularly in the larger sizes. Their main limitation is that the diaphragm material is subject to high localised stresses, and the maximum pressure which can be developed is limited by the strength of this material.

In the case of a mechanically driven elastomeric diaphragm, maximum pressure is limited to about 3 to 3·5 bar (40 to 50 lb/in^2) and is generally less, depending on the size of the diaphragm. Pressures of the order of 300 to 350 bar (4500 to 5000 lb/in^2) are readily attainable with a piston diaphragm pump. Much higher pressures can be obtained with metallic diaphragms. Mechanically driven diaphragm pumps are widely used in the construction industry where pumps may suck in stones or other debris. The spring can compress and can thus keep a stone from being pushed through the wall of the pumping chamber or cause the cranking mechanism to fail. Other applications include their use in dewatering foundations and coffer dams and in sewage treatment plants.

Vehicle fuel pumps are often of the diaphragm type. The diaphragm is moved mechanically by a cam on a suction stroke and is returned by a spring for the discharge stroke. Thus, the spring determines the discharge pressure and provides a nearly constant pump pressure to the carburettor regardless of pump (engine) speed or rate of fuel consumption.

Hand-operated diaphragm pumps are used extensively as bilge pumps on sail boats, where the absence of power is a major concern and hand operation is essential.

Hydraulically driven diaphragm pumps

Hydraulically driven diaphragm pumps (piston-diaphragm pumps) can work at much higher pressures since the load on the diaphragm is balanced by opposing hydraulic forces. They are also more precise in action and readily adjustable to give variable delivery. Piston-diaphragm pumps are thus widely used for metering and proportioning duties. Much larger piston-diaphragm pumps are also produced for process work with flows up to 70 000 l/hr per pump head and pressures up to 3000 bar (45 000 lb/in^2). These pumps are positive displacement pumps and must be provided with a bypass arrangement in case the discharge is blocked. Primary markets for these pumps include water and waste treatment plants and the chemical process, pulp and paper, petrochemical and petroleum industries. Typical liquids handled are hydrazine, phosphate, acids, filter aids, aluminium chloride, caustic solvents, vinyl acetates, mercaptan and glycol.

Air operated diaphragm pumps

Diaphragm pumps may be designed to operate directly from a compressed air supply through a solenoid valve – see Figure 3. This valve alternately admits and releases compressed air at the pump head at a rate determined by the setting of a simple timer. Such pumps normally work under a positive suction head of at least 2 metres (6 ft), this head being required to return the diaphragm for the next delivery stroke. If the air is vented to a vacuum system instead of to atmosphere, however, a positive suction head is not necessary and suction lifts can be accommodated.

An alternative type of air driven diaphragm is shown in Figure 4 where the diaphragm is hydraulically operated *via* a double-acting air motor. This is, in effect, a standard piston diaphragm set up but using an air motor instead of a mechanically driven piston pump. Speed may still be controlled by a timer (or more simply by a restricting valve in the air outlet) to achieve variable delivery. In this case the diaphragm pump will generate suction lift.

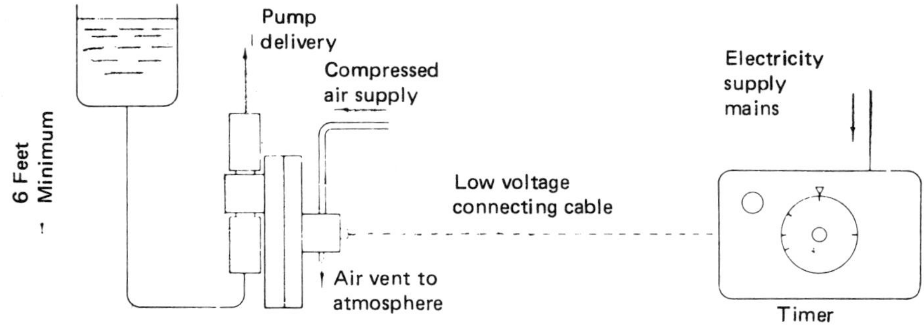

Figure 3

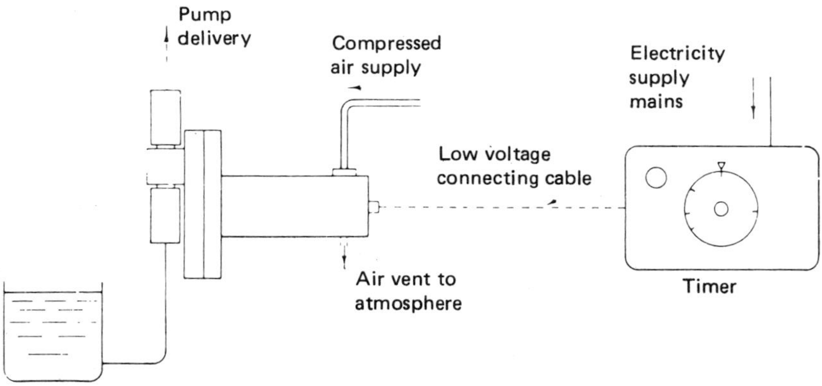

Figure 4

The most common types of pneumatically operated diaphragm pump is the double diaphragm pump, *ie* duplex pump. It comprises two identical fixed diaphragm pumps connected by a pump rod, central stationary assembly and two product manifolds. Each of the pumps has a pair of non-return valves interposed between the product chamber branches and the manifolds, and an air chamber attached to the central assembly. The hand-operated valve that controls the rate of air input and hence the pump's performance is usually attached to the central assembly from which the used air is also released into the atmosphere.

The central assembly contains a means for admitting compressed air into one air chamber, whilst allowing used air to be exhausted simultaneously from the other chamber. This process is caused to reverse automatically when the reciprocating parts reach a predefined position relative to the chambers. Various means for accomplishing this action are used. In the majority of pumps, however, a shuttle valve is employed whose position is switched by reference to the pump rods position. The switching is often achieved pneumatically through air passages intercepted by valves formed around the pump rod.

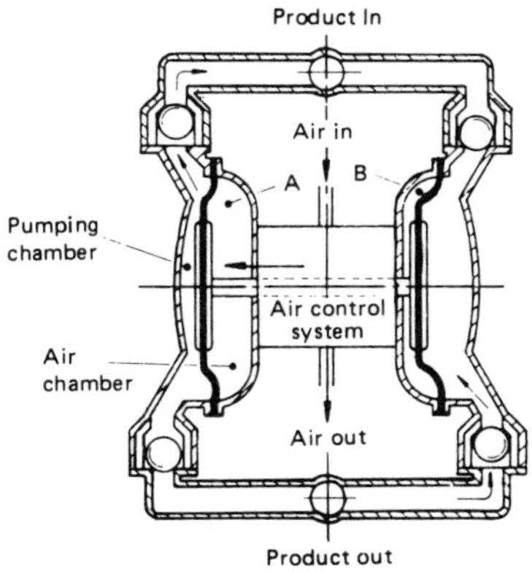

Figure 5(a)

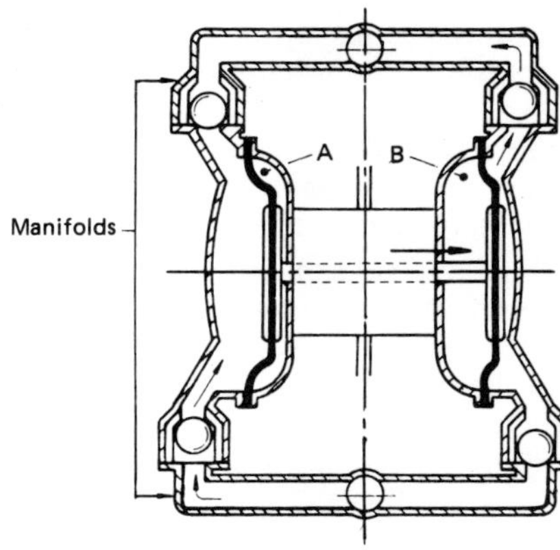

Figure 5(b)

From Figure 5(b) it will be seen that when the pump is working,admission of air into the air chamber of pump 'A' has a two-fold effect: it decreases the volume of pumping chamber 'A' whilst increasing the volume of pumping chamber 'B'. These volume changes occur because the axial force created by the compressed air exceeds the forces due to the product's pressure, the pump's internal friction and the pressure of the air being exhausted from chamber 'B'.

Figure 6 shows that the basic displacement cycle is composed of two components essentially of square wave form. But it should be appreciated that in practice, each predominantly pulse free displacement will only arise when the pump is lightly loaded and running relatively slowly. When these conditions do not exist and high pressure air has to be admitted into and released from the chambers, pressure transients occur which create clearly defined flow pulses.

Recourse to pulsation dampers is usually made in the event of aforementioned pulses being unacceptable.

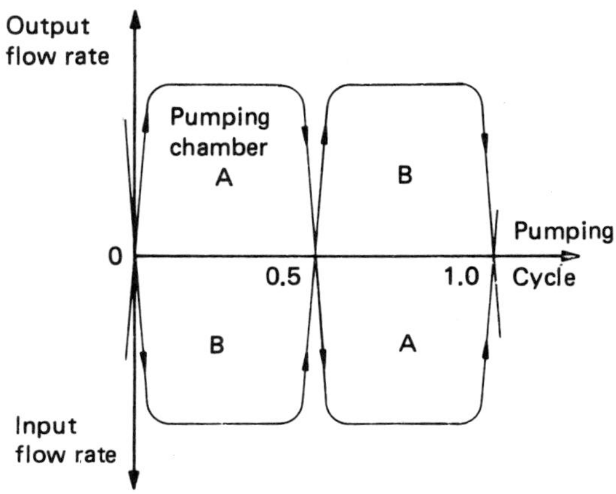

Figure 6

Although the term 'balanced diaphragm' is sometimes associated with these machines, the condition of pressure balance in each pump head is only likely to be approached during half of its full cycle, that is, whilst it is discharging. During the induction stroke, the air pressure acting on the diaphragm is likely to be well in excess of the product pressure, giving rise to the cyclical stress condition which ultimately limits diaphragm life.

Unlike displacement pumps driven by mechanical power, air operated double diaphragm pumps suffer no damage when operated against a closed discharge line. Under such circumstances the product pressure will be limited by the air pressure and the pump will stop working and cease to consume power. The forms of the product output and air input characteristics are shown in Figure 7. The limiting effect of air pressure on product pressure should in particular be noted.

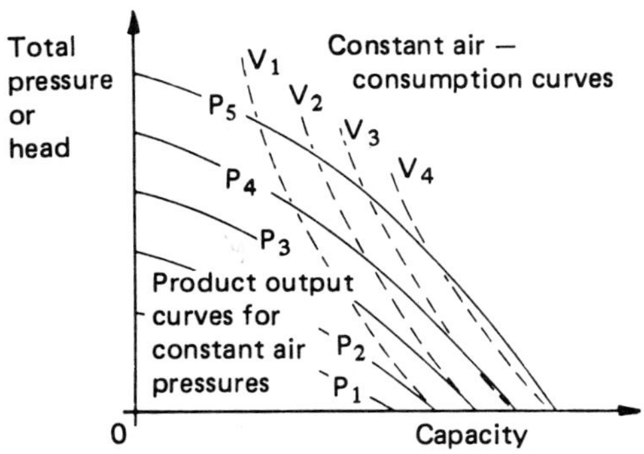

Figure 7

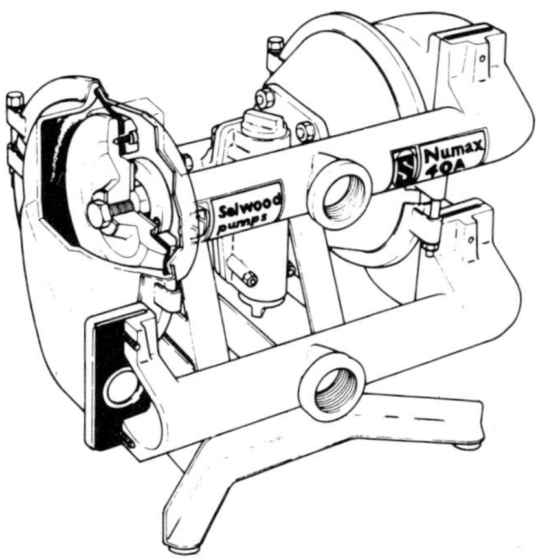

Double diaphragm pump, cutaway to disclose valve and diaphragm clamp design.

Two further versions of an air operated diaphragm pump design are shown in Figure 8, both developed to accommodate the physical properties of PTFE for the diaphragms and ball valves. Each incorporates two pumping chambers with diaphragms mounted on a common shaft each in a chamber in effect forming a pneumatic 'cylinder' with the inner side of each diaphragm a 'piston'. The shaft is then driven in continuous oscillatory motion by compressed air *via* a pilot operated distribution valve. Speed, and thus delivery, is controllable from zero to maximum *via* an adjustable air inlet valve.

The flap valve version is designed to handle liquids with large solids in suspension up to the full pipe size and has proved particularly suitable for such products as cement grout containing fly ash, certain food products, sump and bilge waste.

The ball valve version is designed for handling viscous and/or gritty materials and is particular efficient with products with specific gravity such as sludge, ceramic slip, texturised paints, *etc*. Both types can, of course, also handle virtually all chemically active fluids up to the maximum service temperature rating of PTFE.

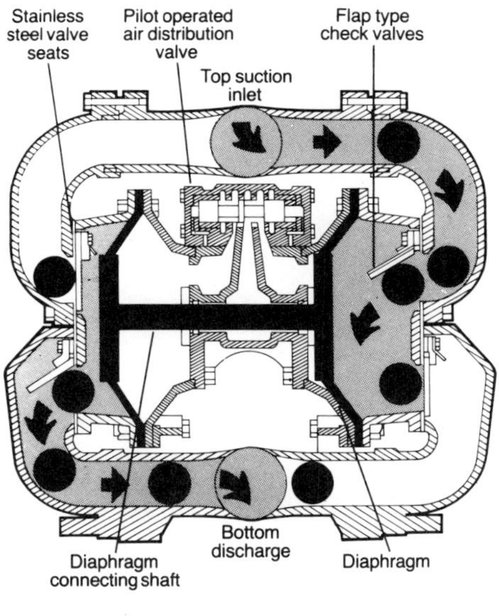

Flap valve type

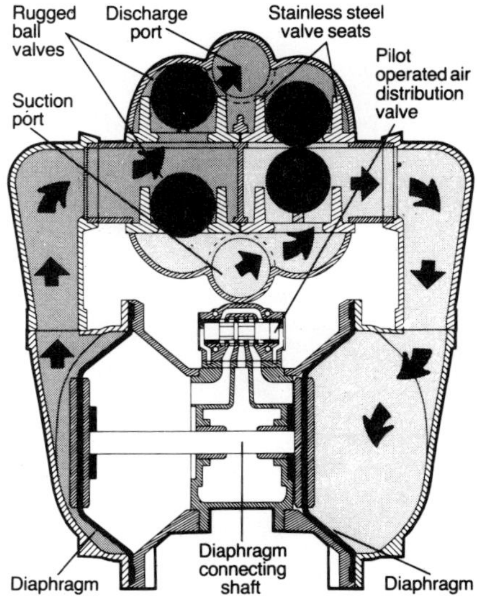

Ball valve type

Figure 8
Double diaphragm pump showing flap and ball valve versions.

Non-metallic air operated double diaphragm pump.

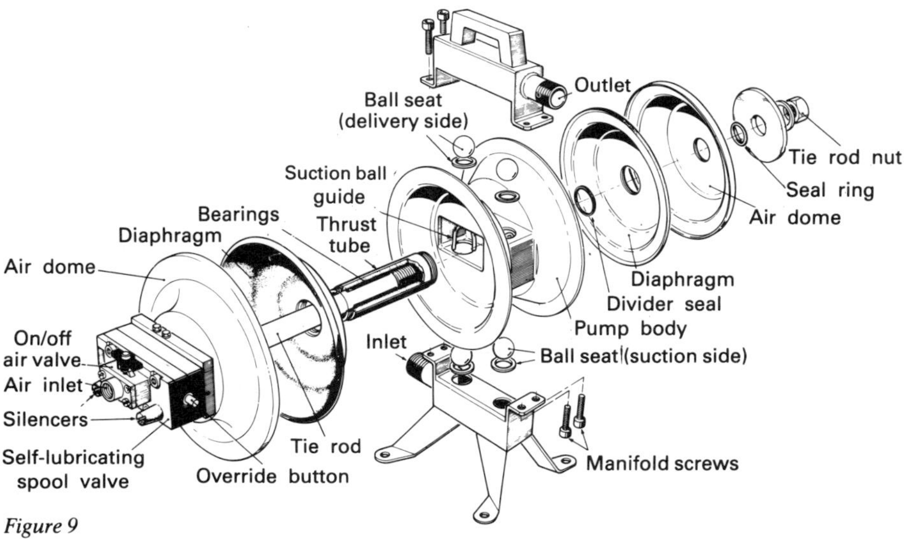

Figure 9

A new concept in double diaphragm pump design is shown in Figure 9. In this pump fluid flows through the centre of the pump 'between' the diaphragms. Suction/delivery pipework is protected by the pump body and an air system incorporating 'positive' pilot bleed signals will, when operated from an adjacent air valve, permit first time starting. There is no risk of mid-position stall and the pump will perform on air supply pressures as low as 1·5 bar (22 lb/in^2) subject to head conditions.

The pumps have proved particularly successful in the chemical, pharmaceutical, food and beverage industries and also for pumping anything from acids to adhesives, cosmetics to ceramics, petrochemicals to paper stock and solvents to solids in suspension.

Electro-magnetically driven diaphragm pumps

These are limited to small sizes and are particularly useful for metering, proportioning or dosing duties used in conjunction with digital electronic controllers. Here, the diaphragm movement is generated by the plunger of an electro-magnet, the coil of which is energised by pulses of electric current.

Diaphragm pumps are ideally suited for handling abrasive slurries because the liquid velocity through the check valves and pumping chambers does not exceed pipeline velocity and so there is minimal scouring and abrasion from slurry.

Because there are no close-fit sliding or rubbing parts and velocities are low, these pumps can be used for liquids with viscosities up to 11 000cSt (50 000 SSU). Because there is minimum turbulence and mixing, they are ideally suited for shear-sensitive materials such as latex.

Whilst air operated diaphragm pumps are displacement pumps they are not positive displacement pumps. Maximum pumping pressure can out exceed the pressure of the compressed air powering the pumps. Advantages of diaphragm pumps are as follows:

(i) self-priming from dry start;
(ii) infinitely variable pumping rate and pressure within pressure and capacity range of pump;
(iii) no seal or packing;
(iv) run dry indefinitely;
(v) discharge can be throttled to zero flow indefinitely;
(vi) explosion-proof for hazardous environments;
(vii) power used in proportion to pumping rate;
(viii) can be used in confined areas; no heat build-up;
(ix) can pump abrasive slurries and solids in suspension;
(x) can pump viscous liquids up to 11 000 cSt (50 000 SSU);
(xi) gentle pumping of shear sensitive materials;
(xii) can pump dry powders in air suspension;
(xiii) no close-fit sliding or rotating parts in contact with liquid;
(xiv) no bypass required as in other displacement pumps;
(xv) zero leakage;
(xvi) simple to maintain and to repair;
(xvii) no bedplate or couplings to align;
(xviii) can be used in handling aggressive chemical solution;
(xviv) can handle a wider range of materials than any other pump type.

Disadvantages are:

(i) not practical for pumping rates above 58·3 m^3/h (250 gal/min);
(ii) not manufactured for operating pressures above 8·6 bar (125 lb/in^2).

TABLE 2 – VISCOSITY

Poise	CENTIPOISE	DuPont Parlin 7	DuPont Parlin 10	Fisher 1	Fisher 2	Ford Cup 3	Ford Cup 4	Gardner Holdt Bubble	Gardner Lithographic	Krebs Units KU	Saybolt Universal SSU	Zahn 1	Zahn 2	Zahn 3	Zahn 4	Zahn 5	Sears Craftsman Cup	Redwood No. 1 Sec.	Engler Degrees	Saybolt Furol Sec	Redwood No. 2 Sec.
.1	10	27	11	20			5	A-4			60	30	16					54	1.84		
.15	15	30	12	25			8	A-3			80	34	17					70	2.35		
.2	20	32	13	30	15	12	10				100	37	18					98	2.90		
.25	25	37	14	35	17	15	12	A2			130	41	19					106	3.48		
.3	30	43	15	39	18	19	14	A1			160	44	20					125	4.10		
.4	40	50	16	50	21	25	18	A			210	52	22				19	165	5.39		
.5	50	57	17		24	29	22			30	260	60	24				20	203	6.78		
.6	60	64	18		29	33	25	8		33	320	68	27				21	245	8.05	30.8	
.7	70		20		33	36	28			35	370		30				23	286	9.40	35.0	30.05
.8	80		22		39	41	31	C		37	430		34				24	327	10.60	40.0	34.00
.9	90		23		44	45	32			38	480		37	10			26	368	11.80	44.7	37.85
1.0	100		25		50	50	34	D		40	530		41	12	10		27	409	14.25	47.8	41.90
1.2	120		30		62	58	41	E		43	580		49	14	11		31	485	15.95	58.2	49.80
1.4	140		32			66	45	E		46	690		58	16	13		34	570	18.55	66.8	57.90
1.6	160		37				50	G		48	790		66	18	14		38	645	21.10	76.4	66.00
1.8	180		41				54		000	50	900		74	20	16		40	735	23.90	86.3	74.15
2.0	200		45				58	H		52	1000		82	23	17	10	44	815	26.75	95.8	82.35
2.2	220						62	I		54	1100			25	18	11		900	28.15	104.6	90.00
2.4	240						65	J		56	1200			20	12	12		985	33.60	113.5	97.75
2.6	260						68			58	1280			30	21	13		1060	34.65	124.5	105.60
2.8	280						70	K		59	1380			32	22	14		1140	37.25	137.5	114.90
3.0	300						74	L		60	1475			34	24	15		1235	39.85	143.2	123.75
3.2	320							M			1530			36	25	16		1300	42.35	151.8	131.65
3.4	340							N			1630			39	26	17		1390	45.00	161.3	139.50
3.6	360							O		62	1730			41	28	18		1465	47.75	171.5	149.00
3.8	380										1850			43	29	19		1550	50.10	180.0	157.55
4.0	400							P		64	1950			46	30	20		1635	52.45	189.5	166.35
4.2	420										2050			48	32	21		1695	52.95	199.5	171.65
4.4	440							Q			2160			50	33	22		1790	54.20	209.5	183.50
4.6	460							R		66	2270			52	34	23		1837	60.60	218.4	188.65
4.8	480								00	67	2380			54	36	24		1950	63.85	228.9	198.75
5.0	500							S		68	2480			57	37	25		2045	65.95	239.4	208.85
5.5	550							T		69	2660			63	40	27		2240	72.85	259.7	229.95
6.0	600							U		71	2900			68	44	30		2433	79.50	287.6	248.50
7.0	700									74	3375				51	35		2850	92.30	332.4	289.60
8.0	800								0	77	3880				58	40		3270	106.45	380.1	329.75
9.0	900							V		81	4300				64	45		3690	119.50	427.8	368.85
10.0	1000							W		85	4600					49		4000	133.50	479.6	408.70
11.0	1100									88	5200					55					

CONVERSION CHART

Poise	CENTIPOISE	DuPont Parlin 7	DuPont Parlin 10	Fisher 1	Fisher 2	Ford Cup 3	Ford Cup 4	Gardner Holdt Bubble	Gardner Lithographic	Krebs Units KU	Saybolt Universal SSU	Zahn 1	Zahn 2	Zahn 3	Zahn 4	Zahn 5	Sears Craftsman Cup	Redwood No. 1 Sec.	Engler Degrees	Saybolt Furol Sec	Redwood No. 2 Sec.
12.0	1200									92	5620					59					
13.0	1300							X		95	6100					64					
14.0	1400								1	96	6480										
15.0	1500									98	7000										
16.0	1600									100	7500										
17.0	1700									101	8000										
18.0	1800							Y			8500										
19.0	1900										9000										
20.0	2000									103	9400										
21.0	2100										9850										
22.0	2200										10300										
23.0	2300							Z	2	105	10750										
24.0	2400									109	11200										
25.0	2500							Z-1		114	11600										
30.0	3000									121	14500										
35.0	3500							Z-2	3	129	16500										
40.0	4000									133	18500										
45.0	4500							Z-3		136	21000										
50.0	5000										23500										
55.0	5500										26000										
60.0	6000							Z-4	4		28000										
65.0	6500										30000										
70.0	7000										32500										
75.0	7500										35000										
80.0	8000										37000										
85.0	8500										39500										
90.0	9000										41000										
95.0	9500										43000										
100.0	10000							Z-5	5		46500										
110.0	11000										51000										
120.0	12000										55500										
130.0	13000										60000										
140.0	14000										65000										
150.0	15000							Z-6			69500										
160.0	16000										74000										
170.0	17000										80000										
180.0	18000										83500										
190.0	19000										88000										
200.0	20000										93000										
300.0	30000										140000										

All viscosity comparisons are as accurate as possible with existing information. Comparisons are made with materials having a specific gravity of one.

To extend range of only the kinematic Saybolt Universal, Redwood No. 1 and Engler Scales: Multiply by 10, the viscosities on these scales between 100 and 1000 Centistokes on the Kinematic Scale and the corresponding viscosities on the other 3 scales. For further extension multiply these scales as above by 100 or a higher power of 10.

(Example:
1500 Centistrokes = 150 X 10 CS 695 X 10 SUS)

Rotary Pumps

THE GENERAL description rotary pump is given to machines with an impeller form providing positive displacement of the fluid being handled with delivery directly proportional to (rotational) speed and substantially independent of head. These two performance characteristics distinguish them from centrifugal pump (and other turbo machines). Their performance also differs from piston type (reciprocating) positive displacement pumps in that delivery flow is continuous and thus smoother, although their internal losses are generally higher. They are thus less suitable for generally higher pressures since slippage intends to increase more rapidly with increasing pressure than with piston type positive displacement pumps. Also practical sizes which can be realised are more limited, especially compared with turbo machines.

Rotary piston pump – to API 676.

Basic types of rotary pumps are summarised in Table 1. These are restricted to pump types employing an impeller or rotor form providing a 'suck' and 'squeeze' action. Screw pumps can be regarded as a special case since single screw pumps provide only 'lifting' action unless running in a close-fitting elastomeric stator. Twin and multiple rigid screw pumps on the other hand provide 'squeeze'. Figure 1 shows basic types of rotary pumps.

Numerous variations in rotary pump operating principles are illustrated in Table 2

TABLE 1 – MAIN TYPES OF ROTARY PUMPS

Single impeller types	Rotor-form types	Screw-form
Gear (i) external (ii) internal	Lobe rotor (numerous forms)	Screw (i) single-screw* (ii) twin-screw (iii) multiple-screw
Vane (i) sliding vane (ii) swinging vane (iii) scraper (iv) cam-vane		**Note:* The Archimedean screw is not generally classified as a rotary pump.
Flexible impeller (flexible vane)		
Liquid ring		

TABLE 2 – SUB-TYPES AND CHARACTERISTICS OF ROTARY PUMPS

Basic Type	Sub-Types	Remarks
Gear pump	External gear	Good efficiency; generates high-frequency pressure 'ripple'.
	Internal gear	Gentler pumping action than external gear pump.
Vane pump	Sliding vane	Good efficiency; lower-frequency pressure 'ripple' than gear pump.
	Swinging vane	Low speed; heavy duty types for handling slurries, *etc.*
	Rolling vane	Generally excellent performance as high-pressure water pump.
	Cam vane	Reduced friction and wear; particularly used as a vacuum pump.
	Flexible stator	Versatile but limited in pressure capabilities and size.
Lobe rotor	Numerous	Wide variety of rotor forms employed.
	Roots pump	Based on two 8-shaped rotors; mostly used as an air blower.
	Waukesha	Extension of lobe rotor principle giving 'external circumferential piston' pump with absence of pressure and 'ripple'.
Screw pumps	Single screw	–
	Eccentric screw	Single rigid screw rotating in an elastomeric stator.
	Twin and multiple screw	–
	Goodyear	Special form of screw rotor allied to a wiper wheel.
	Other variants	Other combinations of single screw and matching stator.
Rotary piston		
Shuttle block		
Semi-rotary		

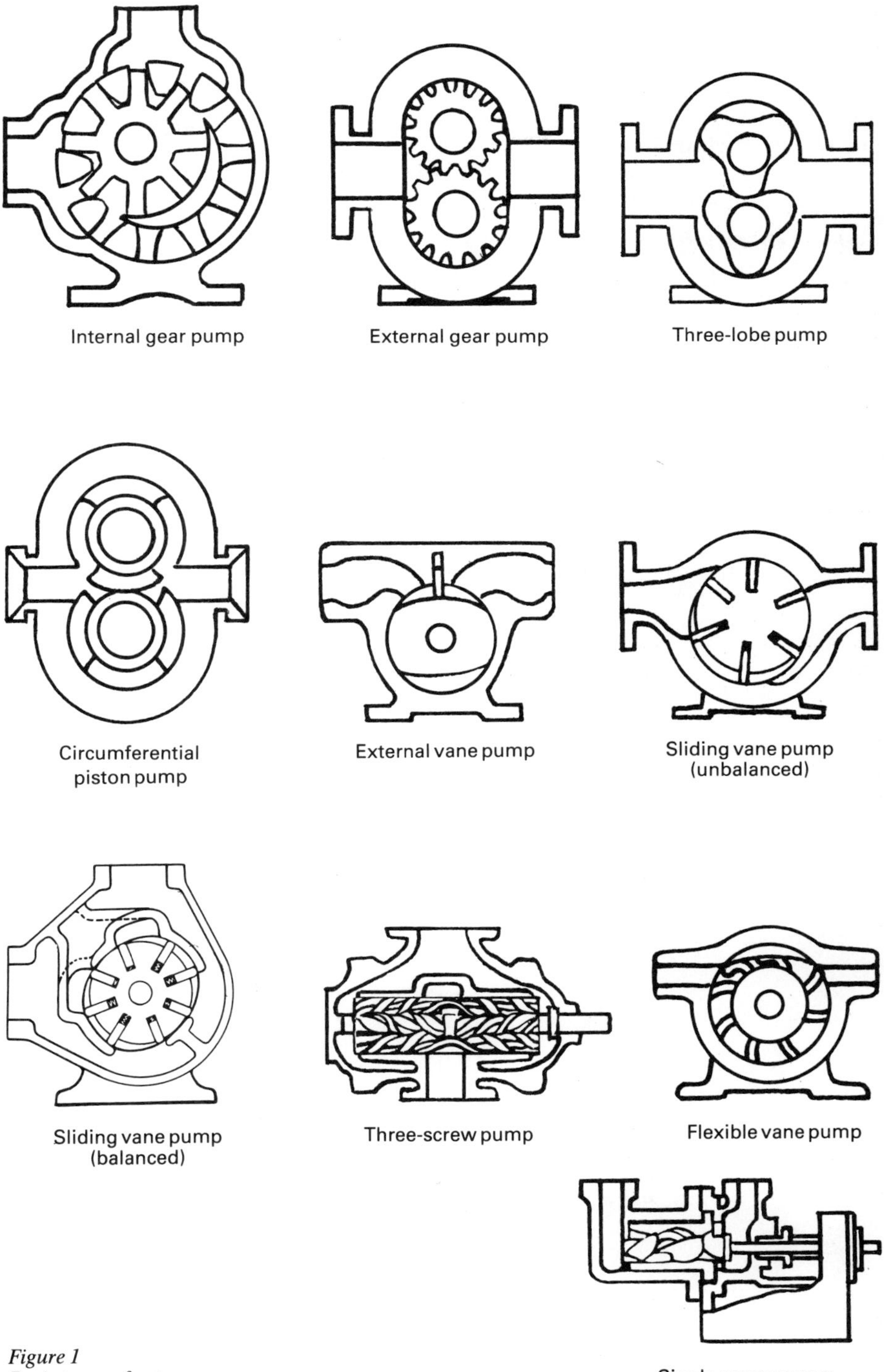

Figure 1
Basic types of rotary pumps.

Rotary pumps are a particularly useful type since they are suitable for handling a wide variety of fluids from the very lowest to the very highest viscosities (with suitable modification of design when very high fluid viscosities are concerned). As a general rule, however, they are suitable only for handling fluids free from solid contaminants which could jam in the small clearance spaces involved or produce high wear. Their main application is for the handling of clean fluids from light oils upwards, although many are equally suitable for water and some types are eminently suitable for handling gases.

General characteristics

Characteristic performance of a rotary pump is shown in generalised form in Figure 2.

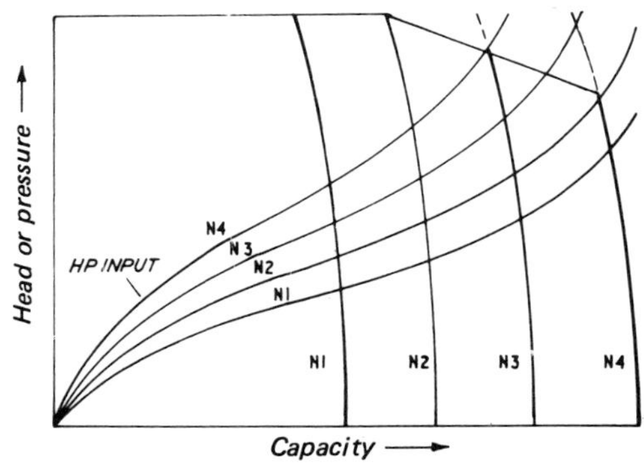

Figure 2

Capacity increases directly with speed, but slippage will increase with delivery head or pressure. The working envelope is thus bounded by a falling head limit and an increased speed curve. In theory, at least, a rotary pump can be operated anywhere within the performance envelope. The required head (or head range) can establish a suitable theoretical capacity (TQ) and pump size (DQ) depending on whether speed is a controlling parameter or not. See Figure 3.

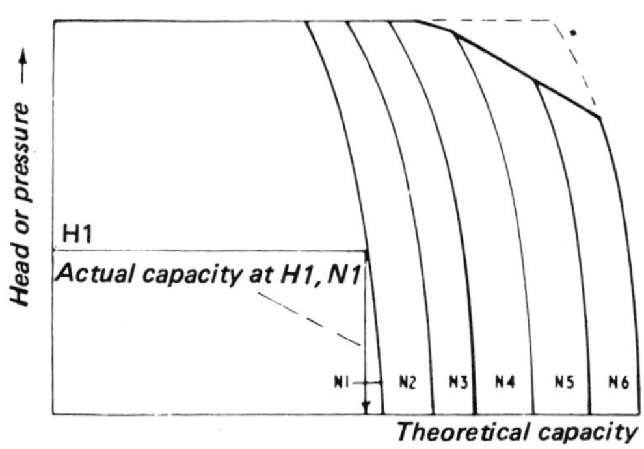

Figure 3

A more useful form of presentation of pump characteristics is to relate horsepower, speed, head and capacity on a single graph of the form shown in Figure 4.

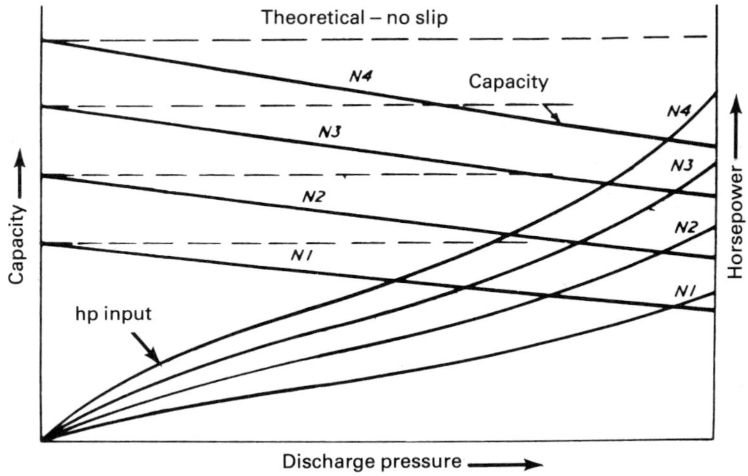

Figure 4

It is common practice to rate a rotary pump in terms of theoretical capacity (TQ), equivalent to the pump displacement at zero total dynamic head (algebraic sum of suction and discharge heads). The delivered or rated capacity (DQ) is then equal to TQ minus the slip. Slip is theoretically only dependent on total dynamic head.

Slip will generally be low where the pump elements are of rigid construction and clearances are small, but will become increasingly marked with increase in head on pumps with flexible elements and/or more generous clearances.

Basically, the capacity and power input will vary with speed for a constant head and with head (or pressure) for a constant speed. The fluid viscosity will also influence power input and practical operating speed.

Capacity and slip

The theoretical capacity per revolution (Q_1) can be derived directly from the displacement per revolution, which in turn can be related to the rotor geometry, *viz*:

$$Q_1 = K(D^2 - C^2) \times W$$

where:

D is the diameter of the rotors

C is the centre distance of the rotors

W is the width of the rotors

K is a constant (or rotor coefficient) depending on the rotor geometry and arrangement

Since Q_1 represents the displacement per revolution:

$TQ = Q_1 \times r/min$

$DQ = TQ - slip$

$= Q_1 \times r/min - slip$

In the case of an external gear pump a typical value for K is of the order of 1·50 to 1·57. Displacement is then given in the cubic form of the dimensional units employed. For example, for D, C and W measured in cm, displacement (or capacity) is given in cm^3. The value of K for other types of rotary pump is specific to the design geometry and can only be determined by calculation direct from empirical data. This method of analysis, however, can provide useful comparative information.

Efficiency

Efficiency can be calculated only by comparing input power required with the hydraulic output power achieved. Thus, whilst increasing the running speed increases capacity more or less *pro-rata*, the corresponding increase in horsepower does not necessarily follow the same relationship. This will depend both on the design of the individual pump and on the viscosity on the fluid being handled. For a constant viscosity there is an optimum design speed which pump efficiency will be a maximum, although this is usually non-critical with fluids of low to moderate viscosity. A rotary pump can often, therefore, be used at very different speeds from its nominal design speed without suffering any appreciable loss of efficiency. There is also the point that relatively small capacities are normally involved so that the actual cost of any wasted power is usually negligible.

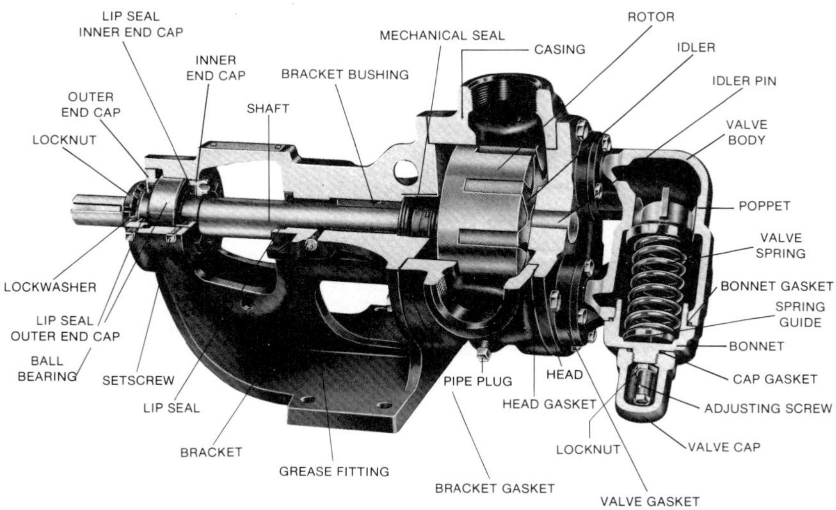

Cutaway view of heavy-duty bracket mounted internal gear pump.

Pressure limits

With rigid elements there is no theoretical upper limit to pressure developed other than the strengths of the elements or casing involved. In pratice, however, high pressure working calls for considerable attention to detail design and accuracy of construction in order to avoid excessive slip and consequent marked loss of efficiency. In many types of pump intended to operate against unlimited heads, a pressure relief valve may be put into the casing to guard against the possibility of abnormally high internal pressures being generated.

In the case of rotary pumps with flexible elements there will be definite limits to the delivery pressure which can be achieved.

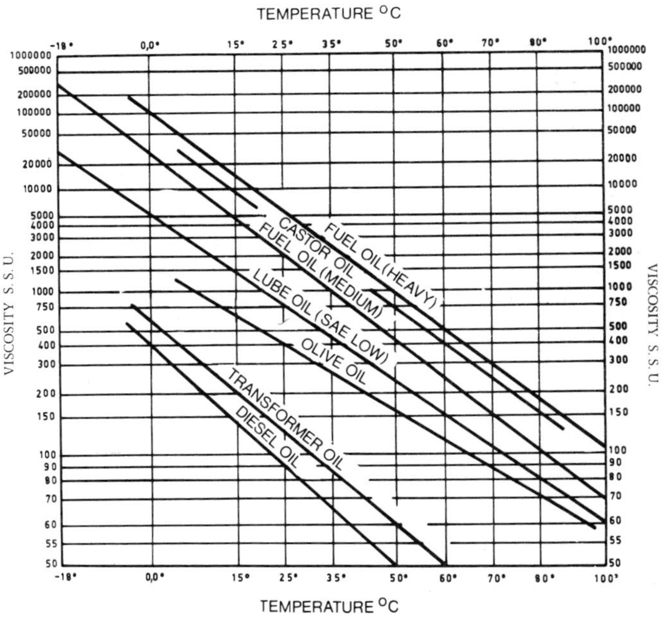

Viscosity-temperature chart.

Effect of viscosity

With increasing fluid viscosity the problem of efficiency can become more acute. Apart from the fact that this will inevitably increase the input power required to maintain a given capacity, efficiency will also tend to decrease with increasing viscosity due to modifications of flow conditions. This can even set a limit to capacity by establishing a critical speed at which flow breakdown or separation takes place because the fluid cannot flow into the casing rapidly enough to fill it. To some extent this may be countered by modification of the detailed design or form of rotor, but the more usual solution is to reduce the speed and thus the capacity available when handling a more viscous fluid. This, coupled with any desirable modification of rotor form, can maintain high pumping efficiency.

In theory, at least, this effect can be self-adjusting with certain types of rotary pump. As for any given horsepower an increase in fluid viscosity will increase the

APPROXIMATE VISCOSITIES AND SPECIFIC GRAVITIES OF COMMON LIQUIDS

Liquid	Specific gravity	Temp °F	Viscosity SSU	Temp °F
Asphalt Virgin*	1.03	60	7,500	250
			2,000	300
Blended RC-1, MC-1 or SC-1*	1.0	60	3,700	100
			1,100	122
RC-3, MC-3 or SC-3*	1.0	60	9,000	122
			3,700	140
RC-5, MC-5 or SC-5*	1.0	60	55,000	140
			4,500	180
Gasoline	.71	70	31	70
Glucose*	1.4	60	70,000	100
			7,500	150
Glycerine	1.25	70	3,000	70
			800	100
Glycol: Propylene	1.04	70	240	70
Triethylene	1.13	70	190	70
Diethylene	1.12	70	150	70
Ethylene	1.13	70	90	70
Milk	1.03	70	33	70
Molasses "A"*	1.43	60	12,000	100
			4,500	130
"B"*	1.45	60	33,000	100
			9,000	130
"C"* (Blackstrap)	1.48	60	130,000	100
			40,000	130
Oils Petroleum Crude (Penn.)*	.82	60	130	60
			60	100
Crude (Texas, Okla.)*	.85	60	400	60
			120	100
Crude (Wyo., Mont.)*	.87	60	650	60
			180	100
Crude (Calif.)*	.85	60	2,600	60
			380	100
No. 1 Fuel Oil*	.88	60	37	70
			34	100

Liquid	Specific gravity	Temp °F	Viscosity SSU	Temp °F
No. 2 Fuel Oil*	.88	60	43	70
			37	100
No. 3 Fuel Oil*	.88	60	40	100
			36	130
No. 5A Fuel Oil*	.88	60	90	100
			60	130
No. 5B Fuel Oil*	.88	60	250	100
			175	130
No. 6 Fuel Oil*	.88	60	1,700	122
			500	160
SAE No. 10*	.91	60	200	100
			105	130
SAE No. 30*	.91	60	490	100
			220	130
SAE No. 50*	.91	60	1,300	100
			90	210
SAE No. 70*	.91	60	2,700	100
			140	210
SAE No. 90 (Trans.)*	.91	60	1,200	100
			400	130
SAE No. 140 (Trans.)*	.91	60	1,600	130
			160	210
SAE No. 250 (Trans.)*	.91	60	Over 2,300	130
			Over 200	210
Vegetable Castor	.97	60	1,300	100
			500	130
China Wood	.94	160	1,400	70
			600	100
Cocoanut	.93	60	140	100
			80	130
Corn	.92	60	140	130
			50	212
Cotton Seed	.90	60	170	100
			100	130
Linseed, Raw	.93	60	140	100
			90	130
Olive	.92	60	200	100
			110	130
Palm	.92	60	220	100
			125	130
Peanut	.92	60	200	100
			110	130

Liquid	Specific gravity	Temp °F	Viscosity SSU	Temp °F
Rosin	.98	60	1,500	100
			600	130
Sesame	.92	60	190	100
			110	130
Soya Bean	.94	60	170	100
			100	130
Turpentine	.86	60	33	60
			32	100
Syrups Corn*	1.43	100	250,000	100
			30,000	130
Sugar	1.29 (60 Brix)	60	230	70
			90	100
	1.30 (62 Brix)	60	300	70
			110	100
	1.31 (64 Brix)	60	450	70
			150	100
	1.32 (66 Brix)	60	650	70
			200	100
	1.34 (68 Brix)	60	1,000	70
			280	100
	1.35 (70 Brix)	60	1,700	70
			400	100
	1.36 (72 Brix)	60	2,700	70
			650	100
	1.38 (74 Brix)	60	5,500	70
			1,150	100
	1.39 (76 Brix)	60	10,000	70
			2,000	100
Tar Coke Oven*	1.12	60	5,000	70
			1,000	100
Gas House*	1.24	60	150,000	70
			11,000	100
Road RT-2*	1.07	60	250	122
			60	212
RT-6*	1.09	60	1,500	122
			110	212
RT-10*	1.14	60	40,000	122
			300	212
Water	1.0	60	32	70

*Values given are average values and the actual viscosity may be greater or less than the value given.

horsepower required and automatically re-adjust the speed to a lower operating point. Unless the driver has a particularly flat bhp curve, and is also flexible enough to accommodate a speed change with increasing load, the real loss in speed and, therefore, capacity can be lower than anticipated as shown in Figure 5.

It is usually more realistic, therefore, either to adjust the drive speed gearing to provide an optimum pump speed for handling a viscous fluid (which will give a reduced capacity whilst maintaining a similar overall efficiency figure), or to increase the power input to maintain the required capacity. The former method is

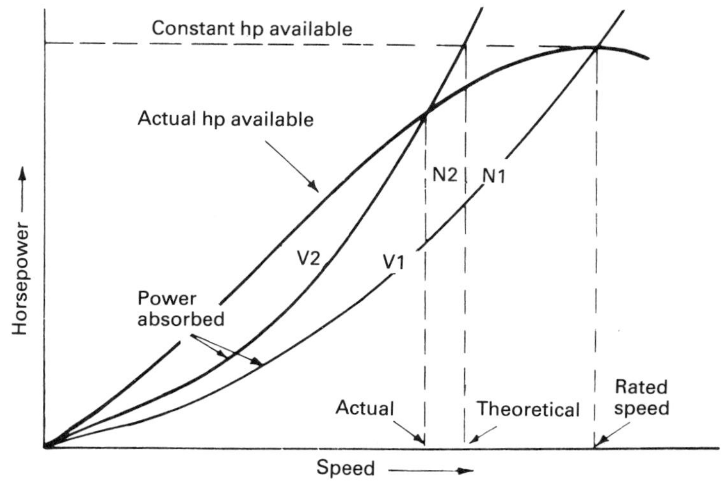

Figure 5

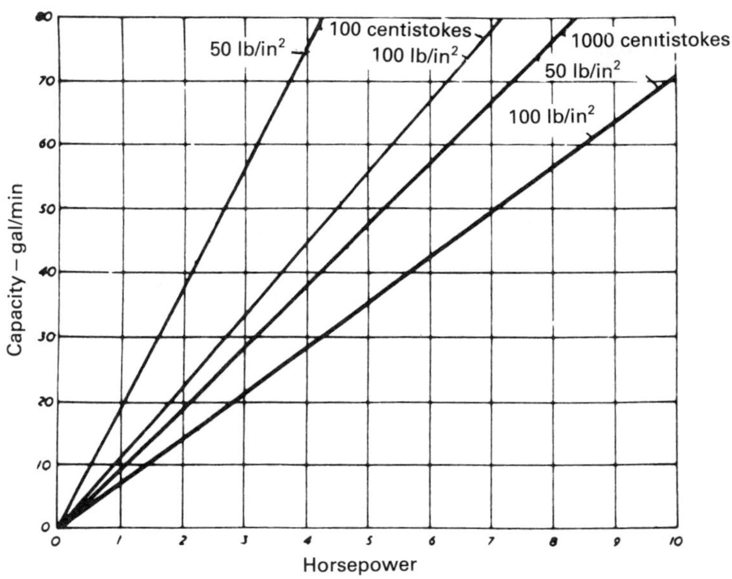

Figure 6

commonly adopted by pump manufacturers who give a 'speed reduction' factor (or percentage) for handling more viscous fluids (usually only significant above a fluid viscosity of about 250 centistokes). Loss of capacity is directly proportional to speed reduction with the pump requiring the same power input as the original rating. If capacity is to be maintained, this can be done only by increasing the power input. Comparative performance figures for a typical three-screw rotary pump are shown in Figure 6.

With very high liquid viscosities it may be necessary to adopt special designs of rotary pump (*eg* screw pumps) and low operating speeds in order to avoid channelling *etc*. In such cases the only way to increase capacity is to increase the size of the pump so that although flow velocity is low, flow rate and efficiency can be quite high. Standard rotary pumps, however, may be quite capable of handling fluids up to 10 000 or 20 000 centistoke viscosity with no more than 50% speed reduction; at still further reduced speeds they may even be workable at viscosities up to 50 000 centistokes. Special designs are required to handle higher viscosities.

Rotary pump applications

The number of applications system conditions and different kinds of fluids handled in rotary pumps are too numerous to enumerate in this handbook. A few of the more common applications are listed here:

Chemical products

Oil burners

Lubrication nets

Paints and varnishes

Sugars, syrups and molasses

Soaps and cosmetics

Asphalt, creosote, dilute glycerines *etc*

Dyes, inks, bleaches

Vegetable and mineral oils, alcohol, benzene, gasoline

An excellent source of application information for a specific type of pump is a manufacturer of that particular pump. Many manufacturers have available application, installation and maintenance manuals.

Mechanical installation

All rotary pumps, particularly rigid rotor pumps, must be installed so that no large mechanical forces of any kind, other than those imposed by pump operating pressures, can act to warp or distort the pump chamber or rotating assembly. Relatively small distortions of a few thousands-of-an-inch may cause interference between rotating and stationary parts and generate high wear for pump damage.

To avoid such unwanted distortions, the pump must not be installed with rigid fittings to long rigid piping systems, either where the weight or the piping system is supported by the pump body or where large mechanical forces on the pump body can be generated by thermal expansion of the piping system.

The problem of distortion of operating clearances in the pump chamber is not as severe for flexible member pumps, but large mechanical forces tending to distort the pump body may cause serious distortion of mechanical sealing arrangements and unusually high wear rates on bearing systems. A cardinal rule then is that a rotary pump must not be so rigidly coupled to either the fluid piping system, or the

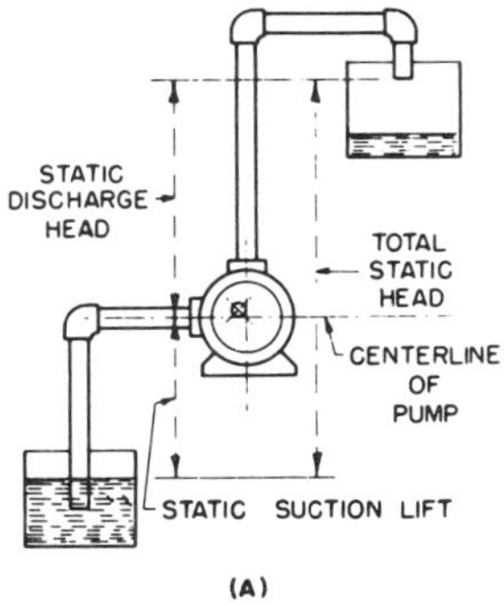

This installation shows static suction lift with free discharge.

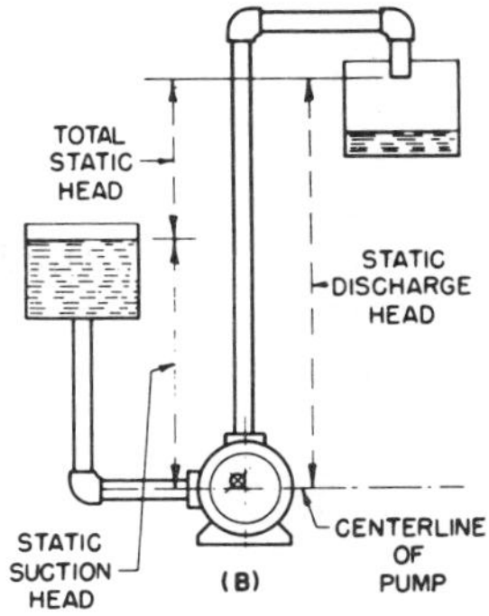

This installation shows static suction head with free discharge.

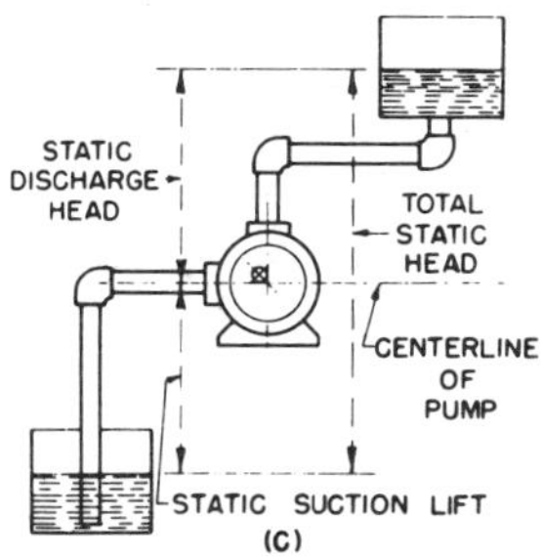

This installation shows static suction lift with discharge to bottom of tank.

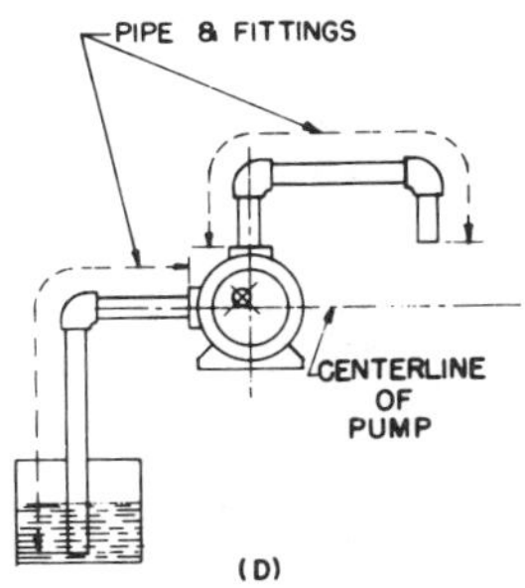

This installation shows pipe friction losses.

Installations showing various suction and discharge conditions.

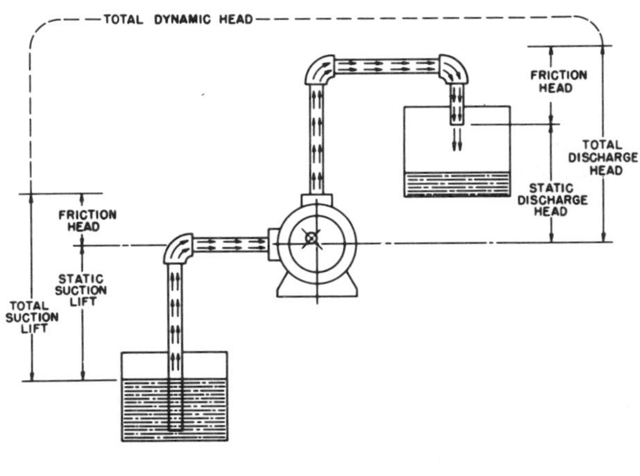

Typical installation showing total dynamic head.

driver, that it supports the weight of either or that it is exposed to high forces caused by thermal expansion of either. A poor mechanical installation of a pump might be the sole cause of an unsatisfactory operation.

Performance flexibility

The flexibility of operation of a rotary pump is further enhanced by the fact that it is usually self-priming (provided some fluid is retained in the casing) and can, if necessary, handle entrained and dissolved gases or air. In the latter case the capacity of the pump is reduced in direct proportion to the amount of entrained gas, since this will tend to separate out within the pump and occupy a proportion of the internal volume. The actual capacity loss will normally be greater than the proportion of entrained or dissolved gas and will increase with developing vacuum at the pump inlet. Under unfavourable conditions and with high vacuum at the inlet a loss of 20% to 40% capacity can be experienced. Such conditions can also lead to pump chatter and noisy operation so that rotary pump applications involving the handling of fluids which may contain high proportions of entrained or dissolved gases or air may need special consideration. On the other hand, rotary pumps are widely – and successfully – used for handling petroleum fluids which tend to contain a high proportion of dissolved air at normal atmospheric pressure and temperature. The main point to be appreciated in such applications is that a loss of capacity over rated performance may be anticipated as a consequence of the dissolved air present in the fluid.

It is a general characteristic of many types of positive rotary pumps, particularly the simpler designs, that they will pump in either direction with equal efficiency simply by changing the direction of rotation. Also, where the pumping action is derived from an eccentrically mounted rotor, variable delivery characteristics can often be achieved quite simply by geometric displacement of the casing or stator or an internal wear ring.

Rotary Lobe Pumps

ROTARY LOBE pumps are used in all branches of industry. In the general food and beverage producing industries, as well as in pharmaceutical production, their hygiene qualities are highly valued. Industrially, their high efficiency, robustness, reliability and potential for handling corrosive and often aggressive chemicals are particularly attractive.

The pumps are frequently used for medium to high viscosity fluid transfer duties, and give rates of relatively predictable accuracy. They handle corrosive and edible fluids, entrained gases and some solids in suspension, have good suction performance, may be easily and quickly cleaned and are simple to install and operate. Efficiencies are normally high and performance is often independent of changes in process pressures. They are reliable and have a long working life.

The basic configuration and working action of a rotary lobe pump is shown in Figure 1. Positive fluid displacement is achieved by means of a pair of conjugate rotors which rotate with continuous contrary motion within a pumping chamber. A pair of timing gears housed in an integrally associated gear case synchronise the

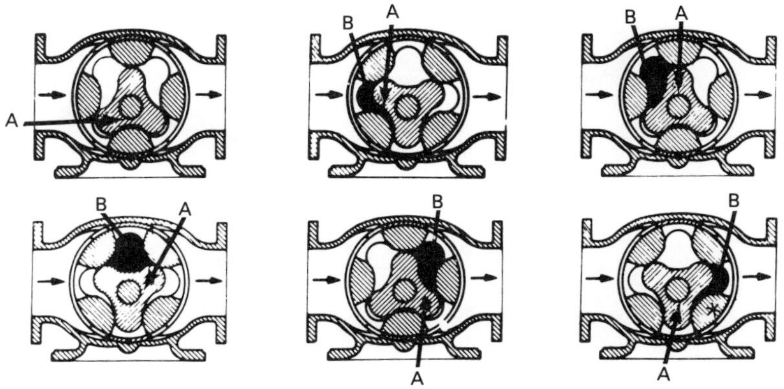

Figure 1
The lobe rotor pump and principle of operation through one revolution. Lobe (A) forms a suitable pocket (B) which becomes charged with fluid and subsequent views show how the fluid is carried round and finally discharged with pulseless flow. Reversible flow is obtained by simple reversing rotation.

rotor motions and ensure that power is not transmitted between the rotors by their mechanical inter-action. This absence of contact between rotors or between the rotors and the pumping chamber is an important characteristic of this type of machine which allows mechanically non-compatible head materials to be specified, and minimizes wear of the product wetted surfaces. When rotating, the rotors give rise to constantly changing volumes in the meshing sections adjacent to the pumping chamber ports. These sections are open to the ports, but are bounded by the rotor and pumping chamber surfaces and their sealing lines.

Fluid intake is the result of the lobe of one rotor gradually moving out of association with the volume defined by an associating pair of lobes on the mating rotor. The reverse action occurs on the discharge side of the pump. Between these two processes slugs of fluid are conveyed around the pump head in a relatively isolated and undisturbed manner. In principle, although not always in practice, the pumps are bi-directional and consequently flow is reversible.

Fluid flows into the inlet chamber under the influence of external forces (gravity, atmospheric pressure, *etc*) and is positively displaced through the delivery port by the energy supplied to the pump drive shaft. This energy ultimately limits the pressure against which the pump may operate, but as this pressure is invariably greater in excess of the maximum working pressure of either the pump or the plant it serves, it is important to realise that the pumps must never be operated against a closed line unless a pressure relief valve is fitted. The mitigating effect of slip is rarely of sufficient magnitude safely to limit the discharge pressure.

Typical construction

Construction of a positive displacement rotary lobe pump is shown in Figure 2. The components form two groups: the pump head embodying in the main product – wetted components such as the rotors, rotor case and cover and shaft seals, and the gear case, which houses the shaft bearings and timing gears. Generally speaking,

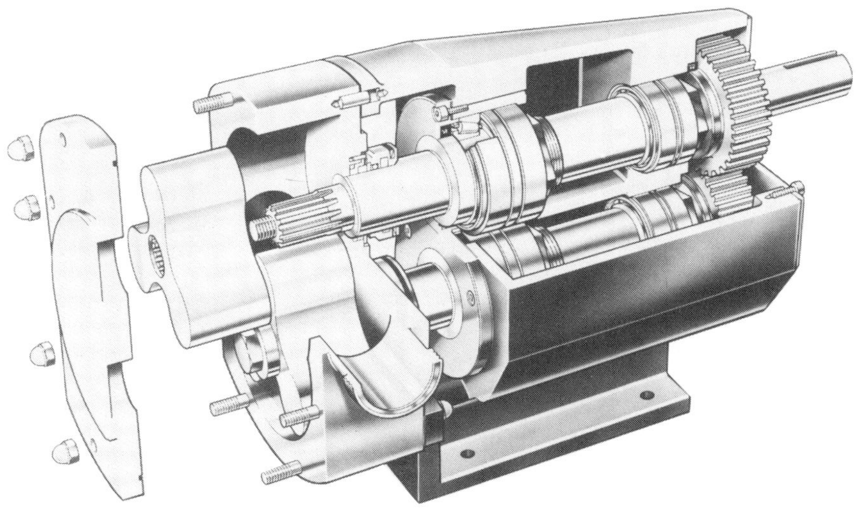

Figure 2
Positive displacement rotary-lobe pump which embodies a modular design.

the shafts are made from continuous lengths of material that is compatible with the product and are each supported at two bearing stations. Invariably, rolling-element bearings are used and frequently only one bearing on each shaft is responsible for axial constraint. Power is applied to the pump by means of an extension provided on one of the shafts, and is in part transmitted to the second shaft through the timing gears. These gears are also responsible for rotor synchronization and consequently have very little backlash.

Rotor forms

The displacement of any pair of rotors is given by:

$$Q = K \times (D^2 \times C^2) \times W \times n$$

where:

Q = volumetric displacement rate
K = rotor coefficient
D = rotor outside diameter
C = rotor centres
W = rotor width
n = rotor angular speed

The co-efficient K depends on rotor fall, number of lobes and the efficiency of the liquid seal between the lobes. The latter is determined by the clearances used for the particular working conditions. Emphirically determined values for coefficient can be used by the pump designer to anticipate the performance of larger and smaller machines provided a family relationship exists. Typical rotor profiles are shown in Figure 3.

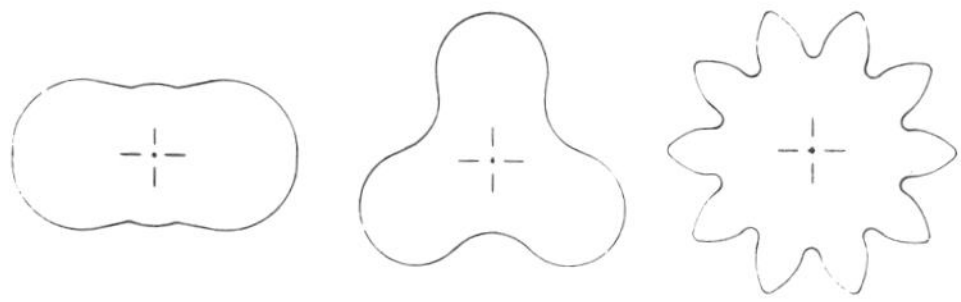

Figure 3
Typical rotor profiles.

The degree of clearance has a profound effect on volumetric efficiency (and hence on power requirement) which is especially noticeable when free flowing liquids of viscosity below about 250 cP are being handled. Under these circumstances, slip is significant and requires a compensating speed increase which is accompanied by a greater hydraulic power requirement. However, lobe rotor pumps are frequently used for low viscosity duties due to their many attractive construction and performance qualities such as the gentle pumping action which is substantially free from shearing and agitating effects.

Characteristics and capacities

Theoretically, capacity is directly proportional to pump speed, but due to rotor clearances, some of the volume displaced by the rotors will flow from the high to the low pressure regions in the pumping chamber and result in decreased output. Figure 4 shows characteristics and maximum capacities for a typical range of lobe rotor pumps.

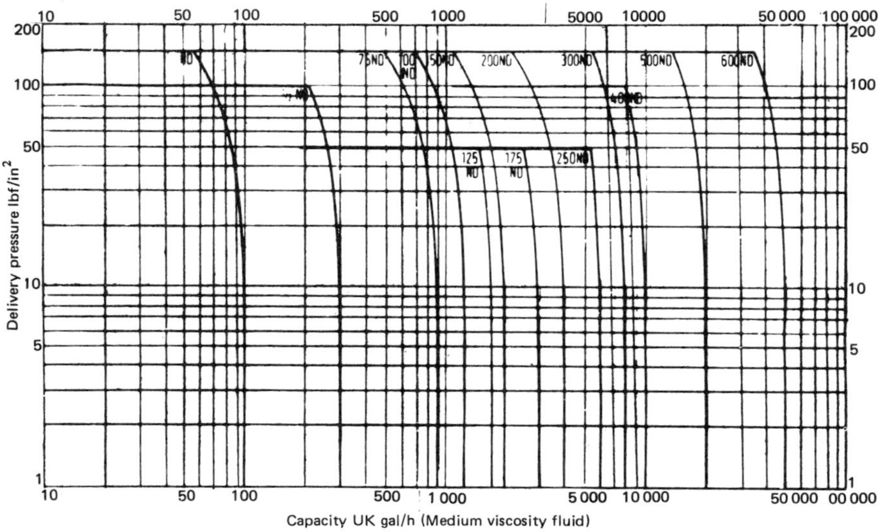

Figure 4
Range charge for a typical family of lobe rotor pumps.

Figure 5 shows that slip increases with differential pressure, but decreases as viscosity increases form. The form of these curves is influenced by produce rheology and pump head dimensions. Rotor clearances are adjusted by the pump designer to optimize volumetric and mechanical efficiencies in relation to specific duty conditions; also taking account of production parameters such as component interchangeability.

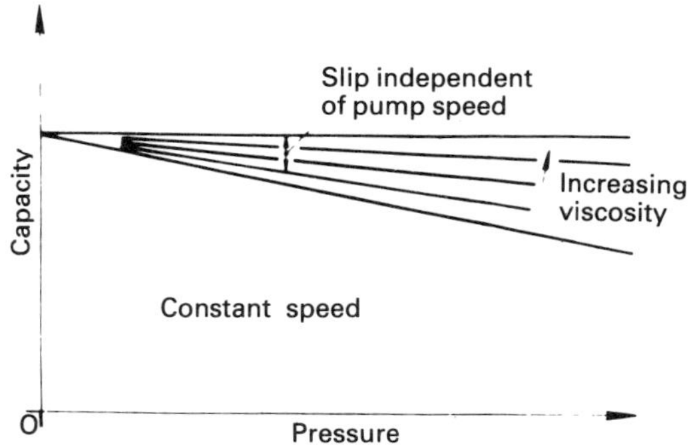

Figure 5

The difference between a large pump run slowly and small pump running at a higher speed may well hinge on their NPSH requirements thus, the adequacy of the supply system becomes a matter of great significance. Economy in general will be best served by avoiding unnecessarily high suction lifts.

To prevent cavitation, the NPSH available at the inlet port must be at least equal and preferably exceed the NPSH required by the pump when handling the product under duty conditions. Manufacturers often prepare NPSH data for each pump in the graphical form given in Figure 6, and whilst pumping under cavitation conditions is sometimes allowable, it should only occur with the pump maker's approval.

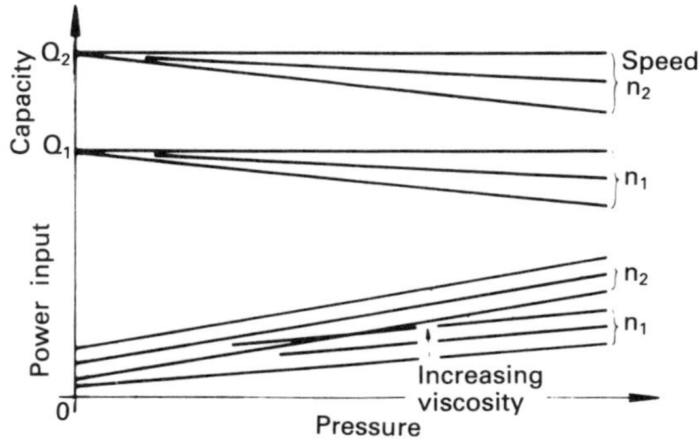

Figure 6

A further check on the relationship between pump speed and product viscosity is sometimes made by means of curves of the type shown in Figure 7. In these cases the duty speed should not exceed the lower of the two speeds obtained by reference to Figures 8 and 9.

Product seals

Generally, each shaft is sealed at its point of entry into the pumping chamber by means of either packed glands or mechanical seals. Duty requirements exercise the main influence over selection, although this must at all times take account of housing constraints and notably the length of shaft between the gear case and pump

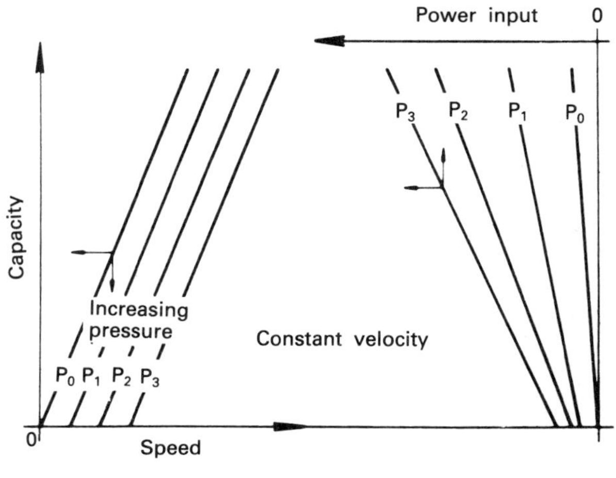

Figure 7

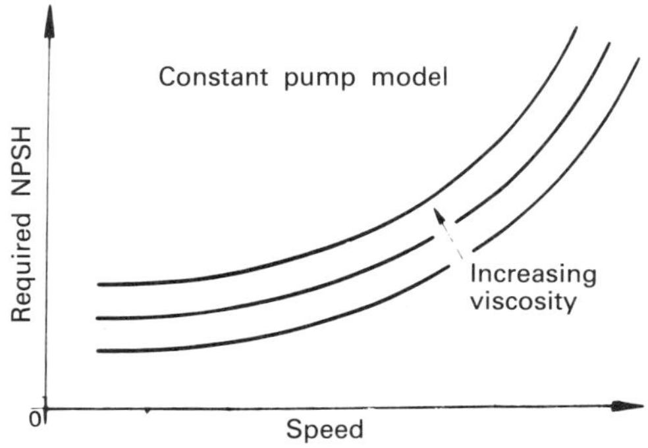

Figure 8

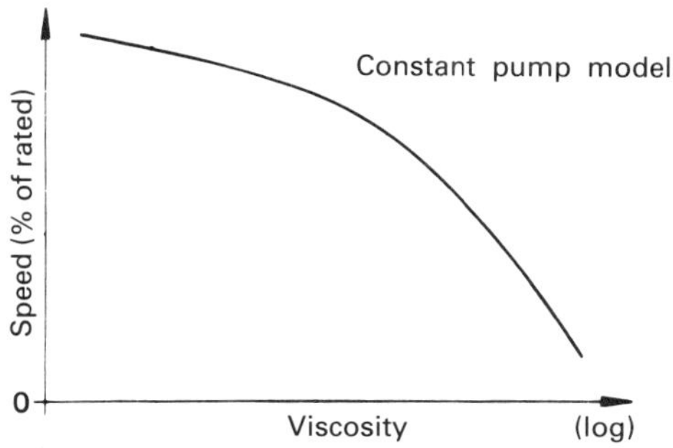

Figure 9

head assemblies. In view of the specialised character of seal manufacture and application, it is customary for pump makers to refer many respective duty requirements to seal suppliers who will accept responsibility for the selection of product seals.

As a rule, rotary lobe pumps can be provided with packed glands of most commonly used configurations, or single mechanical seals mounted in the internal or external attitudes. In addition, it is frequently possible to provide flushed single seals and also double mechanical seals.

Product wetted surfaces

Standard lobe rotor pumps may be divided into two main groups according to the metals used for the pump head components. However, the absence of rubber contact in the pump head allows manufacturers to produce pumps in exotic alloys against special order requirements.

(i) the first group is founded on materials having low corrosion resistance such as mild steel and cast iron. Despite their price advantages, they do not represent a large proportion of pump sales.

(ii) the second and more important group based upon highly corrosion resistant materials such as austenitic stainless steel. Their qualities are of particular significance in the hygiene-conscious industries as well as the chemical and process fields. Nitrile Viton* rubbers and PTFE are frequently used for sealing purposes in these pumps.

*Du Pont's registered trademark.

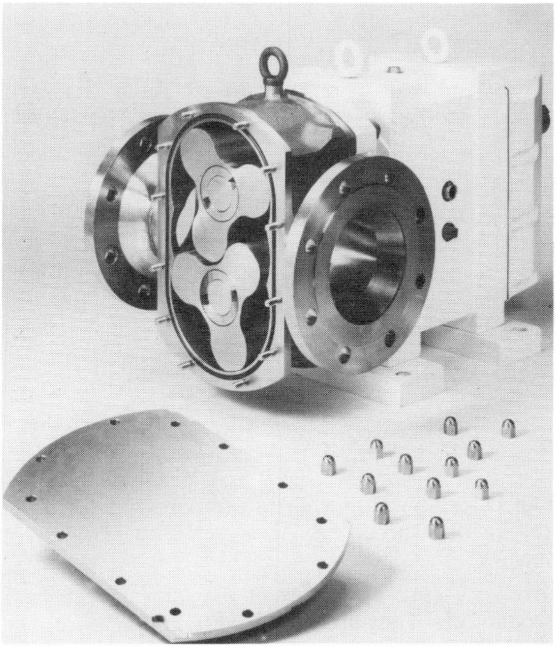

Typical lobe pump.

In-place cleaning
Rotary lobe pumps are inherently suitable for duties involving in-place cleaning procedures. Furthermore, as they can be easily dismantled, they also meet the manual cleaning requirements which frequently form part of the complete sterilization régime.

It must be remembered, however, that in-place cleaning often exposes plant surfaces to temperatures of about 100 °C for periods of time that, whilst being short, are of sufficient duration to require slightly larger rotor clearances on this account, the pump maker should be given information about the chemicals being employed as they may well require PTFE or other fluoroelastomer to be used for sealing purposes.

Priming, starting and suction performance
Self-priming efficiency is improved by the presence of a small quantity of product in the pumping chamber, as this partially seals the clearances and thereby reduces gas leakage across the rotors. Under dry conditions, efficiency is dependent upon pump speed, displacement, rotor clearances and process pressures.

Starting or running must never be conducted against a closed line. If the pump has to exhaust the suction line, it is appropriate to fit the delivery line with a gas venting valve which may be closed by hand immediately the system is filled with liquid. Although some lobe rotor pumps may be run dry for limited periods of time without sustaining damage as a general rule, it is a good practice to introduce liquid into the pumping chamber before the pump is started. The liquid will serve to lubricate the product seals or glands which are usually the only components likely to give rise to mechanical friction effects in pump head.

Stainless steel rotary lobe pump designed for arduous industrial duties.

The magnitude of transitory fluid inertia pressures on starting and stopping, seldom causes problems that should be considered if the duty involves unusually long lengths of pipework.

The pumps shown in Figure 10 represent the latest development in positive rotary lobe pump technology. They are true 'modular build' pumps developed from a computer data base of user information, covering all relevant industries. Modern computer-aided design and production methods ensure high component accuracy and repeatability.

Figure 10
Modular build means having a choice of pumpheads of differing displacements and long or short gearboxes to accommodate the full range of sealing arrangements.

Flow rates are from 5 l/min to 160 m^3/h, port sizes from 25 mm to 100 mm diameter and differential pressures up to 20 bar.

By virtue of the modular design, the pump has two rotorcase sizes for high and low displacements and up to three gearbox modules. Other aspects of this new approach to rotary lobe pump design include on-site rotor interchangeability, positive drive and precise rotor location without the need to adjust timing gears *etc*.

The rotary lobe pump when correctly selected and engineered for the duty is capable for pulling a high degree of vacuum and for example is often used for evaporator extraction duties in which only a small pressure margin exists above the product's vapour pressure. Reference to manufacturer's technical data should be made when determining the required NPSH and the suction lift capability.

TABLE 1 – TYPICAL APPLICATIONS FOR ROTARY LOBE PUMPS

Dairy
Cream
Cheese curd and whey
Cottage cheese
Yogurt
Margarine, butter

Meat packing
Meat – emulsions
Ground meats
Pet foods
Extracts
Minced meat
Sausage meat

Pharmaceutical
Pill pastes
Syrups
Slurries
Extracts
Latex emulsion

Bakery
Batters
Flavourings
Frostings
Fruit fillings
Fats and oils
Sweeteners
Yeast slurry
Dough

Beverage
Beer, wort, yeast
Alcohols and wines
Soft drinks
Fruit concentrates
Fruit drinks
Essences

Canning
Potato salad
Baby foods, soups, stews

Canning
Tomato paste
Fruit purée
Cream style vegetables
Vegetables, diced, slurries
Puddings, jams, jellies
Salad dressings, mayonnaise

Confectionery
Syrups
Cream fillings
Chocolate
Coffee

Cosmetics
Hand and face creams
Lotions
Shampoos
Dyes, alcohols
Essential oils

Advantages of rotary lobe pumps

Positive displacement, normally proportional to pump speed especially at low differential pressure and with medium to high viscosity product. Changes in plant pressure often have a small or negligible effect on capacity.

Product wetted surfaces may be made from austenetic stainless steel or other highly corrosion-resistant materials such as Hastelloy alloys and Monel. Non-metallic pump head parts can be made from carbon, nitrile or viton* rubbers, PTFE, plastics *etc*.

Differential pressures up to 20 bar (300 lb/in^2) are common.

Self-priming element: excellent performance when wetted, limited performance when dry.

*Du Pont's registered trademark.

High suction lift and excellent vacuum extraction abilities.

Generally high volumetric and mechanical pumping efficiencies.

Suitable for all product viscosities – solvents, emulsions, slurries, magmas, and entrained gases. Especially suitable for medium to high viscosity fluids.

Part of a sludge holding system with one of three rotary-lobe pumps. Pumps and pipework are insulated against very low winter temperatures.

Pumps will handle solids in suspension, provided their size and character are within the pump manufacturer's limits.

No rubbing surfaces in pumping chamber of many models. Thus rotor wear should only arise when liquids containing abrasive solids are being handled.

Low flow and shearing velocities within pumping element. Flow is uninterrupted, although slightly pulsating in some models. Pumping action causes little product disturbance and is usually suitable for shear- sensitive fluids.

Dry running is possible for limited periods of time.

Pumping chamber and components usually free from product-collecting crevices. There are no valves.

Rapid access to pumping chambers of some models for cleaning without the need to release pipe connections.

Basically suitable for in-place cleaning (CIP).

Possibility of lubricating oil contaminating product is greatly reduced in models having ample distance between pump head and gear case.

Flow direction is often reversible.

Standard pumps are built for approximate temperature range –20 °C to +100 °C. Lower temperatures and higher temperatures up to 200 °C are satisfied but with special attention to rotor clearances, seal materials and gear case lubricant.

Pumps are available with various mechanical seals or packed glands.

Ports may be machined by manufacturer to suit customer requirements.

Pumps have potentially long lives and need little maintenance.

Compact overall dimensions, occupying relatively small floor area.

Design is suitable for most forms of driver.

Ancillary equipment, such as pressure relief valves, bypass valves, heating jackets *etc* may form integral part of pump assemblies.

Disadvantages of rotary lobe pumps

Downstream line closure when pump is running will almost certainly damage the pump and perhaps the associated plant.

Delivery pressures usually limited to 17 bar (250 lb/in^2).

Temperatures generally limited to 200 °C.

Entry of unexpected hard solids may cause seizure or other serious pump damage.

Slightly pulsating flow.

Limited self-priming capability, unless liquid is present in pumping chamber.

Variable speed drive or bypass required to reduce change in pumping rate.

Volumetric efficiency depends on slip, particularly when product viscosity ⅛ to 250 cP.

Low capacity pumps tend to be larger in size than their rotor dynamic counterparts, hence are usually more expensive.

At least two dynamic product seals are required.

Gas compression is inefficient due to the comparatively large rotor clearances.

Screw Pumps

RIGID SCREW pumps fall into two main categories:

(i) the single screw (Archimedean) pump;

(ii) intermeshing screw pumps with two or more screws.

The Archimedean screw pump consists of a long continuous metal spiral or single screw mounted on a control shaft and rotating in a semi-circular open channel with close clearances. Screw and clearance are inclined at an angle to the horizontal (usually of the order of 30°), when the lift obtained is approximately half the length of the screw. Figure 1 provides an explanation of this principle.

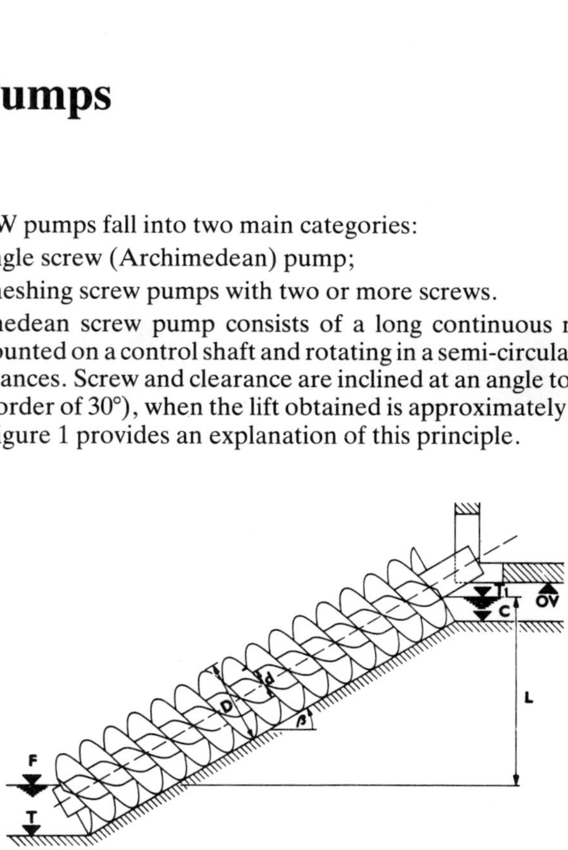

Figure 1
Archimedean screw pump.

D – Outside diameter of the screw pump.
d – Centre tube diameter.
Inclination, angle of screw to horizontal.
F – Filling point, at which the screw works at its maximum capacity.
T – Touch point, at which the capacity is reduced to zero. For water levels between F and T the capacity of the screw pump adapts itself to the supply of water.
C – Chute point, at which the screw trough passes into the receiving channel.
T_1 – Maximum pumping point, to which the water is lifted for maximum efficiency.
L – Lift of screw.

Modern designs of Archimedean screw pump are used for water raising and other duties and may achieve efficiencies of up to 75%. Practical considerations limit the length of screw to about 15 metres (50ft) giving a lift of 7·5 metres (25ft). For high lifts a number of screws can be arranged to pump in series.

Archimedean screw pump installed at a paper mill. Design flow of 2000 l/s.

Typical sizes range from about 300 mm (12 in) diameter yielding a delivery of about 900 l/min (200 gal/min); up to very much larger diameters, with deliveries up to 365 m^3/min (80 000 gal/min). Where diametric space may be restricted, capacity can be increased by working a number of screws in parallel in separate troughs. Rotational speeds are usually of the order of 60 to 30 r/min depending on size.

There are also versions of the Archimedean screw pump where the single power driven screw rotates with close clearance in an accurately bored cylinder or loose fitting casing – this is again mainly used for water raising duties.

Intermeshing screw pumps

Intermeshing screw pumps are a special type of rotary positive displacement pump that generate axial flow, that is to say that the liquid is carried between screw threads on one or more rotors and is displaced axially as the screws rotate and mesh. A single screw set generates axial fluid flow with a corresponding reaction in the form of axial thrust that has to be accommodated by the screw bearings. In a balanced configuration two opposite hand screws are mounted in tandem, when the axial thrust developed by one will counter balance that developed by the other. The outlet is then usually at the centre of the pump with a separate inlet at each end, or alternatively there is an outlet at each end with central inlet. Typical examples of intermeshing screw pumps are shown in Figure 2.

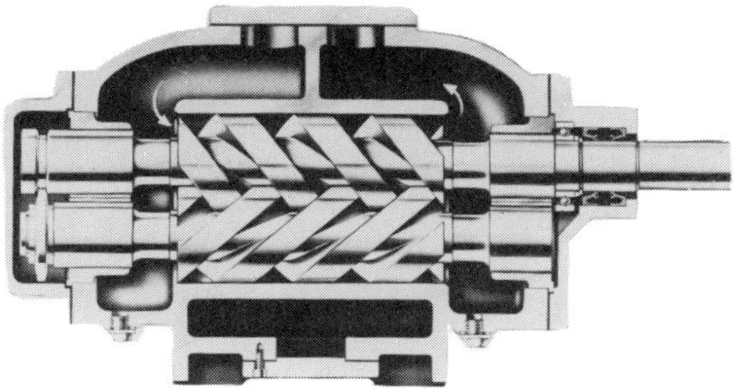

Screw pump with five spindles.

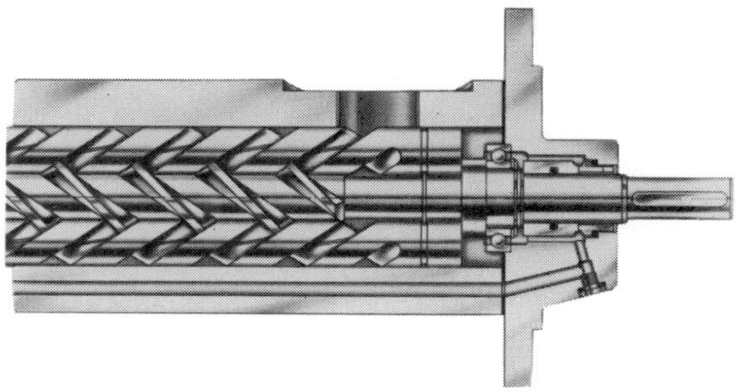

Flanged screw pump with three spindles.

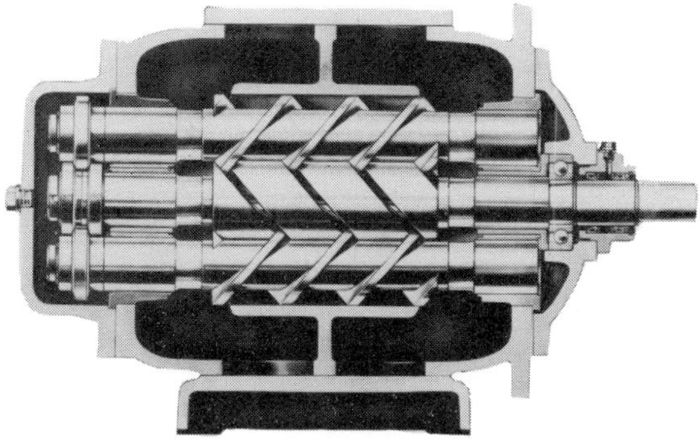

Screw pump with two spindles and internal bearings.

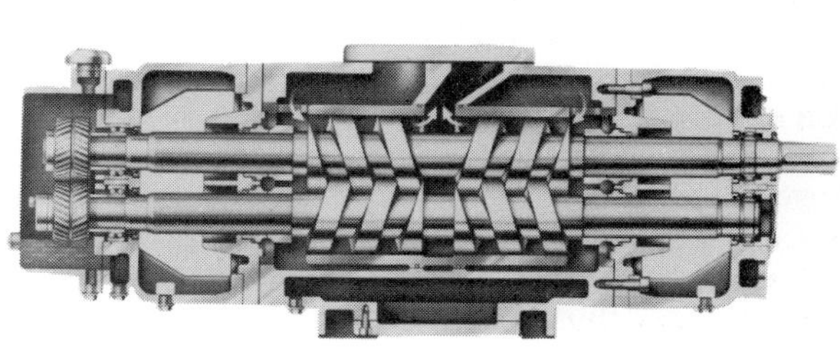

Figure 2 *Double flow screw pump with two spindles and external bearings.*

Two screw pumps

The usual configuration of a two screw pump is two pairs of identical screws on two shafts connected by external gears. This form is in effect two pumps in one housing which has the advantage of not only doubling the output but also of balancing the end thrusts on the spindles. When the screws rotate, chambers of fluid are closed off, such as chambers (a) or (b) as shown in Figure 3.

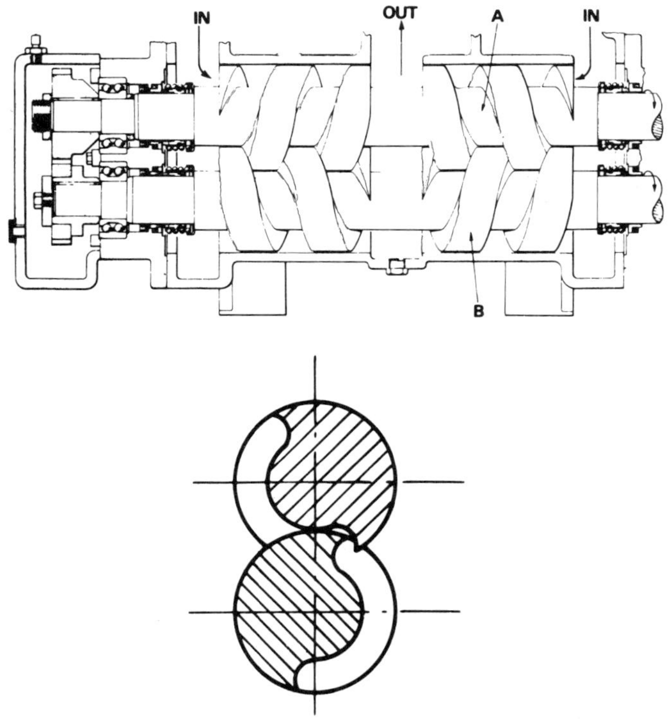

Section through screws

Figure 3
Section through external bearing twin-screw pump.

As the screws continue to turn, these chambers are carried axially towards the centre until the end of the screw is reached and the chambers open to the discharge cavity when the fluid is pushed out. Various screw shapes are offered by different manufacturers but difference in performance would appear to be marginal.

Characteristics

All screw pumps can maintain good efficiency while operating at low speeds which, together with the low flow velocities induced, make them suitable for handling viscous and shear-sensitive fluids, with suitable modification of screw form as necessary. Designs which work with positive clearance can accommodate contaminated fluids, also bearings and timing gears can be external to the pump and independently lubricated. Fine pitches can also be used to permit high rotational speeds without cavitation.

Delivery is pulse free and since the whole of the pumping chamber is displaced there is no unswept volume. This can be particularly advantageous when working under vacuum with air or vapour present in the fluid. Because of the relatively low inertia of rotating parts, screw pumps are capable of operating at higher speeds than other rotary or reciprocating pumps of comparable displacement. Some turbine-attached lubricating oil pumps operate at 10 000 r/min and even higher. Screw pumps like other rotary positive displacement pumps are self-priming and have a delivery flow characteristic which is essentially independent of pressure.

Limitations

Particular limitations of two screw pumps are that maximum pressures are normally limited to about 13·5 bar (200 lb/in^2) because of the flexural problems associated with long spindles; also, practical fluid viscosities which can be handled are limited to about 1500 centistokes. Higher viscosities can, however, be handled at reduced speeds.

Sizes

Two screw pumps are generally available with capacities from 6 to 600 m^3/h and larger pumps with capacities up to 1600 m^3/h have also been produced.

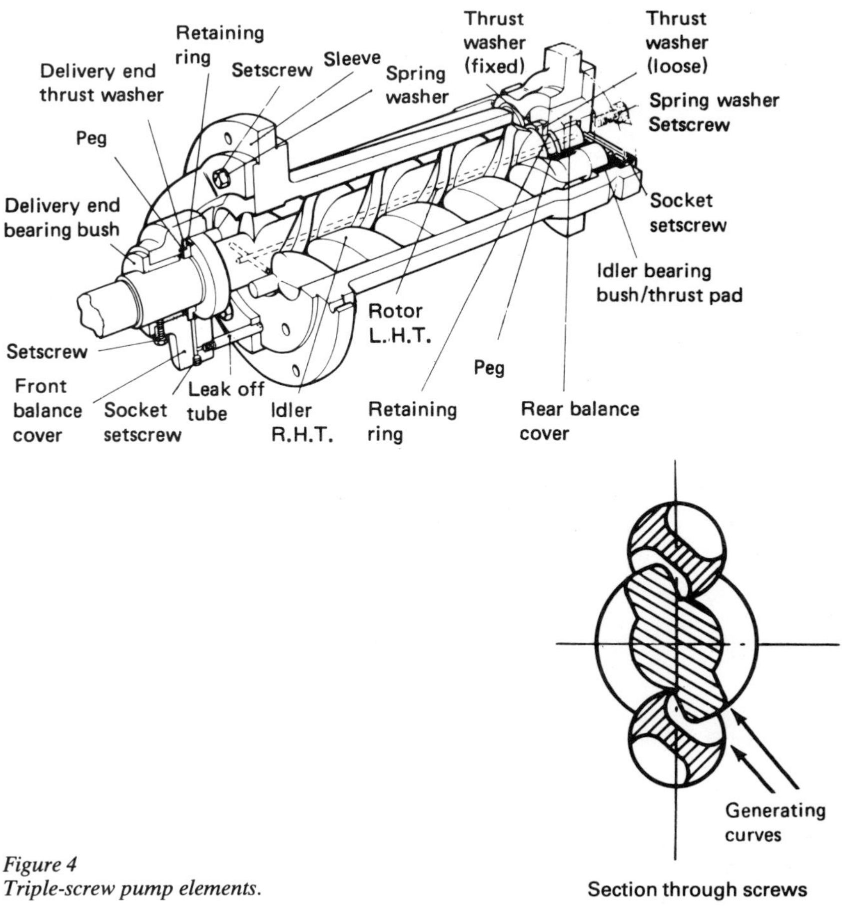

Figure 4
Triple-screw pump elements.

Three screw pumps

The usual configuration for a three screw pump is a centrally driven rotor screw with two smaller idler screws meshing with, and driven by it, as shown in Figure 4. Opposed pumping chambers can be used as on the twin screw pump but are usually confined to large capacity pumps.

The shapes of the screws are based upon the curves of the epicycloid type. These are basically the lines drawn by the contact corner of one rotor section upon the opposing rotor section. If the whole screw is then considered, line contact is produced which forms the fluid seal. These shapes are very sophisticated in detail and have to be manufactured with considerable accuracy if the pump is to be satisfactory.

Drive takes place between the lip of the idler and the root of the rotor screw, which have the same diameters, so true contact occurs. As with the twin screw pump, chambers of fluid are closed off by the rotation of the screws. When the screws continue to turn, each chamber is carried axially along the screws until it is opened to the discharge end where the fluid is expelled.

A particular advantage offered by the three screw pump is that by making the screws longer a number of chambers can be enclosed at the same time. This has a similar effect to putting a number of pumps in series, or 'multi-staging' allowing high pressures to be attained. Efficiencies can range up to 85% and even higher pressure pumps operate with low noise levels. A further development is in the greatly reduced size of pump now produced. Figure 5 for example compares the size of a modern screw pump designed to operate at a system pressure up to 150 bar (2000 lb/in^2) with that of a triple screw pump produced for a similar duty some 25 years ago.

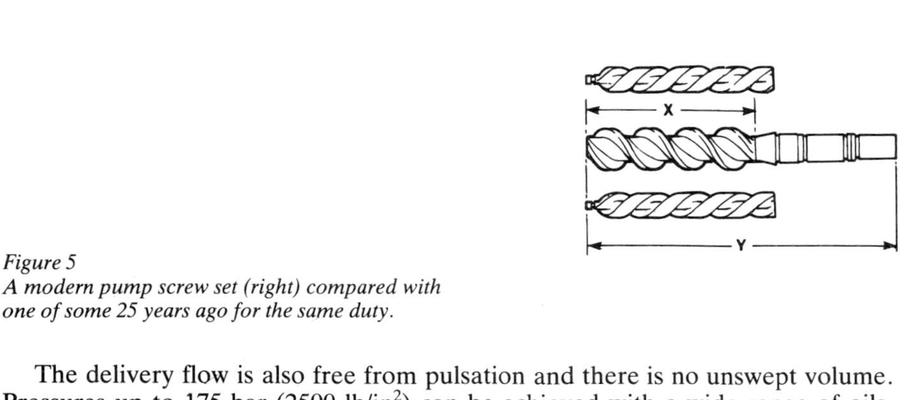

Figure 5
A modern pump screw set (right) compared with one of some 25 years ago for the same duty.

The delivery flow is also free from pulsation and there is no unswept volume. Pressures up to 175 bar (2500 lb/in^2) can be achieved with a wide range of oils. Typical applications include oil firing, lubricating systems, hydraulic systems, oil pipelines and many general oil duties.

As with twin screw pumps, delivery is pulse free with marked absence of hydraulic 'noise' and the type has a good performance on difficult suctions. It is also particularly attractive as a pump for hydraulic oils, being less sensitive than any other types to contaminants. Figure 6 shows the effect of impurities on the efficiency of positive displacement pumps.

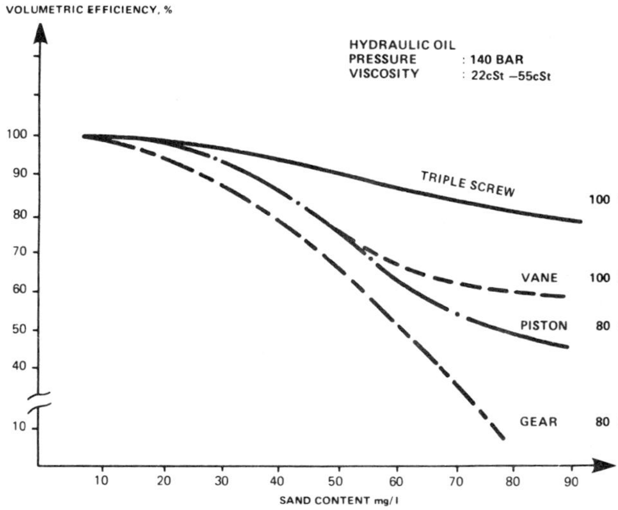

Figure 6
The effect of impurities on the efficiency of positive displacement pumps.

For such services, triple screw pumps will usually operate satisfactorily with filtration of 600 to 1000 microns on the pump suction, though on the discharge or return line filtration of about 25 microns is still usual to protect valves and other parts.

Limitations
As the screws run in contact with each other and with the casing, the fluids handled are limited to oils having reasonable lubricating properties and being reasonably free from solids. A satisfactory minimum viscosity is about 5 centistokes; maximum viscosity 250 centistokes. Higher viscosities can be handled at reduced speeds.

Sizes
Pumps of this type are normally limited to capacities of about 2000 m^3/h because of the special screw cutting facilities required. For hydraulic services they are readily available with capacities up to about 2500 l/min for system pressures of 100 bar (1500 lb/in^2); and 1000 l/min for system pressure of 250 bar (3600 lb/in^2).

Multiple screw pumps
The configuration adopted for three screw pumps can also (in theory at least) be adopted to have from 1 to 5 idler screws around a central rotor.

General considerations
In any screw pump application – regardless of design – suction lift, viscosity and speed are inseparable. Speed of operation, therefore, is dependent upon viscosity

and suction lift. If a true picture of these two latter items can be obtained, the problem of making a proper pump selection becomes simpler and the selection will result in a more efficient unit. The key to obtaining good performance from a screw pump, as with all other positive displacement pumps lies within a complete understanding and control of inlet conditions and the closely related parameters of speed and viscosity.

Screw pumps require at least one rotary seal on the drive shaft. For drive shafts rotary mechanical seal as well as stuffing boxes or packings are used depending on the manufacturer and/or customer preference. Double back-to-back arrangements with a flushing liquid are sometimes used for very viscous or corrosive substances.

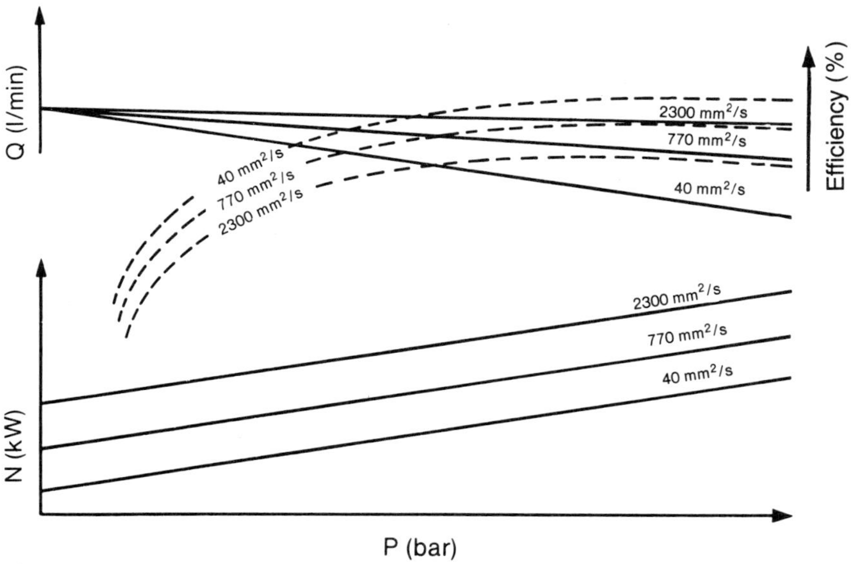

Typical performance graph of a screw pump.

In order to minimize the ill-effects of entrained or dissolved gas on screw pump performance, liquid velocity should be kept low in the suction pipe to reduce turbulence and pressure loss.

A large and well-rounded suction bell should be used to reduce entrance loss. Locate pump to provide positive head on the inlet in order to keep suction lift low.

Suction piping should be located inside a reservoir to obtain maximum submergence. Submerge all return lines, particularly from bypass and relief valves and locate them away from the suction.

Keep circulation rate low and avoid all unnecessary circulation of the fluid. Do not exceed rated manifold pressures on the machinery lubricating systems as the increased flow through sprays and bearings increases the circulation rate.

Heat the fluid where practical to reduce viscosity and to drive off entrained air, fluids of high viscosity will entrain and retain more air than fluids of low viscosity.

Avoid all air leaks no matter how small.

Provide ample vents.

Exhauster fans to draw off air and vapours have been used with good results.

Centrifuging will break a foam and remove suspended foreign matter which promotes foaming.

Use a variable speed drive for the pump to permit an adjustment of pump capacity to suit the flow requirements of the machinery.

As with every pump type there are certain advantages and disadvantages characteristic of screw pump design. These should be recognized in selecting the best pump for a particular application.

Advantages

(i) wide range of flows and pressures;
(ii) wide range of liquids and viscosities;
(iii) high speed capability of allowing freedom of driver selection;
(iv) no internal velocities;
(v) self-priming with good suction characteristics;
(vi) high tolerance for entrained air and other gases;
(vii) minimum churning or foaming;
(viii) low mechanical vibration, pulsation free-flow and quiet operation;
(ix) rugged compact design, easy to install and maintain;
(x) high tolerance to contamination to comparison with other rotary pumps;

Disadvantages

(i) relatively high cost, because of close tolerances and running clearances;
(ii) performance characteristics sensitive to viscosity change;
(iii) high pressure capability requires long pumping elements;

Applications

Screw pumps operate with high reliability in many sectors of industry including:

Chemical and paints industry – for pumping, spinning solutions, paints, lacquers, materials for making enamel paints, plasticisers, waxes, paraffin wax, soap.

Construction of steam and water turbines – lubricating oil and control gear oil pumps.

Hydraulic lifts – pressure oil pumps for hydraulic drive units.

Boilers and burners – as fuel oil delivery transfer and burner pumps.

Cosmetics manufacture – for conveying creams, pastes, detergents and soaps.

Engineering – as hydraulic pumps, gear or bearing oil supply pumps.

Mixing and filling plant – as dosing transfer and filling pumps.

Food industry – for dosing or conveying syrup, glucose, jelly, fats, creams, chocolate, molasses.

Petrochemicals – as dosing pumps or process pumps.

Shipbuilding – as lubricating or cooling oil pumps, fuel pumps, sweet oil pumps as residue pumps, tank drainage pumps, cargo pumps, bilge pumps.

Tank installations – as filling and loading pumps also for reversing direction of flow.

Heat transfer installations – as transfer pumps.

Cellulose industry – for pumping pulp, viscose, lye *etc*.

Progressing Cavity Pumps

THE PROGRESSING cavity pump also known as the eccentric screw/worm pump and helical rotor pump, in its basic form, consists of a single-headed helical rotor rolling eccentrically in a double-threaded helix of twice the pitch length (Figure 1). In so doing, the rotor and stator form a series of sealed cavities 180° apart, that progress from suction to discharge as the single helix rotates. As one cavity diminishes, the opposing cavity is increasing at the same rate; so, the sum of the two discharges is a constant. The result is a pulsationless positive displacement flow.

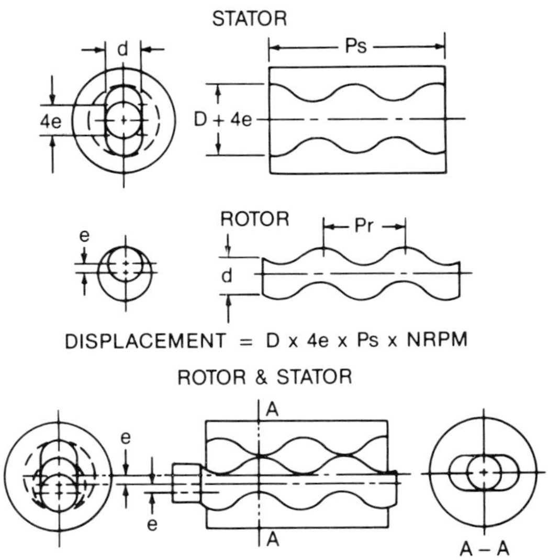

Figure 1
Progressing cavity pump is a single-helical rotor rolling eccentrically in a double-threaded helix of twice the pitch length.

The displacement in addition to being a function of speed, is directly proportional to three design constants: the cross-sectional diameter of the rotor (D); its eccentricity (E), (or radius of the helix); and the pitch of the stator helix

(Ps). Pressure capability in a progressing cavity pump is the function of the number of times the progressing seal lines are repeated. Flow through the elements is not far removed from the straightest distance between suction and discharge. The result is relatively low velocity and shear for a given displacement, and excellent capabilities for handling highly viscous slurries. Another feature that gives the progressing cavity principle added advantages for slurry handling is the use of elastomers for the outer gear in the majority of its applications. Through the use of a compression fit between the rotor and stator (much like an 'O' ring seal along the elements), clearances have been eliminated between the rotor and stator elements. Gear, lobe or multiple screw pumps require clearance between the intermeshing pumping elements and depend on the fluid viscosity to form the seal required to compensate for pressure. The progressing cavity pump has even been used in certain applications as an air compressor where lubricant is added. The pump is capable of pumping low viscosity and mixed phased fluids as well as highly viscous fluids.

The elastomeric outer gear also adds abrasion resistance beyond that of conventional rotary pumps. The particles tend to embed temporarily in the elastomeric gear rather than abrade. The elastomeric gear also allows deformation to partially accommodate large solids.

The length of the pump can be extended to provide two or more complete pitches, if necessary giving the effect of a two-stage multi-stage unit. Diameter pitch and eccentricity are factors controlling the actual performance per stage and can be varied as necessary to match the requirements of the product being handled.

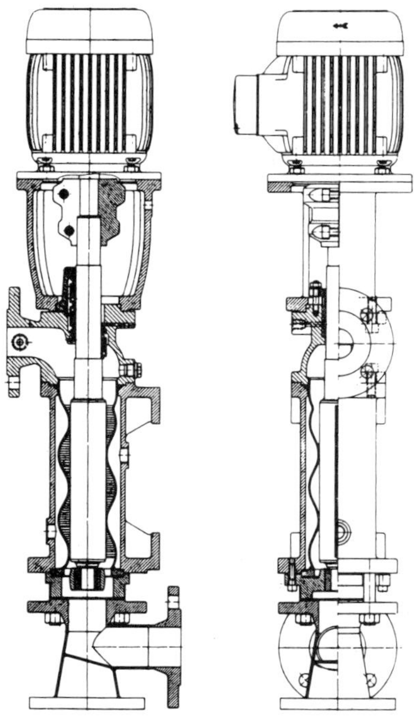

Upright helical rotor pump with lantern and motor.

No valves are required and the end discharge port allows straight through flow or can accommodate a 90 degree bend. The suction port is in the centre with drive shaft and bearings on the opposite side of the pumping chamber. A seal and stuffing box is located in a separate gland section and can be a packed gland or a mechanical seal. Drive is normally by flexible couplings at each end of the drive shaft although one particular version employs a rigidly mounted flexible shaft drive. The eccentric motion of the rotor is accommodated entirely by the flexing of this shaft.

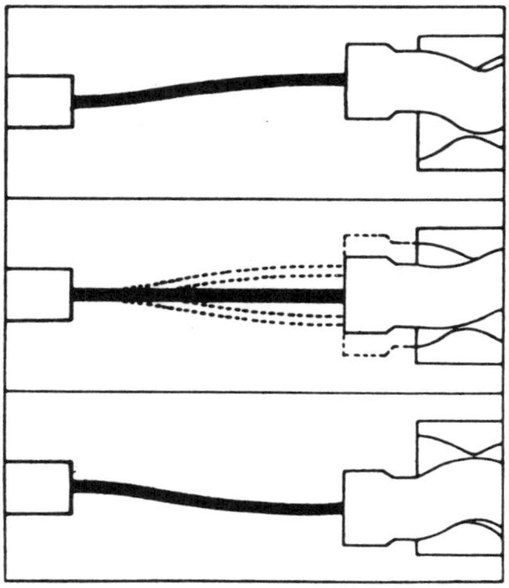

Flexishaft principle.

For handling highly viscous products, the basic form of the pump can be modified to incorporate a hopper section on the suction side, carrying a auger which is rotated with the rotor (Figure 2). The hopper shape and auger are designed to engage the product and provide positive constant feed to the pumping section. Pumps of this type can successfully handle cement grout, compounded coal tailing, filter cake, dewatered sewage, sludge, *etc.*

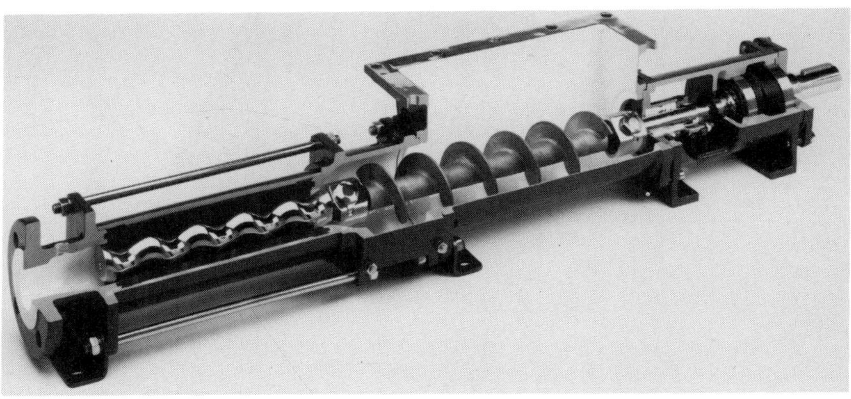

Figure 2
Wide-throat progressing cavity pump with hopper and auger.

TYPICAL SELECTION GUIDE FOR PROGRESSING CAVITY PUMPS

NOM CAPACITY M³/HR AT PRESSURES STATED

INDUSTRIAL PROCESS PUMPS

PUMP \ SPEED	2850	1440	960	720	600	400	PRESSURE BAR	MAX CAPACITY AT ZERO BAR HEAD
B14	—	0.12	0.08	0.06	0.05	0.03	2.0	0.16
B15	0.42	0.21	0.14	0.11	0.08	0.05	2.0	0.60

PUMP \ SPEED	1750	1440	960	720	600	400	PRESSURE BAR	MAX CAPACITY AT ZERO BAR HEAD
GF	0.85	0.70	0.45	0.30	0.25	0.15	3.5	1.40
GG	1.05	0.80	0.55	0.40	0.32	0.20	3.5	1.92
GH	2.40	2.00	1.20	0.80	0.60	0.35	3.5	3.50

PUMP \ SPEED	1440	960	720	600	400	200	PRESSURE BAR	MAX CAPACITY AT ZERO BAR HEAD
MERLIN A	2.20	1.35	1.00	0.80	0.50	0.20	3.5	2.40
MERLIN B	5.00	3.20	2.30	1.80	1.10	0.40	3.5	5.70
MERLIN C	12.40	8.00	6.00	5.00	3.00	1.40	3.5	14.30
MERLIN E	—	24.00	17.50	14.00	9.00	3.50	3.5	25.00
MERLIN F	—	29.00	20.00	15.00	8.00	—	3.5	38.00
MERLIN G	—	—	56.00	46.00	30.00	12.00	3.5	60.00

PUMP \ SPEED	1200	800	720	650	540	480	240	Pres Bar	MAX CAPACITY AT ZERO BAR HEAD
LL	20.0	17.0	11.5	10.0	8.0	7.0	2.0	3.5	23.40
LM	—	34.0	31.0	27.0	22.0	19.0	8.0	3.5	38.60
LN	—	—	52.0	48.0	39.0	33.0	15.0	3.5	58.40
LX	—	—	—	69.0	58.0	50.0	21.0	3.5	76.00
LP	—	—	—	—	90.0	79.0	33.0	3.5	102.00
LR	—	—	—	—	—	135.0	56.0	3.5	150.00

FOOD PUMPS

PUMP \ SPEED	1440	960	720	600	400	200	Pres Bar	MAX CAPACITY AT ZERO BAR HEAD
J3	1.60	1.00	0.70	0.50	0.25	—	3.5	2.25
J4	3.00	1.90	1.40	1.10	0.60	0.20	3.5	4.40
J5	5.30	3.70	2.70	2.30	1.50	0.80	3.5	7.80
J6	11.50	7.50	5.60	4.80	3.00	1.50	3.5	14.00
J7	—	20.00	15.00	12.00	8.00	3.50	3.5	25.00

WIDE THROAT PUMPS

PUMP \ SPEED	350	300	200	100	50	PRESSURE BAR	MAX CAPACITY AT ZERO BAR HEAD
CB2	1.24	1.05	0.68	0.28	0.12	9.0	1.45
CC2	3.30	2.80	1.80	0.80	0.35	9.0	3.70
CE2	7.80	6.60	4.20	1.80	0.60	9.0	9.00
CF2	—	11.00	7.40	3.60	1.90	9.0	11.00
CG2	—	—	15.50	7.00	3.00	9.0	16.50

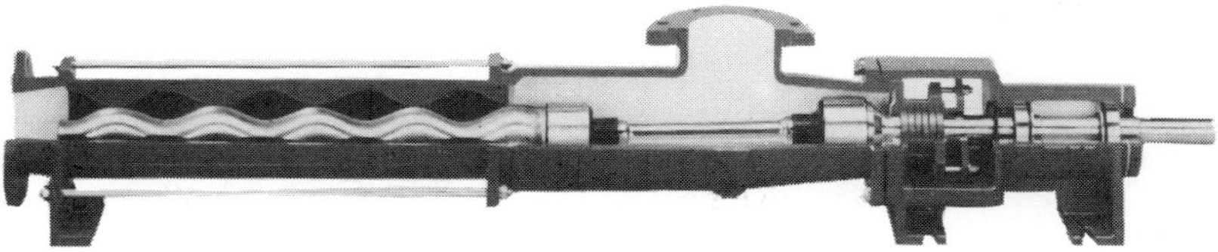

Cutaway of progressing cavity pump.

Advantages

Progressing cavity pumps are self-priming, provide positive displacement with proportional flow with low emulsification, low shear and negligible pulsation. They can handle virtually any liquid from water to abrasive slurries, entrained gases and froth to viscous and non-Newtonian pastes in suitably modified form where necessary. They are produced in the widest ranges of sizes with capacities up to 150 m^3/h (33 000 gal/h) and delivery pressures up to 20 bar (290 lb/in^2). They are one of the most versatile types available with minimal wear and maintenance requirements. About their only limitation is that maximum service temperature is limited to that of the elastomeric stator material which may be in natural of synthetic rubber or fluorelastomer such as Dupont's Viton.

Gear Pumps

THE COMMON form of gear pump consists of two intermeshing gears, one driven and one idling in a close fitting casing. There are two basic types of gear pump – (i) the external gear pump and (ii) the internal gear pump. External gear pumps are the simpler design and most commonly employed. Internal gear pumps can offer larger displacement relative to overall sizes. Gear pumps are rotary positive displacement pumps in which the main pumping action is caused by relative movement between the rotating and stationary elements of the pump. The main characteristics which distinguish gear pumps from lobe pumps are that in gear pumps the mechanical contacts between the gears form a part of the moving fluid seal between the inlet and the outlet port and the outer radial tips of the gear and the sides of the gears form a part of moving fluid seal between inlet and outlet ports. The gear contact locus moves along the tooth surfaces and then jumps discontinuously from tooth to tooth as the gears rotate. In lobe pumps the rotors are not capable of driving each other and the fluid seal contacts locus between the lobes moves continuously across all the radial surfaces of the lobes.

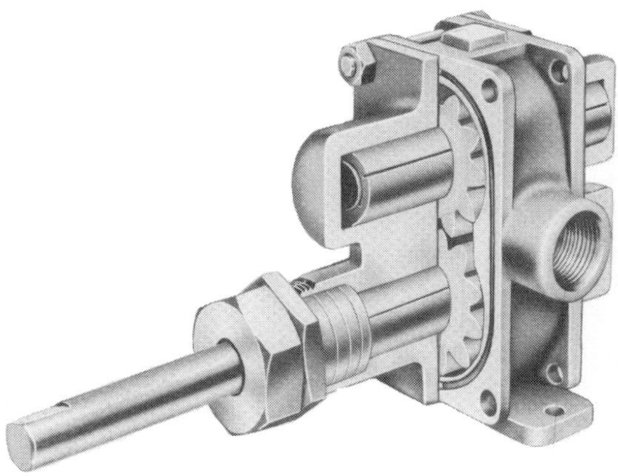

External gear pump.

Gear pumps are generally suitable for handling all clean liquids and are particularly effective where the fluid has lubricating properties. They are also suitable for high pressure working (up to 220 bar), especially with oil fluids. This however places a premium on detailed design, precision workmanship and rigidity; and calls for particular attention to the reduction of internal leakage to a minimum as well as to bearing design to resist torque and pressure loads.

A general formula for estimating the performance of a gear pump is:

$$\mathbf{Q} = K_1 (D^2 - C^2) \times W - K_2 \ \frac{\mathbf{B^2}}{N^2}$$

where:

Q = delivery per revolution
D = outside diameter of gears
C = centre distance of gears
W = width of gears
B = base circle diameter of gears
N = number of teeth in each gear
K_1 = is an empirical factor dependent on gear form, and also units employed.
Typical values $K_1 = 0{\cdot}0025$ for D and C in mm;
and $K_1 = 1{\cdot}57$ for D and C in inches
K_2 = 0·05 for B in mm
K_2 = 1·3 for B in inches

This formula should give reasonably accurate predictions of performance for conventional involoute tooth forms. It will be less accurate for other tooth forms and also when tooth venting is employed for pressure relief. On low pressure pumps, relief may be provided quite simply by allowing the gears to run with a small but definite backlash, and or by designing the gears with a small number of teeth in simultaneous contact. On high pressure gear pumps, grooves are commonly cut in the side plates to provide communication between the inter tooth spaces.

External gear pumps

The basic form of an external gear pump is shown in Figure 1.

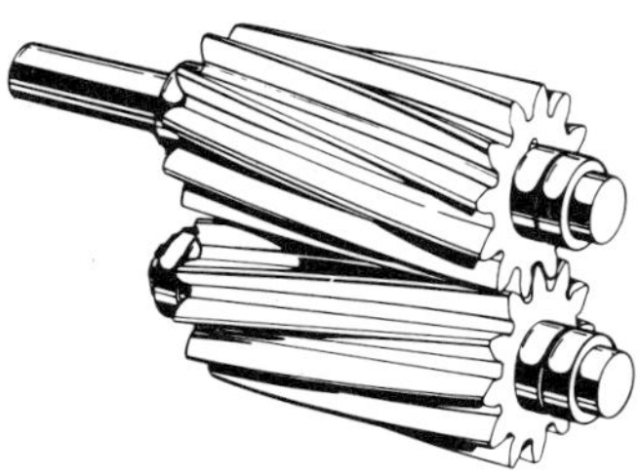

Helical gear
External helical gear pumps provide higher pressure in a smaller unit.

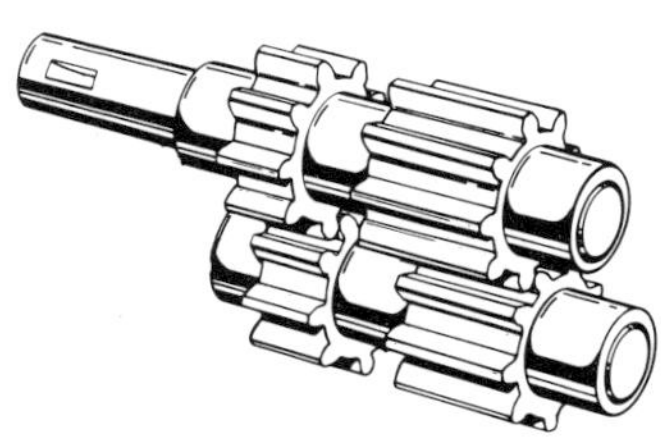

Spur gear
For low-capacity high-pressure transfer applications or fluid power needs.

Figure 1

Two intermeshing gears of the same diameter and form are mounted on separate spindles and housed in a close-fitting casing. Inlet and outlet ports are formed directly in the sides of the casing in line with the point of meshing. One gear shaft is driven whilst the other idles. Both shafts are carried in low friction bearings (usually rolling bearings).

During rotation, as each pair of teeth intermesh on the inlet side, the volume on that side is reduced by the volume of two tooth spaces, providing a suction effect. Oil flowing into the suction space is then trapped on each side by a tooth quest approaching the bore of the housing and carried round to the delivery side by the 'pockets' between adjacent pairs of teeth. On the delivery side, the oil is displaced from the delivery port under pressure.

For maximum volumetric efficiency there should be no leakage between the teeth and no leakage across the end faces of the gears. Even if such internal leakages are reduced to a practical minimum, there may be a further penalty to pay in the high bearing loads and unbalancing loads introduced by fluid trapped in the teeth pockets, which can result in increased friction and lowered mechanical efficiency. Thus a compromise may have to be reached in order to achieve maximum overall efficiency although usually attention to increasing volumetric efficiency results in higher gains than any corresponding reduction in the mechanical efficiency.

Characteristics

Gear pumps are inevitably associated with internal leakage losses and slip. Slip is largely independent of speed and increases only with increasing load. It is however affected by fluid viscosity. Increasing viscosity tends to decrease slip but at the same time increase the power input required at a particular speed. The overall result is that increasing fluid viscosity tends to decrease pump efficiency. Thus speed may have to be reduced to maintain a good efficiency figure when handling higher viscosity fluid. Generalised performance characteristics are shown in Figure 2.

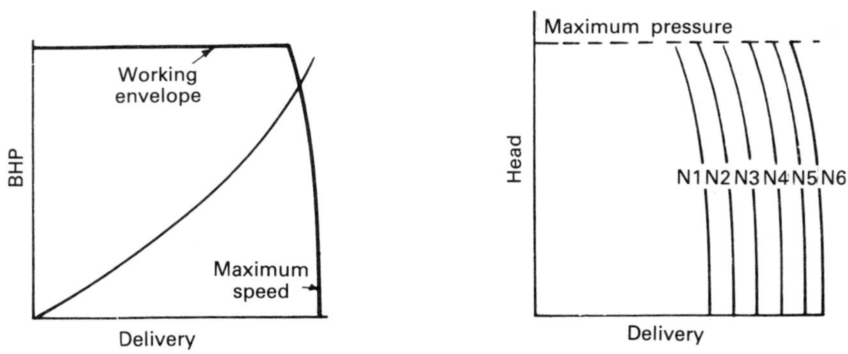

Figure 2

Normally performance of a gear pump is quoted for a specific oil viscosity. The effect of a higher viscosity will be to reduce efficiency, except that if the driver is not a constant speed type it may adjust to the higher load by reducing speed and thus delivery. With fluids of lower viscosity, slip will increase and reduce delivery again unless the driver adjusts to the lower load by speeding up (when the loss of capacity will be less marked).

For any given size of pump, capacity is directly proportional to speed and for any particular speed it decreases slightly with increasing head. This is because slip tends to be constant regardless of speed but increases with increasing head. The effect of increasing fluid viscosity is normally to decrease slip, whilst increasing the horsepower required to maintain speed. Thus efficiency tends to fall with increasing viscosity. This however, is not normally compensated for by the fact that speed is reduced to accommodate higher fluid viscosities and the pump delivery decreases accordingly.

Rated delivery may be expressed in terms of displacement per revolution, or actual delivery given from some specified speed (often maximum speed for continuous running). In the former case, delivery at any particular speed can be obtained by multiplying by the speed in r/min. In the latter case, delivery at any other speed follows from simple proportion. It should be noted however that delivery is normally determined empirically, using a low or medium viscosity oil discharging freely (*ie* zero discharge pressure). Actual delivery will be modified by a different fluid viscosity any will be reduced slightly when working against an output load.

Gear pumps should not normally be run at speeds above the manufacturers rated maximum nor should they be run continuously at high pressures and very low speeds. Otherwise they can be regarded as particularly versatile type of pump which can be run at any speed. Variable delivery operation would not normally be obtained by varying the speed. It would be better to use two or more gear pumps if off-loading of individual pumps is necessary. Multiple units can then be mounted in tandem with a common drive.

Standard ranges of gear pumps are normally based on a number of standard gear diameters. Various capacities for the same (diameter) gears can then be provided by lengthening the gear case to accommodate wider gears. For high pressure work, the diameter to gear width radio may be determined by the type of bearing and the rigidity of the casing. A high diameter to width ratio reduces bearing loads whilst a low diameter width ratio tends to produce less casing stress and minimises leakage across the ends of the gears. The proportions chosen thus have to effect the most suitable compromise between these two requirements. The general solution for optimum performance at high pressures is a 'square' gear with width equal to the pitch circle diameter. Additional provision to reduce end leakage may be included on high pressure gear pumps such as the use of pressure balanced side plates whilst inter tooth venting may be necessary to prevent the build up of high localised pressures on the gear teeth.

Tooth forms

Different tooth forms will also provide different degrees of sealing. Various gear forms have been tried but the stub gear still remains the favourite and about the best for sealing even though the displacement per revolution may be less than that which can be achieved with other tooth forms. Single- and double-helical forms are also used but mainly where a quieter running pump is required. Apart from the doubtful possibility of achieving any real performance gains, the use of more complex tooth forms is usually undesirable from the point of increased complexity and cost of manufacture. The tendency therefore is to use simple stub tooth forms and use the smallest possible number of teeth consistent with smooth continuous drive. Reducing the number of teeth has the advantage of increasing the displacement revolution regardless of gear form to minimise wear it may be necessary to use hardened gears which will be suitable only where the fluid being handled is an effective lubricant for the gear teeth.

Pressure Balancing

Methods of detail design, aimed at reducing internal leakage across the end faces of the gears, are based on pressure loading techniques. One such method is to fit side plates between the gear faces and end covers, with high pressure oil fed to specific areas on the outside of these plates. The plates are thus pressurised to bring them into contact with the gear ends and prevent end leakage, with a forced proportional to the speed and internal pressure of the pump. Numerous variations on this theme have been developed by individual manufacturers and although this involves additional components, the overall cost is usually less than the cost of the more precise manufacture necessary to achieve similar end leakage control with fixed side characteristics. A comparison between the simple gear pump and a pressure compensated gear pump is shown in Figure 3.

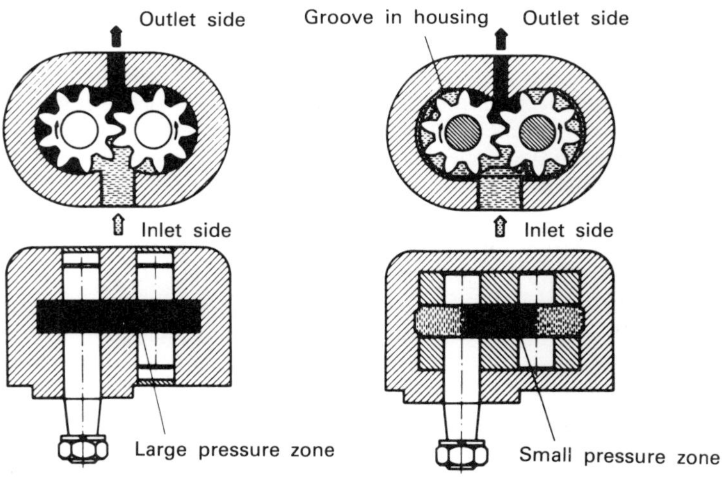

Figure 3
Simple gear pump (left) and pressure-compensated (double-gland) gear pump (right).

Bearing Loads

Bearing loads comprise a torque load combined with a pressure load. In the case of the driving gear the pressure gear opposes and so relieves the torque load. In the case of the driven gear the pressure load supplements the torque load. As a consequence the effective load on the drive gear is higher than that on the driving gear bearings. Theoretically at least, the torque load on the driving gear bearing is zero since it is equalised by the torque applied to the driven gear but torque load is added to the pressure load on the drive gear. In practice the bearing load on the driven gear is normally of the order of 1·5 times that on the driving gear.

Applications

Cast iron gear pumps are widely used by manufacturers of turbines and compressors for the petrochemical industry, for offshore platform and natural gas pipelines. Pumps for these applications comply with API 676 and are often required to give a service life of 25 000 hours or more. Manufacturers of gas turbines and electrical generation equipment require a pump service life of 37 000 hours and are usually fitted with high grade rolling element bearings. Oil pumps for lubricating large low speed compressors may operate at the speed of the compressor itself or of its drive motor. Rotational speed on very large compressors may be as low as 200 to 300 r/min and consequently a high capacity gear lubrication pump would be required. Deliveries of 3000 l/min at 330 r/min are not uncommon.

Gear pumps are suitable for handling low volumes of low viscosity liquids as in the case of on-line sampling and analysis systems for diesel fuel. For instance a sample of fuel may be needed to be drawn continuously from a pipeline running at a pressure of 10 to 12 bar, passed through an on-line analysis system then reinjected into the pipeline. The pump compensates for the pressure drop through the analysers.

Bitumen and asphalt

Bitumen is a lubricating fluid and gear pumps are used for transfer duties with pressure up to 7 bar although more usually 3·5 bar at speeds around 720 r/min. For temperatures up to 250 °C cast iron pumps are normally recommended with cast steel units for higher temperatures. They may be supplied in unheated form with lagging if required; jacketed for heating oil at a temperature of 200 °C; or electrically heated with a single phase element. Figure 5 shows a vertically mounted 75 mm jacketed pump.

On a heated pump the jacket is usually an integral part of the casting, designed to give uniform heating throughout the body. Its main function is to raise pump temperature on start up to liquify residual material in the pump and to avoid cooling of hot liquids on initial contact with the pump. Jacketed pumps may also be used as heating elements in ring main circulation systems. Vertical pumps are also used for immersion in horizontal bitumen tanks. Typically their capacity ranges from 135 to 985 l/min. An externally operated cock allows the pump to circulate within the tank or to supply from it. Pumps of this type are usually self-draining and fitted with a relief valve to guard against motor overload.

Gear pumps are available to handle fluids such as Trinidad Lake asphalt or paint with fine abrasive solids of approximately 0·15 to 0·2 mm in suspension. The gear rotors have external bearings and are driven through timing gears. Inside the pump casing two hinged shoes partially surround the rotors and are adjustable to take up the rotor hence this type of pump is known as an ‘adjustable wear’ pump. In addition off set liner plates are provided inside the pump end covers these may be reversed to take up any wear against the end faces of the rotors. This arrangement is to give at least three times the operating life of ordinary pumps.

Molasses Pumps

Most molasses pumping problems arise from the use of wrongly sized suction pipes. The molasses gear pump should be installed as near to the storage tank as possible and a large diameter pipe with the minimum amount of bends, valves and fittings should be used. Table 1 shows typical pipe sizes for molasses pumps 10 °C (50 °F).

The diameter quoted in Table 1 can be reduced by about one-third when the molasses is heated to 21 °C (70 °F) and by a half at 37 °C (100 °F). All heating systems should be temperature controlled to a maximum of 104 °C (220 °F) to avoid caramelisation.

TABLE 1 – PIPE SIZES FOR MOLASSES PUMPS 10 °C (50 °F)

Length of pipe metres (in)		l/min (gal/min) pumped 0 to 9 (0 to 2)		9 to 25 (2 to 5)		25 to 45 (5 to 10)		45 to 90 (10 to 20)	
		Suction pipe diameter							
		mm	in	mm	in	mm	in	mm	in
0 to 1·2	0 to 4	50	2	63	2½	75	3	100	4
1·2 to 2·4	4 to 8	63	75	3	100	4	125	5	
2·4 to 6	8 to 20	75	3	100	4	125	5	150	6
		Discharge pipe diameter							
0 to 1·5	0 to 5	32	1¼	38	1½	50	2	63	2½
1·5 to 3	5 to 10	38	1½	50	2	63	2½	75	3
3 to 7·5	10 to 25	50	2	63	2½	75	3	100	4
7·5 to 15	25 to 50	63	2½	75	3	100	4	125	5

In sugar factories molasses is usually pumped at 40-70 °C with a pump speed of 250 to 280 r/min. Pumps are normally in the range of 50 to 100 mm with cast iron bodies and geared motors.

In the feed mill industry molasses is usually supplied cold and pumping speeds are 120 to 180 r/min because viscosity is high (over 10 000 centistokes in winter climates).

Figure 4
Vertically-mounted 75 mm jacketed pump.

Hot water jacketed gear pumps are used for pumping animal fats at pressures up to around 7 bar. Flow rates are usually from 27 to 135 l/min. Other applications for gear pumps include:

(i) Cocoa butter – a non-abrasive material for which standard steam jacketed pumps may be used running at 960 r/min. These pumps are usually of cast iron construction but occasionally of stainless steel or bronze.

(ii) Cocoa liquor – an abrasive material which requires slow speeds normally 80 to 100 r/min a correctly rated pump should give a service life in excess of ten years. Pumps are generally cast iron with conventional internal bearing design though external bearing pumps provide for better service life where larger sizes are demanded.

(iii) Chocolate – chocolate and cocoa liquor are very abrasive though not viscous and are pumped hot at low pressures. Slow speed pumps again are required usually with external bearing design and sometimes with timing gears to minimise abrasion.

Gear pumps are used throughout the chemical, pulp and paper, food, petroleum and metal processing industries for circulation, injection, drum transfer, metering and process applications.

Magnetically-driven gear pumps

Magnetically-driven gear pumps are self-priming and usually external spur gear pumps. Their design is suitable for continuous duty industrial applications over wide temperature, viscosity and pressure variations. These pumps provide constant volume pulsation free flow and are safe for use with clear, non-abrasive, hazardous and or corrosive chemicals over the entire small pH range.

Rare earth ceramic, samarium cobalt, barium ferrite or neo-dimiam iron magnets are used.

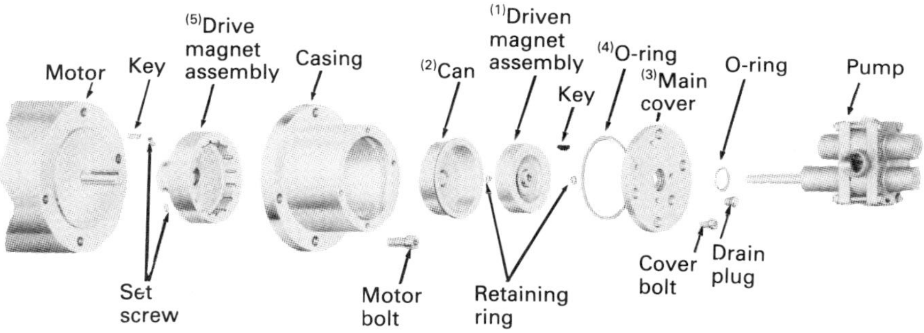

Figure 5
Magnetically driven pumps.

In operation (Figure 5) rotation from the motor shaft to the pump shaft is transmitted by means of a magnetic-drive coupling. An encapsulated driven magnet assembly is mounted on the end of the pump shaft. It is then contained by a closed end (can) which seals against the pumps main cover a drive magnet assembly attached an electric motor shaft rotates around the containment can. When the drive magnet assembly rotates lines of magnetic force cause the driven magnet assembly to rotate which in turn causes the pump shaft to rotate. Pumps of this type also have the ability to operate bi-directionally.

The magnetic gear pump shown in Figure 6 incorporates a 'suction shoe' design which creates a pressure loaded pump. Pressure loaded means that the pressure of the fluid being pumped is applied across the suction shoe and gears to aid in the pumps sealing capabilities. In operation the driven magnetic is connected to the pumping parts and is sealed within a magnet cup. The driving magnet encircles this cup. The two magnets align themselves pole-to-pole and rotate together with no slippage until the decoupling limit is exceeded.

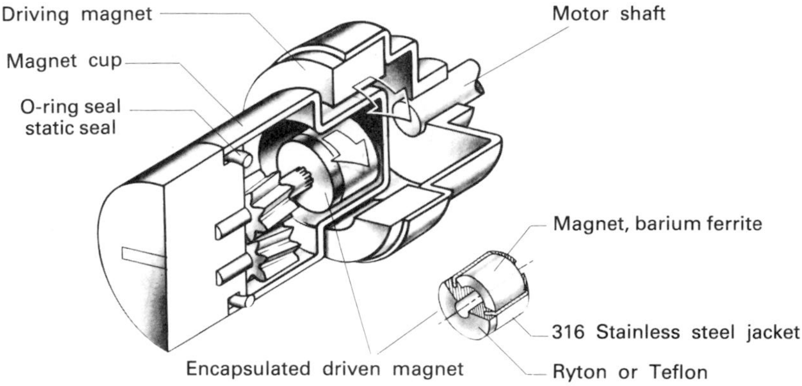

Figure 6

Decoupling occurs when the pump load exceeds the coupling tool between the magnets. This feature can act as a safety device to protect pump and motor from inadvertent damage.

The driven magnet is encapsulated in polyphenylenesulphide or tetrafluoroethylene to protect the ceramic magnet from damage caused be thermal shock.

Magnetically driven gear pump designed to handle aggressive and difficult fluids.

Internal gear pumps

The internal gear pump is based on different geometry to that of an external gear pump, *ie* internal gear is located within an outer gear ring, the tooth form being chosen so each internal gear tooth is in contact with the inner surface of the outer ring as shown in Figure 7. There are numerous design variations possible but all

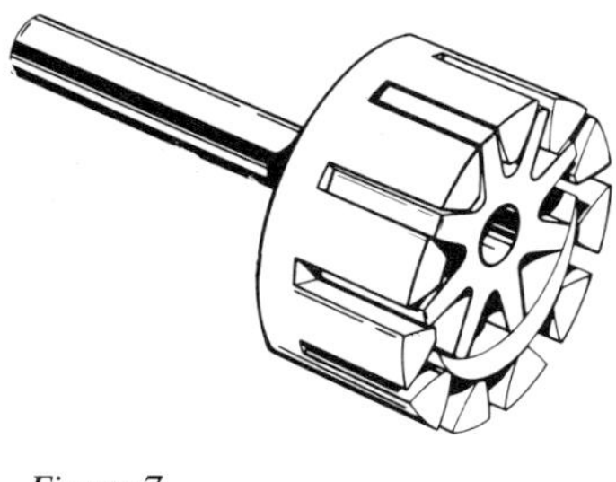

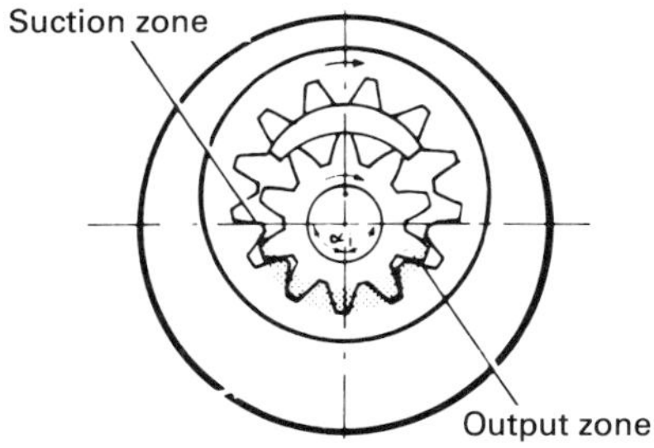

Figure 7
Internal gear pumps stand up to a wide variety of service conditions.

work on the principle of producing a sequence of expanding and contracting pockets into which liquid is drawn from the inlet side, transferred to the outside and forced out under pressure. This geometry has some specific advantages over the external gear pump, notably the lower localised fluid pressures generated and the lower shearing forces on the fluid. It can also show much lower operating noise levels than a comparable external gear pump and readily lends itself to multi-staging.

With simple gear forms, the necessary blocking action to prevent back flow from the outlets to the inlet side may be provided by the gears themselves by a crescent-shaped partition fitted to the case between the gears. Internal gear pumps are better suited to handling higher viscosity and shear sensitive fluids, although they are equally suitable for handling low viscosity fluids and even volatile liquids with suitable shaft seals. They are not suitable for handling low viscosity fluids which are non-lubricants or contaminated fluid. Certain types of internal gear pump are produced for handling fluids with limited lubricating properties when the bearings for the two gears are mounted externally and separately lubricated. Figure 8 shows a cutaway of a heavy duty internal gear pump. In general the internal gear pump is a specialised rather than general-purpose pump and the principle of working has been further developed in lobe rotor forms.

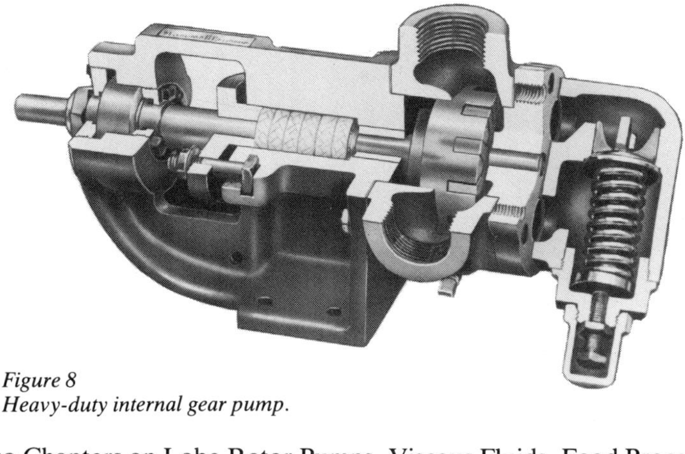

Figure 8
Heavy-duty internal gear pump.

See also Chapters on Lobe Rotor Pumps, Viscous Fluids, Food Processing and Fire Pumps.

Vane Pumps

CONVENTIONAL VANE pumps, or sliding vane pumps as they are sometimes known, are particularly suitable for low and medium pressure duties requiring a compact low cost pump. Lightweight vane pumps are suitable for handling both liquids and gases and find particular application for pressure reduction, handling air down to and into the medium vacuum range.

The pump itself consists of a circular rotor with radial slots mounted eccentrically in a substantially circular casing. Each rotor slot carries a rigid vane, free to slide in a radial direction. Rotation throws the vanes to outwards so that the tips always rub against the inner surface of the casing providing a seal. The actual shape of the casing and the eccentric location of the rotor inlet port communicates with the casing on the expanding volume side (or suction area); and an outlet port connects on the contracting valve side (or pressure area). Fluid is thus sucked in through the inlet port and squeezed out under pressure through the outlet port. In pumps for liquids the ports completely cover the whole inlet and outlet. Where air or gas is being pumped it may be desirable to reduce the port size to achieve a higher degree of compression on the delivery side.

There are various types of rigid rotor vane pumps where generally movable sealing elements in the form of rigid blades, rollers, slippers, shoes, buckets, *etc*, are moved generally radially inward and outward by cam surfaces to maintain a fluid seal between the open to inlet volume and the open to outlet volumes during the operation of the pump. When the cam surface is internal to the body member and vanes are mounted in or on the rotor, the pumps is called an internal vane pump or vane in rotor pump. When the cam surface is the external radial surface of the rotor and the vane or vanes are mounted in the body or stator, the pump is known as an external vane pump or vane in body pump.

The simple single-cell vane pump is unbalanced hydraulically and tends to suffer from low volumetric efficiency because of the difficulty of controlling internal leakage. The geometry does however readily lend itself to providing variable delivery characteristics simply by adjustment of the relative positions of the rotor spindle and outer ring modifying the capacity of the 'pockets' swept during revolution. The casing can also be readily fitted with a replacement liner to take wear.

Variable Capacity Vane Pumps

In variable capacity vane pumps, the displacement of the pump is changed by movement of the cam ring relative to the rotor, effectively modifying 'pocket' volumes. Ring movement in such cases is usually spring controlled with a pre-determined spring precompression opposing the horizontal force developed on the ring. Vertical movement on the ring is constrained by a thrust block. The spring rate the determines the change in pressure necessary to move the ring from full flow rate to zero. Delivery remains directly proportional to the ring setting or effective 'stroke', between the range of full eccentricity and concentricity, unless the drop off 'knee' is reached when the ring will move automatically to reduce the stroke to compensate for increasing pressure. The pump is thus pressure compensated and does not need a relief valve as over-pressurisation will simply reduce the delivery to zero by moving the ring to the concentric position. The main requirement is to establish a suitable delivery/eccentricity gradient so that the pump cannot become unstable and attempt to oscillate over its normal working range. Figure 1 shows the general workling principle of a standard vane pump. Figure 2 depicts the general working principle of a variable capacity vane pump.

Figure 1
Standard vane pump principle.

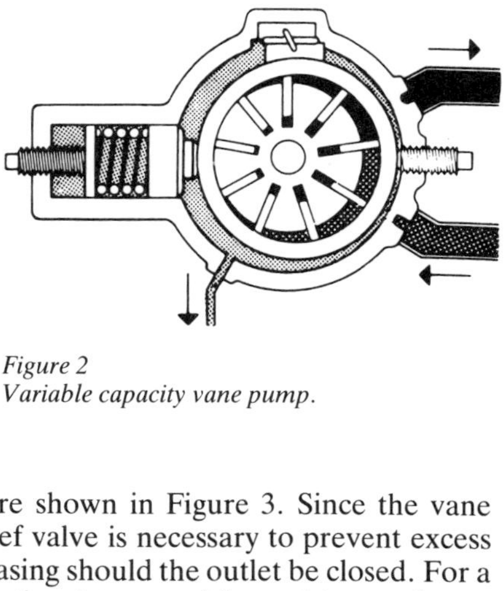

Figure 2
Variable capacity vane pump.

Characteristics

Generalised performance characteristics are shown in Figure 3. Since the vane pump is a positive-displacement type a relief valve is necessary to prevent excess pressure being generated inside the pump casing should the outlet be closed. For a given geometry, delivery is directly proportional to speed but subject to losses through internal leakage. Theoretically delivery per revolution is given by:

$$Q = K(D_c^2 - D_r^2) \times W$$

where:

Q = delivery/rev

D_c = casing internal diameter

D_r = rotor diameter

W = length of rotor

K is an empirical factor determined by internal geometry

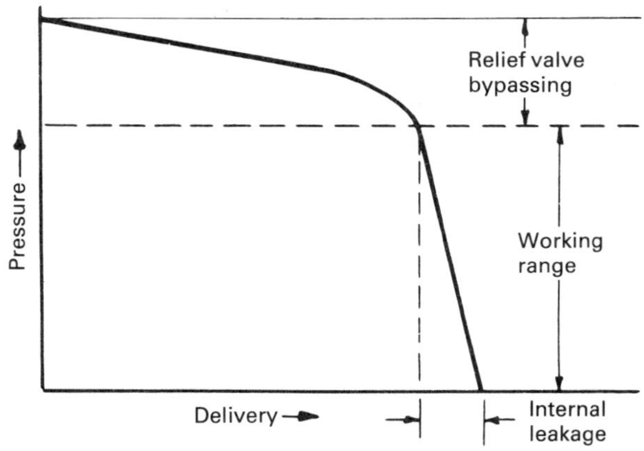

Figure 3

Number of Vanes
The optimum number of vanes depends on the fluid viscosity, with the shape of the casing designed to provide uniform acceleration and deceleration of the blades as well as to avoid trapping the vanes. In general, a large number of blades are used in a vane pump designed for handling gases, (*eg* compressors and exhausters) and a smaller number (typically six or eight) for low viscosity liquid. For handling higher viscosity liquids it is advantageous to decrease the number of blades still further and it may also be necessary to reduce the operating speed.

Instead of relying purely on centrifugal force to throw the vanes outwards, they may be individually spring loaded to ensure an adequate sealing pressure at all speeds, or fluid-assisted by shaping the blade so that pressure is laid down to the bottom of the blades to force them outwards. Cam rings may also be used to ensure positive outward movement of the vanes when the pump is started from cold, especially when such pumps are used on intermittent duty. Without mechanical or pressure extension lightweight vane pumps are likely to be unreliable if operated at speeds below 500 r/min.

Wear
Normally wear on both vane tips and casing is taken up by corresponding outward movement of the vanes. The vanes themselves are relatively simple elements which can readily and inexpensively be replaced when excessively worn. Casing wear is more serious however and can eliminated by fitting the casing with a replaceable liner or wear ring. The same pump cases could be designed to accommodate a number of wear rings of different thicknesses with the same rota, providing a range of capacities. In the case of a variable delivery pump, the wear ring becomes the obvious movable element to adjust the eccentricity. The main problems in this case are properly to control the movement of the ring and to minimise leakage around the side of the ring (usually controlled by the use of pressure plates). To minimise wear it is desirable that the geometry is such that the vanes are static relative to their slots (*ie* have no sliding motion in the slots) during the period they are under differential pressure and are fully balanced regarding side loads when they are sliding in their slots. These conditions minimise wear on the vane faces on the sides of the slots.

Internal Leakage

Since the radial pressure exerted by the vane tips is directly dependent on the speed of rotation sealing at low speed may be poor. This can be overcome by spring loading the vanes to extend underspring pressure at low rotational speeds; or as is now more common by feeding pressurised fluid to the inner ends of the vane slots via the end plates. In the latter case, the vanes can be hydraulically balanced at all times when again they depend on centrifugal force to keep them extended during rotation. Unlike the spring-loaded vane system, therefore, such pumps still need a minimum rotation speed to ensure proper pumping action.

End leakage is more difficult to control. For lower pressure pumps and where some of efficiency can be tolerated, fixed end clearances may be accepted. On other designs pressure-loaded end plates may be incorporated.

The sliding vane pump shown in Figure 4 incorporates fixed vanes and is suitable for pumping low to medium viscosity liquids. With flow rates up to 4900 l/min at differential pressures up to 150 lb/in^2. The shaft can be sealed with adjustable packing, single double-mechanical seals or bellows type of mechanical seals for special applications. The pump incorporates a replaceable liner and the unit can be maintained in place without special tools, without dismounting the pump or disconnecting the piping.

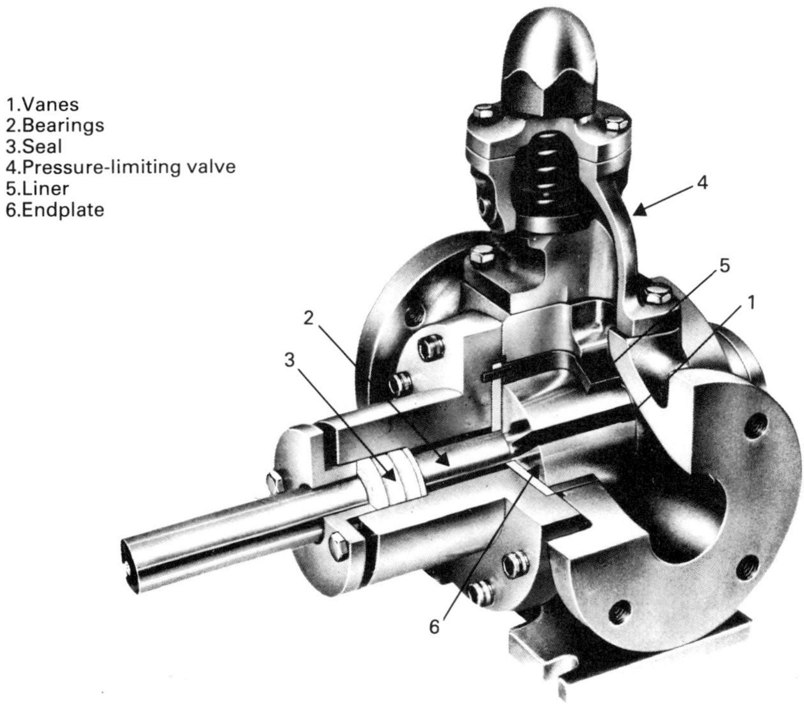

Figure 4

TABLE 1 – TYPICAL BENEFITS CLAIMED FOR VANE PUMPS

	Fluid types		
	Non-lubricating low visc,clean	**Lubricating hi/visc,clean**	**Slurries abrasives**
Production and performance features			
Non-metallically fitted for longer life	X		
Self-adjusting sliding vanes maintain higher volumetric efficiency longer	X	X	X
Internal self-lubricating bearings	X	X	
External bearings, anti-friction and gland types	X		X
Full or partial jacketing available	X	X	X
Alloy pumps are designed to resist galling	X	X	
Oversize porting available for high viscosity to minimise NPSH req.	X	X	X
Maintenance features			
Maintenance-in-place (MIP) – eliminates the need for disconnecting of piping and dismounting of pumps when servicing	X	X	X
Parts interchangeability between type and size groups	X	X	X
Standardised motor speeds of 1800 r/min for 60 Hz (or 1500 for 50 Hz)	X	X	X
Sealing control flexibility w/shaft packing, single- or double-mechanical seals (inside or outside; balanced or unbalanced or with flush connections)	X	X	X
Abrasive-resistant construction	X		X
Wear parts easier, quicker and less costly to replace	X	X	X
Safety features			
Pressure limiting valves fully sized for flow rate and viscosity to be pumped. Oversized valves are available for higher viscosity service	X	X	
Pressure limiting couplings used when fluid solidification is a threat or if the fluid or slurry character might cause a relief valve to be undependable	X	X	X
Inlet line strainers available for industrial, chemical and food service, including jacketing, for pump, drive, and system protection	X	X	X
Return to source PLV for shear, sensitive, volatile or flammable liquids service to avoid liquid recycling and overheating	X	X	X

Figure 5 shows a food processing sliding vane pump with capacities up to 2000 l/min and a differential pressure to 200 lb/in^2.

Typical design benefits claimed for sliding vane pumps are shown in Table 1.

Figure 5

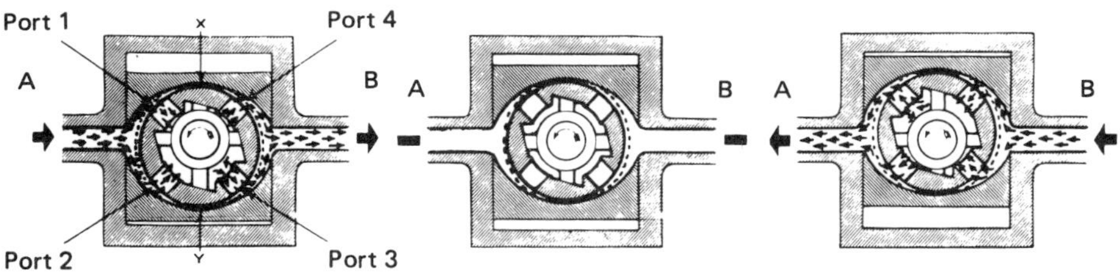

(1)

Port 1 is increasing in volume and drawing liquid in as indicated by the small arrows.
Port 2 has almost reached its maximum volume and is about to pass the seal at (Y) to the discharge side of the pump.
Port 3 has passed the rotor seal (Y) and is decreasing in volume, thus the liquid between the shaft and rotor is forced out on the discharge side B.
Port 4 has practically reached minimum volume and is completing discharge, it is about to pass to the suction side and thus commence another cycle.

(2)

Here the whole of the working parts are concentric, consequently there can be no displacing action, *ie* the pump is in neutral and no pumping can take place.

(3)

The inner body has been elevated to its highest position. The centre of the rotor being above the centre of the driving shaft, the filling of the ports is from the opposite side to that in *(1)*; the discharge now through the branch indicated by A.
In the case of *(1)* the liquid is passing through the pump from left to right below the driving spindle and in accordance with its directon of rotation.
(3) is the reverse of*(1)*, the liquid passing from right to left over the top of the shaft, although the direction of rotation remains unchanged.

Figure 6
Working principle of Plenty vane pump.

Plenty Vane Pump

The Plenty vane pump operates on a distinctly different principle to the standard type of vane pump. The major difference to a standard vane pump is that another component, the rotor has been interposed between the vanes and the stationary body (Figure 6) this rotor rotates in the body of the pump and has two sets of parallel flats machined on its inside surface against which run the flat ends of the vanes (or blades). The vane ends are angled and this gives a component of force to drive the rotor around. The pumping action is effectively the same as the standard vane pump *ie* the shaft centre-line is offset from the rotor centre-line giving expanding and contracting cavities as the shaft rotates.

The reasons why this pump has proved so successful is:

(i) Low wear rate. The tip of the Plenty vane pump is flat and gives a large rectangular area of contact and in one revolution travels up and down the short face of the rotor once. The result of this is that in one revolution the vane tip slides approximately one-tenth of the distance that a standard vane in an equivalent body bore would *ie* a standard vane pump would need to run approximately ten times slower to give the same sliding distance.

The periphery of the rotor in the Plenty vane pump travels roughly the same distance that a standard vane tip pump does so a high wear rate at the body/rotor interface might be expected. However, the contact here is similar to that of a plain journal bearing with a large area of contact around which hydro dynamic pressures are generated to support it and in practice a low wear rate is seen in this area.

(ii) Good volumetric efficiency. The large rectangular area of contact between the vanes and the rotor is reduced slip (or internal leakage) at the vane tip and therefore good volumetric efficiency.

(iii) No small parts. In a standard vane pump the vanes are held in contact with the body by push-rods, small springs, discharge pressure or centrifugal forces. The limitations of these methods are that the push rods are not self-compensating and as the vane tips wear the push rods become ineffective; small springs are prone to break under the cycling loading; discharge pressure does not give constant force and at high discharge pressures can increase the wear rate significantly; centrifugal force is only effective at higher shaft speeds and limits the pumps use on high viscosities where low shaft speeds are required.

The vanes in the Plenty pump are in fact one continuous vane (shaped like the letter 'H' passing through the shaft and two half vanes butting and overlapping each other in the middle of the shaft. As the vane tips wear very little this ensures that close contact with the rotor is maintained. There are only four vanes located at one position on the shaft allowing vane thicknesses to be made high without weakening the shaft.

(iv) Low shear rate. Because the pumping cavities are not in direct contact with the body bore, turbulence due to the cavity moving rapidly over a stationary surface is greatly reduced. This results in a much improved gentle pumping action which inparts low shear rates to shear sensitive products (*ie* additives, polymers, inks *etc*) and considerably reduces risks associated with foaming of the product which can cause severe production, quality and dispensing problems.

A common problem with standard vane pumps is pulsation resulting from only four or six vanes rotating a relatively low speeds. The frequency of pulsation is a multiple of the shaft speed and the number of vanes and generally the lower the frequency the worse are the results in terms of pump and pipework/system vibration. To overcome this, two complete sets of vanes on one shaft are mounted in two banks offset by 45 degrees to each other (Figure 7). The frequency of pulsation is therefore the same as having eight vanes.

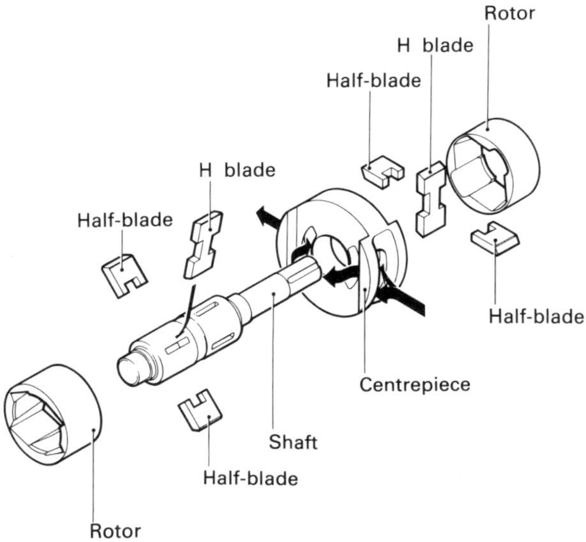

Figure 7

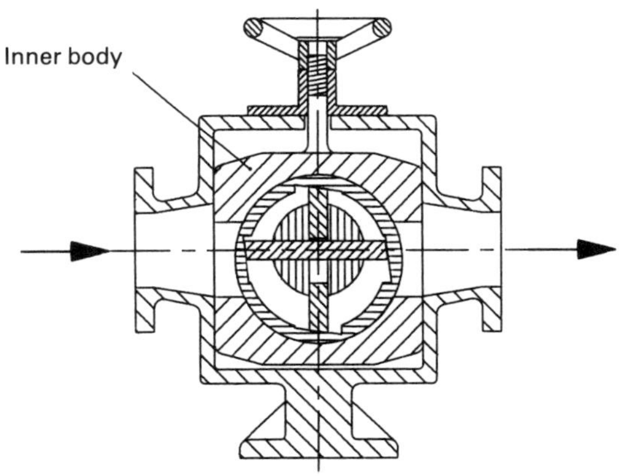

Figure 8
Plenty variable flow vane pump principle.

The principle of the Plenty vane pump may be taken one stage further if, instead of the rotor running in the main body, it runs in a movable inner body which can slide in the vertical plane in the main body (see Figure 8). By doing this it is possible to vary the eccentricity of shaft relative to the rotor which has the effect of giving infinite variation of the flow rate from full flow in one direction through zero flow to full flow in the opposite direction this is done with no variation of the input shaft speed.

Flow rates of Plenty vane pumps are up to 250 m^2 (from a single pump) and discharge pressure up to 13·8 bar are possible.

Energy Savings

An area where potentially high energy savings are to be made is in the application of variable flow rate vane pumps (using constant pressure control) to systems and processes where fluid demand is not constant. Examples of this are:

(i) Suction boost to high pressure pumps.
(ii) Drum/can filling applications.
(iii) Fuel oil ring main systems.
(iv) Blending systems.
(v) Road/rail car loading.

Consider the two systems illustrated in Figures 9 and 10. Figure 9 shows a fixed capacity pump installed in a system where the demand at B is either at variable or intermittent. As the flow rate from the pump is fixed the varying demand at B requires the excess to be recircled and this is generally achieved using a pressure control valve (relief valve) to return the excess to the suction side of the pump. Power input to the pump is proportional to flow and pressure. Therefore as the flow from the pump is always fixed pressure will rise marginally when recirculating (due to valve accumulation) the power input will be higher than the normal running power, *ie*, if 30% of the flow is recircled then approximately 30% of the power input is wasted and dissipated as heat.

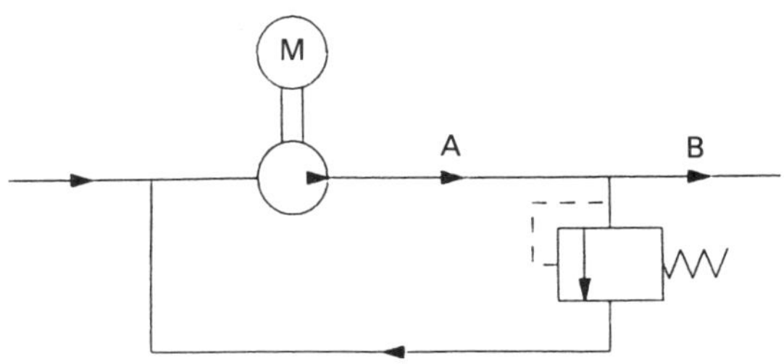

Figure 9
Fixed-flow pump with pressure control valve.

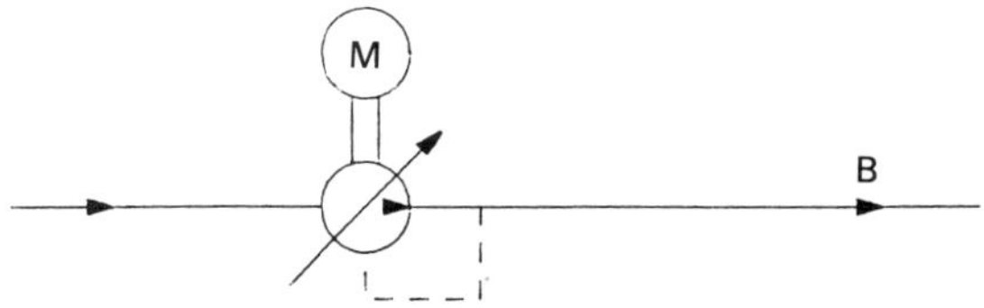

Figure 10
Variable-flow vane pump fitted with constant pressure control.

Figure 10 shows a variable flow rate vane pump with constant pressure control in a similar system. In the variable flow vane pump the variation is achieved by altering the eccentricity of the rotor relative to the centre-line of the shaft. This, therefore, modifies the basic theoretical throughput and does not require any shaft speed variation. Because the theoretical flow rate is varied, heat generation at low flow rates is minimal. Control of the flow variation may be achieved either:

(i) Manually with a handwheel.

(ii) Remotely using an electric or pneumatic actuator.

(iii) Automatically using the constant pressure control system.

The constant pressure control (CPC) system operates by hydraulically sensing the discharge pressure and when it rises above a preset (and adjustable) reference value the eccentricity and therefore flow reduced until flow rate matches demand and pressure is constant as shown in Figure 11. With zero demand the pump is in the neutral position and delivers no flow.

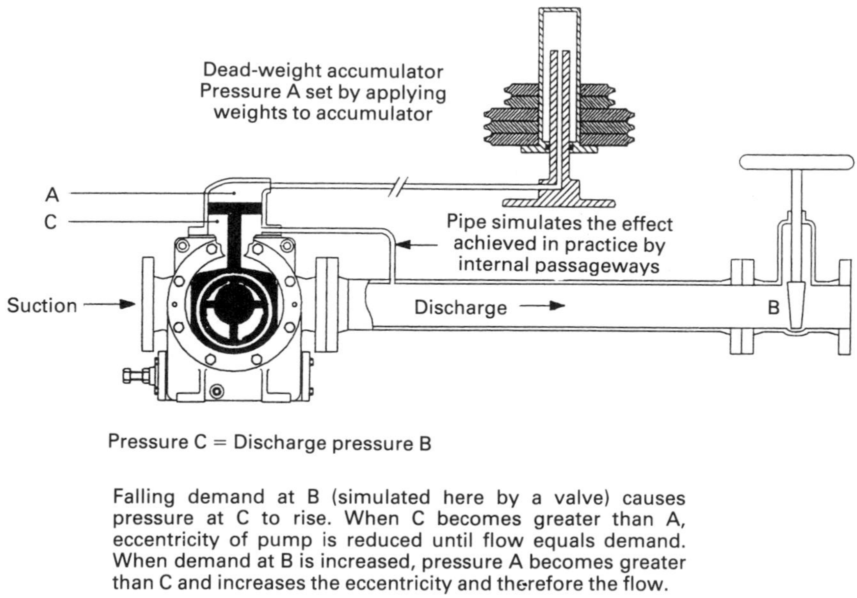

Figure 11
Variable-flow vane pump fitted with constant pressure control.

If demand is zero the power input is only the small value required to overcome friction in the pump and drive plus the small power absorbed by internal slippage. Compare this to the fixed flow rate pump system (Figure 9) where zero demand requires power input of approximately 10% to 20% higher than the normal running power *ie* 110% to 120% of the normal running power is being wasted.

Variable flow rate pumping in general may save costs in many ways for example motors are often oversized to cope with the infrequent requirements of cold starts. The high viscosity is associated with these will increase pipeline frictional losses and therefore the pump discharge pressure. This increases the required driver power size by an amount in proportion to the pressure rise. If flow rate is not critical it may be reduced at start up to reduce the absorbed power to an acceptable level. Likewise if power costs in a factory are related to various tariffs dependent on demand, the flow of the pump may be adjusted to bring the power close to the maximum for that tariff band without jumping into the band.

Variable flow pumps fitted with either hand- or remote-control are also particularly suited to other systems. Bitumen and grease production for example require the flow away from the production process to be varied in accordance with the rate of production. Blending systems are another example of where a variable flow rate is important and can simplify the quality control of the finished product.

Reverse flow feature of some variable flow pumps offer benefits in a number of systems. For example road/rail cars may be loaded or unloaded using the same systems. Also by using reverse flow, lines handling a variety of products may be stripped to reduce cross-contamination.

There are of course other ways of achieving variable flow rate pumping. One common way is to drive a fixed flow pump with a variable speed drive *eg* thyristor control,variators *etc*. Limitations here are that infinite variation right down to zero is difficult to achieve, response times can be slow and initial costs can be very high. Also as most contains sophisticated electronics the skill of maintenance supervisory personnel has to be of a high calibre.

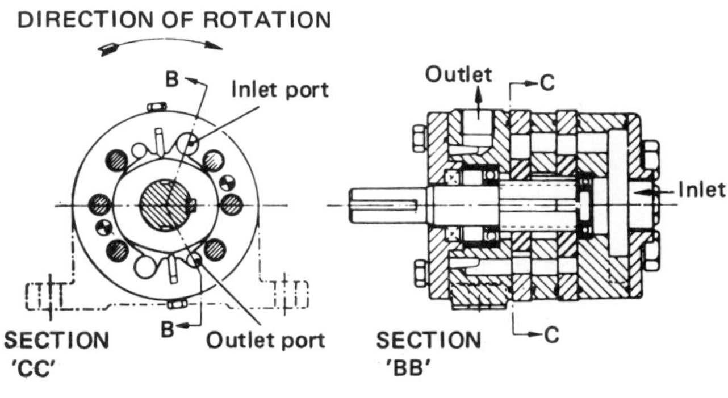

Figure 12

Other vane pump designs

The cam vane pump (Figure 12) reverses the normal configuration of a vane pump employing two sliding vanes mounted in slots in the casing. The rotor itself is plain and cam shaped, rotation producing a sinusoidal-type vane form displacement. Two such cells are mounted in tandem, keyed to a common shaft but with the rotors 90 degrees apart circumferentially. The combined output from such a double unit provides a constant delivery flow without pulsations normally present in a conventional vane pump output.

The push-rod vane pump (Figure 13) employs pairs of diametrically-opposed vanes linked by push rods which ride in a contoured outer casing which forms the roto.. Vane movement also controls the opening and closing of the inlet and outlet ports. Pumps of this type are normally limited to low speeds but can develop relatively high pressures or high torques when used as a motor.

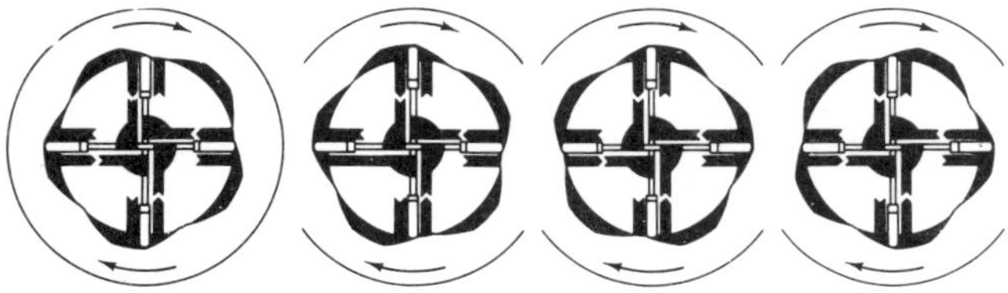

Figure 13
Push-rod vane pump.

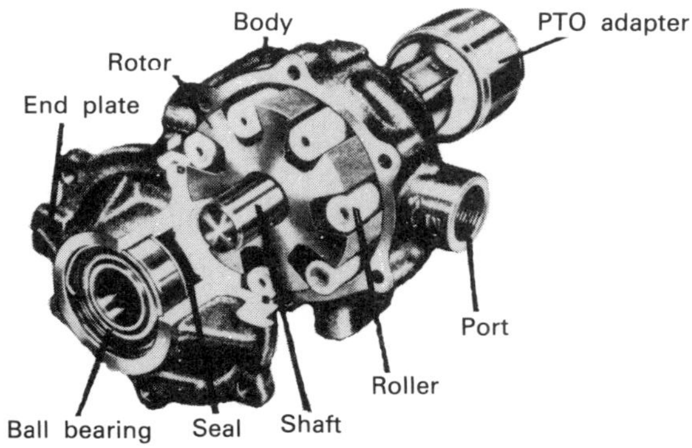

Figure 14
Hypro rolling vane pump.

Rolling vane pump

A further type of pump operating on the vane principle is known as the rolling vane pump (Figure 14) In this, the eccentrically mounted rotor is grooved instead of slotted carrying elastomeric rollers in place of the rigid vanes. A particular feature of this type of vane pump is an ability to handle fluids containing small solids and in this respect, it is similar to the flexible vane pump. It is however capable of generating higher delivery pressures than a flexible vane pump and finds particular application for agricultural spraying work *etc*.

Flexible Impeller Pumps

FLEXIBLE IMPELLER pumps have been available for around 40 years. Yet, although they have come to be regarded as almost the standard pump in certain applications such as the wine industry, the milk tanker business and in engine cooling, the full potential of this simple and relatively low cost product has not yet been realised.

In general the flexible impeller pump has much of the characteristics of a sliding vane pump but is limited in maximum head (pressure) it can develop because of the flexible nature of the elastomeric impeller. It is also more limited in terms of practical sizes in which it can be produced, but is a very useful type for handling a wide variety of non-viscous and low viscosity fluids provided a suitable casing and shaft material and a compatible elastomer are employed.

Usually a flexible impeller pump is similar in appearance to a rotary semi-positive displacement pump which combines the characteristics of roto dynamic (centrifugal pumps) and rotary positive displacement pumps. The pumping action of a flexible impeller pump is shown in Figure 1. A flexible elastomeric impeller is mounted centrally in a substantially circular casing incorporating an eccentric section. Intake and outlet ports are positioned at the ends of this eccentric section.

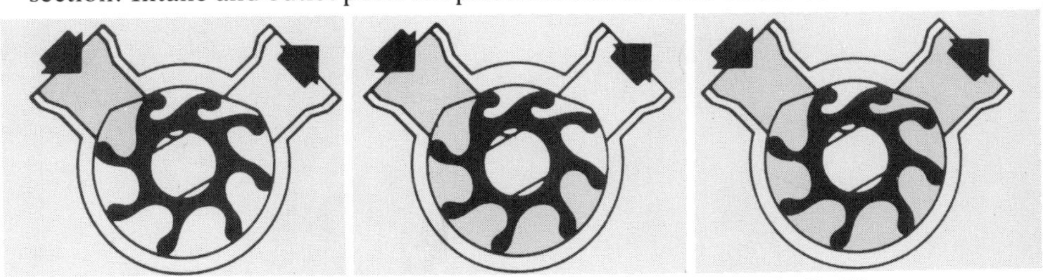

Flexible vane creates increased volume when leaving the eccentric cam piece creating a vacuum thus drawing in liquid, instantly priming the pump.

As the flexible vanes rotate the liquid is carried through the pump from the inlet to the outlet port, each successive vane drawing in liquid.

When the flexible vanes again contact the eccentric cam piece they bend with a squeezing action which provides a continuous, uniform discharge of liquid.

Figure 1

On rotation, when the impeller leaves the eccentric section of the pump body, the flexible impeller blades extend to create a partial vacuum (*ie* the volume in the pump chambers increases), as a result of this, the liquid is suction into the pump. As the impeller rotates, the fluid accompanies it from the suction to the feed side – while the following blade sucks in more liquid. Since the impeller blades are not rigid, this means that sensitive fluid can be pumped without any change in consistency and that comparatively large particles can pass through. When the flexible impeller blades come into contact with the eccentric part of the pump body, the blades are bent and the liquid is squeezed out of the pump in a smooth flow. It follows that such a pump will work in either direction of rotation (reversing suction and delivery), since the vanes will adopt a backwards curve on entering the eccentric section.

Priming

A flexible impeller pump has 'fixed' clearances only in the axial direction and therefore slip flow is only proportional to differential pressure across the end faces of the impeller. Around the periphery, there is physical contact between the impeller blade tips and impeller bore. The resulting sealing effect gives the flexible impeller pump a highly effective air pumping capability *ie* without liquid in the pump all but the smallest pumps will prime with water to a suction height of 4 to 5 m (13 to 16 ft) within a few seconds. No foot valve is required.

Dry running

The flexible impeller depends for its lubrication on the liquid being pumped. However as priming generally does not take more than a few seconds, the dry friction heat generated is minimal. A dry running period of up to 30 seconds is generally a safe length of time. After the pump has primed, air slip becomes liquid slip. It has been shown that increased viscosity reduces slip and it follows that effective priming increases with liquid in the pump.

Impellers

Impellers are normally made of neoprene for general-purpose applications. For handling oils a Nitrile† rubber gives better compatibility and for handling chemically-active fluids, a fluorocarbon rubber would be chosen.

The use of a fluorocarbon elastomer will however normally reduce the pressure rating and possibly also the self-priming ability. Polyurethane impellers may be

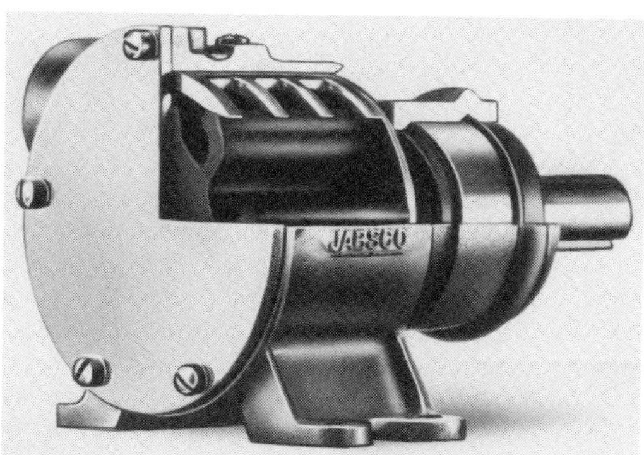

Flexible impeller pump – typical section.

†Du Pont's registered trademark

used where maximum resistance to wear and abrasion is required. The fluid temperature which can be handled by a flexible impeller pump is of course limited by the maximum service temperature of the elastomer employed for the impeller. This is of the order of 80 °C for neoprene and nitrile impellers, 90 °C for polyurethane impellers and 95 °C for fluorocarbon impellers.

Since the impeller is flexible it has the same ability as a swinging vane pump to override solid suspension, so flexible impeller pumps (preferably with a polyurethane impeller) can be used for handling contaminated fluids.

Impeller life depends on the operating conditions, fluid being handled and impeller material. Tip wear will not necessarily go up in loss of performance until relative bearing wear has occurred. Vane failure by cracking however, can result in marked loss of performance well before the vane actually breaks since cracking normally occurs on the 'leading' side rendering that vane ineffective. During long periods of standing idle, it is usually recommended that the impeller be moved from such a pump also when re-fitting an impeller should first be wetted or the vane tips slightly lubricated.

Applications

Flexible impeller pumps are widely used for applications where reliable instantaneous self-priming is essential (*eg* marine engine cooling), or where liquids with a high content of entrained or dissolved gas or air must be handled (fermenting wines and beers). Other applications include food, dairy, chemical, pharmaceutical and engineering industries. Typical products handled include dairy processing – buttermilk, condensed milk, cream, milk, whey. Beverage processing – alcohols, beers, ciders, distillery products and extracts, flavours, fruit juices, soft drinks, syrups, whisky, wines. Food processing – brines, cake icing, cane sugar, mustard, pickle relish, doughnut glaze, gelatine, honey, jams, jellies, molasses, sugar solution and vinegar, flexible impeller pumps are particularly suitable for fragile products without causing damage such as egg whites, cottage cheese, yoghurt, poultry giblets. Industrial – transferring foaming solutions with entrained air such as soaps, circulating abrasive and non-abrasive slurries (low speed), transferring inks, dyes, starches, fuel oil, *etc*. Chemical – circulating and transferring various

New generation epoxy pump.

chemicals such as ammonia, berium, copper sulphate, cyanide solutions, glycerine, nickel, chloride, silver nitrate *etc*; various acids such as boric, carbonic, citric, circulating photo-processing solutions. Pharmaceuticals – processing medicines, lotions, filtering pharmaceutical solutions, transferring thick and thin liquids such as cosmetic lotions.

Flexible impeller pumps can generally be mounted in any position to fit existing piping or if mounting space is limited can be fitted vertically. If mounted vertically, it is recommended that the pump head be in a downward position to prevent damage to ball bearings or motor should seal leakge occur. If the pump is mounted in a position other than shown on the installation drawing, it is recommended that pipework is arranged so that liquid is retained in the pump to lubricate the impeller whilst the pump is priming. Alternatively, if a chemical is handled that may have a deteriorating effect on the impeller, it is recommended that the pump is mounted so that it drains away whilst inoperative. It would then be necessary to limit the suction lift requirements to prevent dry running damage to the impeller whilst priming.

The flexible impeller pump is not generally recommended for process applications but it can be regarded as an ideal answer for all liquid transfer duties.

Peristaltic Pumps

IN GENERAL terms, the peristaltic (flexible tube) pump is a single rotor pump and consists of an elastic tubular element containing the fluid which is subjected to a 'squeezing or rolling' action along a predetermined length by a suitable mechanism – *eg* eccentric cam, fingers, shoes, rollers *etc*. The fluid is positively displaced by each squeeze cycle, repetition of the cycle producing continuous flow. The delivery is established by the bore size of the tube and the frequency of cycling.

In this category of rotary pump, the open to inlet volume, closed to inlet and outlet volume and open to outlet volume is bounded only by the inner surface wall of the flexible tube and defined by the locus of the compression points on the tube by the shoes or eccentric cams *etc*, and the body wall. The open to inlet volume is the tube volume between the inlet and first point of compression. The closed to inlet and outlet volume is the volume contained between the two compression points and the open to outlet volume is that contained in the tube volume between the pump outlet and the adjacent point of compression. Figures 1 and 2 show basic examples of the rotary action and squeezing operation.

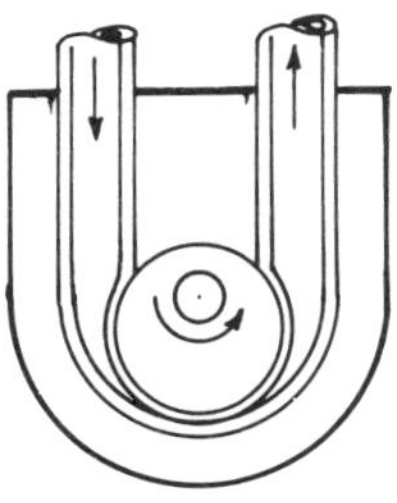

Figure 1

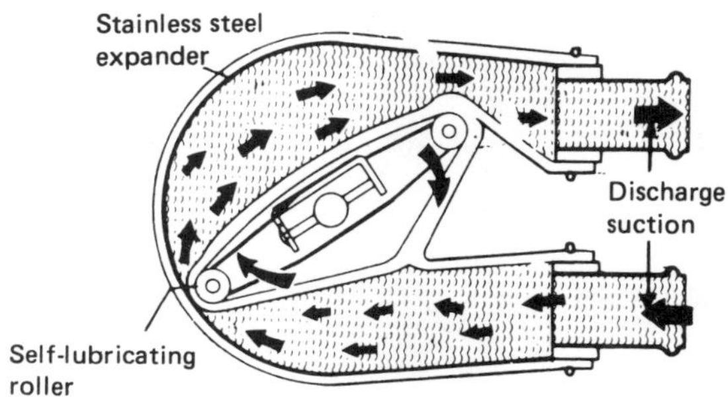

Figure 2

The peristaltic pump shown in Figure 3 is known as the 'hose pump'. In this unit, a composite resilient nylon reinforced and laminated Buna or natural rubber hose is enclosed in a casing flanged at both ends and connected to the suction and discharge lines of the system. A rotor located within the pump casing is fitted with two aluminium pressing shoes located at opposite points about the rotor centre-line.

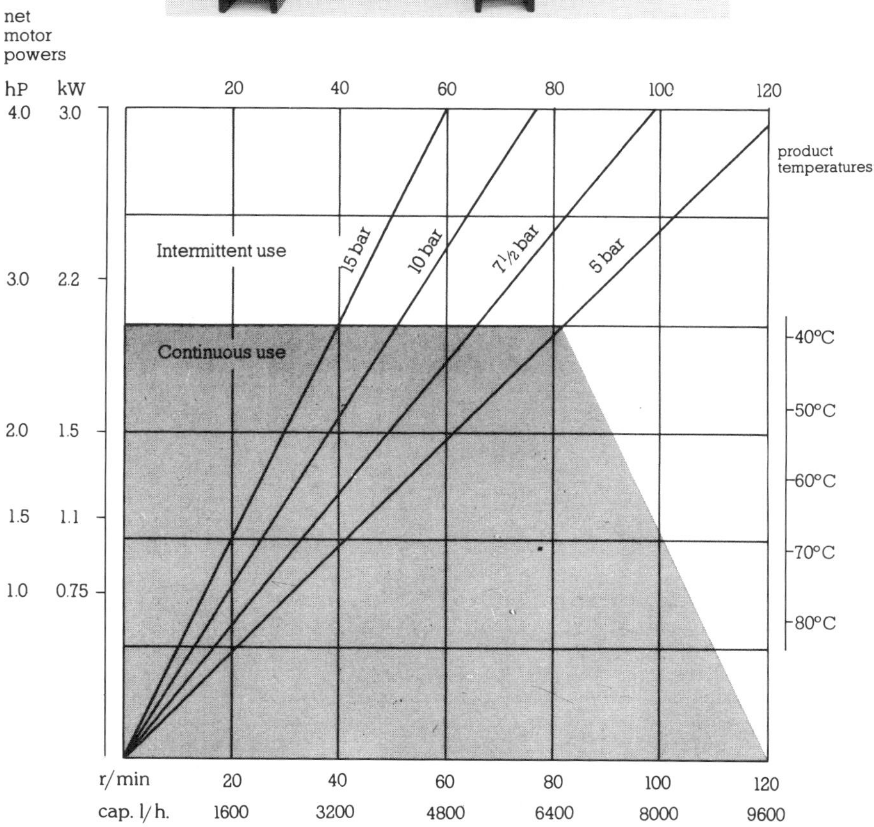

Figure 3
A 25 to 100 peristaltic hose pump.

As the rotor rotates, the hose is totally compressed by the shoes and product within the hose is pushed forward. The pump casing is half filled with a specially formulated glycerine mixture which functions as both lubricant and coolant.

The tendency of certain pumps of this type is to pull or slide the hose through the pump casing as it is fully compressed. The patented design and vulcanising method of the rubber hose fitted to the pump shown in Figure 3 virtually eliminates this problem and ensures that compression is evenly applied across the full width of the hose. Rigidity of the hose is provided by braided layers of nylon reinforcement strategically placed within the hose so that after the pressing shoe has passed and compression ceases, the hose reforms immediately. This makes the pump self-priming and capable of creating a vacuum of up to 95 kPA. The reinforcement also adds considerable mechanical strength producing an expected hose life of between 2000 to 3000 hours and longer.

As the hose is completely compressed twice per revolution of the rotor the natural rubber or Buna elastomers used for the inner layer provide for a wide range of applications.

Total hose compression is particularly important and this is achieved by adjusting the pressing shoes using shims. The number of shims used varying with the pump speed and operating pressure.

Differential pressure required to move the product along is achieved in two ways:

(i) The suction capability is determined by the rigidity of the hose and its ability to recover fully immediately after each compression stroke.

(ii) Discharge pressure is derived from the pushing action of the pressing shoe. As the hose empties product is sucked in. After compression by the pressing shoe, product is forced into the discharge line by the leading edge of the shoe at each half-rotation of the rotor.

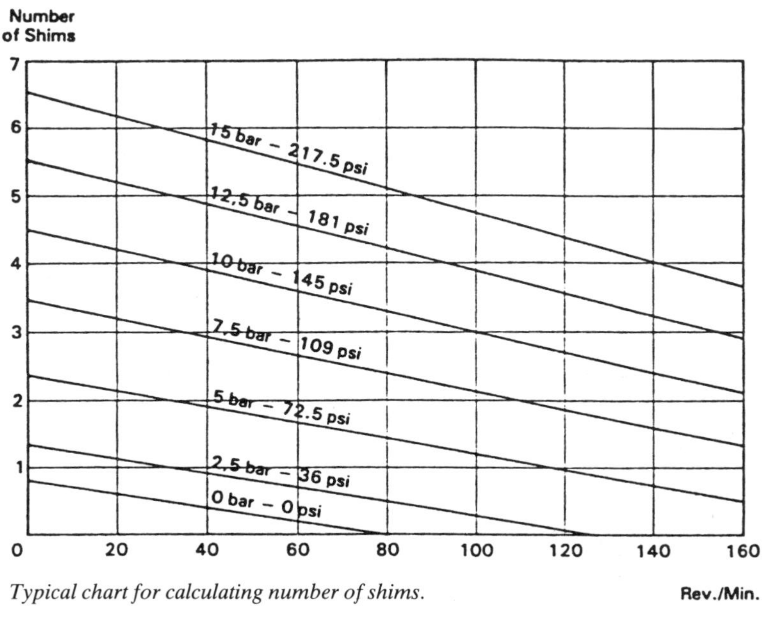

Typical chart for calculating number of shims.

The output of the pump is determined by the contents of the hose and the rotational speed of the rotor. As the shoe compresses the hose, part of the volume of the suction line is displaced by the shoe. As compression ceases, this volume is added to the discharge line. This exchange of volume produces a pulsating flow. The simple construction of the pump permits operation in either direction and in four mounting positions as shown in Figure 4. Because the pump can operate in a clockwise or counter-clockwise manner, the flanges can be used as suction or discharge connections depending upon the direction of rotation.

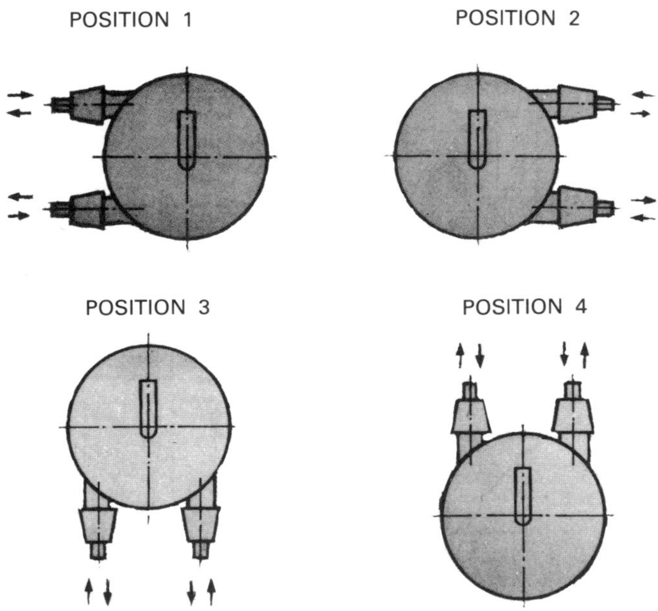

Figure 4

The main characteristics of the pump include:

(i) The hose is connected directly to the suction and delivery lines and no other component is in contact with the pumped product throughout the entire pumping cycle.

(ii) The pump is completely self-priming up to 95 kPa vacuum.

(iii) The pump is suitable for operating pressures up to 15 bar.

(iv) The exterior of the pump hose is permanently cooled and lubricated by the glycerine mixture consequently the pump can run dry without overheating or damage.

(v) Abrasive and aggresive media can be pumped with minimal wear and delicate, easily-damaged products handled without shearing or crushing.

(vi) The pump is capable of a high level of volumetric accuracy and can be used for metering and dosing.

Typical applications for the hose pump include water treatment, chemicals and pharmaceuticals, food and beverage manufacture, sugar refining, paper and board manufacture, ceramics, building construction, mining, tobacco, sewage and effluent treatment and disposal, brewing and pet food manufacture.

Products that can be handled by this type of pump include slurries and flocculants used in water treatment, sewage, sludge and industrial effluents, waste from fish processing plants, metallic oxide slurries, vegetable wastes, diatomaceous earth, molasses, mortar, foamed mortar, limestone slurries, plaster, cement grout, asphalt, carbon slurry, acids, lye, acetone, explosives, latex, paints, glues, resins, filtrate, clay and ceramic slip, wood and paper pulp, radio active waste, caramel, chocolate, jams, marmalade and jellies, meat products, creams, pastes, whole fruit, mayonnaise, thickened milk and other dairy products.

The peristaltic pump shown in Figure 5 consists of a flexible tube wrapped around a rotor machined to form three tangential curves which produce ridges terminating in small radii at three points. The tubing at these points is bent to a smaller radius than its bore and thus kinks occulding the tube. As the rotor revolves, the kinks travel with the radii providing positive displacement of fluid contained in the tube and trapped between the kinks. Again delivery depends on the bore of the tube used and the rotational speed of the rotor. Pump units of this type can be fitted with any number of separate tubes within practical limits (normally ten tubes in a module, but modules can also be coupled together to drive in series). They have proved a particularly economical type of pump for proportioning duties. More recently they are used extensively in biotechnology industry and for laboratory research. Typical examples are peristaltic pumps routinely used during the fermentation process in a biotechnology centre to feed various substrates into a reactor. As the concentration of these substrates is often critical accurate control of input is required. Many compounds including proteins, carbohydrates and alcohols can be used as primary substrates for microbial metabollic conversion into useful end products.

Figure 5

Normally peristaltic pumps are limited to low capacities and low heads. Even with a large diameter tube the rate of squeeze cycling remains limited. Capacity can be increased by operating two or more pumps in parallel and head can be increased by operating two or more pumps in series. A single pump may offer a wide capacity range which can be varied by changing the cycling speed, fitting alternative tube sizes or both.

With the exception of the hose pump, the limited capacity and head normally restricts the use of peristaltic pumps to specialised applications but they have also been employed for more general duties *eg* as hand pumps for water and also handling slurries and sludges. The particular advantage of a peristaltic pump is that

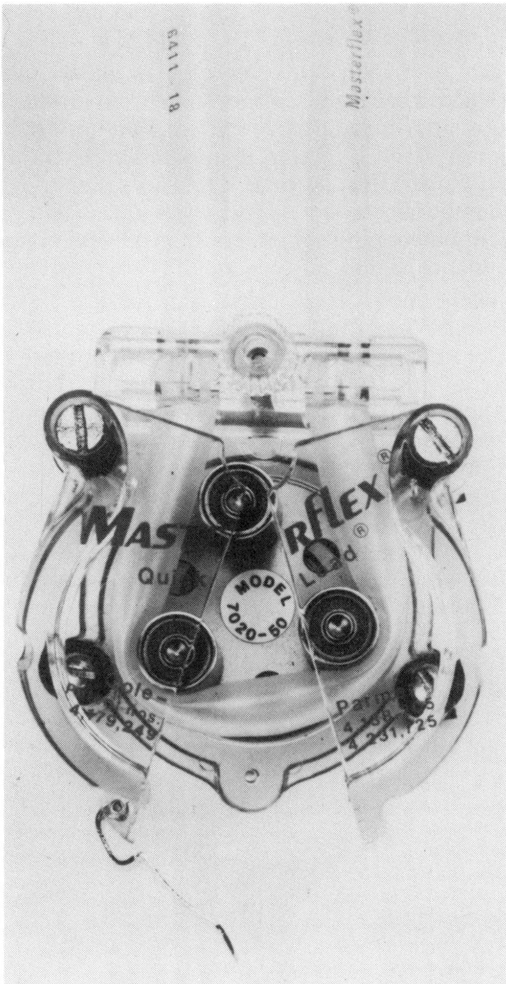

Quick-load pump head.

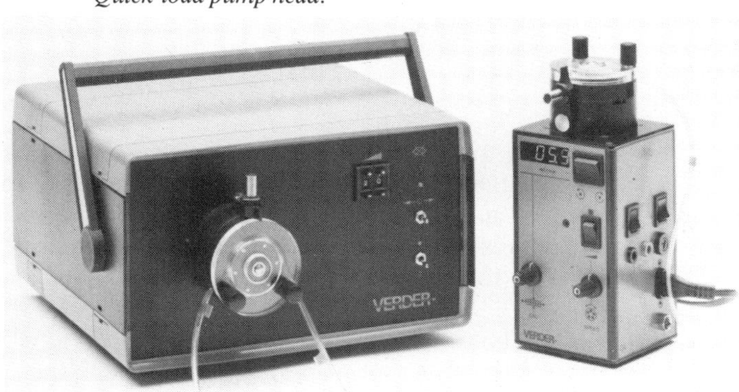

Computer-aided dosing pump.

it is a zero leakage type, in fact valveless pump which has only one component (the tube or hose) in contact with the product being handled. A suitable choice of elastomer enables it to be used for handling chemically active corrosive fluids. The pumping action is gentle though it can also handle shear sensitive fluids.

The pump shown in Figure 6 consists of two opposing revolving rollers alternately compressing a hose. A vacuum is created as the hose returns to its original position and this causes the suction of the material which is pushed forward by a second roller. The action of this pump is somewhat similar to the peristaltic pump shown in Figure 3.

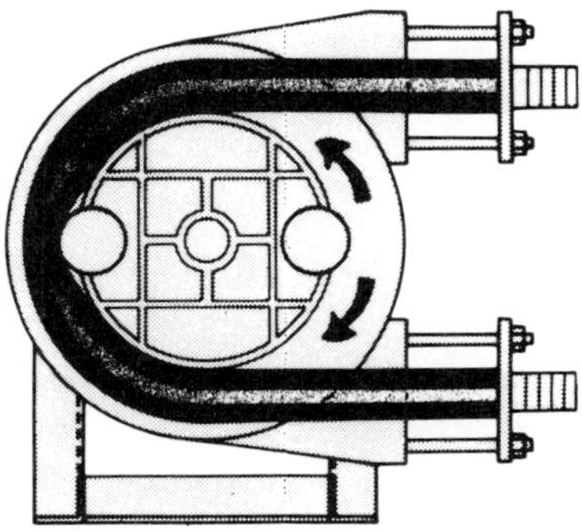

Figure 6
Two opposed rollers alternately compress the hose.

Related Types

The tubular diaphragm pump is a related type also employing a straighter elastomeric tubular element which is subject to contraction and expansion of the internal volume, either mechanically, pneumatically or hydraulically (Figure 7). Whilst the pumping action is similar, it differs from the true peristaltic pump in that it requires inlet and outlet valves to produce fluid transport. Its particular advantage is that it can be made with much larger tube sizes and thus larger deliveries per cycle.

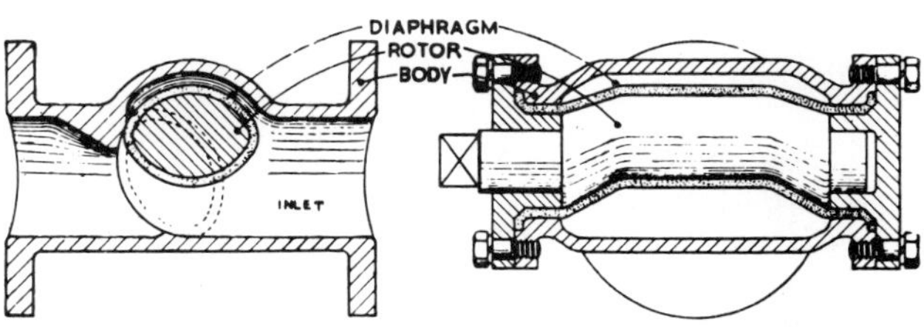

Figure 7
Tubular diaphragm pump.

Another example is shown in Figure 8. In this pump the pumping chamber consists of stacks of alternately flexible and rigid rings with valve assemblies dividing the chamber into three separate volumes. An eccentric drive is applied to the valve units so that they move alternately inwards and outwards, this movement being accommodated by the flexibility of the chamber walls. Through-pumping action is provided by back pressure on a further valve to the inlet side.

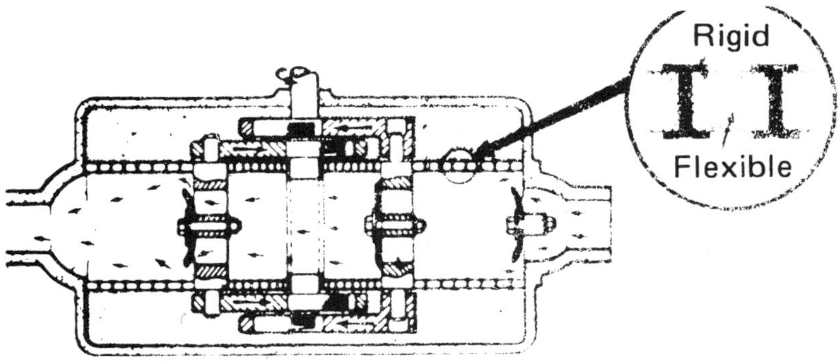

Figure 8
Line pump.

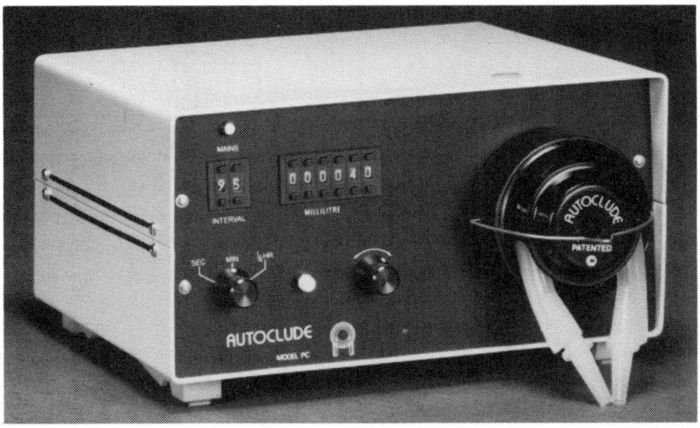

Peristaltic pump with novel 'snap-in' cartridge.

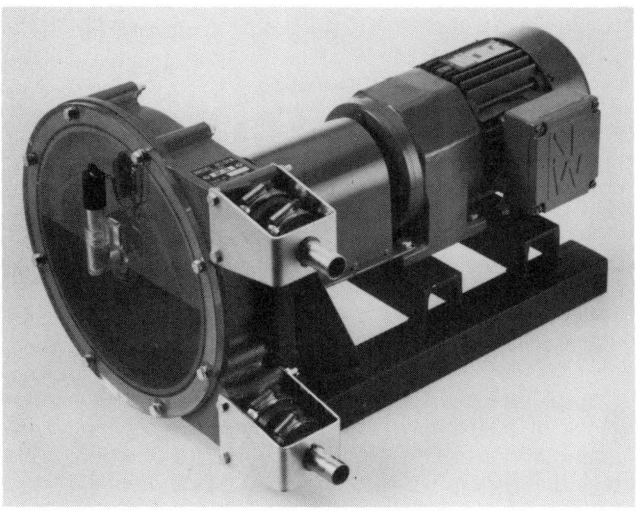

Hose pump, motor and drive unit.

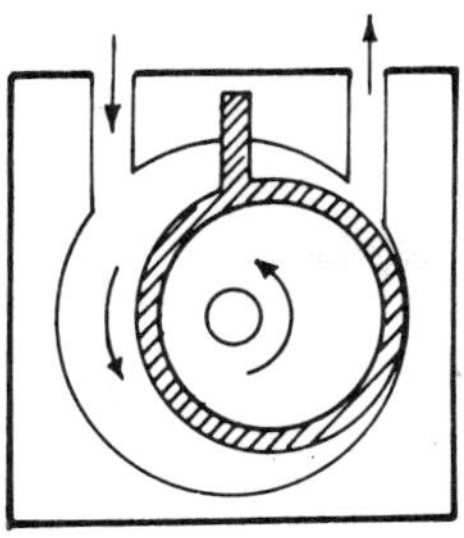

Figure 9(a)
Orbital lobe pump (diagrammatic).

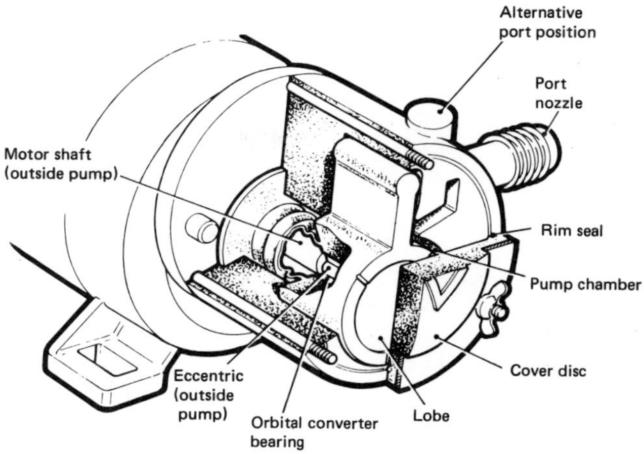

Figure 9(b)
Orbital lobe pump.

The orbital lobe pump (Figures 9a and 9b) also employs an elastomeric tubular pumping element, in this case in the form of a sleeve fitted round an eccentric motor. The interior of the casing is circular with simple inlet and outlet ports. The sleeve is anchored to the casing at one point when rotation of the rotor causes the elastomeric elements to be rolled around the inside of the casing, producing an alternating suction and squeeze action transferring fluid from the inlet to the outlet port. In effect this is a hybrid type combining the movement of a cam-vane pump with peristaltic action.

Metering and Proportioning Pumps

METERING PUMPS are basically special designs of positive displacement pumps capable of achieving a predetermined and consistent (repeatable) delivery. Metering and proportioning duties commonly call for the quantities delivered to be varied from time to time so the majority of pumps developed for such duties are of a variable capacity type.

Methods of metering or delivering measured flows include:

(i) Loss-in-weight systems – (gravimetric feeders) capable of yielding flow accuracies of 0·25% but limited to batching operations.

(ii) Closed-loop centrifugal pumps systems – for handling large volumes of low viscosity liquids, but only accurate within ±20%.

(iii) Piston-diaphragm (rotary) pumps – for metering viscous fluids with an accuracy within ±5%.

(iv) Piston-diaphragm (metering) pumps – specifically designed for metering or proportioning low flows with high accuracy.

Accuracy generally demanded of a metering pump is ±1·5% or better. These conditions are readily met by standard designs of plunger, piston-diaphragm and diaphragm pumps. Accuracies to within 0·2% or better can be achieved, but this normally involves additional expense and complication of equipment and is only justified in limited specialised applications. Also in the case of certain fluids, it may be necessary to accept slightly lower accuracy than normal to obtain better overall performance.

Sizes of such pumps may range from 1 m^1/h to over 30 000 l/h but most fall within the range of 100 m^1/h to 2000 l/h. Very much larger metering pumps are available *eg* capacity up to 70 000 l/h. At the lower end of the scale, where quantities delivered are minute, the type is commonly referred to as a micro-metering pump.

Metering pumps also offer other advantages, one of the most significant being the ability to carry out precise dosing consistently for long periods at time of high pressure. Another important advantage is that the accurate dispacement of the pump is virtually unaffected by widely varying discharge pressures. Metering pumps are often employed where two or more liquids must be proportioned where mixture ratios must be controlled. These effects are achieved by changing the displacement per stroke (by moving the crank pin by special linkages or by partial stroking) or by changing the stroking speed through the use of variable speed transmissions or electric motors.

In addition, a metering pump ensures the fullest use of chemicals by minimising accuracies and elminating spillages. This is particularly important for additives which are concentrated and involve relatively small quantities of metered flow.

The critical part of any metering pump is the pump head, or actual pumping unit. The main types of pump heads used in metering pumps are shown in Figure 1 and can be classified as follows:

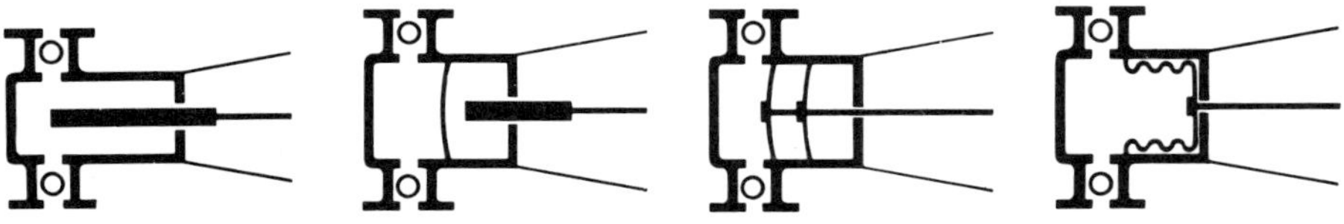

Figure 1
Types of metering pumps (diagrammatic).

(i) Plunger – basically a precision reciprocating pump with a plunger type piston and with a crank or similar mechanical drive. This type is most suitable for higher pressures.

(ii) Mechanical diaphragm – where a conventional diaphragm is driven by a mechanical movement. This type is limited in pressure capabilities.

(iii) Piston-diaphragm – where the diaphragm is actuated by hydraulic pressure developed in an adjacent fluid chamber, this pressure being generated by piston movement. This type can generate higher pressures than a mechanical diaphragm pump because of the more uniform stressing of the diaphragm material.

iv) Bellows – operate on a positive-displacement principle. The rotation of the rotor shaft is transmitted into an up-and-down motion through a lever pivot crank mechanism. This motion provides a continuous squeezing and relaxing force on an elastomeric or conveluted metal bellows module, forcing fluid in and out of the module. This has greater capacity than a diaphragm pump of similar size.

All but the plunger type are glandless pumps (zero leakage type). Rather more limited use is also made of another zero leakage type, the peristaltic pump.

Plunger-type metering heads

A typical plunger head is shown in Figure 2.

The rate of stroking is usually between 30 and 200 strokes per minute and must at all times be slow enough to permit the correct volume to be completely admitted and delivered at every stroke. It is important too that the liquid being pumped should not become aerated or contain an appreciable volume of entrained air, otherwise the pump is really handling liquid and air instead of liquid only and its performance is no longer accurate. On some designs delivery is adjusted by varying the speed of stroking the pumping mechanism itself then being of the fixed displacement type. Micro-metering pumps may exploit speed control more completely to achieve deliveries which may only be of the order of a few cm^3 per hour. To avoid having to use an excessively small size of pump, impulse timing may be applied to operate the pump periodically instead of continuously to deliver the required quantity in the stated time.

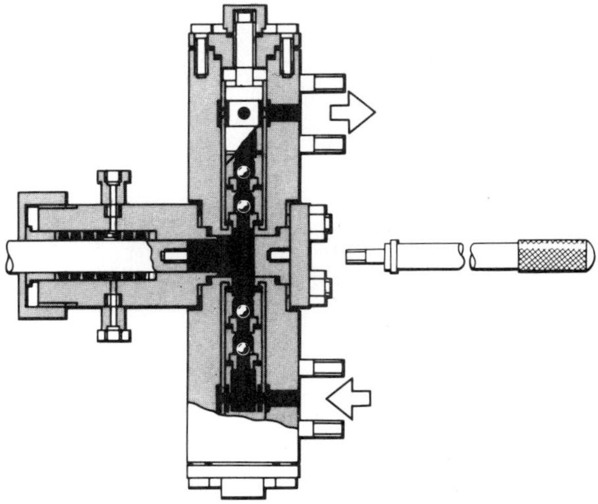

Figure 2
Pumping head for high pressure applications.

Double suction and delivery valves are commonly employed since this safeguards constant delivery in the event of one valve not closing properly due to some contaminant in the fluid lodging on the valve seat. The sealing problem can be reduced to that of the plunger seal, which is critical if accurate metering performance is to be maintained.

When the pump head is of stainless steel, gravity loaded ball valves or duplicated flap valves may be used with closely toleranced valve lift, or they may be of a more intricate design for special purposes. When the pump head is non-metallic, the valves may be of the glass or sapphire ball or cone type, depending on the size of the head.

Power is normally from an electric motor driving through reduction gearing as necessary. A single motor may drive a number of individual metering pumps assembled in block. Where the plunger is hydraulically operated rather than mechanically driven, this also simplifies stroke control.

Displacement is directly proportional to the stroke. Linear stroke (and thus displacement) control can be provided by a micrometer screw altering the throw of an eccentric, or some similar means. The main requirement is that any such method of adjustment should eliminate loss motion as far as practicable, and preferably also provide true linear adjustment (although this is not absolutely necessary). Stroke control can be extended over the full range, but at very small values of stroke, control with tend to become unreliable and critical. The practical working range thus normally ceases a little above zero stroke, *ie* at a positive value for delivery rather than zero delivery. Adjustment for any capacity over the working range becomes less critical with increasing capacity; and is also less critical the higher the stroke:bore ratio. For this latter reason long stroke small bore plungers are normally adopted for metering pumps.

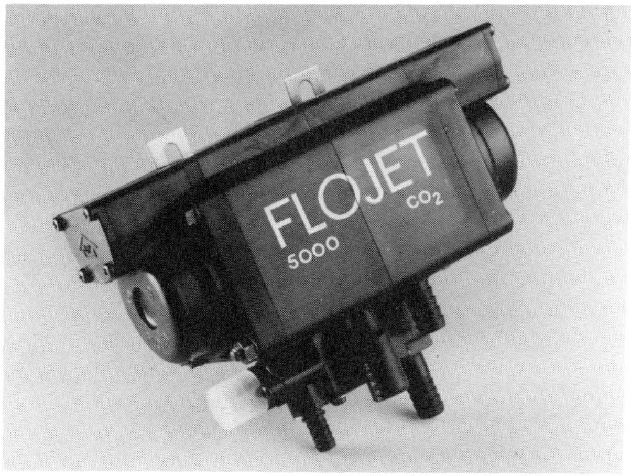

Fully automatic CO_2 driven dispensing pump for Bag-in-Box systems.

The plunger type pump generally provides a rugged durable head suitable for a wide range of applications. Accuracy is good although the slight leakage of the product being pumped may be disadvantageous in certain applications.

Leakage can be kept to a tolerable minimum for a time by good maintenance or by fitting a lip seal with a non-adjustable gland, when no appreciable leakage will occur due to the pressure in the pumping chamber pressing the lip onto the plunger. The seals are available in a variety of materials including synthetic rubbers and plastics. When lip seals cannot be used because of corrosion, PTFE chevron rings may be used.

For higher pressures and temperatures special study must be devoted to the gland. Lantern rings are frequently fitted into the gland packing to flush the plunger or to prevent leakage or dangerous liquids. By the use of newer synthetic materials and packing arrangements, many former hazards associated with toxic or dangerous liquids or abrasive slurries have been overcome.

In the case of inert or inexpensive liquids, any leakage may at the worst be only a nuisance, but if the liquid is corrosive it may damage parts of the pump on which it drips or splashes and if the liquid is flammable, explosive or toxic, the leakage may be dangerous.

In general the advantages of plunger type metering pumps are:

(i) Mechanical simplicity;
(ii) Pressure capability;
(iii) Relatively low cost;
(iv) Wide range;
(v) Accuracy.

Disadvantages are:

(i) Packing leakage making it unsuitable for corrosive or dangerous chemicals;
(ii) Gland adjustment required during the packing and plunger wear;
(iii) Slurries or chemicals which crystalise cannot be pumped.

Mechanical diaphragm heads

The reciprocating drive is connected directly to the centre of an elastomeric diaphragm (or in some cases a stainless steel diaphragm) Figure 3. Only simple valves are required (usually balls, but sometimes cones) since pressures generated are not high. This is the least expensive type to produce but accuracy is not generally as good as that of a plunger pump and the uneven loading of the diaphragm makes it subject to fatigue and eventual rupture. It can however handle a wide range of fluids including those with solids in suspension.

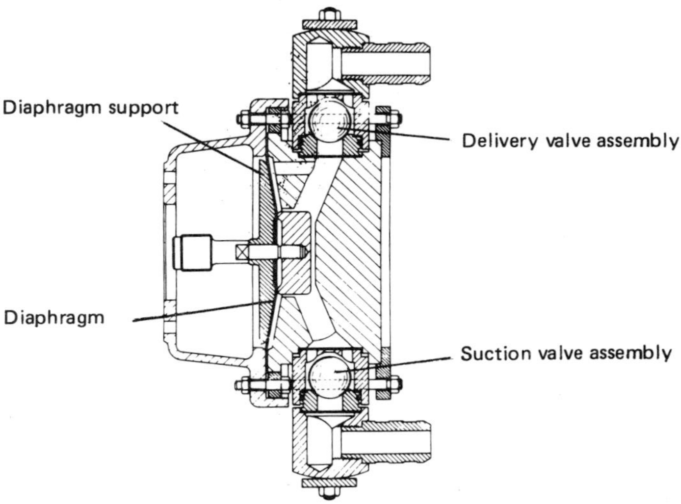

Figure 3
Typical diaphragm head.

The possible consequences arising from diaphragm failure can be obviated by incorporating a second diaphragm to act as a seal in the event of failure of the main diaphragm. Two examples of double-diaphragm heads are shown in Figure 4.

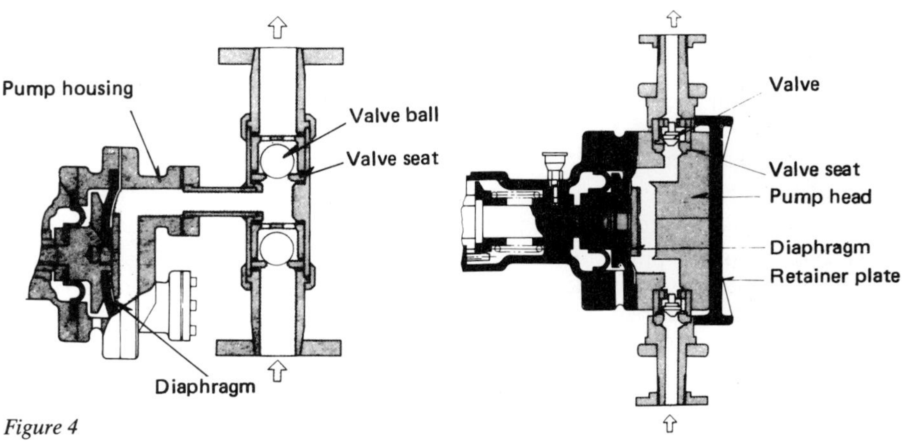

Figure 4

Hydraulic diaphragm heads

The hydraulically-actuated diaphragm pump is a hybrid design which provides the principle advantages of the other two types. A packed plunger is used to pulse hydraulic oil against the back-side of the diaphragm.

A variation of the conventional hydraulically-driven diaphragm pump applies the stroke control directly to the diaphragm instead of to the hydraulic piston. The diaphragm is designed to withstand the large pressure differences generated, and a hydraulically-coupled second diaphragm is used as an unstressed separating membrane (Figure 5).

This arrangement enables one hydraulic cylinder to drive independently multiple-diaphragm pump heads, which can be positioned remotely within several meters. Since the hydraulic pressure cycle is not affected by the medium discharge pressure, the inefficiency due to liquid compression and metal strains does not cause a reduction of flow rate with increased discharge pressure. The flow/pressure characteristic remains flat up to 200 bar.

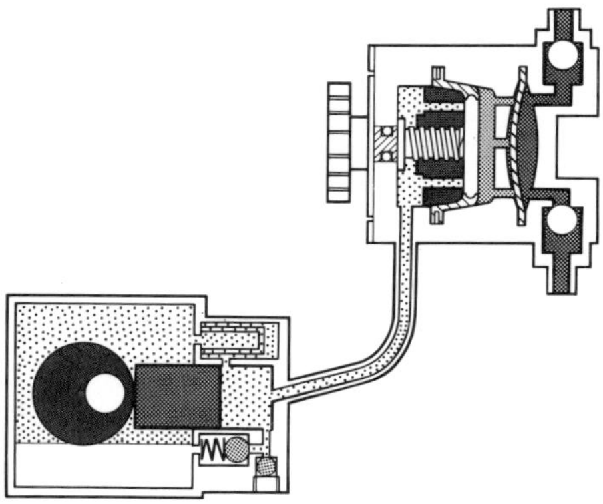

Figure 5

Isolating valves

A head can be removed and replaced with the other heads still running. The hydraulic cylinder can be bypassed to turn the pump heads on or off with the hydraulic pump running. Since the hydraulic pump is stalled against the diaphragm support on each stroke, the pump can operate continuously with the medium discharge shut-off.

A typical hydraulic diaphragm metering pump is shown in Figure 6.

In operation, the pump drive mechanism transmits a reciprocating action to a piston operating in a hydraulic reservoir. The pistons forward movement transmits hydraulic force against a diaphragm/membrane operating the pumping mechanism from the liquid being pumped. The diaphragm moves in direct relationship to the piston displaces process liquid through the outlet check valve. Backward movement of the piston reverses the cycle allowing fresh liquid to enter the metering head through the inlet check valve.

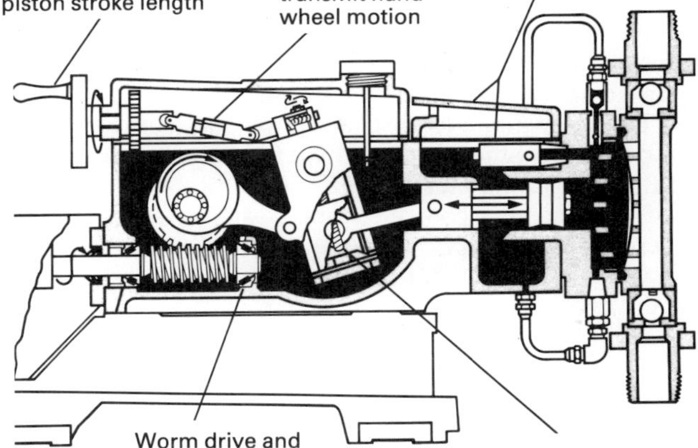

Figure 6
Hydraulic diaphragm metering pump showing drive mechanism including pump head.

The hydraulic diaphragm pump head in particular is finding increasing acceptance for those chemical and process applications involving the handling of additives. Currently, the most sophisticated of design, the hydraulic pump head offers the advantages of extreme accuracy, high pressure operation and the elimination of seals, thus preventing any potential escape of liquid.

The accuracy and working life of the diaphragm is dependent on the careful selection of materials and the geometry of the pump head, and the diaphragm head should be effective under widely varying operational conditions.

Horizontal metering pumps are designed to allow optimum space utilisation and future expansion.

The most common materials used are rubber or PTFE-faced rubber. However, the former has a low resistance to solvent or chemical attack and the latter can be worn away rapidly, exposing the backing, especially when particulate matter is present in the pumped medium.

Again, pumps of this type may incorporate a double diaphragm. In this case the space between two diaphragms is filled with an inert liquid, giving the unit 'fail safe' characteristics. That is in the event of failure of one diaphragm the fluid being handled cannot become contaminated with oil from the hydraulic socket. The use of double-diaphragms with an inert or buffer fluid between them also provides a simple means of displacement control, *ie* increasing or reducing the buffer fluid volume will increase or decrease respectively, the stroke of the diaphragm. Alternatively, variable displacement can be achieved by varying the stroke of the piston pump in the hydraulic circuit.

Bellows metering heads

In bellows metering pumps the flow rate of each pump is regulated by three factors:

(i) Diameter of the bellows module;

(ii) Speed of the gear motor;

(iii) Adjustment of the module/length.

Generally poppet valves are utilised to prevent backflow through the pump. Springs are available to provide a positive shut-off preventing syphoning through the pump in applications where a positive suction head exists. Bellows metering pumps generally operate within a flow range from 1·9 m^1/min to 3 000 m^1/min depending on pump configuration, gear motor speed and stroke length. Discharge pressures generally range from 5 to 50 lb/in^2 depending on the bellows module size.

Bellows pumps are repeatable from stroke to stroke to ±5% have a dry-run capability, are self-priming and have no dynamic seals. The single-stroke dispensing pump shown in Figure 7 is triggered by a switch . The crank makes one revolution before a micro-switch stops the pump. This unit can operate with a variable speed motor. A permanent magnet d.c. motor with a rectifier and control will permit adjustments from 12 to 60 r/min. The advantage here is that speed control combined with bellows stroke adjustments enables a wide range of flow rates to be selected.

Bellows metering pumps have been successfully used in a wide range of applications. The most common include: film processors, X-ray processors, soft drink vending machines, detergent and bleach dispensing system, medical and scientific equipment, silver-recovery machines, industrial floor scrubbers, water and waste water treatment systems, pollution control equipment, water and silicone chip washers and processors, and hundreds of other chemical handling and dispensing systems.

The complete pumping unit

Whatever the type of pump, the complete pumping unit usually consists of the prime mover – normally an electric motor, a gear box or reduction gear unit, and the pump head, sometimes called the liquid end. All may be mounted on the same baseplate, the motor being mounted above the gear box or in any other convenient position. Electric motor is usually of a standard type and of a horsepower to suit the application. The pump may be of the duplex type that is with two pump heads or liquid ends driven by the same motor and reduction gear.

Figure 7
Bellows type dispensing pump.

The two heads can be used to pump different liquids each at an adjustable rate of flow and at a set ratio to each other or they can be connected in parallel thus increasing the total capacity of the unit to double, if required. Other advantages are that a small pump with the two pump heads may be less expensive than a larger unit with one head. Also, the use of two pump heads out of phase will reduce the pulsations inevitable with one head, and will thus even out the discharge flow.

By means of shaft extensions or other means, additional pumps – forming triplex, quadruplex or multiplex units can be driven by the same motor to deliver liquids at rates in fixed proportions to one another as desired (see Figure 8). In some applications, where several liquids have to be blended in fixed or adjustable proportions to each other, three or more pumps are arranged on a common baseplate drive by the same motor each pump having its own capacity characteristics and all having an adjustable rate of output. Multiplex pumps may be arranged horizontally or vertically – an advantage of a multiplex pump that is arranged vertically being that the vertical shaft is driven by the electric motor at the base, when only a relatively small area is required even for 10 or possibly more pumps. Also installation and maintenance may be easier.

In some types of pump the shaft of the motor is coupled directly to that of that pump unit, speed reduction being by means of an integral worm gear. In other cases that shaft of the pump unit is driven through a belt-and-pulley and then through a worm gear. An eccentric maybe mounted on the low speed worm gear shaft, which together with the eccentric rod converts the rotary motion of the worm gear into linear motion. In some types of pump the eccentric rod operates the plunger or

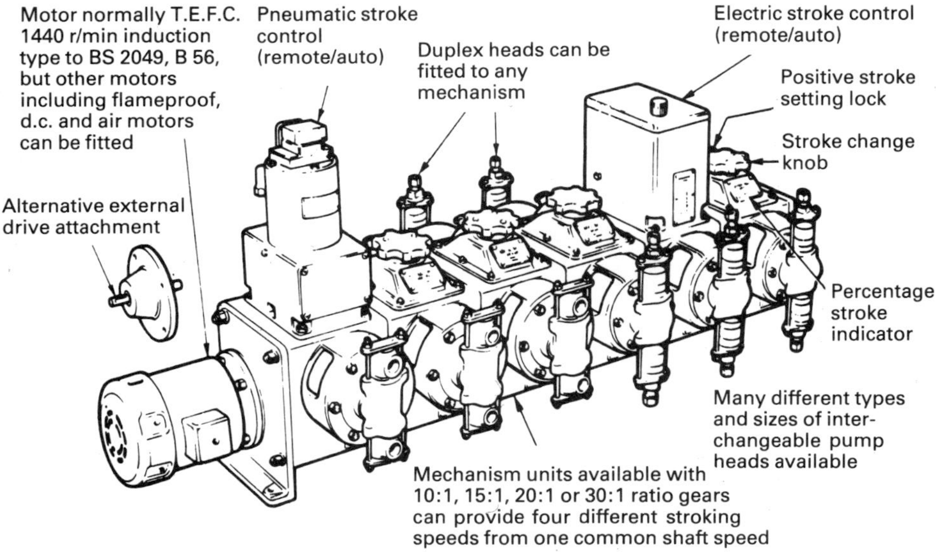

Figure 8
Multiple pump. A six unit assembly showing some of the versatile features.

diaphragm direct and in others through an oscillating arm or rocker arm. The reciprocating speeds vary from about 30 to 200 strokes per minute. In some cases a fixed throw eccentric is used and in such cases the pump can deliver only a fixed rate unless another form of stroke adjustment is used or a variable speed motor is incorporated.

Packaged units

A particular development in the application of metering pumps is the increasing use of fully-packaged chemical dosing units. These usually incorporate several pumps for active and standby duty chemical storage tanks and all interconnecting pipework controls and instrumentation.

Such units commonly operate with remote control or automatic control linked to microprocessors. Pneumatic control systems based on a low pressure air pilot signal are also used to effect pump stroke setting and/or speed control. These systems, being intrinsically safe have a significant role to play in installations in hazardous environments.

The choice of pneumatic or electric control of the pump is normally influenced by the plant conditions. This need not necessarily define the method of controls since the signal may be easily changed from either digital or analogue electronic form to pneumatic signal by means of straightforward converter.

Proper installation of metering pumps is very important if reliable pump operation is to be obtained. NPSH must be kept as high as possible, and the manufacturer's recommendations as to pipe size and length, strainers, relief valves and bypasses must be observed. The lubricating oil in speed reduction gearing, either separate integral units or built-in, must be changed at six-monthly intervals.

Diaphragm pumps usually require replacement of the diaphragm as part of routine service at approximately six-month intervals. On hydraulically actuated diaphragm pumps, the hydraulic fluid must also be changed.

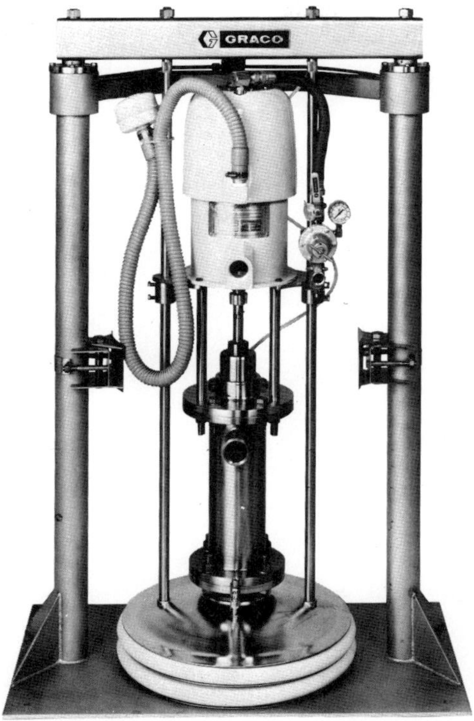

Air-operated metering and proportioning pump for sanitary applications in pharmaceutical and food processing.

Metering plus proportioning

A metering pump can fulfill the duties of both metering and proportioning. However in the case of a proportioning service the quantity delivered is made directly proportional to one major parameter (commonly main flow rate). In this case the metering pump used has its output directly or indirectly controlled by the parameter concerned (*eg* main flow rate). Where the control parameter remains constant for substantial periods of time, adjustment may be manual. However, in many processes, control is automatic, when the metering pump becomes the final regulating unit in a closed loop system.

In such systems it is first of all necessary to have a sensing or measuring device which will detect or measure the value of the parameter – *eg* an orifice plate or venturi to signal flow rate in terms of differential pressure or an impeller type flow meter to interpret flow in terms of an electric current signal. Changes in measured signal (variation in flow) then provide difference of error signal detected by a comparator. In the presence of an error signal, output from the comparator (a controller) adjusts the output of the metering pump until the error signal falls to zero.

Self-priming Pumps

PARAMETERS AFFECTING suction entry losses, and thus the suction performance of different types of pumps are:

(i) *Centrifugal pumps* – The pressure at the entry may not be reduced below the vapour pressure of the liquid. The entry must be designed to make the liquid flow into the eye and meet the impeller vanes at a favourable angle.

(ii) *Reciprocating pumps* – The liquid must pass the intake valve and follow the piston without pressure being reduced below the vapour pressure of the liquid. The liquid mass entering the pump must not 'channel' or form empty pockets.

(iii) *Gear pumps/lobe rotor pumps/diaphragm pumps* – The liquid must flow into an opening pocket during rotation of that pocket over a suction port without pressure being reduced below the vapour pressure of the liquid. The formation of empty pockets must be avoided.

(iv) *Screw pumps* – The liquid must flow into the screw chamber and follow the axial movement of the screw into the first chamber without reducing the pressure below the vapour pressure of the liquid. The formation of empty pockets must be avoided.

Of these basic pump types only positive displacement pump types (ii) (iii) and (iv) have the ability to create suction when started dry and are thus self-priming although there are exceptions. Thus gear pumps are not self-priming unless sufficient residual fluid is present; and vane pumps are only self-priming above a certain minimum speed. Centrifugal pumps (and other types of rotor-dynamic pumps) are not self-priming though it is possible to design them with self-priming properties, or incorporate secondary devices to give self-priming characteristics. An exception with these types is that the 'regenerative pump' is inherently self-priming.

Centrifugal pumps

Conventional centrifugal pumps, mixed flow and axial flow (rotor-dynamic) pumps are not self-priming because when dry they are unable to pump air out of the pump casing, and thus cannot create suction at the intake. This limitation can be overcome by operating such pumps on flooded suction, or fitting the pump with a suitable self-priming device in the latter case they are classified as self-priming pumps. Priming devices include priming nozzles, diffusers and ejectors; also separate air pumps. The same end can be achieved by ancilliary priming devices which may normally be associated with the driver rather than the pump itself; or by a separate mechanical, electrical or hydraulic system. A distinction is thus drawn between a self-priming pump (in which the necessary device to promote self-priming is incorporated in the pump itself) and ancilliary priming devices which may be employed to prime a pump lacking self-priming characteristics.

The self-priming pump shown in Figure 1 has been specifically designed and built for pumping water containing sand, mud and solids in suspension on construction sites. The vacuum produced as the impeller rotates draws air into the pump where it is mixed with the liquid contained in the pump casing. The air/liquid mixture is driven into the priming chamber where the air separates out and is expelled through the delivery port while the liquid due to the higher density falls back and is recirculated. When all the air has been evacuated from the suction line, the pump is primed and operates like a normal centrifugal pump. It can also handle a mixture of air and liquid.

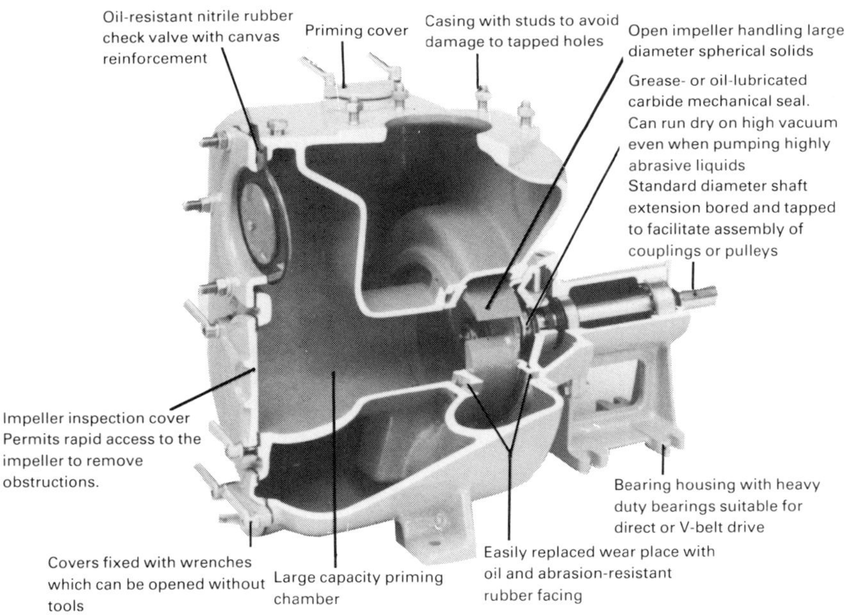

Figure 1

The check valve mounted in the pump suction port prevents the liquid from draining out of the suction line so that when the pump is restarted no time is wasted on self-priming. Should air enter the suction line, the check valve ensures that sufficient liquid remains in the pump casing for the pump to reprime.

Figure 2 shows the priming cycle for a horizontal self-priming pump of back pull-out design incorporating a reverse vane impeller.

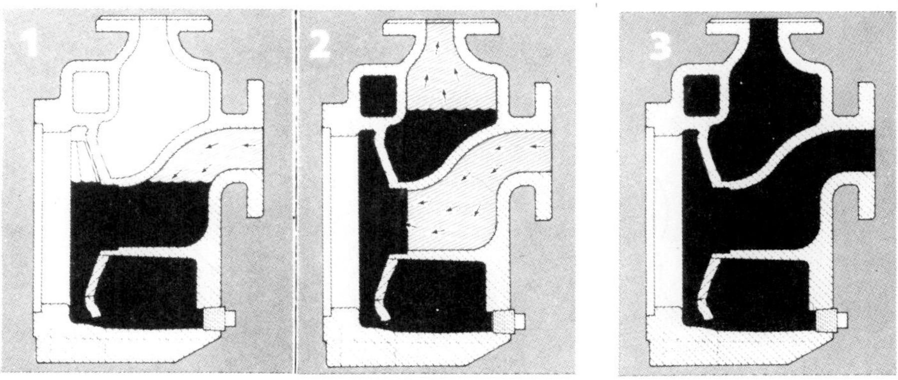

1.
For good priming a sufficient volume of liquid should be available in the casing. The liquid entrains air within the impeller.

2.
The air/liquid mixture leaves the volute and enters the separating chamber. The air/liquid mixture separates in the chamber with the liquid 'settling' and the air venting out the discharge. The air-free liquid returns to the impeller through the bypass opening for re-entrainment. The air re-entrainment and removal cycle continues to reduce the pressure in the suction line.

3.
The liquid rises in the suction pipe until the pipe is flooded. The pump then functions much like any end suction centrifugal pump. Once primed, the increased pressure in the volute reverses the flow through the bypass opening.

Figure 2

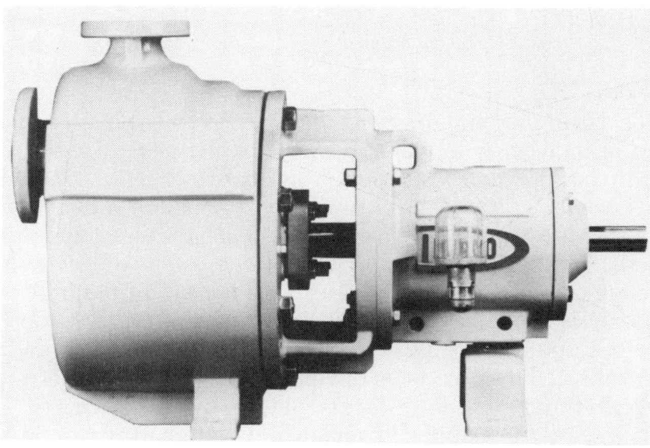

Unitised self-priming pump for capacities up to 318 m^3/h (1 400 gal/min).

Self-priming diaphragm pumps

Self-priming diaphragm pumps have a wide range of applications for pumping thick liquids or sludge containing abrasives or solids. A particular example is shown in Figure 3 where the flow generated by the movement of the diaphragm is controlled by flap valves at the suction and delivery. As the diaphragm rises away from the bottom of the casing it produces a vacuum which draws the liquid into the casing through the suction valve. When the diaphragm is on the downstroke the liquid is expelled through the delivery valve. A spring coupling rod comes into operation if irregularly shaped solids block the diaphragm downstroke. It also operates when the pump is used on flooded suction and sand or powders tend to settle and harden while the pump is stopped. When the pump restarts, the spring operates for a few strokes until the powder is remixed with the liquid.

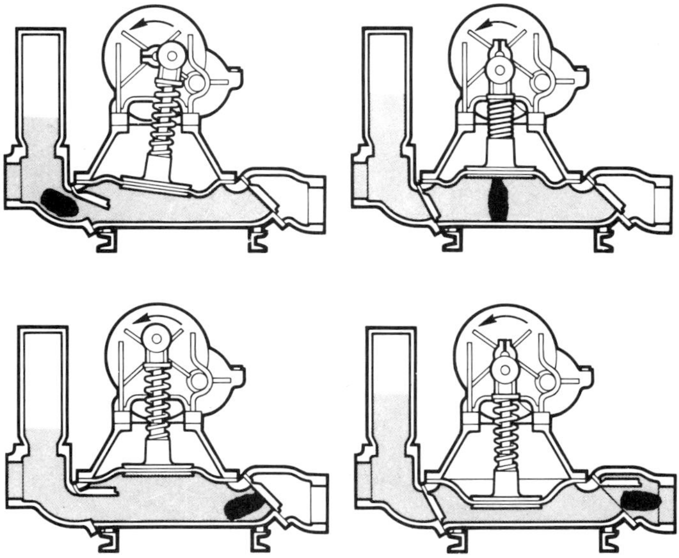

Figure 3
Self-priming diaphragm pump.

Priming nozzles

The principle of priming nozzles is to supply fluid to the eye of the impeller on starting up, this fluid being drawn from a residual charge retained within the casing after the pump has previously stopped. This involves the use of a casing modified shape, which has the suction branch at the top with a non-return valve to prevent syphoning back through the suction line, or a separate residual liquid chamber attached to the pump. On starting up, a continuous flow of this residual liquid is poured through a priming nozzle directed into the eye of the impeller. The flow from the nozzle is broken up into a spray, sweeping through the impeller and entraining air. Entrained air escapes through the delivery pipe and the liquid is recirculated until all the air has been discharged and normal flow is established into the suction pipe, through the impeller and out through the discharge. Flow through the priming circuit is then stopped by manual or automatic operation of a shut-off valve.

Self-priming jet pump suitable for water boosting etc.

Other designs of self-priming pump may have special volute designs or guide vanes to promote a 'nozzle effect' which generates a liquid air mixture in the impeller passages when the pump is started up. Air is then separated in a nozzle section; air passes into the discharge branch and liquid returns for recirculation. This continues until all the air has been evacuated from the suction pipe, when full fluid flow is established. The efficiency of the pump under normal working conditions is reduced to an extent controlled by the form of the nozzle device, which remains in the socket although with good design the loss can be very slight.

Diffusers

The principle of a diffuser is similar to that of the priming nozzle, provision being made to retain a residual charge of liquid in the casing when the pump is stopped. On starting up again this liquid is circulated through the diffuser passages to impinge on the impeller and be turned into spray. Air is then removed by entrainment as in the nozzle system. When the pump is running normally the diffusers merely act as recouperators.

Self-priming pump and engine.

Ejectors

Definitive ejector pumps or jet pumps may also be used as auxiliary devices to promote self-priming in centrifugal pumps. A certain level of liquid is retained in the ejector circuit, drawing in air from the suction pipe. Air passes through the pump to be discharged on the delivery side (usually separating out in a reservoir mounted on the pump outlet), whilst circulation continues until the suction pipe is completely evacuated and normal pumping is initiated (completing discharge of air from the reservoir if fitted). Since energy losses are caused by the flow through the injectors a self-balancing circuit is often employed, automatically stopping circulation through the ejector circuit once normal pumping is achieved. Ejectors have the advantage that they can generate quite high suction heads and are generally not sensitive to impurities in the liquid being handled unless these have a clogging action. In the case of solid contaminants a settling tank may be used on the suction side to reduce the possibility of solids entering the ejector circuit.

Secondary Air Exhausting Pumps

This self-priming system employs a secondary pump combined with the main centrifugal pump. The secondary device is commonly a liquid ring pump (the pumps may be in tandem on the same shaft) or a peripheral pump, which may be incorporated on one face of the centrifugal pump impeller (when provision must be made to retain a certain residual charge of liquid with the attendant side channels). The purpose of the secondary pump is to evacuate the air within the pump casing and suction line. As soon as the casing is filled with liquid the centrifugal pump starts up after which both pumps will continue to work in parallel.

Canned Motor Pumps

WHERE THE necessity arises for a zero leakage pump, mechanical seals replace packed glands. Even greater integrity is provided by canned motor pumps. A typical form of canned motor pump unit is shown in Figure 1. Major parameters related to canned motor design, construction and performance are covered under separate headings.

The basic principle of construction is that the fluid being pumped is allowed to enter the motor cavity with impeller, rotor and shaft running in the process fluid but the motor windings and stator are separated by a thin walled jacket or 'can' in the magnetic gap. Fluid circulating within the can both lubricates the shaft bearings and removes motor head. The shaft length is completely confined within the fluid system and there are therefore no external seals and complete leak tightness is provided *via* the can and pump casing. Canned motor units are particularly adaptable to vertical in line pump construction with either single- or multi-stage impellers. On larger units, where simple fluid circulation may not be adequate for motor cooling, a secondary impeller may be employed to circulate the fluid over an internal heat exchanger, heat being removed by water circulated over or through tubes in the heat exchanger. In such cases a separate source of cooling water is required.

Wash Loss

The most significant effect of flooding the water is the drag – or 'wash' loss – induced by the fluid friction. This wash loss is a function of rotor surface speed (Figure 2). Since power and mechanical losses are also functions of speed, it follows that the designer will be searching for an optimum between these parameters and electrical efficiency. The net effect of these considerations is that the design tends towards unusually large length to diameter ratios. Fortunately such an arrangement also offers the most efficient design from a pressure vessel point of view.

Can losses

The cage rotor design is eminently suited to flooded operation in liquids which may or may not be conducting since no external voltages are developed. While there is thus no electrical reason to shield the rotor from the liquid, it may become

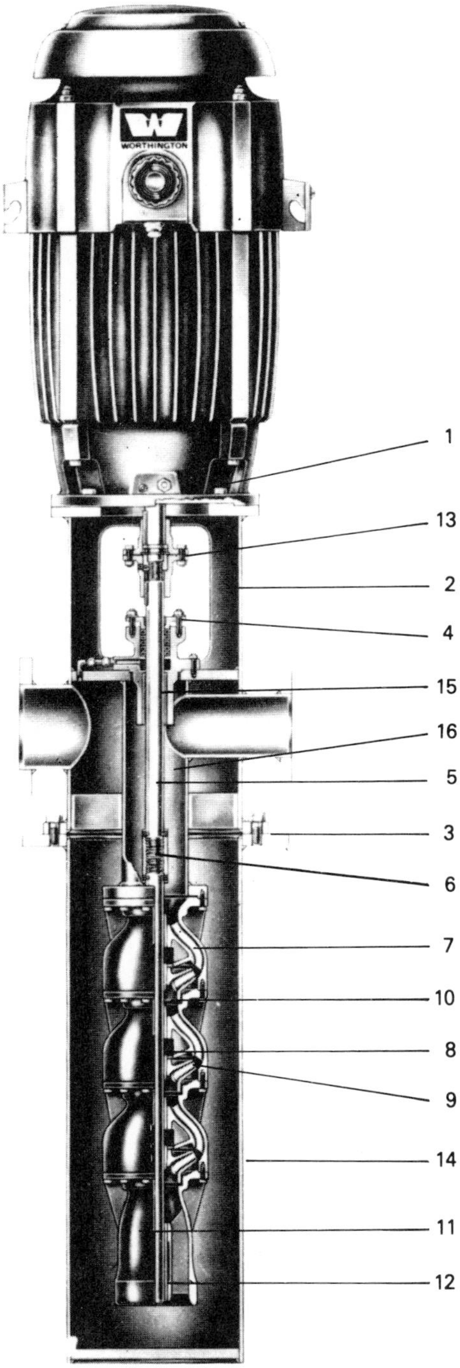

1. Electric motor
2. Discharge head
3. Base plate
4. Stuffing box
5. Shaft
6. Shaft coupling
7. Top bowl
8. Intermediate bearing
9. Intermediate bowl
10. Impeller
11. Suction bell
12. Suction bearing
13. Coupling
14. Can
15. Stuffing box bearing
16. Discharge pipe

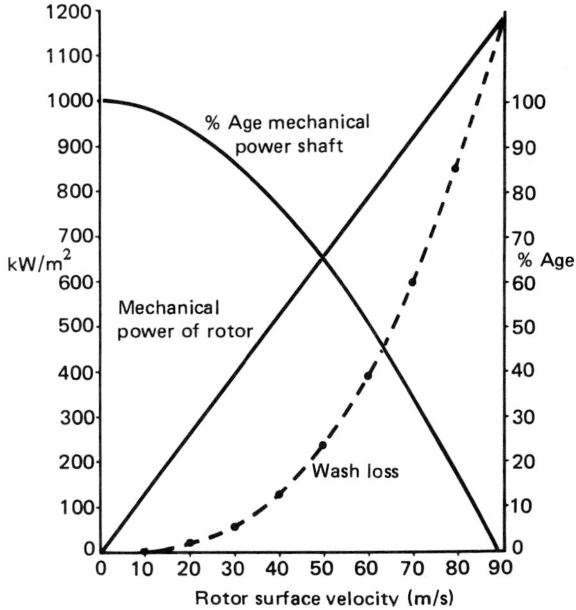

Figure 2
Losses in a canned motor.

necessary to avoid corrosion if the liquid is aggressive. In such circumstances a rotor 'can' similar to the stator 'can' may be welded to the rotor as shown in Figure 3 with little or no efficiency penalty.

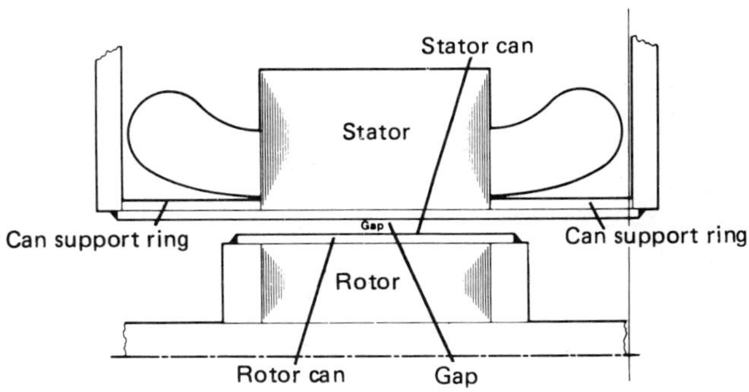

Figure 3

The presence of the stator 'can' and where necessary the rotor 'can' obviously has some effect on the performance of the motor. Mechanically, the stator 'can' must separate the windings from the liquid at whatever pressure. Electrically it would disrupt the magnetic couple between the stator and rotor as little as possible. At present these considerations together with the liquid compatibility aspect are best met by metallic materials.

Because the stator 'can' is subject to the main alternating flux of the motor, it experiences an appreciable eddy current loss. This loss is inversely proportional to the ‘can’ thickness and also to the resistivity of the material. Typically stator ‘cans’ have a thickness in the order of 0·010 to 0·.020 inches and resistivity greater than 0·75 micro-Ohm metre.

Such a thin wall thickness will be suitable only for low pressure applications even when partially supported by the bore of the stator. For this reason, back-up sleeves are normally fitted over the unsupported parts of the ‘can’. The behaviour and effect of the rotor ‘can’ is fundamentally different from the stator ‘can’ since it is rotating with the rotor at a speed only slightly below that of the fundamental magnetic field of the motor. Consequently, the large eddy current losses of the stator ‘can’ do not occur.

Magnetic gap

The magnetic gap between the stator bore and the rotor is typically two to five times greater than that of a conventional motor. Such large gaps do not directly affect efficiency but they do cause the power factor to be lower than normal, particularly at less than full load. The extra current flowing in the windings is no great disadvantage if the motor has been purpose designed. However it may cause extra heating in those designs manufactured from general-purpose stator than a rotor units as a cost saving measure.

Stator enclosure filling

Unlike the conventional motor, very little of the heat generated by the canned motor is radiated off the motor casing. Thus, the machine relies for cooling largely on the heat being effectively transferred to the motor cooling bleed. In some design, heat transfer is aided by a suitable solid or liquid filling in the stator enclosure. Others favour an inert gas. Generally, the advantage of filling the stator enclosure is size, hence cost reduction. In favour of the unfilled stator enclosure is the greater maintenance facility leading to reduced operating cost.

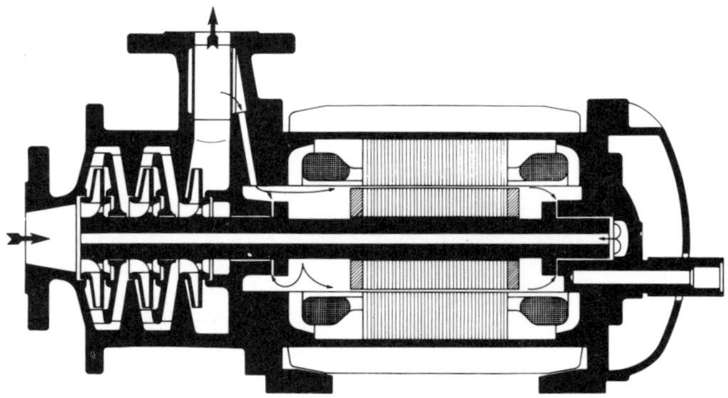

High temperature hermetic pump.

Temperature/pressure balance

As the motor cooling bleed passes through the motor, fed from the discharge side of the pump, it experiences a simultaneous increased in temperature and a decrease in pressure. Figure 4 illustrates a typical effect. When pumping volatile liquids, it is essential to ensure that this combination of circumstances does not cause the liquid to boil. Obviously, were this to happen, the cooling effect would be lost as would all lubrication to the motor end bearing.

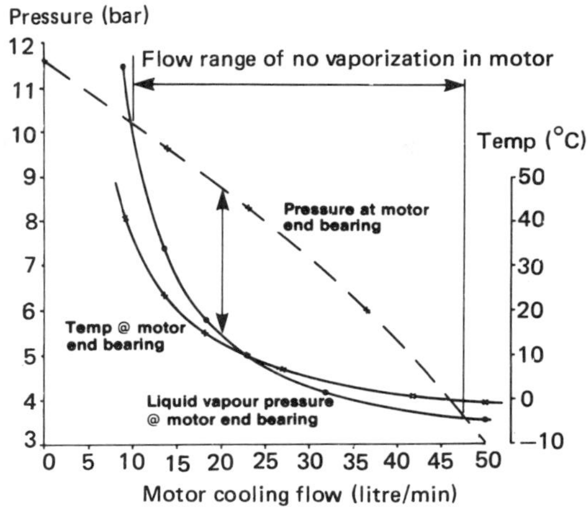

Figure 4
Fluid conditions inside a 55 kW motor – chlorine @ 10 °C pumping temperature.

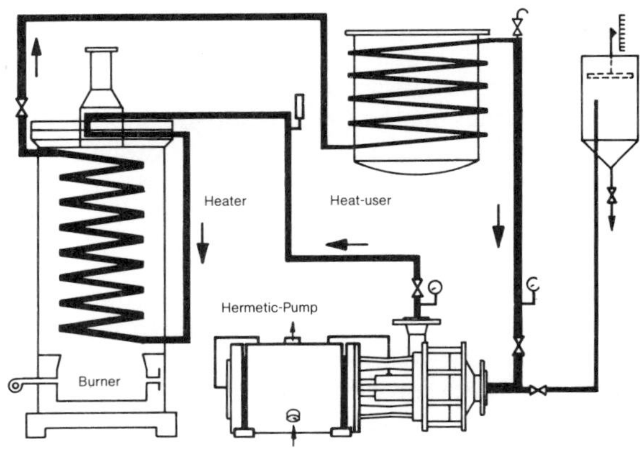

Diagram of a typical heat transfer system.

Control of cooling conditions
The motor cooling bleed is usually controlled in terms of flow and pressure by a fixed orifice outboard of the motor end bearing. With this arrangement, the optimum flow will be have been set on test by the manufacturer. It is very unwise for a user to vary this flow 'to help the pump' without consulting the supplier.

Disposal of cooling flow
From the controlling orifice, the most common arrangement is to return the motor cooling bleed to the suction side of the pump. Again the designer must be wary when pumping volatiles. The motor cooling bleed will by definition have picked up heat and to return it directly to the suction side of the pump is obviously to risk NPSH problems, particularly at low flows. This is the weakness of those designs which return cooling bleed through an axial tapping in the shaft where the hot liquid is introduced directly into the eye of the impeller. With such arrangements, the very least effect will be an increase in the minimum flow requirement of the pump.

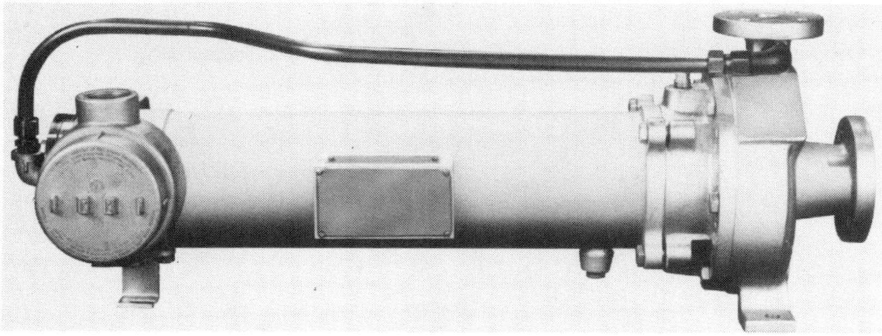

Canned pump designed to handle toxic, volatile, carcinogenic and other potentially dangerous chemicals in the most critical process applications.

Fairly simple sleeve-type bearings with a suitable lubrication groove are normally found to be perfectly adequate for radial loadings. For axial loadings however, the individual characteristics of the liquids to be pumped demand more careful consideration. For this reason various methods of either supporting or eliminating the axial loan are employed. It is probably in this area that the various manufacturers show the greatest originality.

For liquids having reasonable lubricating properties, conventional plain face type or tilting pad thrust bearings may be used. Where the lubricating properties of liquid are very poor (generally defined by a viscosity level below 0·25 cP) thrust balancing is advisable in that it permits a relatively end float. This in turn makes it possible to use self-positioning devices to absorb thrust.

Thrust control

One particular design utilises a thrust balancing disk. As the name implies, this arrangement employs a disk fitted to the shaft immediately above the impeller. The underside pressure is influenced by discharge from the impeller while the top side is relieved back to suction. Thus a force is generated on the under side of the disk which causes the disk to lift, leaking pressure until the axial forces are balanced.

On those designs relying on a small clearance between the rotor and stator cam, the pressure difference at either end of the rotor can be used a 'piston' effect acting on the rotor. A simple port with a tapping backed to suction pressure situated such that it will be opened or closed by axial movement of the shaft; thus when the axial force on the rotor becomes too great, the flow is reduced which in turn reduces the force. In this arrangement it is obvious the rotor is being used as a balancing drum. While this device has the advantage of low cost and simplicity, the small clearance demands between the rotor and stator 'can' is a major potential for failure in the event of bearing wear. Also flow reductions for pressure balancing purposes may well be detrimental from cooling point of view particularly when pumping volatile liquids. The designer has no stable condition to calculate his temperature balance in the motor.

Reasonable potential for thrust control is offered by balancing the thrust at source, *ie* the impeller, using oversized backwear rings with controlled leakage back to suction. Again, the advantages of low cost and simplicity apply. However such a design tends to be hydraulically inefficient and presents design difficulties at low specific speeds.

Pressure vessel design

The pump and motor casings are in effect a pressure vessel which contains the pump and motor. With the higher quality designs this vessel will be manufactured to the requirements of a recognised code of practice such a ASME VIII. For nuclear applications, ASME III may be applicable. In the motor end of the enclosure however, the primary liquid enclosure is the stator can, for which manufacture to pressure vessel codes is obviously appropriate since the result would be unreasonably poor electrical performance. It is evident therefore, that the function of the motor case is to act as the ultimate enclosure which guarantees zero leakage in the event of failure of stator can.

All normal design and manufacturing considerations apply to the outer casings. Due regard must be taken of stress requirements, material selection, welding procedures and quality assurance. Electrical penetrations through the pressure vessel are by means of composite metal/insulator sealing stems which are normally seated on O-rings for lower pressure design or steel welded for high pressures. It is important that such penetrations do not de-rate the integrity of the vessel.

Nuclear duties

For toxic and radio-active liquids the canned motor pump is essential, but as in the case of submersible units, the design problems arise in the motors and not necessarily in the pumps. In the nuclear power stations, the escape of one drop of radio active liquid could be quite disasterous. The designers of nuclear plant therefore demand absolute sealing so that not one drop of radio-active liquid can escape.

Cost comparisons

The cost of a canned motor pump is generally high compared with a conventional motor driven pump of similar performance with mechanical shaft seals (Figure 5). The cost difference is less in the case of a submersed motor pump or an oil filled motor pump although both types are less readily available.

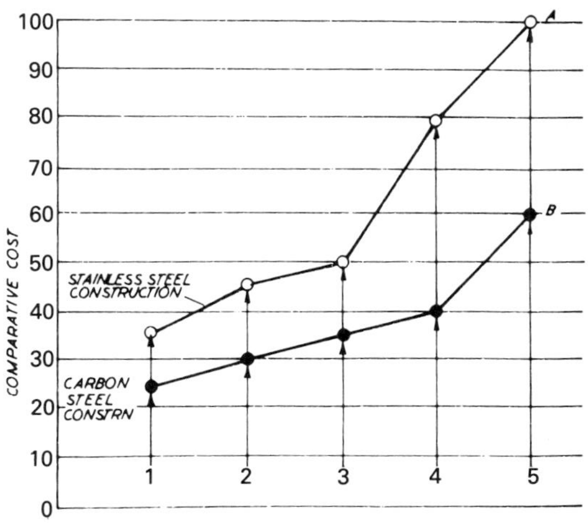

Figure 5

Comparative costs of:
1. Standard pump.
2. Gas-filled motor pump.
3. Oil-filled motor pump.
4. Submersed motor pump.
5. Canned motor pump.

Hygienic stainless steel pump with shroud.

Comparative costs of:
(i) Standard pump;
(ii) Gas filled motor pump;
(iii) Oil filled motor pump;
(iv) Submersed motor pump;
(v) Canned motor pump;

Maintenance

Many of the applications for which canned motor units are used present particular difficulties from a maintenance point of view. Nuclear applications involving radioactivity in particular call for designs which can be rapidly serviced to limit the exposure of fitting staff to hazard. For similar reasons of hazard, it is often essential that all maintenance should be carried out on site.

Design features which offer maintenance advantages include:
(i) Spigotted mating components to ensure rapid and accurate realignment.
(ii) Avoidance of shims to obtain recommended clearances.
(iii) Removable can assembly and unfilled stator enclosures to avoid the need for factory repair of electrical failures.
(iv) Replacable wear parts such as bearing sleeves and bushes, wear rings *etc*.

The close-coupled feature of canned units avoids the need for complicated shaft coupling arrangements.

Typical applications for canned motor pumps include oils and petro- chemicals – the handling of liquified petroleum gas systems such as rail and road tanker unloading and transfer; feed and circulating duties; the pumping of liquid gases such a chlorine and sulphur dioxide, the handling of ammonia trichlorethylene, nitric acid, vinyl chloride, hydrogen cyanide, amines/ammonia, dowtherm/thermex, pumping frion/artcon and general chemical pumping duties where absolute leak tightness and low maintenance costs are primary requirements.

See also chapters on Glandless Pumps and Submersible Pumps.

Glandless Pumps

A GLANDLESS pump is one which has no conventional packings or seals in contact with the product being handled. It is thus particularly suitable for handling solvents, abrasives or chemically active fluids, (*eg* acids) which are not compatible with bearings and seals. At the same time the product remains completely isolated so that the possibility of leakage is eliminated.

The conventional diaphragm pump is inherently glandless, its main limitation being the possibility of diaphragm failure. This can be guarded against by the use of double-diaphragm designs, or further variations in the diaphragm working principle, particularly the stacked diaphragm. Failure of an elastomeric diaphragm is usually due to its limited life when cycle stressed intention (and particularly when stressing is localised). A method of overcoming this is to construct the diaphragm in the form of a bellows comprising alternate elastomeric and metallic rings in a stack. When reciprocated the metallic joints between the rubber and metal is unstressed and the rubber is loaded in compression only. Compression strength only is thus required in the elastomer.

A centrifugal pump which is also glandless can be a very attractive proposition. The vertical glandless pump shown in Figure 1 is similar in hydraulic design to any conventional pump. It is always installed in the vertical position and the design is such that the need for any form of mechanical seal or packed gland is eliminated by allowing a controlled leakage of the liquid being pumped to return to the suction tank by way of an overflow action in the upper body of the pump.

The most widely used method of installing a glandless pump is that shown in Figure 2. The pump is installed beside the tank and positioned so that the pump impeller is flooded at normal maximum liquid level in the vessel. When the pump is started up it will deliver liquid until the suction pipe becomes uncovered when it can be allowed to run dry until the liquid level is restored to the point where re-priming can take place. This cycle of operation may be repeated indefinitely. The majority of applications for which this pump is used involves continuous circulation, for example gas scrubbers and heat exchanger circulating pumps. It is also suitable for use as a filter press feed pump where the controlled leakage acts as an integral bypass which allows for release of back pressure from the filter.

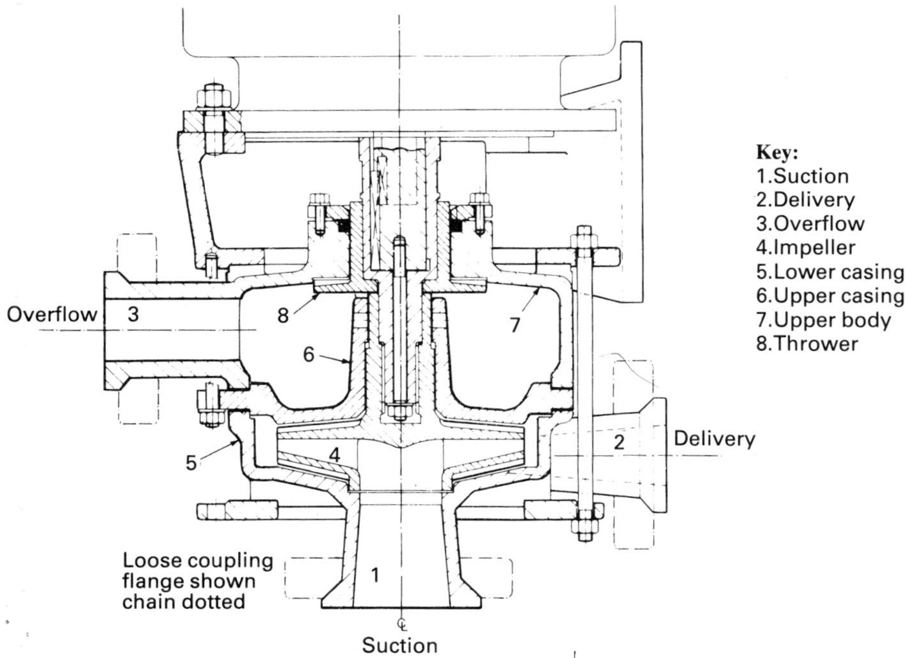

Figure 1
Section through glandless pump.

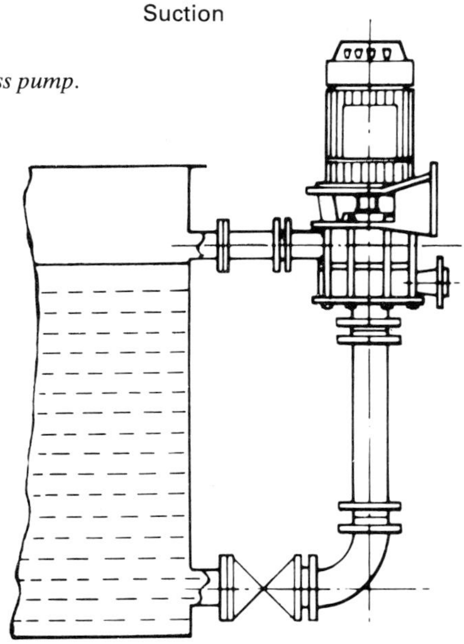

Figure 2
Installation of vertical glandless pump.

Some of the main advantages of this type of pump are the elimination of any form of liquid shaft sealing arrangement, the absence of glands, seals, bearings and neck bushes inside the pump mean that it can be run completely dry for indefinite periods without ill-effect thereby enabling the pump to be used for intermittent duties such as the transfer of industrial effluent from a collection vessel to a treatment plant. The pump can operate against a partially or fully closed discharge valve without ill-effect. The controlled leakage or overflow acts as a built in by pass as the pump circulates liquid through itself and back into the suction tank.

Limitations on vertical glandless pumps arise from the type of installation required. A pump mounted beside a tank from which liquid is to be withdrawn must be arranged so that the maximum liquid level does nıot rise above the centreline of the pump overflow, otherwise it would flood the upper body and leak from the vapour seal. The pump must therefore operate with very little positive head of liquid on the impeller. Unlike conventional floor mounted horizontal centrifugal pumps, it does not take full advantage of the net positive suction head made available to it by the pump installation. A glandless pump is not normally suitable for use as a transfer pump from bulk storage tanks. The pump mounted on the top of a storage tank so that the normal maximum liquid level covers the pump impeller can be started-up and will empty the tank since it is capable of quite high suction lifts. However when it is required to take only a portion of liquid from the tank and the pump is stopped, it will not become reprimed until the tank has refilled or that the liquid level rises to the pump impeller. The presence of an overflow can be a disadvantage when installed on an enamel, glass or rubber lined vessel. In this case the pump overflow is fed into a vertical pipe which serves as a feed tank for the pump.

Maintenance is considerably less than for a conventional pump and even vapours can be contained by fitting a vapour seal/stuffing box which is not in contact with the product and therefore not subject to leakage of the liquid.

Wet rotor pumps

The 'wet rotor' concept employs a more or less conventional centrifugal pump with a conventional motor drive, but with transmission through a magnetic coupling (Figure 3). The pump itself can thus remain fully sealed provided the liquid to be handled is clean and its lubricating properties compatible with the rotor bearings fitted.

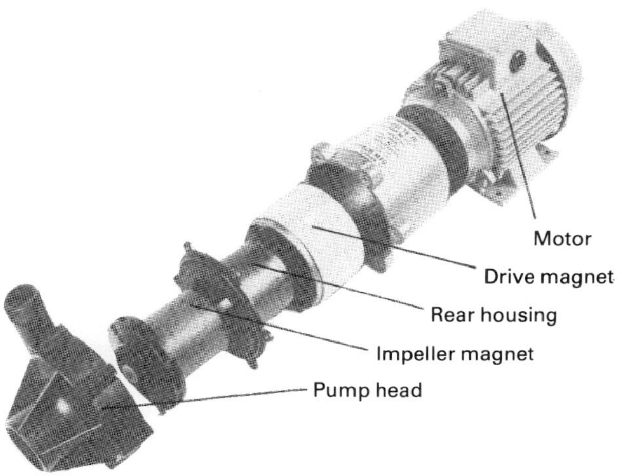

Figure 3
Glandless diaphragm pump.

Magnetic drive for sealless pump.

Pumps of this type generally fall into three categories reflecting construction materials and the degree of resistance to aggresive chemicals:

(i) Mildly corrosive – Pumps in this category resist the action of low concentrate acids, photographic solutions and some solvents. They are ideal for light oils, inks, dyes and pure foods or drugs. Applications include refrigeration equipment, vending machinery and dispensers, aquariums, fountains or agitator pumping equipment.

(ii) Semi-corrosive – These are pumps for more aggressive solutions they handle many acids, alkalines, salt solutions, photographic bleach and a wide range of industrial and scientific compounds including all those in the 'mildly corrosive' section but at generally higher pumping rates. Applications here include photoprocessors, temperature controllers and ice-makers.

(iii) Highly corrosive – For high concentrations of acids and bases all known solvents and mixtures at high specific gravities. Important applications include plating, etching, battery chemicals and brine pumping.

Wet stator pumps

Glandless centrifugal pumps and particularly the larger sizes normally employ squirrel cage induction motors which require no commutators or slip rings. The stator windings can be of either 'wet' or 'dry' type. Stators with wet windings or wound with wire covered with a layer of plastic. Usually this plastic is either PVC or polyethylene. The winding is either star or delta connected and the ends of the winding are brought out of the motor through three or six pressure tight electrical glands. Depending on the nature of the service, the stator laminations are made either of formal electrical sheet or of stainless iron. However, stators made of the latter material have iron losses about double the normal value.

The heat generated by the electrical losses within the motor is removed by circulating the liquid filling the motor through a heat exchanger supplied with low pressure cooling water as shown in Figure 4.

The motor temperature is normally kept between 15 °C and 40 °C and this allows a larger safety margin. It should perhaps be pointed out that plastic coverings on stator windings need to be of a specially developed grade considerably superior to average commercial materials. These special compounds are capable of working at much higher temperatures and are non-porous. The glandless wet stator

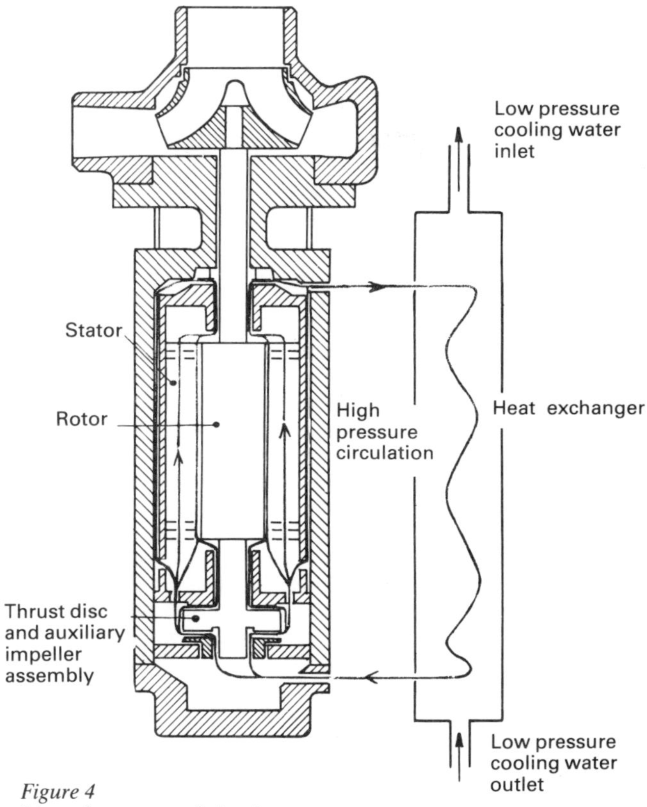

Figure 4
Motor heat removal circuit.

circulating pump shown in Figure 5 is a fully submerged wet motor and rotor dynamic pump arranged inside a pressure-tight enclosure with the minimum number of static seals. The pressure containment comprises three continuously connected vessels:

(i) A pump case which accommodates fluids to the highest boiler temperatures and pressures.

(ii) A motor case maintained at a low temperature but high pressure.

(iii) A heat exchanger sized to maintain the motor cavity cooling liquid at the low temperature level required.

Glandless circulating pumps are in operation in numerous nuclear reactor systems as well assisted circulation boiler systems.

A secondary impeller incorporated in the motor rotating element circulated water through the motor cavity to the top of the heat exchanger and back to the lower part of the motor. This recirculation dissipates the heat generated by motor electrical losses. Bearings are of the tilting pad type and are self-aligning. They incorporate ferrobestos and carbon steel – hard chrome-plated mating surfaces.

Dry stator pumps

'Dry' stator construction employs ordinary stator winding separated from the liquid by a thin 'can' made of inconel or Hastelloy - Figure 6. The main advantage of

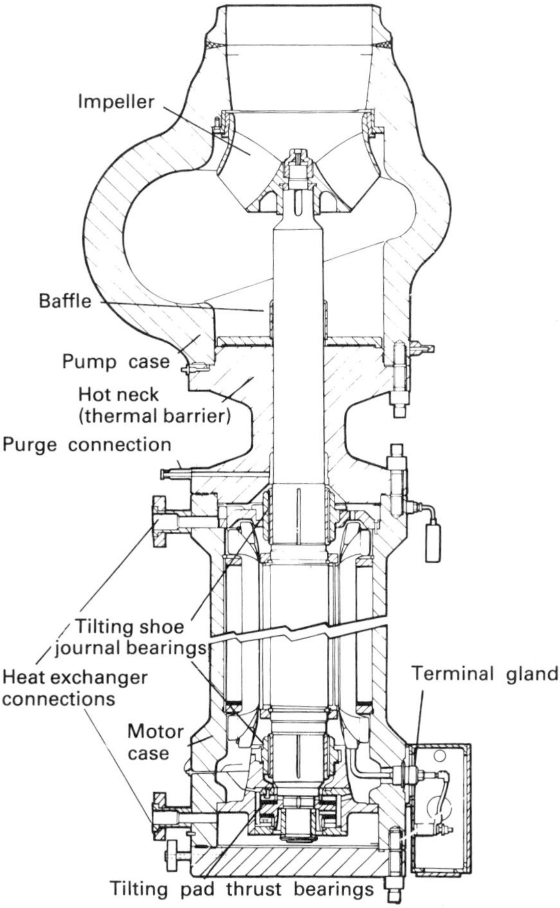

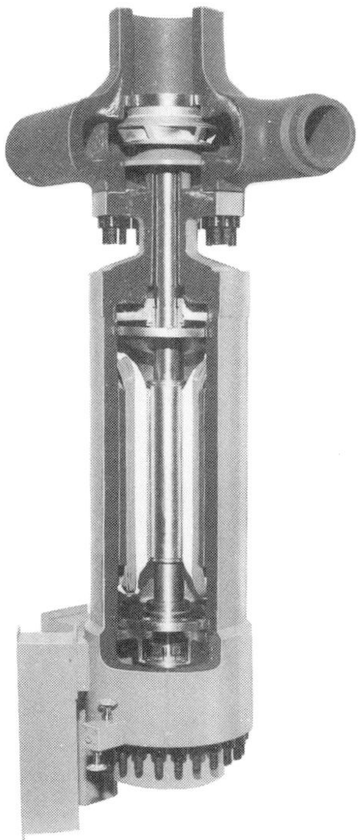

Cutaway of wet stator unit showing double discharge pump case and phase separated 6·6 kV terminal boxes.

Figure 5
Glandless boiler circulatory pump.

canned construction is that the motor can be filled with liquids which would attack the plastic wire insulation. Although high temperature insulation is employed in canned motors, the maximum temperature of the liquid inside the motor cannot be much higher than those in wet stator motors. The reason for this is that the windings in a canned motor are surrounded by stationary gas, so that most of the heat dissipation takes place through the stator laminations and the motor shell. Thus the hottest part of a canned motor is the overhanging portion of the coils at the two ends of the stator. In very large canned motors it become necessary to fill the ends of the stator enclosure with solid compound designed to increase the heat conduction from the coils.

The electrical eddy current losses in the stator can are high due to it being situated in the region of high flux density. Moreover, as motors are made larger these losses tend to increase rapidly with an increase in horsepower.

'Wet' *versus* 'Dry' stators

It has been shown that for geometrically similar motors, even if the can thickness is kept constant the can losses are proportional to the fourth power of the linear

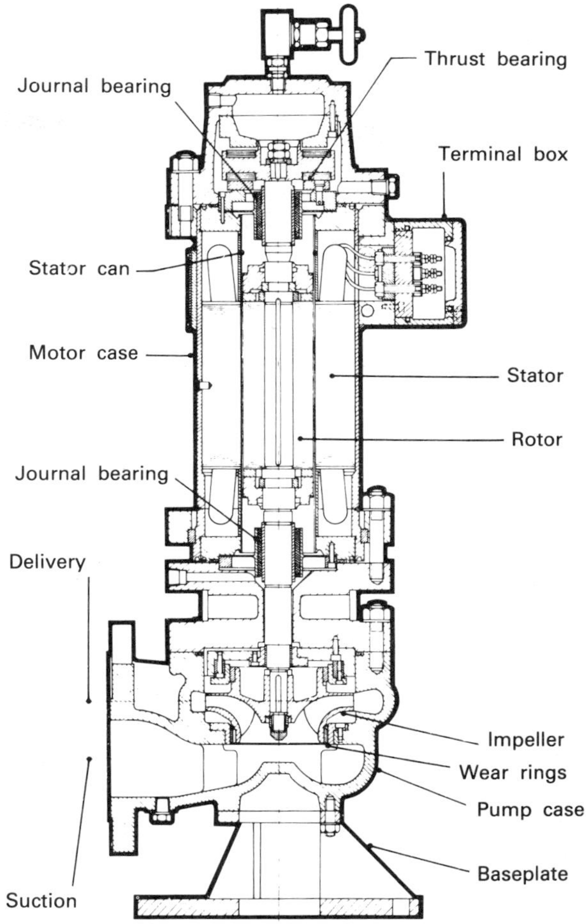

Figure 6
A dry stator glandless circulating pump.

dimensions. This affects adversely the efficiency of the larger 'dry stator' glandless units. Thus a 'dry stator' motor of 400 to 500 hp is normally some 10 points lower in efficiency than a 'wet stator' motor of the same size.

On the other hand, when it comes to small motors, below 10 hp, it is the performance of the 'wet stator' motors which tends to be inferior. This is largely due to the fact that small motors have a large number of turns of fine wire per slot. In 'wet stator' windings each turn, being surrounded by conductive liquid has to be insulated for full voltage to earth. This makes the space factor of the slots poor and the motor bulky and inefficient.

Canned pumps

Canned glandless pumps are conventional centrifugal pumps driven by a canned 'sealed' induction motor. The stator windings are isolated by a can of about 0·40 mm (0·015 in) thickness made of stainless steel or other corrosion-resistant materials. The rotor is also sealed in a can to protect it from the pumped liquid.

Single- and twin-head glandless circulators.

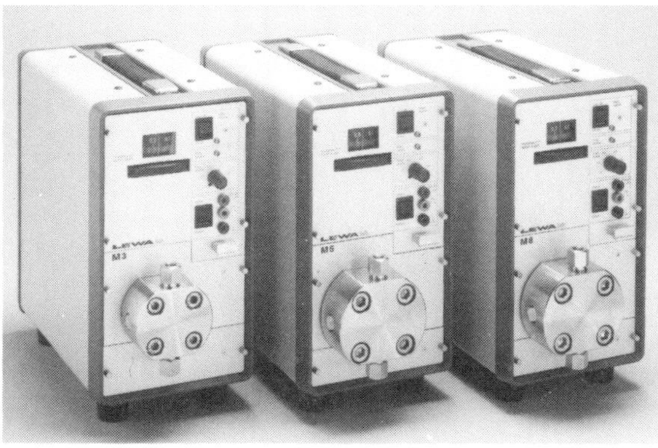

Glandless diaphragm pumps.

The main advantages of the canned glandless pump from an environmental aspect can therefore be summarised; no leakage of any sort, minimal noise and vibration, minimum access requirement which influences sighting, minimum maintenance, limited visits to operating areas.

Canned motor pumps are covered more comprehensively in a separate chapter in this handbook.

Pump bearings

Choice of bearing depends to a large extent on the size of the pump and the fluid to be handled. In the case of large glandless pumps for handling water, two main types of bearing are employed. One type consists of a hard gel running in a cylindrical bush of carbon. Sometimes the bearings are self-aligning and this is a desirable feature because carbon is brittle and cannot accommodate itself to corner loading. Special grades of carbon are employed in these bearings. Because carbon bearings must be protected from large loads, it is desirable to avoid unbalanced magnetic pull by very careful location of the bearings inside the stator. Diffuser pumps are also commonly employed because they exert low radial hydraulic forces, as compared with volute pumps.

A more robust form of journal bearing is the pivoted shoe bearing in which self-

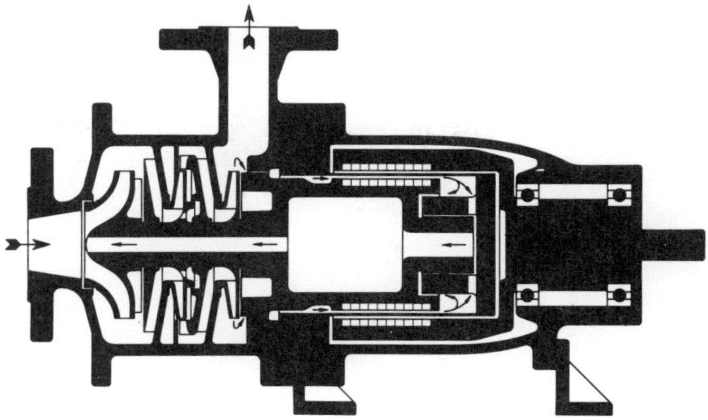

Magnetic pump without shaft and shaft bearings.

aligning pads or shoes of stainless steel run on a journal covered with a layer of reinforced phenolic resin. Because such bearings generate a fully developed fluid film, they are capable of carrying much larger loads per square centimetre of the bearing surface (over 20 bar).

As well as being self-aligning, these bearings are much less vulnerable to grit. Such bearings have proved extremely satisfactory in boiler circulating pumps where they permit the use of volute pumps which often impose considerable side forces on the impeller. Also because the bearings must be kept inside the motor, glandless pumps are invariably of the 'overhanging impeller' type. When the pump is small, several impellers can be mounted in this way. However, the larger pumps are usually of the single-stage type.

Liquid Ring Pumps

LIQUID RING pumps utilised the principle of an expanding and contracting inter-vane pocket, such as is produced by a conventional vane pump but also include a ring of liquid rotating with the impeller. In its simplest form it consists of a multi-bladed impeller mounted eccentrically in a circular housing which is partially filled with a liquid (usually water). When the impeller revolves the liquid is thrown outwards under centrifugal force to form a liquid ring concentric with the casing.

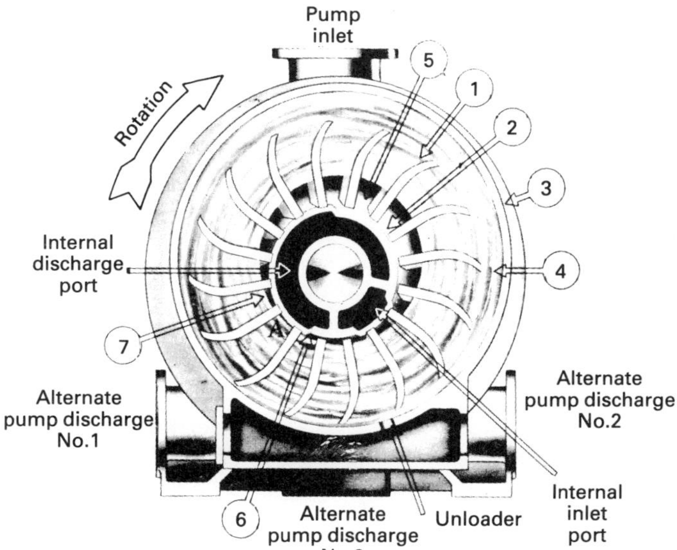

Figure 1

A typical pump of this type is shown in Figure 1. The rotor (1) revolves freely without metallic contact in a circular casing (3). Starting at point 'A', the chambers of the rotor are full of water (4). This water rotates with the rotor but follows the contour of the casing due to centrifugal force. The water recedes as the rotor advances until at (5) the rotor chamber is empty. The converging casing forces the water back into the rotor chamber until at (6), it is again full. This cycle occurs once per bucket in each revolution. As the water is forced to recede from the rotor chamber at (7), it is replaced by air entering through the inlet port in conical casting (2), connected with the pump inlet. As the rotor turns 360 degrees, and the water is forced by the casing back into the rotor chamber, the air that has filled the chamber is forced through the 'discharge port' provided in the conical casting (2) to the pump discharge. The majority of liquid ring pumps are of this simple type with side ducts. There are however designs with ports arranged radially instead of axially. The more usual alternative is the two cell liquid ring pump where the impeller is mounted concentrically in an elliptical housing. Intake and discharge phases occur twice in every revolution with the further advantage that radial forces on the rotor are balanced. This makes it particularly attractive for compressor duties.

The two basic types can be considered as single-acting (eccentric impeller, circular casing) or double-acting (concentric impeller, elliptic casing). Both types are produced in single- and multi-stage configurations.

A third type of liquid ring pump employs an eccentric screw impeller in a circular casing (Figure 2) the mixture of gas and liquid enters the casing axially, when the liquid is thrown outwards by centrifugal force to form a cylindrical ring rotating with the impeller. The screw form of impeller then delivers the gas trapped between the liquid ring and the impeller.

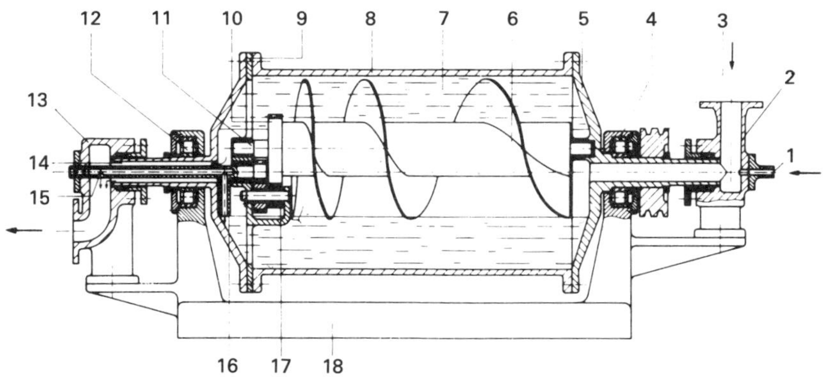

1.Ring liquid inlet.
2.Intake branch mounting.
3.Drive pulley.
4.Guide bearing.
5.Revolving casing cover.
6.Screw impeller.
7.Liquid ring.
8.Revolving casing.
9.Bearing disc.
10.Impeller pinion.
11.Bearing pins.
12.Expansion bearing.
13.Discharge branch mounting.
14.Gas outlet duct.
15.Ring liquid outlet.
16.Level control.
17.Gearing.
18.Main bearing pedestal.

Figure 2
Longitudinal section of liquid-ring pump with eccentric screw impeller.

Performance

The discharge of the simple liquid ring pump is largely governed by the volume of the largest *ie* bottom-most cell. The theoretical performance (Qth) can be calculated from the following formula:

$$Qth = b \times \int_{r_i}^{r_a - a} u_r \times d_r$$

where:

b	=	width of blade
u_r	=	$\omega \times r$ = circumferential speed
ω	=	angular velocity
r	=	mean radius
r_a	=	outer blade radius
r_i	=	inner blade radius
a	=	immersion depth

This is valid only for infinitely thin blades. If the actual blade thickness is taken into account the equation becomes:

$$Qth = \frac{t_m - s}{2t_m} \times \omega \times [(r_a - a)^2 - r_i^2]$$

where:

s	=	blade thickness
t_m	=	mean pitch of cell filled with air

The ratio $\frac{t_m - s}{t_m}$ *ie* the mean pitch minus the blade thickness divided by the mean pitch, is called the blade narrowing factor. The effective discharge Q_{eff} is lower than the one calculated theoretically by the amount of the internal losses:

$$Q_{eff} = \simeq \times \frac{t_m - s}{2t_m} \times \omega \times b \times [(r_a - a)^2 - r_i^2]$$

This shows that the effective discharge capacity of a liquid ring pump depends on the principle dimensions, the angular velocity and the internal losses. As the pressure ratio between the intake and the discharge sides increases, the internal losses get bigger and consequently the effective discharge capacity diminishes.

Duties

Liquid ring pumps are used almost exclusively for pumping gases or vapours and can also be employed as vacuum pumps or compressors. Pumping against back pressure from the vacuum range is also possible. They are also capable of handling certain combinations of liquids together, provided the two liquids are immiscible, but flow losses are inevitable, increasing the power consumption.

All liquid ring pumps have a limiting minimum speed below which the liquid ring will collapse and the pump will no longer work. As a compressor the liquid ring pump has the advantage of producing an oil free delivery, although the air may be fairly heavily saturated with water vapour (if water is the pump ring liquid). Performance is not affected by slight impurities such as dust or small quantities of liquids or vapours entrained with the gas. For vacuum pumping duties, optimum circumferential speed range for liquid ring pumps is of the order of 17 to 20 m/s (50 to 60 ft/s). The discharge volume and maximum attainable vacuum are dictated by the vapour pressure of the ring liquid at a given temperature. Using water at a temperature of 15 °C at the outlet, a vacuum of about 26 torr is reached with a one-stage pump or 15 torr with two-stages. Below this absolute pressure, there is a risk of cavitation. If a higher vacuum is demanded, either another ring liquid should be used or else a liquid ring vacuum pump in combination with some other type of pump such as air and steam ejectors, a reciprocating vacuum pump, rotary and multi- slide vane pump, or rotary piston pump.

Cavitation protection may be obtained by selecting material with particularly high cavitation resistance by providing a suitable cavitation safeguard such as air admission, or by coupling an air ejector to the suction side. Cavitation reveals itself in the form of knocking sounds and vibration of the pumps.

Fristam 'FZ' series self-priming liquid ring pump of cast construction.

Materials

Liquid ring pumps can be constructed in a variety of materials chosen according to the nature of the gases to be pumped. Cast iron is still a common choice followed closely by bronze but pumps are also available in stainless steel and coated aluminium. For particularly arduous duties, parts can be protected against corrosion or errosion by coatings of hard rubber, titanium, epoxy and other resistance materials. There is also an unrestricted choice of ring liquids, although water is the usual choice. Other liquids which may be used to match the chemical properties of the gas handled include various alcohols, oils, petrol, chloroform, paraffin, sulphuric acid, lyes *etc*.

See also Chapter on Self-Priming Pumps and Vacuum Pumps.

Vacuum Pumps

VACUUM IS 'negative' pressure measurement from atmospheric pressure, practical units being mm Hg or inches Hg. A basic limitation of this form of measurement is that atmospheric pressure is variable with weather and altitude. In vacuum practice 'positive' pressure measurement from absolute zero pressure is general, the 'engineering' unit employed in the torr or 1/760 of a standard atmosphere. ISO recommendations, specify 'positive' pressure measurement (*ie* from absolute zero pressure) in pascals (N/m^2) or mbar. The relationship between these units is:

At STP (0 mm Hg or 0 in Hg) : 760 torr = 1013 mbar = $1{\cdot}01325 \times 10^{-5}$ pascals.
At absolute zero pressure (0 torr, 0 pascal, 0 mbar) : 760 mm Hg = 29·92 Hg

There is also considerable variation in the units employed to measure flow in a vacuum service. The ISO recommendation is cubic metres/h (m^3/h) but litres per second (l/s) is more useful. Flow may also be given in mass units, *eg* kg/h or lb/s.

Vacuum stages
For convenience the complete vacuum range from atmospheric pressure down to absolute zero pressure can be divided into five stages of vacuum classes as follows:

(i) Low (or coarse) vacuum – pressures down to 25 torr (33 mbar).
(ii) Medium vacuum – pressure range 25 torr down to 10^{-3} (33 to 0·001 mbar).
(iii) High (or fine) vacuum – pressure range 10^{-3} torr down to 10^{-6} (10^{-3} to 10^{-6} mbar).
(iv) Very high vacuum – pressure range 10^{-6} torr down to 10^{-10} (10^{6} to 10^{-10} mbar).
(v) Ultra-high vacuum – less than 10^{-10} (less than 10^{-10} mbar).

Classes of vacuua are illustrated in Figure 1.

High vacuum systems
The two major parameters in the design of a high vacuum system are the rate of evacuation required and the ultimate pressure to be realised and held. These parameters determine the size and number of pumps required. This may involve the use of backing pumps capable of pumping from atmospheric pressure downwards followed by further pump(s) which only begin to operate below a

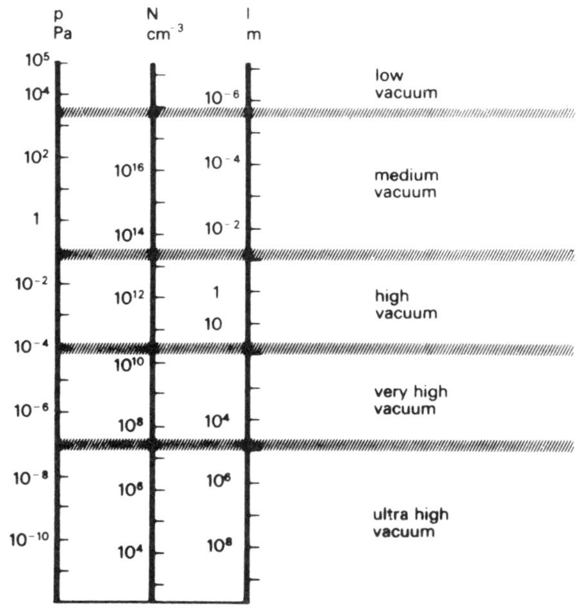

Figure 1
Classes of vacuua.

certain limiting pressure level. The majority of backing pumps are of the mechanical type or a liquid ring type although fluid jet pumps, condensers, liquid air traps and cryogenics pumps will work from atmospheric pressure down.

The first stage is then effectively acting as a fore-pump for the second stage in pumping off the quantity of gas removed by the second stage against the fore-pressure provided by the first stage. Evacuation time down to the vacuum level required can be calculated from the following formula:

$$\text{time in minutes} = \frac{2{\cdot}3V}{Qe} \log_{10} \frac{P_1}{P_2}$$

where:

V = volume in litres
Qe = effective pump speed (litres/min)
P_1 = initial system pressure in torr
P_2 = final system pressure in torr

In both corrosive and clean duties the widely used oil-lubricated rotary pump can have some disadvantages. In corrosive applications aggressive vapours and/or abrasive particles tend to contaminate the lubricant of the pump, which shortens its service life, whilst in a clean application the lubricant may cause contamination of the vacuum process. Figure 1 shows a multi-stage vacuum pump designed to work from atmospheric pressure to below 0·01 mbar, without any lubricant or sealing fluid within its swept volume. The pump is a positive displacement rotary machine in which a number of intermeshing rotor pairs of different profiles, mounted on common shafts are held in correct phase relation without contact by a pair of timing gears. This vacuum pump system has been specifically developed for clean, particulate, toxic and corrosive applications particularly in the semi-conductor industry.

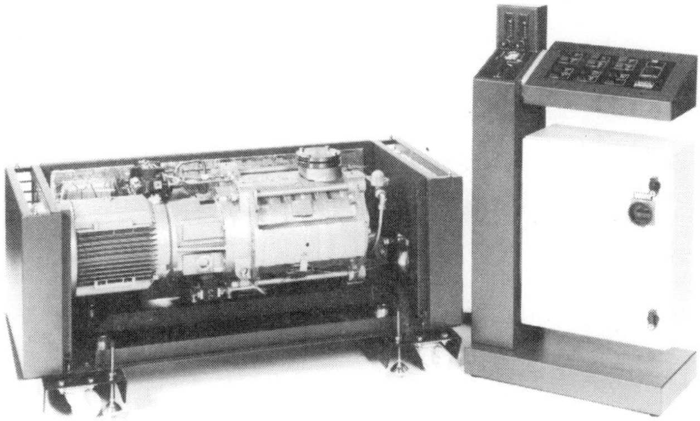

Figure 2
Advanced multi-stage vacuum pump with control and diagnostics module.

Blank-off pressure

It is normally recommended that in selecting vacuum pumps, the minimum blank-off pressure capabilitiy of a pump should be of the order of a half to one decade lower than the ultimate operating pressure to be attained by the pump. Thus a rotary piston pump with a blank-off capability of 0·01 torr would be suitable for use on a system requiring an ultimate operating pressure of from 0·05 to 0·2 torr. Increasing the margin between blank-off and operating pressure is advantageous but decreasing it below the recommended figure will result in reduction in system reliability.

Many single-stage rotary piston pumps are capable of reaching blank-off pressures of 0·010 torr or lower which represents a compression ratio capability of the order of 1 000 000 to 12. In terms of operating pressure range such pumps perform efficiently between 75 torr and 0·075 torr and thus have operational compression ratios ranging from 10 to 1 to 10 000 to 1.

Gas ballast

If water vapour (or other vapour) is likely to be present in the system it will cause trouble by condensing during the compression cycle of mechanical pumps, contaminating the oil circulating in them. On entering the high vacuum side, this condensation will re-evaporate, reducing the ultimate pressure and pumping speed. This can be overcome by using the technique of gas ballasting on the backing pump in the system. Gas ballasting involves the ingestion of a small quantity of gas (usually air) at a constant rate of mixture; this prevents condensation during compression provided the seal oil temperature is above the saturation temperature of water vapour at the reduced partial pressure. Normally, for effective gas ballast, the oil temperature should be maintained at 60 °C to 70 °C (140 °F to 160 °F) where its lubricating and sealing properties are not impaired due to reduction in viscosity (see Figure 3).

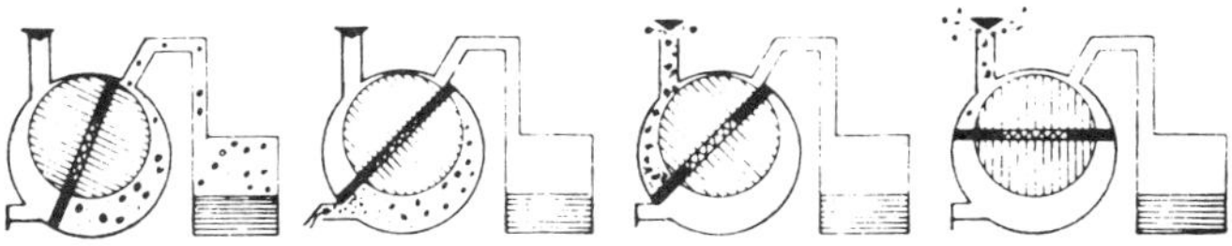

Vane pump working with gas ballast (water vapour ejected with gas ballast).

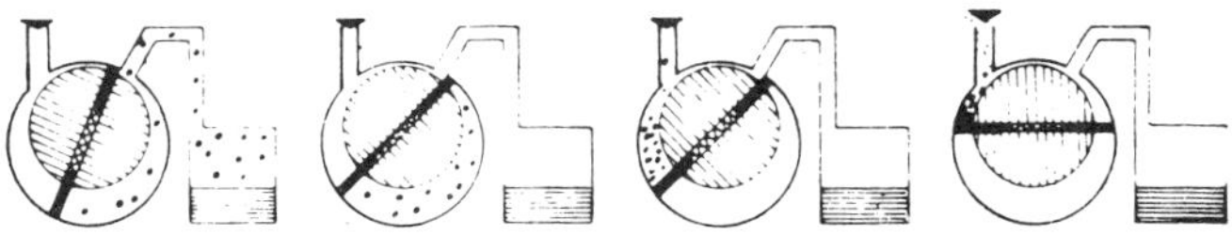

Vane pump working without gas ballast (condensed water vapour remaining over a certain level if partial evacuation is needed).

Figure 3

The use of gas ballast limits blank-off and operating pressure capability of the pump. Depending on the particular design and the characteristics of the pump there is an upper limit to the pressure at which gas ballast is effective. This is normally in the region of 25 to 30 torr which limits the quantity of water vapour which can be handled by a particular capacity pump. Where large quantities of water vapour have to be handled, the mechanical pumps should be protected by a water cooled or refrigerated condenser or trap, as condensing is the most efficient means of pumping water vapour.

Vacuum pump capable of handling corrosive gases and suitable for use on processes where the recovery of condensed vapours is required. Has a wide range of applicaitons in the chemical, petroleum, pharmaceutical, plastics, food and other related industries.

Condensers

Condensers usually consist of a vacuum envelope containing tubes or parallel plates which may be either water-cooled or refrigerated. The most efficient vapour trapping path is achieved by correct positioning of the vapour inlet and outlet. Condenser performance is independent of the capacity of the backing pump which merely maintains the required low partial pressure. However, high permanent gas pressures must be avoided as they will blanket the cool surface and reduce the condenser efficiency.

An ideal pump/condenser combination which has excellent vapour handling characteristics, and will operate efficiently in a variety of conditions is a two-stage mechanical system consisting of a rotary pump and a mechanical booster pump with an interstage condenser. Very fast vapour pumping is possible due to the fact that the interstage pressure is high and vapour can be condensed and collected in a suitable receptacle.

Contamination of the primary low pressure pump is avoided by maintaining an interstage vapour pressure below that at which condensation occurs in the pump. The backing pump, which has a much smaller capacity is protected by gas ballasting. Using this system, it is possible to cope with water vapour with a partial pressure of up to 100 torr. Furthermore, solvents particularly those with a high vapour pressure, can be easily pumped, trapped and recovered.

Mechanical pumps are not capable of producing partial pressure less than 10^{-3} torr (the best that can be obtained with a Roots-type booster or rotary vane pump). Production of high vacuum thus demands the use of specialised pumps operating on different principles.

Considerable use of vacuum pressure made in industrial applications and processes also for mechanical handling and low cost automation. Here the order of vacuum required is not normally very high. Many such applications can be met by air compressors working as exhausters. For others a particular type of pump may be chosen.

Turbo-molecular pump

In general, turbo-molecular pumps operate in the molecular flow range between 1×10^{-3} and 1×10^{-11} mbar. A turbo-molecular pump (Figure 4) mainly comprises a rotor and a stator. Rotating and fixed disks are arranged alternately. Each of the

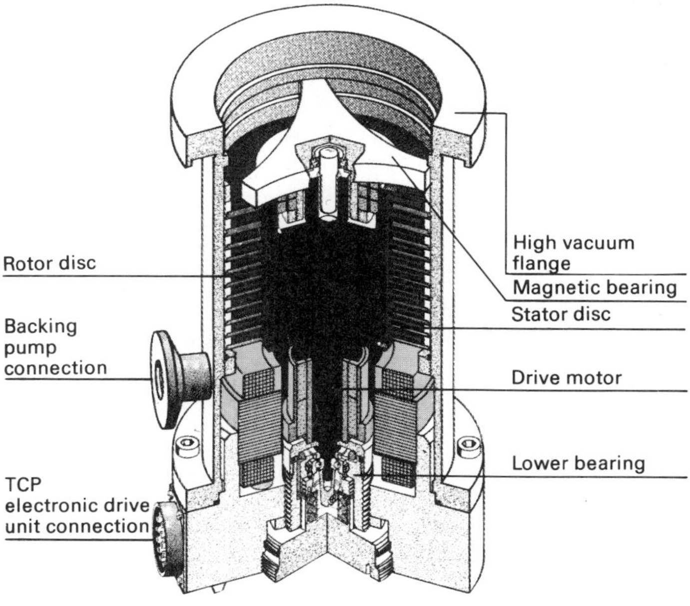

Figure 4
Turbo-molecular pump.

disks has sloping channels, the channels of the rotor disk being arranged at a mirror image attitude to the channels of the stator disk. Each channel of a disk forms an elementary molecular pump. All slots of a particular disk are parallel to one another. This means that it is possible to attain technically and economically high volume flow rates using turbo-molecular pumps.

A rotor disk and a stator disk together form a pump stage which produces a particular compression. Gaps are left between the rotor and the stator and between the rotor and the housing for reasons of operational dependability.

Typical applications for turbo-molecular pumps include specimen locks, differential pumping on analysis equipment, micro-analytical balances, backing pumps for large turbo-molecular pumps, production of hydrocarbon free insulating vacuums, helium leak detectors, residual gas analysis equipment, surface analysis equipment, laboratory evaporation and atomising systems, vacuum tube and rectifier evacuation, electron microscopes, mass spectrometers, plasma etching devices, vacuum furnaces, space simulation chambers and pumping radio active gases.

When selecting turbo-molecular pumps the following factors should be considered:

(i) Required ultimate pressure – the ultimate pressure depends on the flange type and backing pump, the characteristics of the vacuum chamber including overall leak rate, de-gasing rate and permiating rate as well as the compression ratio and volume flow rate of the turbo-molecular pump.

(ii) Required operating pressure – if it differs from the ultimate pressure, the operating pressure depends on the gas loads encountered during the vacuum process and on the volume flowrate of the turbo-molecular and backing pump.

(iii) Gas type – with a large number of processes in which chemicals such as chlorine or fluorine, for example are employed, a corrosion-resistant or plasma pump must be used.

(iv) Conductants – a drop in conductants as a result of lines of valves between the pump flange and the vacuum chamber may result in the effective volume flow rate being reduced considerably. In extreme cases pumps with a totally different volume flow rate attain almost the same effective volume flow rate at the vacuum chamber. For this reason consideration should be given to conductants in order to select the most economical pumps.

(v) Cycle time and frequency – the number of program cycles per day and the duration of each cycle are key factors when determining the pump type.

Liquid ring pumps

Liquid ring pumps are a good choice for duties where gases have high liquid content or are corrosive. They are virtually unaffected by carry-over of liquids and even occasional soft solids and are much less damaged by grit and dirt than other types of pump, such matter being flushed through by the seal liquid. Typical applications are de-watering, de-aeration, pump priming, vacuum filtration, gas extraction and condenser duties. They are often used as backing pumps for other types of unit such as steam ejectors and Roots blowers.

Figure 5
Hermetic vacuum pump package unit with permanent magnetic coupling.

Figure 5 shows a single-stage vacuum pump installation for handling process gas consisting of two liquid ring vacuum pumps with permanent magnet couplings one operating and one on standby together with a heat exchanger and liquid separator.

Roots blowers

With a Roots blower, as no sealant is normally used between the moving and stationary parts of these pumps, gas leakage occurs, opposite to flow, and this is dependent on the pressure ratio existing across the pump and the specific gravity of the gas, greater slip occuring for less dense gases. Noise levels are fairly high and efficiency drops as vacuum increases, but the machines are often used with an oil sealed rotary or liquid ring pump as a backing unit when higher vacuums are required. Typical applications for these pumps are vacuum conveying of powders and granules and dry gas exhausting from process plant.

Rotary vane vacuum pumps

Generally rotary vane vacuum/pressure pumps are used for rough continuous vacuum, high intermittant vacuum and high continuous vacuum duties including de-watering, vacuum forming, milking systems, agricultural waste, septic and industrial waste, and also pneumatics for agricultural food products such as grains and high mixture corns. Figure 6 shows a vacuum pump developed for hot climates and industrial waster haulers. The entire compression phase is enclosed with a cast iron jacket to standardise temperature differences between the intake and exhaust cycle. When a suitable service liquid is circulated through the jacket, heat is removed.

Figure 6

Positive displacement rotary vane vacuum dairy pumps (Figure 7) are usually low speed units (600 r/min to 1150 r/min), and can incorporate fan or liquid cooling. Where a reclaimer/silencer is fitted oil is drawn through an oil filter to site valves where the flow rate can be adjusted and inspected. It then enters through the bearings into the pump chamber to lubricate the vanes. The hot exhaust causes moisture to boil off in the reclaimer. Oil is screened from the air stream and returned to an oil reservoir.

Figure 7
Dairy vacuum pump.

Axial flow pumps
These are high speed units dependent on gas kinetic energy to achieve performance and are more often used as compressors. The gas passes along the pump axially between alternate rotating and stationary blades. These units like centrifugal blowers are only suitable for clean gas streams at constant flow and moderate pressures, otherwise efficiency reliability is impaired.

Centrifugal gas pumps
These units are characterised by radial gas flow and are available in single- and multi-stage configurations. They are high speed units using centrifugal force to effect the compression of the gas speeds of 20 000 to 100 000 r/min being common.

Centrifugal units are best chosen for operation on dry gases where there is no risk of carry-over of liquid or foreign matter into the gas stream. They are best for steady-state conditions are their efficiency is greatest at the design flow rate and drops off as the gas flow changes above or below the design rate; they are very sensitive to these changes.

For multi-stage high flow pumps, it is possible to generate more isothermal compression by intercooling between stages, thus improving efficiency.

If gases with low specific gravity are to be pumped, this type of unit becomes inefficient when compared with a positive displacement unit, but reliability is high on clean gas duties.

Rotary screw pumps
These units work on the principle that a constant mass of gas is compressed between contra rotating intermeshing screws which converge as the gas passes along the machine. Reliability is good but efficiency is reduced as vacuum increases, due to slippage of gas between moving parts as it becomes dense. There is little operating experience on these units as vacuum pumps as they are normally used as compressors.

Submersible Pumps

TRUE SUBMERSIBLE pumps comprise a pump and motor directly coupled as a unit capable of being fully immersed, the only connections with the surface being a rising main and a power cable for the motor. They are normally centrifugal pumps produced in a wide variety of types and sizes ranging from single-stage units for pit drainage, contractors' working, shallow well pumping, sewage and slurry handling, general de-watering, *etc*, to multi-stage units for deepwell pumping, mineshaft pumping, offshore engineering *etc*.

Submersible pump for sewage and waste water.

Wet motors and dry motors

Submersible pumps are generally classified as wet or dry motor types, the former are more common. In wet motor designs the motor is normally mounted immediately below the pump and the motor compartment is filled with oil or clean water when assembled, stator windings being insulated accordingly. The motor thus operates under control and consistent wetted conditions, for which it was designed, provided adequate provision is made to prevent outside fluid being sucked in by the thermal expansion and contraction of the casing, or through any other leakage. In dry motor designs, the motor is mounted above the pump separated from it by a cylindrical section or air cylinder which has a number of holes in the bottom. Air is trapped in the upper part of this cylinder when the pump is immersed and acts as a barrier to exclude water (or liquid) from entering the motor itself. This, in its simplest form will only provide temporary protection and in practice the air trapped in the cylinder needs periodic charging to replace air losses (*eg* when the water level in the cylinder reaches a critical height). This recharge is normally accomplished by directing compressed air into the cylinder. On some designs the necessary compressor is located within the pump unit itself. In other cases it is fed from a separate compressor at the surface. It can be operated automatically by a level sensing switch in the air cylinder, although, in the built in compressor, protection is only maintained as long as the pump is running.

Impellers

In the case of simple single-stage pumps, impeller and pump casing design has to be balanced to suit the product being handled. Most applications can be covered by three impeller forms -- freeflow, single-vane and closed two- or three-channel impeller. (Figure 1).

Free-flow impeller *Single-vane impeller* *Closed two-channel impeller*

Figure 1

These impeller types can handle raw sewage, stringy media, sludges containing large amounts of solids and gas, as well as all types of effluent. The nature of the product determines the choice of impeller, with factors such as passageway, efficiency, wear resistance and gas entrainment predominating. Another impeller selection criterion ranking with reliability in importance is low energy cost. It is especially important for pumps destined for continuous running to be equipped with maximum efficiency impellers matched to the particular medium handled. A progressive submersible pump programme is nowadays inconceivable without advanced impellers because these are indispensable to energy saving pump operation.

Mounting arrangement

The most suitable of three different mounting arrangements can be selected to match the service and site conditions:

(i) Permanent wet well (Figure 2).

(ii) Portable wet well (Figure 3).

(iii) Dry well (Figure 4).

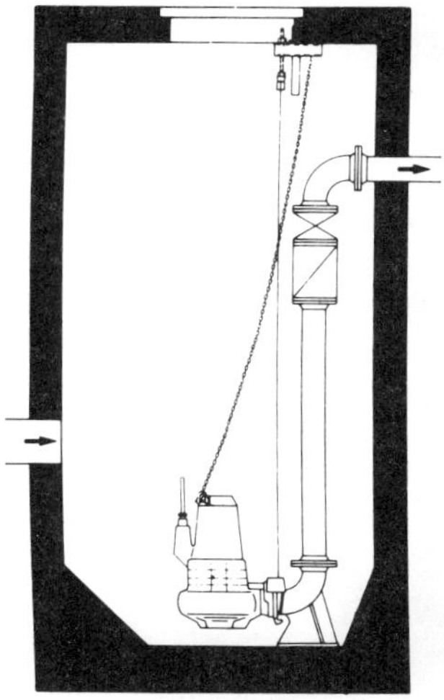

Permanent wet-well single pump with suspension device

Figure 2(a)

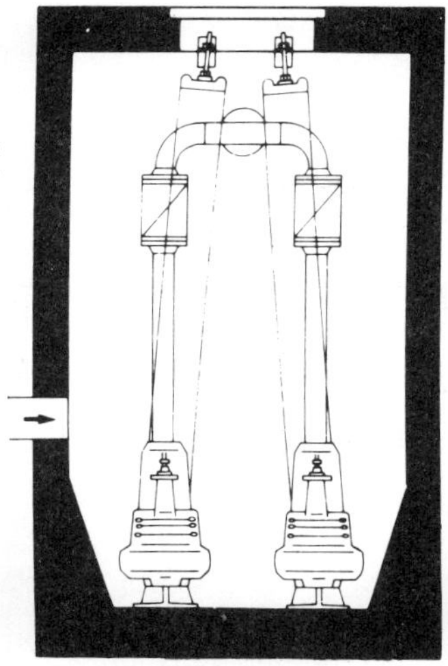

Permanent wet-well duplex pumps with suspension device.

Figure 2(b)

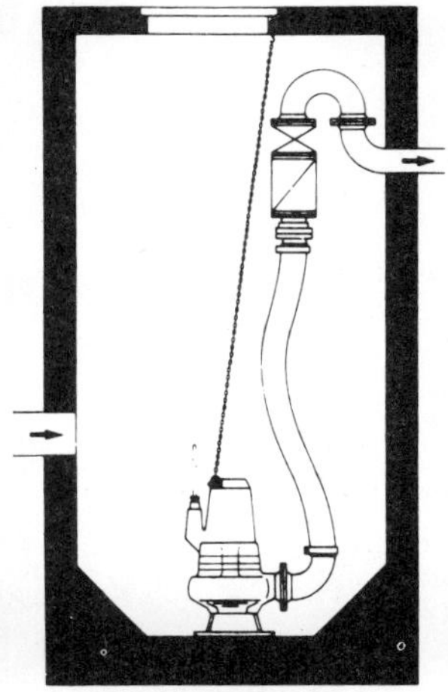

Portable wet-well pump with support stand.

Figure 3

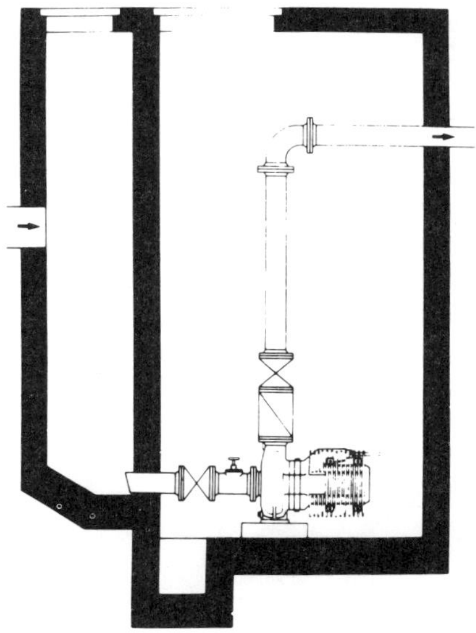

Permanent dry-well; up to 14 kW horizontally-mounted, floodable.

Figure 4(a)

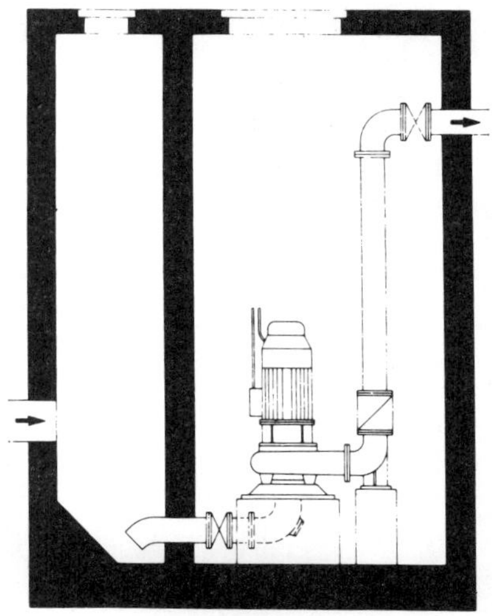

Permanent dry-well; from 16 kW upwards vertically-mounted, with fan, floodable.

Figure 4(b)

The most widely used is the permanent wet well type. With such an arrangement, it should be possible to move the pump into and out of the sump with the liquid at any level neither should it be necessary to enter the sump for pump inspection or maintenance.

TABLE 1

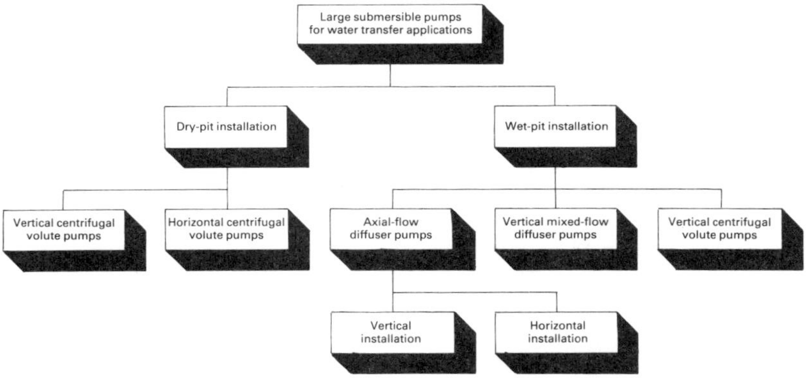

The different designs of large submersible pumps that are of practical interest in water lifting, drainage and transfer schemes are detailed in Table 1.

The water filled submersible bore hole motor has been used in water lifting schemes for decades and is a well proved solution in the majority of tubewell installations. These pumps are also suitable for many water transfer applications and are available with power ratings in excess of 400 kW, with or without external cooling circuits for wet or dry pit installation. The submersible mixed flow pump can be used in place of the mixed flow diffuser bowl pump in lifting large water volumes for irrigation purposes.

For booster pumping stations particularly in desert or otherwise remote environments with harsh climatic conditions, the submersible volute pump with an external cooling system can offer certain advantages against the conventional solution which is either a standard end suction centrifugal pump mounted on a common baseplate with an air-cooled electric motor driven through a flexible coupling or a vertical diffuser bold pump with discharge head and suction barrel.

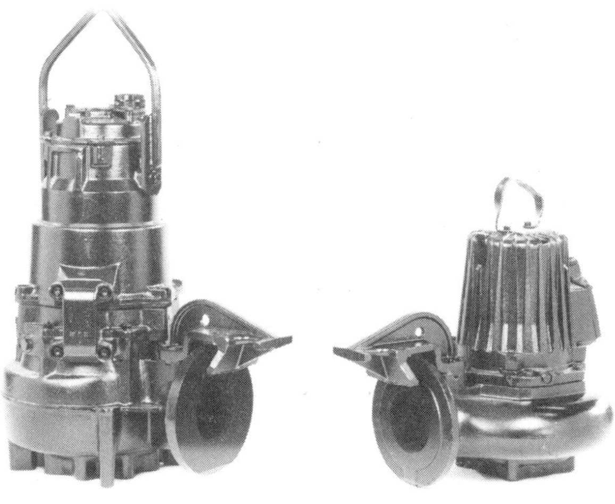

Submersible pumping units.

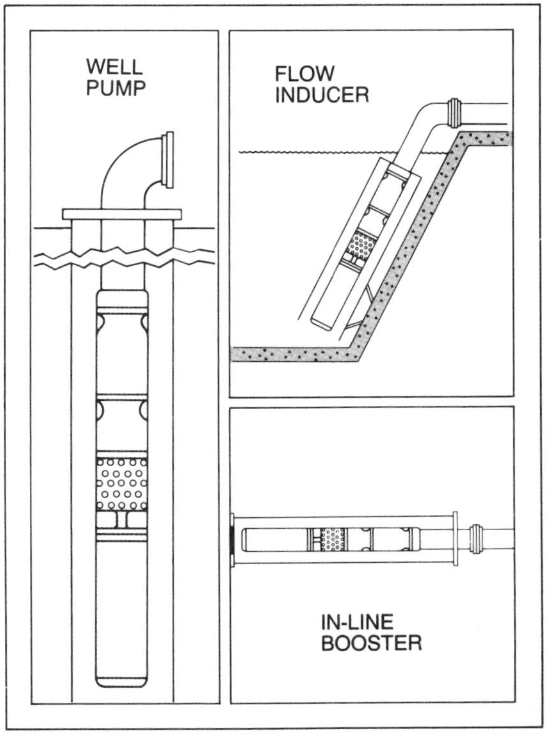

Typical installations.

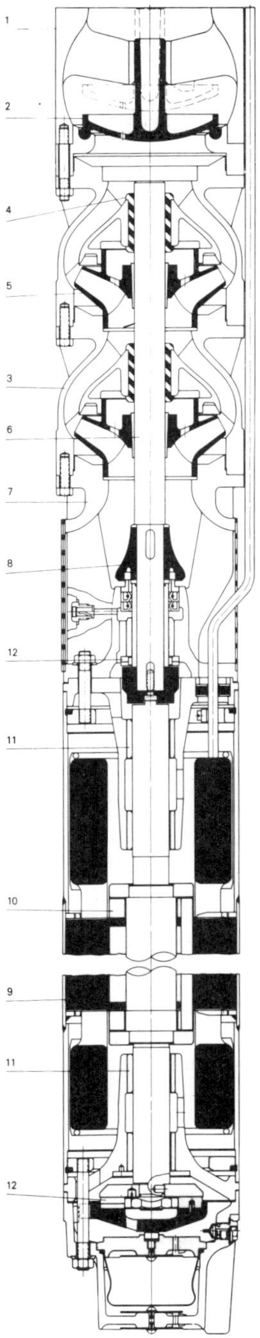

1. Check valve casing
2. Valve
3. Intermediate bowl
4. Intermediate bowl bearing
5. Impeller
6. Shaft
7. Suction casing
8. Sand collar
9. Stator
10. Rotor
11. Radial bearing
12. Axial thrust bearing

Figure 5
Cross-section through typical submersible pump.

Advantages

The following advantages can be said to apply to submersible pumps:

(i) They do not require suction pipes.
(ii) Less friction losses.
(iii) Less space at ground level.
(iv) Quiet operation.
(v) Easy installation and removal of discharge pipe.
(vi) Can be installed in uneven wells and in countries subject to flooding.
(vii) Advantage in extremely deep wells which present problems with shafting.
(viii) Small diameter.

When selecting submersible pumps the following considerations should be borne in mind:

(i) Origin of water – well, river *etc.*
(ii) Liquid – clean, containing sand *etc.*
(iii) Diameter and depth of the well
(iv) Flow – assumed or measured.
(v) Water depth – static and dynamic levels.
(vi) Maximum head relative to ground level at well head.
(vii) Head losses – existing or planned piping.
(viii) Electrical supply characteristics – voltage, frequency, phases, start-up method.
(ix) Requested automation – for start-up and shut-down.

Figure 5 shows the cross-section of a typical submersible pump.

Power cable

Electric power is supplied to the downhole motor by a special submergable cable. The cable is usually constructed with three individual conductors one for each power phase. Each copper conductor is enclosed by insulation and sheathing material. The thickness and composition of the insulation material determines the cables resistance to current leakage, operating temperature capability and resistance to permeation by well fluid and gas.

Detailed information on the design, construction, selection and installation of submersible pumps can be found in the handbook of 'Submersible Pumps and Their Applications' by H. H. Anderson, published by the Trade and Technical Press Limited, publishers of this manual.

Hydraulic Drive Downhole Pumps

THE HYDRAULIC drive downhole pump is a small compact unit designed as a reliable alternative to the electro-submersible pump (ESP).

The pumping system represents a significant departure from current accepted technology and has a wide range of applications both onshore and offshore including oil well production, water lift for re-injection and geothermal well pumping. Pumps of this type are capable of operating for long periods in deep highly deviated wells handling fluids which are hot, corrosive and abrasive and can withstand frequent stop/start sequences without distress.

The basic system is shown diagrammatically in Figure 1.

In operation, the power fluid is bled from the well production line and fed through cylone separators (if required) to achieve a level of filtration of 100 ppm, 100 microns. The power fluid passes to a surface charge pump and from there through a control valve or choke, down the power supply tubing on which the downhole unit is suspended and into the turbine to provide the power required to drive the pump.

The pump takes its suction from the reservoir and increases the fluid pressure to overcome static and friction heads and deliver the required quantity from the wellhead at the designed pressure. Outlet from the pump mixes with the turbine exhaust and the combined fluids flow up the annulus between the power supply tubing and the production tubing and out of the wellhead into the production line, so beginning the cycle once again.

Variations of power fluid systems are illustrated in Figures 2 to 7.

The hydraulic turbine driven downhole pump has variable speed capability and will use all hydraulic power in the form of flow and pressure energy being fed to it. The applications of artificially lifting wells containing heavy oils are extremely difficult to predict, particularly in the estimating of the required downhole pump horsepower. Both the under-estimating and over-estimating of the motor driven power in and ESP installation can lead to rapid motor failure due to overloading in the former and high starting currents in the latter. By far the main cause of ESP failure has been attributable to the electric motor, its sealing element and associated electric power transmission system. In addition, with electric

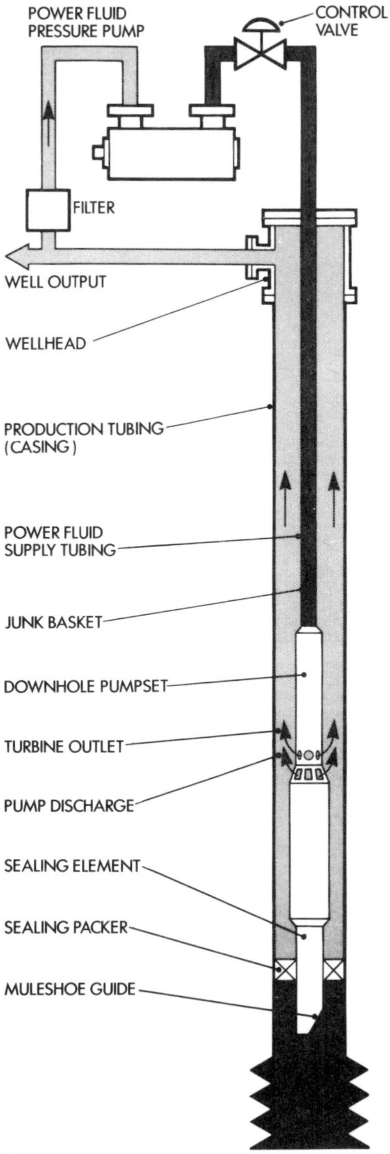

Figure 1
Typical hydraulic turbine driven downhole pumping system.

submersible pumps, there are also the problems associated with starting torques when pumping high viscosity liquids.

Overloading is not possible with the hydraulic drive downhole pump since only a controlled finite power is available to the turbine in the form of flow and pressure energy. The maximum expected horsepower required over the pump life can be estimated at the design stage. The downhole unit simply increases or decreases in speed to match the particular well operating conditions. High torque problems are alleviated since the hydraulic machine has no time limit to achieve operating speed and turbine output torque can be more easily controlled.

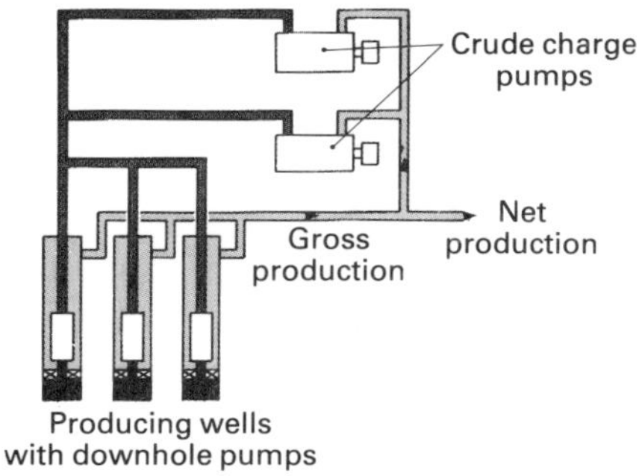

Figure 2
Oil lift – well product drive.

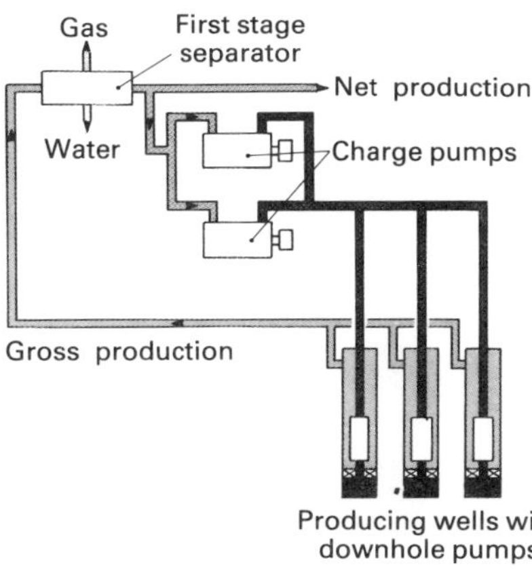

Figure 3
Oil lift – crude oil drive.

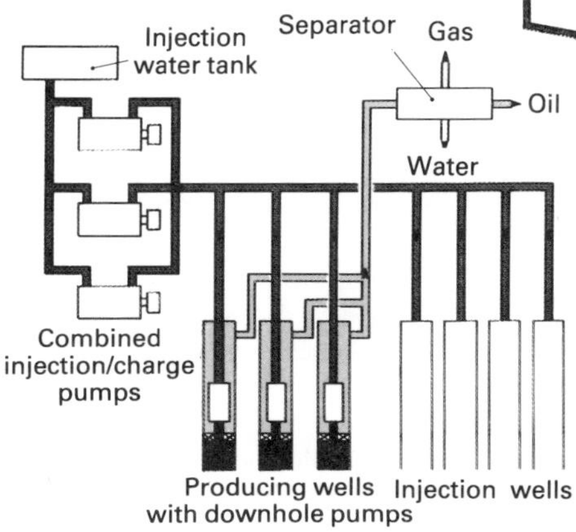

Figure 4
Oil lift – injection water drive.

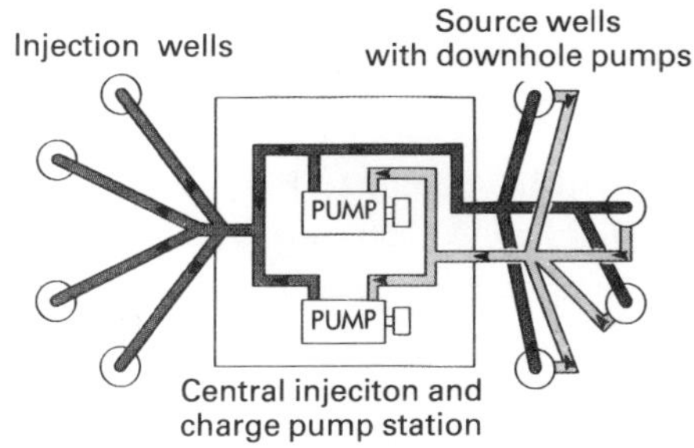

Figure 5
Water lift – central injection/charge system.

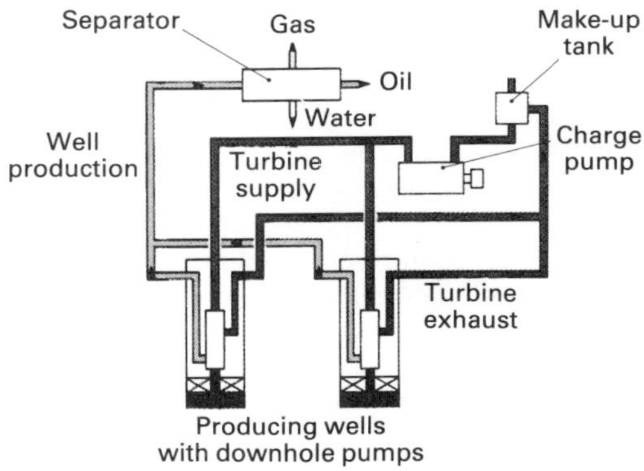

Figure 6
Oil lift – closed power supply system.

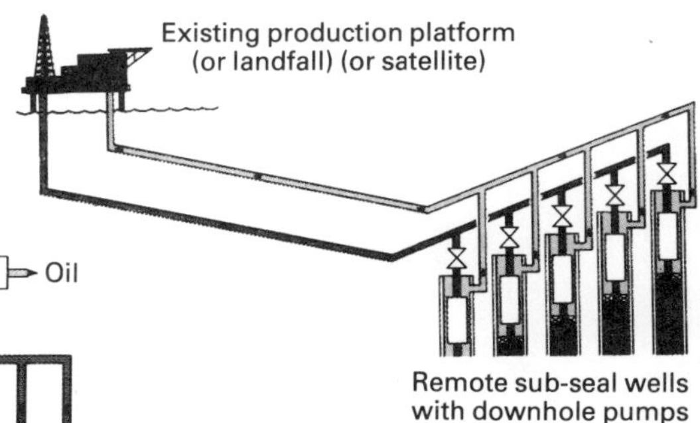

Figure 7
Oil lift – sub-sea production.

Typical operating range is as follows:

Flow 1200 bbl/D to 100 000 bbl/D

Head up to 3300 metres (11 000 ft)

Temperature up to 200 °C in standard form.

Selection criteria

When selecting a suitable hydraulic turbine drive downhole pump for either an oil or source water well application, by far the simplest approach is to break the method down into a step-by-step procedure. The following outlines the methods that are used when selecting a unit for either an oil lift or source water well application. There are always some anomolies peculiar to either oil or water examples.

Prior to beginning the selection of the unit/units, it is important that all the information relating to the particular application is known since any changes or alterations may have a direct effect on the selection made.

A source of power fluid is required to drive the downhole turbine driven pump set. The turbine itself maybe powered by well product, dead crude oil, produced water from the separation facilities, aquified water, or by sea water. The selection of the power fluid will therefore depend on fluid availability and on individual application requirements. In addition, chemical compatibility of power and produced fluids should be considered.

The choice of type and size of surface charge pumps will be dependent on and may be influenced by many factors.

The downhole pump set may be driven from the surface on an individual basis *ie* one charge pump serving one downhole unit. However, it may be possible to power a group of downhole pumps from a single large charge pump. This method makes most efficient use of available space and weight capacity and is the least expensive from a capital and operating cost viewpoint. The well completion and pump setting depth play an important role in the choice of top side unit since in many instances, the effect of friction losses can significantly reduce the overall system operating efficiency.

As a guideline, where there is a large well casing bore or the pump is set close to the surface of the well, the most efficient method of providing power to the turbine is *via* a high flow rate low pressure charge pump arrangement, however, if the pump requires to be set in the well or a small diameter casing bore is used, then the best choice of top side machine would be a high pressure/low flow rate pump, thus minimising the pressure losses as a result of friction in the well.

In general, if possible, it is best to select as low a pressure top side pump as is practical from a friction head loss viewpoint as it is normally less expensive and inherently more efficient to produce a high flow low pressure machine than a high pressure low flow rate pump.

In many applications a high degree of flexibility is required, this can be as a result of expected changes in well performance or a requirement to vary the well output. This may be effected by the use of a throttle valve on the power supply fluid line at surface thus reducing the power going to the turbine. However, the most efficient method of obtaining this flexibility is with the use of a variable speed charge pump by either using a fluid drive coupling or by the use of a gas turbine driver. A further method of achieving this ability to cope with changing well conditions or well output is to add or remove pump stages from the charge pump as required, the latter is obviously done over a lengthy period of the field life.

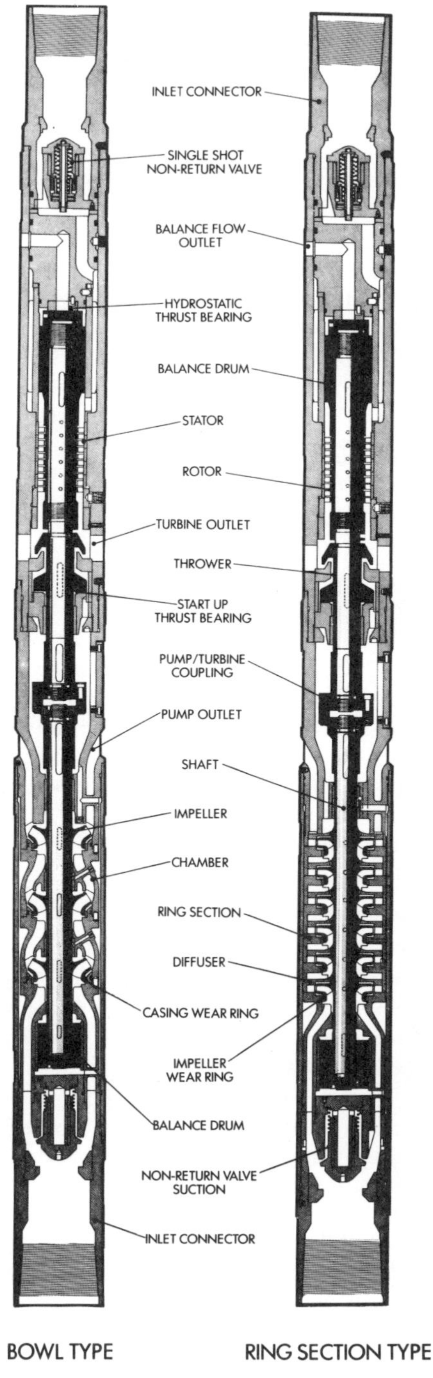

Hydraulic drive downhole pumps – sectional view.

In addition to the use of charge pumps, it may be possible and is often more cost effective to use pumps which have been (or may be in the future) selected for other duties. An excellent example of this is where a field requires water injection to maintain reservoir pressure. In this instance, injection pumps will normally be rated at a pressure also suitable for powering the downhole turbine. An example here is where water injection pumps have been sized to provide the quantity of injection water required , plus the power fluid flow rates required to drive the turbine driven downhole pumps which provide the well source water for the injection system.

The final decision required prior to proceeding, is to select the size of the power supply tubing. In general, the supply tubing diameter should be around half that of the well production tube or casing. Taking into account the combined downhole pump/turbine efficiency this will minimise power losses in the two flow paths.

In addition the following calculations should be made:

(i) Clearly define the well and system parameters for the required operating conditions.

(ii) Select the pump frame size.

(iii) Establish the specific gravity of the fluid below and through the downhole pump.

(iv) Determine the downhole pump suction pressure *ie* the minimum pressure at the downhole pump suction that will enable the pump to operate in a safe, reliable and efficient manner.

(v) Determine the downhole pump setting depth *ie* depth at which the pump must be set to give the required pump suction pressure.
6. Determine the downhole pump discharge pressure. This pressure will be influenced by pressure losses as a result of fluid friction in the return annulus.

(vii) Calculate pump generated head.

(viii) Calculate pump flow rate.

(ix) Calculate pump performance.

(x) Calculate downhole pump shaft horsepower.

(xi) Calculate downhole pump shaft torque. Since the downhole pump is a variable speed machine dealing with fluids of varying specific gravities it is essential that the torque being transmitted by the pump/turbine shaft is within acceptable limits.

(xii) Determine downhole turbine selection/performance. The efficiency characteristic of the downhole turbine is extremely 'flat', *ie* the efficiency changes little over a wide power range. It is however important that the turbine frame size and blade height be selected to suit the available combination of head and flow for the required output and speed.

(xiii) Determine approximate value of head available to expand across the downhole turbine.

(xiv) Calculate turbine design power. Since the turbine performance curves are prepared for a specific gravity of 1·0 the downhole pump power is required to be corrected for the turbine power fluid's specific gravity.

(xv) Select turbine and approximate turbine power supply flow rate.

(xvi) Correct required values to the turbine chart speed using the 'Affinity Laws'.

(xvii) Select the number of turbine stages required.

(xviii) Calculate actual turbine head drop.

(xix) Balance leakage flow rate. The turbine balance drum and hydrostatic thrust bearing require that a small quantity of power fluid be passed over the drum and through the thrust bearing to provide the necessary rotor axial balance.

(xx) Calculate actual power turbine flow rate.

(xxi) Check that top side supply pressure is adequate.

(xxii) Compare actual power supply flow rate with assumed value.

The hydraulic turbine driven downhole pump is gaining operating experience worldwide, many of the features incorporated in the unit design are being utilised by operators to pump wells which to date have proven to be extremely difficult to produce.

SECTION 4

Pump Construction

Pump Materials and Corrosion

CAST IRON (normally close grained SG irons) remains a popular choice for casings for general-purpose pumps handling water, solvents and caustic solutions (at low temperatures). Impellers may also be in cast iron or bronze.

The other main type is the stainless steel pump with casing, impeller and shaft all in stainless steel. Stainless steel, however, can embrace a whole range of nickel-chromium alloy steels, which can vary considerably in corrosion-resistance. In general, low allow steels are less resistant to corrosion than those having higher alloy content, whilst resistance can be further improved by the addition of nickel or molybdenum. The corrosion resistance of austenitic chromium-nickel stainless steels is also adversely affected by improper heat treatment and fabricating techniques resulting in carbon precipitation, *eg* exposure to the carbon precipitation range, especially during welding, can lead to inter-granular corrosion developing. Stabilisation can be achieved by the introduction of columbium or titanium, and such alloys are satisfactory for welding and stress relieving without damage of carbon precipitation, provided the proper ratio between the carbon and stabilising element is maintained.

With the much greater number of pumps produced in stainless steel, more limited use is made of the all-bronze pump with bronze or gun metal casing and impeller and wear parts also in bronze. Neither bronzes in particular nor to a lesser extent, austenitic stainless steels are particularly suited to working at high temperature because of their relatively high thermal expansion (causing difficulty in maintaining correct fits and running clearances) and loss of strength at elevated temperatures. (See Table 1).

Duplex stainless steels

The attraction of duplex stainless steels – alloys of austenitic – ferritic steels – is that they combine the toughness and general corrosion-resistance of austenite with the strength and resistance to stress-corrosion of ferrite. First produced some 50 years ago they offered few real advantages and several disadvantages over conventional stainless steels as casting alloys until comparatively recently with the introduction of the original Langalloy 40V, followed by the even more carefully balanced Ferralium alloy 255.

TABLE 1 – TYPICAL TEMPERATURE RANGES FOR FERROUS MATERIALS FOR PRESSURE RATING

Material Type	Temperature Range °C (°F)	Standard Specification			
		Castings		Forgings	
		British Standard	Comparable ASTM	British Standard	Comparable ASTM
Carbon steel	−30 to 540 (−20 to 1000)	1504–161 Gr.B	A.216 Gr.WCB	1503–161 Gr.B or C	A.105 Gr.1 or 11
1¼% Cr ½% Mo steel	−30 to 650 (−20 to 1200)	1504–621	A.217 Gr.WC6	1503–620	A.182 Gr. F11
2¼% Cr 1% Mo steel	−30 to 650 (−20 to 1200)	1504–622	A.217 Gr.WC9	1503–622	A.182 Gr. F22
5% Cr ½% Mo steel	−30 to 650 (−20 to 1200)	1504–625	A.217 Gr.C5	1503–625	A.182 Gr. F5a
Austenitic chromium nickel steels	−200 to 815 (−325 to 1500)	1504–801	A.351 Gr.CF8	1503–801	A.182 Gr. F304
		1504–821 Gr.Nb	A.351 Gr.CF8C	1503–821 Gr.Nb	A.182 Gr. F347
				1503–821 Gr. Ti	A.182 Gr. F321
		1504–845 Gr.B	A.351 Gr.CF8M	1503–845 Gr.B	A.182 Gr. F316

Modern duplex steels (and Ferralium alloy 255 in particular) are now becoming recognised as having superior corrosion resistance to salt solutions and particularly seawaters with or without a variety of contaminants, compared with austenitic stainless steels and many other corrosion-resistant metals. (See Table 2).

TABLE 2 – CORROSION FATIGUE STRENGTH AT 10^8 CYCLES OF VARIOUS MATERIALS IN SEAWATER

Wrought Alloys	UTS (kg/mm^2)	Corrosion Fatigue ($\pm kg/mm^2$)
Inconel alloy 625 (21Cr, 9Mo, 3.5Cb, 2.5Fe, Ni)	105	33
Hastelloy alloy C (16Cr, 16Mo, 5Fe, 4W, Ni)	76	22.5
Monel alloy K500 (29Cu, 3Al, 1Fe, 6Ti, Ni)	124	18.3
Incoloy alloy 800 (32Ni, 21Cr, 4Ti, 4Al, Fe)	63	17
Type 304 Stainless (19Cr, 10Ni, 2Mn, 0.08C)	56	10.6
Type 304L Stainless (19Cr, 11Ni, 2Mn, 0.03C)	53	9.8
Type 316 Stainless (18Cr, 12Ni, 2Mn, 2.5Mo, 0.08C)	60	9.8
Type 316L Stainless (18Cr, 12Ni, 2Mn, 2.5Mo, 0.03C)	56	9.7
18% Ni Maraging Steel (18Ni, 7Co, 5Mo, 0.4 Ti)	176	3.5
Mild steel	42	1.4
Ferralium alloy 255 (wrought)	125	35
Cast Alloys	**(kg/mm^2)**	**($\pm kg/mm^2$)**
Ni-Al Bronze CA 955 HT	81	10.6
Ni-Al Bronze CA 955	61	8.8
Mn-Ni-Al Bronze CA 957	70	6.3
Mn Bronze CA 865	51	5.6
Ferralium alloy 255 (cast)	125	22

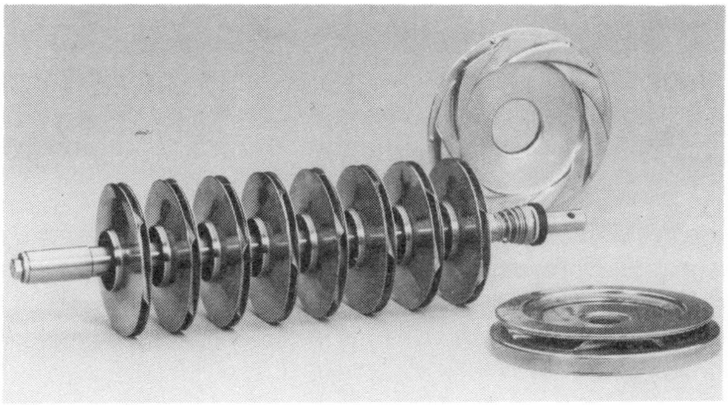

Stainless steel pump components.

Titanium
The use of titanium and titanium alloys for pump construction has increased as both designers and users have come to appreciate its outstanding resistance to corrosion by a wide range of aggressive media, its long and trouble-free service, and the savings in cost attendant upon reduced maintenance and downtime in chemical and process industry applications.

Although pumps in titanium were at one time produced on a one-off basis from bar and forgings (and some still are) titanium castings are commonly used for bodies, impellers and backplates of chemical pumps over a wide range of sizes delivering from a few litres per hour to several hundred litres per minute. Pump parts produced from patterns designed specifically to take advantage of the nil or low corrosion rate of titanium and the innate high strength level of the metal can be much cheaper than those produced on the patterns used for the production of castings in less costly material. The ability to use existing patterns for the production of titanium castings is however essential where the total requirement may be small or for unit production.

Full details on the corrosion-resistance of titanium in various media are available from metallurgists and corrosion specialists at the major titanium supply companies. Advice on the suitability of parts for the casting process is similarly available in order that wherever possible design and material specification may be optimised for the application concerned. In general terms titaniums greatest resistance is to the chloride ion and its derivatives, chlorides, chlorine dioxide, sodium hypochlorite *etc*. Pumps operating in such environments for periods in excess of 10 years and in some cases for more than 15 years show little or no sign of wear or deterioration. In some cases the original machining marks continue to be visible. The cost-effectiveness of titanium over a long period of operation in chemical plant can therefore be extremely favourable.

Materials for corrosive duties
A wide variety of metals is used for the construction of chemical and process pumps ranging from basic cast iron and steels through numerous alloy steels and nickel alloys to the more exotic titanium and zirconium alloys. Alternatives include lined and coated pumps (with basic metallic construction) and the use of non-metallic materials. Selection of a material for pump construction based on published corrosion data for a particular corrosive service does not always mean that it will perform as expected. The use of so-called material corrosion tables is very

questionable as the corrosion data listed have usually been determined under stagnant conditions (total immersion tests). Also, the possibility of attack is not limited to straightforward chemical activity but can be initiated by contaminants in the fluid capable of catalytic action, electrolytic effects, erosion – corrosion and stress corrosion. The problem of containing corrosion is therefore not a simple one.

Corrosion

DIN 50900 describes corrosion as 'the reaction of a material with its environment causing a measurable change in the material and possibly leading to corrosive damage'. Corrosive damage is defined as an 'impairment of the function of a component or an entire system through corrosion'. Corrosion is therefore fundamentally a chemical process.

The cause of all corrosion reactions is the thermodynamic instability of metals in relation to air, water or other oxidising agents. They tend to revert to a compounded state, corrosion products being formed from the pure metals and energy being released in the process. In the case of corrosion a material conversion takes place, the speed of which represents the corrosion rate. This material conversion rate is governed by a general physical principle, according to which a current or a mass flow is proportional to a motive force and inversely proportional to resistance.

Electrochemical potential is a measure of the ability of a system to function. By way of simplification it may be said that it characterises the tendency of a metal to pass into the ionic form *ie* to transferelectrons. Potentials are usually indicated in relation to the hydrogen electro, which is taken as zero; metals with negative potentials are designated as 'base', those with positive potentials as 'noble'. The corrosion-resistance of a metal is essentially determined by its potential and the pH value of the solution.

Corrosion phenomena on metallic materials in hydrous media can be classified into three groups:

(i) Uniform corrosion – in which the rate of corrosion is the same at all locations of the metal surface (*eg* metal dissolution in acids, simple rusting processes).

(ii) Local corrosion without mechanical stressing – during which the corrosion is limited to local narrowly defined locations (pitting corrosion, crevice corrosion, inter-crystalline corrosion, galvanic corrosion, selective corrosion).

(iii) Local corrosion in the presence of mechanical stressing – it being possible to distinguish additionally between the mechanical stressing acting on the material in depth (stress corrosion cracking, corrosion fatigue) or only on its surface (erosion-corrosion, cavitation corrosion).

Forms of corrosion are illustrated in Table 3.

Uniform attack

In the case of uniform attack metal removal takes place more or less evenly over the entire metal surface. Certain differences can occur in the micro-domain which lead to roughing. This form of corrosion is characteristic of aggressive media, there being no resultant insoluable corrosion or surface clinging products to influence the rate of corrosion locally. Uniform attack is observable on numerous materials in acids.

TABLE 3 – FORMS OF CORROSION

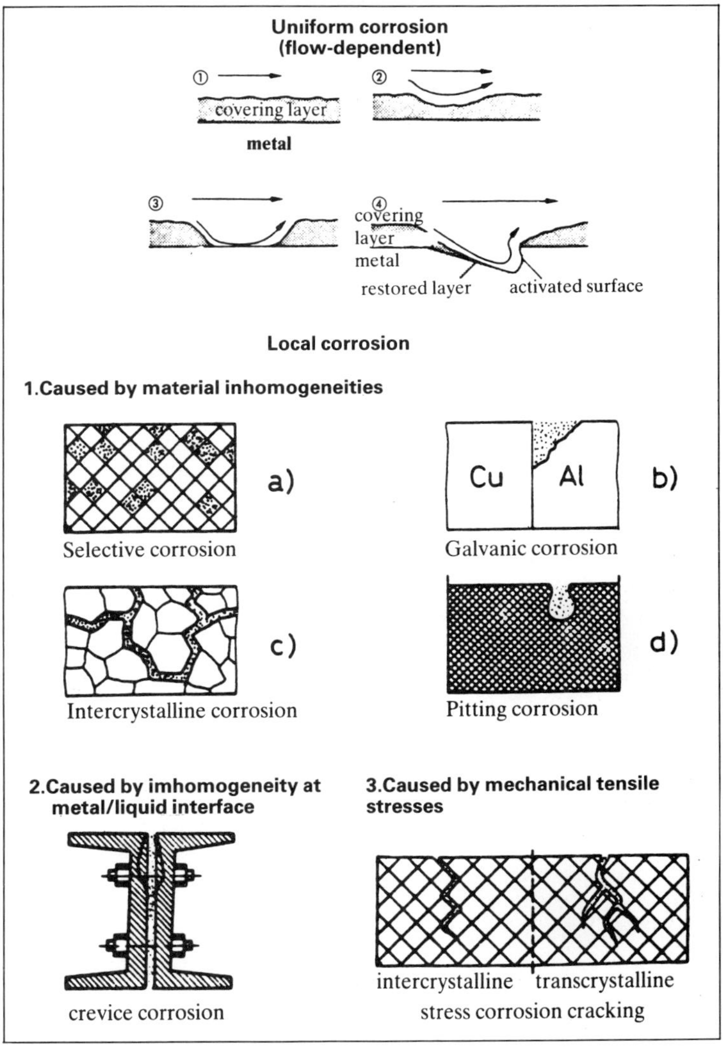

Pitting corrosion

Characteristics for this type of corrosion are individual, mostly hemispherical small cavities which can lead to perforation of pipes and tanks, while most of the metal surface shows no corrosion at all. The cause of pitting corrosion is local destruction of the passive layer with formation of small corrosion anode, while the oxygen reduction can proceed unhindered on the large passive area. As a result of hydrolysis of the corrosion products, the pH value can fall to very low values in the cavity.

Pitting corrosion is initiated by chlorides in particular. It occurs especially frequently in stagnant solutions, *eg* during machine outages. This type of corrosion is furthered by rising temperature. All passivatable materials and especially austenitic stainless steel, are prominent among those susceptible to pitting corrosion. This can be countered by using steels with molybdenum additive, the amount of molybdenum required to ensure protection rising in proportion to chloride content and temperature.

Crevice corrosion

This is an attack on surfaces in a crevice filled with liquid. Such crevices can be a consequence of the design but may also result from encrustations and deposits on metal surfaces formed during operation.

Crevice corrosion may be regarded as local breakdown of the passive condition resulting from oxygen deficiency and/or a pH decrease due to hydrolizing corrosion products in the crevice caused by impediments to emigratory diffusion. Crevice corrosion occurs frequently with stainless steels, in particular when medium contains chlorides.

Inter-crystalline corrosion

Inter-crystalline corrosion is the term used when corrosion primarily affects the grain boundaries of a polycrystalline metal. Even when total metal loss is very small this form of attack leads to the breakdown of crystallite cohesion and as a consequence of grain dissociation – grain disintegration. The most important factor affecting the inter-crystalline corrosion is the material itself or rather its composition.

Typical examples of the materials susceptible to this type of corrosion are high alloyed austenitic chromium-nickel steels and ferritic chromium steels.

Galvanic corrosion (contact corrosion)

If two different metals are in electrically-conducting contact galvanic corrosion can occur if their individual potentials are sufficiently far apart. In such cases the baser metal corrodes more quickly than if it were isolated from the nobler one. Conversely the content results in a reduction in corrosion of the nobler metal (cathodic protection). It is especially critical, if the surface of the baser metal wetted by the medium is small compared with the surface of the nobler one.

The danger of galvanic corrosion is greater the higher the salt concentration (electrical conductivity) of the medium. It is for example very small in organic liquids or demineralised water; in seawater however even potential differences of 100 mV can become a problem.

Selective corrosion

Selective corrosion can occur in two-phase alloys, in that the baser phase is selectably dissolved out while the nobler phase remains undamaged. The form of the component is practically unchanged. The damage is finally manifested by porosity or mechanical failure. The technically most important cases of selective corrosion occur with cast iron (graphitization, spongiosis) brass (dezincification) and certain aluminium bronzes (de-aluminification).

Causes of selective corrosion include chlorides, slightly acid pH values, a reduced oxygen supply and insufficient circulation of the medium. The danger of selective corrosion can be prevented by technical alloying measures.

Stress corrosion cracking and corrosion fatigue

These types of corrosion are characterised by the occurence of cracks and/or brittle fractures at stresses far below the yield point of the undamaged material.

Centrifugal pump constructed in Hastelloy.

Stress corrosion cracking occurs at static tensile load, and in fact only with certain medium-material combinations. The stress corrosion cracking of austenitic CrNi steels in chloride containing media is of special technical significance. The danger of damage increases with the chloride content, the temperature and the stress level. Below about 70 to 80 °C the occurrence of stress corrosion cracking is however unlikely.

Since in practice the composition of the medium cannot usually be changed, design measures (*eg* low mechanical stresses) or alloy-technical measures must be taken to avoid stress corrosion cracking. The use of CrNi alloys with increased Ni content (above 25 to 30%) in many cases enables the danger of stress corrosion cracking to be minimised. Duplex steels also show enhanced resistance.

Fatigue cracking occurs in the case of a cyclically alternating mechanical load; it is not specific to either materials or media, *ie* it can occur with all metallic materials and in all corrosive media.

Erosion-corrosion

Erosion-corrosion is the accelerated destruction of metallic materials in fast flowing corrosive liquids. With increasing flow rate corrosive substances are brought more quickly to the metalled surface, while reaction products are completely or partially removed.

In the velocity ranges controlled by transport as well as those controlled by phase reaction the shear forces generated by the flow at the surface of the metal cause partial or total destruction of the covering film, thus making it possible for corrosion to increase abruptly. At very high flow rates and/or with unfavourable hydraulic profiling, high mechanical forces can act on the metal surface (liquid impact, cavitation) and so cause direct mechanical destruction of the material. In general corrosion is accelerated here as well. The term used for this is mechanochemical metal damage.

For every material there is a flow rate which must not be exceed in engineering installations. Furthermore, this flow rate is dependent upon the respective medium and the more corrosive this medium packs, the lower is the allowable flow rate.

Cavitation corrosion

If the static pressure in a pump falls below the vapour pressure of the liquid being pumped, vapour bubbles are formed, which on their implosion can cause cavitation damage. As with erosion-corrosion, the material cavitation consists of an interplay of mechanical stresses and corrosion-chemical reactions. Although in many cases the mechanical influence predominates, the chemical components must never be neglected. This alternating effect is the more strongly defined, the more aggresive the medium.

In only slightly corrosive media (*eg* water) the cavitation resistance of a material improves with rising hardness. In a corrosive liquid on the other hand, the choice of a cavitation-proof material may not be based on its hardness alone. On the contrary, the best cavitational resistance is displayed by materials with good toughness coupled with a high hardness value and an optimal corrosion-resistance.

Axial flow pump constructed in Hastelloy for phosphoric acid.

Corrosive properties of liquids being pumped

A distinction is drawn between non-aqueous and aqueous liquids. The non-aqueous liquids, typically organic substances such as oil, petrol *etc*, usually have no corrosive properties at all in relation to metals. If these substances contain water, then an increase in corrosivity will only be observed if the waters solubility level is exceeded. Caution is required with organic acids, amines, chlorinated hydrocarbons and the like.

Aqueous liquids often contain dissolved salts and gases, their pH value fluctuates from acid *via* neutral to alkaline. Depending on salts the following groups of waters can be distinguished:

(i) Natural waters – ground water, surface water, seawater *etc*.

(ii) Treated waters – soften, demineralised and/or degased water.

(iii) Special chemicals and salt solutions – cooling brines, effluent from chemical processes and other industrial sectors.

Most metals are unstable in acid media. From case-to-case highly alloyed Cr or CrNi steels, titanium, Hastelloy alloys, silicon iron and the like can be used, but limits also exist for these materials, depending on the type of acid, acid concentration and temperature of application. If necessary recourse must be made to plastics, ceramics, glass or graphite.

Examples of metal materials recommended for pumps are given in Table 4.

TABLE 4 – EXAMPLES OF MATERIALS RECOMMENDED FOR PUMPS

	Material No. as per DIN (examples)	Natural waters, equil. water	Treated waters: softened, deminer-alized	Water or boiler feedwater O_2-free	Salt Water			Sea-water	Injection water	Organic liquids e. g. oil, hydro-carbons
					neutral	acid	alkaline			
Cast iron, incl. low-alloyed	0.6025 0.7040	+	–	+	$\oplus$	–	+	–	–	+
Steel casting incl. low-alloyed	1.0619 1.7706	+	–	+	$\oplus$	–	+	–	–	+
Ni-Resist	GGG-NiCr 202	+	+	+	+	$\oplus$	+	+	–	+
Si cast iron	G-X70 Si 15	+	+	+	+	+	+	+	+	+
13% Cr steel 16% Cr steel	1.4027 1.4313 1.4405	+	+	+	+[1]	$\oplus$	+	–	–	+
CrNi steel type 18/8	1.4306 1.4308	+	+	+	+[1]	$\oplus$	+[1]	–	–	+
CrNi steel type 18/8/2.5	1.4404 1.4408 1.4581	+	+	+	+	$\oplus$	+	+	$\oplus$[3]	+
DUPLEX steels	1.4460 1.4462	+	+	+	+	$\oplus$	+	+	+[3]	+
NiCrMo steel	1.4500	+	+	+	+	$\oplus$	+	+	+	+
Bronze (Sn)	2.1050.01	+	+	$\oplus$	+[2]	–	–	–	–	+
Al bronze	2.0966	+	+	$\oplus$	+[2]	–	–	+[3]	–	+

Symbols: + resistant
$\oplus$ conditionnally usable
– unstable

1) in the absence of much chloride
2) in the absence of ammonia or NH_4^+
3) according to H_2S content and pH

Lined pumps

One basic approach to providing corrosion-resistance with metal pump components is to line or coat the wetted surface with a (non- metallic) corrosion-resistant material. Possible lining coating materials are rubber, plastics and ceramics.

Rubber is an attractive lining for pump components since the choice of rubber components is wide, offering resistance to most chemicals including acids and alkalines. The hardness of the coating or lining can also be selected across a very wide range. At one extreme is a very soft rubber, and at the other a hard rigid ebonite. Abrasions, unlike normal wear problems caused by rubbing, can best be resisted by a soft lining or coating. A rigid ebonite surface on the other hand is much smoother (and can be further smoothed by polishing if necessary) and has appreciably lower moisture absorption. The choice between rubber and ebonite may be decided on these grounds and also on whether a flexible rather than rigid lining is desirable to accommodate mechanical shock. The latter is not a complete criteria, however, as rigid ebonite coatings can be mounted on a soft rubber interlayer, or a flexible form of ebonite may be employed. Soft rubbers are generally to be preferred for handling crystalline substances, slurries and fluids containing abrasive solids.

Plastic coatings and linings

The range of plastic materials which can be used as linings or coatings for pump components is even wider, but in practice is rather more limited. Where chemical

Typical non-metallic pump.

resistance is required, for example PTFE will meet nearly all such requirements within the softening temperature of the material, although thermosetting epoxy resins can be an attractive alternative. Two basic methods of approach are used:

(i) Plastic coating of metal parts for corrosion protection.

(ii) Application of plastic linings by a moulding operation.

The first method can be applied by dip techniques, although this will have several limitations – notably the fact that the thickness of the coating achieved may be relatively low and choice of plastic is limited to those materials suitable for dip-coating. The effectiveness of the bond and the permeability of the plastic are other critical features. Corrosive fluid which permeates through the protective coating attack the basemetal, setting up corrosion and loosening the bond. In consequence the lining does not provide complete protection and fails at the bond over localised areas. Increasing the coating thickness may combat permeability but greatly increases the difficulty of establishing a satisfactory bond with thermoplastic materials. Also the materials selected on the basis of chemical compatability may be difficult to bond to a basemetal.

Thermoplastics can also be applied successfully as thick linings by modern injection moulding techniques to yield wall thicknesses of 4 to 6 mm, so that permeability problems are unlikely to arise; also such a thickness can show a long life under the most adverse conditions such as in contact with abrasive fluids. Linings of this type can be stabilised by moulding into dovetailed grooves in the base component.

Such difficulties are not normally present with thermosetting polymers since the bond is established by the curing process. Both epoxy resin (particularly) and polyester resins bond well to clean metals and can form hard, durable chemical-resistant liners and coatings. Costs however, can limit their application.

Rigid non-metallics

Originally the only rigid non-metallics used in the construction of special duty pumps were of organic origin *eg* stoneware, porcelain, and glass (with the two latter materials also being used as hard linings). Much easier construction together with far better mechanical strength is achieved using thermosetting resins suitably reinforced producing a composite material which not only has a reasonably high maximum surface temperature but excellent chemical resistance (*eg* epoxy, polyester and furane resins reinforced with glassfibre). There is also considerable scope for application of homogenous (non-reinforced) thermoset plastics which are even easier to form by injection moulding, *etc*. Main limitations here are that they are not strictly rigid materials and have high moduli compared with metals. Maximum service temperatures are relatively low with progressive degradation of mechanical properties, from normal ambient upwards.

Another outstanding material is carbon, although difficult to work and brittle. Carbon has a full pH resistance of 0 to 14 (*ie* is virtually immune to chemical attack), a higher maximum service temperature than metals and good dimensional stability.

Apart from their chemical-resistance carbon materials can also be self-lubricating which again can be put to advantage. Figure 1 shows a vane pump for pumping fluids which have no lubricating properties, the rotor, casing and vanes all being in carbon. Where necessary, certain mechanical limitations of carbon can be minimised using resin-impregnated grains or carbon metallics, although this will affect other properties (*eg* maximum temperature rating and chemical resistance).

Glass reinforced plastics (GRP)

The use of glass (laminate) reinforced thermosetting resins for the construction of pump casings and impellers can be attractive, both on a cost and performance basis. Choice of resin is usually epoxy or polyester; the former has superior chemical resistance but is more costly. Alternative reinforcing materials include cotton/asbestos carbon fibre and Du Pont's Kevlar. Choice can be based on hardness and other physical properties required, as well as corrosion-resistance. Equally such mouldings can be produced under high pressure to give added strength.

Reinforced thermoset plastic components normally require no internal or external metal strengthening but casings normally require bearing sections and possibly local ribbing to give sufficient rigidity. The wetted surface of a component may be resin rich (*eg* rather like a very thick gel coat) to achieve the best possible chemical-resistance.

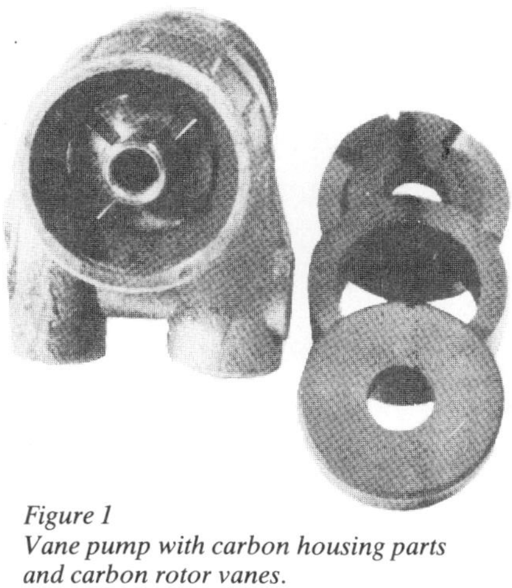

Figure 1
Vane pump with carbon housing parts and carbon rotor vanes.

The two main problems with GRP mouldings are the high modulii of the material components with metal and the more limited maximum service temperature. The problem of high modulii of expansion in plastics is mainly related to the axial direction, mostly due to the difference in expansion of the metal shaft and plastic parts. This can be overcome by the use of generous axial running clearance. Similar generous clearances may be necessary in the impeller and casing. The former can however cause high wear or even seizure when dirty liquids are being pumped and the latter lead to a loss of efficiency. It is largely a case of designing the pumps specifically to accommodate the limitations set by the high moduli of plastic materials.

Under certain conditions too, cavitation can be very destructive to these materials, therefore suction conditions are very critical, but even with good suction conditions, 'aerated' liquids can cause problems. Inpact resistance is good and wear resistance normally fairly good.

The corrosive properties of the conveyed medium essentially determine the choice of materials for pumps. In this connection the influence of flow rate is to be taken into particular consideration. Erosion and cavitation damage can only be avoided by an optimal flow profile, by observing hydraulic requirements and by a correct choice of materials. The selection of the materials for pumps is at best a compromise between the cost of manufacture and the anticipated maintenance costs. Many pump installations start out with a low service factor and through operating experience are gradually upgraded in materials until an acceptable and scheduled replacement programme is achieved.

Plastic Pumps

THE DESCRIPTION all-plastic pumps is generally taken to refer to pump constructions where all the wetted parts are plastic materials. Shafts, pedestals and other non-wetted parts may be in metal or other appropriate materials. The particular advantage of selected plastics is their ability to reject attack by corrosive or aggressive chemicals. In fact, few saturates or combinations of chemicals occur which cannot be handled successfully by plastics of one kind or another. Plastic materials may also offer considerable advantages in cost and ease of fabrication of pump parts. The main limitation of plastics compared with metals is a more limited maximum service temperature. Thus the majority of plastic pumps are produced for handling fluids at normal ambient temperatures. Other disadvantages are the lower mechanical strength (although this can be offset by the use of reinforced or 'filled' plastics) and the generally higher moduli of plastic materials.

In the main, basic metal pumps fitted with plastic components for the wetted end seldom prove popular as the original all metal pump since the combination of materials do not necessarily compliment each other. It is thus necessary to consider the design of a plastic as an original exercise in plastic materials throughout. This may be based on conventional metal pump geometry or incorporate original features to exploit fully the potential advantages offered by various plastic materials. Also an original design may be able to remove all metal parts from contact with fluid, by coating the shaft in plastic and using plastic coated bolts for securing the casing *etc*.

In the case of smaller impeller pumps, nylon is a common choice for rigid impellers, whilst flexible impellers are made from synthetic rubber (neoprene or nitrile) or synthetic elastomers such as Du Pont's viton and polyurethane depending on the chemical resistance required. The remainder of the construction can also be non-metallic (with the exception of the shaft) with bodies or casings in nylon, PVC, PTFE, polypropylene, polyacetal, polycarbonate or fluorocarbons for higher temperature services; or phenolic resin or expoxy resin for high rigidity.

Plastic materials

Of the materials in general use, high molecular, low pressure polyethylene (PE) compares favourably with rubber-lined or hard metal-lined pumps. It will withstand almost all acids and alkalines at temperatures up to 90 °C with the exception of the concentrated acids like HNO^3 in concentrations of 30% or more and a few specific solvents.

Another material with wide application is polypropylene (PP); this material has an ability similar to that of PE to withstand temperature although its resistance to aggressive media is not quite so comprehensive as that of PE. It is however weldable so that the potential for making joints is that much wider and it is therefore a particularly useful material for pipes as well as pumps.

Figure 1
Chemical pump manufactured in a modified epoxy resin.

One of the most versatile plastics is polyvinylidene fluoride (PVDF). This has exceptional resistance to nearly all media, especially chlorinated fluid and chromic acid, both difficult media to deal with. Even more relevant in some applications is its temperature resistance which reaches 120 to 130 °C before significant loss of strength occurs, a fact which makes it the only choice in many cases.

Polytetrafluoroethylene (PTFE) and its extreme chemical resistance is well-known. For pump applications it has a temperature resistance of 150 °C, its only major limitation being that its wear-resistance is not as good as that of some other plastics.

Glassfibre reinforced materials based on polyester resin can be fabricated into almost any form and are therefore especially valuable for certain sizes and designs of equipment. With a temperature limit of approximately 110 °C they are particularly resistant to salt solutions and to any fluids acidified with hydrochloric acid, though their application is much wider than that.

Epoxy resin based GRP is an even more versatile reinforced plastic and in pump applications may be reinforced with carbon/graphite fibres as well as glassfibre

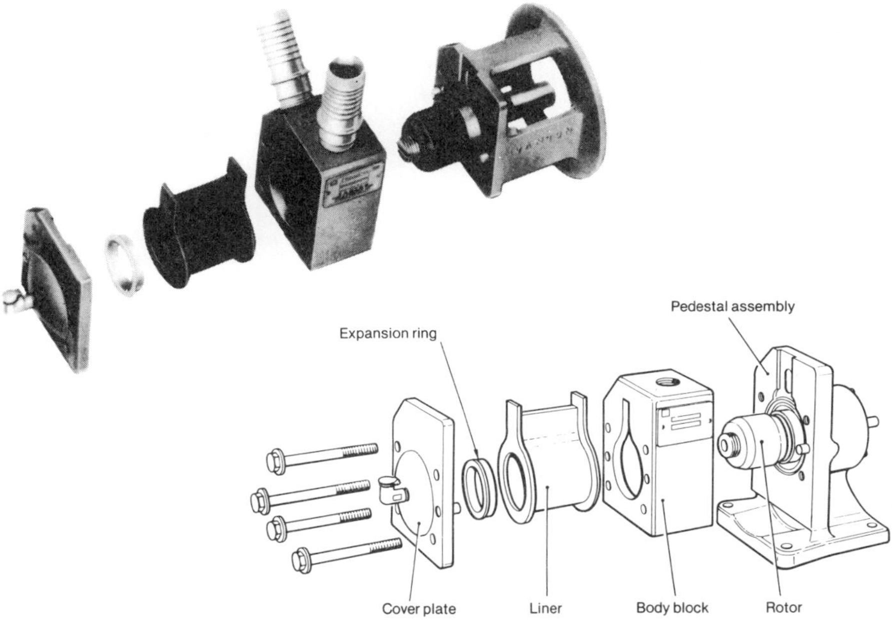

Rotary plastic pump.

Portable electric rotary plastic pump.

TABLE 1 – PROPERTIES OF RIGID PLASTICS SUITABLE FOR PUMP CASINGS, BODY BLOCKS AND IMPELLERS

Name (Common or Trade) Chemical Name	PVC Polyvinylchloride (normal impact)	CPVC Chlorinated polyvinylchloride	PE Polyethylene (high density)	PP Polypropylene (unmodified)	PTFE Polytetra-fluoroethylene	RULON All-polymeric reinforced PTFE	PVDF Polyvinylidene fluoride	ETFE Modified copolymer of ethylene and TFE	PPS Polyphenylene sulphide
Specific gravity (density)	1.30–1.58	1.49–1.58	0.926–0.940	0.902–0.910	2.14–2.20	2.24 min	1.75–1.78	1.7	1.34
Tensile strength lb/in^2	6000–7500	7500–11000	3500–4500	4300–5500	2000–5000	1200 min	5500–7400	5000–7500	10000
Compressive strength lb/in^2	10000	9000–16000	–	5500–8000	1700	1200	8680	7100	–
Impact strength ft lb/in notch (Izod test)	0.4–2.0	0.61	1.5–12	0.5–2.2 at 73°F (0.125 x 0.5 in bar)	3.0	6.0	3.6–4.0	No break	0.3 at 75°F (0.5 x 0.25 in bar)
Hardness Rockwell	R113	R12.1	D65 Shore R35–40	R80–110	D50–55 (Shore)	D60–75	D80 (Shore)	R50, D75	R124
Thermal expansion 10^{-5} in/in/degF	2.8	4.4	6	5.8–10.2	10.0	3.3 (degF)	8.5	5–9	5.5
Heat Resistance °F (continuous) °C	130–140 55–60	230 110	200 93	225–260 105–125	500 260	550 290	300 150	300–360 150–180	400–500 200–260
Chemical Resistance: Effect of weak acids Effect of strong acids	None None to slight	None None	Resistant Attacked by oxidizing acids	None Attacked slowly by oxidizing acids. Avoid chromic acid.	None None	None None	None Attacked by hot conc. sulphuric acid	None None	None Attacked slowly by oxidizing acids.
Effect of weak alkalis	None	None	Resistant	None	None	None	None	None	None
Effect of strong alkalis	None	None	Resistant	Very resistant	None	None	None	None	None
Effect of organic solvents	Resists alcohols, aliphatic hydrocarbons, oils; swells in ketones, esters, aromatic hydrocarbons		Resistant below 60°C except to chlorinated solvents.	Resistant below 80°C	None	None	Resists most solvents.	None	Resistant below 375–400°F (190–204°C)
Pump components	Casings, impellers, bolts, nuts, shaft sleeves	Impellers, bolts nuts, shaft sleeves.	Body blocks	Body blocks, bolts, nuts, shaft sleeves	Body blocks	Sleeve bearings	Casings, impellers, bolts, nuts, shaft sleeves	Impellers	Impellers, sleeve bearings

TABLE 2 – PUMP BODY BLOCKS IN PLASTICS COMPARED WITH ELASTOMERIC LINERS

	Material	Operating Temperature Range	Applications
BODY BLOCK	Polyethylene	Up to 185°C (365°F)	Excellent for weak and strong acids and weak and strong alkalis; attacked by strong oxidizing acids and aromatic solvents.
	Polypropylene	Up to 185°C (365°F)	Excellent for weak and strong acids and alkalis. Excellent for many solvents.
	PTFE	Up to 265°C (510°F) but may be limited by flexible liner	Excellent for weak and strong acids, weak and strong alkalis, and organic solvents; generally inert to chemical attack.
	PVDF	−20°C to 130°C (−4°F to 265°F)	Excellent resistance to solvents.
	Epoxy resin	−20°C to 140°C (−4°F to 284°F)	Normally used only when reinforced, *eg* as GRP.
	Polyester resin	−20°C to 140°C (−4°F to 284°F)	Normally used only when reinforced, *eg* as GRP.
	Nylon 6/6	Up to 105°C (221°F)	Good resistance to alkalis, dilute acids, solvents. Glass-filled nylon preformed for strength and rigidity.
LINERS	Flexible liners Natural rubber	Up to 165°C (329°F)	Good resistance to weak and strong acids and alkalis; attacked by oxidizing agents; good resistance to oxygenated solvents and alcohols; swells in vegetable, mineral and animal oil. Excellent abrasion resistance.
	Buna N	Up to 185°C (365°F) intermittent to 200°C (329°F)	Good resistance to weak and strong acids and alkalis; excellent resistance to aliphatic hydrocarbons; excellent resistance to petroleum oil, petrol, mineral and vegetable oils. Excellent water swell resistance.
	Neoprene	Up to 225°C (437°F)	Excellent resistance to dilute acids; weak and strong alkalis; good resistance to concentrated acids; good resistance to oil and petrol.
	Hypalon (chlorosulfonated polyethylene)	Up to 210°C (410°F)	Excellent resistance to dilute and concentrated acids, weak and strong alkalis. Exceptional resistance to strong oxidizating acids. Good resistance to concentrated mineral acids.
	Butyl	Up to 225°C (437°F)	Good resistance to corrosive chemicals. Outstanding resistance to dilute mineral acids. Excellent resistance to vegetable and mineral oils and solvents. Excellent heat resistance and low gas permeation.
	Viton	Up to 250°C (482°F)	Excellent resistance to oils, solvents and missile fuels and most chemicals at elevated temperatures.
	Compar (polyvinyl alcohol)	Up to 150°C (302°F)	Extremely resistant to organic solvents; attacked by water, weak acids and alkalis.
	Nordel	Up to 225°C (437°F)	Resistant to weak acids, most alkalis and ketones.

when a temperature limit of 125 °C is possible. It is particularly useful for its resistance to solvents, to H_2SO_4 and to a wider range of media than the polyester-based GRP.

Nylon is another well-established engineering plastic, although its application to pump components is largely restricted to non-corrosive duties. Nylon is attacked by concentrated mineral acids and is soften by and absorbs polar solvents such as alcohol. It is also less abrasion-resistant than polypropylene ultra-high molecular-weight polyethylene (UHMWP).

Table 1 gives properties of rigid plastics suitable for pump casings, body blocks, impellers, *etc*. Table 2 compares pump body blocks in plastics with elastomeric liners.

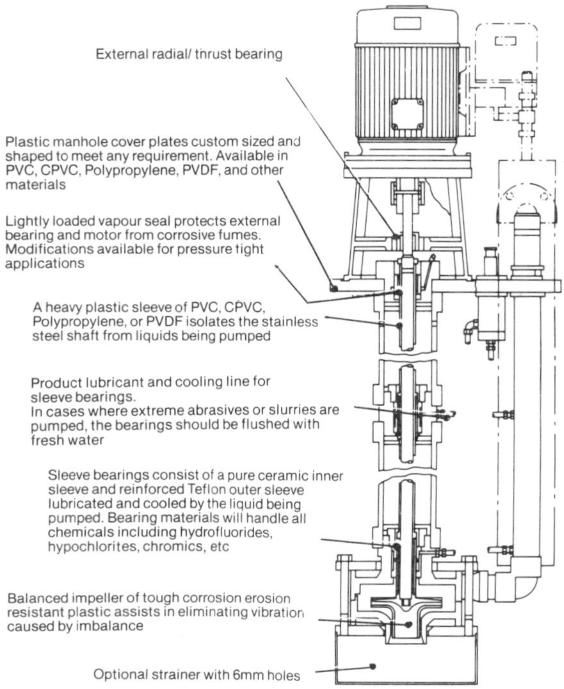

Figure 2
Heavy-duty plastic sump pump.

Plastic pump design

Because the mechanical and thermal properties of plastics differ from those of metals the all-plastic pump needs to be designed around the material being used, *ie* plastics are not a simple direct substitute for metals. Rigidity can be a particular problem, calling for special attention in the design of an all-plastic pump. Figure 2 shows a heavy-duty sump pump designed to handle corrosive fluids and hazardous chemicals stored in sumps or tanks. This type of pump finds wide application in chemical processing, waste treatment, electrolysis and electroplating, pollution control, on fume scrubbers and wherever corrosive liquids must be transferred.

The pump shaft is completely encased in plastic to isolate the metal from the solution. The pump head bolts are of heavy sectioned plastic and this construction eliminates pit corrosion of the shaft in the sleeve bearing area. Semi-open or fully-closed plastic impellers are used depending upon the application. Radial vanes on the back of the impeller increase the flow of fluid through the sleeve bearing. The sleeve bearing consists of a pure ceramic inner sleeve and reinforced Du Pont's teflon outer sleeve lubricated and cooled by the liquid being pumped. The all-plastic air-operated double-diaphragm pump in UHDPE (Figure 3) is another example of the successful use of plastic materials.

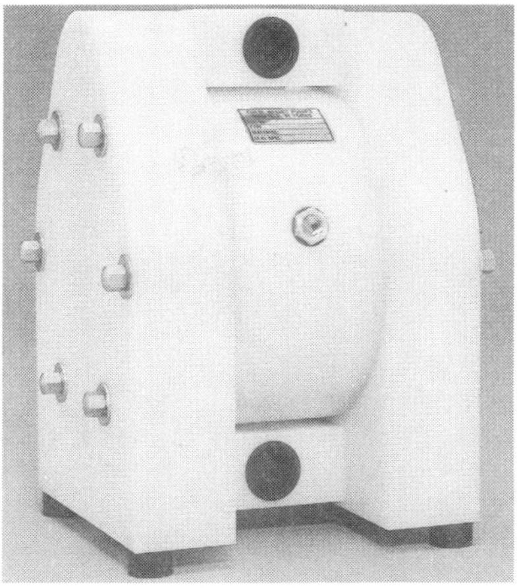

Figure 3
Corrosion-resistant sealless double diaphragm pump in ultra-high density polyethylene and PTFE.

Figure 4
Horizontal centrifugal pump for sustained high pressure applications.

The self-priming centrifugal pump shown in Figure 4 is specifically engineered to serve a variety of process industry needs in the handling of corrosive fluids at temperatures to 120 °C. With a broad flow range; 1 to 65 m/h it is used for sump evacuation, and in-line pump service where headroom precludes the use of vertical sump pumps.

Many of the advantages of plastic construction for handling corrosive fluids can in fact be lost if necessary non-plastic parts remain wetted by the fluid being handled. This applies particularly to the shaft and impeller fastenings and to the type and form of the shaft seals used. Where no attempt is made in the design to protect the shaft, then shaft and locknut must be in suitable materials for the liquid being handled.

One of the main points to consider in the design of plastic pumps intended to handle a wide range of different chemically-active fluids is that the presence of unprotected (metal) parts wetted by the fluid may limit the variety of fluids that the pump can handle, or call for a change in metal specification to handle particular products.

Pump Construction

TURBO MACHINES (centrifugal, mixed flow and axial flow pumps) are commonly described and/or classified by their construction geometry (this also being a form of categorisation) *ie* number of stages, mounting, entry, casing geometry and casing construction.

Table 1 gives the classification of turbo machines by geometry and Table 2 the classification of centrifugal pumps by construction.

The number of stages refers to the number of separate impellers mounted on a common shaft and contained within the casing. A single-stage pump implies a single impeller (although in some cases it may be double-sided) and a single-stage of pressurisation of the liquid passing through the pump. Pumps with more than one stage are generally referred to as multi-stage machines, with the number of stages appended where applicable. Thus in the case of unit construction, often employed for multi-stage pumps, any number of stages may be added within practical limits, by bolting on additional sections.

Mounting refers to whether the pump designed for horizontal or vertical mounting. Horizontal pumps are the more common and have advantages from the point of view of ease of maintenance, resistance to corrosion and abrasion and ease of mounting with minimum floor space, ease of priming and reduction in required NPSH and general flexibility to adapt to a particular duty. With certain types of pump the application may dictate mounting – *eg* submersible and immersible pumps are invariably of vertical type.

Entry refers to the suction side connection (s). In the simplest form of centrifugal pump, the suction branch is mounted on the axis of the pump and opens into the central eye of the impeller. The liquid is then flung out under centrifugal force into a volute casing terminating in a recouperator section, to the end of which is attached the delivery flange. The impeller itself is overhung and the single-entry flow imparts and axial thrust on the impeller which can be partially relieved, if necessary, by holes in the back shroud. The balance of the axial thrust is then taken by the shaft bearings.

With a double-entry pump, the inflow is divided and taken to each side of a double-sided impeller, thus balancing the axial thrusts. Pumps with double-entry are usually of large size, with higher specific speeds. Suction and delivery branches

TABLE 1 – CLASSIFICATION OF TURBO-MACHINES BY GEOMETRY

Basic Type	Stage(s)	Layout	Entry	Casing
Centrifugal	Single-stage	Horizontal	Single	Volute-split or end pull-out.
	Single-stage	Horizontal	Double	Volute-split or end pull-out.
	Multi-stage	Horizontal	Axial (single or double)	Ring type for low to medium heads. Barrel type for high pressures.
	Multi-stage (balanced)	Horizontal	Back-to-back	Volute (usually).
	Single-stage	Vertical	Single	Volute-split casing
	Single-stage	Vertical	Double	Volute-split casing.
	Multi-stage	Vertical	Single	Volute
Mixed flow (helical)	Single-stage	Horizontal	Single	Volute-split casing or end pull-out.
	Single-stage	Horizontal	Double	Volute-split casing.
	Single-stage	Vertical	Single	Volute-split casing.
Mixed flow (diagonal)	Single-stage	Horizontal	Single	Concentric.
	Single-stage	Vertical	Single	Concentric.
	Multi-stage	Usually vertical	Single	Concentric.
Axial flow	Single-stage	Horizontal	Single	Concentric.
		Vertical	Single	Concentric.
	Multi-stage	Usually vertical	Single	Concentric.

TABLE 2 – CLASSIFICATION OF CENTRIFUGAL PUMPS BY CONSTRUCTION

Construction Parameter	Classification	(Alternative Descriptions) Sub-Types or
Alignment of axis	(i) Horizontal	
	(ii) Vertical	
Suction entry	(i) Single	(a) Top suction (top inlet)
	(ii) Double	(b) Side suction (side inlet)
		(c) Bottom suction (bottom inlet)
Casing	Split casing	(a) Horizontally split (axially split)
		(b) Radially split
Impeller support	(i) Overhung	(a) Internal bearings
	(ii) Between bearings	(b) External bearings
Mounting	(i) Integral	
	(ii) In-line	(ii) (Pipeline mounted)
	(iii) Foot mounted	
	(iv) Frame mounted	
	(v) Lantern mounted	(v) (Skirt mounted; lantern based)
	(vi) Pedestal mounted	(vi) (Headstock mounted)
	(vii) Bung mounted	
	(viii) Flange mounted	(viii) (Flanged overhung pump)
	(ix) Tank mounted	(ix) (Suspended pump)
	(x) Wall mounted	
	(xi) Skid mounted	(xi) (Bulkhead mounted)
Rotor disassembly	(i) Pull-out	(i) Withdrawable rotor assembly
	(ii) Horizontally split casing	
Seals	(i) Packed glands	
	(ii) Mechanical seals	
	(iii) Glandless	

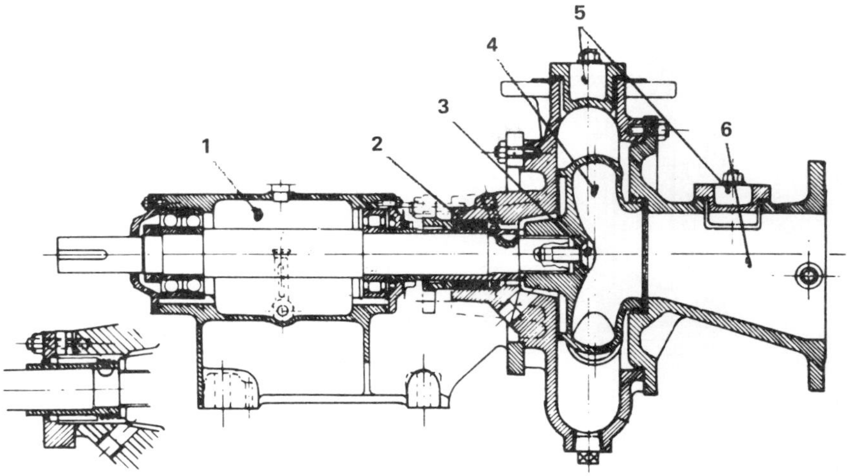

1. Large bearing bracket
2. Stuffing box
3. Recessed impeller nut without obstruction at impeller entry
4. Single-channel impeller
5. Inspection cover
6. Suction cover

Single-channel impeller sewage pump.

are commonly situated on one half of a split casing, the other half being removable for inspection or for dismantling the pump without the necessity of first disconnecting the suction and delivery pipes.

As a general characteristic the suction branch diameter is a little larger than the delivery branch on single-stage pumps. This basically is to encourage the use of a generous size of suction pipeline to minimise suction pipeline to minimise suction losses; but in practice it does not necessarily determine the corresponding pipe sizes. Delivery and suction branch sizes are normally standardised (to mate with a standard pipe flanges, or with standard pipe threads in the case of small pumps).

Impellers can be classified according to the major direction of flow in reference to axis of rotation. Accordingly centrifugal pumps may have:

(i) Radial-flow impellers.
(ii) Axial-flow impellers.
(iii) Mixed-flow impellers (combining radial and axial flow principles).

In addition, impellers can be further classified as:

(i) ingle-suction with a single inlet on one side.
(ii) Double-suction with water flowing to the impeller symmetrically from both sides.

The mechanical construction of impellers gives a still further sub-division into:

(i) Enclosed, with shrouds or side walls enclosing the water ways.
(ii) Open with no shrouds.
(iii) Semi-open or semi-enclosed.

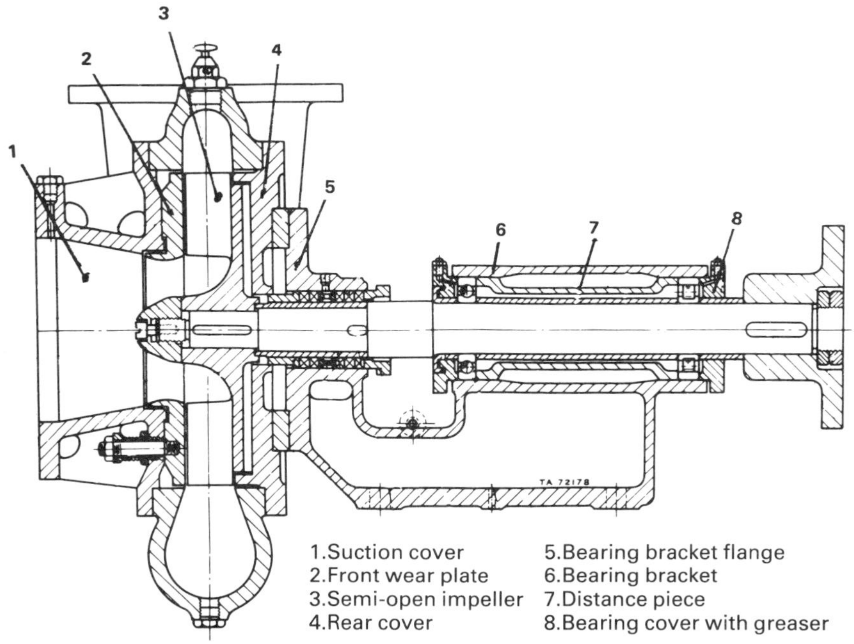

Slurry pump
Pump of very heavy construction with semi-open impeller running between replaceable wear plates. Usually requiring special stuffing box arrangement, allowing the use of mechanical seals for this often difficult duty. Bearing bracket is often equipped with adjusting device for the correct positioning of the impeller.

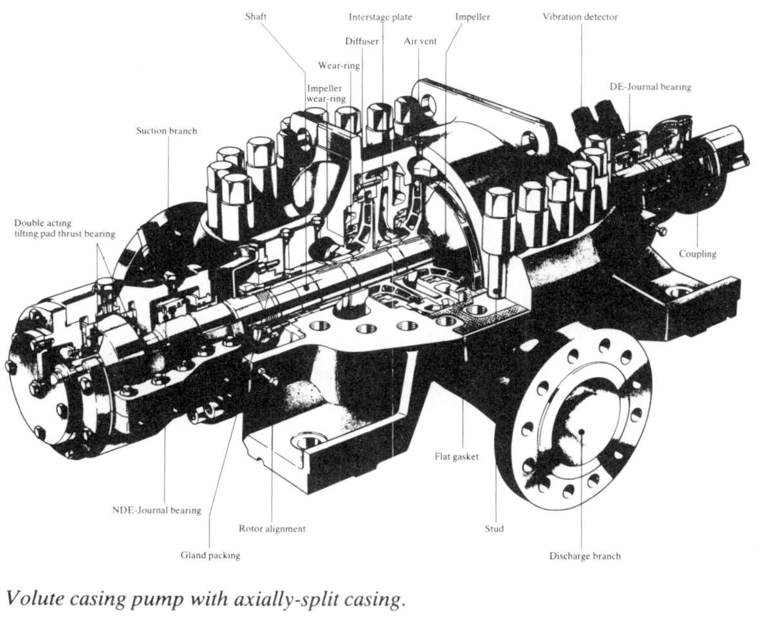

Volute casing pump with axially-split casing.

Accordingly a pump in which the head is developed by a single impeller is known as a single-stage pump and as previously stated two or more single-stage pumps can be connected in series or all the impellers can be incorporated in a single casing. The unit is then called a multi-stage pump.

Horizontal shaft centrifugal pumps are classified still further according to the location of the suction nozzle:

(i) End suction.

(ii) Side suction.

(iii) Bottom suction.

(iv) Top suction.

Some pumps operate in air with the liquid coming to and being conducted away from the pumps by piping other pumps most often vertical types are submerged in their suction supply. Vertical shaft pumps are therefore called either dry-pit or wet-pit types. If the wet-pits are axial flow, mixed flow or vertical turbine types, the liquid is discharged up through the supporting drop or column pipe to a discharge point above or below the supporting floor. These pumps are consequently designated as above ground discharge or below ground discharge units.

Low type number impellers for small quantity high head duties have relatively large diameters and small axial widths. These impellers often have plain radial flow and their vanes have single curvature. For medium and high type numbers, the impellers are generally of double curvature, variously described as mixed flow or Francis impellers. The liquid, normally water enters the impellers almost axially and is turned in the impeller to radial flow, hence the term mixed flow. Impeller passages have generally been produced by the error triangle, conformal transformation or aerofoil methods.

The path of the water through the impeller takes the form of a quadrant, usually of varying width. The combination of impeller rotation and water rotation about this quadrant from inlet to outlet can therefore be said to resemble a gear drive. With pure axial inlet the combination of impeller rotation and water flow will result in purely helical inlet vanes. At outlet the flow will be purely radial which, combined with impeller rotation, will result in the outlet vanes being purely spiral.

Casing geometry may be described in various ways, but particularly should refer to the manner in which the casing can be opened for disassembly (*eg* split casings or end pull out). In the case of multi-stage pumps the method of assembly of the individual stages is usually specified – *eg* ring type or barrel type. The latter are normally used for high pressure designs, and have an inner casing fitting within an outer barrel. Discharge pressure acting on the inner casing provides a sealing force to hold the casing halves together, whilst the construction also minimises the number of connections and sealing points required.

The most common type is the horizontally-split casing with suction and delivery branches located in the bottom half of the casing. The upper half can then be removed for servicing without disturbing the pipework. Vertically mounted split casing pumps are however coming into great use particularly where saving in floor space is important.

Most single-stage centrifugal pumps are intended for service at moderate pressures and temperatures. As a result pump manufacturers usually design a special line of pumps for high operating pressures and temperatures rather than make their standard line unduly expernsive by making it suitable for too wider range of operating conditions.

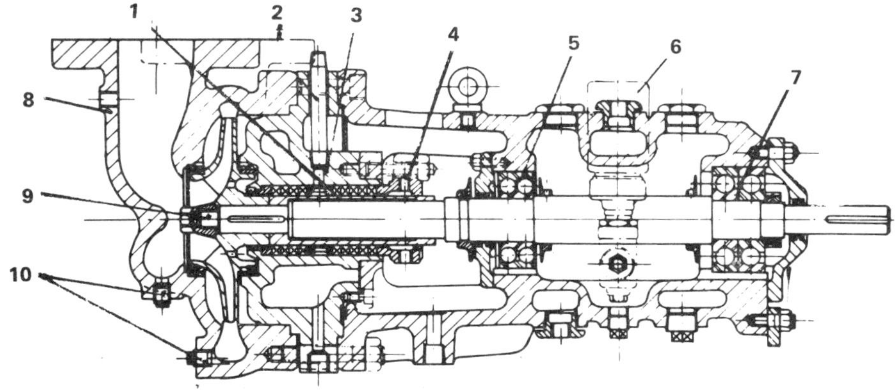

1.Stuffing box sleeve
2.Injection to soft packing
3.Stuffing box
4.Split gland with smothering device
5.Radial bearing
6.Constant oil level and reservoir
7.Thrust bearing
8.Pump casing
9.Impeller nut
10.Drain plugs

Back pull-out design heavy process pump
This type of pump is mainly used in refineries and other process plant for the pumping of hot and sometimes flammable fluids, often at high (suction) pressure. It is therefore of heavy construction with the emphasis on suitable stuffing box design which, in most cases, must be suitable for mechanical seals. The illustration shows a soft packed box which is often of considerable length and suitable for the injection of cooling and/or lubricating fluid to the packing. The design is suitable for back pull-out with suction and discharge branches located on the pump casing. Often the suction branch is vertical in order to provide a direct connection to the suction system. For hot duties the casing feet are arranged in the centre line in order to retain shaft alignment. Cooled bearing bracket and stuffing box and large oil reservoir are normally essential features.

For general service, the end suction single-stage pump design is extensively used for small pumps up to 102 and 152 mm (4 and 6 inches) discharge size for both motor-mounted and coupled types. In all these the small size makes it feasible to cast the volute and one side integrally. Whether the stuffing box side or the suction side is made integrally with the casing is usually determined by the most economical pump design. For larger pumps, especially those for special service such as sewage handling there is a demand for pumps of both rotations. A design with separate suction and stuffing box heads permits use of the same casing for either rotation if the flanges on the two sides are made identical. There is also a demand for vertical pumps that can be disassembled by removal of the rotor and bearing assembly from the top of the casing. Many horizontal applications of the pumps of the same line, however, require partial dismantling from the suction side. Such lines are most adaptable when they have separate suction and stuffing box covers.

Casing construction is normally only applicable as a form of classification in the case of multi-stage centrifugal pumps (particularly boiler feed pumps), when the following descriptions apply:

(i) Split casings – which in general are restricted to a maximum pressure of about 100 bar or less on account of the difficulty of sealing the casing joint although some higher pressure units are made with this form of construction.

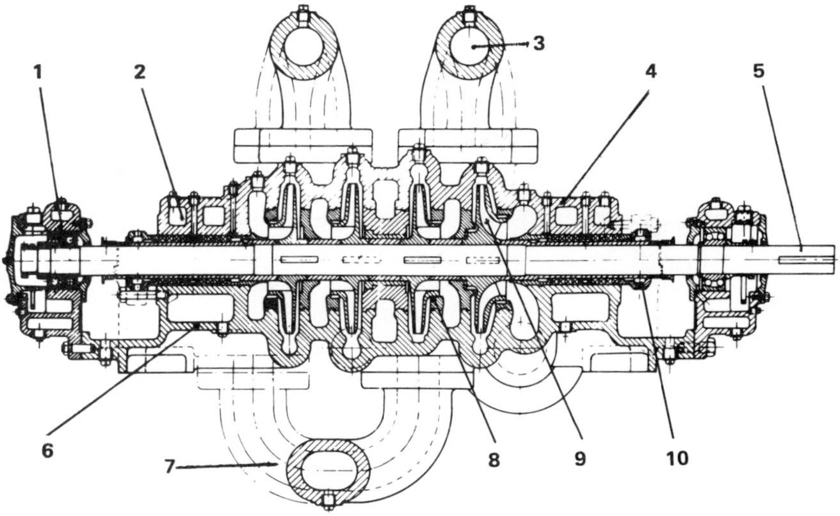

1.End bearing
2.Cooled stuffing box
3.Transfer pipes.
4.Top casing halve
5.Shaft
6.Bottom casing halve
7.Transfer pipe
8.Wear rings
9.First-stage impeller
10.Split gland

Multi-stage casing pump.

A split casing is made of two or more parts fastened together. The term horizontally-split had regularly been used to describe pumps with a casing divided by horizontal plane through the shaft centre line or axis. The term axially-split is now preferred. Since both the suction and discharge nozzels are usually in the same half of the casing, the other half may be removed for inspection of the interior without disturbing the bearings or the piping. Like its counterpart horizontally split, the term vertically split is poor terminology. It refers to a casing split in a plane perpendicular to the axis of rotation. The term radially split is now preferred.

(ii) Ring or unit construction – where each stage comprises a separate casing with its suction chamber and delivery chamber. A multi-stage casing is then built up by bolting together the required number of units with external tie bolts. Gasket type seals may be used between the casings for pressures up to about 70 bar. For higher pressures the jointing surfaces are usually ground and lapped. Whilst this form of construction is straightforward, a difficulty is the possibility of distortion of the complete pump body under pressure and temperature changes. Thermal conditions may call for pre-heating or a gradual warm-up of the pump on certain designs. On high pressure designs, some pressure relief may be obtained by dividing the length of the assembly into high pressure and low pressure sections by means of an intervening partition. Such pumps are capable of working up to the highest feed pressures required without aggrevating distortion problems.

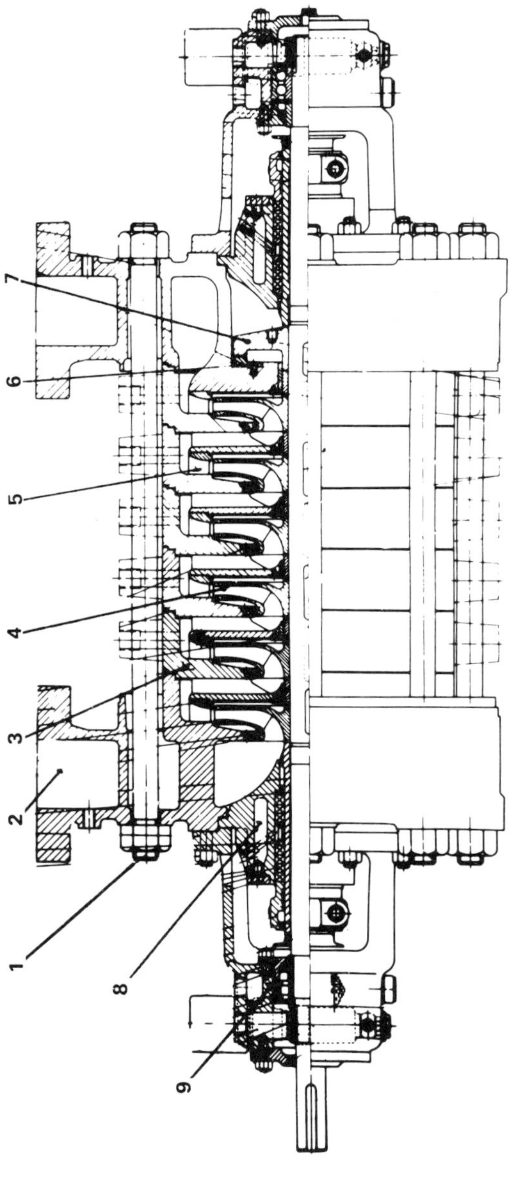

1.Tie bolts
2.Suction stage
3.Interstage
4.Impeller
5.Diffuser
6.Stationary balance disk
7.Rotating balance disk
8.Watercooled stuffing box
9.Oil lubricated bearing

Multi-stage pump.

(iii) Barrel-type casings – here an inner casing fits into an outer barrel; pressure acting on the inner casing then provides the force necessary to seal joints between individual stages. This pressure is equal to the pressure in the delivery branch, but is partly balanced by the internal pressure in the stages so that inner casing walls are not necessary. A further advantage is the small number of high pressure fluid joints which have to be sealed and so this form of construction is particularly suitable for high pressure designs. Barrel-type pumps are also less liable to distortion, although they are generally heavier and more expensive to produce. They are a particularly popular type in America for medium and high pressure services, but less so in the European productions.

Machining the classicial helical pump rotor has been developed into a fine art.

Rigidity

In general, a two-stage pump will have a more rigid shaft than that of a single-stage because, although the span between bearings is greater, the shaft diameter is generally larger to transmit the greater power and in addition a certain amount of support is derived from the water lubricated central sleeve bearing. The gland conditions are more onerous on a two-stage pump since the gland at the delivery stage is subjected to first-stage pressure instead of inlet pressure. It is often convenient to provide a restriction bush to break down the pressure to a reasonable value for the type of packing or seal that is used, the discharge from this restriction bush being used to seal the first stage gland against air leakage.

Axial thrust

Single-stage pumps with closed impellers – the pressures generated by a centrifugal pump exert forces on both stationary and rotating parts. The design of these parts balances some of these forces, but separate means may be required to counter-balance others. Axial hydraulic thrust on an impeller is the some of the unbalanced forces acting in the axial direction. As reliable large-capacity thrust bearings are now readily available, axial thrust in single-stage pumps remains a problem only in larger units. Theoretically, a double suction impeller is in hydraulic axial balance, with the pressures on one side equal to and counter balancing pressures on the other. In practice this balance may not be achieved for the following reasons:

(i) The suction passages to the two suction eyes may not provide equal or uniform flows to the two sides.

(ii) External conditions such as an elbow located too close to the pump suction nozzle, may cause unequal flow to the two suction eyes.

(iii) The two sides of the discharge casing waterways may not be symmetrical, or the impeller may be located off-centre.

These conditions will alter the flow characteristics between the impeller shrouds and the casing, causing unequal pressure on the shrouds.

(iv) Unequal leakage through the two leakage joints can upset the balance.

Combined, these factors can create axial unbalance. To compensate this, all centrifugal pumps even those with double-suction impellers, incorporate thrust bearings.

The ordinary single-suction closed radial flow impeller with the shaft passing through the impeller eye is subject to axial thrust because a portion of the front wall is exposed to suction pressure and thus relatively more backwall surface is exposed to discharge pressure. If the discharge chamber pressure was uniform over the entire impeller surface, the axial force acting towards the suction would be equal to the product of the net pressure generated by the impeller and the unbalanced annular area.

Actually, pressure on the two single-suction closed impeller walls is not uniform. The liquid trapped between the impeller shrouds and casing walls is in rotation and the pressure at the impeller periphery is appreciably higher than at the impeller hub.

To eliminate the axial thrust of a single-suction impeller, a pump can be provided with both front and back wearing rings; to equalise thrust areas, the inner diameter of both rings is made the same. Pressure approximately equal to the suction pressure is maintained in a chamber located on the impeller side of the backwearing ring by drilling balancing holes through the impeller. Leakage past the backwearing ring is returned to the suction area through these holes. With large single-stage single-suction pumps, balancing holes are considered undesirable because leakage back to the impeller suction opposes the main flow, creating disturbances. In such pumps a piped connection to pump suction replaced the balancing holes. Another way to eliminate or reduce axial thrust in single-suctionn impellers is to use pump-out vanes on the back shroud. The effect of these vanes is to reduce the pressure acting on the back shroud of the impeller.

Axial forces acting on an overhung impeller with a single stuffing box are affected by suction pressure. In addition to the unbalanced force found in a single suction two box design there is an axial force equivalent to the product of the shaft area through the stuffing box and the difference between suction and atmospheric pressure. This force acts toward the impeller suction when the suction pressure is less than atmospheric or in the opposite direction when it is higher than atmospheric.

Mixed flow and axial flow impellers – the axial thrust in radial impellers is produced by the static pressures on the impeller shrouds. Axial flow impellers have no shrouds and the axial thrust is created strictly by the difference in pressure on the two faces of the impeller vanes. In addition, there may be a difference in pressure acting on the two shaft hub ends one generally subjects discharge pressure and the other the suction pressure. With mixed flow impellers, axial thrust is a combination of forces caused by the action of the vanes on the liquid and those arising from the difference in pressures acting on the various surfaces. Wearing rings are often provided on the back of mixed flow impellers with either balancing holes through the impeller hub or an external balancing pipe leading back to the suction. Except for very large units and in certain special applications the maximum axial thrust developed by mixed flow and axial flow impellers is not significant because the operating heads of these pumps are relatively low. This thrust is carried by thrust bearings with the necessary load capacity.

Multi-stage pumps – most multi-stage pumps are built with single suction impellers in order to simplify the design of the inter-stage connections. Two obvious arrangements are possible for the single-suction impellers; several single-suction impellers may be mounted on one shaft each having its suction inlet facing in the same direction and its stages following one another in ascending order of pressure. The axial thrust then balanced by a hydraulic balancing device. An even number of single-suction impellers may be used one half facing in one direction and the other half facing in the opposite direction. With this arrangement, axial thrust on the first half is compensated by the thrust in the opposite direction on the other half. This mounting of single suction impellers back-to-back is frequently called opposed impellers.

An uneven number of suction impellers may be used with this arrangement, provided the correct shaft and inter-stage bushing diameters are used to give the effect of a hydraulic balancing device that will compensate for the hydraulic thrust on one of the stages. It is important to note that the opposed impeller arrangement completely balances axial thrust only under the following conditions:

(i) The pump must be provided with two stuffing boxes.

(ii) The shaft must have a constant diameter.

(iii) The impeller hubs must not extend through the inter-stage portion of the casings separating adjacent stages.

Except for some special pumps that have an internal and enclosed bearing at one end, and therefore only one stuffing box, most multi-stage pumps fulfil the first condition. Because of structural requirements however, the last two conditions are not practical. A slight residual thrust is usually present in multi-stage opposed impeller pumps and is carried on the thrust bearing.

Radial thrust

In pumps with volute casings radial forces caused by non-uniform pressure distribution over the impeller circumference acts on the impeller at part-loads and overloads. For double volute casings with common delivery branches, the radial thrust at 180° peripheral angle between the two tongues is about 25% of the thrust for single spiral casings. With reducing peripheral angle between the tongues, the radial thrust factor increases rapidly.

Pumps with diffusers are subject to lower radial thrust than pumps with volute casings. The stable component of the radial thrust becomes greater with increasing eccentricity of the impeller in the casing, while the unstable component is greatest during concentric running.

Bearings and Lubrication

THE TYPE and placement of bearings on a pump can affect the application potential and also, to a lesser extent, installation requirements. In the case of general purpose pumps, main features may offer alternative bearing (and gland) designs to adapt the machine for specific duties. A basic point is whether the bearings are external (mounted outside the casing); or internal (contained within the casing). Internal bearings will be at least partially, and often exposed to the product being handled. Thus external bearings would be preferred when the product is aggressive, corrosive or abrasive, or otherwise incompatible with the type of bearings fitted.

Bearings that give radial positioning to the rotor are known as line bearings and those that locate the rotor axially are called thrust bearings. In most applications the thrust bearings actually serve both as thrust and radial bearings.

Plain bearings are widely used on all types and sizes of pumps, being favourable on cost and simplicity of fitting, suitability for high speeds, wide compatibility with fluids when wetted and generally quieter operation than roller bearings. On small pumps simple bushes may be employed, press fitted into the pump casing. These may be in a suitable bearing metal or low friction plastic material with good dimensional stability.

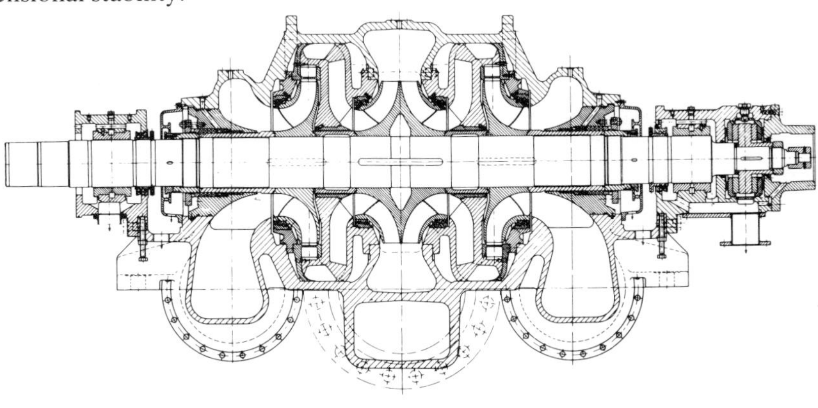

Typical water transport pump with tilting pad thrust bearing.

Larger plain bearings are normally of the sleeve type, the sleeve material being a bearing metal or a non-metal. Metal sleeves have the highest load carrying capacity and are generally suitable for wetted bearings where the fluid being pumped has adequate lubricating properties. Water is not excluded as water lubricated metal bearings are capable of satisfactory performance with suitable choice of materials, provided the water is clean and neutral in characteristic. More usually, however, bearing sleeves for water lubrication are made of rubber, synthetic fibre, laminated thermoset plastic, 'filled' plastic, special polymers of an elastomeric nature, or carbon graphite.

Modern polymeric bearing materials can offer specific advantages when the fluid in contact with the bearing contains abrasive as they reject this abrasive and allow the particles to be washed out of the bearing rather than, as happens with softer plastics, become imbedded in it; or in the case of harder materials such as metals, scoring and scratching it. Hard plastics, such as phenolics, can cause rapid shaft wear, as can nylon.

Rubber is a common choice for large bearings, with relatively generous clearances and flushing channels in the rubber section, a rubber sleeve being bonded to a metal sleeve (usually bronze) to form the complete bearing sleeve. Rubber bearings are capable of handling dirty as well as clean water although other types of water lubricated bearing sleeves are usually suitable for clean water only. If the wetting fluid is dirty, the bearing sleeves would then normally be lubricated by clean water from a separate supply. Exceptions again are the modern polymeric bearing materials which are directly competitive with cutless-type rubber bearings. These (and also to some extent carbon graphite) have the ability to accept dry start-up running which can avoid the necessity of a separate bearing lubrication system on vertical pumps.

Pump bearings may be rigid or self-aligning. A self-aligning bearing will automatically adjust itself to a change in the angular position of the shaft. In sleeve or babbeted bearings, the name self-aligning is applied to bearings that have a spherical fit of the sleeve in the housing. In anti-friction bearings, the name is applied to bearings the outer race of which is spherically ground or the housing of which provides a spherical fit.

Rolling contact bearings

Where the bearing load and speed permit, as is mostly the case with standard pumps, rolling contact bearings of the ball roller type are frequently used. Figure 1 shows the shaft bearing of a single-stage process pump. Such bearings provide both radial and axial guidance of the shaft. The most common ball bearing used on centrifugal pumps are:

(i) Single row deep groove.

(ii) Double row deep groove.

(iii) Double row self-aligning.

(iv) Angular contact – either single or double row.

All except the double row self-aligning bearings are capable of carrying thrust loads as well as radial loads.

Sliding contact bearings

Sliding contact bearings are employed where the service conditions (*eg* speed, radial and axial loads) no longer allow the use of rolling contact bearings and also wherever it is necessary to use the pumped medium to lubricate the bearings.

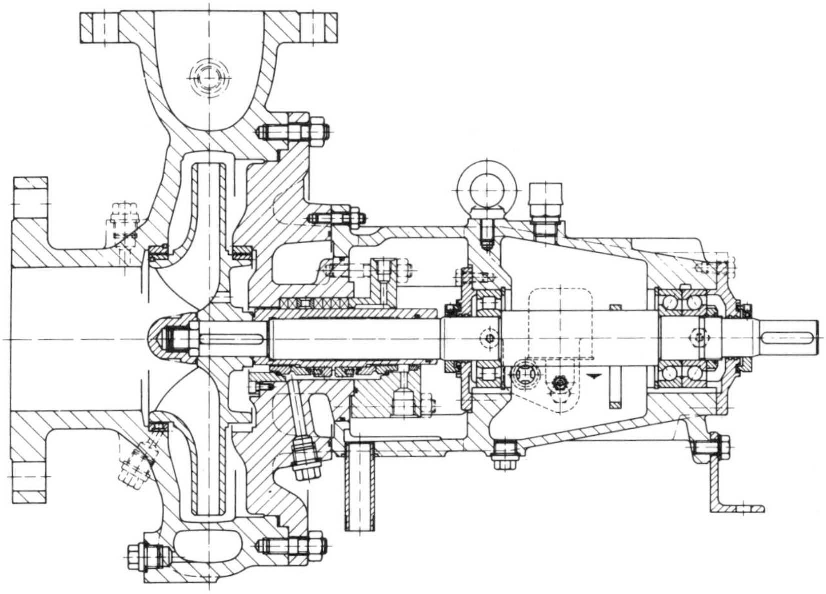

Figure 1
Shaft bearings of a single-stage process pump.

Oil lubricated journal bearings
These are mainly employed in the following types:

(i) Cylindrical bearing shell.
(ii) Bearing shells offset horizontally.
(iii) Multi-lobe sliding contact bearing.
(iv) Tilting pad bearing.

A journal bearing is essentially a viscous pump and it derives load capacity by pumping the lubricant through a small clearance region. The most common type of journal bearing is the plain cylindrical bushing. It may be split and have lubricating feed grooves at the parting line. Axial grooves can be incorporated to enable better cooling and to improve whirl stability. The principle advantages of cylindrical bearings are:

(i) Simple construction.
(ii) High load capacity relative to other bearing configurations.

Oil lubricated journal bearings (where the bearing shells are offset horizontally) and lobe bearings have non-circular geometries. These bearings are often used because they provide better resistance to whirl than do cylindrical configurations because they have multi-load producing pads that assist in preventing large attitude angles and cross coupling. They are generally used for high speed, low lobe applications where whirl might be a problem. They generally have poor horizontal stiffness because of the large clearances along the major diameter of the lips. Lobe bearings are usually clearance and tolerance sensitive.

Tilting pad thrust bearings are used extensively on high speed applications such as on boiler feed pumps, vertical pumps and on any multi-stage pump where violent pressure fluctuations occur. If fitted, provision must be made to carry away any

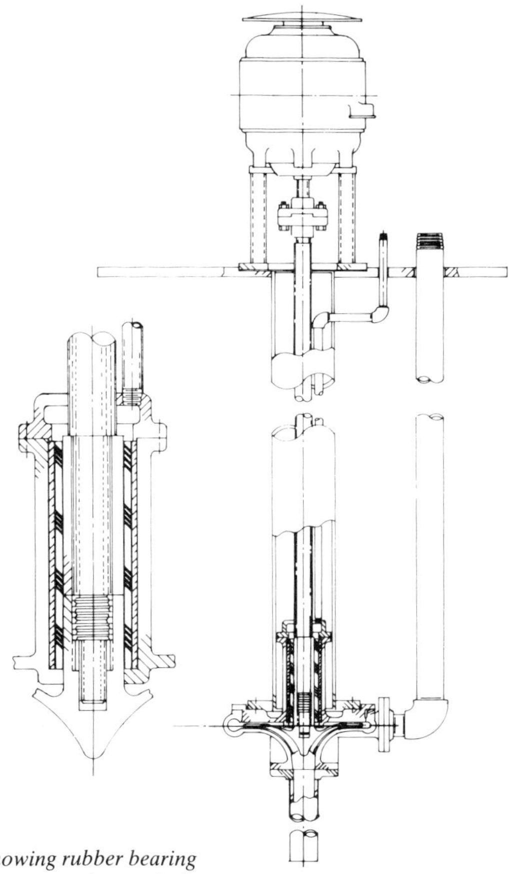

Figure 2
Applications showing rubber bearing installation arrangement into typical sump pump.

excess heat by a coil of water cooling pipes in the bearing housing or in a separate chamber. Extreme care is necessary to avoid any ingress of water into the oil. In the case of vertical shafts, a tube must be placed in the bore of the elongated thrust element of the rotor, to ensure that the thrust pads and the journal portion are always immersed in oil, whether standing or running.

Water lubricated bearings
Water lubricated rubber bearings were originally developed for marine applications. They are designed to generate a film of water at the bearing surface which provides ample support for pump shafts. In addition, grooves in the surface allow water to flow freely through the bearing. If sand or other foreign abrasive materials are present, they are flushed through the grooves. Water lubricated rubber bearings are not normally suitable for use with carbon steel shafts because of the chances of corrosion roughening the shaft. Solutions which may be adopted include the use of a stainless steel shaft (or monel for handling brines); stainless steel or bronze sleeving of the shaft over the bearing area; and hard chromium plating of the shaft, or similar surface treatment. Such shaft protection is not normally necessary with other types of water lubricated bearing sleeves.

Water lubricated rubber bearings.

Generally speaking, a journal surface speed of 3.2 ft/s is required to establish a fully hydrodynamic film of lubricant. Figures 3, 4 and 5 show typical water lubricated bearing installations.

Modern non-metallic bearings

Non-metallic bearing materials such as nylon, PTFE, laminated phenolics, acetal copolymers and ultra-high molecular-weight polyethylene, can offer major advantages over traditional metallic bearings for many applications requiring resistance to corrosive attack, abrasion, *etc.*, and specifically for bearings which have to operate in contact with fluids which are poor lubricants. No such polymeric material combines all the individual advantages offered by specific types, but very interesting properties compared with all the others can be offered by elastomers. Their particular advantages are:

(i) Exceptional resistance to abrasion.

(ii) Tolerance of very high shock loads.

(iii) Non-malleability (*ie* they are not pounded out of shape and are not easily damaged in handling).

(iv) High resilience (*ie* they can stand large and repeated deformation with no permanent effect).

(v) Retention of flexibility at low temperature.

Generally speaking, it is not possible to utilise them as bearing materials except where a high coefficient of friction is acceptable.

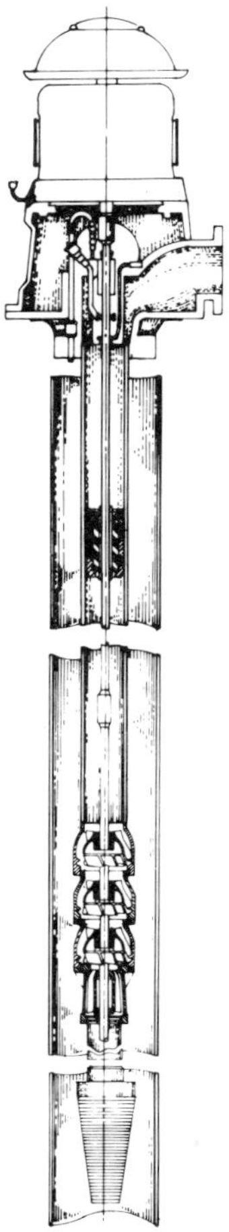

Figure 3
Arrangement of rubber bearings in bowls of vertical turbine pump.

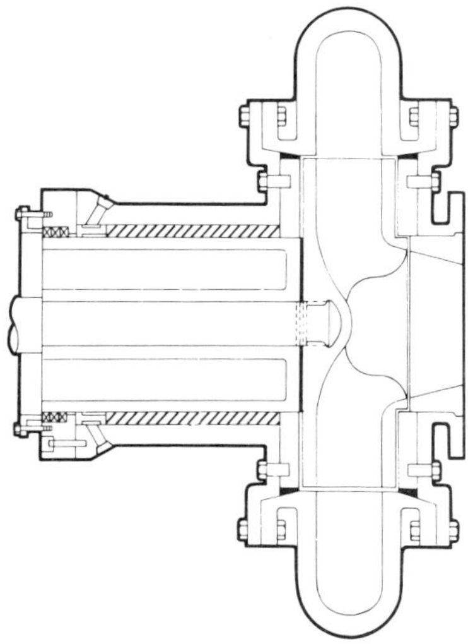

Figure 4
Rubber bearing in pump shaft provides support close to impeller, with stuffing box or sealing head placed outboard.

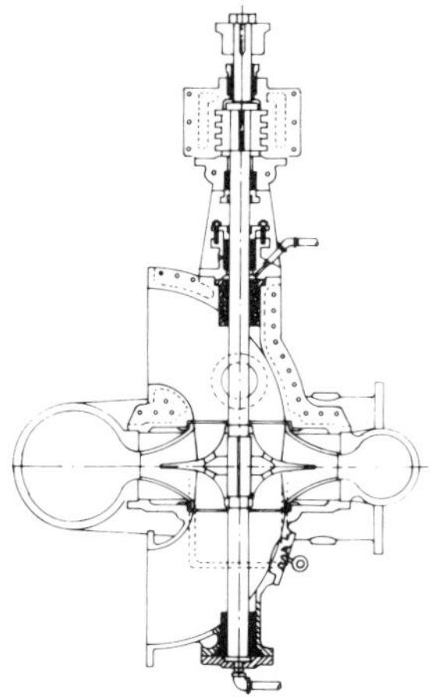

Figure 5
Centrifugal pump cross-section shows details of rubber bearing assemblies.

The more recent combination of elastomers with plastics of polymer alloys with a predominant elastomer component has produced further new bearing materials offering the advantages of elastomers with the greater load carrying capabilities and lower coefficient or friction of plastics. They could become a first choice for arduous conditions such as dirty, abrasive environments, shock loadings, inadequate lubrication and/or the need to work as well at low temperatures as at ambient and high temperatures (up to say 100 °C).

Bearings of this type of hard elastomeric material can give excellent results as pump bearings since the pumped medium will act as the lubricant. It is therefore unnecessary to seal these bearings from most media unless they are incompatible. Also, where there is abrasive content in the fluid this is accommodated without leading to excessive wear. Such bearings can also have the ability to operate dry for some time which can be of significant benefit while the fluid is being pumped up.

Lubrication

The choice of the lubricant for pump bearings in centrifugal pumps is dictated by applicational requirements by cost considerations and some times by the preference of a group of purchasers committed to the major portion of the output of that line. In vertical wet bit condenser circulating pumps water is the lubricant choice in preference to grease or oil. Most centrifugal pumps for refinery service are supplied with oil lubricated bearings because of the insistence of refinery engineers on this feature. In the marine field on the other hand the preference lies with grease lubricated bearings. For very high pump operating speeds (5000 r/min and above) oil lubrication is found to be the most satisfactory.

In small pumps the main consideration is cost so the most economical lubricant is chosen depending upon the type of bearing used. Ball bearings used in centrifugal pumps are usually grease lubricated although some services use oil lubrication. In grease lubricated bearings the grease packed into the bearing is thrown out by the rotation of the balls creating a slight suction at the inner race. As the expelled grease is cooled by contact with the housing thus attracted to the inner race, there is a continuous circulation of grease to lubricate and cool the bearing.

In vertical pumps the bearing housings require seals to prevent the escape of the lubricant, grease is usually preferred here as it lessens the chance of leakage. A bearing fully packed with grease prevents proper grease circulation in itself and its housing as a general rule therefore it is recommended that only one-third of the void spaces in the housing be filled. An excess amount of grease will cause the bearing to heat up and grease will flow out of the seals to relieve the situation. Unless the excess grease can escape through the seal or through the relief cock that is used on many large units, the bearing will probably fail early.

For oil lubricated ball bearings, a suitable oil level must be maintained in the housing this level should be at about the centre of the lowest ball of a stationary bearing. It may be achieved by a dam and an oil slinger to maintain the level behind the dam and thereby increase the leeway in the amount of oil the operator must keep in the housing. Oil rings are sometimes used to supply oil to the bearings from the bearing housing reservoir. Constant level oilers can also be used. See Figure 6.

Figure 6
Constant level oiler.

With all types of bearings – but with plain bearings in particular, the operating temperature of the bearing will have a considerable influence on bearing performance and life. If the bearing temperature is likely to become excessive – *ie* due to a hot liquid being handled or bearing loads being high – provision may have to be made to cool the bearing. This may be done by fitting a jacket around the bearing through which coolant is circulated or, if the bearing is separately lubricated by water or oil feed, by controlling the temperature or flow rate of the bearing lubricant. The provision of bearing cooling is quite distinct from gland cooling which is much more commonplace.

Compression Packings

Definition of compression packing

A COMPRESSION packing can be described as a deformable material used to prevent or control the passage of a fluid between surfaces that move in relation to each other.

Packings are the traditional form of *gland* seal and can be manufactured from a wide variety of different materials. A packing may be in shredded form (usually mixed with a lubricant) with which the gland or *stuffing box* is packed; in made-up sections (normally rectangular but sometimes circular); wound in position spiral fashion from a suitable cut length; or fabricated sections assembled in the gland as cut rings. In all cases sealing is obtained by tightening the gland, so that the packing is forced against or compressed on to the surface to be sealed.

The operating principle of a packed gland is illustrated in Figure 1. The compressive force generated by tightening of the gland spigot produces a radial pressure providing the sealing effect. The radial pressure distribution varies throughout the packing length in an exponential manner. To keep the packing 'dry' the radial pressure on the inner ring must be at least equal to the internal pressure, implying that the radial pressure of the outer ring will be considerably higher – and excessively high for most purposes (resulting in excessive friction, shaft wear and pneumatic seal failure). Thus in the majority of applications the compressive force is adjusted to give very *slight* leakage past the last ring, *ie* the radial pressure of this ring is very slightly less than the internal pressure. It follows, however, that if the gland is adjusted to *minimum* compression for *no* leakage, there will be some leakage past the majority of the rings.

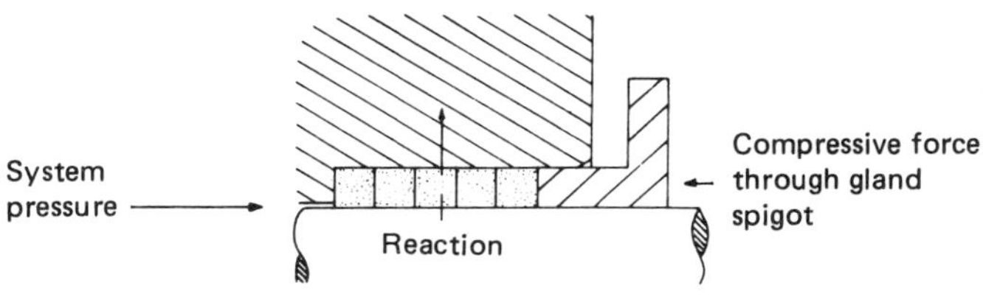

Figure 1

The question of optimum gland tightening is also complicated by the fact that some packings expand under service conditions, such as may be encountered due to a rise in temperature, and very little initial tightening of the gland may be necessary. In other cases periodic re-tightening of the gland may be necessary to compensate for wear and relaxation of the packing and to maintain a satisfactory seal.

With a typical packing material the ratio of radial pressure generated to applied axial pressure in tightening the gland is of the order of 0·6 to 0·7. Typical radial pressure throughout the gland is then as shown in Figure 2.

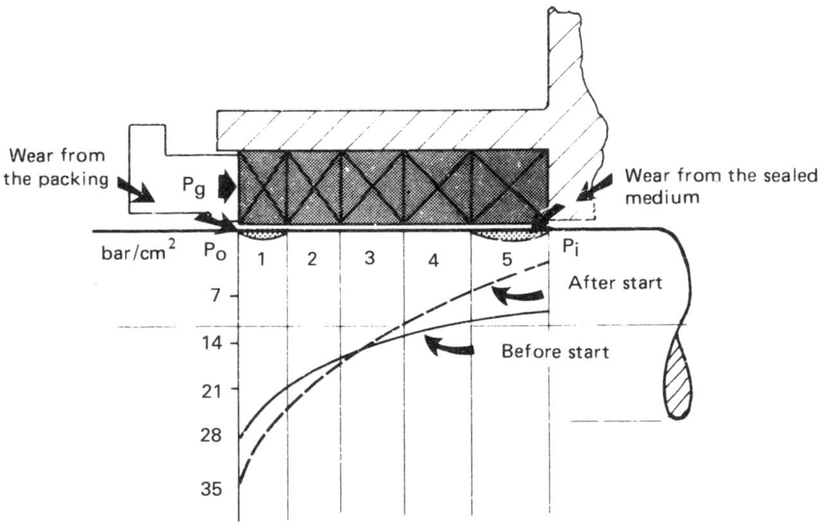

Figure 2

Uses of compression packings

The major uses for compression packings are in the process industries such as petrochemical, paper, steel, *etc* and also in service industries such as marine, water, sewage, food and nuclear. They seal all types of fluid such as steam, water, acids, alkalis, solvents, oils and gases, *etc*. They are also used in rotary, centrifugal and reciprocating shaft pumps, agitators, valves and many other types of mechanical equipment.

Flexible seal sets or single seals may replace packings for many reciprocating duties, particularly in large sizes and heavy duty applications, unless minimum leakage is a primary requirement, when a mechanical shaft seal may be preferred. It is significant, however, that with the widespread use of mechanical seals, the demand for gland packings shows no sign of falling off.

The degree of 'softness' of packings may vary considerably. They usually contain lubricants and excessive compression or over-heating during service can produce loss of lubricant, with subsequent reduction in packing volume and loss of radial pressure leading to leakage.

Where lubrication is a problem, or a degree of gland cooling is required, additional lubricant/coolant can be fed to the centre of the gland (Figure 3). The degree of cooling which can be provided by this is limited and for higher

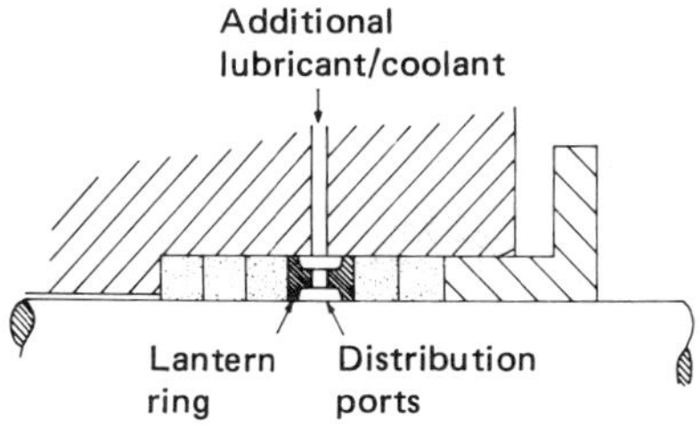

Figure 3

temperature working cooling may have to be applied to the complete gland housing to maintain the operating temperature of the gland within the limits of the packing material. Many of the problems associated with high friction and heating through necessary high compression shrinkage of fibres and/or lack of adequate lubrication have largely been eliminated by the latest packing materials based on PTFE-coated aramid fibres.

Packing sizes

Compression packings are normally of substantially square section (although round braided packings may be used on reciprocating rods and valve stems and loose packings may be used for sealing valves and some pump glands). Thus most packings are made in a standard range of section sizes from about 6 mm (¼ in) square upwards. Section size is largely arbitrary, but as a general rule housing width should be of the order of 25% of the shaft (or rod) diameter for shaft sizes of 12 mm (½ in), reducing to 10% for shaft sizes of the order of 150 mm (6 in).

Again there are no exact rules as to the optimum number of rings, but for average duties a total of four or five square rings is typical – see also Figure 4.

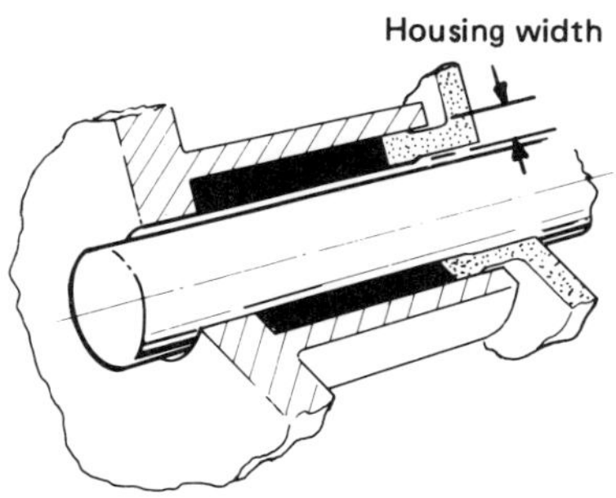

Figure 4

Gland design

Gland design for handling clean, non-abrasive fluids under positive pressure is straightforward (Figure 5a). Detail requirements are the provision of an adequately tapered lead-in at the mouth of the gland to facilitate fitting the packing rings without damage, and a reasonably good surface finish on the gland surface; $2{\cdot}5\mu$ mm (64μ in) Ra is generally considered satisfactory for most applications.

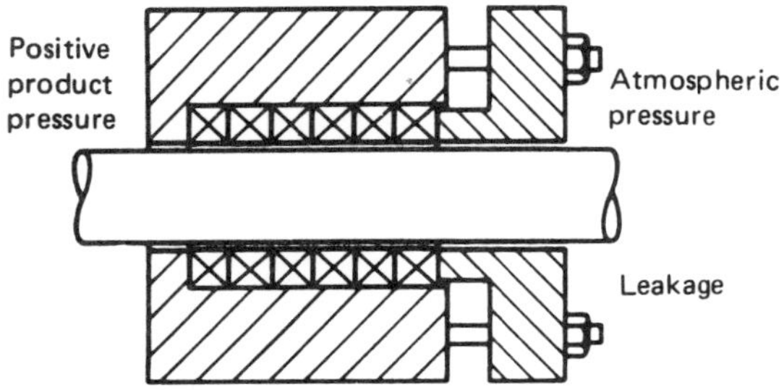

Figure 5a

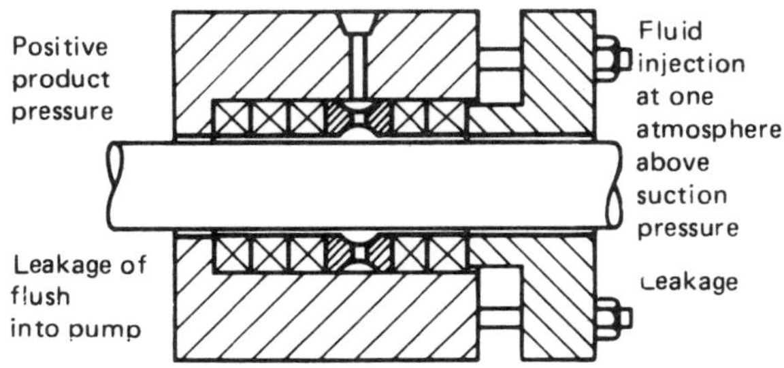

Figure 5b

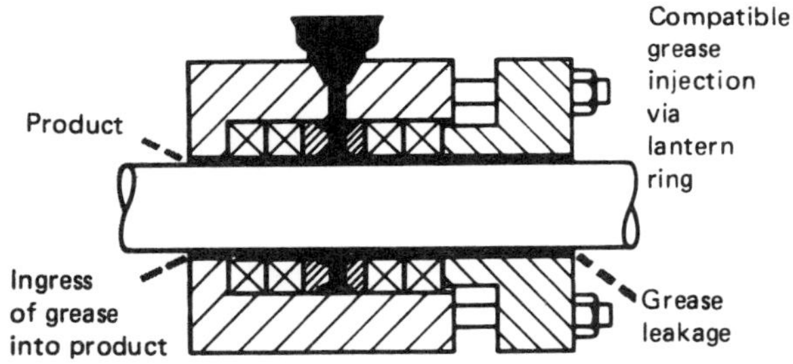

Figure 5c

Where the product being sealed contains abrasive, it is highly desirable to keep this out of the packing area. This can be done by injecting a compatible flushing fluid through a lantern ring in the centre of the gland (Figure 5b). It can be noted here that the controlled leakage in this case is that of flushing fluid which, because of the distribution of radial pressure, will also leak back into the product. Where it is not possible to arrange a suitable liquid flush, a grease flush may provide a solution (Figure 5c). The grease in this case must be clean and compatible with the product.

Two other gland arrangements are shown in Figure 6. In Figure 6a the product being handled is at less than atmospheric pressure, requiring a fluid barrier to prevent air being drawn in through the gland. This barrier is provided by tapping the discharge side of the product and feeding it into the gland *via* a lantern ring. Controlled leakage in this case is that of the product.

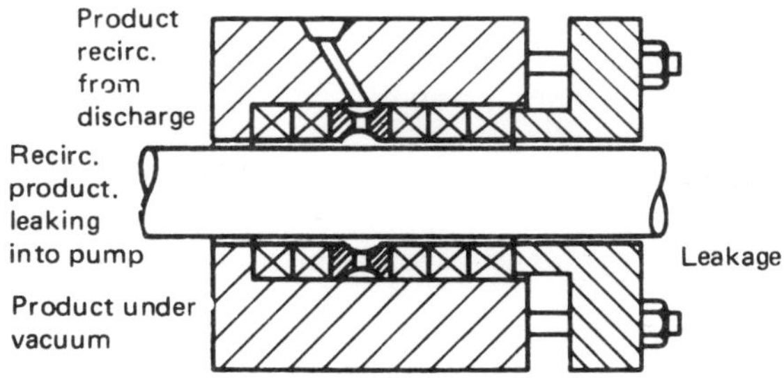

Figure 6a

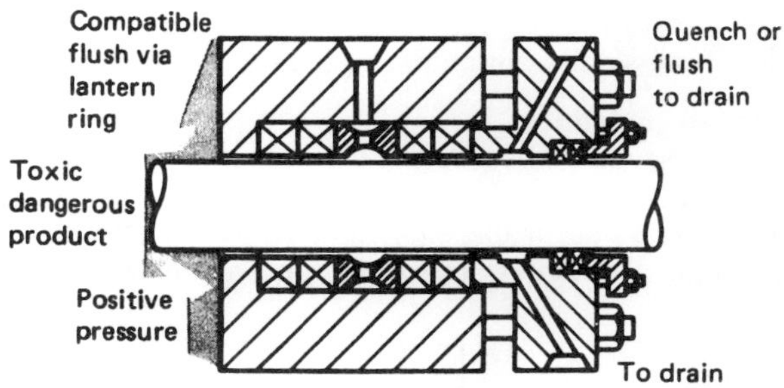

Figure 6b

In Figure 6b the product being handled is toxic or hazardous, so a flushed gland is again used to provide a primary barrier. This is backed up by a *quench (flushing annulus)* in the *gland follower* and an *auxiliary packed gland* to exclude leakage.

Operating principles

To generate the necessary compressive force it is usual to have a bolted gland follower. Adjustment of the retaining nuts (or studs) enables the axial movement of the follower to be easily controlled.

In hazardous or inaccessible situations spring loading is sometimes used, *eg* Figure 6c shows Belleville washers assembled between the gland nuts and the gland

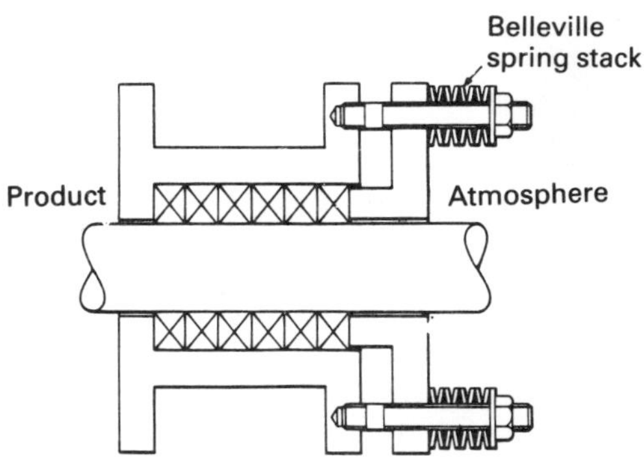

Figure 6c

follower. This can prove acceptable where there is slow or infrequent shaft motion, *eg* in valves, but the inherent lack of fine control demanded by some packing types, particularly on high speed shaft applications can cause problems. The range of load capability available from springs is also a limiting factor.

On applications where there is slow or infrequent shaft motion, compression packings are required to seal without leakage. This condition can be achieved by ensuring the compressive force exerted by the gland follower causes the packing radial force to exceed the pressure to be sealed.

For high speed shaft applications fluid leakage is essential for heat dissipation and lubrication purposes and must be controlled. Fluid leakage ensures the frictional heat generated at the packing/shaft interface is dissipated. The sealing force can be adjusted to cater for service wear but care must be taken to avoid over compression and loss of adequate fluid leakage with the consequent friction increase, shaft wear and premature packing failure.

Design guidelines
There seem to be very few international standards defining the design of the installation environment for compression packings. Furthermore, stuffing box depths vary according to specific service conditions such as the pressure of the fluid being sealed, lantern ring inclusion, *etc*. Figure 6d shows general design guidelines.

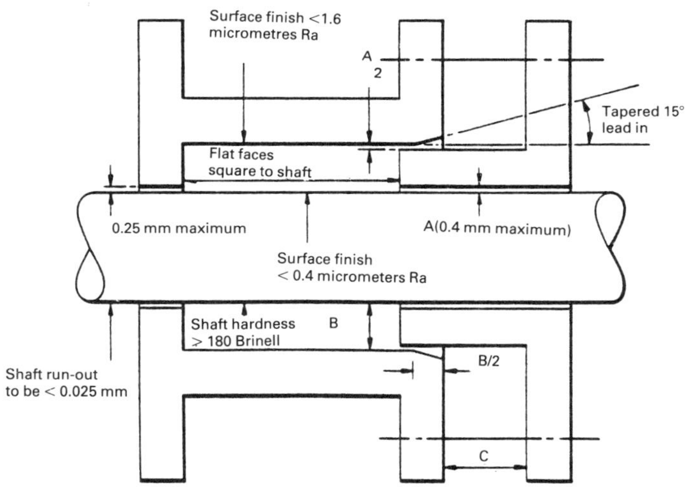

Figure 6d

Points to note are:

(a) Assuming square section packing is to be used, dimension C should be at least 1·5 times B.

(b) The shaft must be adequately supported. The packings must not be used as a bearing. It must also be free from scores, pits, grooves and ridges.

(c) If the clearances exceed those stated then suitable anti-extrusion rings must be fitted. These can be machined from metal or suitable plastic with appropriate clearances or formed from a suitable packing material.

(d) If metallic packings are to be used the shaft hardness should be at least 500 Brinell. There are a number of techniques and materials available that can be employed to achieve this, *eg* spray deposition of stellite or chrome oxide, *etc.*

(e) The use of a sleeve over the length of packing reduces refurbishment/replacement costs particularly when hardening is necessary.

When a lantern ring is required in the installation its length should be at least 1½ times the packing radial section (dimension B) and the same clearances in the stuffing box bore and over the shaft as the gland follower should be applied in order to minimize the possibility of it contacting, and therefore damaging, the shaft. PTFE is particularly suitable as a lantern ring material because of characteristics such as chemical inertness and relative non-abrasiveness. The cross section of a lantern ring should balance the need for structural strength with minimum restriction of injection fluid flow to the packing and shaft. On installation it should be positioned below the barrier fluid inlet in such a way as to allow for slight compression of the inboard packing rings.

TABLE 1

Shaft diameter mm	Packing section mm
Up to 16	3
Above 16 to 25	5
Above 25 to 50	6.5
Above 50 to 90	8
Above 90 to 150	10
Above 150	12.5

TABLE 2

Stuffing box pressure bar	Number of rings
Up to 35	4
Above 35 to 70	6
Above 70 to 140	8
Above 140	10

Tables 1 and 2 provide general guidance on:

(a) The cross section of packing to use related to the shaft diameter (all types of equipment).

(b) The number of square section rings required in relation to the pressure of the fluid to be sealed.

With reference to Table 2 it is not possible to be definitive. Decision-making will be influenced by practical experience coupled with the knowledge that a particular packing:

(a) is resistant to deterioration by the fluid being sealed;

(b)is capable of withstanding the fluid temperature; and

(c) can be formed in such a way as to ensure that the fluid pressure alone will not cause loss of packing volume, *eg* through lubricant squeeze out, *etc.*

To exceed the cross-section and number of rings recommended is unnecessary and can be detrimental. Too many rings of too large a section means:

(a) Excessive area of packing/shaft contact with excessive heat generation.

(b) Possible loss of packing thermal conductivity efficiency.

(c) As the stuffing box increases so does:
   (i) the difficulty of installing/dismantling and adjusting the packing rings properly; and
   (ii) the chance of shaft malalignment with its inherent adverse effect on packing sealing performance.

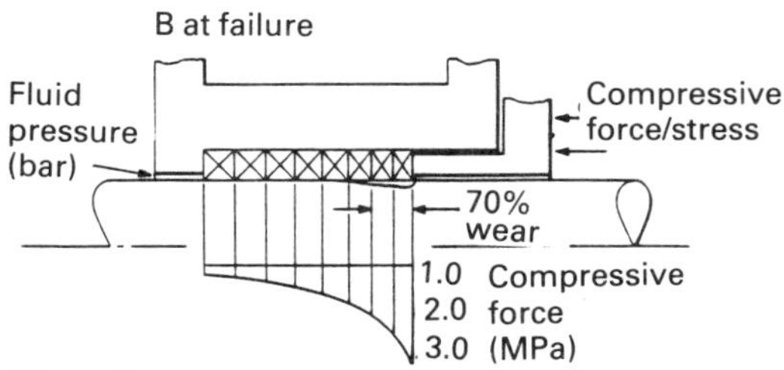

Figure 6e

Furthermore, reference to Figure 6e shows how the fluid pressure is progressively throttled by each successive packing ring. It can be seen that the five rings nearest to the gland follower do the majority of the sealing and most of the wear on the shaft occurs under the outer two to three rings. Unless considered desirable because the fluid being sealed is:

(a) At high temperature.
(b) At high pressure.
(c) Corrosive.
(d) Abrasive.

Four or five rings should be sufficient.

PTFE filament yarn braided packing impregnated with PTFE dispersion for acid duties.

Traditional materials

The traditional type of packing based on lubricated fibre yarns remain in common and widespread use. The range of materials employed is quite wide (see Table 3, which is only a partial list) and further extended by the introduction of synthetic yarns to upgrade certain performance characteristics, although rayon and nylon have proved to have only limited benefits, (see also Table 4).

TABLE 3 – TRADITIONAL PACKINGS

Material and construction	Maximum pressure lb/in^2	bar	Maximum service temperature °C	°F	Main application(s)	Fluid(s)
Asbestos – plaited	1000 to 2000	20 to 140	340 to 540	650 to 1000	Reciprocating and rotary up to 750 ft/min.	General service.
Asbestos – proofed	3000	210	120 to 260	250 to 500	Rotary and reciprocating.	Oil resistant packings.
Asbestos – resistant binders	2000 to 3000	140 to 210	up to 315	up to 600	Rotary and reciprocating.	Acids, corrosive fluids, *etc.*
Asbestos – braided sleeve			120	250	Rotary	Dilute acids, alkalis, ammonia.
Asbestos – wire reinforced	750 to 2000	50 to 140	260	500	Up to 1250 ft/min.	Steam, hot water, aqueous solutions, oils, *etc.*
Asbestos – plaited – metal braided	1500	105	650	1200	Reciprocating and rotary.	High temperature service.
Asbestos – white metal (inserts)	700	50	260	500	Reciprocating and rotary.	Steam.
Asbestos – wire, plaited	700	50	260	500	Rotary up to 2000 ft/min.	Steam, water, acids, alkalis.
Asbestos cloth – rubber core	1000	70	315	600	Reciprocating.	High pressure steam.
Asbestos – wire – rubber	700 to 1000	50 to 70	260 to 315	500 to 600	Reciprocating	Steam, air, gases, water.
Soft cotton (lubricated)			95	200	1250 ft/min.	High speed centrifugal pumps, suitable with solids in suspension.
Cotton yarn (lubricated)			95	200	Up to 1250 ft/min.	Water, oil, aqueous solutions, ammonia.
Cotton – plaited			65	150	Reciprocating and rotary pumps.	Air, water, refrigerants.
Cotton duck – rubber			140	280	Piston rods, heads of reciprocating pumps.	Hot and cold water, petroleum products.
Cotton duck – metal reinforced	50 (steam) 3000 (water)	3.5 (steam) 210 (water)	150	300	Piston rods, *etc.*	Low pressure steam, water, oils, ammonia.
Canvas covered cotton			120	250	Centrifugal and rotary pumps.	Water, caustic solutions, ammonia.
Cotton cloth – bonded	3000	210	140	280	Reciprocating low-medium speed rotary.	Oils, solvents, hydro-carbons, *etc.*
Flax – plaited (lubricated)			65 to 140	150 to 280	Circulating water pumps.	Fresh and salt water.
Flax – wire reinorced cotton covered	50 (steam) 3000 (water)	3.5 (steam) 210 (water)	140	280	Water feed and circulating pumps.	Fresh and salt water.
Foil – wrapped fibres	500 to 700	35 to 50	65 to 800	150 to 1500	High speed rotary.	Steam, water, hot oils, mild acids and alkalis.
Foil – wrapped, plaited core	500	35	190 to 800	300 to 1500	High speed rotary.	Oil pumps, high temperature steam.
Hemp (lubricated)	500	35	65 to 95	150 to 200	Medium speed rotary pumps.	Water.
Plaited vegetable fibre			65	150	Rotary and reciprocating, medium speeds.	Fresh and salt water.
Plain and plaited leather			37 to 50	100 to 120	Low and medium pressure reciprocating.	Cold water and cold oils oils.
Leather – fibre – metal			37 to 50	100 to 120	Reciprocating (low-medium pressures).	Water, oils, limes, *etc.*

TABLE 4 – TYPES OF MATERIALS

Type	Construction	Maximum Performance Parameters*			Application	pH*
		Rubbing Speed m/sec	Temp. °C	Pressure bar		
Cotton	Plaited or braided with grease graphite or mica lubricant	7.5	90	–	Seals for water.	6–9
Hemp	Plaited or braided with grease graphite or mica lubricant	–	–	–	Seals for water	5–9
Flax	Plaited or braided with grease graphite or mica lubricant	–	70–120	–	Rotary seals or pumps and slow reciprocating seals; ships' stern glands, etc.	–
Textile	Plaited or braided cotton, nylon, rayon, hemp, etc, with PTFE impregnation	–	–	–	Seals for water services, solvents, weak alkalis, oils, greases, foodstuffs, etc.	–
Asbestos (dry)	Round or square plaited or braided white asbestos	–	500	–	Autoclaves, boiler stop valves, etc.	
Asbestos (lubricated)	Round or square plaited or braided white asbestos with graphite, mica or mineral oil lubricant		–40 – +300		Steam services, evaporators, cannisters, liquors, etc.	5–12
Asbestos (wire reinforced)	Square section plaited or braided with brass or inconel wire reinforcement. Impregnated with graphite or mica lubricant		–50 – +750	250–650	Water, air, steam, solvents, hydrocarbons, weak acids and alkalis	4–11
Asbestos (PTFE)	Plaited or braided asbestos yarn coated with PTFE dispersion	15	280	100	Acids, solvents, oils, hydrocarbons, etc (not caustic solutions)	0–8
Asbestos (Glass fibre)	Plaited or braided asbestos yarn and glass fibre with added lubricant	5	200	250–300	Corrosive duties with equivalent chemical resistance to blue asbestos, except caustic solutions	0–11
Blue asbestos	Braided asbestos fibres with added lubricant	15	280	60	Limited production because of health hazard and not made in many countries	0–12
Asbestos (lead)	Manufactured from asbestos fibres and granulated lead with added lubricant	–	–	–	–	–
Ramie (PTFE)	Ramie yarn impregnated and coated with PTFE. Plaited or braided with added lubricant	15	120	400	Water, mildly aggressive clean fluids and mildly abrasive slurries	4–11
Acrylic	PTFE coated, lubricated and plaited or braided	10	120–200	100	For low temperature, low general service slightly acidic fluids	2–8
PTFE	Yarns or tape	–	200–250	–	Soft packings, services involving corrosive media	0–14

TABLE 4 – TYPES OF MATERIALS (contd)....

Type	Construction	Maximum Performance Parameters* Rubbing Speed m/sec	Temp. °C	Pressure bar	Application	pH*
PTFE and lubricant	PTFE braided and impregnated with graphite and/or molybdenum di-sulphide lubricant	20	–100 to +250	30+	Water, steam, acids, alkalis, solvents, oils, greases, hydrocarbons, etc	0–14
	Braided pure PTFE fibres treated with PTFE dispersion	10	–200 to +300	100	Sealing all media	0–14
PTFE (graphite)	Extruded fibrillated PTFE and graphite with mineral oil lubricant	10	–100 to +250	100	Water, acids, alkalis, solvents, oils, de-greasing fluids, oxidizing agents, foodstuffs, etc.	0–14
Aramid – PTFE	Braided PTFE coated Kevlar yarn impregnated with lubricant and PTFE	10–20	–220 to +300	200–1000	High duty 'super-packing'	1–14
PTFE – Silk	Braided PTFE – silk yarns with added lubricant	5	280	200	Water, steam, acids, alkalis, oils, oxidizing agents, dye stuffs, etc.	0–14
Graphite yarn	Woven or braided graphite yarn treated with graphite powder	–	–200 to +600	–	High temperature services	0–14
Carbon fibre	Amorphous carbon yarns treated with graphite powder	–	–200 to +600	–	High temperature services	0–14
Graphite/ asbestos	50/50 wet spun, with added inert lubricant	25	500	80	For water, air, steam, hydrocarbons	3–12
Graphite/ asbestos	50/50 wet spun, inconel wire, reinforced yarn	–	650	900	Steam, gases,	2–14
Expanded graphite	Flexible plait or tape form	35	–200 to +600	300	High temperature services, foodstuffs, etc	0–14
Glass fibre	Braided glass fibre yarns with added lubricant	–	–	–	Suitable for use with acid and corrosive fluids (except caustic solutions)	–
Alumina silicate	Plaited with inconel wire	–	1200	–	Extremely high temperature services. Limited to static seals or slow movements	–

*Depending on actual construction, type of lubricant used, etc.

Vegetable-based fibre yarns are generally suitable for oil, water and non-corrosive chemical duties where the working temperature does not exceed 90 °C and rubbing speeds are moderate (not more than 8 m/s). Cotton and flax are the most widely used fibres, and to a decreasing extent hemp. Ramie, jute and sisal have largely disappeared from the scene.

Asbestos yarns are the traditional choice for higher temperature services (up to 320 °C) and higher rubbing speeds (up to 20 m/sec). Asbestos has, of course, been the subject of much concern as a health hazard and the use of blue (crocidolite) has virtually ceased. Blue asbestos, however, has better corrosion resistant properties. There is less realistic objection to white (chrysotile) asbestos, which produces the principal yarns now used for asbestos packings, particularly if the fibres are securely bound by impregnation during the manufacture of packings and will not emit asbestos dust which is the main quoted source of health hazards.

Traditional lubricants

Apart from specialized applications where physically dry packings are required, yarn packings are invariably combined with a lubricant.

Graphite is the lubricant commonly introduced into packing sections and provides excellent self-lubricating properties for many services where the packing would otherwise have to run dry, or in contact with a fluid which is not a lubricant. Thus graphited lubricant is particularly suitable for steam and water services, and especially salt water. In certain cases, however, the presence of loosened graphite may be objectionable; or in the case of the packing operating against a stainless steel rod, graphite may produce pitting of the steel through electrolytic action. An alternative lubricating impregnant which overcomes these difficulties is mica. These lubricants, together with molybdenum disulphide and PTFE, remain the standard 'dry' lubricants.

Traditional 'wet' lubricants such as tallow, have been superseded by mineral oils, greases, waxes and soaps. Silicone greases are particularly used with asbestos packings for high temperature services, but are now no longer regarded as suitable for use with edible products or drinking water. The lubricant employed for such services is usually an inert mineral oil.

The actual percentage of lubricant employed will vary with the service. Thus a packing intended for high speed movement, and particularly high rotary speeds, would normally be of a softer type to maintain flexibility for long periods and contain a large percentage of lubricant. A packing used only for a static application would not normally contain any lubricant at all. That for a reciprocating motion may contain anti-friction wire reinforcement in preference to lubricant, with perhaps a final dressing of graphite. Others may contain both soft anti-friction wire reinforcement and be impregnated with lubricant. The value of soft anti-friction wires is that they provide continuous lubrication to the shaft and also assist in conducting heat away from the working surface.

With the notable exception of packings constructed from exfoliated and multi-filament yarn graphite, those commonly used for high speed shaft applications contain both dry and wet lubricants.

These lubricants perform a number of important functions including:

(a) Provision of initial lubrication and sealing during start up and running in of equipment. The sealed fluid or external injection fluid eventually takes over this function.

(b) Provision of a fluid barrier. By filling voids in braided packings, sealed fluid penetration into the packing is minimized and sealed fluid passage through the packing is prevented.

(c) Provision of inter-fibre lubrication. This minimizes fibre on fibre abrasion/breakage and aids even distribution of the compressive force.

(d) Improvement of thermal conductivity/heat dissipation characteristics of the packing.

Figure 6f shows an installation used when handling fluids at high temperature. Injection of coolant *via* the lantern ring alone may be inadequate. In this case a jacketed stuffing box can be used with coolant passing through it.

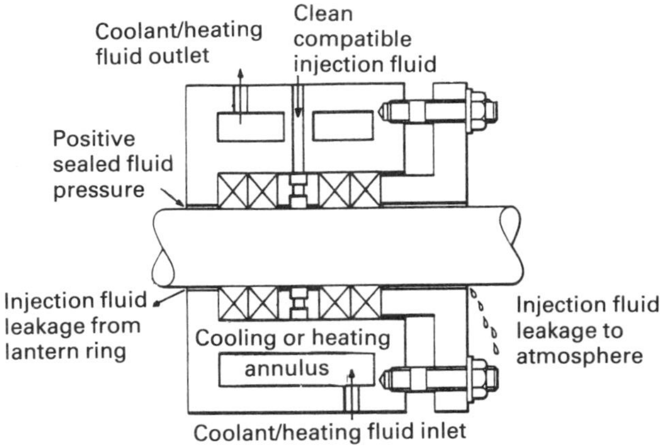

Figure 6f

If the fluid being handled crystallizes, becomes highly viscous or a solid when cooled, *eg* sugar, bitumen, wax, *etc,* then heaters or a jacketed stuffing box must be used to restore the fluid state before equipment start up. In this case steam may be suitable to pass through the jacket.

N.B. The packing rings should be made from a material which has a high thermal conductivity characteristic.

When the packing installation is required to hold a vacuum, or where a suction lift is involved, the fluid injected into the lantern ring can be a grease. In this case, a screw or spring-loaded Stauffer cap type lubricator is recommended.

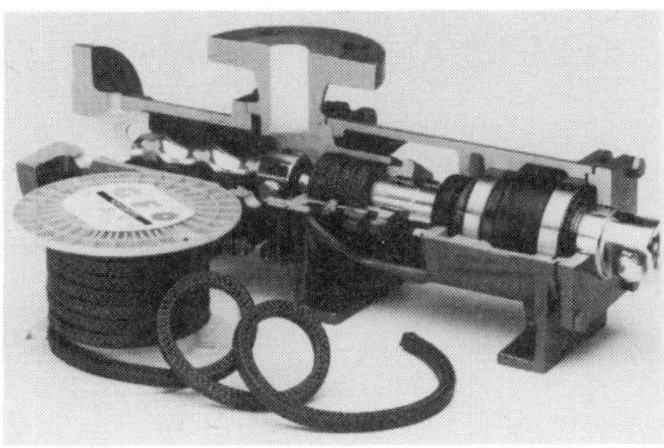

Non-asbestos compression packing.

Gland packings – installation and maintenance

Gland packings are supplied either as a continuous length in the form of a spool coil or spiral of packing material or as a pre-shaped split ring, when the exact size required must be specified when ordering.

The recommended method of cutting rings from a continuous length of packing is as follows:

(i) Place the packing round the shaft, or round a mandrel of the specified diameter (Figure 7a). The bore of metallic and extruded packing spirals should conform to this diameter.

(ii) To assist in cutting rings, two guide lines parallel to the shaft axis and separated by a distance equal to the packing section may be drawn on the spiral (Figure 7b).

(iii) Cut the rings from the spiral at an angle of 45°, diagonally across the guide lines so that no gap is left between the ends (Figure 7c).

(iv) Metallic and extruded packing rings are spirally open ready for fitting by pulling the ends axially apart. (Figure 7d).

(v) When the rings cannot be opened without risk of damage to the packing section, they are hinge-cut, cutting diagonally about two-thirds through the packing (Figure 7e).

(vi) Check the first ring to ensure a correct fit in the stuffing box, before cutting further rings in the same way.

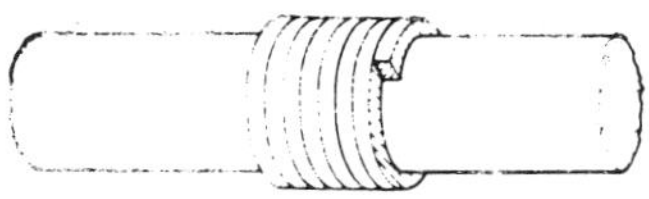

Figure 7a

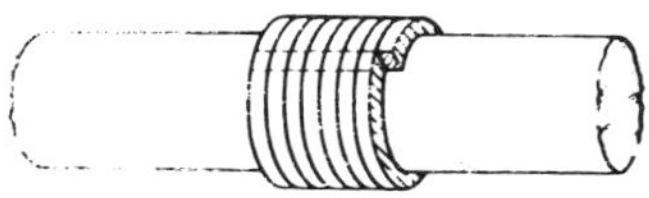

Figure 7b

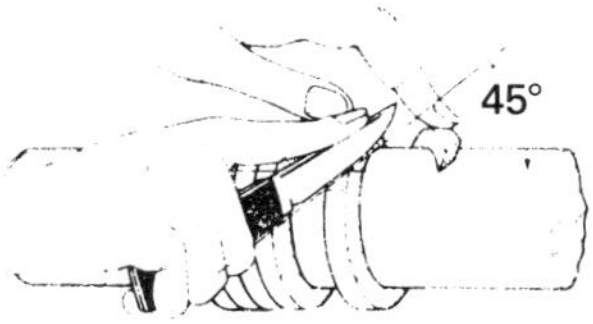

Figure 7c

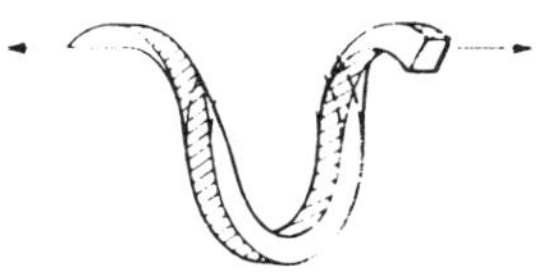

Figure 7d

Figure 7e

Removing old packings

The system should be depressurized where appropriate and/or drained. The nuts holding the gland follower are then released, allowing the follower to be withdrawn along the shaft and clear of the stuffing box (Figure 8a). The old packing rings should then be withdrawn carefully. The best way is to use a pair of extractor tools inserted on diametrically opposite sides of the shaft (Figure 8b). After removal of the old rings, make sure that the inside of the stuffing box is clean. Check also that the shaft is in good condition, *ie* not scored, pitted, ridged or corroded. New packings will only have a short life rubbing on a damaged or rough shaft.

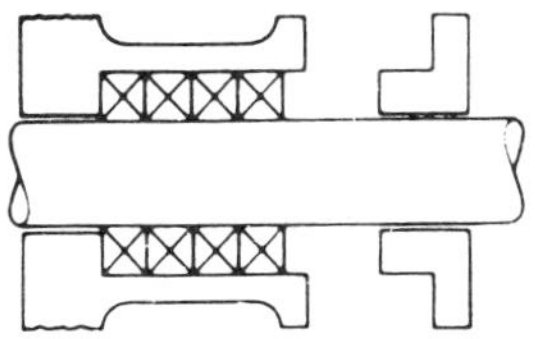

Figure 8a

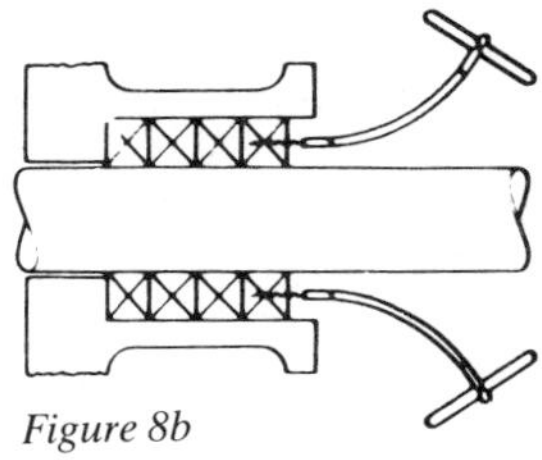

Figure 8b

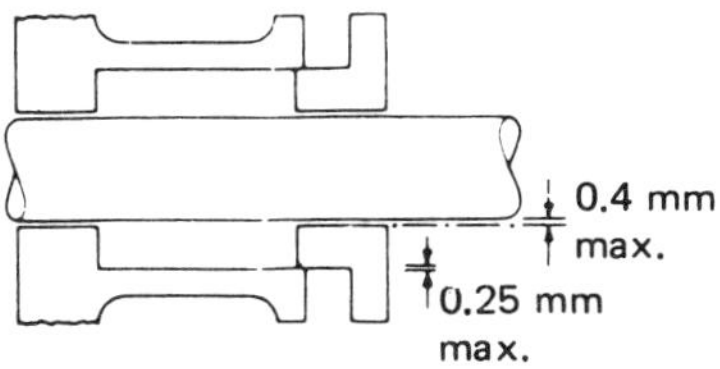

Figure 8c

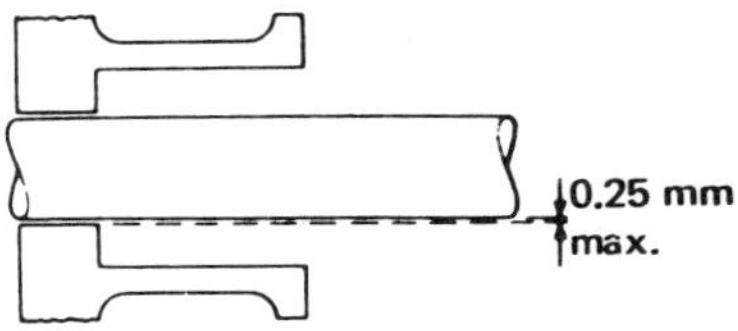

Figure 8d

The following checks should be carried out:

(i) Check the shaft for concentricity with the stuffing box bore.

(ii) Check the shaft to ensure run-out does not exceed 0·025 mm (0·001 in) TIR.

(iii) Examine the gland follower for general condition and fit. The inner radial clearance should be 0·4 mm (0·015 in) maximum, and the outer radial clearance should be 0·25 mm (0·010 in) maximum, to prevent risk of cocking or touching on the shaft (Figure 8c).

(iv) Check the clearance between the neck bush and the shaft (Figure 8d). If this is greater than 0·25 mm (0·010 in) radially, it may be advantageous to employ a thin, close clearance spacer ring in the bottom of the stuffing box, to prevent risk of packing extrusion.

The number of rings required will be obvious from the number of old rings removed. However, if a different packing is to be used, measure the depth of the stuffing box and deduct a suitable allowance for the entry of the gland follower to arrive at the total depth of packing rings required.

Fitting new packings

Having checked that the shaft turns freely and is concentric with the housing bore, rings can be fitted up individually. A tamper can be used to ensure that each ring is pushed home true and square, but the use of a split sleeve in conjunction with the gland follower is better (Figure 9a). *There are exceptions to this practice.* Gland rings of PTFE multi-filament yarns or graphite should not be tamped or driven home. They are only to be slid in place, otherwise they may suffer permanent damage.

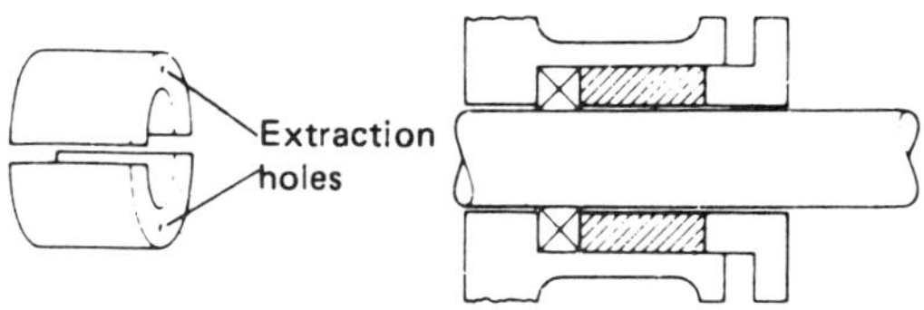

Figure 9a

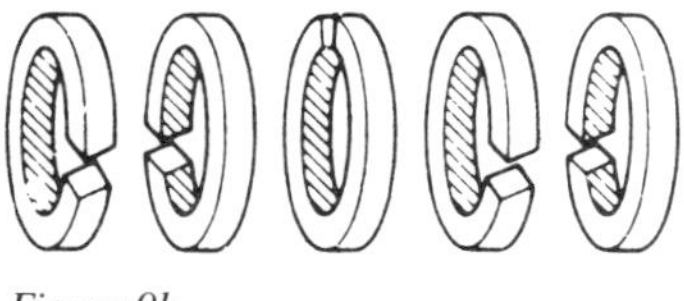

Figure 9b

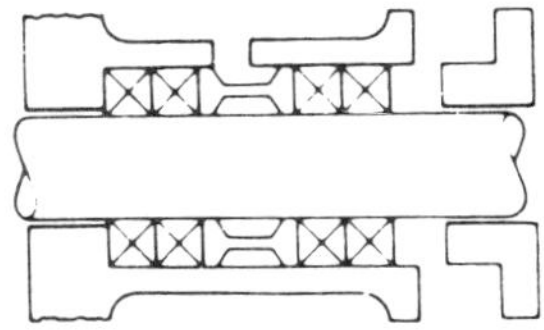

Figure 9c

Joints in succeeding rings should be staggered by 120° (Figure 9b). After fitting each ring, check that the shaft can be turned.

The actual position of each ring after installation can be checked by measuring the free depth remaining, *ie* this should be equal to the gland depth less the depth of the ring(s) installed. This is a particularly useful check in the case of a gland which incorporates a lantern ring to ensure that the lantern ring is positioned below its inlet. Note that the initial position of the lantern ring will be biased towards the 'open' end of the gland (Figure 9c) to allow for the compression of the bottom rings when the gland is tightened.

TABLE 5 – FAULT-FINDING CHART

	Observations	**Possible causes/actions**
At start-up	No leakage	1. Incorrect installation — negative stuffing box pressure requiring lantern ring. 2. Slight overtightening — follow stop/start procedure.
At start-up	Excessive leakage	1. Wrong section packing. 2. Incorrect installation procedure. 3. Shaft run-out.
Packing set removal	Packing section reduced under horizontal shaft	1. Shaft misaligned with stuffing box. 2. Worn bearings — packing acting as bearing.
Packing set removal	Packing section reduced above horizontal shaft	1. Shaft misaligned with stuffing box. 2. Worn bearings.
Packing set removal	Whole or part of an end ring missing	Excessive clearance between shaft and stuffing box neck or gland follower allowing extrusion.
Packing set removal	Wear on the outside of one or more rings	Rings rotating with shaft, packing section too small.
Packing set removal	Rings next to gland follower worn, other all right.	Incorrect installation procedure, gland follower overtightened.
Packing set removal	Ring i.d.'s burnt, dried or charred, remaining material all right.	1. Incorrect packing selection re : temperature limit/shaft speed. 2. Inadequate lubrication.
Packing set removal	Innermost ring deteriorated	Incorrect packing selection re : compatibility with product.
Packing set removal	Packing seizure on shaft after equipment shutdown	Product crystallizing or solidifying in packing bore through: 1. Inadequate lubrication. 2. Lack of heating or cooling.

After fitting the final ring the gland follower is brought up into position and tightened evenly with finger pressure on the nuts. Check that the shaft turns freely. The system can then be started and pressurized, which should produce appreciable steady leakage past the gland. After running for some time in this condition (*eg* five to ten minutes) the gland nuts should then be spanner-tightened in rotation about one-sixth of a turn at a time until leakage is reduced to an acceptable level.

This adjustment should be repeated at ten to fifteen minute intervals until leakage is reduced to drip leakage at an acceptable level. This level depends very much on the application, *eg* with careful running-in and light operating conditions, leakage may virtually be eliminated; with heavier operating conditions, a fair rate of drip leakage may be necessary to ensure that the gland does not overheat.

After the running-in period, further adjustments should only be necessary after prolonged intervals. All such adjustments should be made with the system operating at normal temperature and pressure, *ie* not under static conditions.

Mechanical Face Seals

Design

MECHANICAL FACE seals, known generally as mechanical seals comprise rotating and stationary elements in 'rubbing' contact to form a sealing face with a minimal leakage path, following the basic principle shown in Figure 1. They are essentially rotary shaft seals. Successful operation depends on achieving the right conditions at the face, the faces themselves being lubricated by a thin hydrodynamic film (generally of the order of 0·0006 μm to 0·00006 μm (0·025 μin to 0·25 μin) thick of the fluid being contained. While the basic principle of operation remains the same, mechanical seals vary widely in detail design and construction to cater for normal operating conditions – *eg* shaft size, speed, pressure and the fluid to be contained.

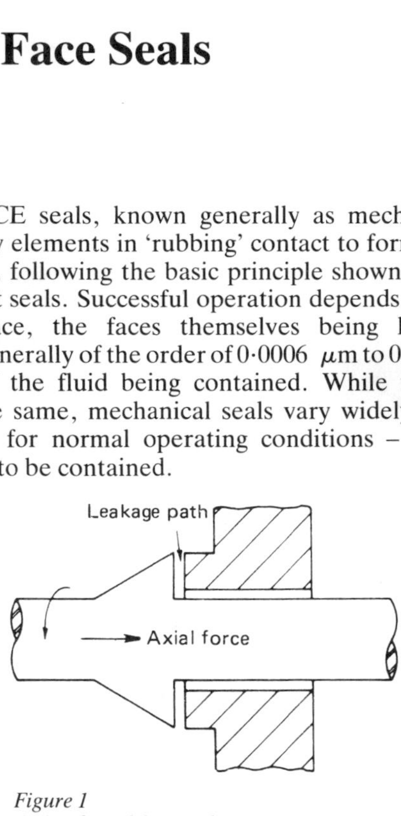

Figure 1
A simple end face seal.

Component parts of unbalanced single spring seal.

The majority of mechanical seals are used as pump shaft seals.

Other significant applications include mixing vessels (approximately 10 to 15% of the total of all mechanical seals) and marine propeller shaft seals.

A particular advantage of a face seal is that besides being capable of providing positive sealing it places no wear on the shaft itself. All rubbing wear is concentrated on the sealing faces which are normally self-compensating for wear (*eg* by spring loading); and their continual rubbing action maintains a lapped finish and very close fit in the absence of abrasive contaminants. Some flexibility can also be introduced into the design to accommodate small amounts of axial or radial misalignment which may be present.

An example of a simple mechanical seal which meets these requirements is shown in Figure 2, where for general descriptive purposes the rotating elements are referred to as the *rotor* and the static elements as the *stator*.

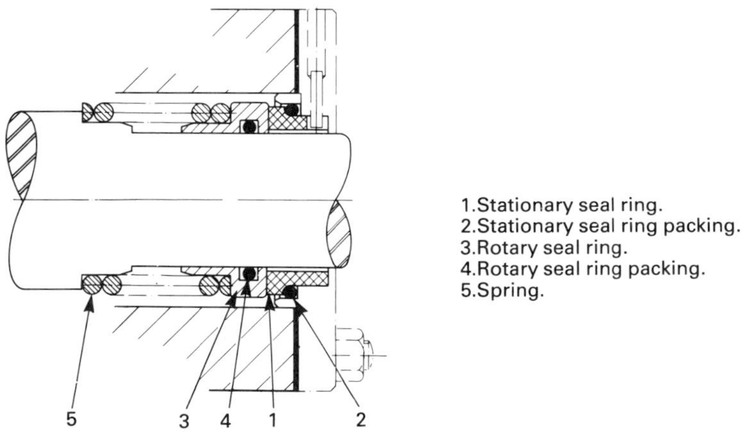

Figure 2
Mechanical face seals.

The rotating sealing ring which contains the rotating face is mounted on the shaft through the rotor static seal. Although this sealing ring will travel with the path of the shaft, it does have sufficient flexibility to compensate for shaft misalignment and maintain itself in flat contact with the stator. Likewise, the stationary sealing ring which contains the stationary face is mounted flexibly in the gland plate with sufficient flexibility to compensate for angular misalignment of the gland plate. The spring which energizes the rotating sealing ring through the rotor static seal keeps the two sealing rings in intimate contact in the absence of hydraulic pressure. Typical constructions are shown in Figure 3.

The leakage path across the two sealing surfaces is the heart of any mechanical seal. Proper lubrication of the sealing faces is necessary to minimize wear and provide reasonable life. This lubrication is normally accomplished by the establishment of a fluid film across the faces. It is, therefore, imperative that the fluid in the seal cavity be one that will provide adequate lubrication. If the process fluid will not perform this function, it will be necessary to provide an artificial environment in the sealing cavity.

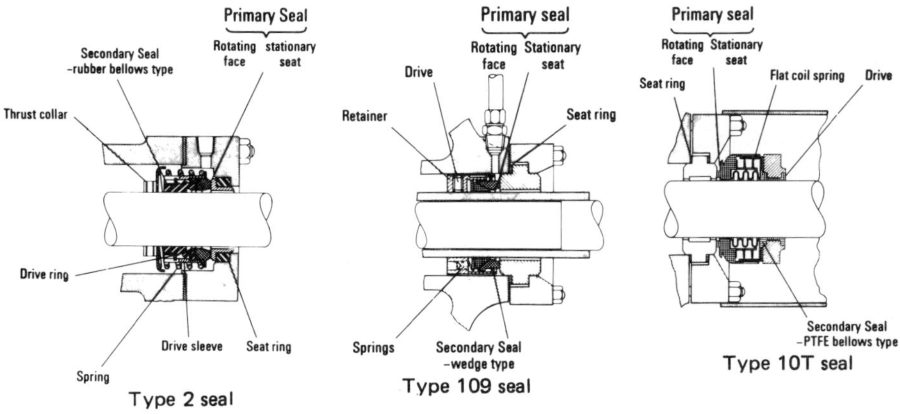

Figure 3
Basic types of seals in a proprietary range.

Control of the distance between the sealing faces is necessary to limit the amount of leakage that can occur across them. Although the amount of leakage that will occur is dependent upon many factors: density and viscosity of the fluid, seal face materials, differential pressure, size, speed, *etc*, experience has shown that maintaining the sealing surfaces flat to within three light bands of a helium lamp, 0·87 μm (34·8 μin) will provide a positive seal with no visible liquid leakage.

Basically, therefore, any mechanical seal includes the following components:

(i) A stationary sealing ring.
(ii) A secondary seal for this ring.
(iii) A rotating sealing ring.
(iv) A secondary seal for this ring.
(v) A method of pressing the two ring faces together *via* an axially flexible member (*eg* a spring or bellows).
(vi) A method of driving the rotary sealing ring (*eg* either mechanically or through the friction of its secondary seal).

Materials

Standard seal ranges are generally offered in a variety of materials of construction. Materials of principal components (seal ring bodies, spring housings, springs, *etc*) range from the more common stainless steel, bronze, *etc*, to materials with special corrosion resistance such as *Hastelloy C* or even *Titanium*. Occasionally copper alloy is chosen as a seal ring body material because of its high thermal conductivity, which effects efficient heat removal from the faces.

Face materials range from plain stainless steel, lead bronze, Ni-resist, *etc*, to more exotic materials such as tungsten carbide, silicon carbide *etc*. In most instances, the counterface material is a carbon composition with either a metal or resin filler. Face materials are selected on a duty/life/cost basis.

Secondary seal materials are selected on the basis of chemical compatibility with sealed fluid and temperature. Some practical duty limits for the more common face and packing materials are shown in Tables 1 and 2.

TABLE 1 – PV (PRESSURE X VELOCITY) LIMITS

Face Materials RSR/SSR	FACE MATERIAL PV LIMITS BAR M/S†			
	Water and Aqueous Solutions		Other Fluids	
	Unbalanced Seals	Balanced Seals	Unbalanced Seals	Balanced Seals
Stainless steel carbon	5.5	–	30	–
Lead bronze carbon	23	–	36	–
Stellite/carbon	49	85	52	580
Chrome oxide/carbon	70	440	–	–
Alumina ceramic/carbon	36	250	88	420
Tungsten carbide/tungsten carbide	44	500	71	420
Tungsten carbide/carbon	70	700	88	1225

†1 bar m/s = 2855 lb/in^2 ft/min

TABLE 2 – SECONDARY SEAL TEMPERATURE LIMITS

Seal material	Temperature °C	
	Minimum	Maximum
High nitrile rubber	–30	120
Ethylene propylene rubber	–50	150
Viton fluoroelastomer	–40	250
†Kalrex perfluoroelastomer	–50	310
PTFE	–100	250
High temperature polymers	–100	300
Compressed asbestos fibre	–100	400
Pure graphite materials	–200	3000

†Registered trademark

Maximum temperature 500 °C in oxidizing media

The majority of seals use one of the 'contact' faces in carbon, which is mechanically weak against distortion. Its main advantage is its excellent self-lubricating properties for start-up conditions and excellent heat transfer to remove heat from the faces. It is generally held that a rotating carbon face is preferable because the heat emission from the rotating face is greater than from a stationary face (the stationary face is usually insulated from the surrounding metal parts by the elastomer seals). Furthermore, the fitting of a stationary carbon face into a housing can often result in the fracture of this relatively weak carbon part. Since seals with both stationary and rotating carbon faces appear to offer equal life under similar conditions, the argument tends to be more academic than practical but the structural weakness of carbon is not in doubt.

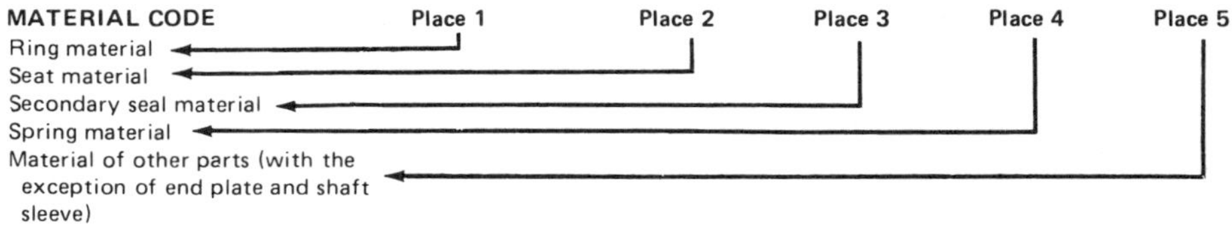

TABLE 3 – MATERIAL CODE

Place 1/2	Place 3	Place 4/5
Material of ring or seat	Material of secondary seal	Material of springs and other metallic parts (with the exception of end plate and shaft sleeve)
Mechanical Carbon	**Elastomers**	
A = Hard carbon impregnated	P = Nitrile rubber	
B = Hard carbon resin impregnated	N = Chloroprene	
C = Other carbon	B = Butyl rubber	
	E = EP rubber	
	S = Silicone rubber	
	V = Fluor rubber	D = C-steel
Metal	M = PTFE-encased	E = Cr-steel
D = C-steel	X = Misc. elastomers	F = CrN1-steel
E = Cr-steel		G = CrN1Mo-steel
F = CrN1-steel		
G = CrN1Mo-steel		
H = CrN1-steel, stellited	**Non-elastomers**	
K = CrN1Mo-steel, stellited	T = PTFE	
L = Stellite	A = Asbestos impregnated	M = High nickel alloy
M = High nickel alloy	F = IT seal	N = Bronze
N = Bronze	Y = Misc non-elastomers	
P = Cast iron		
R = Alloyed cast iron		
S = Cast chrome	**Special case**	
T = Misc metals	U = Differences in secondary sealing materials	T = Misc metal
Metal Carbide		
U = Metal carbide		
Metal Oxide (ceramic)		
V = Al-oxide		
W = Cr-oxide		
X = Misc metal oxides		
Plastics		
Y = PTFE, strengthened		
Z = Misc plastics		

Standards for mechanical seals

The development of European national standards has produced the German DIN 24960 and ISO 3069 seal installation standards; and also in the UK the BS 5257 : 1975 pump standard which effectively incorporates ISO 3069. A number of other national standards generally require seals conforming to the dimensional sizes specified in DIN 24960. Nomenclature and material coding given in this standard are not necesssarily followed by all manufacturers, however.

The (German) VDMA nomenclature for single internal mechanical seals with rotating seal head is as follows (see also Table 3):

GLRD (specifying a mechanical seal)   VDMA

3 symbols (specifying type and size)   5 letter code (specifying materials)

In the first group of letter symbols:
1st letter – U = unbalanced or B = balanced.
2nd figure gives nominal diameter in mm.
3rd letter gives direction of rotation or direction of winding of spring, *viz:*
R – right hand, with single spring.
L – left hand, with single spring.
S – rotation independent of single spring.
A – direction independent of multiple springs.

Single spring *versus* multi-spring
The single spring has two main advantages:

(i) The axial tolerance allowed on the setting length can be greater because a larger diameter spring requires a greater axial movement for a given change of force.

(ii) The wire section of the single spring is much heavier than the multi-spring section and, therefore, if the spring is in contact with a corrosive environment or can readily clog due to solid particles and/or coating, the single spring has a far greater chance of success. Locating the multi-spring external to the handled fluid overcomes fouling (except for 'coking' conditions) but corrosion can still occur.

On the debit side the single spring has inferior pressure distribution, since no matter how well a single spring is manufactured, it is very difficult to obtain the

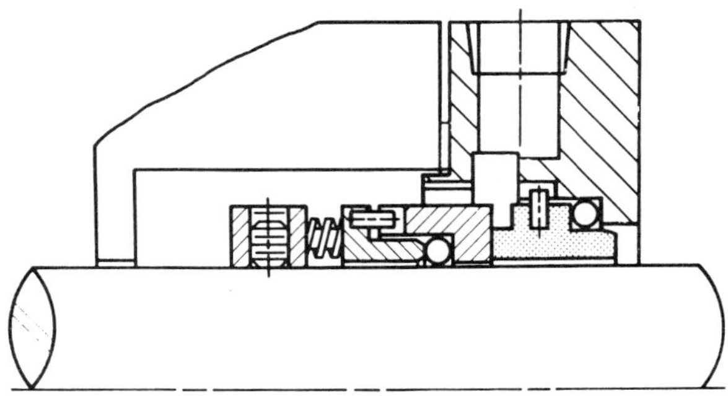

Figure 4
Mechanical seal with multiple spings.

Large multi-spring single seal.

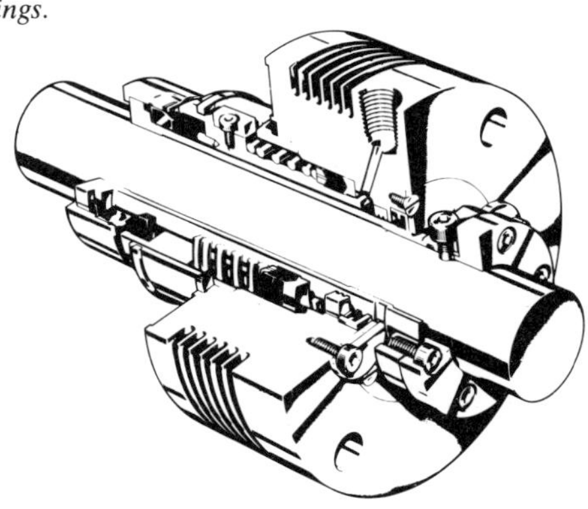

High temperature single spring seal.

desirable even face loading around the complete seal circumference which the multi-spring design can achieve (*eg* see Figure 4). A length problem may also exist since the single spring design is of necessity of much greater length than the multi-springs. In addition, single springs become progressively more difficult to compress during fitting as shaft sizes increase. At high speeds they may also resonate and fracture. Multiple spring designs, however, may have corrosion problems in service due to the small diameter of wire employed, but see also Table 4.

TABLE 4 – ADVANTAGES AND DISADVANTAGES OF SPRING TYPES

Spring type	Advantages	Disadvantages
Multiple	Smaller seals. Even face load. Higher rotational speeds.	High stress levels. Low corrosion allowance. Prone to blockage.
Single	Low stress levels. Greater corrosion allowance. Readily coatable in *eg* PTFE.	Uneven loading. Larger and longer seals. Speed restricted.
Rat-trap Wavy washer Belleville washer	Space-saving.	High rate.

Secondary seals

In addition to providing necesssary static sealing, the secondary seals normally provide flexibility to both the rotary and stationary seal elements. Standard pressure-energized seals such as an O-ring, V-ring or U-cup, *etc*, or wedge seals are commonly employed; although in some cases the stationary ring may have no seal, *eg* Figure 5. Axial movement of the rotary sealing ring is required and this can be provided by its secondary seal sliding on the shaft itself, the seal then being described as a *pusher* seal. Pusher seals predominate in the US, but are limited by temperature.

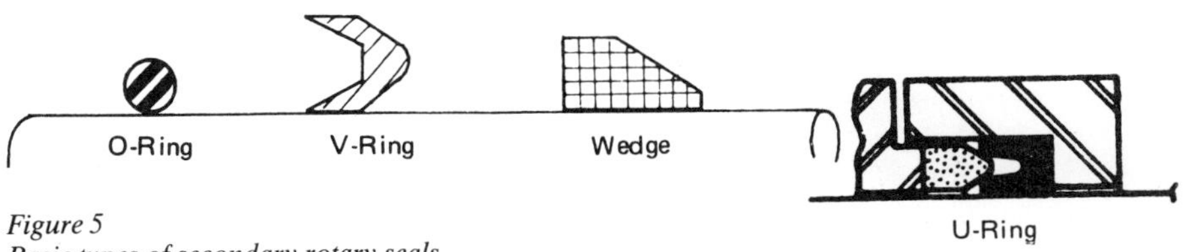

Figure 5
Basic types of secondary rotary seals.

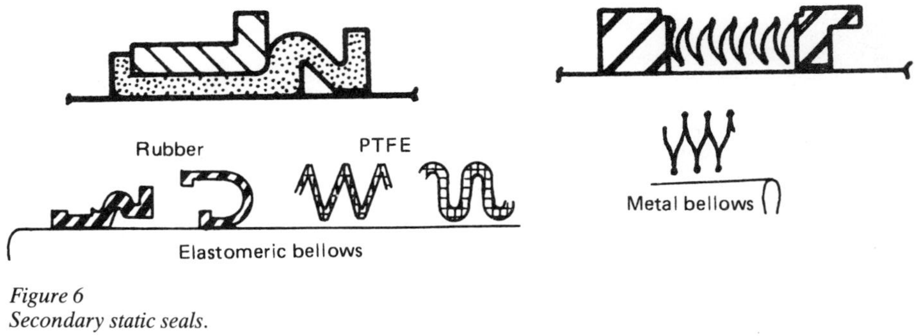

Figure 6
Secondary static seals.

For a pusher seal to be capable of axial sliding movement, however, the shaft itself must remain in good condition, with no corrosion or pitting to inhibit seal movement, and there must be no solids build-up for a similar reason. Any problems in these respects can be eliminated by using a *pseudo-static* seal instead of a pusher seal, this takes the form of an elastomeric or metal bellows (Figure 6).

The operating parameters, liquid, pressure, temperature, *etc,* normally dictate the materials of the secondary sealing members and the material in many cases dictates the secondary seal design. For example, the use of PTFE for corrosion resistance requires that secondary seals take the V-ring or wedge form. This further requires that the rotor static seal be mechanically loaded and the stator include an anti-rotation pin because of the anti-frictional characteristics of a PTFE stator mounting.

Type classifications

Mechanical seals can be classified in several ways, *eg:* (Figure 7).

(i) Inside or outside seals

(ii) Unbalanced or balanced seals.

(iii) Single or double seals.

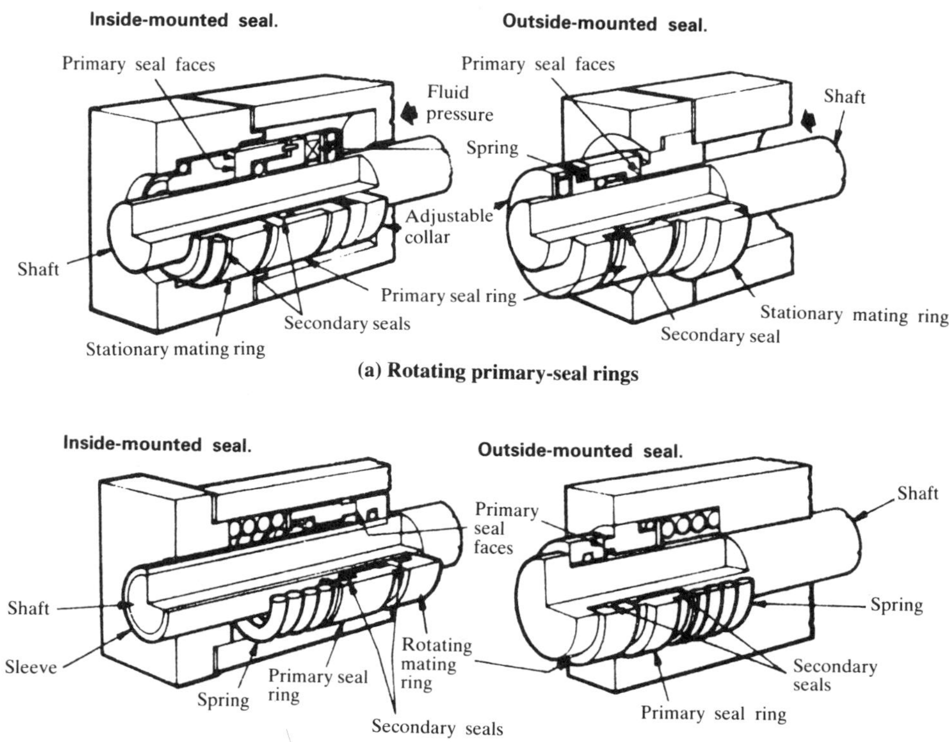

(a) Rotating primary-seal rings

(b) Stationary primary-seal rings

Figure 7
Inside-mounted and outside-mounted mechanical face seals incorporating rotating and stationary primary-seal rings.

Mechanical seals are described as *inside* if the hydraulic pressure being contained acts in a 'closing' direction, when any leakage is from the o.d. of the seal. With an *outside* seal hydraulic pressure acts in an 'opening' direction, with any consequent leakage from the i.d. of the seal. Actual seal mounting position on the shaft (*ie* externally or internally) does *not* define whether the seal is an internal or external type.

The internal seal is a more stable type; the external seal tends to lose face 'contact' with a sudden surge and quite often it is impossible for it to remake normal face 'contact'. Excessive leakage will then occur with the only remedy usually being to shut the unit down and restart. This phenomenon is far less likely with internal seals. Secondly, the cooling of an internal seal is usually better than the external seal, with the pumped fluid having better contact to remove heat. Even with a cooling injection, the injection positioning for heat removal is usually easier to place in the optimum position on an internal seal installation. This cooling problem makes thermal distortion (and, therefore, leakage failure) a greater problem on the external seal. A basic limitation of the external seal is that solid particles in the fluid which is being sealed can readily collect by centrifugal force against the sealing faces, and cause physical damage by chipping the edges and then entering between the faces to accelerate the process.

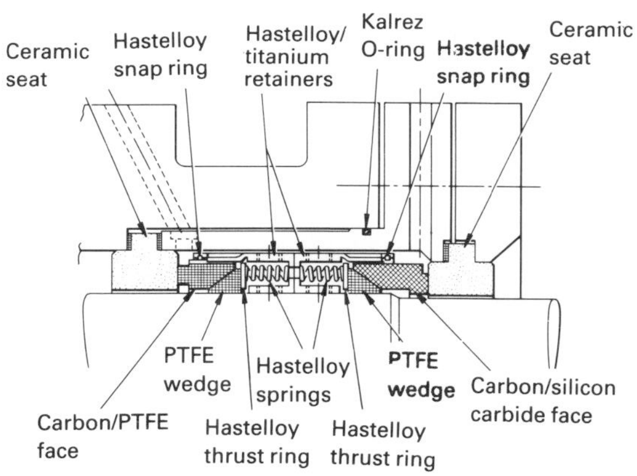

Detail of double mechanical seal with V-seats.

Examples of DIN standard seals.

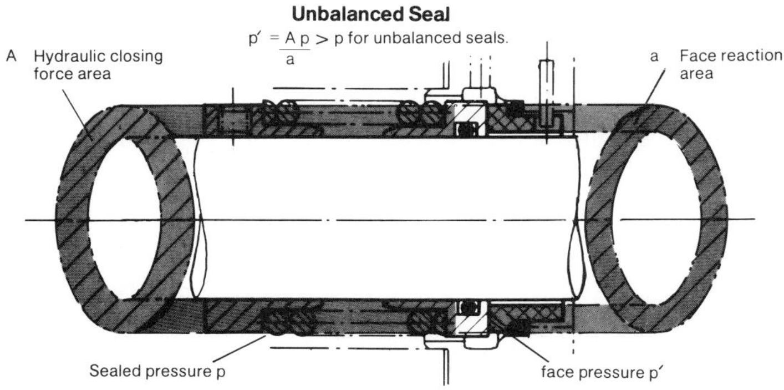

Hydraulic balance/unbalanced seal.

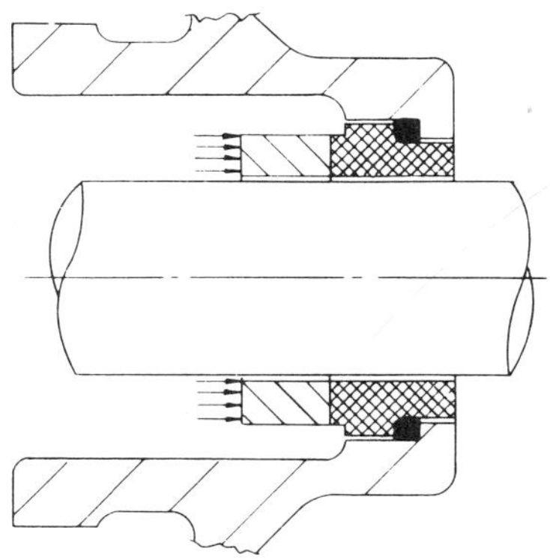

Pressure acting on unbalanced seal face

Figure 8

Hydraulic balance

Hydraulic balance refers to the relationship between the pressure of the fluid being sealed and the contact pressure between the seal faces. In the case of an *unbalanced seal,* hydraulic pressure is unrelieved by the face geometry so that the face contact pressure is equal to or greater than the fluid pressure (Figure 8). With a *balanced seal* the design proportions the radially disposed areas so that the effective contact pressure is always less than the fluid pressure (Figure 9). In practice, the lowest face pressure that will give effective sealing is normally selected.

The immediate advantage of a balanced seal is that friction is reduced at the seal faces (because of the lower face contact pressure), with less heat generated and reduction in rubbing wear. Also such a seal can accommodate higher pressures than its unbalanced counterpart. The disadvantage is that construction is more complicated and costly, and commonly calls for a *stepped shaft* (but not in all designs). Thus unbalanced seals are more widely used for pressures up to 10 bar (150 lb/in^2). API 610 specification calls for balanced seals to be used for pressures above 75 lb/in^2, and specifically balanced seals only for all process duties, while balanced seals extend this application of mechanical seals up to about 85 bar (1250 lb/in^2).

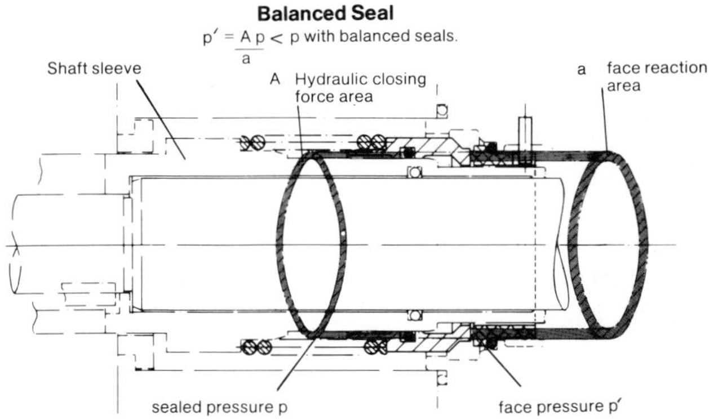

Hydraulic balance/balanced seal.

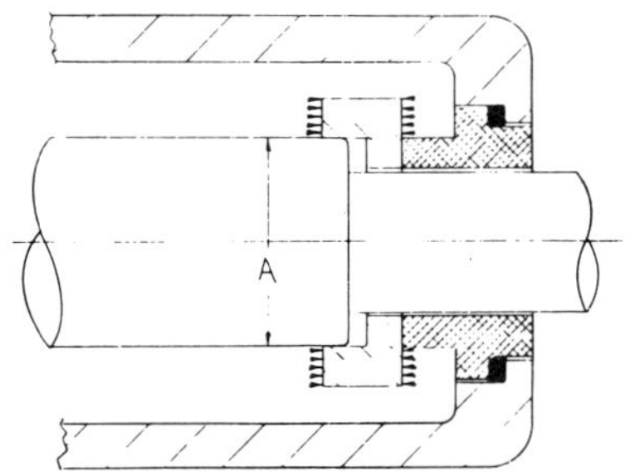

Pressure acting on balanced face

Figure 9

Variations of seal balance are illustrated in Figures 10, 11 and 12, showing various face arrangements. Here 'S', the diameter of the seal sleeve shoulder, represents the effective sealing diameter which may also be referred to as the *hydraulic* or *sliding diameter* because all thrust loads are computed about this surface. 'A' represents the hydraulic piston area of the *sliding seal ring* and 'B' represents the contact face area of the sealing faces. The spring force is ignored in all cases.

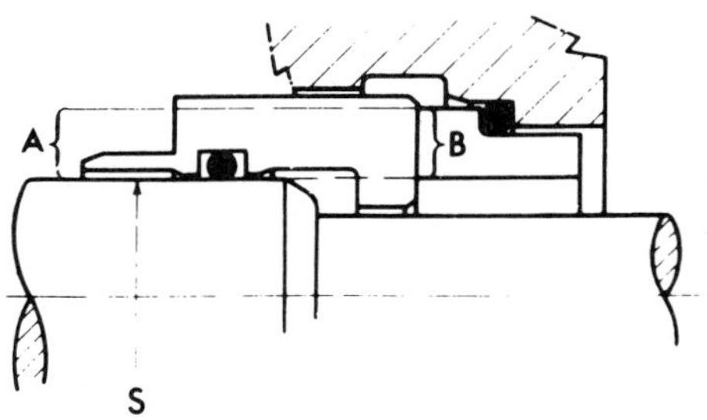

Figure 10

In Figure 10 all the contact face area B is disposed outside the effective sealing diameter S and the hydraulic piston area A is equal to the contact face area B. This diagram, therefore, represents a condition of 100% out-of-balance which also indicates that the average contact face pressure will be exactly 100% of the hydraulic pressure sealed.

In Figure 11 all the contact face area B is disposed outside the effective sealing diameter S and the hydraulic piston area A is greater than the contact face area B and the loading will actually be higher by an equivalent percentage than the hydraulic pressure being sealed. This is the condition existing in most unbalanced seals.

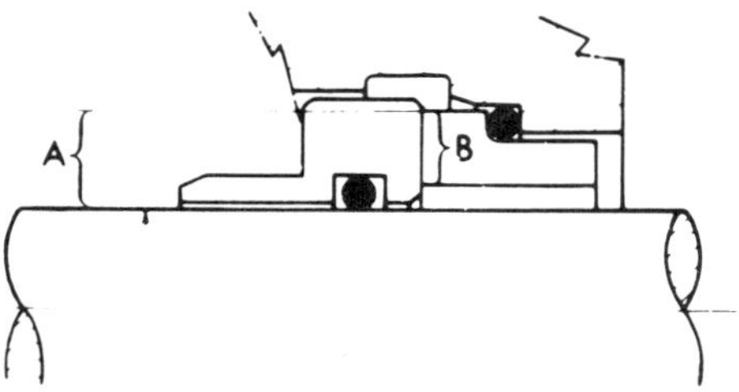

Figure 11

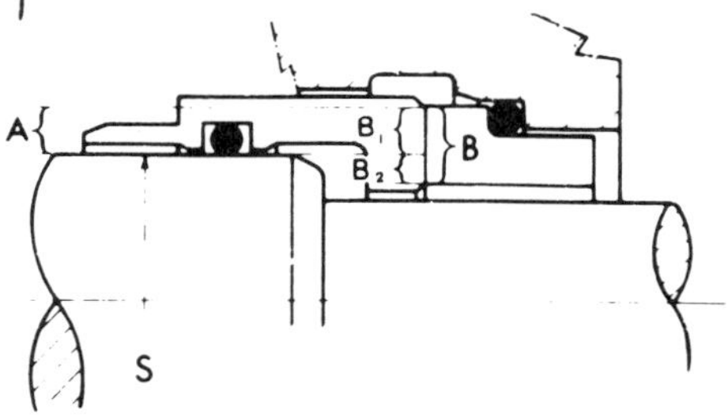

Figure 12

Figure 12 shows the relationship of most balanced seals. Here part of the contact face area B, designated as B_1, is disposed outside the effective sealing diameter S. Area B_1 is, therefore, equal to the hydraulic piston area A. Because the rest of the seal face area B_2 is located inside the effective sealing diameter S, the total seal face area B will equal the sum of $B_1 + B_2$ and the unit face loading will be less than the pressure sealed in accordance with the ratio of the two areas, *ie:*

$$\frac{B_1}{B_1 + B_2} = \frac{A}{B}$$

This value, expressed as a percentage, indicates by how much the seal is out of balance.

Single and double seals

Single seals have one set of sealing faces and are generally suitable for sealing fluids which will provide adequate lubrication at the seal faces. They can also be used with non-lubricating fluids by introducing separate flushing fluid into the seal cavity, cooling and lubricating the seal faces. The problem then is the control of product dilution. Where this cannot be tolerated, *double seals* are used. These are, basically, back-to-back mechanical seals containing the flushing fluid/lubricant in a chamber isolated by the secondary seals of the two seals. The seals themselves may be unbalanced or balanced – see also Figure 13.

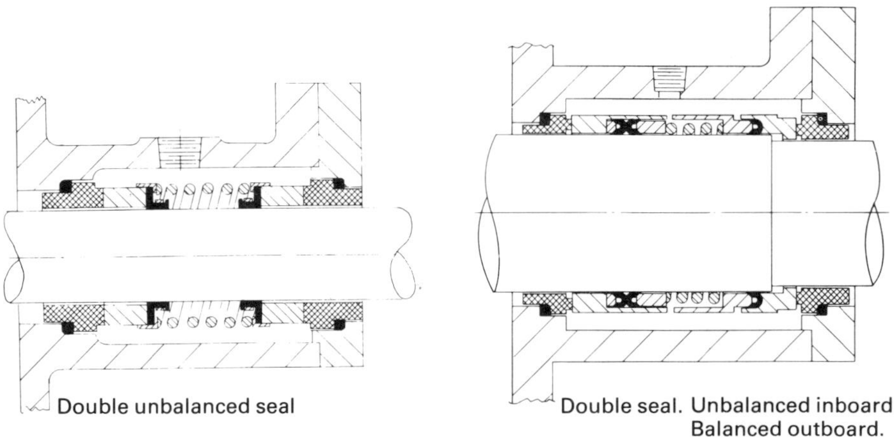

Figure 13
Examples of double seal.

Shaft sizes and PV

The pressure x velocity (PV) value largely determines the suitability of material combinations for the seal faces, and specifically the amount of heat generated at the face. It also follows that, for given rotational speeds, an increase in shaft diameter automatically implies an increase in PV because:

$$PV = \text{pressure} \times \pi \times \text{seal diameter} \times \text{rotational speed}$$

Units normally applicable are:

$$\text{bar m/s} = \text{bar} \times \pi \times \text{mm} \times \text{rev/s}$$

N.B. The formula shown applies to unbalanced seals. For balanced seals, the figure obtained should be multiplied by the degree of balance applied to the seal design, usually of the order 0·75. Note also that the pressure referred to is that actually put on the seal. When product recirculation is used, the pressure will be somewhere between discharge and suction pressures.

Typical values of the PV capability of difference face material combinations are as follows (see also Table 1):

Materials	**PV (bar m/s)**
carbon *vs* hard faced stainless steel	190
carbon *vs* ceramic	190
carbon *vs* leaded bronze	350
carbon *vs* nickel iron	400
carbon *vs* tungsten carbide	900

It should be noted that one way of reducing the working PV value for a given size of seal is to use a balanced seal, reducing the effective value of P.

Face temperature

To maintain an adequate lubricating film between the seal faces it is essential to limit the temperature at the interface to below that at which the film tends to vaporize or boil away.

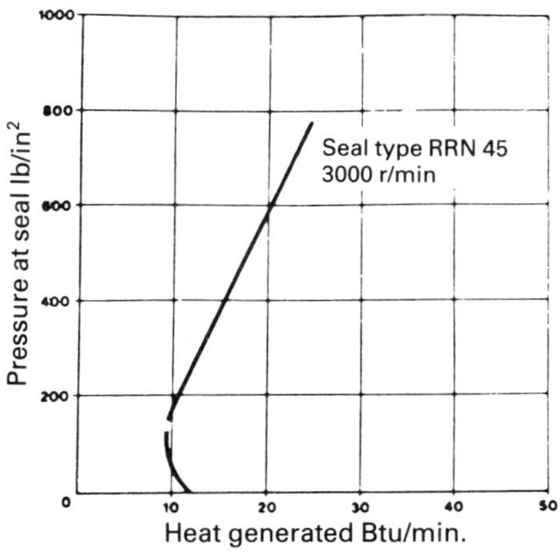

Heat generated by seal on water

$Qd = Qg$

$Qd = mk\,A \tanh(ml)\,\triangle T$ $m = \sqrt{\dfrac{hc}{kA}}$

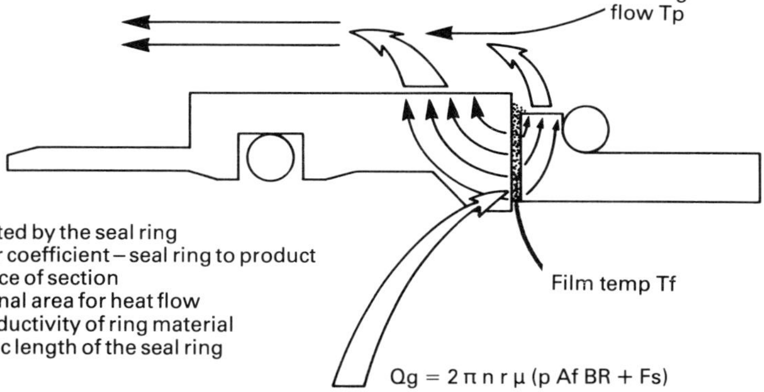

$Qg = 2\pi n r \mu (p\,Af\,BR + Fs)$

$\triangle T = Tf - Tp$

Qd = heat dissipated by the seal ring
h = heat transfer coefficient – seal ring to product
C = circumference of section
A = cross-sectional area for heat flow
k = thermal conductivity of ring material
l = characteristic length of the seal ring

Qg = heat generated at the seal face
n = shaft speed
r = mean face radius
Fs = spring load
p = product pressure
Af = face area
BR = balance ratio
μ = coefficient of friction

Heat generated at seal faces.

Figure 14

The amount of heat generated will depend on the face contact and pressure related to stuffing box pressure. Figure 14 shows the amount of heat generated by a typical seal at different pressures.

The heat generated at the seal faces has to be conducted through the seal rings to the liquid in the stuffing box. Thus the product temperature, or, strictly speaking, the difference between the temperature at the seal faces and the temperature of the product in the box, has an influence on seal stability. Similarly, the thermal properties of the seal ring material play an important part.

As a consequence of this heat dissipation the temperature within the stuffing box will increase and some means must be provided to remove it, *eg* by jacket cooling of the stuffing box or more generally by the circulation of the relatively cool product *via* a tapping from the discharge nozzle to the seal faces.

It is possible to determine stability limits for a seal by running it at various speeds and pressures and increasing the temperature until the seal becomes unstable. Figure 15 shows limits produced in this way. The curve represents the maximum allowable temperature in the stuffing box in order for the liquid film to remain stable.

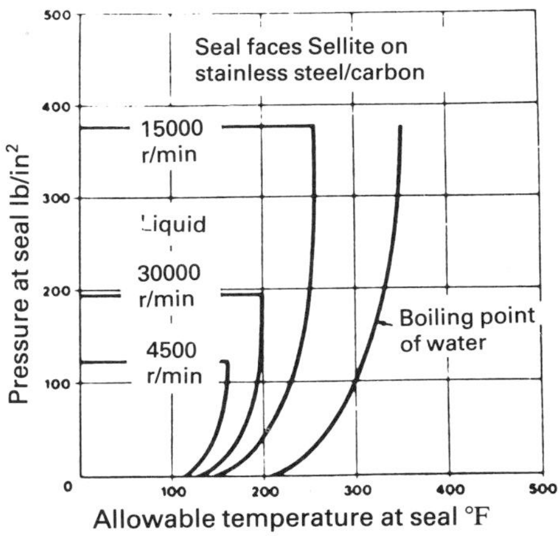

Pressure temperature limitations at various speeds RRN 45 on water

Figure 15

The most common cause of premature seal failure arises from the loss of the liquid component of the fluid film between the seal faces. Just before this occurs, the seal emits a puff of vapour every few seconds and there is local boiling-off of the liquid film, causing the seal faces to open and tilt momentarily. This allows more liquid to enter between the seal faces giving a temporary cooling effect. When the frictional heat generated at the seal faces has built up sufficiently to vaporize more liquid, another puff of vapour is emitted and the cycle is repeated. At this stage the only bad effect suffered by the seal is a chipping of the edges of the carbon seal face caused by the tilting of the rotating seal ring.

If the temperature of the product surrounding the seal is increased slightly, the rate of emission of puffs of vapour also increases until there is heavy leakage of liquid. This is caused by the eruption of carbon from a small crater in the face of the seal when product which has permeated below the surface of the material is vaporized suddenly. The carbon debris from the crater is ground between the seal faces leaving a 'comet trail' pattern on the carbon face.

This is the prelude to complete loss of the liquid component between the seal faces and 'dry running' with resultant heavy face wear occurring. Both carbon and metal rotary seal ring faces are then heavily grooved – somewhat like a gramophone record.

A dry-running seal may also produce shaft wear under the secondary seal. As the liquid at the face gasses off, it pushes the secondary seal along the shaft. When the gas has escaped into the atmosphere, the box pressure closes the faces. This phenomenon is known as 'popping' and can occur with great rapidity. The result is shaft wear, known as 'O-ring drag' or 'wedge-etching'.

The cure is to stabilize conditions at the seal face by cooling; hardening the shaft under the secondary seal also helps.

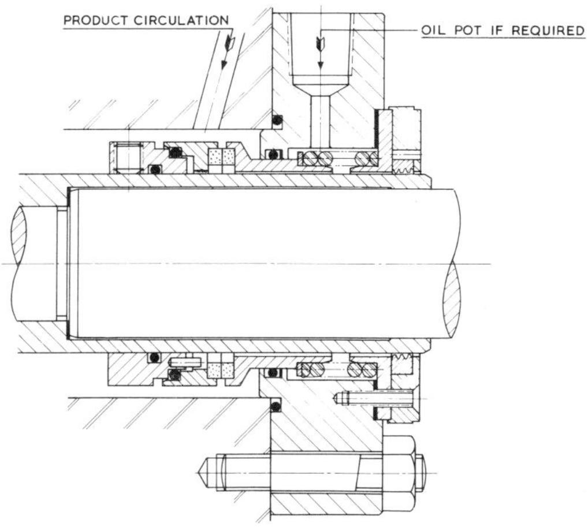

External stationary spring seal for high viscosity and abrasive duties.

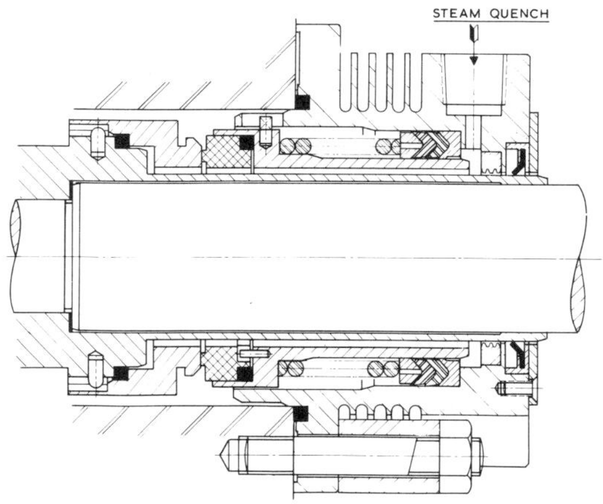

High temperature single spring seal.

Cooling

The heat generated by the rubbing faces of a mechanical seal must be removed if the seal is to work with minimum leakage and wear. Equally, to be most effective, the coolant should be directed at the point where the most effective heat transfer occurs. This applies whether cooling is achieved by recirculation of the pumped product, or by an external source of coolant independent of, and not in direct contact with, the rubbing faces. Examples of good and bad practice in inlet connection location are summarized in Table 5.

TABLE 5 – INLET CONNECTION PRACTICE

Ideal		Troublesome	
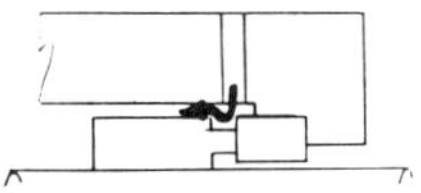	Vapour ring broken down, maximum cooling effect.	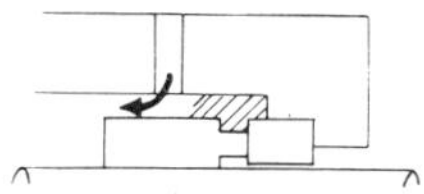	Avoid dead pockets – overheating will result.
		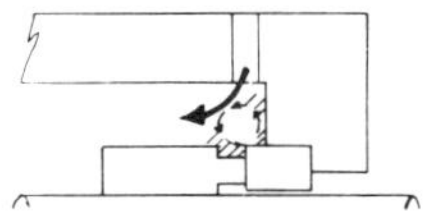	Clearance around seal too large – vortex prevents liquid flow.
		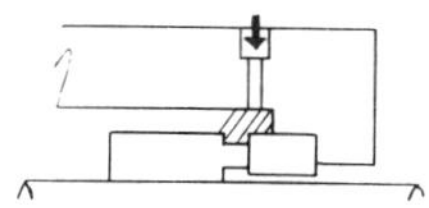	Avoid restrictor in clamp plate – change of velocity on entering seal chamber may cause vaporization.
		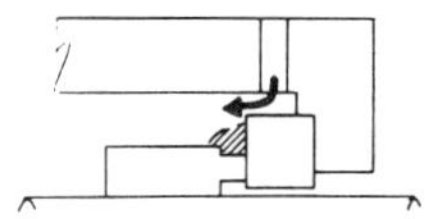	Avoid axial flow with entry remote from seal face – vaporization may occur in vicinity of rubbing face.

Leakage

Because mechanical seals are designed to operate with a lubricating film between the contact faces there is always the possibility of some leakage, if only minimal. Thus, in practice, all mechanical seals tend to leak although this may be of such a low order that the fluid evaporates or vaporizes and is not apparent as liquid leakage, or is perhaps observed as occasional drips. Any more generous leakage, however, is likely to be an indication of wear on the seal faces, bearings, wear rings, *etc.* (See Figure 16).

Factors which have an overriding influence upon the leakage experienced are:

(i) Accuracy of fitting and installation.
(ii) Plant mal-operation and plant upset.
(iii) Integrity of the secondary seal.
(iv) Characteristics of the liquid handled.
(v) Adequacy of cooling.
(vi) Correct selection of the seal and materials.
(vii) Vibration and stability of the equipment.

Wear

Manufacturers establish wear rates by testing different face material combinations on several products until a satisfactory level of wear rate is established from which they are able to specify an average seal design life. Figure 17 is an example of such data expressed as operating limits for a proprietary range of unbalanced and balanced seals covering product, temperature, pressure, shaft size and speed. Also

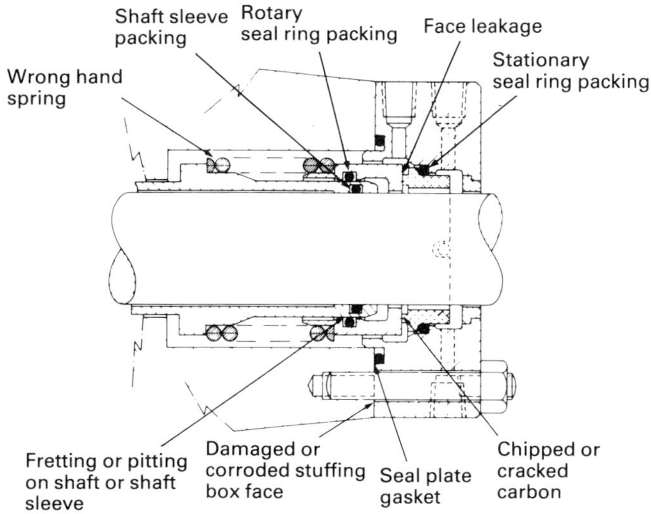

Figure 16
Possible leakage paths from a standard balanced seal.

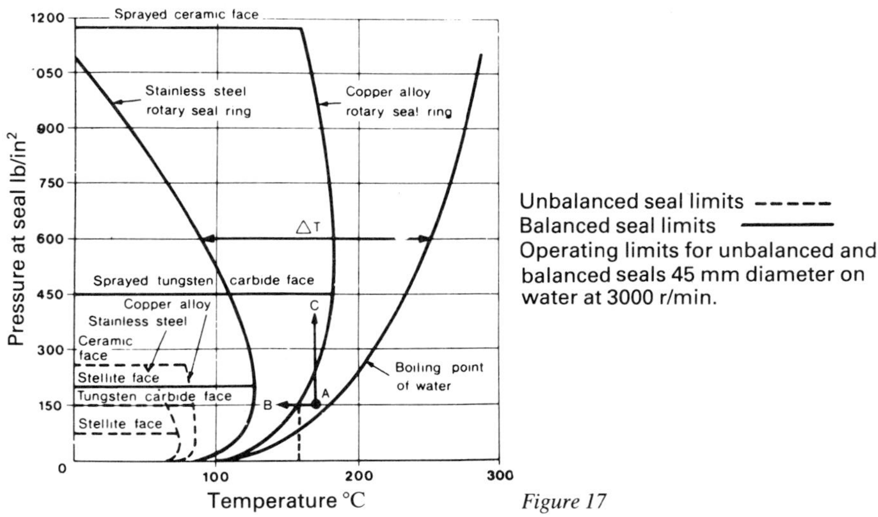

Figure 17

indicated is the symbol ($\triangle$T), a parameter used to denote the temperature difference between product temperature at the seal and vapour or boiling point. The curve on the graph indicates the maximum stability conditions for this size seal with different body and face materials. Therefore, a 45 mm size seal with stainless steel body and tungsten carbide face will not give a satisfactory life beyond this curve. Built into the manufacturer's seal selection guide is a minimum $\triangle$T to indicate this curve for seals working under different conditions. The condition shown on the graph could be a boiler feed duty at 150 lb/in^2 and 170 °C failing at point 'A' – an unstable region. The nearest curve to the left of point A selects a seal

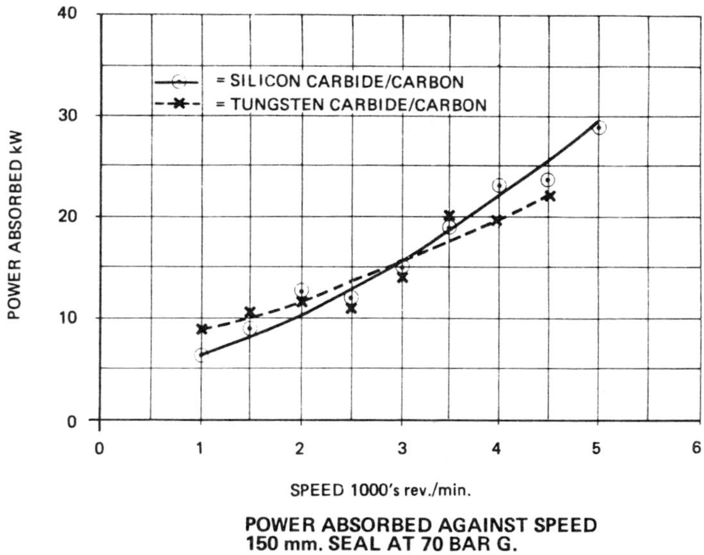

Power absorption/speed comparison.

with a copper alloy rotary and ceramic face, this being the only single seal that will operate under these conditions. Even then cooling would have to be applied to the seal area to bring the temperature down to where it intersects our curve at approximately 160 °C.

Seals for abrasive services

The most common sources of abrasive content in a fluid being handled are crystallization solidification of the product occurring as a result of temperature changes or chemical reaction(s), or the normal presence of abrasive solids in suspension. Crystallization occurs mostly as a result of the product passing across the seal faces, with an accompanying pressure drop to atmospheric pressure. The liquid is lost in the form of vapour, leaving behind a deposit of crystals. These crystals can build up sufficiently to disturb the stationary face in the gland plate. This can be overcome by fitting a lip seal, close clearance bush or an auxiliary packed gland in the outer portion of the gland plate, with a quench to the space between it and the seal faces. This creates a liquids barrier between the product and atmosphere, and any crystals that form and pass across the faces are washed away by the quench medium. Liquids with abrasive solids in suspension can be more difficult to deal with, particularly as the solids may vary widely in size, density and concentration. Also they can produce wear both by impingement erosion and abrasion of the seal face(s).

Problems associated with impingement erosion can be minimized by arranging a suitable flow pattern to carry abrasives away from the seal face. Thus centrifugal pumps with bell housings can have a vortex breaker fitted in the bell housing to prevent solids being drawn to the seal face and circulation pipes (where fitted) should be of generous diameter and direct re-entry of fluid into a region where solids do not accumulate. In more severe cases, the addition of a cyclone separator will remove the bulk of large solids and reduce the possibility of erosion and blockage of the seal mechanism.

TABLE 6 – TYPICAL SEALS FOR ABRASIVE FLUIDS

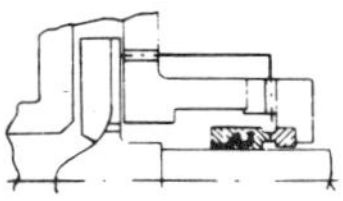	Single Type 2, tungsten carbide opposing tungsten carbide with product recirculation from behind the impeller with no restrictions in the seal chamber.	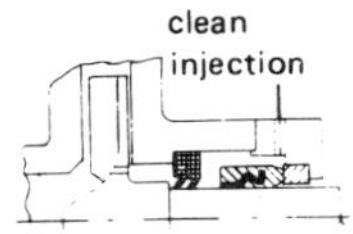	Single Type 2 or Type 299 (split face) opposing ceramic or tungsten carbide seat. Restricter rings fitted at bottom of seal chamber with clean injection from external source.
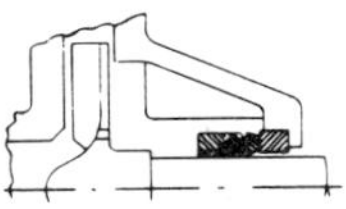	Single Type 2 or Type 299 (split face) opposing ceramic or tungsten carbide seat in bell housing incorporating a vortex breaker.	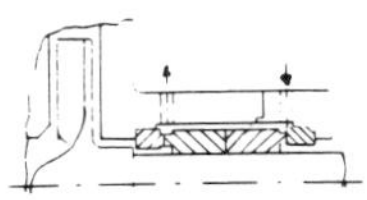	Double seals incorporating pressurized sealant, tungsten carbide opposing tungsten carbide for inboard seal and conventional materials outboard.
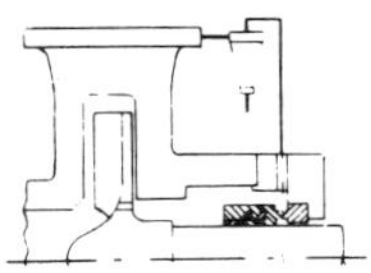	Single Type 2, tungsten carbide opposing tungsten carbide with product recirculation from behind impeller with no restrictions in the seal chamber, but with cyclone separator incorporated in the recirculation line.	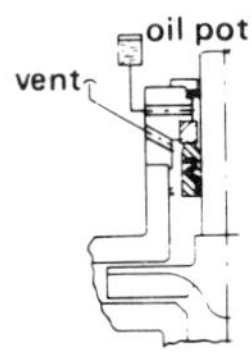	Vertical pumps – single Type 2, product circulation, no restrictions in seal chamber, with external lip seal and an oil pot.

There remains, however, the distinct possibility of finer particles penetrating the fluid film between the seal faces, causing abrasive wear. Normally this is accommodated by a suitable choice of materials, *eg* hard faces or at least one face of split form if long seal life with minimum of maintenance is to be achieved.

Some specific recommendations for seal types and installations for handling liquids containing abrasives are summarized in Table 6.

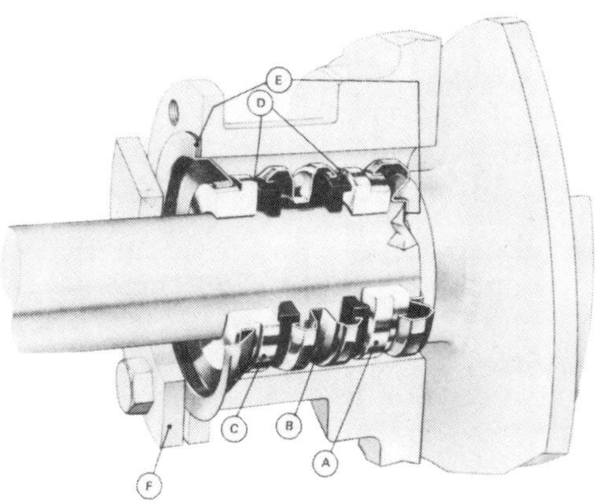

A–Drive element
B–Floating element
C–Stationary elemen
D–Dynamic point, no additive lubrication
E–Static joint gaskets
F–Gland or draw flange

Dry face mechanical seal.

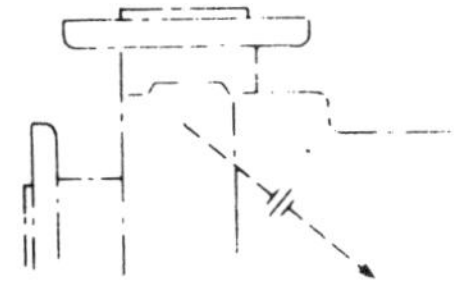

Integral (internal) recirculation from pump discharge to seal.

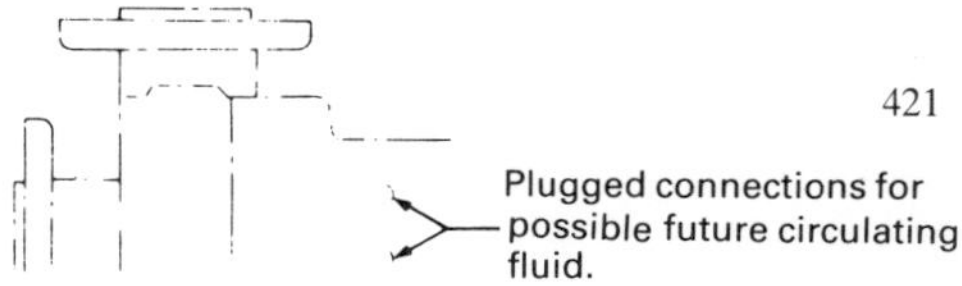

Dead-ended seal box with no circulation of flush fluid. Water-cooled box jacket and throat bushing required, unless otherwise specified.

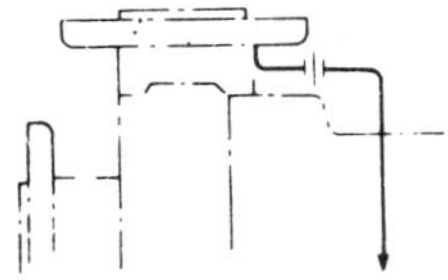

Recirculation from pump case through orifice to seal.

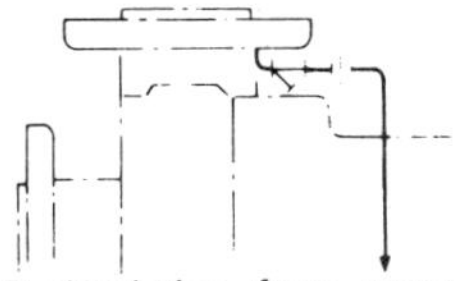

Recirculation from pump case through strainer and orifice to seal.

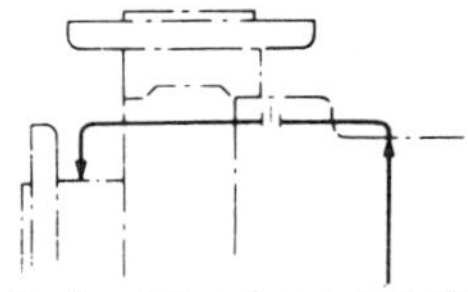

Recirculation from seal chamber through orifice and back to pump suction.

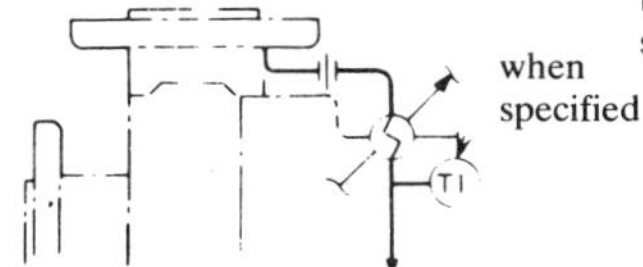

Recirculation from pump case through orifice and cooler to seal.

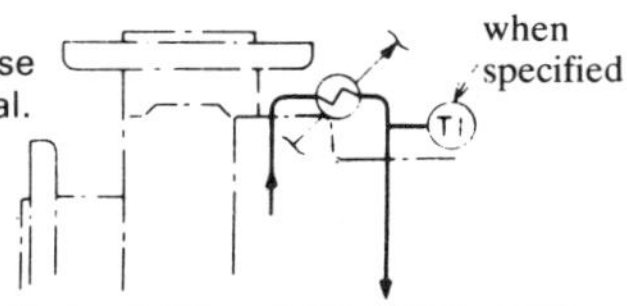

Recirculation from seal with pumping ring through cooler and back to seal.

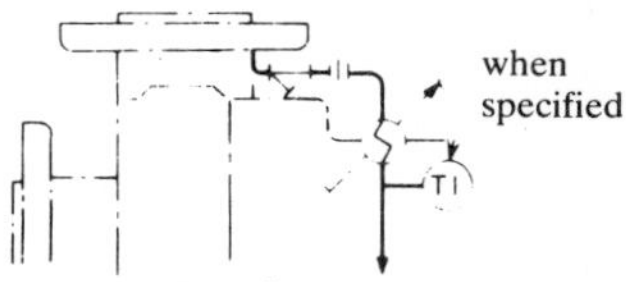

Recirculation from pump case through strainer, orifice and cooler to seal.

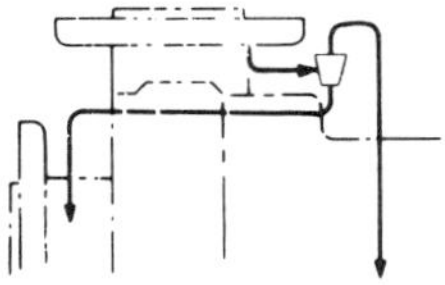

Recirculation from pump case through cyclone separator delivering clean fluid to seal and fluid with solids back to pump suction.

Dirty or Special Pumpage

When specified By vendor Recommended by purchaser

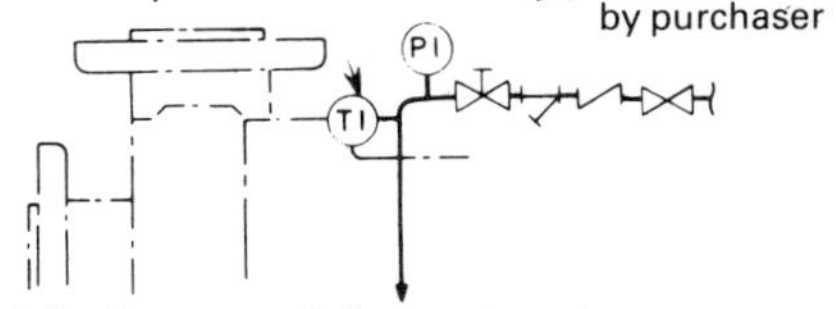

Injection to seal from external source of clean cool fluid. [See Note (b)].

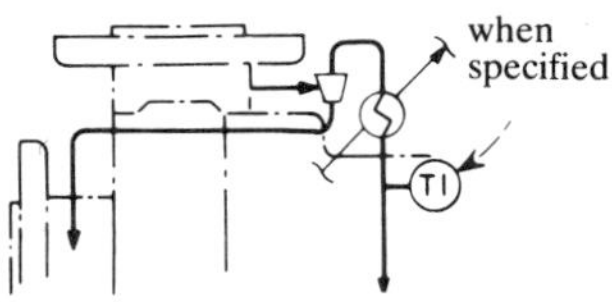

Recirculation from pump case through cyclone separator delivering clean fluid through cooler to seal and fluid with solids back to pump suction.

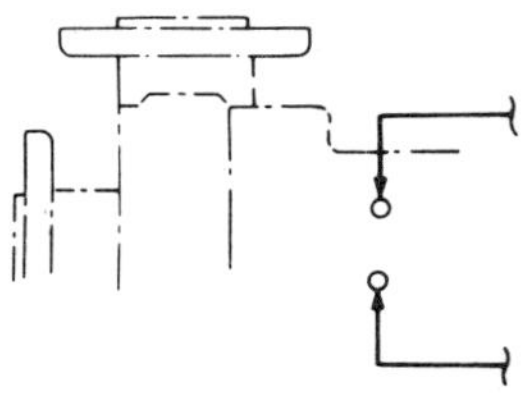

Circulation of clean fluid to double seal from an external circulation system.]See Note (b)].

NOTES:

- Cooler.
- Pressure gauge, with block valve.
- Dial thermometer, when specified.
- Pressure switch, when specified, including block valve.
- Cyclone separator.
- Y-Type strainer.
- Flow-regulating valve.
- Block valve.
- Check valve.
- Orifice.

Figure 18
Piping arrangements.

cont...

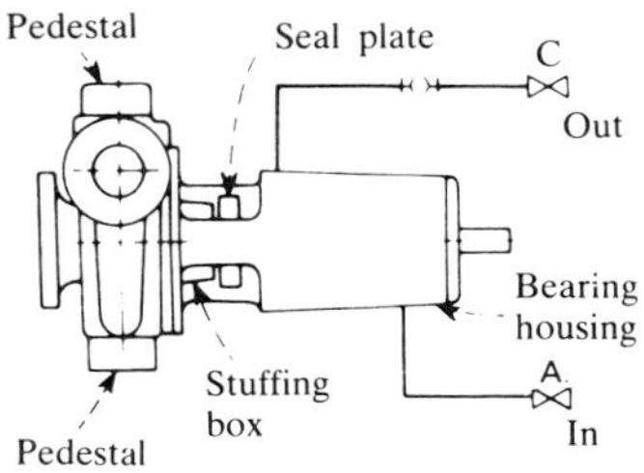

Cooling to bearing housing.

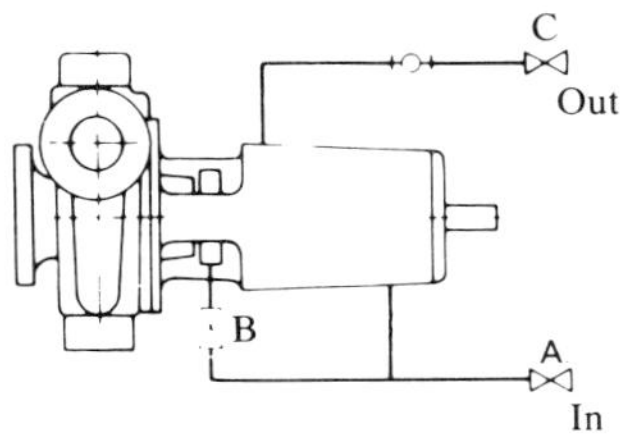

Cooling to bearing housing with parallel flow to seal plate.

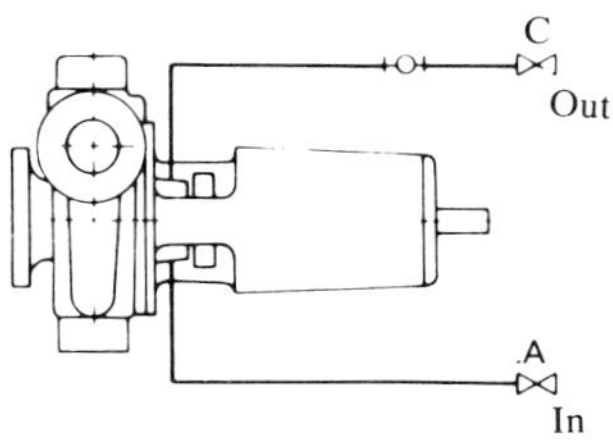

Cooling to stuffing box jacket.

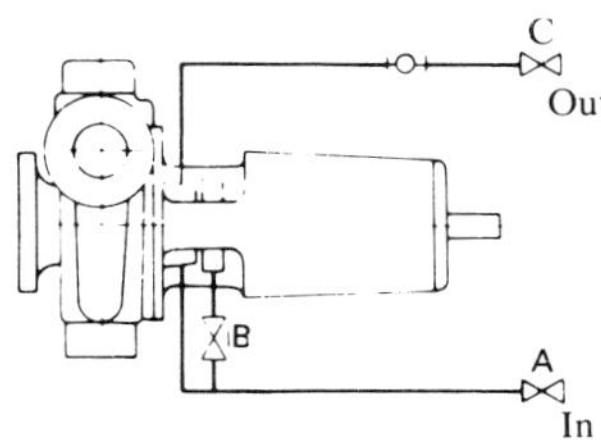

Cooling to stuffing box jacket with parallel flow to seal plate.

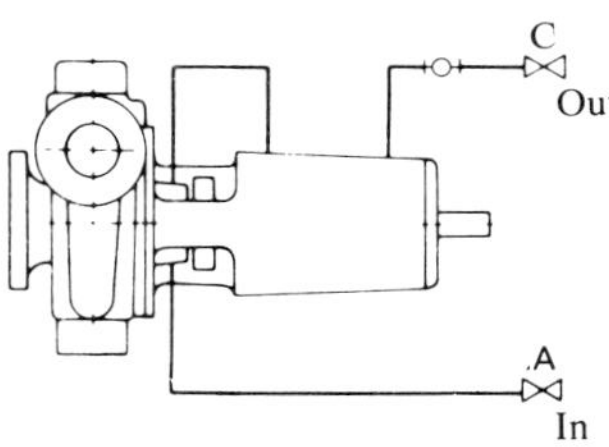

Cooling to stuffing box jacket and bearing housing in series.

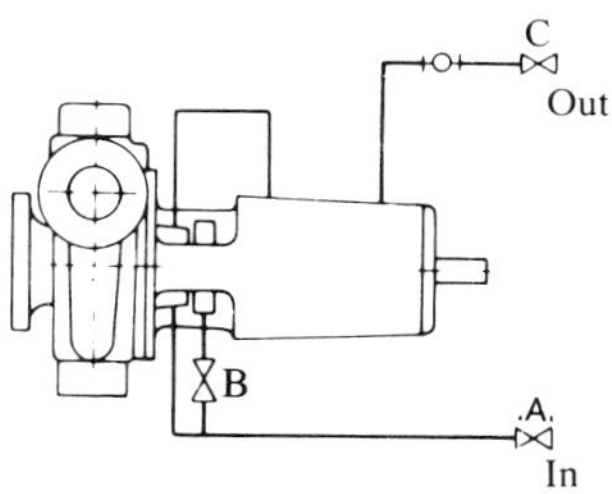

Cooling to stuffing box jacket and bearing housing in series with parallel flow to seal plate.

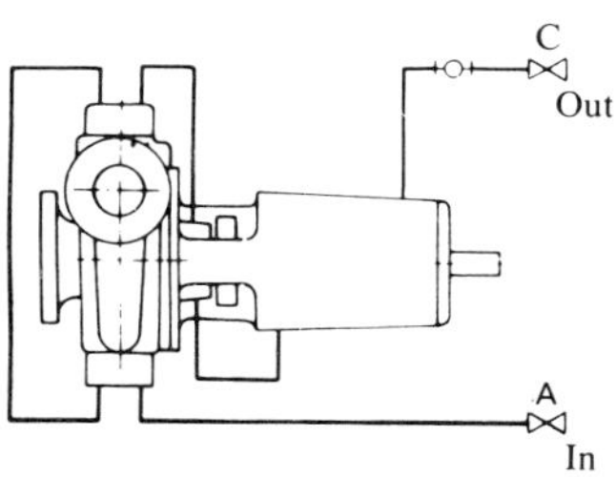

Cooling to pedestals, stuffing box jacket and bearing housing in series.

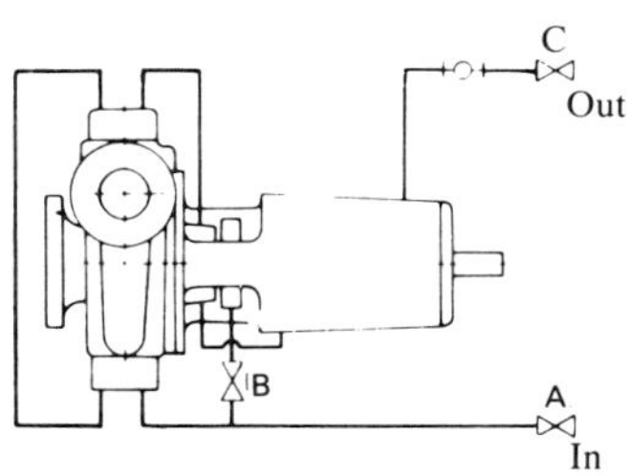

Cooling to pedestals, stuffing box jacket and bearing housing in series with parallel flow to seal plate.

NOTES:

Valve

Sight flow indicator, when specified.

Valve "A" inlet, shutoff valve.

Valve "B" branch flow control valve.

Valve "C" outlet, shutoff valve (optional).

Figure 18 (contd...)
Piping arrangements.

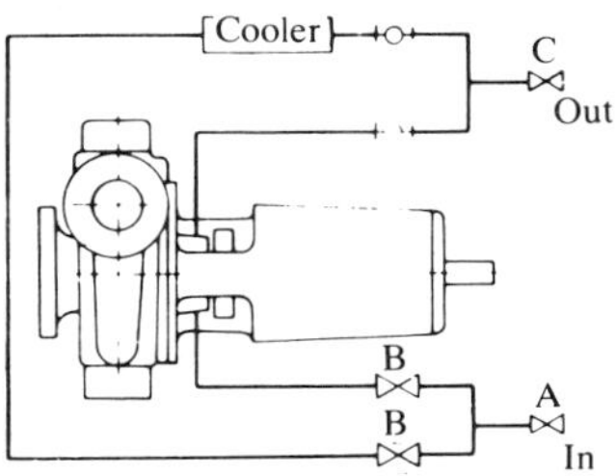

Cooling to stuffing box jacket with parallel flow to cooler.

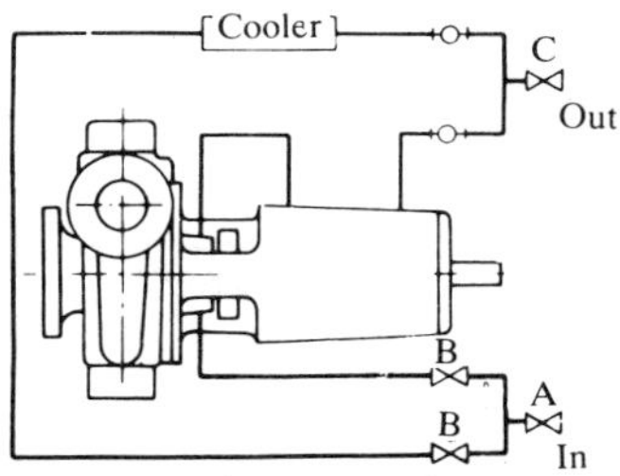

Cooling to stuffing box jacket and bearing housing in series with parallel flow to cooler.

NOTES: Valve

Sight flow indicator, when specified.

Valve "A" inlet, shutoff valve.

Valve "B" branch flow control valve.

Valve "C" outlet, shutoff valve (optional).

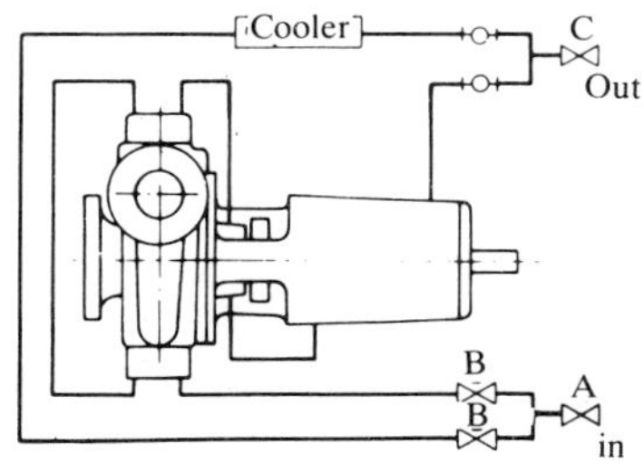

Cooling to pedestals, stuffing box jacket and bearing frame in series with parallel flow to cooler.

Figure 18 (contd...)
Piping arrangements.

Auxiliary systems

Conditions favourable to the employment of mechanical face seals are that the liquid: is clean, always available to flood the seal (lubricated and cool), has a pumped liquid 'condition' which is well below the vapour pressure, does not require heating before start-up to reduce the viscosity, has sufficient heat transfer to remove the generated heat, does not require a quench gland because of very dangerous or toxic vapours, and does not require extra pressurization at the seal because of very low 'flash point'.

Mechanical seal installations which do not conform to the aforementioned requirements need special designs of auxiliary systems to ensure adequate performance. Such systems have, in fact, been well developed by seal/pump manufacturers over the years, and API 610 publishes a series of figures which enables either the user, the pump manufacturer or the seal manufacturer, singly or jointly, to quote the figure reference denoting the auxiliary system to be used in accordance with his experience, *eg* see Figure 18.

These plans represent commonly used systems and give broad guidelines for system selection. Other variations and systems may be specified by individual pump manufacturers. Other items which can be incorporated in the auxiliary system include cyclone separators, filters and leakage detectors.

A vortex separator is used when the liquid handled is dirty; its function is to clean the liquid which is being supplied to the mechanical seal for lubricating/cooling purposes, thus increasing the seal life and reducing maintenance down-time. The separator operates as follows: the dirty liquid enters the separator, being piped from the pump discharge; and enters tangentially into the side/top of a conical chamber, the tangential flow creates a vortex so that the liquid swirls around in the conical chamber, thus forming a 'coarse' centrifuge. The rotation throws the solid particles to the wall of the cone by centrifugal action and then dirt moves gradually downwards to the outlet from the cone apex (bottom) and back into the main stream of the liquid at a low pressure point. The clean liquid is extracted from the top of the cyclone separator and led to the mechanical seal faces (Figure 19).

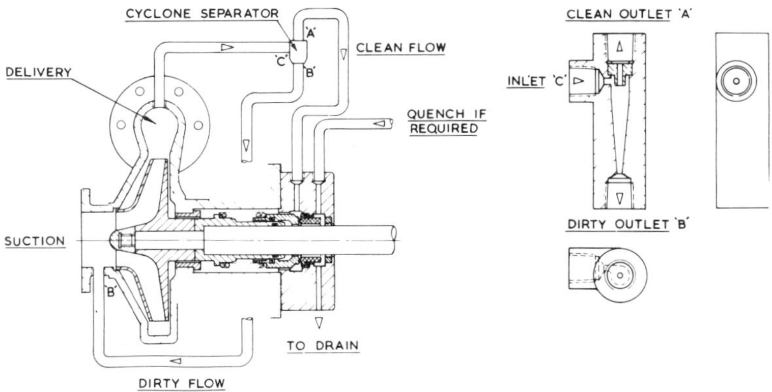

Figure 19

In general the following conditions must be observed for the unit to operate successfully:

(i) The solid particles must not be too large, in general less than 1 mm (very large cyclone separators can be manufactured for larger particles, but the flow rates would not be economical). Minimum size depends on specific gravity of the solid and the liquid viscosity, but is in the order of 5 micron.

(ii) The solids should not exceed 10% by weight, but 5 to 7% is the normal maximum.

(iii) Because the operation is by centrifugal force the solid particles must have a higher specific gravity than the liquid.

(iv) If the liquid is viscous the centrifugal action is so retarded that it is commercially non-operative. Maximum viscosity should therefore not normally exceed 20 centistokes.

(v) There must be a pressure difference between the inlet and outlet of the cyclone to achieve the necessary velocity of flow for separation purposes.

Filters

Filters are used when the solids content has specific gravities which are close to or even lower than the liquid media (otherwise a vortex separator is a preferred choice) or in a closed circuit (say through a heat exchanger) where the mechanical seal is separated from the main body of dirty liquid by a neck bush. The greatest problem with filters is that they choke with remarkable rapidity and therefore require frequent attention.

Example of sealant system

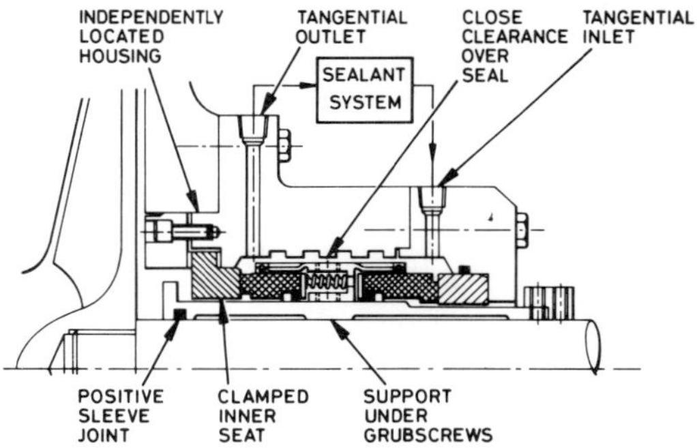

Example of back-to-back double seal with sealant system.

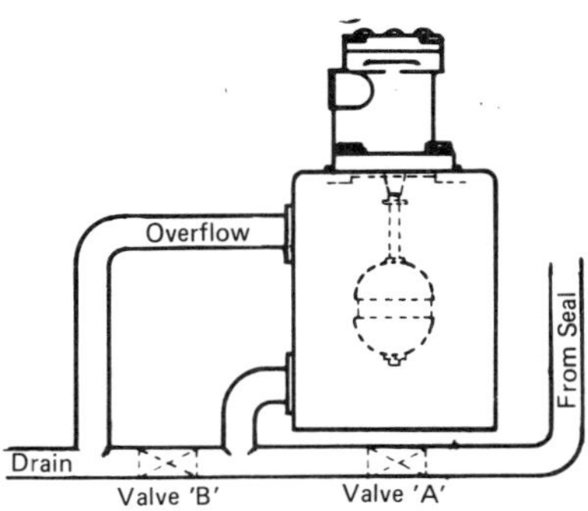

Leakage detector (non-solidifying)

Figure 20

Leakage detectors

Leakage detectors are normally only used where the contained liquid is very dangerous (explosive or toxic). The detectors are fairly simple in operation provided the contained liquid does not solidify.

A typical leakage detector is shown in Figure 20. The operation is extremely simple in that normally valve 'A' is open and valve 'B' is closed so that any leakage will build up in the chamber and trigger the flow alarm. Generally only an alarm is actuated, but the signal can also be used to shut down the unit if this is deemed necessary.

Cartridge seals

The true cost of a seal failure is frequently substantially more than the refurbishing or replacement cost. Typically a UK refinery has estimated the average cost of a seal failure to be £1000, covering only such factors as labour and replacement costs. Production losses are generally minimised by using standby, duplicate, equipment, but significant consequential costs can accrue when hazardous products leak to the environment. On a world-wide scale an international oil exploration and processing group have estimated they spend some $20M per year on seal maintenance.

Cartridge type mechanical seals have in recent times been developed to combine the mechanical seal benefits of long-life and reliability with the practical simplicity of gland packings.

Whilst the concepts of a cartridge seal is not new, the combination of cartridge construction, its applicability to a number of international standards, factory testing, material rationalisation and suitability for use on hundreds of different products, represent a significant advancement. The design of cartridge seals was intended for a wide-ranging market in such industries and applications as chemical processes, paper and pulp, coal and iron, marine and refinery off sites. It is particularly suitable for applications where abrasives or suspended solids are present. Fibrous products and slurries which would normally prevent a conventional seal from functioning by clogging springs or bellows, are ideal applications.

The cartridge design has been produced to minimise the necessary fitting skills and reduce installation time. In any industry where down time is crucial the cartridge seal can fulfil the need for rapid seal replacement. Even on non-critical pumps, cartridge type mechanical seals have shown short payback periods and have also proven to be labour saving conversions.

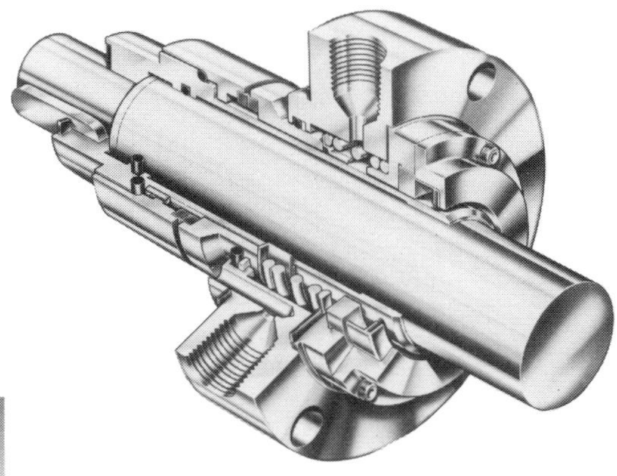

Seal for high viscosity, and abrasive duties in cartridge form.

A modular mechanical seal system.

MECHANICAL SEALS SELECTION GUIDE

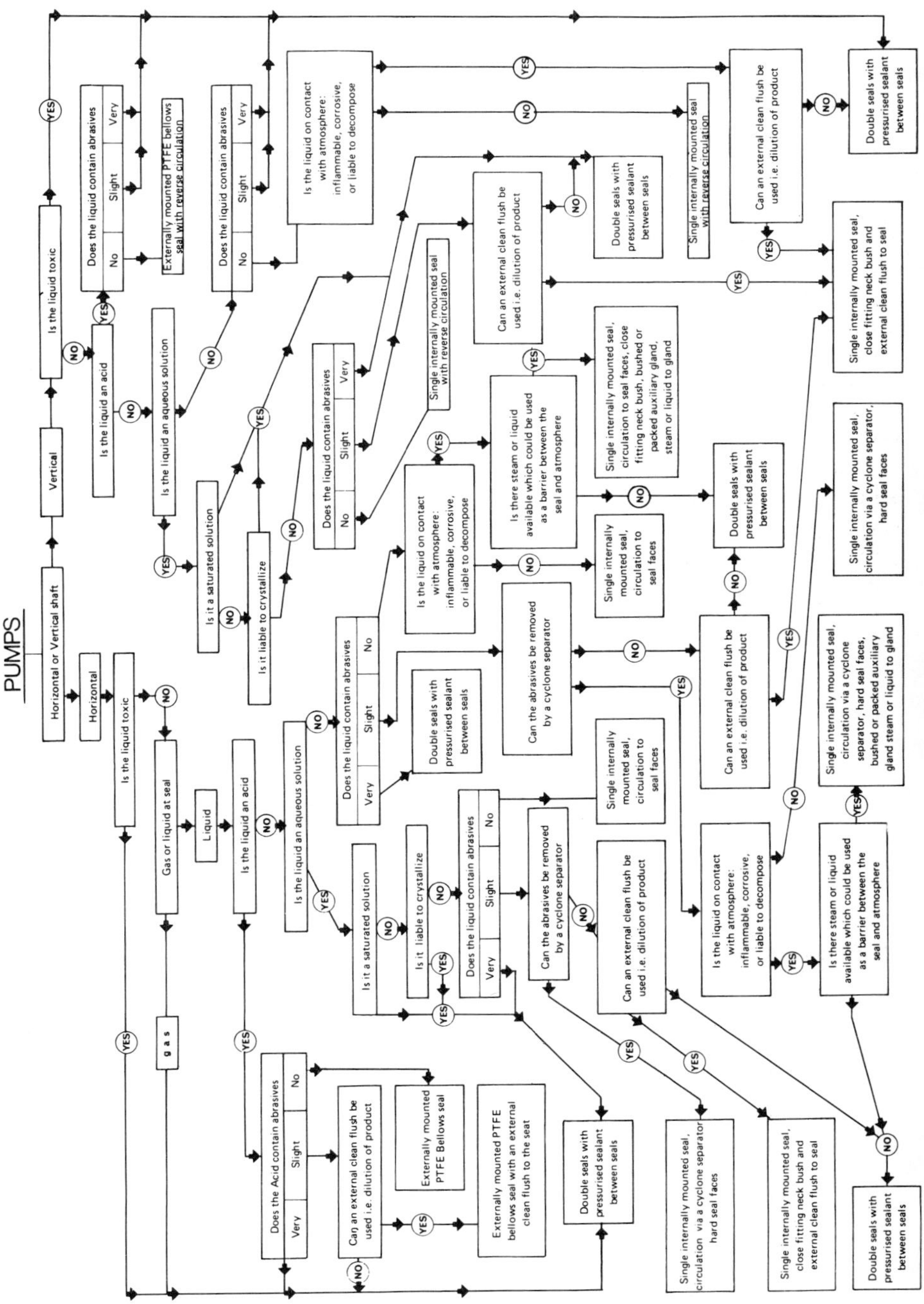

MODES, CAUSES AND CORRECTIONS OF MECHANICAL FACE SEAL FAILURES

Failure mode	Cause	Correction
PRIMARY SEAL FACES		
Overall corrosion	Improper materials.	Upgrade materials.
Intergranular corrosion	Improper materials.	Upgrade materials.
	Improper processing.	Correct processing, such as welding and heat treating.
Stress-corrosion cracking	Improper material.	Upgrade material.
	Improper processing.	Correct processing, such as stress relief.
Leaching corrosion	Improper material.	Upgrade material.
Seal-face distortion (concavity, convexity, waviness or non-uniform contact)	Excessive fluid pressure on seal.	Lower fluid pressure; upgrade material, upgrade design.
	Excessive swell of confined secondary seal.	Change secondary-seal materials or design.
	Improper seal assembly — excessive or non-uniform clamping or bolting stresses, or weight or misalignment of suction piping on end-suction over-hung-type pumps.	Correct assembly.
	Internal stress.	Stress relieve and refinish.
	Improper finishing.	Refinish.
	Foreign material trapped between faces.	Remove foreign material.
	Excessive PV value of seal operation.	Reduce PV value or upgrade design or materials.
	Improper equipment operation resulting in adverse seal environment (for example, insufficient seal lubrication).	Correct environment, such as cooling of fluid flow rate; upgrade materials or design.
Fracture	Improper handling.	Handle parts with care.
	Improper assembly (jamming).	Correct assembly.
	Stress-corrosion cracking.	See above, at Stress Corrosion Cracking.
	Excessive thermal stress by: Improper operation such as insufficient seal lubrication.	Improve equipment operation or environment; upgrade design or materials.
	Excessive PV value.	Reduce PV value.
	Excessive fluid pressure on seal.	Reduce fluid pressure or upgrade design or materials.
	Excessive swell of secondary seal.	Upgrade materials; change fluid or lower temperature.

cont...

MODES, CAUSES AND CORRECTIONS OF MECHANICAL FACE SEAL FAILURES (contd)....

Failure mode	Cause	Correction
PRIMARY SEAL FACES contd...		
Edge chipping	Excessive fluid pressure on seal.	Reduce fluid pressure; upgrade design or materials.
	Excessive shaft run-out.	Reduce run-out or upgrade seal design.
	Excessive shaft deflection.	Reduce deflection or upgrade seal design.
	Excessive shaft whip.	Reduce shaft whip or upgrade seal design.
	Seal faces out-of-square.	Square faces to shaft axis.
	Seal face vibration.	Reduce fluid temperature to 28 °C below boiling point.
Severe, uniform adhesive wear	PV value too high.	Reduce PV value; upgrade materials; improve seal balance or lubrication.
	Deposition of dissolved solids.	Reduce fluid temperature to 28 °C below boiling point; reduce dissolved solids; upgrade face materials.
	Incorrect assembly (jamming).	Correct assembly.
	Fine abrasives in sealed fluid.	Remove abrasives from fluid; upgrade materials.
	Failure of axial holding hardware (jamming).	Correct for axial slippage of set screws or collar.
	Excessive shaft end play.	Correct end play.
	Poor environment, such as insufficient seal lubrication or loss of cooling.	Correct equipment operation; upgrade face materials or design.
Heavy, non-uniform wear, galling and grooving	Abrasive contaminants.	Remove contaminants or upgrade materials.
	PV value too high with one or both faces of metal.	Reduce PV value; upgrade materials or design.
Erosion	Abrasive flow into seal face.	Remove abrasive from sealed fluid; shroud seal faces or direct flow away from seal.
Blistering of carbon-graphite faces	Improper materials.	Upgrade seal-face material.
	PV value excessive or cyclic.	Reduce PV value and cycling.
	Inadequate seal cooling.	Improve seal cooling.

cont...

MODES, CAUSES AND CORRECTIONS OF MECHANICAL FACE SEAL FAILURES (contd)....

Failure mode	Cause	Correction
SECONDARY SEALS		
Extrusion	Excessive pressure.	Reduce pressure or upgrade design or material.
	Excessive temperature.	Reduce temperature or upgrade design or materials.
	Excessive swell.	Upgrade materials or change seal fluid.
Chemical attack	Improper material.	Select proper material.
Cracking	Excessive temperature.	Reduce temperature (by cooling); upgrade materials; reduce PV value.
	Chemical attack.	Select proper material.
	Ozone attack.	Upgrade materials; reduce ozone concentration; reduce stress.
Cuts, tears and splits	Improper handling.	Correct handling.
	Poor dispersion.	Correct manufacturing.
	Poor knit.	Correct manufacturing.
	Inclusion.	Correct manufacturing.
	Material overstressed.	Lower stress or upgrade materials.
Corrosion of interface	Crevice corrosion.	Eliminate crevice; apply corrosion-resistant coating.
	Fretting corrosion.	Eliminate vibration caused by out -of-square faces or excessive deflection; end-play or run-out of the shaft.; apply corrosion-resistant coatings. Lubricate interface. Upgrade resistance to corrosion and wear.
HARDWARE, GENERAL		
Overall corrosion	Improper material.	Upgrade material.
Stress-corrosion cracking	Improper material.	Upgrade material.
	Improper processing.	Correct processing, such as stress relief.
Intergranular corrosion	Improper material.	Upgrade material.
	Improper processing.	Correct processing, such as heat treating and welding.
Hydrogen embrittlement	Improper processing.	Correct processing.
Fatigue	Excessive stress or vibration.	Reduce stress or vibration.
	Seal-face vibration.	Reduce fluid temperature to 28 °C below boiling point.

cont...

MODES, CAUSES AND CORRECTIONS OF MECHANICAL FACE SEAL FAILURES (contd)....

Failure mode	Cause	Correction
MECHANICAL DRIVE		
Torsional shear	Excessive torque due to: Improper lubrication.	Correct for stoppage of lubricant flow to seal faces; clean out or install (if needed) bypass flushing line.
	Failure of axial holding device.	Check set screws or other means of securing collar for slippage or jamming.
	Excessive fluid pressure.	Reduce fluid pressure or re-design (for example, seal balance).
Axial shear	Excessive shaft end play.	Correct end play.
	Improper assembly (jammed).	Correct assembly.
	Excessive pressure loading.	Reduce pressure or upgrade design.
Wear	Excessive torque.	See Torsional shear.
	Out-of-square seal faces.	Square faces to shaft axis.
	Excessive shaft run-out.	Reduce run-out.
	Excessive shaft deflection.	Reduce deflection.
	Excessive shaft end play.	Reduce end play.
	Seal face vibration.	Reduce fluid temperature to 28 °C below boiling point.
Seal hang-up	Deposition of dissolved solids, or products of corrosion, seal-fluid oxidation or decom-position.	Change to non-pusher seal; upgrade corrosion resistance of material; lower temperature of fluid; quench seal.

When a seal manufacturer is asked to make a seal selection, it is necessary to know the product being handled, the suction discharge and sometimes vapour pressures, the temperature, speed of rotation, shaft diameter, stuffing box bore and depth, the pH value, and, for some products, the material from which the pump is made. If the wrong materials are chosen for the seals, it is possible to produce electrolytic action which corrodes the seal components. An overall guide for taking all the operating conditions into account is given diagrammatically in the *Mechanical Seal Selection Guide* chart.

Bellows Seals

BELLOWS ARE essentially exclusion devices, normally capable of accommodating both axial and radial movements. They may be used in the form of gaiters specifically to exclude dust, dirt, *etc,* from a machine; as secondary sealing components in mechanical face seals; and as primary seals replacing packed glands on such machines as agitators, pumps, compressors, mixers, *etc.* In this latter category they are a simple form of mechanical face seal.

Bellows may be made of elastomeric or polyamid materials, or from metal. *Elastomeric bellows* used in pusher-type (face) seals normally also incorporate a metal spring or springs to offset fatigue. Metal bellows have inherent spring action and may be of convoluted (formed from tube by rolling) or welded construction. (Other methods of construction include hydro-forming and electro-deposition). *Welded* bellows represent the more costly construction but are stronger, can be given more precisely controlled operating characteristics and have the highest operating temperature range. They are also generally less subject to vibrational fatigue than convoluted bellows. Further improvement in performance for high pressure working can be achieved by using laminated welded construction instead of single ply (welded) construction.

Metal bellows seals.

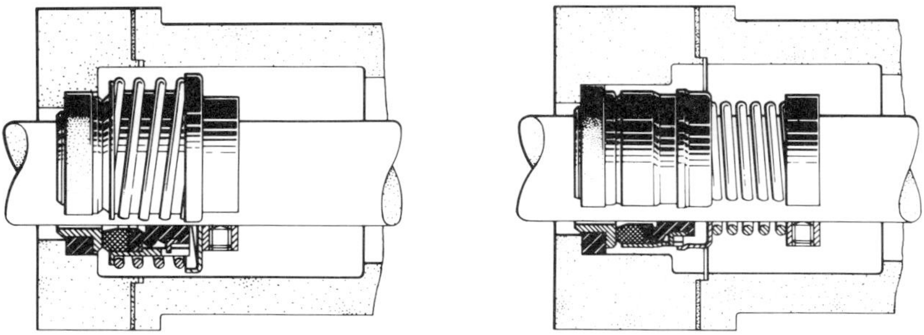

Examples of rubber bellows seals.

Welded metal bellows are fabricated from a series of metal discs or plates normally from 0·1016 to 0·1737 mm (0·004 to 0·007 in) thick in stainless steel or corrosion-resistant alloy in the form of a nesting ripple (Figure 1). This configuration produces a bellows with a long stroke capability without overstressing the material. Other configurations are shown in Figure 2. The *single sweep* is used where space for the ripple configuration is limited and good pressure resistance is required. The *toroid* is used for extreme pressures and constant effective areas. The *flat plate* is used primarily for pressure null and sensing applications, not for seals.

Bellows envelope dimensions may be fixed by the design or the effective diameter of the bellows. *Pitch* is the distance between adjacent convolutions, which varies as the bellows is stroked. Maximum pitch should not exceed the stroke plus nested length (three times the metal thickness multiplied by the number of convolutions). The relationship between differential pressure deflection and probable cycle life is then given in Figure 3. Both maximum pressure capability and maximum deflection per convolution are governed by the material property, *viz:*

$$\text{Maximum pressure capability} = K \times \frac{\text{plate thickness}}{\text{bellows i.d.}}$$

where
K is a constant depending on the material
(*eg* 150×10^3 for AM350 martensitic stainless steel in inches and pressure in lb/in^2)

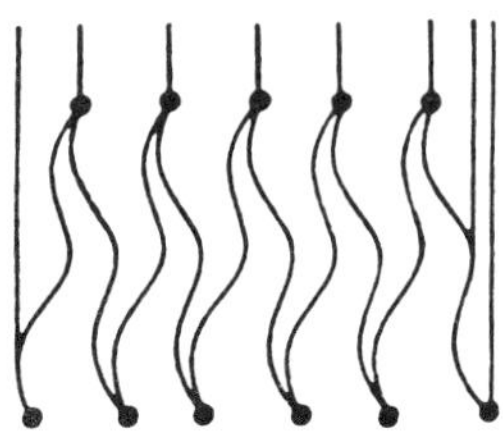

Figure 1
Bellows formed by welded discs.

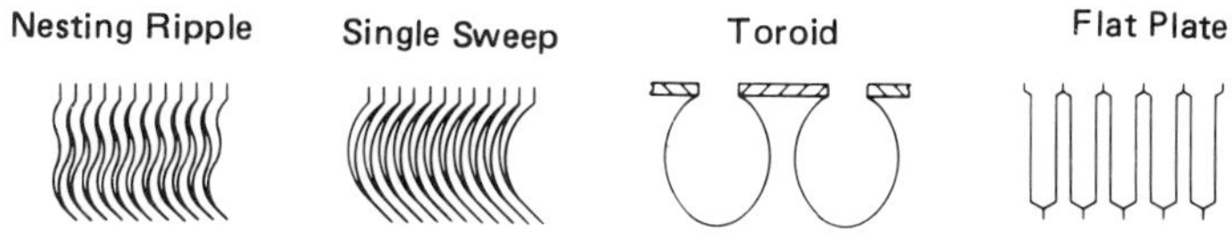

Figure 2

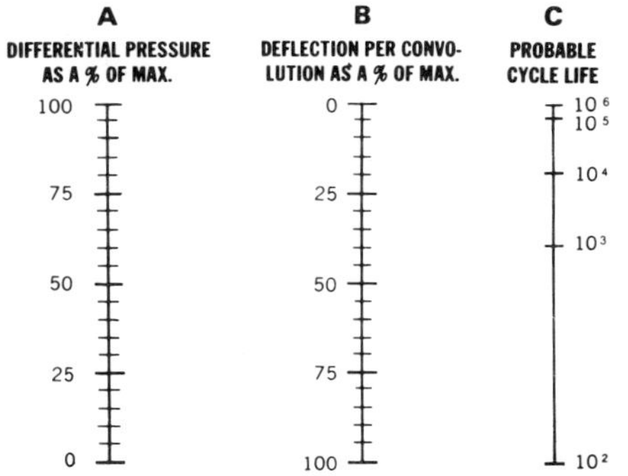

Figure 3

Maximum deflection per convolution is again dependent on the material used, but also bellows form and bellows i.d.

General arrangement of a typical *bellows (face) seal* is shown in Figure 4. The bellows itself acts as a spring to keep the faces together, provides a dynamic seal, and transmits the torque from the shaft to the face. One end of the bellows is welded to an adaptor which is usually clamped to the shaft or sleeve by set screws and which houses the static secondary seal. The other end of the bellows is welded to the shell which retains the seal face, both of these being carried clear of the shaft.

With the product being contained at the o.d. of the seal, the centrifugal action throws any particles away from the bellows and so prevents clogging, hence this design of seal is self-cleaning. As the bellows seal has no sliding elastomer there is no drag or hang-up on the shaft to make the faces separate in the event of shaft misalignment, probably the biggest cause of leakage with face type seals. This feature – which also eliminates shaft or sleeve wear, another common fault of face type seals – has been a major attribute in the rapid popularity of bellows seals. This design of seal can be mounted either directly on to the shaft, on to a hook sleeve,

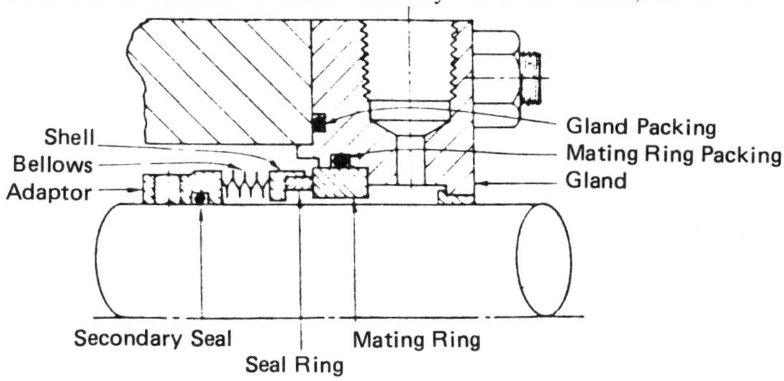

Figure 4
General arrangement of typical bellows seal.

Metal bellows seal.

Rubber bellows seal.

or to a cartridge sleeve in the case of inaccessible or difficult arrangements. Cartridge sleeve arrangements allow the seal to be assembled and set before fitting to the machine, which can be a valuable asset.

Temperature limitations

A major limitation of the face-type mechanical seal, when replacing gland packing, was the temperature range that could be accommodated.

The limiting factor was the safe operating range of the elastomers, generally in the order of 175 °C to 200 °C (350 °F to 400 °F). This necessitated cooling the product, which increased the cost. Also, the attendant problems of increased viscosity and possible shearing of the product at the seal faces, produced a localized increase in temperature.

With the use of glass-loaded PTFE in wedge form, however, the temperature range is taken to 280 °C (536 °F), and with the advent of pure carbon, under a variety of names such as *Grafoil** and *Graftite* to over 500* °C (930 °F).

When sealing high temperature hydrocarbons such as oils and asphalts, 'coking' occurs at the seal faces. Viscosity increases and the faces stick together when the pump is stationary. A way of overcoming this is by dead ending of the stuffing box and introducing a steam quench to the atmosphere side of the seal. The metal bellows seal, although still requiring this steam quench, has a distinct advantage over other forms of seal.

Bellows materials:
1·4571 (AISI 316 Ti)
AM 350
Hastelloy C-4

Typical bellows seal.

In high temperature applications, expansion is a major problem in machines, *eg* pumps, because the shaft expands at a faster rate than the casing, due to its smaller mass. The advantage of the bellows design is that the flexibility of the bellows will accommodate this growth, without the 'bottoming' experienced with other face-type seals.

Balanced bellows seals

Another particular advantage of a bellows seal is that it can provide pressure balancing without the need for a stepped shaft. In the bellows design balancing is related to the *effective diameter* (see Figure 5). Fluid in the stuffing box goes between the convolutions and exerts pressures against the bellows plates, creating an axial force in each direction. The amount of the force depends upon the plate area and the pressure exerted on it. For example, if the pressure is 7 bar (100 lb/in^2) and the plate area is 2 in^2 then the total force would be 200 lb/in^2. This 200 lb/in^2 force is split and shared by each end of the plate so that 100 lb/in^2 is acting at each end. At the i.d. of the bellows the force acts equally against each side of the apex but in opposite directions and so cancels itself out, but at the o.d. the 200 lb force acts as a closing force against the seal face. This means the effective area is 1 in^2 and that the effective diameter is midway up the bellows.

To obtain the 'balanced pressure' designed seal the seal face is positioned in relation to the effective diameter and the closing force is designed to be slightly more than the opening force so that the seal faces are held together during all operating conditions without generating excessive frictional heat.

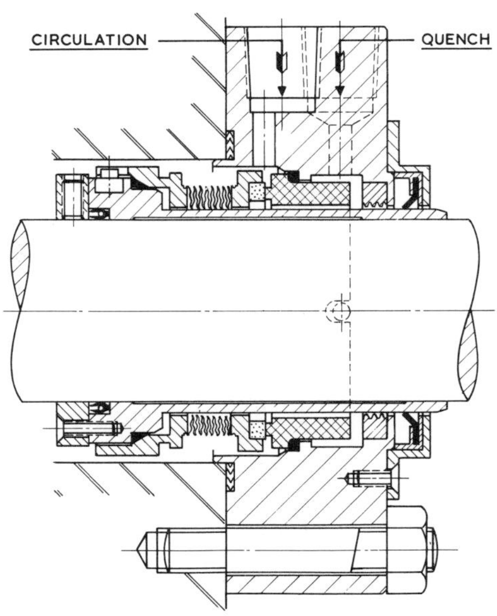

High temperature metal bellows seal.

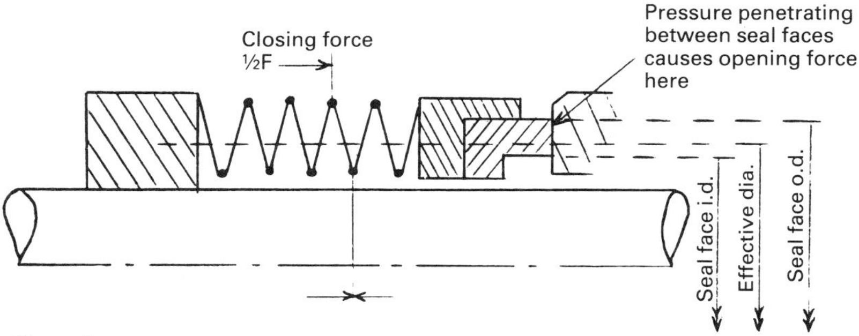

Figure 5
Pressure balancing of bellows seal.

High pressure media
Single ply welded metallic bellows may be designed to accommodate internal (bursting) pressures up to 500 bar (7500 lb/in^2.) depending on pitch. Further improvement in pressure rating is possible by using laminated bellows as shown in Figure 6, increasing the maximum pressure rating to 700 bar (10000 lb/in^2) while retaining the same nesting capabilities and low spring rate.

Handling corrosive media
When sealing abrasive fluids, the entrained solids become trapped, either between the packing and the shaft when using soft packed glands or between the elastomer and the shaft with face type mechanical seals. This causes badly worn shafts and

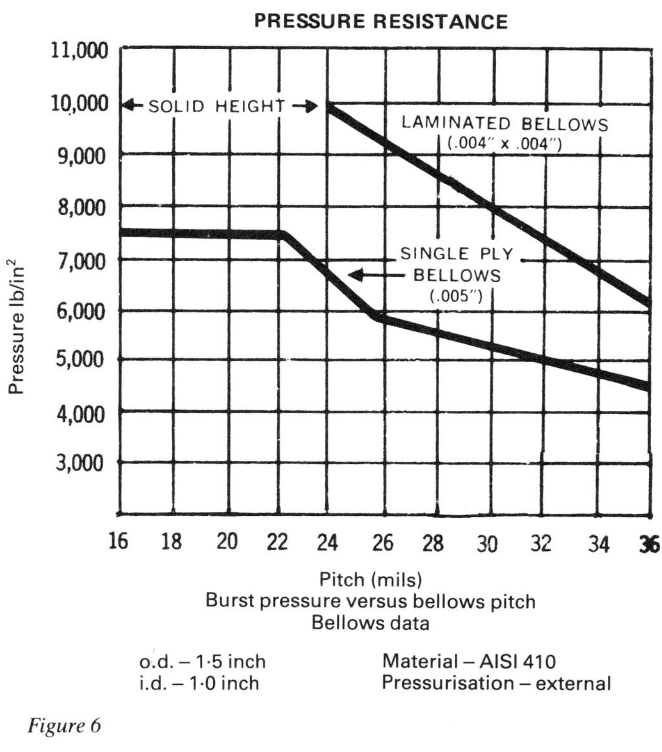

Figure 6

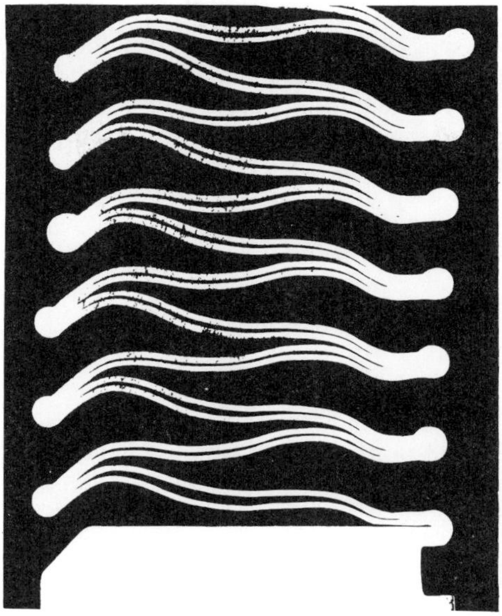

20X macrophotograph of laminated bellows in cross-section. Note the long compression stroke and almost total nesting capability which the plate and weld bead configuration afford.

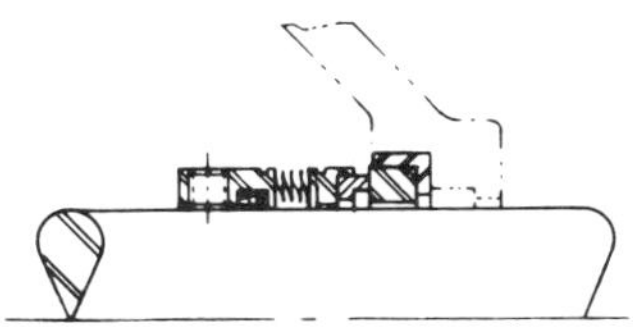

Built-in seal with cup mounted mating ring.

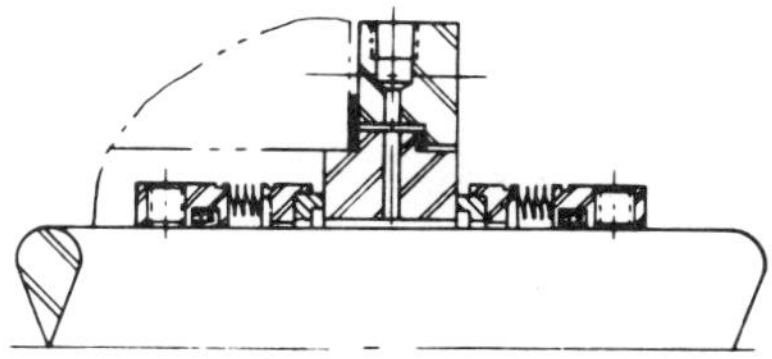

Internal-external flushed double seal.

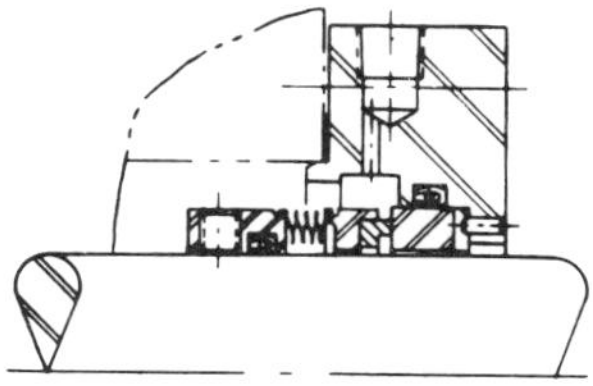

Flush gland with block type tungsten carbide mating ring.

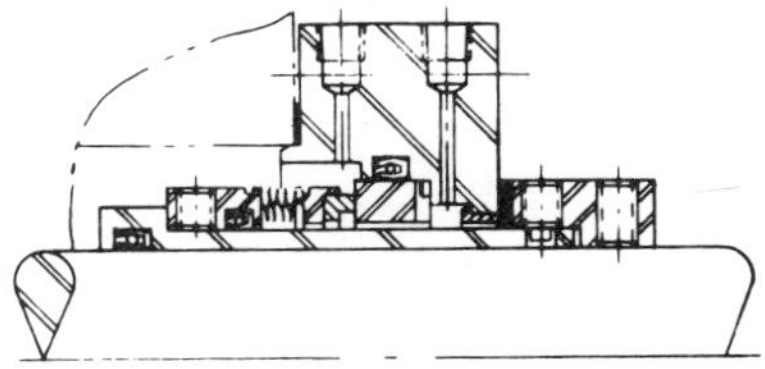

Cartridge type package seal.

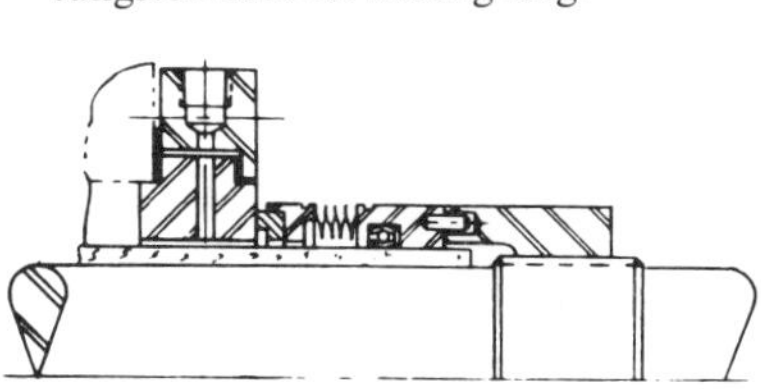

External seal for plastic or glass sleeves.

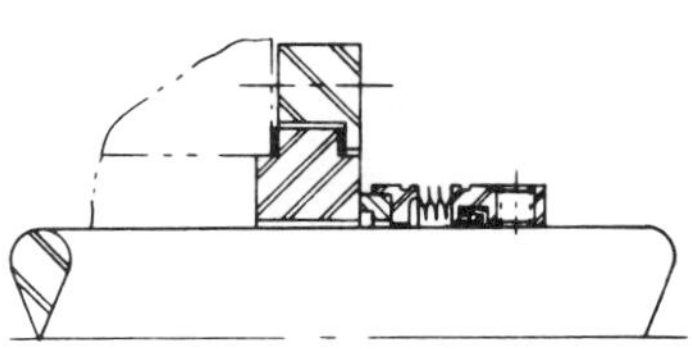

External seal with clamp-type mating ring.

Examples of bellows seal applications.

elastomers, which allows the product to leak out and incurs high replacement costs. This is eliminated with the bellows seal design as there are no sliding elastomers, *etc,* running against the shaft. With fluids which are heavily entrained with solids the bellows can be mounted internally so that the media only come into contact with the outside of the bellows. Any particles will be thrown away from the bellows convolutions by the centrifugal action and so clogging is prevented, a common fault with the smal with the small springs used in face type seals. The bellows itself is usually made from a corrosion-resistant material such as *Hastelloy C.* An advantage with using a bellows design seal is that the need for expensive filters or cyclone separators is generally avoided.

Formed metal bellows seals

One of the most significant developments in metal bellows sealing has been the introduction of the worlds' first multi-purpose formed metal bellows seal. This incorporates an asymmetric profile which does away with areas of high stress in the bellows and fits into the design envelope for single seals to DIN 24960 (LIN) (metric) and ANSI B73.1 – 1974 (imperial), supporting a working pressure of 20 bar and has a higher rate of bellows flexibility than can be achieved with a conventional formed bellows. This high flexibility is the key to the performance of the seal because it absorbs small equipment misalignments found in practice, provides a full follow-up force for seal face movement and thereby protects the sealing fluid film. Seal construction is simplified, and bellows welding for instance has been reduced by up to 98% compared with a normal welded metal bellows seal.

Typical applications include refineries and many chemical process plants or for use in areas where hygiene and purity are critical such as food preparation, the pharmaceutical industry, bio-technology and cosmetics. The seal is also suitable for abrasive fluids, slurries, mining wastes, pulp paper and sewage handling because the bellows profile has excellent anti-clogging characteristics.

The worlds' first multi-purpose formed metal bellows seal. Operating temperatures –40 °C to + 200 °C.

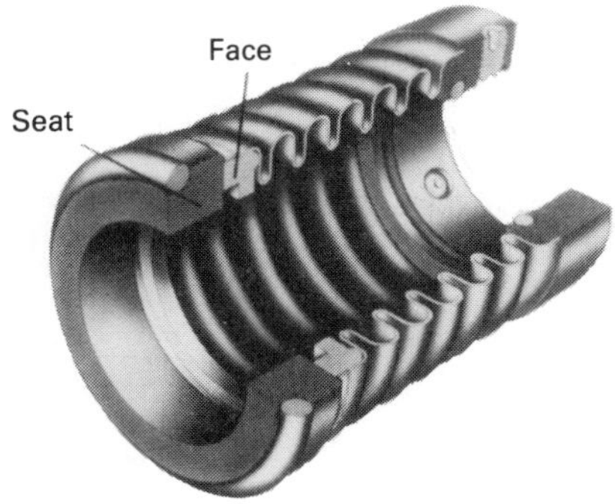

Asymmetric bellows shape provides consistent and even distribution of stresses.

Materials
Fabricated metallic bellows can be made from any readily weldable metal. Martensitic stainless steel is probably the most widely used, but requires heat treatment after welding. High-nickel alloys are normally chosen for higher corrosion resistance and/or higher temperature application – see Table 1.

Elastomeric bellows
Elastomeric bellows may be formed by moulding or welding. Moulded bellows are normally preferred. Deep, narrow convolutions are best for low pressures and rounded, wide-spaced convolutions for higher pressures. For high pressures either a substantial increase in thickness or laminated construction is necessary, which has the effect of stiffening the bellows.

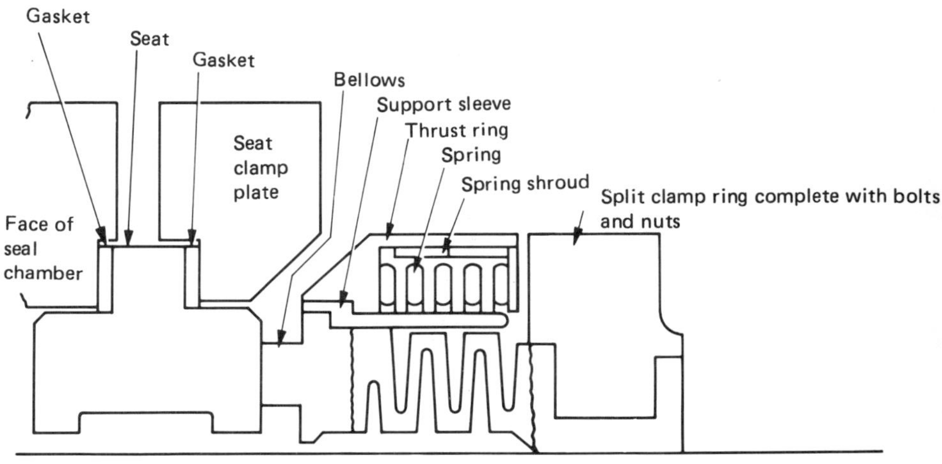

Details of a sophisticated PTFE bellows seal.
The support sleeve limits bellows expansion under pressure surges, thus inhibiting over-stressing which could otherwise lead to failure.

TABLE 1 – METALLIC BELLOWS MATERIALS

Material	Temperature °C	Description
AM 350	−40 +450	Martensitic stainless steel. Toughest and most commonly used material. Very high strength after heat treatment. Not recommended for use in as-welded condition. Corrosion resistance equivalent to 303 (free machining 18/8 stainless steel) before heat treatment and as 400 series after heat treatment.
300 Series	−250 +650	Austenitic stainless steel. Un-heat-treated. Can be used for cryogenics, but weak at high temperatures. Has tendency to take permanent set, so undesirable when spring rate is important. Useful as bellows device in corrosive conditions.
Inconel X750	−250 +750	Good strength at high and low temperatures. Improved corrosion resistance over stainless steel but marginal with sulphur duties. Difficult to weld. Higher cost raw material and expensive heat treatment.
Hastelloy C	+250	Best corrosion resistance. Un-heat-treated. Limited pressure capability. Good strength. Higher raw material cost than Inconel.

Bellows seals for acid duties

Highly corrosive acids can only be handled by seals made from Teflon and mounted externally, so that the metal half-clamps securing the seal to the shaft are outside the product.

TABLE 2 FACE COMBINATION PV LIMITS

Seal face	Mating face	Maximum PV	
		lb/in² ft/min	bar m/s
Carbon	Stainless steel	150000	50
	Stellite	700000	240
	Chrome oxide coating	450000	150
	Tungsten carbide coating	800000	280
	Tungsten carbide	1000000	350
	Sealide	5000000	1750
	Ceramic	500000	170
	Lead bronze	700000	245
	Ni-resist	850000	300
Tungsten carbide	Tungsten carbide	150000	50
	Sealide	500000	170
Stellite	Sealide	250000	90
Sealide	Sealide	400000	140

The above PV values are calculated using mechanical force only.
For values using higher pressures as would generally be found in pumping applications, the above figures may be increased by as much as up to x 2.

Teflon cannot be moulded into complicated shapes and is available only in solid bars or tubes. *Teflon* bellows, therefore, have to be machined, as have all the other seal parts in this material.

In almost all cases, the clamped stationary seal ring, or seat, is made of ceramic, which has a high aluminium oxide content.

The opposing rotating face may be of *Rulon,* tungsten or silicone carbide, or, more generally, glass-loaded *Teflon.*

Pure *Teflon* is slightly porous and would allow penetration by the pumped liquid, which could result in an uneven film thickness.

Dirty/Abrasive acid duties

Abrasive particles in the product can fret the inside of the bellows, allowing the product to escape to atmosphere. This can be dangerous to plant operatives.

TABLE 3 – MATERIALS SELECTION GUIDE FOR HIGH TEMPERATURE BELLOWS SEALS

Media	Media type	Seal face	Other materials	Gland, etc
Cryogenics	–	Carbon	Consult manu-facturer	Circulation. Use tandem seals with barrier fluid.
Heat transfer fluids	Non-abrasive Abrasive	Carbon Tungsten carbide	Standard	Circulation, vent and drain. Bronze throttle bush.
Hydro-carbons and petro-chemicals	Mildly corrosive	Carbon	Inconel	
	Abrasive	Tungsten carbide	Standard	Circulation, vent and drain. Bronze throttle bush.
	Corrosive and abrasive	Tungsten carbide	Inconel	
	Refinery vacuum	Carbon		Circulation, vent and drain. Bronze throttle bush.
	Vacuum bottoms		Standard	Use flush. For low pressure use steam quench.
	Catalyst slurry	Consult seal manu-facturer		
Solvents	Non-corrosive	Carbon	Standard	
	Corrosive		Inconel	
	Abrasive	Tungsten carbide	Standard	Circulation, vent and drain. Bronze throttle bush.
	Corrosive and abrasive		Inconel	
	Hazardous			Circulation, quench. Auxiliary packing.
Thermo-sensitive fluids	Hardening or solidfying	Tungsten carbide		Vent and drain. Bronze throttle bush. Steam quench jacketed stuffing box.

Injection of the same product from a separate, clean source, at a slightly higher pressure than stuffing box pressure, will solve the problem. Its drawback, however, is that the clean injection is lost into the dirty product.

A remedy is to introduce the clean liquid into the seal area *via* a connection in the bottom of the seat, and to return it to its source *via* a similar connection in the top of the seat.

To prevent loss of the clean liquid into the product, a Teflon lip seal, or close-clearance neck bush, should be fitted in the bottom of the stuffing box.

Comprehensive information on all aspects of seals and sealing technology can be found in the Seals and Sealing Handbook published by The Trade and Technical Press Limited, publishers of this manual.

SECTION 5

Pumping Practice and Operation

PUMP INSTALLATION
PUMP START-UP
PUMP CAVITATION AND RECIRCULATION
PUMP OPERATION AND MAINTENANCE
PUMP NOISE AND NOISE CONTROL
VIBRATION AND CRITICAL SPEED
PIPEWORK INSTALLATION

Pump Installation

FIXED PUMPS must be securely anchored to firm foundations, accurately levelled with shafts, coupling faces and flange faces truly vertical or horizontal (as appropriate). Specific instructions for mounting and initial setting up are normally supplied by the pump manufacturer.

Alternative methods of mounting a pump are:

(i) Permanent installation on a foundation with bolts and grout.

(ii) Mounting on isolation/levelling pads.

(iii) Mounting on adjustable base legs.

(iv) Mounting on a portable base.

See also Figure 1.

Pumps of an appreciable size and weight should, if possible, be mounted on a concrete foundation. Alternative schemes for providing adequate rigidity to support the bedplate are usually more costly. The position of the pump should be

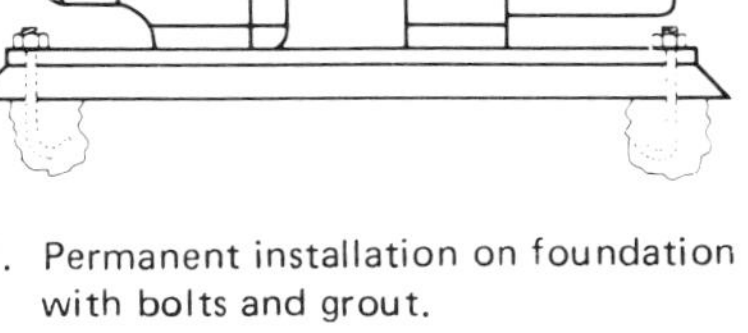

1. Permanent installation on foundation with bolts and grout.

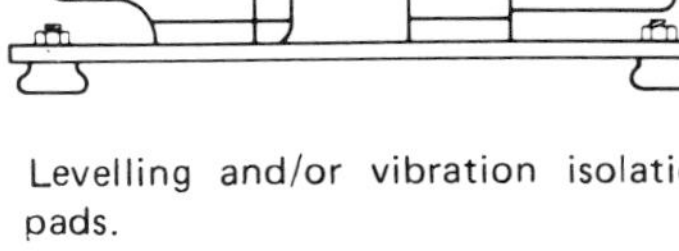

2. Levelling and/or vibration isolation pads.

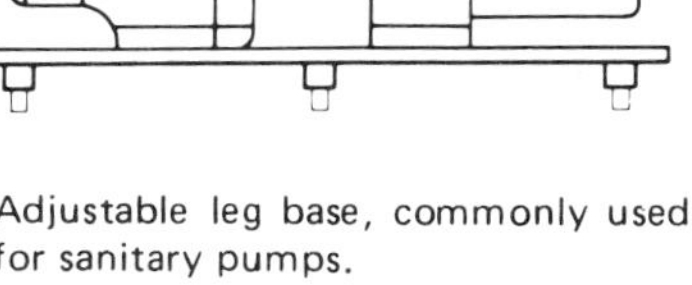

3. Adjustable leg base, commonly used for sanitary pumps.

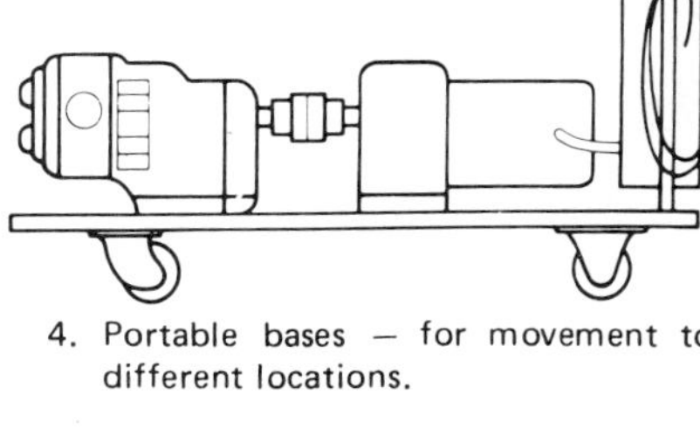

4. Portable bases – for movement to different locations.

Figure 1
Four methods of pump installation.

chosen so that it is readily acceptable for inspection and servicing. In the case of large heavy pumps, there must be sufficient headroom and/or side clearance to accommodate any lifting tackle necessary for opening and dismantling the pump.

Foundation bearing loads are calculated from the total weight of the pump plus concrete foundations, divided by the surface area of the foundation. Table I can be used to estimate the weight of concrete foundations.

Adequate foundations of substantial mass are necessary to provide rigidity of mounting so that the pump and driver cannot be twisted or misaligned. Isolation treatment may also be necessary to reduce as far as possible the transmission of structurally-borne vibrations to other parts of the building.

Anchor or mounting bolts are normally cast in with the concrete base, placing a high premium on exact positioning in conformity with installation or mounting drawing. Removable bolts are to be preferred as these can be replaced if damaged or broken and can also be removed if necessary for ease of sliding the pump into place on its foundations.

Foundation bolts can be erected on a suitable jig or template before the foundation is poured, allowing a sufficient length of bolt to project to accommodate grouting. Normally a space of about 25 mm (1 inch) is left between the top of the foundation and the baseplate for grouting and the top surface of the foundation should be left rough to provide a good key.

TABLE 1 – WEIGHT OF CONCRETE FOUNDATIONS
(Weight in kilograms and [pounds])

Length Metres (Feet)	150 mm (6 inch) Thick Concrete† Foundation Width – Metres (Feet)				300 mm (12 inch) Thick Concrete† Foundation Width – Metres (Feet)			
	0.61 (2)	0.91 (3)	1.2 (4)	1.5 (5)	0.61 (2)	0.91 (3)	1.2 (4)	1.5 (5)
0.91 (3)	395 (870)	600 (1305)	790 (1740)	990 (2175)	790 (1740)	1185 (2610)	1580 (3480)	2000 (4350)
1.2 (4)	525 (1160)	790 (1740)	1050 (2230)	1315 (2900)	1050 (2320)	1580 (3480)	2100 (4640)	2630 (5800)
1.5 (5)	660 (1450)	990 (2175)	1315 (2900)	1650 (3625)	1320 (2900)	1970 (4350)	2630 (5800)	3300 (7280)
1.8 (6)	790 (1740)	1185 (2610)	1580 (3480)	1970 (4350)	1580 (3480)	2370 (5220)	3160 (6960)	3950 (8700)
2.1 (7)	920 (2030)	1380 (3045)	1840 (4060)	2300 (5075)	1840 (4060)	2760 (6090)	3680 (8120)	4600 (10150)
2.4 (8)	1050 (2320)	1580 (3480)	2105 (4640)	2630 (5800)	2100 (4640)	3160 (6960)	4210 (9280)	5250 (11600)
2.75 (9)	1185 (2610)	1775 (3915)	2370 (5220)	2960 (6578)	2370 (5220)	3500 (7830)	4740 (10440)	5920 (13050)
3.0 (10)	1300 (2900)	1970 (4350)	2630 (5800)	3290 (7250)	2600 (5800)	3940 (8700)	5260 (11600)	6600 (14500)

*For average gravel concrete. For other types of concrete factor weights by:

Coke breeze concrete	– 0·70
Coarse clinker concrete	– 0·76
Coarse brick concrete	– 0·86
Limestone concrete	– 0·93
Reinforced concrete	– 1·04

†Weights of other thicknesses can be calculated by simple proportion.

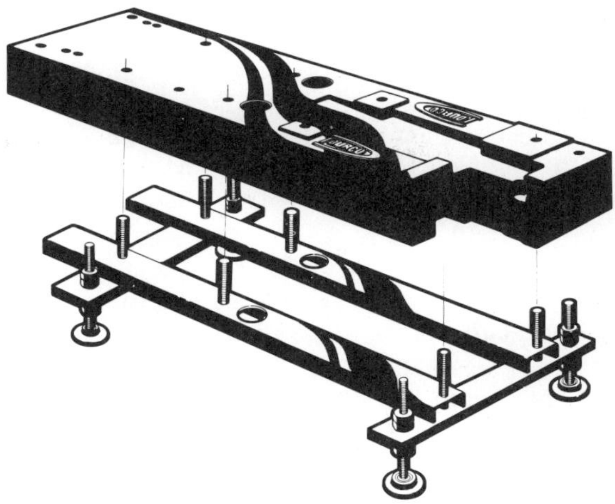

Example of polymer bonded concrete base plate.

Concrete should be mixed and laid by proficient workmen and the correct mix employed. Once poured and levelled, as much time as possible should be allowed for the concrete to harden – 28 days usually being advisable, or this can be reduced to 14 days if necessary and conditions are favourable. Sprinkling with water or covering with a damp cloth will prevent uneven drying of the concrete, this treatment being maintained for about 7 days, or longer in freezing weather.

Many pumps are dowelled to the baseplate. This is primarily to prevent lateral movement and also to hold the pump and driver in place if the anchor bolts slacken off. Small and medium pumps are normally dowelled; large pumps may benefit, but not invariably. Usually the manufacturer specifies whether or not a particular pump should be dowelled. It is important that dowels are used to ensure that they do not restrict any designed freedom for the pump to expand and contract horizontally, in such cases, dowelling should only be attempted at the fixed end.

Where pumps are mounted on upper floors of buildings, the bearing loads must be consistent with any building and factory regulations which may apply. Isolation mounting may have to be considered in more detail, particularly to avoid flanking transmissions of the vibration and sound.

Alignment

Alignment is facilitated by the use of wedges and shims under the baseplate on both sides of each mounting bolt. Initially adjustment should aim at getting the pump and its baseplate level in all directions. Then the pump must be aligned with its driver, if separately mounted. This alignment must be as exact as it is possible to achieve although it does not necessarily follow that pump and driver shafts should be exactly in line horizontally. The manufacturers of some types and sizes of pumps may recommend a specific vertical distance between pump and driver shafts when setting up cold, to compensate for differential vertical expansion of the unit when hot. This vertical distance may be positive or negative depending on the type of pump, its method of mounting and the type of driver. Distances are usually of the order of 0·15 mm to 0·5 mm (0·005 inch to 0·020 inch) but specific instructions should be given for each pump. In the absence of any such instruction exact horizontal alignment can be assumed to be correct.

After satisfactory alignment has been achieved it is usual to grout the bedplates in position. Grouting consists of pouring a thin mortar mix around and under the machine base to take up any uneveness in the base and prevent the unit shifting. A typical depth of grout is 20 mm to 40 mm (¾ inch to 1½ inches) although it may poured to greater thickness into spaces under the baseplate itself. Holes are sometimes left in the baseplate for this purpose. Successful bonding of the grout to the original foundation depends very largely on roughening the top surface and then properly wetting it down.

Checking pump alignment

When the pump is installed, alignment must once again be checked, and then re-checked after the installation of the pipework (see Figure 2).

Pump sets or pumps supplied with driver mounted, normally have driver and pump aligned at the factory, when the two are mounted on their common baseplate. Alignment will however need a complete re-check after installation as some deformation of the baseplate may occur during transit and handling. Specific instructions are usually supplied by the manufacturer for cold setting alignment.

Information regarding installation of particular pumps is normally provided by the pump manufacturer. The type of pump may also govern the positioning required for proper suction performance and required NPSH. As a general rule positioning should be such that static suction lift should be reduced to a practical minimum. In particular cases flooded suction may be desirable or even necessary.

Treatment for different pump types

Centrifugal pumps are normally mounted on a bedplate of iron or steel. In the case of small and medium sized pumps this bedplate may be designed to accommodate both the pump and driver. With larger pumps it is usual to provide a bedplate for the pump and to mount the drive separately. Preparation of the foundations and actual mounting technique follow on the lines described previously.

With small and medium sized centrifugal pumps, pump and driver are commonly connected by a pin type flexible coupling with rubber bushes. With larger sizes of pumps a gear type coupling is preferred.

Where a pump is situated above the inlet water level, a foot valve is generally provided and priming can be effected by funnel for the initial start, after which priming back from the rising main *via* a bypass on the delivery valve is generally practicable. However, the foot valve may leak, and if so the pump will require

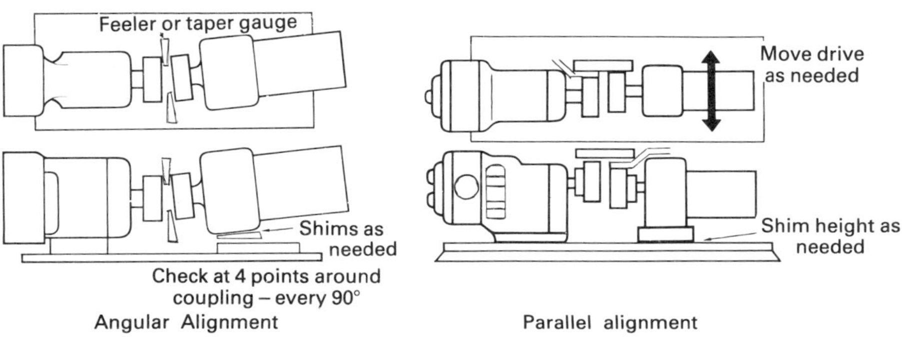

Figure 2
Checking pump alignment.

priming at each start, the leakage being made up from the rising main. On pumps set to start automatically, a low pressure relay may be fitted to prevent starting with less than a nominal pressure at the rising main.

Flooded inlet pumps are readily primed by opening the suction valve, but this valve should never be used as a means of regulating the flow through the pump. Air is removed from the pump by opening the air cocks at the top of each stage and at the top of the suction passage. For multi-stage pumps it is necessary to prime a proportion of the stages representing the proportion that the static head bears to the total head with a suitable margin of say two further stages. It will be appreciated that where the head is wholly frictional, the priming of two stages will suffice to free the later stages of air. It is absolutely essential that the suction passage should avoid any air pockets the suction pipe to this end rising progressively to the pump. Where a suction valve is not fitted, priming may be carried out by a steam, air or water ejector at the top of the casing.

Reciprocating pumps
Large reciprocating pumps require adequate clearance and space all around the mounting site for the manipulation of lifting tackle and the disassembly and assembly of pistons, rods and packings during routine service. Pumps may be delivered in sections to be bolted up on site, which places a premium on alignment. Particular care should be taken to ensure that all internal surfaces are clean – particularly cylinder walls and valve passages. This should be checked before assembly and again before starting up. Similar considerations apply to the pipework, particularly on the suction side.

All pipework should be mounted so that the pump cylinder is relieved of external mechanical loads. Strains transmitted directly to the pumps cylinder can result in misalignment or even a broken cylinder.

Particular care should be given in aligning pumps powered by a separate driver. Although a flexible coupling may be used this does not alter the fact that misalignment will lead to vibration, excessive wear and the loss of input power. Alignment of any belt drive should be checked in order to minimise wear.

Rotary pumps
Rotary pumps are commonly produced as units to be coupled to a suitable driver. They should be installed carefully to ensure satisfactory alignment. It is particularly important that only the correct slinging points be used when handling heavy units and they should be large enough to accommodate the baseplate with a space around the edges and be of sufficient rigidity, height and mass to absorb vibration.

Alignment should be checked after installation as there is always the possibility that baseplates may have been distorted by handling or by bolting down to an uneven foundation.

After initial start-up, a check on alignment should be made when the pump has warmed up and the fluid has reached its normal working temperature. Further checks can be made weekly during the initialy period of service. Any discrepancies which appear may indicate an item which needs regular servicing if they cannot be traced to an installation fault and corrected.

All piping should, as far as possible, be supported independently of the pump so that a minimum of strain is imparted to the pump casing. It is generally recommended that suction piping be larger in size that the pump suction connection and that a strainer, where used, be fitted at the pump inlet. Foot valves are generally considered unnecessary with rotary pumps and should not be used with viscous fluids in any case because of the high resistance to flow. They may, however, be used with water and low viscosity fluids, especially when working with a high suction lift.

The recommended discharge piping size is usually the same as or larger than the pump discharge outlet.

Lobe rotor pumps

Lobe rotor pumps are normally securely bolted to the mounting which carries its driver. The mounting must not distort the pumps gear case. Pumps are normally intended to operate with one shaft above the other in the vertical plane. Obtain manufacturers approval for use in any other attitudes.

The pumping unit should be as near to the supply vessel as possible. A filter should be fitted to the supply line if unacceptable solids are likely to be present. Consider also the need to provide an overload protection device such as a relief valve, slipping clutch or electrical overload trip.

Transmission should be positioned as near as possible to the gear case. Belt loadings must accord with makers' recommendations. Avoid tight hub/shaft fits; do not hammer the pulley or coupling on to the shaft. Carefully align coupling flanges before the pump is finally positioned. Flexible couplings will not tolerate undue misalignment which can give rise to pump and drive component failure.

All moving parts should be guarded. Repeat alignment and adjustment checks after a few hours running on-stream.

Relief valves

Many positive displacement rotary pumps are fitted with a relief valve to prevent excessive pressure build-up inside the casing should the pump be operated against a throttled delivery. In some cases the relief valve bypasses fluid back to the suction side so that under such conditions, there is a continual flow looping the pump which will raise the pump temperature. If a considerable proportion of the flow is carried by the bypass loop, this rise in temperature can lead to the fluid overheating. In such cases a separate pressure relief valve can be used in the discharge pipe, discharging if necessary into the supply tank. This will eliminate the looped flow and appreciably reduce the rise in pump temperature.

Pump Start-up

IN GENERAL, all centrifugal pumps must be filled with water before starting, since the internal running clearances depend upon water for lubrication. There are however exceptions to this rule, for example pumps having very heavy shafts with a total deflection at all times less than the radial clearance, or very large pumps under flooded conditions which are evacuated of water by compressed air in order to reduce the starting load on the motor. In this latter case a water supply is usually provided to the neck ring to prevent risk of seizure.

Normally the centrifugal pump starting torque is so low than it does not require special consideration. Driving units like steam, gas and water turbines, have very high driving torques. The difference between driving and pump torque is sufficient to accelerate a centrifugal pump to its operating speed in a very short time.

Where a pump is driven by an internal combustion engine, the starter must be sufficiently large to bring both engine and pump up to operating speed. However, a clutch is usually interposed to separate the pump from the engine during start-up.

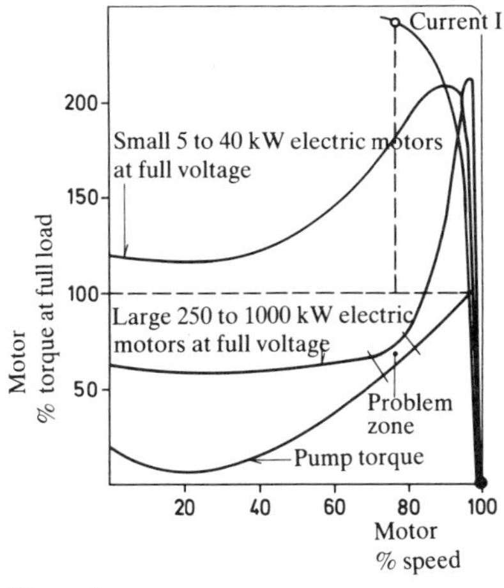

Figure 1
Starting torque curve for electric motor and pump.

Depending upon the type and size, electric motors have various torque characteristics. With high power inputs in particular, start up must therefore be investigated thoroughly at the planning stage. At around 80% of the speed the torque of an electric motor may drop to the pump torque. Acceleration torque is then nil, and the group becomes locked into this speed. As a result, the motor takes up a high current and the risk of destroying the windings. A typical starting torque curve for electric motor and pump is shown in Figure 1.

Start-up (excluding pressure surge)
Centrifugal pumps may be started in four different ways:

(i) Start-up against closed valve.

(ii) Start-up against closed non-return valve with the delivery valve open.

(iii) Start-up with delivery valve open but no geodetic head.

(iv) Start-up delivery with valve open and pressure pipeline drained.

The start-up time for a centrifugal pump depends on the acceleration moment *ie* on the difference between the torque of the driving unit and the starting torque required by the pump. The acceleration moment varies with the speed. The start-up time must therefore be calculated for individual speed increments and then totalled. Depending on whether the pump starts with the delivery valve open or closed, its starting torque and hence its start-up time will also vary.

Submersible pumps
When started against full head or closed valve, the submersible pump approaches full speed before flow can start. The foot valve is generally omitted on submersible pumps since its liability to sticking open and difficulty of maintenance at the bottom of the well render its use impracticable. The omission of a foot valve however involves a start against zero head, which explains the need for consideration of zero head power consumption and thrust loading. Care must be taken in cases where the water stands very high in the well or shaft under certain rainfall conditions thus demanding fairly continuous operation at low pumping heads.

The operating cycle of a submersible pump set is generally as follows – with the well water standing at normal level and with the pump immersed in water, the motor is started. The head at the start is zero if no foot valve is fitted. As the set accelerates the water rises in the delivery column, imposing a head on the pump. During the first minute or so the pump operates against the head which is less than normal. On a low type number pump, this may impose more than normal load on the motor, although this is usually acceptable on short term rating.

After the delivery column is filled, the pump operates at normal duty. When the set is shut down by switching off the motor or by power failure, the water column and the rotor decelerate, stop and then reverse.

The energy in the vertical water column is many times greater than the kinetic energy in the rotor so that overspeed in reverse is reached. The period of reversal is however, relatively short (provided that check valves are installed on surface mains and reservoirs) before the vertical water column and the rotor finally come to rest at zero head.

Reciprocating pumps
With reciprocating pumps, check alignment before starting up by removing the cylinder head and centring the pistons in the liner with shims. Calipers can be used

to check the alignment of rods to make sure that they are correctly centred in their stuffing boxes. When supplied new the stuffing boxes may or may not be packed. If not, the correct packing must be inserted according to specific instructions. The gland can then be tightened up evenly but should not be over-tightened. A slight leakage is usually tolerable, or even necessary, to lubricate and cool the packing adequately all bearings, pivot points *etc.*, should be properly lubricated.

Pumps should be primed according to the specific instructions before attempting to start and all valves in the suction discharge, steam and exhaust lines should be opened, together with any drain valves on the steam end.

In the case of steam pumps, the exhaust is opened then the steam valve just enough to warm the pump. The steam pump can be opened slowly until the pistons begin to move. The valve can be further opened as the pump comes up to working speed. the drain valves can be closed as soon as the steam end is free of condensate.

Starting-up technique for power driven pumps is similar, first opening suction, vent, discharge and bypass valves. The pumps can be turned over by hand first to check for freedom of movement before starting the driver. During initial running a check should be kept on temperature and lubricating oil pressure (if fed by a separate pressurised system). If there is any excessive temperature rise the pump should be stopped immediately and the cause investigated. Normally a new pump (or a reconditioned one) should be run at reduced speed for the first several thousand strokes, after which, if all is well, it can be continuously operated at maximum rated speed. Manufacturers recommendations for running-in specific pumps should always be followed.

Rotary pumps

With most rotary pumps it is important that they should not be run dry, although there are exceptions. Pumps may be primed manually or by a primary loop in the piping which traps a supply of liquid in the bottom of the loop when the pump is stopped. When starting a new pump for the first time it should be primed through the discharge side until filled. Once it is started a check should be made that the flow is maintained. If not, the pump should be stopped, reprimed and started again. If the pump is packed the temperature of the gland should be checked after a short run and the gland loosened if there are signs of over-heating. Where the pump is fitted with seals – and the seals are of the type specified by the manufacturer – there is not likely to be excessive friction when starting from new, nor are any adjustments called for.

It is particularly important when starting-up rotary pumps that all valves should be fully open to prevent any possibility of excessive pressure built up and that the system be free from air leaks. When priming, the pump casing should be completely filled so that any air inside at the beginning is driven out; it is an advantage to be able to vent the discharge line so that liquid flowing through the discharge pipe for the first time can completely displace and air present.

If a pump handling a hot liquid is being started up for the first time, it is a wise precaution to prime it with a hot liquid and then allow a period of 'soak' so that all internal components can expand to the full extent consistent with the service temperature at which they would normally operate. If started immediately after priming with hot liquid there is the possibility that certain components may expand faster than others and cause temporary interference.

Where a rotary pump is designed to handle a fluid which has lubricating properties, ball bearings are usually internal and all necessary lubrication is supplied by the fluid itself. If the fluid is non-lubricating then the main bearings are usually either externally fed from lubrication points or of a sealed type which normally require no attention other than at specified maintenance intervals.

As overall considerations with positive displacement pumps, never start or run a pump against a closed line; check that the direction of rotation agrees with the manufacturers instructions and the required flow direction; and check that the fluid being handled can flow freely into the pump.

Pump Cavitation and Recirculation

CAVITATION CAN be explained as the formation of vapour bubbles in any flow that is subjected to an ambient pressure equal to or less than the vapour pressure of the liquid being pumped. Cavitation damage is the loss of metal produced by the collapse of the vapour bubbles against the metal surfaces of the pump impeller casing. NPSH is the net positive suction head required to prevent cavitation.

Pump operation in the presence of cavitation will reduce both the total head and the output capacity. A steady crackling noise in and around the suction indicates cavitation. A random crackling noise with high intensity knocks indicates suction recirculation rather than cavitation from inadequte NPSH.

Cavitation damage from inadequate NPSH occurs on the low pressure or the visible surface of the impeller inlet vane. A suction gauge or manometer in the pump suction can be used to determine whether the NPSH available is equal to or greater than the NPSH required from the manufacturer's rating curve. If the additional NPSH cannot be supplied the capacity of the pump should be reduced to the point where the required NPSH is equal to or less than the available NPSH. If this is not possible, then a small amount of air can be bled into the suction to reduce the damage associated with cavitation.

The shape of the suction passage, the diameter of the hub, whether double or single entry, the blade angles at pick-up, the profile of the blade at pick-up and blade length will all have a direct bearing on cavitation performance. It is therefore usual to group together in cavitation analysis pumps of similar geometric shape.

The temperature, pressure, viscosity and saturation pressure of the liquid are important factors, concerned more with the application of the pump than the initial design since the original designing and testing of a pump or range of pumps is usually carried out on cold water. The operating speed of the pump and its size will affect the inlet type number.

Vapourising liquid duties

If the liquid in the vessel supplying the pump is at boiling point, the free surface of the liquid must be at a level above the impeller inlet vane corresponding to NPSH in order to ensure that the liquid can pass into the impeller without vapourising.

This condition can serve to control the pump flow so that at all times it is equal to the flow into the vessel. A reduction into the flow into the vessel will lower its level until the pump by partial vapourisation reduces its flow to correspond to the lower NPSH. Vapourising liquid pumps must operate at relatively low speeds of rotation and flow so as to minimise any cavitation attack to an acceptable level.

Inducers

Where high heads are involved it is essential to operate in the safe zones of 3000 to 4000 inlet type numbers. This generally involves a booster pump at lower speed or an inducer at full speed to avoid harmful cavitation in the main pump. An inducer fitted to the inlet of the first impeller of the main pump resembles a screw which can have a constant or variable lead and a parallel or tapered periphery or hub. Inducers were first developed for the fuel pumps of space rockets and operated at inlet type numbers up to 40 000 but here the life need only be a few minutes and inlet type numbers of this order are not possible on continuously operated pumps.

In general the provision of an inducer can increase the inlet shape number of a high speed pump by two to three times thus giving a generous margin of safety in respect of permissible NPSH. Inducers are however less able to accept off-peak flow conditions than conventional impellers and here vibratoin difficulties can occur.

Pumps with supercavitating inducer

Here the inducer vanes are sufficiently short and run at a high enough speed to ensure that the cavitation bubbles do not recondense until they are clear of the vane and therefore can do no harm since they collapse in the liquid. The inlet shape number attained by a supercavitating inducer is comparable with that of a normal inducer but the margin of safety in respect of life is greater. Several pumps with supercavitating first stages are now in operation for chemical duties.

Cavitation tests

The incidence of cavitation is detected by the following in order of appearance:

(i) Stroboscopic observation of bubble appearance and size.

(ii) Sensitive acoustic tests of cavitation and noise.

(iii) Reduction of efficiency and/or head of 3% which is the basis of ISO and BSI test codes in determining NPSH and inlet shape number.

Long-term basis

The major factors causing cavitation erosion are high relative vane velocity, adverse angle of attack and at impeller periphery, close proximity of moving and stationary vanes. NPSH should increase approximately as velocity to the power of 3·2 (not the square) to avoid long term erosion.

Cavitation erosion is assessed by depth of attack or by weight of metal removed or by the cost of weld repair. Mild steel impellers and runners are often protected as vital parts by stainless steel weld deposits.

Temperature effects

At the critical temperature of 374 °C water and steam densities are the same. Hence there is no volume change or bubble collapse. In practice, cavitation erosion is negligible above about 300 °C but increases progressively as temperature falls.

Recirculation

Recirculation occurs at reduced flows and is the reversal of a portion of the flow back through the impeller. Recirculation at the inlet of the impeller is known as suction recirculation. Recirculation at the outlet of the impeller is known as discharge recirculation. Suction and discharge recirculation can be very damaging to pump operation and should be avoided for continuous operation.

Suction recirculation will produce a loud crackling noise in and around the suction of the pump. Recirculation noise is of greater intensity than the noise from low NPSH cavitation and is a random knocking sound. Discharge recirculation will produce the same characteristic sound as suction recirculation except that the highest intensity is in the discharge volute or diffuser.

Suction and discharge recirculation produce cavitation damage to the pressure side of the impeller vanes. Viewed from the suction of the impeller, the pressure side would be the invisible or underside of the vane.

An analysis of the symptoms associated with recirculation should consider the following as possible corrective procedures:

(i) Increase the output capacity of the pump.

(ii) Install a bypass between the discharge and the suction of the pump.

(iii) Bleed air to the suction of the pump to reduce the intensity of the noise, vibration and cavitation damage.

(iv) Substitute a harder material for the impeller to reduce the rate of cavitation damage.

Pump Operation and Maintenance

OPERATING AND maintenance requirements vary with the type of pump as well as with needs of the specific installation. Generalised details are thus described under specific pump headings – Centrifugal pumps, Reciprocating pumps and Rotary pumps. Operating and maintenance requirements and recommendations specified by the manufacturer take precedence in individual cases.

Centrifugal pumps

Centrifugal pumps are normally subject to hourly checks for a period after installation and initial start-up, and thereafter routine checks and maintenance at regular intervals as specified by the pump manufacturers. Most manufacturers specify the intervals for bearing lubricant changes and also the type of lubricant to be employed. Time intervals may, however, vary considerably according to the design of bearing, service conditions and other factors.

A complete progressive record should be kept for each pump, detailing check data, maintenance intervals and operations carried out at these intervals. The usual intervals recommended for preventative maintenance are monthly, three monthly, six monthly and annually, but the necessary actions at these intervals are governed largely by the service conditions. A maintenance routine should therefore be planned with the service conditions in mind rather than as an arbitary routine. Thus the checking of pump bearing temperatures, normally recommended as a regular monthly check, may be carried out at shorter, *eg* weekly, intervals if thought desirable. Similarly, packings and seals, which are normally checked at six monthly intervals for possible replacement, may need earlier (or later) attention in a specific installation, depending both on the original design of the pump and service conditions.

The annual check was originally held to require complete disassembly of the pump to check parts for wear *etc*, and to replace all components worn beyond specified limits. Again the necessity for detailed inspection in this manner is almost entirely dependent on service conditions and shorter or longer periods may be better – the former demanded by necessity or the latter by the greater economy afforded by increasing the periods between complete shut-downs and the relative high cost of major servicing operations.

In many designs of pump intended for severe service conditions provision is made for easy inspection, removal and replacement of wear parts without

TABLE 1 – CENTRIFUGAL PUMPS – FAULT-FINDING

Fault	Cause	Remedy or Action
Pump not turning	Driver not running	Check fuses, circuit breakers.
	Keys sheared	Replace.
	Drive belt slip	Check and adjust.
	Coupling fault	Check if slipping or broken; replace if necessary.
	Shaft or gears sheared	Check; replace if necessary.
Pump not priming	Inlet valve closed	Open valve.
	Inlet clogged or restricted	Check and clear.
	Air leaks on suction side	Replace seals; check line(s) for leaks.
	Liquid drained or syphoned from system	Fit check or foot valve to prevent draining.
	Worn pump impeller	Inspect; increasing pump speed might help; also fitting foot valve.
No discharge	Lack of prime (see also above)	Open all vent cocks to release trapped air and fill pump and suction pipe completely with fluid.
	Excessive suction lift	Check pump inlet for clogging, *etc*, causing excessive friction head. Check suction head.
	Excessive discharge head	Check that valves are open. Check piping for obstructions or blockage. Check total head.
	Speed too low	Check that pump rev/min is consistent with manufacturer's recommendations.
	Pump clogged	Check that impeller is not clogged.
	Wrong direction of rotation	Check that pump is running in the correct direction.
	Vapour lock	Bleed suction pipe to clear air lock. Check that suction pipe is properly submerged.
	Relief valve not properly adjusted	Check adjustment; check for dirt on valve seat.
	Air leak	Check seals; check line(s) for air leaks.
Low delivery	Air leaks	Check suction piping and pump for air leaks. Check pump gaskets.
	Vapour lock	Check NPSH and fluid temperature to ensure that liquid in suction line is not 'flashing'.
	Low NPSH or damage	As above, and also check suction pipe, foot valve, *etc.*
	Clogged strainer(s)	Check and clean if necessary.
	Excessive inlet friction	Suction line too small; or too many fittings adding fluid friction.
	Relief valve incorrectly set, or jammed.	Check and adjust as necessary.
	Excessive system back-pressure	Reduce system friction by re-design.
	Worn impeller	Inspect and replace if necessary.
	Worn wear rings	As above.
	Wrong direction of rotation	Check against manufacturer's specification.
	Constriction in suction line	Check that foot valve size is adequate (if fitted). Check for other possible obstruction.
	Wrong pump size	Check that pump is adequate for the job.
	Poor suction	Check that suction pipe is properly submerged and in best position.

TABLE 2 – RECIPROCATING PUMPS – FAULT-FINDING

Fault	Cause	Remedy or Action
Low delivery (cont)	High fluid viscosity	Check that fluid viscosity is consistent with anticipated performance.
	Excessive fluid temperature	Reduce speed and/or delivery; decrease suction head.
	Speed too low	Check operating rev/min against specification for pump performance.
Over-heating	Stuffing box over-heats	Check that packing is not too tightly or badly fitted. Check packing lubricant (where applicable). Check that packing is consistent with manufacturer's specification. Check cooling flow (where applicable).
	Bearings over-heating	Check oil level or lubricant condition. Check if correct lubricant is being used. Check bearing for misalignment or excessive tightness. Check fitting and condition of oil seals. Check that operating speed is not excessive.
	Fluid too viscous	Reduce fluid viscosity (*eg* by heating).
	Excessive pressure	Reduce pump speed; increase delivery line size(s).
Vibration and noise	Cavitation	Check pump operating conditions.
	Excessive fluid viscosity	Check product suitability.
	Entrained air	Check for air leaks.
	High vapour pressure fluid	Check product/pump suitability.
	Improper pump assembly	Check and rectify.
	Unbalanced impeller	Check that impeller is not damaged or clogged.
	Misalignment	Check alignment with driver.
	Non-rigid mount	Check mounting for rigidity.
	Bent shaft; faulty bearings	Check and replace if necessary.
	Pump wear	Strip down and check for wear.
	Relief valve chattering	Re-adjust, repair or replace as necessary.
Excessive wear	Misalignment	As above.
	Out-of-balance	As above.
	Non-rigid mount	As above.
	Bent shaft	As above.
	Lack of lubrication	Check quantity and quality of lubricant.
	Dirt in pump	Use filter to remove.
	Corrosion	Check that pump materials are compatible with fluid being handled.
	Too high operating speed	Check against manufacturer's recommendations for fluid viscosity.
	Operating pressure too high	Reduce speed or pressure, *eg* change in system.
	Abrasives present in fluid	Check product/pump suitability.
Pump requires excessive power	Speed too high	Check against recommended rev/min.
	Misalignment	Check alignment of pump and driver, also foundations.
	Internal friction	Check for rubbing contact, clogging, *etc*.
	Tight bearings	Check bearings and packings (bearing temperature will be a clue).
	Lack of lubrication	Check quantity and quality of lubricants.
	High fluid viscosity	Check that fluid viscosity is not too high for economic handling.

completely stripping down the pump, thus simplifying maintenance and making it both logical and economic to attend to maintenance at frequent intervals. The only reason that really justifies shut down and complete dismantling of the pump for inspection and overhaul is a marked loss of performance. If this is suspected the pump can first be tested to establish if head, capacity or power input figures have deteriorated and whether remedial action is needed.

Mounting brackets fitted to base plates simplify dismantling and reassembly.

Reciprocating pumps (direct-acting)

Steam pumps are generally trouble-free in operation and require little attention other than routine lubrication. Gaskets and packings will however require periodic replacement and maintenance will be required to correct for mechanical wear *etc*. Disassembly is usually straightforward and a specific procedure is usually detailed in the manufacturer's instruction manual.

The valve chest at the steam end will normally show wear by rounding of the ends of the slide valve together with wear on the valve chest face itself, terminating in a rounded shoulder. There will come a point where the rounding of the valve and the shoulder will open a leakage path to the steam port. The valve face must then be re-faced and the valve faced down. The valve face can be scraped or filled, depending on the depth of wear and the extent of the shoulder formed, taking care that the face is rendered flat and true. The slide valve itself is best re-faced in a lathe. The two can then be ground in for a final finish. Grinding in alone will not effect a cure unless the shoulders on the face are first removed, although in certain valve designs the tendancy to 'shouldering' is eliminated, *eg* by using a raised valve face the whole length of which is lapped by the slide valve or by grooving the valve chest to produce a similar effect. In such cases light wear can be taken up merely by re-grinding.

Valves are usually adjusted with the piston at mid-stroke. This position can be detemined by marking the rod relative to some convenient fixed reference point, *eg* the gland, for the extreme positions of the stroke, then finding the mid-position between these two marks and moving the rod to bring this centre against the fixed

TABLE 3 – RECIPROCATING (PISTON) PUMPS – FAULT-FINDING

Fault	Cause	Remedy or Action
No discharge	Not primed	Prime. Open vents on discharge side to release trapped air and leave open until all air is discharged.
	Excessive suction lift	Reduce suction lift or reduce suction friction with larger diameter pipe or eliminate bends, *etc.*
	Air leaks	Check system and eliminate air leaks by sealing, *etc.*
	Vapour bound	Check fluid temperature and vapour pressure – fluid temperature may be too high, or suction lift excessive for fluid temperature.
	Blockage	Check for blockage in suction pipe, foot valve or strainer. Check pump suction valves.
	Deterioration	Check suction valves, piston packing, piston rod packing, worn valves or badly scored cylinder.
Low discharge pressure	Low steam pressure	Check for obstruction, leak or partially closed valve in steam system.
	Tight packing	Loosen gland until leakage is apparent.
	Excessive backpressure	Check that pump is not operating against excessive system head.
	Deterioration	Check cylinder bore for wear, also condition of piston packings and valves.
Pump stops or hesitates	Intermittent steam supply	Check for blockage, *etc.*
	Valve trouble	Check for excessive valve wear and leakage. Check that valve timing is correct.
	Excessive backpressure	Check that system head is not excessive.
Variable delivery	Air leaks	Check system for air leaks.
	Misalignment	Check alignment of pump and possible distortion due to unsupported piping connected to pump cylinder.
	Excessive suction lift	As above.
	Vapour bound	Reduce fluid temperature, or reduce suction lift.
	Tight packing	Loosen gland.
	Excessive speed	Check that operating speed is consistent with specification.
Pump short-strokes	Excessive cushioning	Adjust cushioning valves to obtain correct stroke.
	Worn valve	Check valve for leakage, re-face as necessary.
	Entrained gas	Modify suction intake as necessary.
	Incorrect valve timing	Check against specification and adjust as necessary.
	Worn bore	Replace liner, or re-bore and fit oversize piston.
Piston over-strokes (hits head)	Cushion valves	Close down as necessary to reduce stroke.
	Piston leakage	Replace piston packing; replace worn liner or re-bore cylinder.
	Valve leakage	Check valves on liquid head for leakage – re-grind or re-set if necessary.
Excessive wear	Misalignment	Check alignment.
	Bent piston rod	Check for straightness.
	Worn bore	Replace liner or re-bore.
	Fluid	Check that pump is compatible with fluid being handled.

reference point. The actual method of adjustment then depends on the lost motion design employed in the particular pump. In some cases the valve gear may be adjustable from outside, in others by opening the valve chest cover. It is important to bear in mind that adjustment of lost motion, controls the stroke of the piston and care must be taken that the piston does not strike the head. Similarly, when cushion valves are fitted, opening these has the effect of increasing the stroke and, if overdone, the piston could strike the head. Normally, cushion valves should be set almost closed for high speed and light load operation, and progressively opened for higher loads and slower speeds.

Liquid end valves may be of several types, *eg* disc valves for low and medium pressures; ball valves or hemispherical valves for handling abrasive of viscous fluids; wing valves for higher pressures; *etc*. All such valves when enclosed mate with a seat, which may be screwed or pressed into place. Normal wear or slight pitting can be accommodated by lapping into the valves with a suitable grinding compound. Heavier wear or pitting calls for removal of the seat and re-facing (or fitting a new seat). Any slight distortion of the seat produced by re-fitting is then taken up by grinding the valve.

Other detailed maintenance requirements are usually logical or straightforward *eg* withdrawal of piston and rod, removal of a cylinder liner *etc*. Removable liners are usually designed to be removed with a drawbolt. Pressed-in liners will normally have to be chipped out but a replacement can be fitted with a drawbolt. The main sources of trouble are likely to be corrosion, wear and pitting of the liner and piston rod. Corrosion should not be a problem if the pump materials were correctly chosen or the components surface treated to withstand the particular operating conditions.

Power driven reciprocating pumps are somewhat simpler and normal detailed maintenance is largely confined to checking the valve condition together with periodic attention to seals or packings. Valve seats may be re- ground, re-faced and ground, or replaced and ground in, depending on the severity of the wear. Operating time before such attention is required will vary widely with the type and design of pump and the service conditions. It is good practice to check the valves on a new pump after three months' service unless there is some indication that earlier attention is needed. After that, maintenance periods can be based on experience.

Rotary pumps

Rotary pumps in general have a minimum of moving parts and porting rather than valve systems, hence maintenance is normally held to a minimum and is largely confined to inspection for wear, corrosion or material defects, together with keeping the seals in good condition. Disassembly normally follows a logical sequence when individual parts may be inspected for condition and wear and clearance is checked against permitted tolerances. Excessively worn or defective parts should be replaced. Where corrosion is also present it is advisable to check the material specifications against the liquid being handled as a replacement part of a better material may be available.

There may be specific instructions for disassembly, *eg* a spindle should be withdrawn in one direction only to avoid damage to a seal. The manufacturers instruction book will, therefore by the primary guide for maximum permissible wear on individual components. When timing gears have to be removed, the gears should be marked before disassembling so that they can be reassembled in the in the correct order and position. When new timing gears are required these are often supplied as matched pairs with one slotted for a key and the other not. This is because their position in the shaft is critical in determining clearances between the driven rotor or screw elements, and the correct place for the new gear key slot can only be established by keeping the specified clearance between the rotors while assembling. Having found this position accurately the gear is removed, the slot cut in the marked position and the gear reassembled for checking. If it is incorrect it will be necessary to reposition, mark and cut another key slot. The performance of many rotary pumps, particularly of the lobe rotor and multi-screw types, depends on accurate timing and the maintenance of prescribed clearances between the rotating elements. Any deviation from such settings normally results in a marked reduction in pump life and loss of efficiency. The importance of periodic timing and clearance checks is also emphasised.

In vane pumps the principal wear is on the vanes themselves and the liner or casing on which they rub. With sliding vanes replacement is usually a straightforward matter. In some designs it is possible to reassemble a worn vane the other way round and so double its effective life. With swinging vanes the shape of the pivoted portion of the rotor is such that a substantial degree of wear can take place without interfering with the sealing efficiency. There will, however be a limit to the amount of wear which can be taken up purely by geometry and once this is exceeded it will be necessary to replace the vane. With both types, vanes may usually be replaced merely by removing the cover plate or head plate, leaving the rotor in position.

The vanes may run on a liner which can be withdrawn and replaced after it has worn beyond acceptable limits. In some pumps of this type it is possible to withdraw the liner without removing the rotor first, although there is always the possibility that it will have become 'frozen' in the casing due to corrosion. If it is difficult to remove, the pump must be disassembled completely and the liner driven out from one side. Care should be taken that the replacement liner is refitted the correct way round, so that intake and discharge port openings are not reversed and the interior of the casing should be cleaned out thoroughly before refitting. It may also be necessary to remove any burrs on the new liner before it can be fitted easily.

Lobe-rotor pumps

Lobe-rotor pumps are precisely-made machines; undue force must never be used during servicing. Be especially careful not to damage the means of alignment between rotor case and gear case. Ensure that sealing surfaces of mechanical seal rings are not scratched or damaged in any way. If in doubt, obtain correct fitting length from manufacturer.

For shut-down and maintenance, isolate the pump from electrical and hydraulic supplies. Do not allow the product to solidify in the pumping chamber or on shaft sealing surfaces. Product wetted parts can often be cleaned with hot water and detergent.

It is advisable to hold components of the following types in stock. Quantities depend on pump design, service conditions and stocking policy:

O-ring seals – pump head, shaft sleeve, front valves, mechanical seals, port connections, gear case.

Oil seals and joints – gear case.

Glands – packing sets, preferably pre-formed rings.

Mechanical seals – rotating and stationary sealing rings, springs.

Transmission – flexible coupling parts, belts, gear box parts.

Miscellaneous – lubricating oil, relief valve springs, fasteners.

TABLE 4 – ROTARY PUMPS – FAULT-FINDING

Fault	Cause	Remedy or Action
No discharge	Not primed	Prime to fill pump.
	Excessive suction lift	Reduce suction lift or reduce friction in suction side with large pipe.
	Air leaks	Check and rectify; check gaskets.
	Blockage	Check adjustment and setting.
	Excessive wear	Check components for wear against manufacturer's permitted tolerances.
	Wrong rotation	Check that pump is being rotated in the correct direction.
	Insufficient speed	Check that pump is running at rated speed.
Low discharge pressure or reduced capacity	Insufficient speed	As above.
	Wrong rotation	As above.
	Excessive suction lift	As above.
	Air leaks	As above, check gaskets particularly,
	Air entrainment	Re-position suction inlet.
	Relief valve or bypass valve	Setting may be too low. Check and re-set.
	Excessive wear	Check as above.
Excessive noise	Misalignment (where applicable)	Check alignment of driver and pump and drive connection.
	Internal damage	Bent or broken rotor.
	Unbalance	If suspected, check rotor for static and dynamic balance.
	Air entrainment	Re-position suction inlet.
	Air leaks	Check and rectify.
	Cavitation	Check against causes of cavitation.
	Excessive pressure	Relief valve set too high, adjust to correct setting consistent with pump rating.
	Deterioration	Check for excessive wear or clearances on components.
Excessive discharge pressure	System pressure	If system pressure is too high for pump rating a larger pump will have to be used, when some relief may be possible.
	Relief valve or bypass valve	Check and re-set relief valve for correct pressure.
	System throttled	Discharge valve may be partially closed or system partially blocked.
Excessive wear	Abrasive liquid	Check that pump is suitable for handling liquid if abrasive solids are present; or check that filter or strainer used is adequate.
	Distortion	Pipework loads transmitted directly to the casing may cause distortion.
	Excessive pressure developed	See above.
	Excessive speed	Check that speed is consistent with pump specification for viscosity of liquid handled.
Excessive input power required	Damage	Check for bent or damaged shaft, *etc*.
	Excessive pressure	As above.
	Excessive fluid viscosity	Check speed rating against actual viscosity of fluid; reduce speed for higher viscosities.
	Excessive speed	Check against pump rating for fluid viscosity handled.
Pump overheats	Relief or bypass valves	Check that settings are correct.
	Excessive speed for fluid handled	Check that speed is consistent with rating for fluid viscosity.
	Excessive pressure	As above.
	Discharge throttle	Looped flow through relief valve will cause heating; may be relieved by separate relief valve discharging to tank.

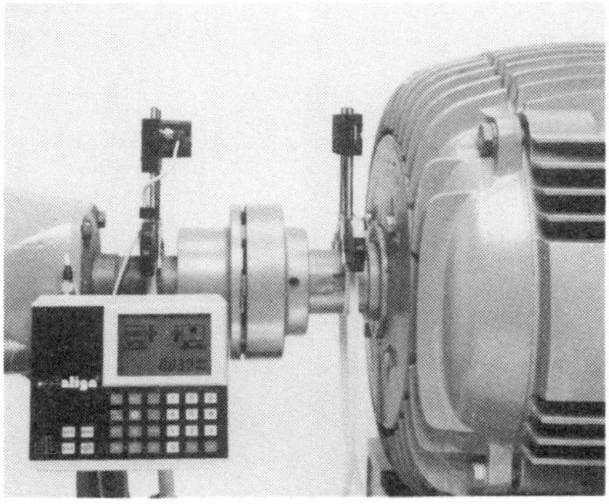

Computer-aided laser shaft alignment.

The development of sophisticated electronics, computers, chemical analysis, lasers, vibration pick-ups, sonic measurements, ultra-sonics and radiographics have permitted the analysis and forecast of the life of any pump component so that opening-up maintenance can be carried out at a reasonable period before expected failure rather than at routine times. There is really no point in the stripping of a machine if it is certain that it is operating satisfactorily. The following methods will minimise maintenance costs:

(i) Chemical analysis of debris from bearings *etc*, in the lubricating oil or balanced leakage.

(ii) Metal wall thickness and integrity measurement by laser, ultra-sonics, videographics, magnetic or other means.

(iii) Vibration and noise analysis by Kurtsosis, *eg* waive form investigation of bearing movements, monitoring of head, quantity and efficiency performance.

It is probable that the cost of monitoring will amount to less than the costs of routine maintenance and disassembly, particularly if continuous/trend monitoring is employed.

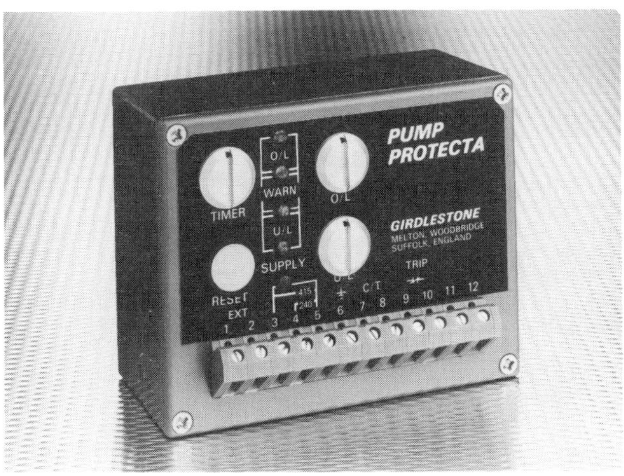

Pump protection device helps reduce repair costs.

TABLE 5 – LOBE-ROTOR PUMPS – FAULT FINDING

SYMPTOMS: No discharge	Under capacity	Irregular discharge	Prime lost after starting	Pump stalls when starting	Pump over-heats	Motor over-heats	Excessive power absorbed	Noise and vibration	Pump element wear	Excessive gland/seal wear	Product loss through gland	Seizure	CAUSES	REMEDIES
X													Incorret direction of rotation.	Reverse motor.
X													Pump unprimed.	Expel gas from supply line and pumping chamber and introduce liquid.
X	X	X	X					X					Insufficient NPSH available.	Increase supply line diameter increase static suction head. Simplify supply line configuration and reduce length.
	X	X	X					X					Product vaporising in supply line.	Reduce speed. Decrease product temperature – check effect of increased viscosity on available and permitted power inputs.
	X	X	X					X					Air entering supply line.	Remake pipework joints. Adjust or repack gland.
X	X	X	X					X					Gas in supply line.	Expel gas from supply line and pumping chamber and introduce liquid.
	X	X	X					X					Insufficient head above supply vessel outlet	Raise produce level. Lower outlet position. Increase submergence of supply pipe.
X	X	X	X					X					Foot valve/strainer obstructed or blocked.	Service fittings.
			X	X	X	X	X	X					Product viscosity above rated figure.	Decrease pump speed. Increase product temperature.
	X												Product viscosity below rated figure.	Increase pump speed. Decrease product temperature.
	X				X			X	X			X	Product temperature above rated figure.	Cool the product/pumping chamber.
				X		X	X						Product temperature below rated figure.	Heat the product/pumping chamber. (Check with pump maker).
								X	X	X	X	X	Unexpected solids in product.	Clean the system. Fit strainer to supply line.
	X			X	X	X	X	X	X			X	Delivery pressure above rated figure.	Check for obstructions. Service system and revise to prevent problem recurring. Simplify delivery time.

					X	X	X			X		X	Gland over-tightened.	Slacken and readjust gland.
	X	X	X					X			X		Gland under-tightened.	Adjust gland.
										X	X		Gland flushing inadequate.	Check that fluid flows freely into gland. Increase flow rate.
		X	X			X	X	X					Pump speed above rated figure.	Decrease pump speed.
	X												Pump speed below rated figure.	Increase pump speed.
					X	X	X	X	X			X	Rotorcase strained by pipework	Check alignment of pipes. Fit flexible pipes or expansion fittings. Support pipework.
	X												Belt drive slipping.	Re-tension to maker's recommendations.
					X	X	X	X					Flexible coupling misaligned.	Check flange alignment and adjust mountings accordingly.
								X					Insecure pump/driver mountings.	Fit lock-washers to slack fasteners and retighten.
					X	X	X	X	X			X	Shaft bearing wear or failure.	Refer to pump maker for advice and replacement parts.
				X	X	X	X	X	X			X	Worn unsynchronized timing gears.	Refer to pump maker for advice and replacement parts.
					X	X	X	X				X	Gearcase oil quantity/quality incorrect.	Refer to pump maker's instructions.
				X	X	X	X	X	X			X	Metal-to-metal contact of pumping element.	Check rated and duty pressure. Refer to pump maker.
	X												Worn pumping element.	Fit new components.
X	X				X								Front cover relief valve leakage.	Check pressure setting and readjust if necessary. Examine and clean seating surfaces. Replace worn parts.
	X							X					Relief valve chatter.	Check for wear of sealing surfaces, guides, *etc* – replace as necessary.
	X							X					Relief valve incorrectly set.	Readjust spring compression. Valve should lift about 10% above duty pressure.

DIAGNOSIS WILL BE GREATLY ASSISTED BY TAKING ON-STREAM PRESSURE READINGS AT THE PUMP'S INLET AND OUTLET PORTS

Pump Noise and Noise Control

SOURCES OF noise in pumping systems are:

(i) Noise generated by pump.

(ii) Noise generated by pump driver and transmission (*eg* gears where applicable).

(iii) Vibrations generated by the pump and/or the driver.

(iv) Hydraulic noise generated within the pump.

(v) Hydraulic noise generated in the pipeline and valves.

All the above may be radiated as air-borne noise, amplified by resonance of coupled structures. Pump noise may be masked by driver noise, in which case practical attempts to reduce noise levels must be aimed at the driver first or, alternatively, the possibility of fully enclosing the pump and driver should be considered. This is often the simplest solution in the case of small pump units, but it may be further necessary to:

(i) Fully isolate the mounting of the pump and driver so that structural-based vibrations are excluded.

(ii) Pay proper attention to sealing the enclosure, particularly at points where piping emerges.

(iii) Isolate pipe connections so that vibrations are not transmitted along the length of piping itself.

(iv) Ensure that there are no system design faults or limitations which can lead to excessive pump noise.

In general, the noise level generated by a particular type of pump is influenced by pressure, size and speed. The noise relationship of these parameters favours the choice of a large pump operating at low speed and generating low delivery pressures. This is likely to be ruled out on an efficiency basis (particularly in the case of roto-dynamic pumps), or by demand requirements.

Measuring noise

To start with it is necessary to define the object to be measured as the source of sound emission. By this the pump maker understands only the pump by itself with pump body, suction and discharge ports and baseplate pads. The user however is interested in the overall noise level of the pump installation. This includes additionally the noise from the motor and any gearing plus emissions from pipes and surfaces excited by structure-borne noise. Because the latter depend on particular installation they cannot be included in the noise data for a given pump type.

The following methods may be used for measuring pump noise:

(i) Sound pressure measurement, prescribed surface method;

(ii) Sound pressure measurement, reverberation room method;

(iii) Sound pressure measurement with reference sound source;

(iv) Structure-borne noise measurement;

(v) Intensity measurement.

Sound pressure is the quantity perceived by the human ear.

Sound power is the acoustic power emitted by sound source.

Sound intensity is the sound power per unit area.

Structure-borne sound is the sound propagated in a solid medium or at its surface. Vibrations on the surface may radiate air-borne sound.

For sound pressure measurements, limiting the extraneous noise often requires considerable outlay.

The structure-borne noise method is insensitive to extraneous noise.

However problems arise from the inexactly known radiation efficiency and from radiating opening where no transducers (*eg* accelerometers) for structure-borne noise can be fixed.

Intensity measurement is the latest method and measures in effect the required physical quantity, sound intensity or sound power.

The noise characteristics of individual pump types are as follows:

Positive displacement pumps

The type of pump concerned has a considerable bearing on noise likely to be generated. Rotary pumps with balanced rotors operating with positive clearances, such as the roots pump, like rotor and screw pumps, are inherently quiet, the principle source of mechanical noise in such cases being the driving gears. Delivery is largely free of ripple (pressure pulsations), leading also to low levels of hydraulic noise. Vane pumps on the other hand, tend to be relatively noisy. Gear pumps also tend to be noisy although with this type it is rather easier to redesign for quiet operation than with other types.

Other types of positive displacement pumps, particularly reciprocating pumps, generate a pulsating flow; thus the actual discharge pressure fluctuates about a mean value. Both the magnitude and form of the pressure fluctuations depend to a large extent on the load against which the discharge is delivered, but the frequency will be that of the generated rate of pulsation plus its harmonics. The noise spectrum will thus contain these frequencies, together with the pump rotation frequency.

Further noise generated within the pump itself is directly related to detail design. Thus poorly designed port and pump passages which can generate high turbulence lead to broad band noise. Lack of internal stiffeners or excessive clearances, tend to generate narrow band noise. Such additional noises are characteristic of individual designs and manufacturing tolerances, *etc*. Thus piston pumps inherently tend to be noisier than rotary pumps.

Although the primary consideration of the pump designer is maximum hydraulic performance, much can be done to reduce pressure pulsations at source. Basically, this can be achieved by reducing the pressure differential between the pumping chamber and the discharge port – typical methods adopted being the introduction of controlled leakage or delayed opening of the discharge port. Unfortunately, any such methods inevitably result in a loss of hydraulic efficiency and notable gains in pressure pulse reduction are usually limited to a fairly narrow operating range. But, as performance is the main selling point, deliberate de-rating to achieve pressure-pulse reduction is not attractive to pump designers.

Some control is also possible by attention to the selection of the pump casing materials. Traditional materials such as cast iron and steel do not readily dissipate vibration energy internally and in particular instances the complete pumps casing may resonate and generate 'solid-body' vibration which is transmitted to connected pipework and the pump mount. In a 'quiet' pump design, therefore it may be necessary to give considerable attention to the selection of the casing material *eg* 70-30 manganese-copper alloy provides far better attenuation than traditional materials at frequencies of over 1000 Hz (10 to 15 dB compared with cast iron). The other problems which may arise in this respect are higher material cost and lower mechanical strength calling for thicker constructions. The latter will improve noise reduction but further add to the cost of the casing.

Centrifugal pumps

In the case of centrifugal pumps the operating conditions can have a significant effect on noise emission. Air-borne noise is normally lowest when the pump is operating at its most efficient point. Further reductions are possible by design modifications which reduce the interference between the rotating and stationary flow actions, *eg* inlet guides moved as far away from the impeller as possible without losing their flow-straightening effect. Poor inlet flow conditions are a common source of noise in centrifugal pumps.

This is particularly true in the case of boiler feed pumps which may have heads per stage in excess of 1000 metres and hydraulic powers in excess of 8000 kW, when even detailed attention to noise reduction and source in design is still likely to

Noise attenuated pump.

realise noise levels in excess of 100 dB at a distance of 1 metre. In general productions where no specific attempt is made to reduce noise at source in the design of wall pumps, a noise level of 90 dB at 1 metre is likely to be achieved by pumps of more than 300 kW running at 3000 r/min; or 600 kW running at 1500 r/min.

Noise generated by the flow in centrifugal pumps is usually of three forms:

(i) Broad band noise due to turbulent flow in the pump.

(ii) Mechanical vibration of the rotating mass with a basic frequency equal to the shaft r/min.

(iii) Individual narrow-band tones with frequencies also proportional to the rotational speed and called impeller-vane passing frequencies.

These in turn occur at the rotor (f_1), stator (f_2) and from rotor-stator interference with the following relationship:

$f_1 = V_i \times n \times m$

$f_2 = V_c \times n \times m$

$f_3 = V_i \times V_c \times n \times m$

where:

V_i = number of impeller vanes

V_c = number of diffuser vanes (or casing tongues)

n = pump speed

m = 1st, 2nd, 3rd order, *etc*

The impeller frequency (f_1) is usually the most pronounced (1st and 2nd order). Principal causes of impeller-vane passing frequency are unequal pressure, flow separation and unequal velocity distribution at the vane outlet. Pumps with high efficiency also perform well with regard to the fundamental broad band noise level because the level of the broad band noise depends most exclusively on the hydraulic efficiency of the pump. A typical noise spectrum (upper curve of Figure 1), shows a marked peak which has a major influence on the overall sound pressure level.

Methods of minimising the peaks of the impeller vane passing frequencies are:

(i) Velocity and pressure gradients at the impeller vane outlet kept to a minimum.

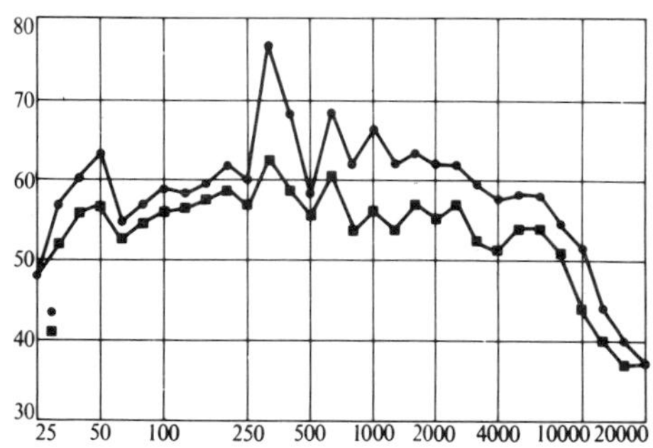

Figure 1
Original (upper curve) and new one-third octave spectrum of the same pump after re-design.

(ii) Avoidance of flow separation.
(iii) Reduction of the pressure shock (impact) when an impeller vane passes a tongue.
(iv) Reduction of the pressure shock (impact) when an impeller vane passes a diffuser vane.

Substantial reductions in the overall sound pressure level are possible through suitable design and shaping of individual pump components. Particular detail parts which are likely to prove effective with little or no reduction in pump performance are:

(i) Clearance between impeller vane and tongue (*ie* varying the outside vane diameter).
(ii) Impeller vanes pointed at outlet.
(iii) Impeller vanes machined obliquely at outside diameter.
(iv) Impeller vanes provided with grooves at outlet.
(v) Impeller vanes provided with holes towards the outlet.
(vi) Impeller vanes oblique to shrouds.
(vii) In voloute casing with oblique edge.
(viii) Tongue in volute casing provided with holes.

Roto-dynamic pump noise and vibration parameters are given in Table 1.

TABLE 1 – ROTO-DYNAMIC PUMP NOISE AND VIBRATION PARAMETERS

Parameter	Cause	Due To	Primary Product
Hydraulic noise	Turbulence	Operating conditions	Noise and vibration
Unsteady hydraulic forces	(i) Excessive turbulence	(a) Inadequate clearances (b) Asymmetric running (c) Badly designed ports and passages	Vibration Vibration Vibration
	(ii) Cavitation	Insufficient NPSH	Vibration and noise
	(iii) Pressure pulsations	Operating conditions and detail design	Vibration
	(iv) Water shedding	Operating conditions and detail design	Vibration
Shaft vibration	(i) Dynamic unbalance (ii) Hydrodynamic unbalance	Shaft speed	Vibration

Generalisations

In the case of a volute pump, blade frequency noise is equally predominant in the spectrum, with shaft frequency noise appearing at low to moderate levels. With a diffuser type pump, shaft frequency noise is moderate to high with blade frequency noise less predominant. The suction and discharge noise spectra are also different. With a two-stage or multi-stage pump, blade frequency noise is again predominant, with shaft frequency noise low other frequencies may also be present with marked fluctuations.

In general a volute pump will produce lower amplitude pressure pulsations than a diffuser pump at most flow rates (certainly up to 100% rated flow). At higher flow rates the diffuser pump may be slightly more favourable. Generalised characteristics are shown in Figure 2.

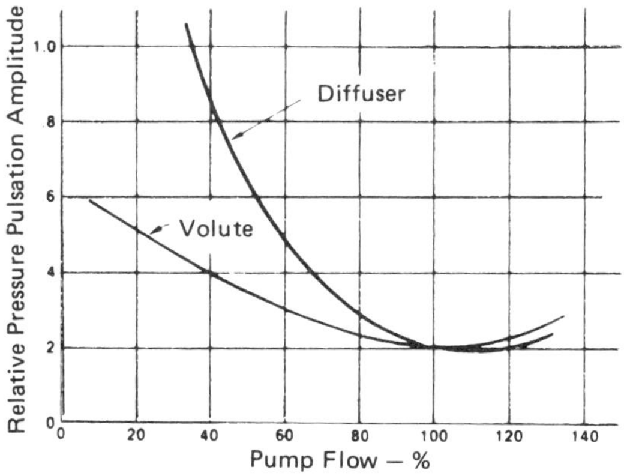

Figure 2
Generalised pulsation characteristics – volute versus diffuser pumps.

From theoretical analysis a formula can be derived for the general noise level, *viz:*

$$20 \log_{10} \quad \frac{P_O Q}{10\,000\, N_S \simeq a_2^2\, tr}$$

where:

P_O = total pressure rise across impeller, bar

Q = flow rate through impeller, m^3/min

N_S = specific speed

a_2 = impeller outside radius, cm

tr = width of impeller at outlet, cm

$\simeq$ = pump angular velocity, radians/sec

This formula can be used to estimate the general noise level of a centrifugal pump within ±2 dB, although the impeller blade frequency noise can be modified by the operating conditions and also by changes in pump geometry for the same specific speed.

It is a general characteristic of hydraulic noise that it is transmitted through the fluid, thus the reduction in noise by isolating the pump on resilient mounts and/or decoupling the pipework will be relatively small (probably 1 or 2 dB at best). Also the main source of noise will be at impeller blade frequency and its harmonics, which may account for up to 90% of the noise energy.

Theoretical considerations indicate that the blade frequency noise level of the pump can change by about 10 dB depending on the operating point of the pump and that minimum noise level should occur at flow rates around 115% of the design operating point. Diffuser pumps show less variations in noise level with load than with volute pumps, due to the smoothing effect of the diffuser blades.

Effect of speed

Noise levels will also increase with increasing rotational speed, the general pattern being as illustrated in Figure 3. This is consistent with the increase in consumption with increasing speed. Equally, the noise level of a pump will tend to increase with a decrease in specific speed – see Figure 4. The most significant fact, as far as noise reduction is concerned is that for similar duty levels a reduction in pump noise of 10 to 12 dB may be realised if the pump speed is halved.

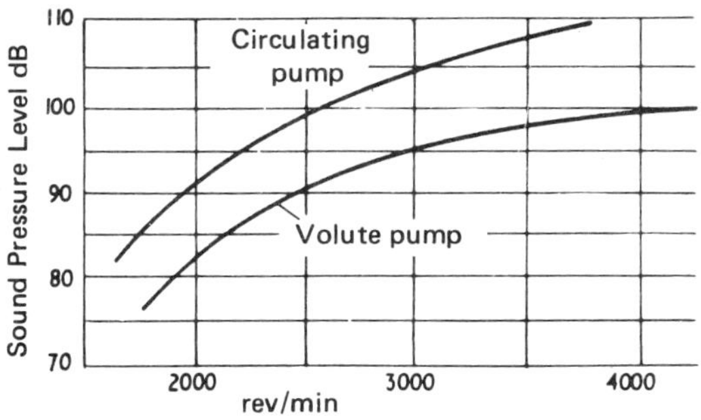

Figure 3

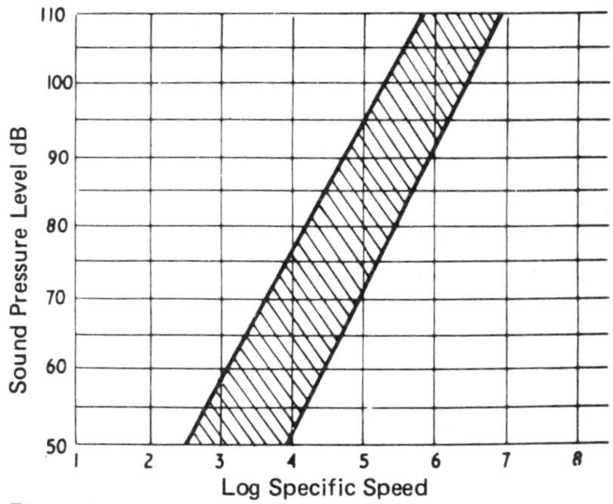

Figure 4

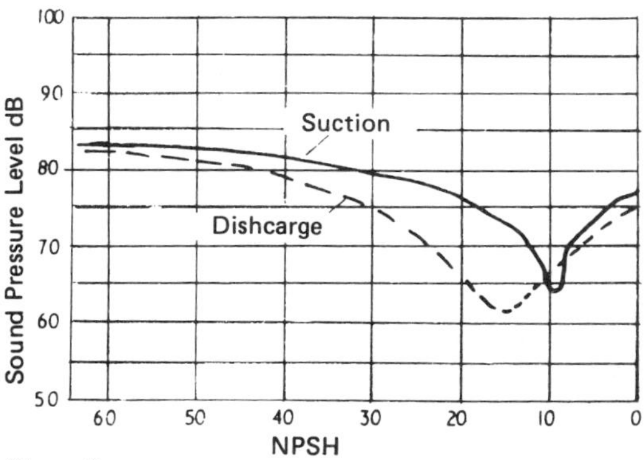

Figure 5

The effect of varying NPSH is a little more difficult to estimate. In general a change in NPSH will produce a change in the impeller blade frequency component, yielding a sharply defined minimum – see Figure 5. The shaft frequency component merely reduces with decreasing NPSH. It would appear, in fact that the onset of cavitation is beneficial for hydraulic noise reduction since this provides marked attenuation of the blade frequency noise, but since cavitation develops more fully as NPSH decreases still further, it provides an additional noise source which raises the overall range. Mild cavitation can produce attenuation and thus a reduction in noise level (consistent with a minimum noise level at about 115% load) but once this cavitation is more fully developed, the overall noise level will increase substantially.

Ways of abating noise

Besides the primary possibilities taken into account by the maker in the design of his pump, the siting in the plant can affect the noise level too. Generally speaking, hydraulically well designed pumps tend to behave well with regard to noise also. Otherwise however it must be remembered that the pump itself often generates relatively little sound power. Other major noise sources are:

(i) Drive motor, gears.

(ii) Excitation of structure-borne noise in adjacent light structures (*eg* chequered plate).

(iii) Radiation from the discharge pipe, to a lesser extent from the suction pipe as well.

Pump drive

During the acoustic planning of the installation the gearing and especially the motor should be selected with an eye to the noise abatement requirements. Water cooled motors are generally much quieter than air cooled ones.

Structure-borne noise

Care must be taken to ensure that the structure-borne noise set up by the machinery (pump gearing, motor) is radiated as little as possible by other adjacent components. Elastic mounting would be best, but this is usually not possible. At all events light structures (thin sheets) which are not part of the fixing should not be joined to foundation supports or other elements to the pump or driving machinery.

Pipelines

Ideally the lines ought to be isolated acoustically by means of compensators and liquid silencers. As a secondary measure sound absorbent insulation of the pipes may be considered. Such insulation can reduce noise from pump pipelines by 5 to 15 dB.

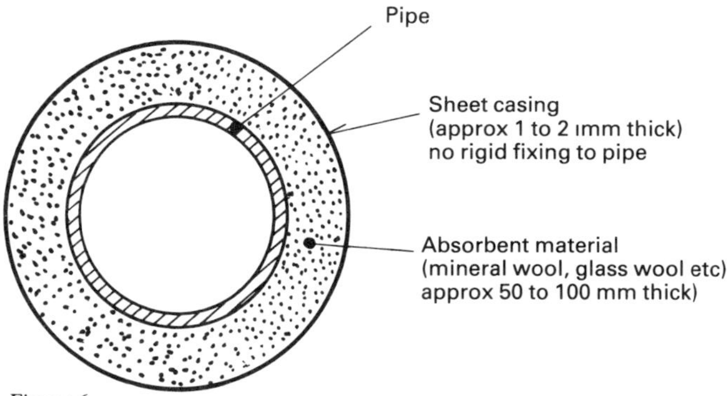

Figure 6
Acoustic insulation round a pipe

Reduced emission from the pump

If the emmisible noise levels are exceeded by radiation from the pump itself there exists two differently effective approaches to reducing it:

(a) Sound absorbent cladding of the pump (possibly providing thermal insulation at the same time. Attainable level reduction up to 5 dB.

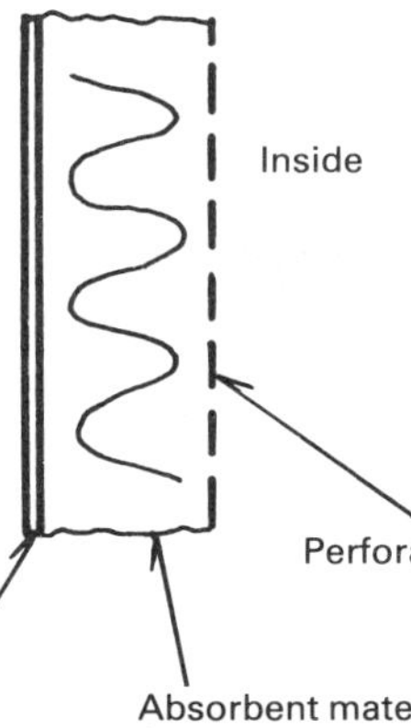

Figure 7
Schematic wall cross-section of sound hood.

(b) Encapsulation (sound hoods). Sound hoods bring abatements up to 30 dB and more, depending on their design. Usually it is advisable to enclose the motor and any gearing as well.

It must be borne in mind that the level reduction attainable in the machine room depends also on the radiation from the component mentioned previously (pipelines, structure-borne noise). The degree of improvement can be achieved by any of the source modification approaches obviously depends on the particulars of each installation, *ie* the basic causes of excess noise. Modification of pump internals for example is extremely difficult in existing installations and can produce undesirable side effects unless the pump was poorly designed or selected initially.

Further information on all aspects of noise measurement reduction and control can be found in the *Handbook of Noise and Vibration Control* published by The Trade and Technical Press Limited, publishers of this manual.

TABLE 2 – LIST OF STANDARDS AND GUIDELINES

Sound level meters	
DIN 45 633, 1970	Precision sound level meters.
Sound measurements	
DIN 45 635	Measurement of air-borne noise emitted by machines.
Part 1 (1984)	Enveloping surface method; basic requirements for three accuracy classes.
Part 2 (1977)	Reverberation room method; basic measurement method.
Part 3 (1978 D)	Engineering methods for special reverberation test room.
Part 8 (1981 D)	Measurement of structure-borne noise; basic requirements.
Part 24 (1976 D)	Enveloping surface method; liquid pumps.
ISO 3741–3746	Acoustics – Determination of sound power levels of noise sources.
ISO 3741, 3742	Reverberation room method.
ISO 3744	Measuring outdoors or in large rooms.
ISO 3745	Laboratory, anechoic room.
ISO 3746	No special test environment.
ISO 4412/1 1979	Hydraulic fluid power – Test code for the determination of air-borne noise levels – Part 1 : Pumps.
Sound emission	
VDI 3743 1982 sheet 1	Emission characteristics of technical noise sources, centrifugal pumps.
Sound insulation	
VDI 2711 1978	Noise reduction by enclosures.

D denotes draft.

Vibration and Critical Speed

VIBRATION IS a direct source of noise, as well as being undesirable. Bending and whirling are usually the only significant forces as far as vibration is concerned, shafts normally being stiff enough to resist tortional and axial loading without excitation.

Even if the rotating mass is perfectly balanced, there will always be a degree of static deflection or bending of the horizontal shafts due to the dead weight. When the shaft is rotating, this static deflection produces a displacement of the centre of the gravity or unbalanced condition giving rise to a centrifugal force producing a dynamic deflection which is superimposed on the static deflection.

A rotating shaft carrying a rotor with any degree of static unbalance will develop transverse vibrations of very low amplitude, normally restrained by the bearings. The level of vibration (amplitude) is determined by the design geometry, dead weights and speed, and a figure for an acceptable level of vibration is somewhat arbitrary since this may depend on a particular designers experience or established design and manufacturing techniques.

Measuring vibration is a good way of checking conditions. On smaller pumps such checking is mostly performed with portable instruments. On large installations, especially feed pumps, water transport pumps and injection pumps, vibration measuring devices are often fitted permanently, in conjunction with alarm tripping and/or continuous recording in a control room.

The causes of aggravated vibration are manifold. Detailed measurements and analyses carried out by a specialist are often needed for a reliable diagnosis. A distinction must be drawn between system-related and pure pump problems.

System related problems

(i) Unfavourable dynamic behaviour of foundations, supporting structures or pipelines (residence excitation by forces at rotation speed).

(ii) Excitations from the coupling, especially due to misalignment.

(iii) Excitations from the drive (motor, steam turbine, gearing).

(iv) Unfavourable inflow conditions such as insufficient suction pressure (cavitation), swirling (intake vortex, suction pipe with bends in more than one plane).

(v) High pressure pulsations due to hydraulic instability of the entire system.

Pump related problems

(i) Mechanical imbalance of the rotating parts due to inexpert balancing, careless assembly or operational influences (cavitation erosion, deposits, corrosion, damaged impellers, jammed parts, abrasion).

(ii) Unfavourable dynamic behaviour of the rotor due to excessive seal or bearing clearances.

(iii) Increased hydraulic forces when the pump is operated outside of the admissible delivery range. (Some increase in vibration is normal departing from the optimum flow rate).

(iv) Mechanically defective bearings.

Admissible vibration limits depend primarily on the machine design and should therefore be fixed by the manufacturer.

The diagnosis of vibrations in positive displacement pumps should usually include dynamic pressure measurements in the cylinders and piping near the pump. These measurements can be obtained by the use of peizo-electric or strain gauge pressure transducers. If cavitation or flashing is suspected, a pressure transducer capable of measuring static and large dynamic pressures should be used; even then, cavitation produced pressure shocks may damage the transducer. Accelerometers with low frequency characteristics may be used with electronic integrators to obtain accurate vibration displacement data from the pump case, cylinders, or piping. Similarly velocity or seismic pick-ups may be employed. Maximum vibrations usually occur at the middle of piping spans and at unsupported elbows (out of plane).

A tracking filter system for vibration analysis.

Critical speed

Critical speed is the rotational speed which inherent running vibration and free vibration are in resonance, producing marked amplification of the vibration amplitude. Determination of critical speed involves complex calculation and is specific to a particular design. This is further complicated by the fact that the same design of pump may be fitted with impellers of different weights (and thus different static deflections), so that a change in impeller will also result in a change of specific speed. In such cases however, it may be possible to simplify determination of critical speed with different alternatives by presenting solutions in graphical form for that particular pump.

As a general recommendation, the first critical speed should be at least 20% higher than the maximum operating speed, which is readily realisable in practical designs by ensuring that the shaft is stiff enough (*ie* static deflection low). In particular cases, however, it may be desirable to employ a more flexible shaft when the first specific speed will be lower than the normal running speed. This is unavoidable.

Apart from actual damage, (*eg* a bent shaft), the primary source of shaft vibration will then be dynamic unbalance. The fact that the rotating system is statically balanced during manufacture does not necessarily mean that it is also dynamically balanced. In fact, the reverse is usually true. Ideally the rotating assembly should be both statically and dynamically balanced during manufacture as treatment of dynamic unbalance can prove particularly troublesome in the field. Also methods of producing dynamic mechanical balance are not always satisfactory as balance weights attached to the periphery of rotating elements do not necessarily provide perfect compensation, since the elements may be hydrodynamically unbalanced. As a consequence it may well generate considerable vibration at pump rotational speed frequency.

In order to ensure operational reliability of high head pumps, it is important to make a careful analysis of the vibrational behaviour of the rotor. A number of sophisticated computer programs are available for carrying out this analysis and apart from analysing complex rotor shapes, they can also take account of the bearings and labyrinths. These programs deliver data not only on the natural frequencies associated with each vibration mode, but also on the corresponding damping values for each frequency. The forces occuring in the labyrinths and any balancing pistons have a considerable influence on the vibrational behaviour of the rotor. The restoring force acting in opposition to rotor deflection has the effect of increasing the natural frequency, while the transverse force acting in the tangential direction can lead to instabilities in the form of self-excited vibrations.

Apart from programs for computing natural frequencies, there are also programs for computing forced vibrations. These allow for calculation of the amplitudes of shaft vibrations caused by imbalance of forces. Vibrations excited by imbalance forces occur at the rotation frequency (synchronous vibrations) or at higher harmonic frequencies, without the occurrence of subsynchronous vibrations. Subsynchronous vibrations only become noticeable in the case of self-excited vibrations. These can occur for example in boiler feed pumps with heavily worn labyrinths, since with increasing labyrinth clearance, not only the natural frequencies but also the rotor damping rates are reduced.

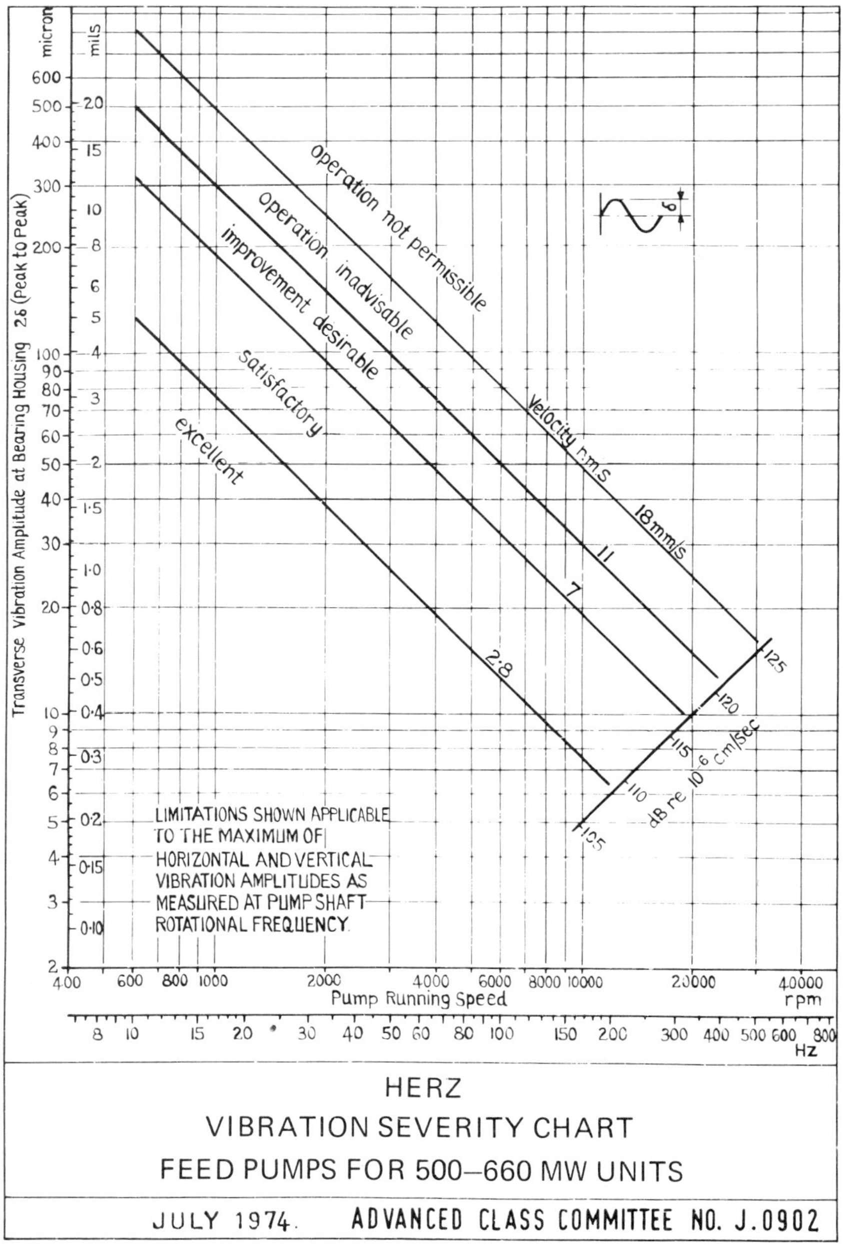

Figure 1
Vibration severity chart showing vibration limits.

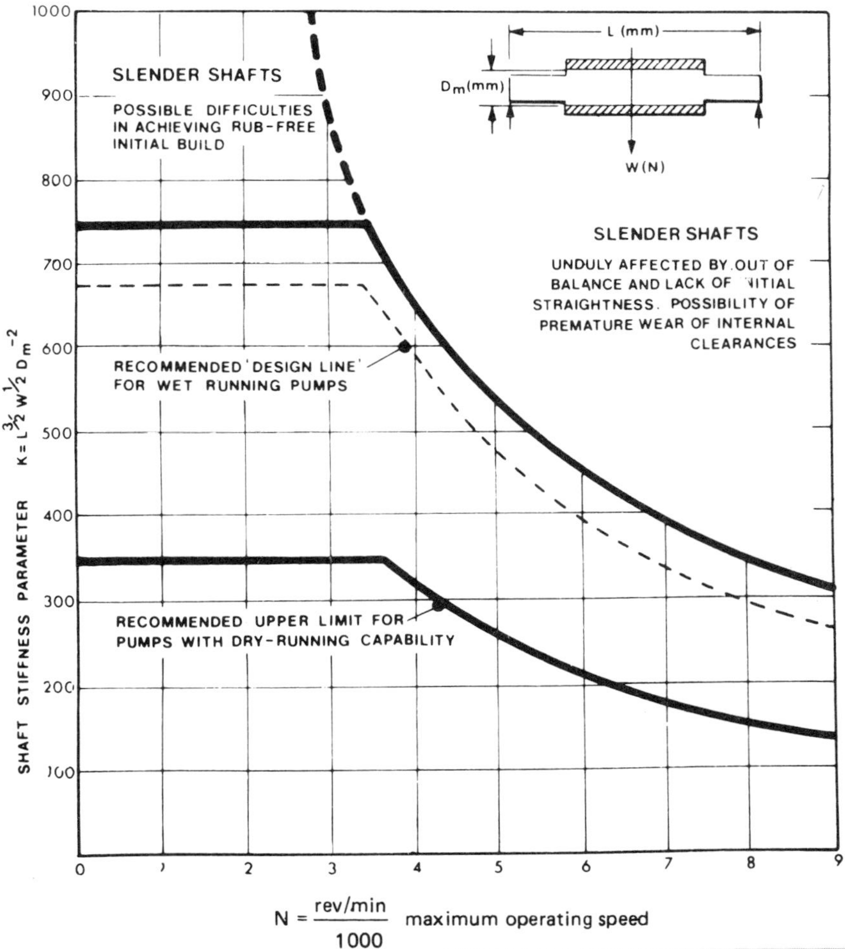

Figure 2
Pump rotor rigidity.

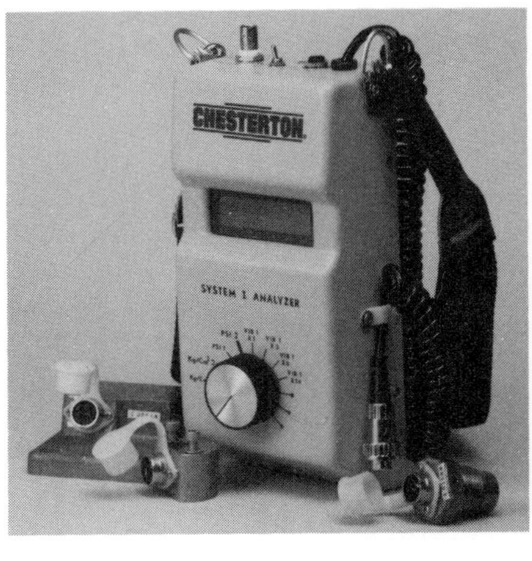

Electronic sensor package

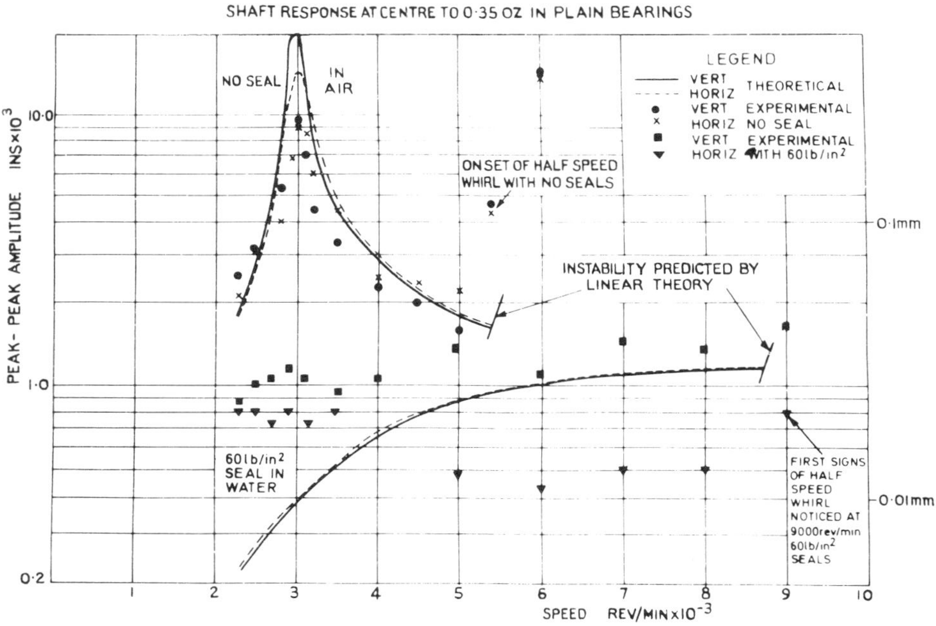

Figure 3
Critical speed of rotor in air and in water.

One of the main tasks of rotor dynamics, especially in the case of high performance pumps, is to modify rotor design so that self excited vibrations are avoided. The natural frequency, abrasion mode configuration and damping depend upon a large number of factors of which only the most important are mentioned here:

Rotor geometry – distance between bearings
Shaft diameter
Mass distribution
Overhung shaft sections

Radial bearings – type
Relative clearance
Loading
Width/diameter ratio
Oil viscosity

Axial bearings – mass
Overhang
Stiffness
Damping
Loading

Shaft coupling – type
Mass
Overhang
Alignment errors

Labyrinths/balanced pistons – labyrinth clearance
- Length
- Diameter
- Surface geometry
- Pressure differential
- Reynolds number, axial
- Reynolds number, tangential
- Inlet and outlet geometry of the gap labyrinth clearance
- Balance piston/sleeve misalignment
- Pre-rotation

Hydraulic excitation – restoring and lateral forces caused by impeller/diffusor interaction
- Dynamic axial thrusts
- Flow separation phenomena (hydraulic instabilities)

Vertical pumps

It is recognised that when vertical pumps are operated at variable speeds, the possibility of vibration increases sharply. Vertical units are often very tall and slender and their bases, pedestals and supports have low natural frequencies. Therefore, rotating unbalance, coupling misalignment, bad bearings, or hydraulic turbulence can exert alternating dynamic forces on the vertical structure. Additionally, as pump speed is changed, frequencies of these dynamic forces also change.

When the frequency of a dynamic force matches the natural frequency of a pump component, resonant vibration occurs. In these cases, vibration is quite vigorous and can be seen without the use of any measuring instrument. When the operating speed varies, the chances that the dynamic force at some condition will match the natural frequency of a base pedestal or support are much greater than if the unit is operated at a constant speed. Vibration at a natural frequency can be difficult to eliminate if not examined in a systematic way.

Vertical units with tall pedestals and supports are less rigid than horizontal units and more likely to possess natural frequencies which are in the normal operating range of a variable speed drive.

Vibration analysis starts with the identification of natural frequencies, determining at what frequencies maximum amplitudes occur. The investigator must operate the pump at many different speeds while the amplitude of vibration is recorded. While amplitude readings must be taken at one location throughout the test, preferably at the location and in the direction where maximum vibration occurs, readings should be taken in many locations through the entire operating range of the pump, recording amplitude, frequency and speed.

Pipework Installation

THE PIPE sizes are determined on hydrodynamic considerations. Pumps are normally fitted with flanges conforming to national or international standard sizes, the branch sizes for a particular pump having been designed to provide optimum performance consistent with the rated performance of the pump. A pipe size matching both the suction and delivery flange should be 'correct' for that particular pump and should establish suitable flow velocities on both the suction and discharge sides.

The flow velocities in individual installations however, may be critical. In such cases it is advisable to calculate the flow velocities given by standard 'flange matching' pipe sizes and to compare them with typical or recommended figures for the type of fluid handled, or the system used. It may be advantageous to adjust the pipe size in certain cases *ie*:

(i) If the suction pipe velocity is too high a larger pipe size will improve NPSH and suction characteristics or increase the suction lift attainable.

(ii) If the delivery pipe velocity is low, some saving in pipework costs may be realised by adopting a small standard size consistent with recommended values of delivery flow velocity (Vd). This will however result in a reduction in working head.

(iii) If the delivery pipe velocity is high, an increase in pipe size will reduce the total head required or increase the available head.

These effects will be most noticeable where the friction head accounts for an appreciable part of the total head. Where the total system head includes only a small proportion of friction head the size of pipe used on the delivery side is mainly significant for its effect on the cost of pipe and fittings.

General rules – suction piping

As a general rule, the suction piping should be somewhat larger than the pump inlet or connection, it should never be smaller. With larger diameter suction piping a reducer is called for between the pipe and pump connection. This should be of the offset or eccentric type to avoid the possibility of an air pocket developing, as could occur with a symmetrical reducing section.

Suction pipe sizing is normally based on recommended flow velocities which vary both with the size of pipe and the type of fluid being handled. The main requirement is to ensure true full bore flow without excessive head loss due to friction and freedom from cavitation, in the case of hot or viscous fluids.

In general a large size of pipe is to be preferred particularly if high losses are anticipated through a long length of suction piping or the presence of bends and fittings; and there is obviously an advantage in reducing the length of the suction piping to a practical minimum. Where no suction lift is present and there are no marked sources of loss, such as excessive length or sharp bends, pipe sizing can be based on arbitary hydraulic gradient and the diameter related to flow rate and fluid viscosity.

General rules – delivery piping

Provided the estimated delivery velocity is not excessively high, a pipe size equal to the delivery flange size should be satisfactory. Further factors which contribute to headloss may, however, have to be considered for finalising the optimum delivery pipe size – *eg* the length of pipe involved, number of fittings and bends and effective head required. In long runs, headloss may become an important factor, favouring the use of larger pipe diameters, although savings in this respect must be weighed against the increased cost of pipework.

against the increased cost of pipework. Anything other than this which can be done to minimise total head loss will provide more economic operation, *eg* runs made as straight as possible, small radius bends or loops avoided, and the number of valves and fittings kept to a minimum. Another factor which may be significant over an extended period of time is deterioration of the pipe bore when handling a particular fluid. Thus the frictional loss in old pipes may increase to several times that of new pipes over a period of 20 years or more or even more rapidly in the case of direct chemical attack.

Delivery pipelines should aim at achieving straight runs with a minimum of bends and gradients. The latter, together with upward loops can contribute to 'water hammer' developing in long runs as well as increasing the head loss. Otherwise, requirements are unlikely to be critical although every attempt should be made to reduce or minimise energy losses.

In large capacity, low head systems, the outlet can contribute a considerable proportion of the total head loss. These losses can be reduced and the efficiency of the system improved by optimum design of the pipe outlet. Open discharge is wasteful of energy since both the velocity head and full distance represent head losses. Such losses are substantially reduced if the outlet is carried below the liquid surface, and minimised if the final section is tapered to give divergent flow.

The following illustrations are guidelines for designing suction and inlet pipelines. It should be noted that these are minimum requirements and must be adhered to.

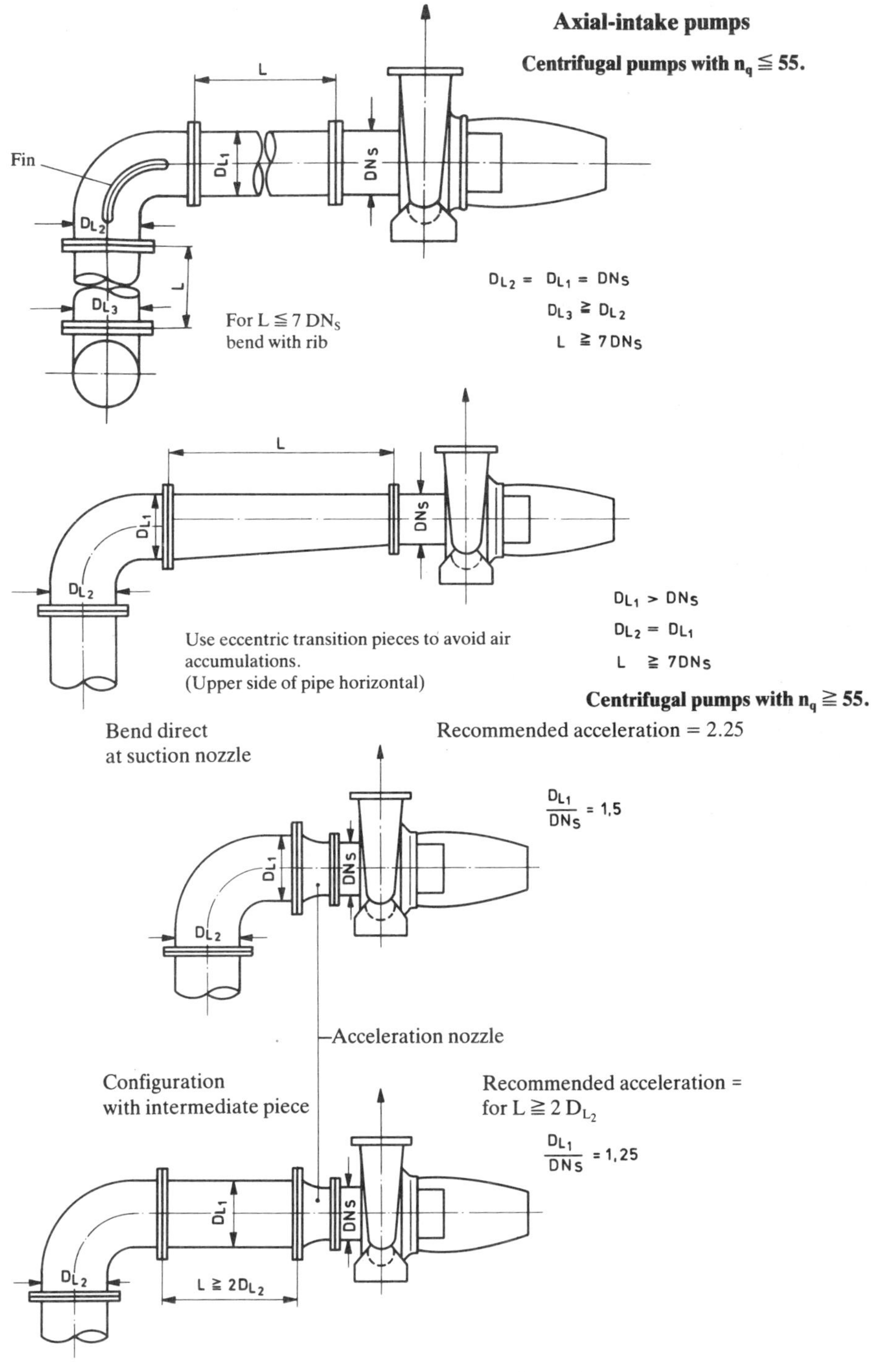

Acceleration nozzle before suction nozzle.

Figure 1
Suction and inlet pipeline design for axial intake pumps and double entry pumps.

Double-entry pumps

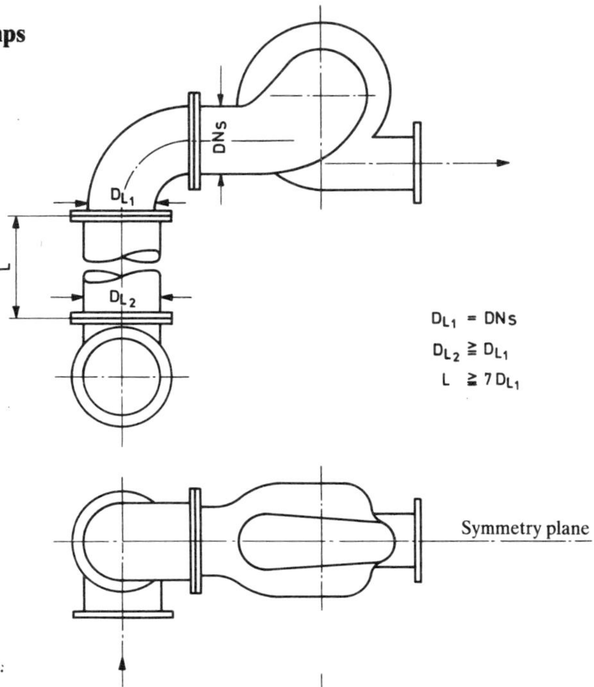

Bend in symmetry plane.

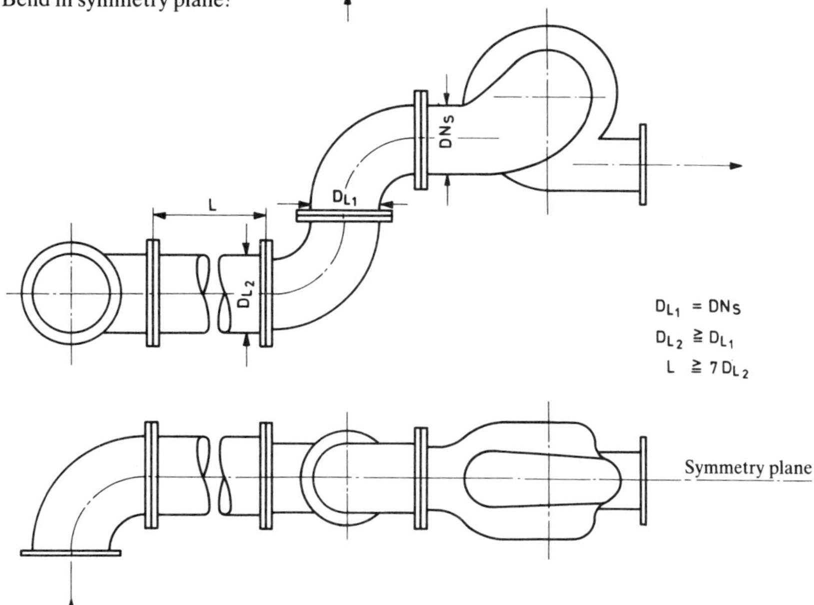

Double bend in symmetry plane.

Figure 1
Suction and inlet pipeline design for axial intake pumps and double entry pumps (contd...)

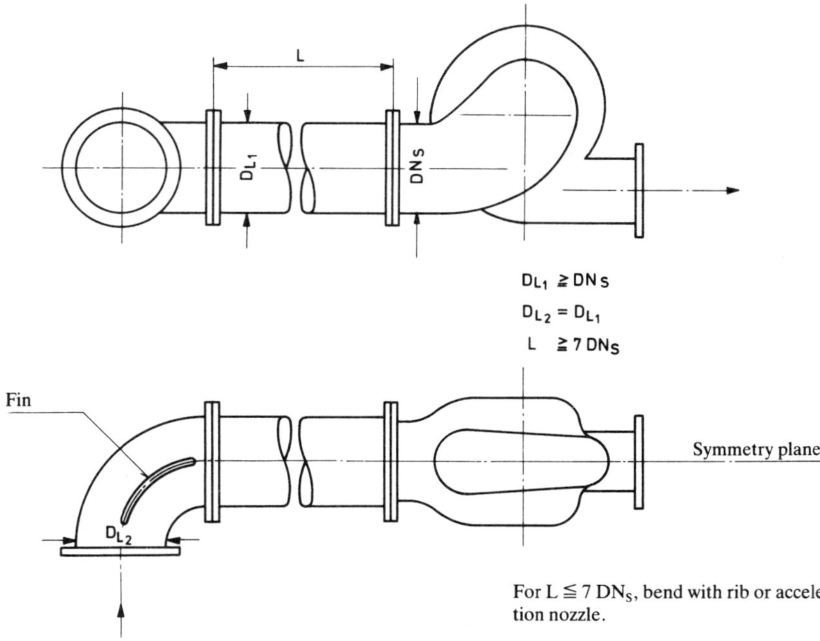

For L ≦ 7 DN_S, bend with rib or acceleration nozzle.

Bend at right angles to symmetry plane.

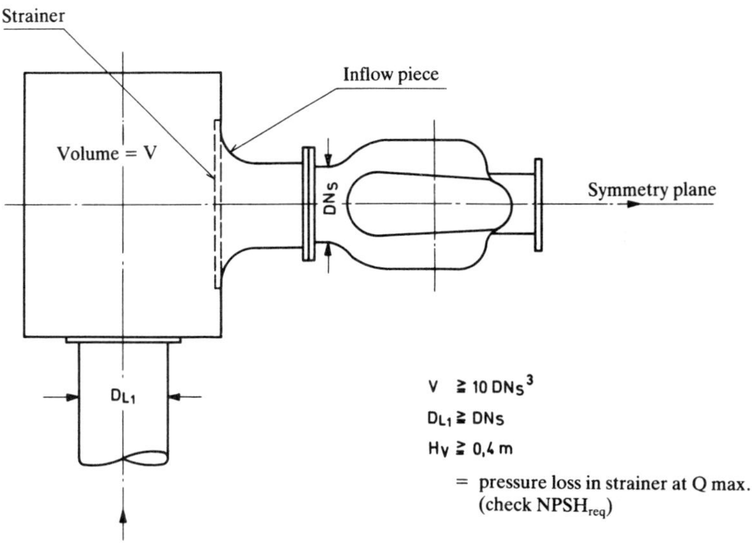

Inlet box with inflow at right angles to the symmetry plane.

Figure 1
Suction and inlet pipeline design for axial intake pumps and double entry pumps (contd...)

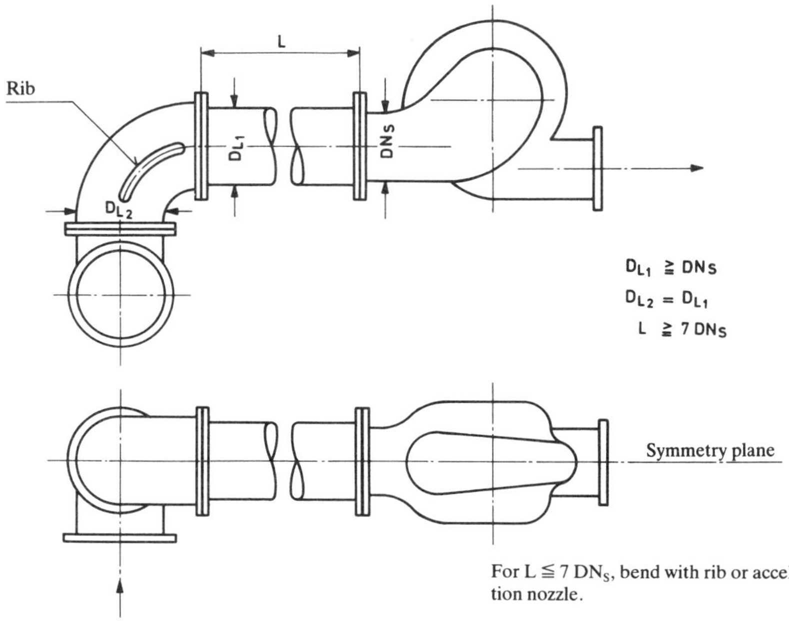

For $L \leqq 7\,DN_S$, bend with rib or acceleration nozzle.

Double bend in different planes.

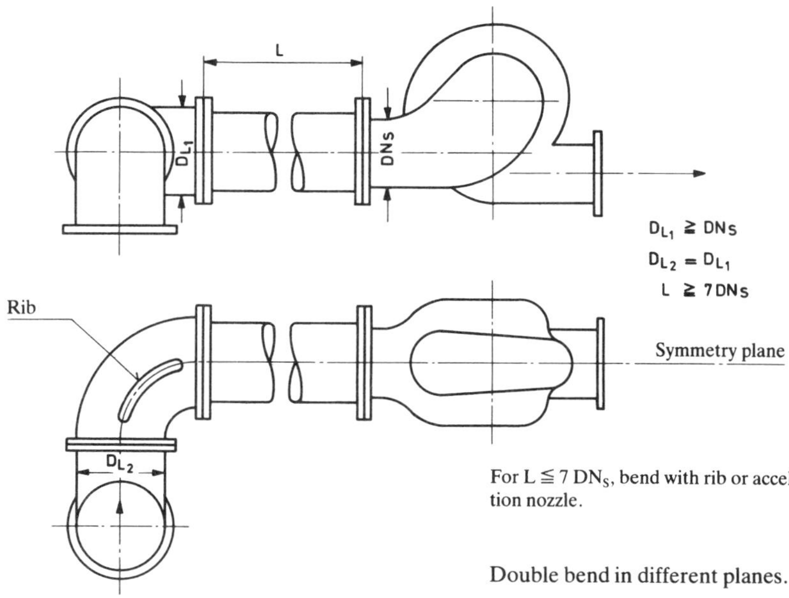

For $L \leqq 7\,DN_S$, bend with rib or acceleration nozzle.

Double bend in different planes.

Figure 1
Suction and inlet pipeline design for axial intake pumps and double entry pumps (contd...)

Reciprocating pumps

Reciprocating pumps may need special consideration because of the pulsating nature of the flow. To minimise the effect of pump pulsation frequency, piping should be as short and direct as possible, with the minimum number of bends. Piping should also be such that the natural frequency of any span is equal to or greater than twice the pump pulsation frequency, and mean flow velocities on the suction side should be held to the following values:

0·6 metres/sec (2·0 ft/sec) for pump speeds up to 250 r/min.

0·45 metres/sec (1·5 ft/sec) for pump speeds up to 330 r/min.

0·3 metres/sec (1·0 ft/sec) for pump speeds above 330 r/min.

This will normally call for suction piping one or two sizes larger than the pump suction inlet. Pipe size is less critical on the delivery side where mean flow velocities can be up to three times the valves given previously.

Pipeline supports

Pipes carrying fluids normally need supporting at regular intervals, both to carry the weight of the pipe and also to restrict movement, particularly at bends, under changing pressure loads (and also to 'detune' them in the case of reciprocating pumps).

Axial movement of pipes can be accommodated by suitable geometry or the incorporation of flexible sections or expansion joints as necessary.

Resilient mounting of pipes, *eg* on clips or mounts with resilient lining, can accommodate movement and also serve to eliminate resonant amplification of noise and vibration by isolation and damping. The original generator of noise and/ or vibration may be the pump itself or pressure pulsations in the pump delivery. The original noise level may not in itself be objectionable or even apparent, until it is amplified by resonant effects. Treatment aimed at eliminating resonance by isolation or decoupling of the source is nearly always simpler and more effective than attempted damping of the source.

Treatment aimed at eliminating resonance by isolation or decoupling of the source is nearly always simpler and more effective than attempted damping of the source.

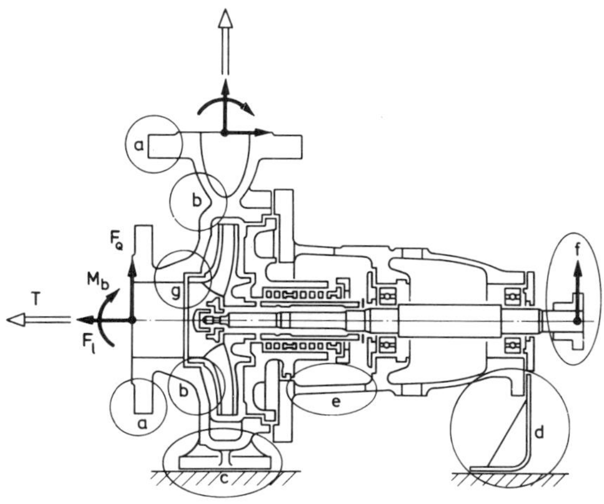

Effect of pipe loads on a pump.

Pipe isolation by means of resilient lined clips or hangers not only prevents pipe vibration from being transmitted direct to possible resonant rigid panels *via* rigid connections, but also provides effective damping of pipe vibrations themselves which can considerably reduce radiated noise.

The same principle of isolation can be usefully applied to throughways and end fittings. It should be borne in mind however, that the effectiveness of isolation depends very largely on the mass to which the isolating fittings are attached; the more solid and massive these masses are the more effective they will be.

Decoupling normally involves the use of a flexible element in the system itself which will absorb and damp vibration. It can thus be effective in preventing noise being transmitted from one part of a system to another, whether or not resonant effects are present.

In the case of a reciprocating pump, mechanical resonance can occur in a pipe span where the natural frequency of the span approximates to the pump 'driving' frequency *viz*:

$$\text{Driving frequency } F_d = n \times \frac{N}{60}$$

where:

n = number of pump pistons or plungers

N = pump r/min

For satisfactory performance (*ie* absence of resonance) the natural mechanical frequency of any pipe span should be equal to or greater than (n x N)/30

At the same time the pipe support structure should be much stiffer than the pipe spans supported, which should not be tied into lightly braced structures. Elbows, flanges, valves and other fittings should be located near supports and not in the central span where they would greatly reduce the natural frequency of the span. Figure 1 summarises good practice.

Auxiliary pipework

The auxiliary piping required may or may not be supplied by the pump manufacturer. If it is not, requirements can normally be met from stock sizes of small bore tubing utilising standard fittings. The exact arrangement, type and size of tubing *etc*, will depend on the type of pump, pumping temperature, liquid handled and other service conditions. In certain cases auxiliary lines may take the form of standard flexible hose with detachable self-sealing couplings for rapid attachment and removal, *eg* auxiliary piping for cleaning processed lines or similar duties.

Pipe joints and couplings

Classical methods of joining pipes rigidly are:

(i) Threaded joints – offering low installation cost but mostly practical for small diameter pipes with thick walls.

(ii) Flanged joints – particularly suitable for installing valves and fittings.

(iii) Welded joints – suitable for any size of pipe but requiring special skills for the welding operation.

Brazing and soldering are alternatives to welding for low pressure work, particularly for copper and copper alloy pipes.

Bonded joints

Adhesive bonded joints are a proposition only where the tube or pipe material is suitable for such treatment – *eg* certain types of plastic tube may be joined by adhesive bonding – but in general the performance achieved will be inferior to that given by alternative methods. Adhesive bonding on the metallic pipes offers no advantages and many disadvantages compared with conventional jointing methods.

Pressure surges in pipeline systems

In pipeline systems any change in the operating state leads to dynamic pressure changes, which must be taken into account in the planning and operation of installations. They are capable of causing serious damages. Water conveyance and supply systems are often extremely varied in nature so that it is impossible to find by approximation procedures a solution that will reliably preclude over-stressing of components in any systems.

In steady operation, the flow velocity is constant in time and place. By contrast, in transient flow, the velocity varies in time and place. Transient flows occur at every change from an existing steady operating state to a new one. Pressure surges result from transient flows.

Consequently the following operations on pumping installations are attended by surging problems:

(i) Starting a pump.
(ii) Stopping a pump.
(iii) Switching over pumps.
(iv) Altering the valve setting.
(v) Altering the speed.
(vi) Power failure on one or more pumps.
(vii) Inexpert operation.

With the exceptions of power failure and inexpert operation, all of them are deliberate actions which can be performed properly. On the other hand power failures are unintentional and generally constitute the most extreme case. Additional safety devices must be provided against power failure in particular.

Control of pressure surges

Although surges in long delivery mains cannot altogether be eliminated when a roto-dynamic pumping set suddenly stops working, there are various ways of bringing them within safe limits. These methods include:

(i) Flywheel on pump or motor shaft – a flywheel mounted on the motor shaft will help to maintain the speed of the rotating part after power has been cut off. A precaution that may be necessary, on account of additional inertia of the rotating parts, is to modify the motor starting gear so that the set can be started from rest more slowy.
(ii) Surge suppressor – this is the name given to a positively operated relief valve or bypass valve mounted in a branch of the delivery main just upstream of the normal reflux valve.
(iii) Air vessel – a capacious closed air vessel or air chamber connected to the delivery pipe upstream of the reflux valve will often reduce the

intensity of surge pressures, although at the cost of propagating low frequency disturbances that depend upon the expansion and contraction of the compressed air in the chamber.

(iv) Surge tank or surge chamber – in low-head installations, the chamber may take the form of an open-top cylindrical tower in which the water surface can freely oscillate. Reserve of water stored in the tank permits the pressure and velocity changes in the pipe to lag behind those in the pump branch and in this way surge pressures are reduced.

(v) Power operated control valves – in very large and important medium-head and high-head installations, no type of reflux valve could be made safe. Instead a single main control valve is interposed in the delivery pipe, which acts either as an isolating valve or as a surge-supressor. Operated by servo-motor this valve begins to close automatically as soon as the electric supply to the pump motor fails.

Heated pipes and piping

The desirability (or in some cases necessity) for heating one or more components in a pumping system depends both on the product involved and the circumstances or specific requirements. These can be considered under the following headings:

(i) Frost protection.

(ii) Maintenance of products temperature for optimum handling characteristics or to avoid heat losses.

(iii) Provision or maintenance of a suitable fluid viscosity for satisfactory or economic pumping.

Frost protection

Where the product may be subject to freezing at low ambient temperatures the simplest treatment is by thermal insulation or lagging, reducing the rate of heat loss from the product itself and so delaying the onset of freezing. This does not eliminate the possibility of freezing in the long term and so some form of heating may also be necessary. This can take the form of heaters used to maintain the ambient temperature above freezing level; immersion heaters to maintain the products temperature; or electric surface heaters applied directly to the pipes (and also pump and valves, if necessary).

Maintaining product temperature

This can be accomplished by immersion heaters in the stock container, associated with pipe lagging as necessary; or by electric surface heaters applied to the container and/or pipework. As a general rule the total loading of heaters should be at least 15% greater than the heat losses anticipated to allow for unforeseen variables. Also in the case of heat sensitive products, it is important that the heat loading should be applied evenly to avoid localised over-heating.

Pump heating

Basic methods of heating a pump are:

(i) Circulation of a suitable heating fluid through a double-walled pump casing.

(ii) Electrical heating by special heating elements incorporated in the pump casing.

(iii) Heating by special jackets incorporating electrical heating elements.

Methods (i) and (ii) demand special pump construction. Method (iii) can be applied to standard (non heated) pumps, with certain limitations.

With method (i) hot water can be used as the heating fluid to achieve temperatures of up to 90 to 95 °C (195 to 205 °F), or somewhat higher in a closed pressurised system. Steam heating can provide temperatures of the order of 150 to 180 °C (300 to 355 °F), depending on the steam pressure available. A wider range of working temperatures can be provided by electrical heating with the advantage that electricity of clean, reliable, easily controlled and capable of repeating performance exactly.

A further advantage of electric heaters is that they can be rendered 'flame proof' using metal sheathed mineral insulation heating elements flameproof glands screwing into flameproof junction boxes which are 'Buxton' certified. It is then necessary to ensure that the stabilisation temperature reached is below the ignition temperatures of flammable concentrations which could be present. This can be ensured by the use of suitable control to maintain the temperature of the equipment at the correct level and at the same time keep power consumption to minimum.

Heated pipelines

Generally speaking heated pipelines are mainly used in the chemical industry for processes involving the conveyance of viscous fluids which do not flow readily at ambient temperatures. These take the form of jacketed pipes in carbon steel (usually) stainless steel or other alloys, through which steam or some other heating fluid can be circulated. Jackets are normally made from the same material as the pipe to avoid difficulties which may arise from electrolytic corrosion due to two dissimilar metals being in contact. Erosion-corrosion may also be a problem and stainless steel impingement plates are often fitted at the point of entry of the heating fluid to protect the pipe from excessive wear. Jacketed pipes are of standard production available in straight lengths, using two different sizes of pipe. Bends may be constructed either by bending the product and jacket pipes by hot forming or by the use of welded fittings depending on size, bend radius, *etc.*.

Heating tapes

An alternative method more applicable to general duties, is pipe heating using flexible electric heating tapes. A loading of approximately 33 watts per metre run (10 watts per foot run) is usually adequate for most general purpose pumping applications and will compensate for temperatures up to 100 °C (210 °F) when straight traced and applied under woven glass cloth. This is suitable for use at temperatures up to 350 °C (660 °F). To render the tape waterproof an additional layer of silicon rubber may be extruded over the standard insulation. Further types are covered by PVC sheeting for full weatherproofing (*eg* for frost protection of water pumps at outdoor installations). A tape with a loading of 49 watts per metre run (15 watts per foot run) will compensate for temperatures of up to 149 °C (300 °F) when straight traced under lagging a spiral lay for the tape will appreciably increase the temperature compensation provided.

An extension of pipeline heating is provided by electrically heated flexible hose. This has particular application where viscous fluids have to be handled through a flexible line and where there may be a serious reduction of flow or even blockage due to cooling in low temperature conditions.

Bursting discs

Bursting discs or rupture discs as they are also called, consist of a thin diaphragm clamped in a suitable holder to fit into the wall of a pipeline or pressure vessel which is designed to rupture a predetermined pressure. They act as a safety valve against over pressure with nominally full bore passage for the discharge of pressure. The large venting area provided, together with the inherently low inertia of the disc, is particularly useful for safeguarding pressure vessels and plant systems against rises in pressure associated with excessive surge pressures, explosions or rapid combustion.

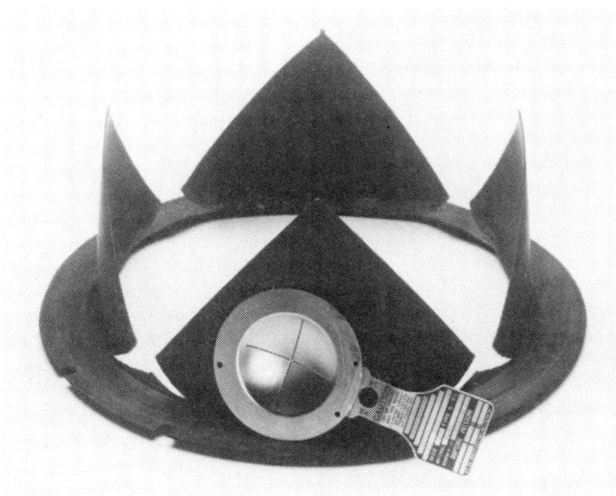

Perfectly burst disc.

The majority of bursting discs comprise a ductile metal foil clamped in an accurately machined circular holder. The disc is either flat, in which case the edges of the holder are radius; or pre-domed, in which case the holder clamps the flange section of the disc. Under pressure a flat disc expands into a spheroidial shape with a thinning of material towards the crown, until eventually with increasing pressure it will burst. Pre-domed discs are normally preferred in modern installations since pre- doming reduces fatigue failure, increases creep resistance and generally prolongs disc life. Pre-doming is normally accomplished by the application of hydraulic pressure to within 90% of the burst pressure. This strains the disc well beyond the normal working range so that under normal operating conditions no further deflection takes place the pre-doming operation also provides a quality check control on the disc material.

Burst pressures available from proprietary discs range from under 0·07 bar (1 lb/in^2) to over 275 bar (4000 lb/in^2). The actual burst pressure realised will be dependent on pressure and creep. Under the effect of creep the disc will eventually fail at a lowered 'burst' pressure which may be realised by the system pressure. Thus the actual working life of a bursting disc is a function of the creep characteristics of the metal employed and the working pressure:bursting pressure ratio. Typical minimum burst pressures for plain diaphragm discs at ambient temperatures are given in Table 1. Table 2 gives pressure factors for creep and temperature effects using conventional discs.

TABLE 1 – TYPICAL MINIMUM BURST PRESSURES FOR PLAIN DIAPHRAGM DISCS – ORIFICE SIZE 25 mm (1 in)

Disc Material	Burst Pressure bar	Burst Pressure lb/in^2	Disc Material	Burst Pressure bar	Burst Pressure lb/in^2
Aluminium	1.75	25	Palladium	6.3	90
Copper	6.3	90	18/8 Ti stainless steel	49	700
Gold	3.15	45	Silver	5.25	75
Lead	4.2	60	Titanium	35	500
Monel	15.75	225	Neoprene	2.52	36
Nickel	8.4	120	PTFE	1.4	20
Platinum	8.4	120	Lead-lined aluminium	6.3	90

TABLE 2 – PRESSURE FACTORS FOR CREEP AND TEMPERATURE EFFECTS (CONVENTIONAL DISCS)

Material	Temperature °C 20	50	60	100	150	175	200	300
Aluminium	0·70	0·50	0·40	–	zero	–	–	–
Silver	0·60	0·50	–	–	zero	–	–	–
Copper	0·70	–	–	–	–	zero	–	–
Nickel	0·95	–	–	–	–	0·90	0·65	0·50
18/8 Ti stainless steel	0·95	–	–	0·90	–	0·75	0·65	0·50
Platinum	0·80	–	0·70	–	–	0·50	–	–
Monel	0·90	–	–	–	–	–	–	–
Neoprene	0·70	0·70	0·70	zero	–	–	–	–
PTFE and PTCFE	0·70	0·70	zero	–	–	–	–	–
Lead-lined aluminium	0·70	0·65	0·60	zero	–	–	–	–

TABLE 3 – EFFECT OF TEMPERATURE ON REVERSE BUCKLING DISCS

Material	0·50	0	20	50	100	150	200	250
Aluminium	1·5	1·03	1·0	0·96	0·89	0·76	–	–
Monel	–	–	1·0	0·99	0·96	0·94	0·92	0·90
Nickel	1·20	1·04	1·0	0·99	0·96	0·94	0·92	0·90
Silver	1·10	1·02	1·0	0·97	0·92	–	–	–
Stainless	1·30	1·04	1·0	0·99	0·99	0·99	0·98	0·97

Figures indicated % change from anticipated bursting pressure calculated at 20 °C.

A general recommendation with metal discs is that the working pressure should not be greated that 70 to 75% of the burst pressure. Alternatively reverse buckling discs can be used where working pressures can be as high as 90% of the burst pressure. Table 3 shows the effect of temperature on reverse buckling discs.

Shear discs

For high pressure working, shearing discs may be preferred to tensile discs. In this case the material is usually hard worked rather than annealed and mounted in a holder which has a sharp rim against which the disc is forced to shear under 'burst' pressure. The centre of the disc may thickened or reinforced to promote shear failure along the intended line. Alternatively, the disc may be thicker throughout and machined with a groove to provide a local sheer line. Repeatability of performance is generally less exact than with tensile discs.

Materials

Standard materials normally used for the discs are aluminium, copper, nickle, stainless steel and silver. In general, pure materials are preferred to alloys as being more suitable for exact reproduction from batch to batch. Gold, palladium and platinum may be selected for extremely corrosive conditions or for eliminating any possible contamination of the product being handled. Titanium may be employed for high temperature services. Other metals used include lead and monel; composite metals may be used with a coating of corrosion-resistant metal on a base

TABLE 4 – BURSTING DISC MATERIALS – MAXIMUM WORKING TEMPERATURE AND PRESSURE RANGE

Action	Type		Maximum Working Temp °C	Diameter		Typical Pressure Range For 25 mm (1 in) Orifice		Remarks
				mm	in	bar	lb/in²	
Tensile	Metal	Aluminium	100	6–500	¼–20	1.5–47	20–680	Used for low pressures.
		Copper	120–150	6–600	¼–24	3–125	40–1 800	
		Gold	80	6–500	¼–20	1–125	15–1 800	
		Lead	70–80	6–450	¼–18			
		Monel	450	6–500	¼–20	7–280	100–4 000	For corrosion resistance at high temperatures.
		Nickel	410–450	6–600	¼–24	7–210	100–3 000	For corrosion resistance at high temperatures.
		Palladium	300	6–300	¼–12	2–210	30–3 000	
		Platinum	400	6–450	¼–18	3.5–140	50–2000	
		Silver	120–150	6–500	¼–20	3.5–100	50–1 400	
		Stainless steel	250–300	6–300	¼–12	50–210	700–3000	Corrosive services.
		Tantalum	150–250	6–300	¼–12	35–50	500–750	Corrosive services.
		Titanium	300	6–300	¼–12	35–210	500–3000	For high temperatures.
	Plated Metals	Noble metal plating						For corrosion resistance and/or improved strength under corrosive conditions.
		Sheffield plate						
	Coated Metals	Plastomers	As for coating					PTFE or PTFCE
		Thermoset resin						Epoxy resin.
	Non-Metallic	Neoprene	65					
		Rubber canvas						
		Compressed asbestos						
Shear	Metallic	Plain metal	As for metal above					Less consistent than tensile discs.
		Grooved metal						
	Non-Metallic	Graphite	160	25–600	1–24	1–85	1–1 200	For corrosive duties.
		Toughened glass	150	150–1 100	6–44			Normally for explosion protection.

metal. The coating metal in such cases provides corrosion resistance and the base metal be necessary mechanical strength at reduced overall cost. Examples include platinum and gold plating lead lined aluminium and Sheffield plate. Table 4 gives details of bursting disc material together with maximum working temperature and pressure ranges.

Installation

Correct installation depends on the disc being mounted in a suitable matching holder. For high pressure working, the periphery of the disc may be V-flanged and the holders shaped accordingly to provide a wedging action. This may be necessary to resist extrusion of the disc under high differential pressures which could appreciably modify the performance of the disc.

SECTION 6

Pump Ancillaries

PRIME MOVERS – ELECTRIC MOTORS
PRIME MOVERS – INTERNAL COMBUSTION ENGINES
PUMP DRIVES AND SPEED CONTROL
CONTROL AND MEASUREMENT
FILTERS AND STRAINERS

Prime Movers – Electric Motors

ELECTRIC MOTORS are normally the first choice for driving pumps requiring input forces up to 250 kW. An a.c. motor being the logical choice as more efficient and more cost-effective than a d.c. motor. The main exceptions are small pumps which may be driven by 12 V or 24 V battery powered d.c. motors to make them independent of any external power supply.

The most common motor used to drive pumps is the squirrel-cage induction motor. This is basically a constant speed machine, the synchronous or no-load speed being dependent on the supply frequency and the number of poles, *viz*:

$$N = \frac{120 \times f}{p}$$

where:

N = speed in r/min
f = line power frequency (Hz)
p = number of poles

When the motor is on load, speed drops slightly, so practical speeds on 50Hz supply are:

2-pole 2900 r/min
4-pole 1450 r/min
6-pole 950 r/min
8-pole 720 r/min
10-pole 580 r/min

Approximate efficiency curves of electric motors as a function of loading are shown in Figure 1.

A cage induction motor can be wound to give two, three or four separate speeds. This can be achieved by a special single winding in which the number of poles is changed by reconnection *via* an appropriate starter to give either a simple 2:1 speed ratio or, by the more complicated Pole Amplitude Modulated system (PAM), wider speed ratios. A speed ratio of 3:1 cannot be achieved using the PAM system. Multi-speed motors are also made by using two separate windings and this system must be employed to achieve three or four speed motors.

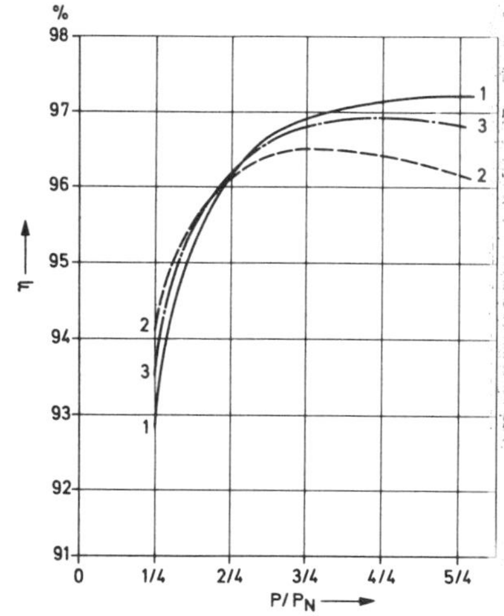

1 = Synchronous motor, 2500 kW, 6 kV, 1500 min^{-1}, $\cos \varphi = 1.0$
2 = Synchronous motor, 2000 kW, 6 kV, 1500 min^{-1}, $\cos \varphi = 0.8$ over-excited
3 = Squirrel-cage motor, 2500 kW, 6 kV, 1500 min^{-1}

Figure 1
Approximate efficiency curves of electric motors as a function of loading P/PN.

Electric motor coupled to vacuum pump in process application.

Type of electric motors

The majority of motors to metric specifications produced today, have a frame size output to speed relationship that has been laid down in both British Standards and documents published by the IEC (International Electro-Technical Commission). Most of these motors are built with class B insulation systems, with a permissible temperature rise of 80 °C when measured by resistance. Other insulation grades are sometimes offered or specified, principally class F; this usually happens in special circumstances, such as where there is a high ambient temperature. If a class F system is run with its permissible temperature of 100 °C, its operating life will be similar to that of a class B system operating with an 80 °C permissible rise.

Smaller pumps may be driven by single phase a.c. motors, though few single phase motors over 25 h.p. are used. Series motors are mainly of a fractional h.p. sizes; they have a high starting torque, but the speed of the motor rises appreciably on reduced load and vice versa. The governor control series motor is an uncommon type, but has the advantage of a high starting torque combined with an almost constant speed over its full range of load.

The squirrel-cage motor is a robust unit and can be regarded as a general purpose type motor. It is suitable for a large number of working machines and is therefore utilised in all branches of industry.

Generally speaking a high speed motor is cheaper for a given torque value. Where a gear train is used, the cost of motor plus gear train must be taken into account when determining the appropriate motor speed.

The slip ring rotor type of three-phase asynchronous motor requires greater expenditure both for purchase and operation, *eg* servicing of slip rings and brushes. It is therefore used for those applications where the simple squirrel-cage motor is inadequate. Its advantages are:

(i) Low starting current.
(ii) High starting torque.
(iii) Easy speed changing (loss-free or dissipative).
(iv) Permits a high switching frequency.

For dryers where the speed is not controlled and where the switching frequency is low, a design incorporating the brush lift-off and short circuiting device is recommended in order to reduce servicing expenditure and improve efficiency.

Unlike the asynchronous motor, the synchronous type requires no reactive power for its excitation. Depending on the field current value the synchronous motor can even delivery reactive power to the electricity supply grid. Its range of application covers drives of medium and high power, at continuous constant speed operation.

Selection

Selection of a motor is dependent on power requirement, speed and drive conditions of a centrifugal pump. Motor size is also influenced by the type of current, the voltage and the frequency of the electricity supply grid.

The following additional information is necessary to assure appropriate sizing:

(i) The requirements imposed by the centrifugal pump.
(ii) The ambient conditions.
(iii) The grid connection data.
(iv) Any special regulations in force.

Pump requirements on the motor

The requirements imposed by a centrifugal pump on the motor are as follows:

(i) Type of centrifugal pump.
(ii) Power requirement or indicator diagram (as a function of flood rate, speed or time).
(iii) Function
Working cycle (switching frequency)
Gear

(iv) Speed
Speed adjustment range
Direction of rotation

(v) Start-up with or without load
Load moment curve
Mass moment of inertia

(vi) Control conditions
Control magnitude
Precision

(vii) Any mechanical or electrical breaking
Breaking torque curve

(viii) Installation
Fastening, foundation
Physical configuration
Force transfer to centrifugal pump
Additional axial and radial forces incident on the end of the motor shaft.
Shaft end dimensions.

Ambient conditions

(i) Ambient temperature
Temperature of cooling medium (air, water)
Contamination of air – acid vapours, moisture, dust.
Analysis of water

(ii) Special conditions
Explosive gas mixtures
Fire – damp (methane)
Installation in open air *etc.*

(iii) Altitude of installation (distance above sea level)

(iv) Type of protection.

(v) Shaking.

(vi) Additional regulations.
Motor noise level
Motor vibrations *etc.*

Grid connection details

(i) Type of current, voltage, voltage fluctuations, frequency.

(ii) Safe operating values; start-up current, power factor.

Special specifications

(i) National regulations

(ii) Climatic conditions

(iii) Special instructions concerning operation, storage, transport, servicing *etc.*

Starting characteristics

During running-up to operating speed, the torque of an asynchronous motor varies in accordance with a characteristic curve which is established by the following quantities:

T_A Starting torque at standstill
T_K Pull-out torque as maximum value during running-up
T_S Pull-up torque as minimum value during running-up,
where T_S is less than T_A

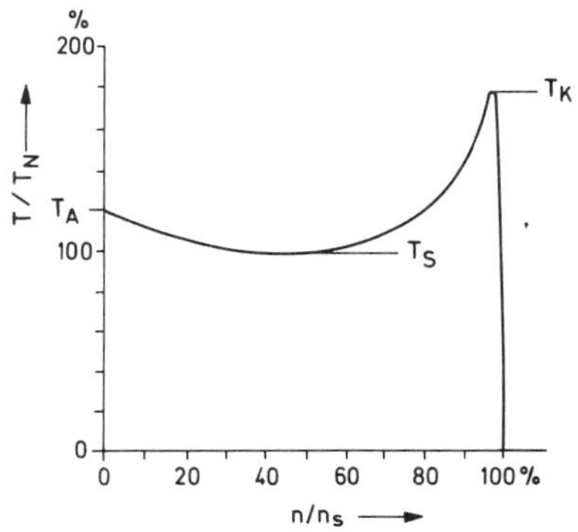

Figure 2
Characteristic curve.

The characteristic curve is dependent on the following:

(i) In the case of squirrel-cage motors the rotor slot shape and cage material hence it can be matched to operating conditions by appropriate choice of these.

(ii) In the case of slip ring motors, on the resistance of the windings and on the external resistance applied to the motor circuit.

Starting characteristics of three-phase squirrel-cage motors

Typical characteristic curves are shown in Figure 3 for the following types of squirrel-cage motor:

(i) Deep slot rotor with low starting torque.

(ii) Deep slot rotor with starting torque.

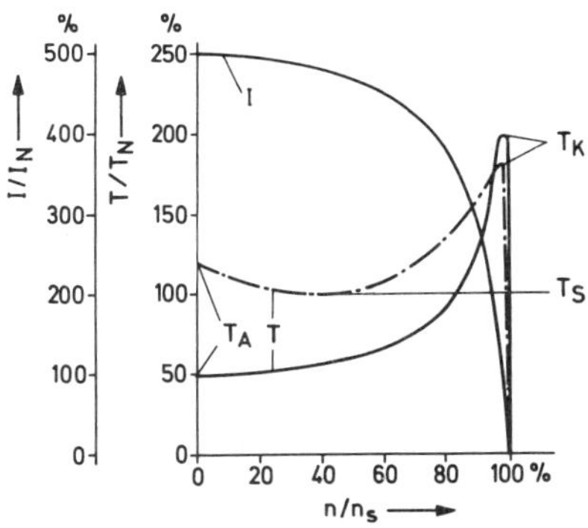

Deep slot rotor ——— Double slot rotor —·—·—
T Torque
T_N Nominal torque
T_A Starting torque
T_S Pull-up torque
T_K Pull-out torque
n Speed
n_s Synchronous speed
I Starting current
I_N Nominal current

Figure 3
Typical starting characteristics of three-phase squirrel-cage motors.

When directly connected at full grid voltage, three-phase squirrel-cage motors make up a transient current which can amount to between 4 and 6 times rated current, depending on power and the number of poles. During run-up the current decreases to a value corresponding to the load, *eg* to rated current when rated load is applied. The starting current can be reduced by special start up procedures (when pump start-up torque so permits).

Starting characteristics of three-phase slip ring induction motors
In the case of slip-ring induction motors, additional resistance Rv inserted into the rotor current circuit serve to raise the torque during start up and also to increase pour-out slip. In general, the resistances are so chosen that it is possible to start up from standstill with rated torque, which corresponds approximately to rated current. In extreme cases, rated pull-out torque is available at standstill. See Figure 4. At the same time, the starting current of the slip ring induction motor, by comparison with that of the squirrel-cage motor is limited by the additional resistances Rv.

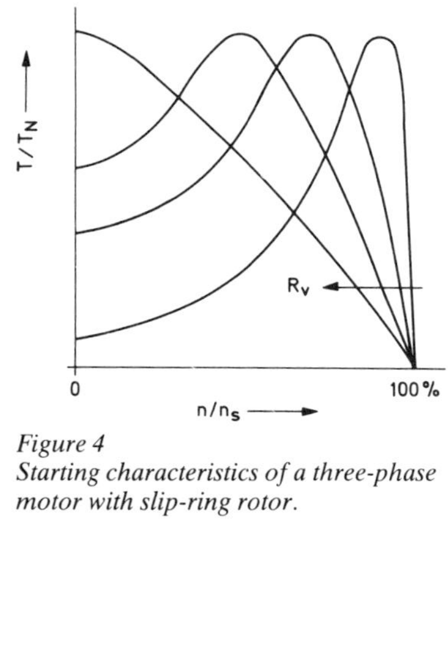

Figure 4
Starting characteristics of a three-phase motor with slip-ring rotor.

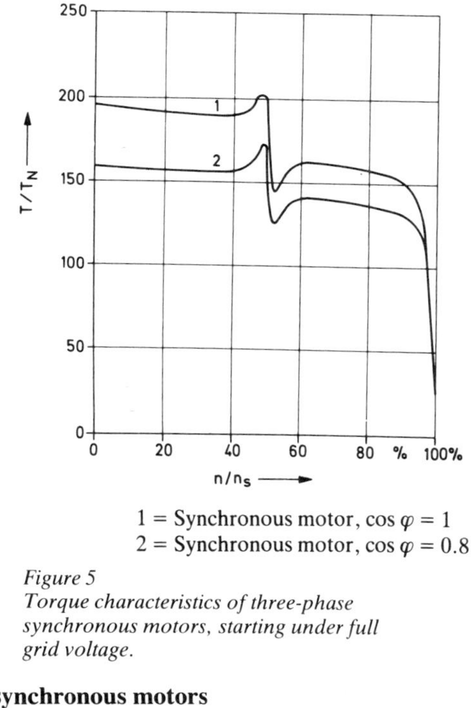

1 = Synchronous motor, cos $\varphi = 1$
2 = Synchronous motor, cos $\varphi = 0.8$

Figure 5
Torque characteristics of three-phase synchronous motors, starting under full grid voltage.

Starting characteristics of three-phase synchronous motors
The start-up of synchronous motors usually takes place asynchronously. The shape of the speed/torque characteristic is dependent on the the design of the pole pieces and the damper winding. The characteristic curve of the starting torque produced by a synchronous motor with solid pole pieces is shown in Figure 5.

The design referred to produces an almost constant torque over the whole speed range. In the case of direct connection, a transient current occurs with asynchronous motors. This can be decreased by suitable start-up procedures (when pump start-up torque so permits). Change over to synchronous speed is brought about by connecting the direct current excitation.

Possible starting procedures

Squirrel-cage and synchronous motors are generally designed for direct connection. When the counter-torque permits, these motors can also be supplied for impedance or part voltage start up and for start-up *via* starting transformer. Slip ring induction motors are run up *via* starting resistances which are inserted into the rotor current circuit.

In the case of centrifugal pumps the starting torque curve of the pump must be taken into account.

Three-phase squirrel-cage motors are designed for direct connection. The characteristic torque and current curves of squirrel-cage motors (standard values) are shown in Figures 6 and 7.

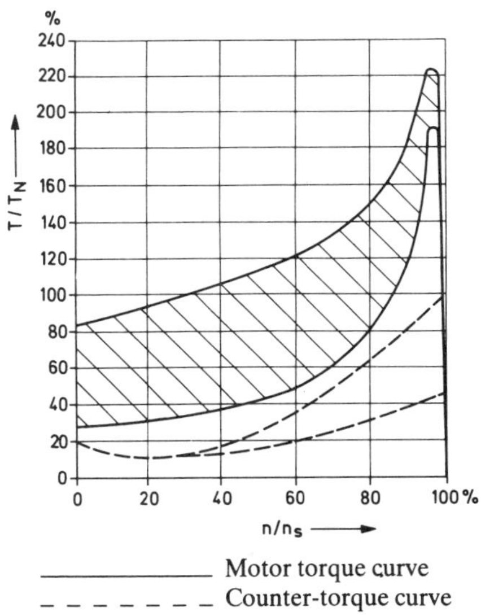

Figure 6
Characteristic torque curves.

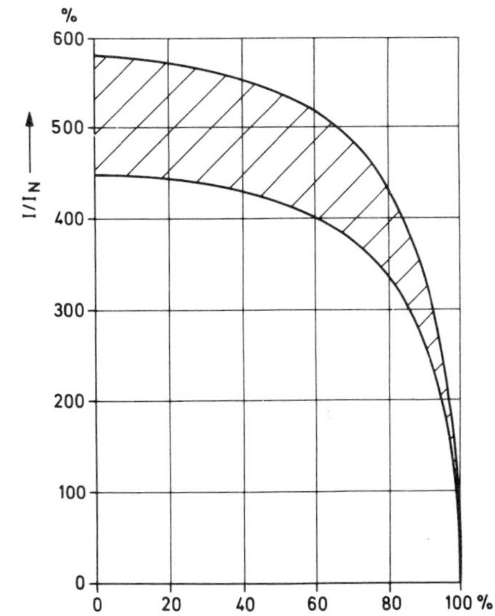

Figure 7
Characteristic starting current curves.

The start-up characteristics of squirrel-cagee motors are shown in the shaded zone as a function of motor size and number of poles. Current and torque curves are valid for start-up at nominal voltage (guide values). When the counter-torque curve so permits, motors suitable for impedance or part voltage starting or for starting *via* block transformer are available.

When starting at reduced voltage, torques decrease approximately in accordance with the square of the voltage current roughly linear to it.

In three-phase slip ring induction motors, starting takes place *via* starting resistances inserted in the rotor current circuit. This increase of the resistance in the rotor current circuit causes a raised starting torque and a reduction of the starting current. The biggest attainable starting torque is approximately equal to pull-out torque. The shaded areas in Figure 8 show the acceleration torque available in each stage, this being a yardstick for starting time.

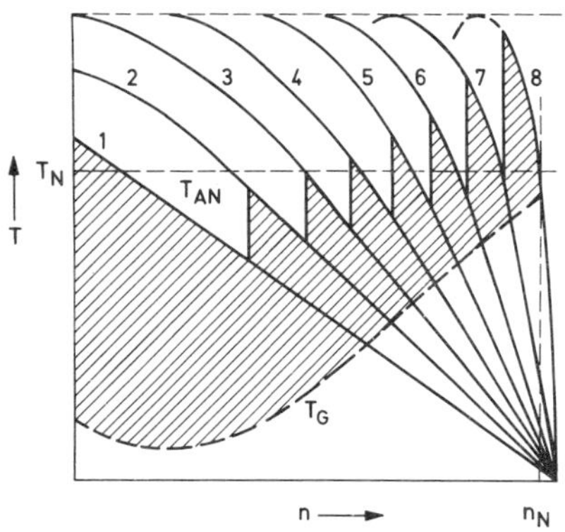

T_{AN} = Torque characteristic in the individual start-up steps
T_G = Curve of counter torque
T_N = Nominal torque

Figure 8
Curve of torque obtained using an 8-stage starter. (Stages 1 to 8).

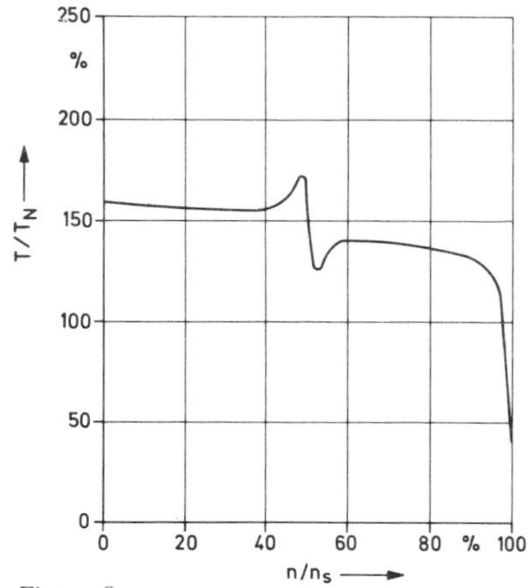

Figure 9
Characteristic torque curve of three-phase synchronous motors with solid pole pieces during starting at nominal voltage (guide values).

The starting heat is dissipated essentially *via* the starting resistance so that motor stressing during run-up is slight.

The starting of synchronous motors takes place asynchronously. The shape of the speed/torque characteristics is determined by the design of the pole pieces. Figure 9 shows the starting torque characteristic curve.

Starting method for three-phase motors

When the supply grid characteristics and the drive permit direct connection, this starting procedure should be used. In other cases the most suitable proven starting methods available should be chosen. See Table 1.

TABLE 1 – PROVEN STARTING METHODS FOR SQUIRREL-CAGE AND SYNCHRONOUS MOTORS

	Applications with Squirrel-cage motor	Synchronous motor
a. *Direct connection*	X	X
Starting at reduced voltage		
Star-delta-starting	X	
b. *Starting via choke:*		
– choke in supply connection	X	X
– chioke in star point	X	X
c. *Starting via starting transformer*	X	X
d. *Starting via transformer*	X	X

The most suitable starting method should be established in consultation with the pump, motor and electricity suppliers.

Hazardous locations

Safety is of paramount importance in the use of electrical equipment in flammable or potentially flammable atmospheres. Correct selection of motors for hazardous atmospheres is therefore essential bearing in mind the economics of the various types of motor available.

A potentially explosive atmosphere is one which could become explosive under certain conditions (the danger is a potential one). An explosive atmosphere is one where a mixture with air, under atmospheric conditions of flammable substances in the form of gas, vapour or mist exists in such proportions that it can be exploded by excessive temperatures, arcs or sparks (the danger is a real one).

The degree of danger varies from extreme to rare. Hazardous areas are classified into three zones as follows:

Zone O in which an explosive gas/air mixture is continuously present for long periods. (No motors may be used in Zone O).

Zone 1 in which an explosive gas/air mixture is likely to occur in normal operation.

Zone 2 in which an explosive gas/air mixture is not likely to occur in normal operatic.. and if it occurs it will exist only for a short time.

By implication an area that is not classified Zone O, 1 or 2 is deemed to be a non-hazardous or safe area.

The minimum temperature at which a gas, vapour or mist ignites spontaneously at atmospheric pressure is known as the ignition temperature. To avoid the risk of explosion, the temperature of any part or surface of a motor must always remain below the ignition temperature of the mixture. The classification of these temperatures is detailed in Table 2.

TABLE 2 – IGNITION TEMPERATURE CLASSIFICATIONS

Temperature class	Maximum surface temperature (°C)
T1	450
T2	300
T3	200
T4	135
T5	100
T6	85

Flameproof theory

A gap between metal surfaces or flame path need not be totally closed to stop the passage of a flame. The smallest gap or flame path necessary to prevent the passing of a flame varies according to the gas or vapour involved. Gases and vapours are sub-divided according to experimental data which has been established to determine the 'maximum experimental safe gap' (mesg). Using the mesg the standards making bodies lay down safe working dimensions for particular gases which are sub-divided or grouped in to A, B, or C, or explosion classes 1 to 3 for PTB certified motors.

In the case of metal-to-metal joints in a flameproof motor, *eg* end shield to frame, these will consist of a long metal spiggot fitting into a long recess which will normally be clamped tight by the fixing bolts. A gap/flame path, however, will always exist between the shaft and the motor interior. Safety is therefore achieved in a flameproof motor by ensuring that all the gaps/flame paths in the motor can never exceed mandatory dimensions and that the motor is physically capable of withstanding an internal explosion without transmitting this to the external atmosphere.

Prime Movers – Internal Combustion Engines

INTERNAL COMBUSTION engines are used extensively as prime movers for centrifugal and displacement pumps particularly where either electrical energy is not available or the set is a standby unit. Depending on the application, the engine fuel may be diesel fuel, petrol (gasoline), natural gas, liquid petroleum gas (LPG), or sewage gas. The engines can be either liquid or air cooled.

The use of the petrol engine as a driver for pumps with its favourable initial cost, good power-to-weight ratio, compactness and flexibility of speed control has declined to some extent with the development of the lightweight high speed diesel engine. Basically, the petrol engine is superior where lightweight, compactness, ease and flexibility of operation are concerned. Thus it is particularly suitable for portable applications. The relatively high fuel cost, however, tends to make it uneconomic for pump drivers in larger sizes. The general ruggedness, lack of electrics, dependability and low running costs of the diesel engine have made it a preferred type for many portable applications at least where diesel fuels are as readily available as petrol – as well as the preferred choice of i/c engines for larger power (stationary) drivers. Running costs can usually be in the order of one-third to a quarter of that of a petrol engine having the same pump, and may even be directly comparable with electric power.

The rating of an internal combustion engine is the most important consideration when making the proper selection. Generally speaking the practice is to rate engines according to the severity of the duty to be performed, the most common rating classifications are maximum, standby or intermittent and continuous. Power ratings of internal combustion engines are always related to specific atmospheric conditions, which are called 'reference conditions'.

In accordance with ISO 3046/1 reference conditions are defined as:

100 KPa = 1 bar,
27 °C air temperature,
60% relative air humidity and
27 °C cooling water temperature for the charging air.

If the conditions at a site are different from these, power must be converted from reference conditions to actual conditions. The following data are guide values:

(i) Engine installation sites at altitudes greater than 500 metres above sea level involve a power reduction of 1% for every 100 metres altitude.

(ii) A power reduction of 1% per 2 °C temperature must be taken into account for ambient temperatures greater than 27 °C.

(iii) Continuous rating – ISO 3046/1 defines this as the power at which an engine can be operated continuously at a given speed and under the conditions subsisting locally during the period between overhauls prescribed by its manufacturers.

(iv) Overload capacity – in the absence of other data ISO 3046/1 defines this as 110% of continuous rating for the duration of 1 hour (with or without interruptions) within an operating period of 12 hours.

General formulae for power required to obtain a given delivery from a water pump are:

$$\text{kW} = \frac{\text{litres/min x total head (metres)}}{\text{pump efficiency}} \quad \text{(approx)}$$

or

$$\text{bhp} = \frac{10 \text{ x gal/min x total head (feet)}}{33\,000 \text{ x pump efficiency}}$$

Pump efficiency may range from as little as 50% for smaller pumps up to 90% or more for larger capacity pumps (and will also depend on the operating point in the case of centrifugal pumps). Even knowing the pump efficiency accurately, a factor of at least 1:2 should be applied to the formula solution to cater for variable site conditions and loss of pump efficiency due to normal wear.

Air breathing internal combustion engines are of course subject to loss of power at high altitudes due to decreased air density. Performance ratings are normally given for sea level operation. As a rough guide hp output can be reduced by 1·5% for each 300 metres (1000 ft) of altitude. Similar loss can be anticipated with high ambient air temperatures *ie* high inlet air temperatures. If necessary, the engine can be supercharged to recover such losses or even to enhance performance at low to moderate altitudes.

Diesel engines

Diesel engines can be distinguished by their relatively high efficiency (35 to 40%) and also by good torque controllability (control of injection quantity). The choice of rotation speed depends in particular on the operating conditions, *ie* for continuous duty a low speed is advantageous, whereas for operation of short duration higher speeds may be chosen lies between 750 and 1500 r/min.

Larger diesel engines may be designed to operate on a dual fuel system. The engine operates on a gaseous fuel with a pilot injection of diesel fuel for ignition. In case of a loss of the gaseous fuel supply, the engine will convert to 100% diesel fuel.

Engine installation

The correct foundation, mounting, vibration isolation and alignment are most important to the success of any engine installation. All stationary engines require a foundation or mounting base. There are many variations but all basically serve to isolate the engine from the surrounding structures and absorb or inhibit vibrations.

Diesel engine power pack.

Portable air-cooled engine driven self-priming pump.

Air requirements

A diesel engine requires fresh air for combustion and for cooling the engine room as compensation for the heat radiated by the engine. Combustion air requirement at normal atmospheric pressure is about 6 to 7 m^3/h/kW. Air volume for cooling the engine, if the temperature rise from engine heat radiation needs to be limited to 10 °C is about 15 to 20 m^3/h/kW.

Air inlets and outlets are usually equipped with silencers. Care must be taken to prevent negative pressure in the engine room.

Exhaust gases

The exhaust gases are ducted to the exterior through the exhaust to which the following conditions apply:

(i) The limits for back pressure stated by the engine makers must not be exceeded.

(ii) The exhaust pipe must be insulated to prevent heat radiation.

(iii) One or more silencers (depending on ambient conditions) must be mounted before the pipe outlet.

Cooling water

With the exception of low-power air cooled engines, engine cooling (cylinder lubricating oil and combustion air in the case of supercharged engines) is generally effected by a closed cooling water circuit common to the engine. This circuit in turn has to be cooled with either air or water.

The diesel engine may be started either by an electric starter motor or by compressed air. To ensure full power development in standby sets within the shortest possible time the engine cooling water circuit and lubricating oil must be kept constantly at a temperature of approximately 50 °C. This is usually achieved by means of electrical resistances.

Depending on the installation site special arrangements must be made to supress noise.

Advantages and disadvantages of various diesel engine configurations are shown in Table 1.

TABLE 1 – APPLICAITONS – DIESEL ENGINES

Configuration	Advantages	Disadvantages
1. Direct driving of pumps	Possibility of individual speed regulation	Number of Diesel engines equal to number of pumps
2a.) Drive via Diesel generating set (auxiliary generating set)	Reasonable price	All the pumps are not in operation simultaneously all the time. When they are not, the Diesel engine operates at part load (un-economical operating mode). No reserve for Diesel engine overhauls or failures
2b.) Distribution among several Diesel generating sets	Better engine workload-ing, reserve during over-hauls	Expensive
3. Pump with electric motor and Diesel engine on single shaft	Diesel engine operates during power failures only	– Disengageable coupl-ing between Diesel engine and electric motor – Electric motor with two shaft ends and a speed matched to that of the Diesel en-gine, otherwise gear transmission required

Steam turbines

Steam turbines are often the best drivers for larger sizes of centrifugal pumps. With steam turbine drives a pass-out system is usually economical since the amount of fuel required to generate steam at 10 bar is only about 3% more than that required

Direct injection industrial diesel engine

to generate the same weight of steam at 1 bar, which is often a more convenient pressure for space and process heating. By combining a pump drive with heating it is possible to utilise some 80% of the heat in the fuel, in comparison with a typical 30% utilisation when the latent heat of the steam is wasted.

The type of governor employed may considerably affect the pump performance achieved, *ie* the shape of the head capacity curve. Constant speed governors normally give a conventional H-Q curve and differential pressure governors a substantially horizontal H-Q curve. The shut-off head will thus vary considerably with the type of governor used.

Gas turbines

Gas turbines have a particular application for high speed drives as well as having a very favourable power:weight ratio. Over the last few decades they have gained a particular importance as pump drives.

The gas turbine is an internal combustion engine differing in many respects from the standard reciprocating engine. The process by which a gas turbine operates involves steady flow; hence pistons and cylinders are eliminated. Also each part of the thermodynamic cycle is carried out in a separate apparatus. The basic process involves compression of air in a compressor, introduction of the compressed air and fuel into the combustion chamber(s), and finally expansion of the gaseous combustion products in a power turbine.

Some of the main advantages of gas turbines are:

(i) Low space requirement and weight per kW.

(ii) Self-contained system of relatively low capital expenditure.

(iii) High reliability.

(iv) Easy maintenance.

(v) Can burn various fuels.

(vi) No cooling water required.

Gas turbines are finding increasing application for driving large capacity mobile pumps, where the high power:weight ratio of the driver can show to full advantage. They can also operate successfully in dirty- or abrasive-loaded atmospheres making them particularly attractive for use on desert sites or for similar applications.

In larger sizes, gas turbines make an attractive alternative to steam turbines. Where fuel costs are important the overall efficiency of the gas turbine can be improved by using the exhaust gases for heating. With a comparatively simple heat exchanger the efficiency can be increased to about 70% and injecting more fuel into the exhaust gases to promote after-burning and the use of unconsumed oxygen can further increase efficiency to 80%. Exhaust heat so extracted can be used for process plant heating, steam raising, *etc*. The performance of the gas turbine itself can also be improved by injecting water into the inlet air when ambient air is hot with low humidity, as may be common in certain localities.

Gas turbines for pump drives are available in a wide range of speeds and for power output from 180 kW to over 50 MW.

An important aspect of crude oil production is secondary recovery. Its purpose is to raise the productivity of an oil field whose natural pressure no longer suffices to raise the oil to the surface. For years it has been the practice to flood such fields with water (seawater, formation water *etc*) under high pressure. The development of high pressure centrifugal pumps permitted the injection of large quantities of water into oil fields. As most oil fields are located in remote areas, pre-assembled gas turbines/pump packages have become more and more popular.

Offshore platform installations require driving machinery with minimum vibration and low unbalanced inertia forces. The gas turbine fulfills these two requirements ideally.

Another suitable field of application for gas turbines as pump drives is the loading of oil tankers. With a gas turbine pump set a high degree of flexibility can be attained, particularly towards the final phase of the loading operation.

The use of gas turbines can vary from simple drives with constant discharge flow and head to complex installations with variable speed, discharge head and flow. The hydraulic characteristics of the pump must be matched and optimised with the gas turbine, as only gas turbines with given power output that are already commercially available can be utilised. The power output of the gas turbine must be equal to or greater than the maximum load the pump may demand.

Pump Drives and Speed Control

THE BASIC equation for power transmission elements is:

$$P\,(\mathrm{kW}) = \frac{1}{9549}\left[\frac{\mathrm{kW \times min}}{\mathrm{Nm}}\right] \times T\,(\mathrm{Nm}) \times \mathrm{r/min}$$

Power = Constant x Torque x r/min

Gear drives

Gear drives may be used where the pump speed and driver speed differ and are usually a preferred choice where speed ratios are 6:1 or greater. Single and double reduction gear units are readily available with ratios up to 25:1. With the use of a timing belt drive on the input this ratio can readily be extended to 150:1 or 250:1 in the case of worm gear reducers. Gear drives are used to vary the speed of a pump by reducing the speed of a prime mover or increasing the speed to enable the pump to operate at a speed higher than that of the prime mover.

Gearing permits the use of a compact power transmission unit which can be completely enclosed and lubricated for life or nominally so. It is particularly applicable to electric motor drives. A gear drive is not subject to slip, normally a high efficiency and can be enclosed in such a way that it is protected from dirty, damp and abrasive atmospheres while accurately cut gears will transmit power smoothly and without shock. Right angle spiral bevel gears, spur gears, helical, double helical and triple helical gears are used to drive between parallel shafts. Straight bevel and high point gears are also occasionally used in right angle drives.

The simplest type of gear drive employs spur gears, with teeth parallel to the axis of the shaft. The sections of the mating teeth on plains perpendicular to the shaft axes are identical, the contact points in such plains lie on lines of contact parallel to the shaft; the lines of contact on each tooth move up or down the profile of the tooth and disappear either near the tip or near the root.

Involute gears permit the centre of either gear to lie within the pitch circle of the other, the larger gear having inwardly projecting teeth and being called an internal gear. The working surfaces of the teeth of the interal gear are concave and thus tend to fit more closely than in the case of external teeth so that they have a relatively high load capacity. Internal gears may be straight or helical and form a very compact drive, since the distance between shaft centres is the difference between the pitch radii of the gears.

Spiral gears are a form of helical gearing which may be used to transmit power between shafts which are not parallel. Spot contact occurs between teeth of spiral gears and they are chiefly used on lightly loaded or infrequently used mechanisms. For light loads at high speed a steel-bronze combination is satisfactory, with case hardened steel gears for higher loads. Bevelled gears are used to transmit power between shafts which are at an angle to each other usually at right angles. They may have straight teeth somewhat similar to spur gears or helical or spiral teeth giving quieter running. Bevelled gears may be employed for such purposes as transmitting power from the horizontal shaft of a prime mover to the vertical shaft of a pump.

Spiral bevel gearing is considered to be superior to straight bevel gearing in that in the former, loading is always distributed over two or more teeth in any given instant. Spiral bevels are also smoother and quieter in action because the teeth mesh gradually.

Helical gears offer better performance characteristics than spur gears; however, size for size helical gears can be more expensive and some users have shied away from them to keep the cost of the gear drive to a minimum. When considering a parallel shaft gear reducer or power transmission drive, the decision must be made as to whether the gears should be spur or helical and if helical whether they should be single or double. A helical gear has a greater effective face width than an equivalent spur gear because of the greater number of teeth in contact thereby enabling it to transmit up to 100% more power than an equivalent spur gear.

Double helical gears have two sets of opposed helical teeth each set having the same helix angle and pitch. Double helical gears are used for high speed pump applications where a large helix angle must be combined with tooth sharing and elimination of end thrust for extremely smooth gear action. Single helical gears have some attractive advantages over double helical gears. The most significant being that the external thrust loads of single helical gears do not affect gear tooth action whereas with a double helical gearing, a thrust load tends to unload one of the helices and overload the opposite one.

Worm gears provide a convenient means of coupling to non-intersecting shafts, which are normally perpendicular to each other. It is a compact arrangement which is capable of quiet transmission of the highest powers. The efficiency of a worm drive falls with increase of speed ratio; 50:1 may be regarded as the upper limit, while few drives have a ratio of less than Figure 4. Suitable means must be provided for taking the end thrust of the driving shaft on which the worm is mounted. Worm gearing tends to be limited in power capacity and has lower efficiencies than parallel shaft and bevel gear types.

Epicyclic gear units are sometimes used for pump drive applications. The most common types of epicyclic arrangements are planetary, star and solar. The planetary arrangement is the most commonly used. The star arrangement is used for higher speed applications and the solar arrangement allows a low ratio.

Most of the aforementioned types of gearing have been incorporated in internally geared electrical motor units, which thus form a compact power source for driving a pump at a different speed from that of a motor. Backlash is provided between the teeth on a gear drive to avoid risk of the teeth jamming due to variation of the distance between the centres, gear eccentricity due to errors in cutting or mounting, lateral run out or errors of pitch, profile or alignment. Backlash allowance is the amount by which the maximum tooth thickness is less than the nominal thickness. The sum of the backlash allowed in a pair of gears gives the nominal backlash. This can be increased by an amount equal to the combined tooth thickness tolerances.

Improper lubrication causes a high percentage of gear reduction unit failures. Too frequently, speed reducers are started up without any lubricant at all. Conversely, units are sometimes filled to a higher oil level than specified in the mistaken belief that better lubrication is obtained. This higher oil level usually results in more of the input power going into churning the oil, creating excessive temperatures with detrimental results to the bearings and gearing. Insufficient lubrication gives the same results.

Gear failure due to overload is a broad and varied area of misapplication. The nature of the load (input torque, output torque, duration of operating cycle, shocks, speed, acceleration, *etc*) determines the gear unit size and other design criteria. Frequently, a gear drive must be larger than the torque output capability of the severity of application conditions by providing a higher nominal power which in effect increases the size of the gear unit. If there is any question in the user's mind that the actual service conditions may be more severe than originally anticipated it is recommended that this information be communicated to the gear manufacturer before start-up. Often there are remedies that can be suggested before a gear unit is damaged by overload, but none are effective after severe damage.

Motors and other prime movers should be analysed while driving the gear unit under full loaded conditions to determine that the prime mover is not overloaded and thus putting out more than the rated torque. If it is determined that overload does exist, the unit should be stopped and steps taken either to remove the overload or to contact the manufacturer to determine suitability of the gear drive under the observed conditions.

Variable speed drive connected to rotor line pump.

Belt drives

V-belt drives are normally the lowest cost installation for constant speed drives where the pump speed is lower than the driver speed. They also offer some flexibility to change pump speed by changing the sheave size.

Belt drive packages may be mounted horizontally, vertically, or at a 45° angle and are available in standard, open or totally enclosed designs. Reliability and accuracy of speed control are advantages of the mechanical adjustable-speed belt drive package. Construction details, size, and mounting dimenions are non-standardised and vary with the manufacture but all employ dual adjustable pitch sheaves mounted on parallel shafts at a fixed centered distance and a special wide section rubber V-belt to provide a compact assembly. Most of the designs utilise spring loaded sheaves for control of belt tension.

The mechanical adjustable speed drive package is usually rated as a constant-torque, variable power device. The power rating is based on the capacity of the whole unit at maximum speed setting. When operating at any output speed below this maximum, the power capacity is reduced in direct proportion.

Timing belt drives offer distinct advantages for speed increase drives involving high shaft speeds since they do not have the lubrication problems associated with gear and chain drives under such conditions. They are not without their limitations, however, particularly a tendency to track towards one side of their pulleys which is exaggerated if any misalignment is present. Special belt construction is also needed to operate successfully at ambient temperatures in excess of about 90 °C.

Powers of up to 150 hp can be transmitted by stock timing belt drives, although belt speed is normally limited to about 1800 m/min (6000 ft/min). Much higher powers (and belt speeds) are however available from special constructions. Single-stage speed ratios of up to 8·5:1 are usually possible over a wide range of shaft centre distances. A possible disadvantage with all belt drives is the transience (bending) load applied to the shaft due to belt tension. If necessary this can be eliminated by employing an outboard bearing or a jackshaft to take the full weight of the drive (Figure 1)

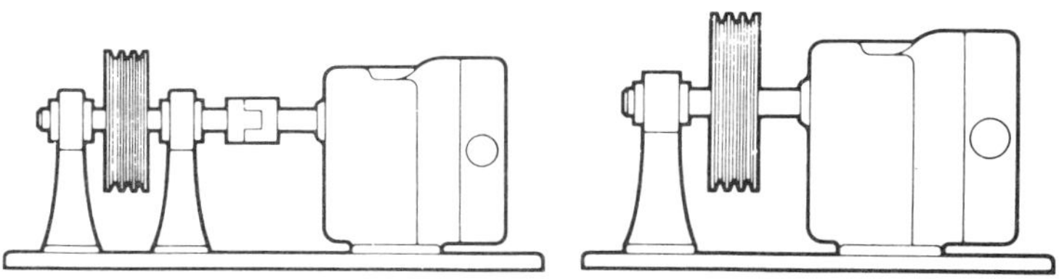

Figure 1

Magnetic drives

The pump shaft/impeller assembly of a magnetic drive pump is driven by a cylinder of permanent magnets external to the containment shell which is mechanically coupled to a separate or close-coupled motor shaft. Within the containment shell a matching set of permanent magnets (synchronous couplings or a torque ring (eddy-current coupling) is mounted on impeller shaft. The shaft bearings are lubricated by the liquid pumped. Magnet drive pumps where developed to eliminate the dangers of pumping hazardous liquids by the use of a hermetically sealed wet end. They are generally more expensive to manufacture than packed or sealed pumps.

See Chapter on Glandless Pumps for further information.

Speed control

Where the system head curve derives wholly or mainly from friction losses, speed control is best, because pump efficiency then remains practically constant. Though speed control can be expensive, it is gentle to the pump and valves so that the life span of both is generally increased. Furthermore operating costs are reduced, because higher pump efficiency means less power input. Unlike throttling, speed control leaves the piping system characteristic unchanged, while the pump characteristic moves down in accordance with the speed change, and smaller flow rates result at the new intersections.

Apart from the speed regulation possibilities afforded by variable speed driving machinery such as electric motors with direct speed control, diesel engines, gas turbine and steam engines, pump speed can also be varied over a wide range by the use of variable speed gearing between the electric motor and centrifugal pump.

Variable speed gearing most commonly used on centrifugal pumps are:

(i) Mechanical stepless speed converters such as belt drives or friction wheel drives.
(ii) Hydraulic speed converters – hydrostatic drives and hydrodynamic converters.
(iii) Electro-magnetic speed converters.

Variable speed hydraulic drives

Variable speed hydraulic drives can offer a speed range of 5:1, which enables a single pump to be operated over a very wide envelope of head/flow requirements.

The variable filling type is preferred since this enables the output speed to be controlled over a wide stepless range, which is used on a majority of pump drives.

Infinitely variable speed regulations provided over a speed range of as much as 5:1. For constant torque drive, *eg* positive displacement pumps, speed regulation of up to 3:1 may be obtained.

The fluid drive is readily adaptable for use with most types of automatic control – pneumatic, electric or hydraulic actuators – sensitive to such functions as pressure, flow, level and temperature. Otherwise simple mechanical or remote manual control may be used.

Generally speaking the advantages of hydraulic drives are:

(i) Stepless control in a range of 4:1 to 5:1 maximum.
(ii) Capable of transmitting very high power outputs.
(iii) Load-free motor starting.
(iv) Gentle pump acceleration.
(v) Damping of any tortional vibrations.
(vi) Simple torque matching by modifying the oil fill.
(vii) Assured protection against expensive heating means of fuseable cut-out.
(viii) Wear-free transmission, as the power transmitting parts have no mechanical contact.
(ix) High efficiency as rated slip is very low.

Some of the disadvantages are:

(i) Price.
(ii) Additional space requirement for the converter and its auxiliaries such as a cooler *etc*.
(iii) Rated capacity of electric motor slightly increased to compensate for converter losses (rated slip and mechanical loss generators such as bearing and gear training driving powers for oil pumps).

Electro-magnetic speed converters

Electro-magnetic speed converters are generally manufactured with a stationary excitation coil or one that turns with the rotor. When the driving rotor is rotating and the driven rotor is stationary, one surface of the opposing rotor is permeated consecutively by a maximum induction field (opposite a tooth) followed by a minimum induction field (opposite a gap). As the magnetic flux taken up by this surface is variable, eddy currents are generated. Like all induced currents these follow Lenz's Law, *ie* they attempt to resist the cause of their generation. The driven rotor starts to rotate. Speed differential between the two rotors is reduced.

There is a torque-slip curve corresponding to every excitation value of the electro-magnetic circuit. Modern semi-conduction technology involving transistors, silicone-control rectifiers and integrated circuits are used extensively in circuit design.

Eddy current couplings are applied to centrifugal pumps for water and waste water pumping in municipal installations, boiler feed pumping, circulating water and condensate pumping in power plants, fan and stock pumping in paper mills and for reciprocating pumping in a multitude of applications and industries.

The range of application is limited thermally, *ie* by the need to dissipate the slip power in the form of heat. Speed converters are built with air or water cooling. In special applications (plants with explosion risk or special environmental conditions) or for large slip power losses, water cooling is recommended. Figure 2 shows the design principle of an electro-magnet speed converter with stationary excitation coils.

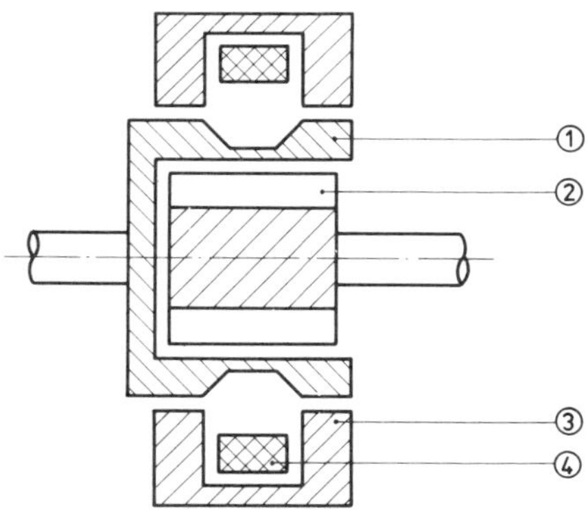

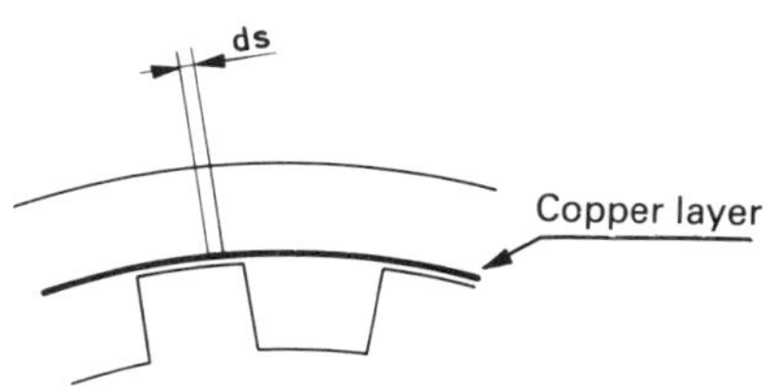

Key:
1. Smooth driving rotor with copper layer driven at constant speed.
2. Toothed driven rotor, the speed of which is variable.
3. Stationary electro-magnetic circuit excited by a coil. The magnetic field so generated flows through both rotors.
4. Coil.

Figure 2
Design principle of speed converter with stationary excitation oil.

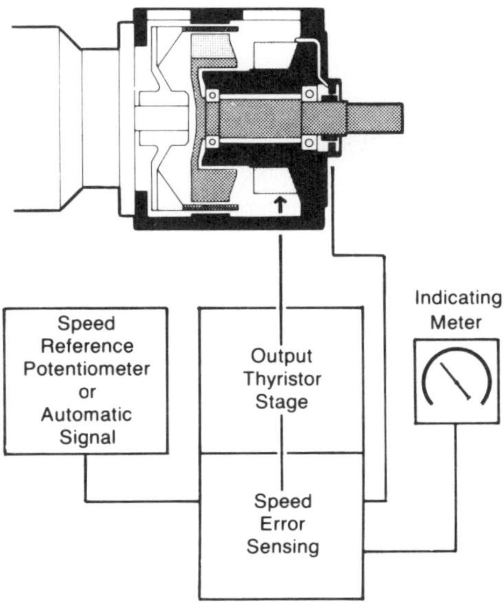

Figure 3
Friction-free infinately variable speed drive.

The variable speed drive shown in Figure 3 is a friction free infinitely variable speed drive. A tube, mounted on a hub incorporating a cooling fan is driven by a standard a.c. motor at constant speed. A rotor, fixed to the output shaft is free to revolve within the tube. The coil is stationary so there is no electrical supply to the rotor. When the coil is energised a magnetic field is set up which causes the rotor to revolve in the same direction as the motor.

Torque is proportional to coil current. Coil power is as low as 2% of transmitted power. The unit is ideal for driving variable speed pumps because it combines low prime cost with reduced energy consumption and zero routine maintenance. It compares favourable with alternative variable air flow systems for example, inlet guide vane systems have high energy losses in the normal operating range of 30 to 90% of maximum volume, require routine maintenance and are not so amenable to automatic control. The same is true of methods of controlling water flow with a fixed speed pump motor. Powers up to 7 kW for centrifugal pumps and 32 kW for positive displacement pumps are obtainable.

The principle of operation of the variable speed drive shown in Figure 4 is that of magnetic attraction. Energisation of a diametrically-opposed pair of stator coils pulls a pair of rotor poles into line. Figure 5 shows a totally enclosed motor which have an eight pole stator with stationary coils and a rotor with six poles. There are no bars or windings on the rotor, producing a very low inertia. Energisation is accurately timed by sensors which mounted on an end casing, are impervious to normal industrial environments. They interact with a revolving segmented ring to provide digital signals indicating the rotor position. The logic circuit then energises the appropriate coil pair to give the most torque-effective current pulse.

The sensors give a frequency proportional to motor speed. This is compared with a set speed reference to produce a torque demand signal. In effect, the speed is not

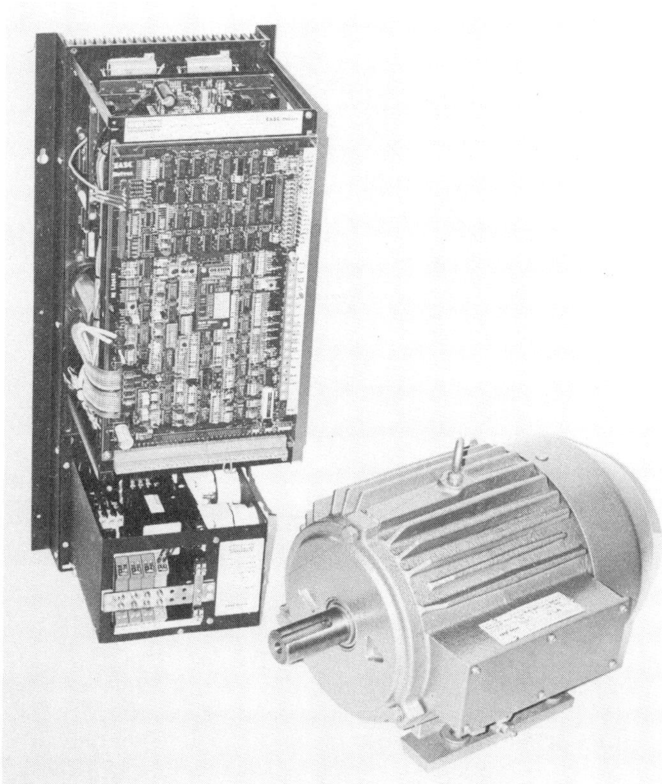

Figure 4
A 7·5 kW system certified EExe.

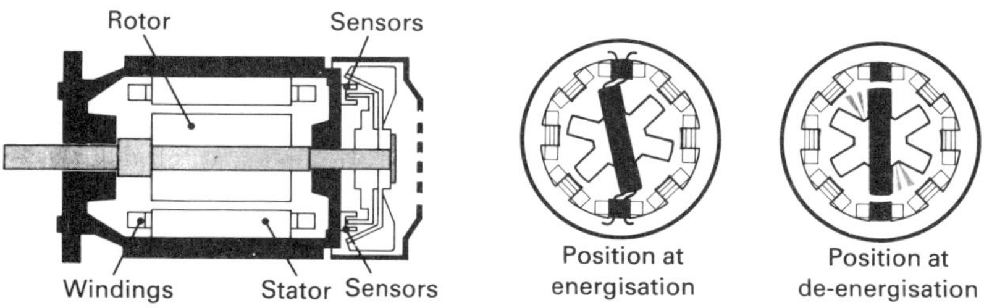

Figure 5
Switched reluctance drive.

controlled by the frequency of impulses but rather the train of pulses is controlled by the rotor position and the speed reference. This promotes high efficiency by supplying current for the optimum time in relation to the torque demand. The controller powers the motor through GTO thrystors.

Belt variators

Variable speed belt variators are available in a range from 0·5 to 200 hp. They are considered to be very efficient (90 to 95%) according to speed setting and a major reason for employing belt variators is to save motor current by driving the machine at the speed required according to varying conditions. Variators have a low capital cost compared with alternative means in this power range such as inverters, thrystors, eddy current or hydraulic variable speed units. Figure 6 shows a number of 150 and 200 hp variators mounted above centrifugal pumps. The pumps circulate hot and chilled water round a complex of shops and offices for heating and air-conditioning purposes. Motor current is saved by varying the pump speed rather than restricting the flow.

Figure 6
Belt variators can save motor current.

The a.c. inverters have proved particularly suitable for use in the efficient control of pumping equipment.

Other variable speed drive units enable submersible pumps to produce a wider volume range than is possible at a fixed speed.

Conditions also change and this can eliminate the need to resize the pump resulting in reduced down time and lower production costs. Variable speed drives of this type control the speed of the pump by varying the frequency and amplitude of the voltage supplied to the motor. Essentially a voltage controlled inverter, the unit accepts three phase fixed frequency a.c. voltage as input. This is converted to d.c. through controlled rectification then reconstructed as three phase a.c. voltage at the output. The reconstruction allows the output to be at any desired frequency. Controlled rectification permits output voltage amplitude to be regulated accordingly.

Couplings

With electric motors, permanent couplings can often be employed connecting the motor shaft to the pump shaft, the motor being mounted either directly on to the end of the pump (in small sizes) or on a stool mounted on the pump. Vertically mounted pump allow the motor to be directly mounted above (or, more rarely, below) the pump and can appreciably reduce alignment problems. With this configuration alignment is less likely to be affected by the effect of thermal expansion on the pump itself, which means that a solid coupling is usually practicable, with no coupling losses involved.

Solid couplings can only be used where the driver and pump shafts are exactly in line, no relative endwise motion can take place and the driver speed is matched to the pump design speed. Many pumps designed for electric motor drives are in fact matched to synchronous motor speeds, synchronous motors commonly being employed to improve plant power factor. In this respect it should be noted that the maximum synchronous speed of a standard a.c. motor operating on 50 cycles frequency is 3000 r/min. However, higher speeds can be realised if necessary by incorporating a frequency changer. A basic solid coupling consists of two matching flanges one on each shaft which are bolted together. In some cases a spacer be may incorporated to locate the motor in a more convenient position, but a disadvantage of this system is that it is even more difficult to align the pump and the driver exactly. It is also essential that misalignment should not develop after a period of service due to foundation settling or other causes, which could induce loads on shafts and bearings.

Apart from simplicity, the main advantage of a solid coupling is its low cost. Its size can be chosen on the basis of shaft diameter alone and this does not require a service factor. Bolt loads can readily be established for a bolted up coupling (deciding the number and size of bolts to be used for joining the flanges). The plain board sleeve located with a key is an even simpler type, although it will involve some de-rating of the shaft performance to account for the keyway, and can also be designed to accommodate a certain amount of end float if necessary.

A common application for solid couplings in the pump industry is in vertical drives where the prime mover is positioned above the pump. In such cases, both machines can employ a common thrust bearing which is generally located in the motor. The coupling flange bolts must be capable of transmitting any down thrust from the pump to the motor. In applications where the thrust from the pump is toward the motor, it is common practice to provide shoulders on the shafts to transmit the axial force.

A range of couplings which use resilient spiders to cope with misalignments and vibration.

Flexible couplings

The use of a flexible coupling would appear to give considerably more latitude. In fact, successful operation again depends on good initial alignment. In other words, a flexible coupling is used primarily to accommodate the slight axial movement which may be necessary to avoid overloading bearings rather than to allow non-axial movement. The latter xcan result in appreciable power losses in the coupling as well as generate vibration which will adversely affect the life of all the components. It should be noted that the vibration generated by a misaligned coupling can cause energy losses in the motor and pump as well as at the coupling itself since vibration will be common to all three components. Various types of flexible coupling are shown in Figure 7.

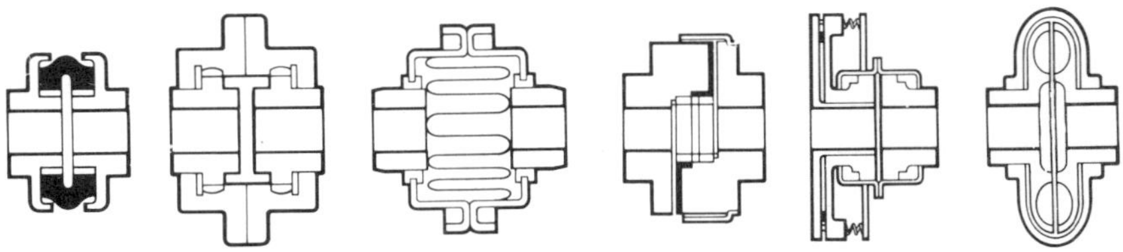

Figure 7
Types of couplings.

Vibration and power losses can also result from insufficient rigidity of mounting if imbalance is present in any one of the rotating elements. This can be absorbed to a large extent by more rigid mounting, but in an extreme case with a relatively light casing and very rigid mount it may be the casing which fails. The dynamic balance or rotating elements is thus an important factor if power transmission losses are to be avoided, particularly at higher rotational speeds.

The metal disc coupling consists of two sets of thin sheet metal discs bolted to the driving and driven hub members each set of discs is made up of a number of thin laminations which are individually flexible and compensate for shaft misalignment by means of this flexibility. These discs may be stacked together as required to obtain the desired torque transmission capability. This type of coupling requires no lubrication; however, alignment of the equipment must be maintained within an acceptable limits so as not to exceed the fatigue limit of the material. Another example of an all metal material flexible coupling is the flexible diaphragm coupling. Here the design of the coupling is principally centred about the contoured diaphragm. This special 'hyperbolic' contouring of the diaphragm permits the accommodation of torque, speed, axial deflection and simultaneous angular misalignment while maintaining uniform shear and low tensile stress. This coupling is particularly suitable for high speed applications.

Where the pump installation requires driver and pump to be separated, the connecting shaft normally needs to be carried on its own bearings and coupled to the driver by some form of flexible coupling. Great care is necessary in lining up the various bearings on the shaft, driver and pump. An alternative method is to use a Hardy Spicer propeller shaft comprising a tube into which is welded a shaft having a universal joint at one end with a multi-toothed splined shaft with universal joints at the other end. Permanent couplings of the rigid or flexible type can only be adopted when the pump is to run at the same speed as the driver and also when the starting torque available from the driver exceeds the starting load torque of the pump. Starting torque requirements vary with different types of pump and also with the viscosity of any fluid which may be present on starting up. Centrifugal pumps, in general, require quite low starting torques of the order of 15 to 20% of the normal running torque. With reciprocating pumps and rotary pumps, starting torque may be higher than normal operating torque, although this can be relieved by fitting a bypass. If insufficient starting torque is available from the driver employed, the coupling must be designed to slip or disconnect so that the driver may be run up to speed, off-loaded then connected to the pump when sufficient torque is being generated. Friction clutches and fluid couplings are two of the main types of couplings employed under such circumstances.

A service factor should be used in selecting a suitable size of coupling to ensure that an economic service life is obtained, irrespective of the value of a loading or the severity of overload or starting conditions (see Table 1). Some flexible couplings may also be subject to speed factors where torque capacity is reduced by centrifugal loading and service temperature factors where elastomeric elements are involved. Tortional stiffness may also need separate examination where the coupling is to be used for tortional and vibration damping. There the manufacturer should be consulted as necessary.

TABLE 1 – TYPICAL SERVICE FACTORS

Driven machine	TYPE OF DRIVER: a.c. motors: squirrel-cage motors, star-delta start. d.c. motors (shunt wound) internal combustion engines (above 600 r/min and multi-cylinder).			a.c. motors direct-on-line start: high torque slip repulsion-induction single phase series wound and slip-ring motors. Series and compound wound d.c. motors. Internal combustion engines – engines – single cylinder or under 600 r/min.		
	Operation : hours per day			**Operation : hours per day**		
	up to 10	**10 to 16**	**over 16 or continuous**	**up to 10**	**10 to 16**	**over 16 or continuous**
Centrifugal pumps	1·0	1·1	1·2	1·1	1·2	1·3
Positive displacement rotary pumps	1·1	1·2	1·3	1·2	1·3	1·4
Piston pumps	1·2	1·3	1·4	1·4	1·5	1·6
Positive displacement blowers	1·2	1·3	1·4	1·4	1·5	1·6
Centrifugal blowers	1·0	1·1	1·2	1·1	1·2	1·3
Special case : reversing drives	Multiply service factor by 1·25			Multiply service factor by 1·25		

Shaft alignment

As far as coupling the pump and driver are concerned it is most important to line up the pump and driver as accurately as possible preferably within two hundredth of a millimetre. This is usually performed with a dial indicator gauge.

Recently however, a laser based system has improved the speed and precision with which horizontal and vertical shafts can be aligned. It eliminates time consuming repetitive checking associated with dial indicators and feeler gauges. The system is designed for correcting parallel offset and angular misalignment between driving and driven shafts. The unit is portable battery power operated and consists of four major components; a low power Class 1 laser emitter/detector; a prism reflector; a hand-held laser beam finder; and a microprocessor with appropriate software. The last emitter/detector and prism reflector are mounted on the driving and driven shafts with hardware supplied. The beam finder is used to locate the invisible laser beam and guide it into the bi-axial photoelectric positioning sensor located in the centre of the detector. The computer which is interfaced with the emitter/detector presents a digital display of the X and Y co-ordinates of the laser beam. The shafts are then rotated through 90° increments making automatic position readings. Distances between laser and prism, laser and front feet and front feet and back feet are entered. The microcomputer displays the direction and the magnitude of the adjustment required at the feet and also calculates and displays misalignment at the coupling. The system permits entry of target specifications for thermal growth, measures and displays ‘soft foot’ conditions and directs and monitors horizontal movement through the computer.

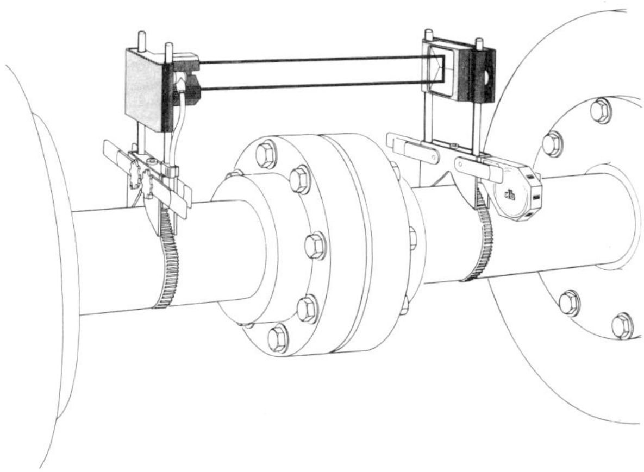

Figure 8
Laser-based shaft alignment system.

Drive shafts

Pump drives system arrangements may be classified in one of two categories; those which are close coupled having a shaft separation of a fraction of an inch (not to be confused with integral motor pumps not having a flexible coupling) and those which for one or more reason have the prime mover located a substantial distance from the pump. These latter types of systems require a modification to the basic flexible coupling designs.

One means of accommodating shaft separation in excess of the normal amount provided in a standard coupling is to employ a flanged tubular spacer between the two coupling halves. These components are lightweight and are commonly used with end suction pumps, where it is possible to move the pump impeller while the pump housing and pump piping as well as the prime mover remain in place. For high speed drive systems, a lightweight spacer is usually the only practical means of achieving the goal. This spacer may be used to tune the system tortionally (as previously discussed) by varying the body diameter and wall thickness. Spacers can be manufactured in lengths of up to several feet but the cost generally restricts its usage to shorter lengths except where no other means is suitable.

Floating shaft couplings have a purpose similar to that of spacer couplings namely to connect two widely separated shafts. The basic difference is in the construction of the component. While spacers are normaly made with the body having an integrally formed flange to connect the two coupling halves, a floating shaft usually is made by attaching a flange to a piece of solid tubular shafting by means of mechanical keys or by welding. Floating shaft arrangements are widely used on horizontal pump applications of all types and are especially common on vertical pump applications, such as in water pumping and sewage treatments.

A rigid intermediate shaft connected to a pump provided with a rigid coupling must be designed to carry its own weight, the axial thrust from the pump and a bending load. Volute-type centrifugal pumps produce a radial reaction on the pump shaft which in turn is transmitted to the vertical shafting through the rigid pump coupling.

Flexible drive shafts consist of universal joints with tubular shafting and can be substituted for flexible couplings whenever it is necessary to eliminate the need for critical alignment, provide wide latitude in placement of pump and drive and permit large amounts of relative motion between pump and driver. This type of shafting can be used horizontally as well as vertically to provide a short spacer arrangement or a large separation between pump and driver such as that required for deep settings.

Pump shafts and sleeves directly affect the life of mechanical seals and bearings. There are numerous choices of shaft that include:

(i) Composite – a steel shaft end-to-end with either a brazed-on alloy sleeve of cobalt based alloy or high silicon iron or bonded, non-metallic sleeve of ceramic or ziroconia. The advantages of this type of shaft material is the strength of the steel, rigidity of a solid shaft corrosion and abrasion resistance.

(ii) Butt-welded – a steel end friction welded to a solid alloy wet end. Advantages here are again the strength of the steel, rigidity of a solid shaft with alloys to match the pump wet end.

(iii) Solid – steel end-to-end or stainless steel alloy end-to-end. Advantages – the strength and economy of solid steel or the process and atmospheric corrosion resistance of solid stainless steel with the rigidity not obtainable in a hook sleeve design.

(iv) Hook sleeve – a steel shaft end-to-end or a steel power end butt-welded to a stainless wet end accommodating a hook sleeve. Advantages – the strength of steel with a wide range of easily replacable alloy sleeves. Easy sleeve renewals without tearing down the bearing housing. Accommodates many new generation cartridge design mechanical seals.

Control and Measurement

GENERALLY, TRADITIONAL type instruments remain in widespread use in duty pumping systems although much more sophisticated instrumentation based on the use of computers and microprocessors have become particularly suited to the requirements of the water industry as well as petrochemical and general process control applications.

Centrifugal pumps are commonly controlled by starting and stopping as demand fluctuates. The flexibility of this type of pump and the fact that the power consumed tends to fall if the outlet is restricted makes it possible to run the pumps continuously under widely varying conditions. Where a continual flow is essential but demand varies considerably, several pumps in parallel are used and may be controlled by variations of flow or level. The most common need for accurate control is where there is danger of, for instance over pumping a bore hole or over filling a tank and this is catered for effectively by level controls described later.

Protection against burst mains signalled by a sudden fall in pressure, is desirable on high pressure mains and becomes more important as they approach the end of their usefui life. New pumping parts supplying old mains should always have this protection, whilst any signs of weakness would make it worthwhile giving protection on older plants.

Positive displacement pumps require protection against over-pressure (unless a relief valve is included in the pump itself) and may also require some form of unloading device so that they can be started against'no load' unloading can be accomplished by lifting suction valves although the more usual solution is the fitting of a bypass (unloading) valve. This can be solenoid operated and controlled by a pressure switch.

Flow control is normally only possible by a change in pump speed unless the pump is a variable capacity type. In this case a linear (manual) movement or linear actuator can perform this duty. Many fluid processes are governed by a control valve in conjunction with a pump. In this case a variable pump can often be used to advantage by eliminating the control valve and transferring the actuator to the pump producing a control pump. This approach has the advantage of avoiding spill-back and of improved flow stability. Also expensive flow sensing equipment can often be avoided. Though process control is traditionally pneumatic actuation by

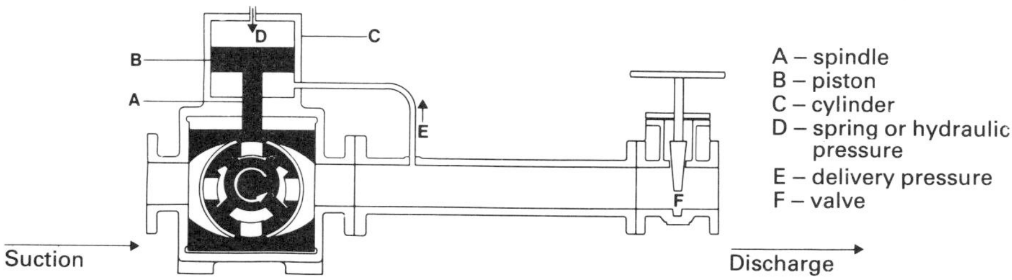

Figure 1
Constant pressure control device attached to variable displacement vane pump.

electric or hydraulic means may be more appropriate for certain duties. Figure 1 shows a constant pressure control device.

The choice of pump control divides into two types: on-off and modulating and can either be operated manually or automatically. Manual control involves pushing a button to stop or start a motor or turning a valve handle to open or close a system.

Open loop control is considered to be the simplest form of automatic control valve setting is adjusted and held at a calculated or calibrated value to produce the required flow output, level or pressure. Open loop systems are generally stable and respond quickly. In a feedback or closed loop control system the output variable is measured and the value compared with an arbitary desired or set value. If the comparison reveals an error the pump speed or control valve setting is changed to correct the error.

Level controls
On-off control of pumps emptying and filling sumps and tanks containing water or watery fluid which have sufficient conductivity to operate an electronic circuit, is usually by the electrode method shown in Figure 2. Here the relay is energised

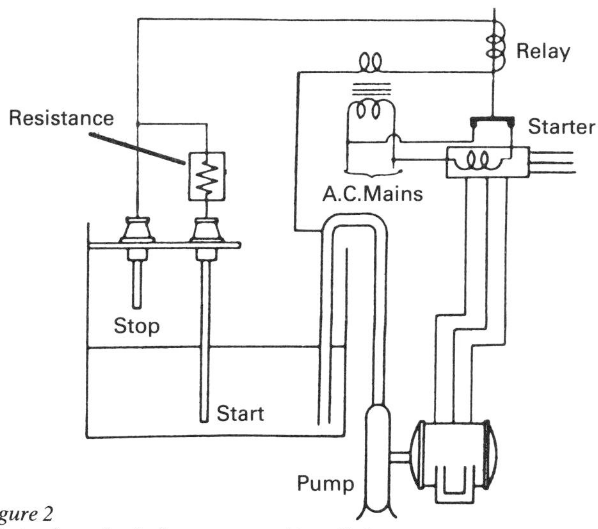

Figure 2
Electrode method of pump control installed in a tank which is filled by a pump. The pump starts when the level falls below the lower electrode and stops when the level reaches the upper electrode.

when both electrodes are immersed and as the upper one is left dry with falling level, the relay is maintained by current passing through the resistance and lower electrode. The circuit is broken as soon as the longer electrode is uncovered; the value of the resistance is such that the relay cannot operate until short circuited by the upper electrode.

When controlling the pump by the level on the suction side, as when emptying a sump, the relay has a contact which closes when it is energised. To start and stop the pump the level on the discharge side, *eg* tank, reservoir, *etc*, a contact is fitted which opens when the relay is energised. A single electrode is sufficient if the object is to provide a safety device to operate a high or low level.

Standard electrodes for tanks and pumps can be single or double units; the latter are very convenient for inserting through a flanged inlet. For boreholes the electrode is suspended by a standard cable and the electrode itself is screened by a perforated insulating sheath to prevent possible contact with the side of the borehole.

For non-conducting liquids a capacity probe is necessary. This may have an electronic detector in the head and is connected to an indicating controller. The two can be several hundred meters apart. The indicator with suitable probe will measure any difference in level from 300 mm (12 in) to 30 m (100 ft) or more. The control points are set by moving the pointers to the appropriate reading on the dial. It will then be appreciated that all these controls operate at 12 volts or less.

Where, as well as pump control, an indication of borehole water level is required a pressure transducer can be used in conjunction with an indicating controller.

Float controls

One of the most simple and reliable methods of controlling level where a float can be accommodated is the type of float switch shown in Figure 3, where the float is connected to the switch either by chain or rod. The minimum level distance is 150 mm (6 in) and this can be extended by altering the stops. The floats themselves can be made of copper, stainless steel and glazed porcelain. Counterweights are needed

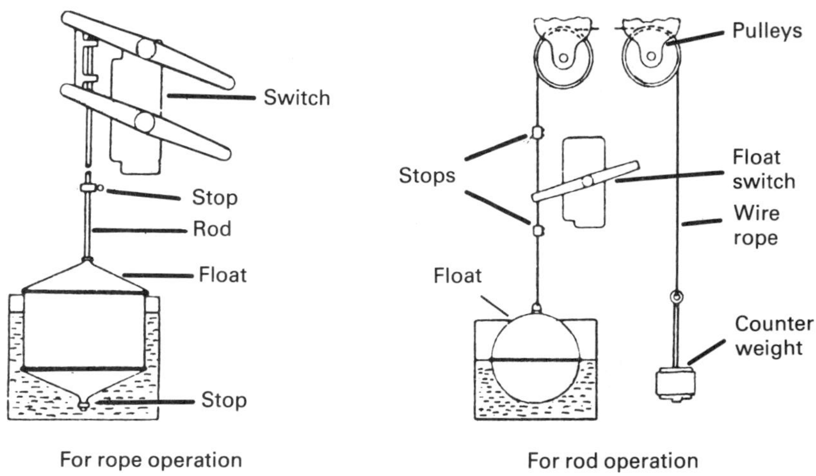

Figure 3
Float switches showing typical arrangement of float gear.

for the heavier floats or where the rod or chain is longer than a metre. These type of switches are available in both indoor and outdoor housings and depending on the type of switch fitted will control d.c. motors up to 4 hp.

One of the more recent and successful level control switch has been the mercury activated level alarm system. This particular switching device consists of a heavy duty mercury to mercury type capsule with omni-directional on-off tumblers so that the float is not sensitive to rotation.

This, together with a novel wiring circuit, prevents relay contact arcing when starting and stopping pump. Figure 4 shows the principle of operation for a double float pump switch. Installation of these devices is usually quite simple with cord, plug and adjustable mounting straps and clamps as shown in Figure 5. Switches of this type are capable of controlling pumps up to 1 hp in single switch versions and 2 hp in double switch versions.

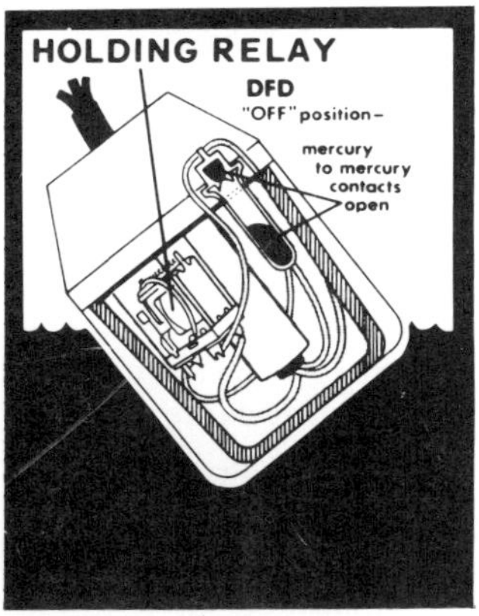

Off position – float is tipped down and mercury remains in non-contact position.

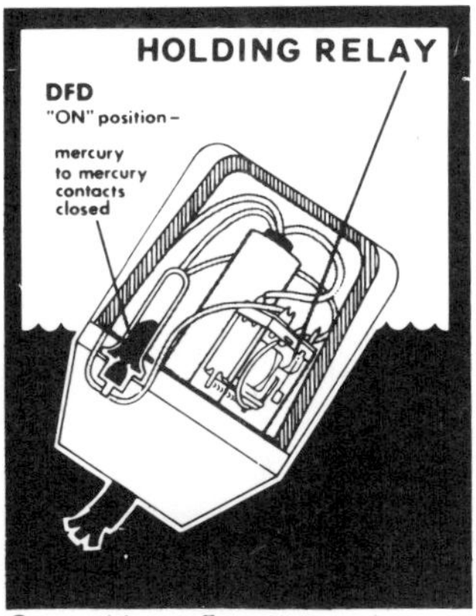

On position – float is tipped up and mercury moves to contact position.

Figure 4
Principle of operation for a mercury-to-mercury double float pump switch.

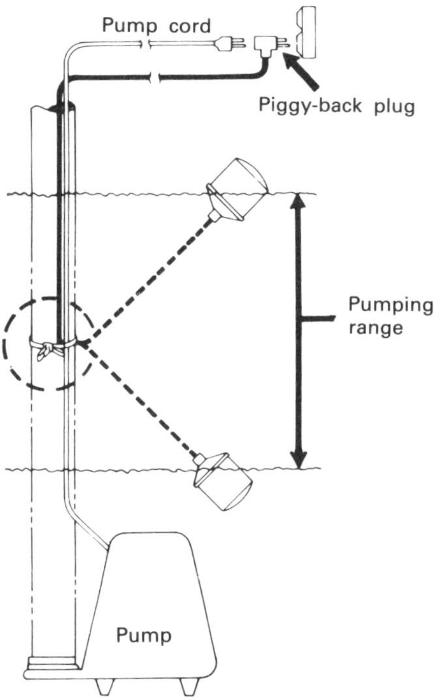

Figure 5
Typical installation of heavy-duty mercury-to-mercury pump switch showing pumping range.

Computerised pump controls
A computerised pump controller produces substantial energy savings on multiple pump installations by optimising pump control and scheduling. These units are designed to be self-contained easy to fit to existing pump installations and packaged in splash-proof housings to withstand the severe operating environments expected.

Unlike alternative general purpose control approaches, which are not designed to meet the particular requirements of pump installations, computerised pump controllers provide an optimum solution by combining special monitoring and control algorithms with simple user configurations to achieve tailored operation on any pump installation.

Monitoring facilities built into units of this type include power and power factor monitoring, enabling plant operating efficiencies to be assessed and optimised as well as pump wear monitoring to assist in maintenance scheduling. Other features include alarm monitoring of plant parameters for out-of-limit conditions and sensor faults and automatic protective plant shutdown on detection of critical events. Figure 6 shows a block diagram of a typical computerised pump controller.

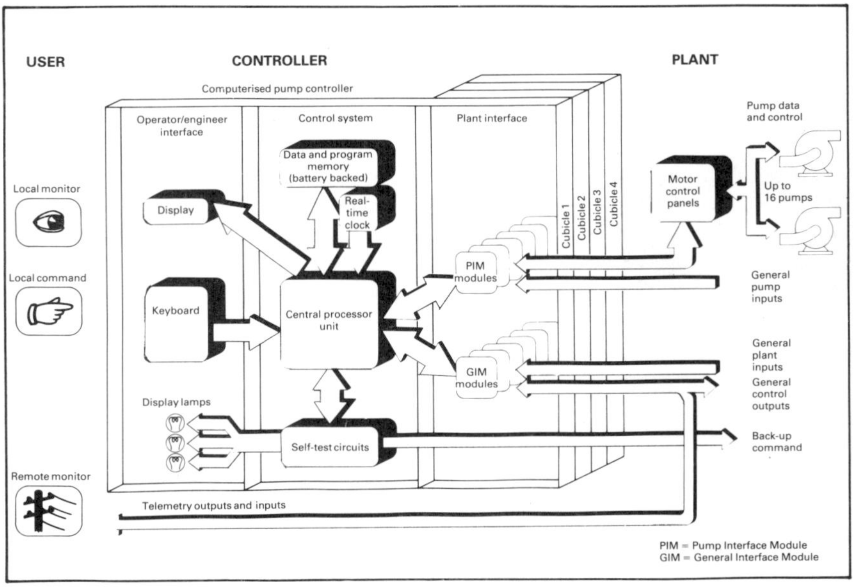

Figure 6
Block diagram of computerised pump controller.

A combination of a variable speed drive and line switching enables this unit to match the pump output precisely with the system demand so achieving considerable energy saving. The capacity is divided among a number of smaller pumps (up to five), which are switched in or out as dictated by system demand. The inverter drive is allocated to one pump to smooth out the steps. This configuration has the advantage that only one, relatively small inverter is required. In order to even out wear on the pumps, the inverter drive can be switched between the pumps on a regular basis.

Faults such as loss of water; high motor temperature; high fluid level and excess system pressure can be indicated and identified on the control panel. The system provides for automatic response if necessary closing down one pump and bringing another into operation – if the spare capacity is available.

Applications for microprocess based pump control systems include constant pressure control of pressure booster systems; control of heating and air conditioning systems; control of vacuum pumping systems; and a variety of configurations for process control applications and on-site efficiency testing.

Speed variation

Large pumps dealing with a variable demand may be run most economically by sympathetic changes in speed. Wound rotor a.c. motors give a speed range of about 2:1 which is sufficient for most practical requirements, as a wider range than this would cause pumps to cut in and out too frequently. Although a proportional automatic controller can be used for controlling the motor speed, a simpler method is to fit a level detector and use this in conjunction with a timer to increase or decrease the speed in steps at suitable time intervals.

Speed sensors

The function of the sensing head of speed sensor is to convert the measured variable 'speed' into a proportional frequency. Magnetic and oscillator sensors are available and both have given good results. Their use depends on the range of application they are required for. Preference is often given to the magnetic sensor due to its wide pulse and speed range and other essential characteristics.

Magnetic sensors generate power and consist of a permanent magnet and coil. By means of moving ferrous objects (gear wheels, screw heads, pins, boreholes in shafts or pulleys) a voltage is induced in the coil. The amplitude of the output signal depends on the space between the sensing head and the pole wheel on the peripheral speed of the pole wheel, and on the form of the poles.

The ouput signal grows from zero at the rate of the increasing speed. In the lower range, however, the signal is below the operating threshold. Equipment operates only after the threshold has been exceeded.

Magnetic sensors are senstitive to external magnetic fields, which may distort the measuring result. It is important therefore that the connecting cable is shielded and the shield earthed.

Oscillator sensors contain a transistor-oscillator. As soon as a metal part approaches the front of the sensor, the oscillator stops oscillating, which influences the internal resistance and thus actuates the connected frequency-voltage converter. The oscillator sensors are mainly used for low speeds and standstill control.

They are not suitable for ferro-magnetic materials and are less sensitive to interference pulses than magnetic sensors.

Instruments

The standard instrument associated with a basic pump installation is a pressure gauge (or gauges) of the Bourdon tube or diaphragm type in the form of a dial gauge. A common arrangement is to have one gauge at the pump inlet and one at the pump outlet although the actual gauges may be remote from the pump itself. In this case the gauging points may be monitored by a 'sender' (pressure transducer) with pressure displayed by an electric meter or LED display.

Liquid column of pressure gauges may be used for test measurements but only where low heads are involved.

The accuracy achieved with a Bourdon tube gauge can be of the order of ±2% of the full scale deflection. Greatest accuracy is normally achieved at the upper end of the scale. The selection of a Bourdon tube gauge should be based on a pressure range where the normal reading point will be towards the upper end of the scale. Consistency of performance, however, is related to the fatigue characteristics of the tube material and some drift is inevitable with time. As a general rule, therefore, Bourdon gauges need regular checking and re-calibration when in use.

Bourdon gauges are susceptible to mechanical shock and pressure surges, and should be protected against the possibility of their occurrence. A simple method of protection against pressure surges is to fit a snubber or restricter in the feed line. In severe cases, it may be best to employ mechanical throttling or a shut-off device, which responds directly to any sudden increase in pressure.

Another possible source of trouble is blocking of the tube by contaminants in the fluid. To obviate this a diaphragm-type seal can be incorporated in the inlet feed. The Bourdon tube is then filled with clean fluid (usually oil) which is isolated from working fluid, the pressure of the latter being transferred to the Bourdon tube through the flexible seal. This principle can be extended by employing a diaphragm unit or capsule as a transmitter separate from the Bourdon gauge and connected to it by a length of tubing. A distinct advantage offered here is that the gauge itself can be distant from the transmitter without affecting the accuracy of the reading.

Simple diaphragm gauges can be made extremely sensitive when designed for use with low pressures, *eg* up to 1 bar (15 lb/in^2). More robust designs are suitable for pressures up to a maximum of about 20 bar (300 lb/in^2). The diaphragm travel and thus the stroke available to operate and indicate movement is dependent on the diameter of the diaphragm and its cross-sectional form. Large movement may only be obtained at the expense of some loss of linearity of scale. The main limitations of diaphragm gauges are a restricted pressure range (although this can be improved by the use of convolute metal diaphragms), susceptibility to pressure pulsations and rather higher cost than a Bourdon gauge. They can however, usually withstand substantial pressure overload without damage, although calibration may be effected.

Differential gauges

It is now common practice to protect pumps, especially high pressure multi-stage pumps from being damaged by solid matter. This may involve fitting filters which are subjected to high inlet pressure. To check the filter condition it is usual to measure the pressure drop across it by differential pressure gauges. Where the allowable pressure drop is not more than one-fifteenth of the working pressure, a Bourdon tube type differential pressure indicator can be used. This instrument has two Bourdon tubes which are connect to either side of the filter. A simple mechanism subtracts one tube movement from the other and the resulting difference is shown on a circular scale. For high pressure a more elaborate instrument embodying either a diaphragm or metallic bellows has to be used. The pressures are then applied either side of the diaphragm bellows and the result of deflection due to pressure difference taken to the point through a magnetic coupling stuffing box or rocker arm.

Electronic pressure gauges

Electronic pressure gauges are based on a pressure transducer in a resistance bridge circuit, an amplifier and an indicator. The latter can be meter or digital readout through LED's. The pressure range depends on the type of transducer used.

Accuracy is normally to within ±1% of the maximum pressure rating of the transducer.

Pressure recorders

Chart-type pressure recorders are commonly based on a Bourdon gauge with the movement limited to the chart pen. Instead of the older type of pen carrying ink, modern instruments use pressure-sensitive chart paper and a 'chapter bar'. The latter is actuated by the chart drive motor momentarily to press the pointer against the paper to produce a small dot. Repetition of this produces a trace which appears as a continuous line on the chart.

Vacuum gauges

Cavitation due to too high a suction vacuum or too low a pressure has been the cause of many premature pump failures. On normal pumping duties the most common cause may be excessive suction lift combined with a partial blockage, particularly of foot valve strainer. This can be taken care of by a vacuum gauge fitted with an electric contact which either operates alarm or shuts the pump down. A gauge has the advantage over a pressure switch that it gives a continuous indication of the conditions as well a providing automatic protection.

Pumps handling hot liquids especially feed water pumps, must have sufficient nett positive suction head (NPSH) to prevent vapour flashing in the impeller. The onset of this condition can be indicated by a suitable instrument located on the suction side of the pump, giving a visible and/or audible warning of the approach of cavitation conditions.

Flow meters

Flow meters can be classified under the following types:

(i) Mechanical meters, or those having moving or mechanical elements. These may provide positive measurement, semi- positive measurement, or measurement by inference (inferential meters). There are also a number of special types and individual proprietory designs properly classified as mechanical meters. Table 1 gives various examples and applications of mechanical flow meters.

(ii) Differential flow meters, which are based on a detecting element modifying the flow and generating a differential pressure across the device. Such devices must be combined with a further separate measuring element to measure the differential pressure developed, so that it can be rendered in the form of a flow measurement.

(iii) Variable aperture flow meters which operate in the reverse manner to a differential pressure element but are capable of giving direct indication of flow rate by displacement of a float or similar device.

(iv) Electro-magnetic devices of various types, ranging from basic d.c. generators to capacitance or resistance change detecting elements.

(v) Weirs and venturi flues, mainly applicable to open channel measurement, but also used for pump test measurements, the measurement of boiler feed and condensate, *etc*, in the form of weir tanks.

(vi) Current meters, basically velocity-measuring devices. These are again mostly used for open channel measurement.

TABLE 1 – CLASSIFICATION OF MECHANICAL FLOW METERS

Classification	Sub-Types	Principle	Accuracy	Applications
Reciprocating piston	(i) Packed piston	Reciprocating pump being driven as a 'motor'.	±2%	Metering and dosing – most types of liquids.
	(ii) Non-packed piston	Reciprocating pump being driven as a 'motor' (usually duplex).	Very high	Metering of fluids with lubricating properties – not suitable for water.
Rotary	Duplex rotor	Rotary pump being driven as a 'motor'	Better than ±1%	Greater capacity than reciprocating types.
Rotary piston (semi-rotary)	(i) 'Dry'	Pressure-tight gland between semi-rotary motor and counter	±2%	Numerous designs available with material selection to suit all types of liquids.
	(ii) 'Wet'	Fully submersible unit		
Inferential	(i) Impeller (fan)	Rotational speed of driven fan proportional to flow velocity	±2%	Most liquids.
	(ii) (a) Helix (vertical) (b) Helix (horizontal)	Rotational speed of driven axial flow impeller proportional to flow velocity.	±2%	Suitable for larger sizes.
	(iii) Turbine	Damped rotation; calibrated		Usually used as shunt meters
	(iv) Electro-magnetic	Rotor carrying magnet in a.c. generator circuit – output proportional to flow rate	±½% with digital integration	
Compound	Various	Usually an inferential meter covering high high and medium flow ranges; combined with smaller mechanical meter for indicating low flow rates. Changeover can be automatic		Coverage of widely varying flow rates.

(vii) Mass flow measuring devices, which may be based on torque sensing or gyroscopic elements. These are capable of reading mass flow independently of the density of the fluid involved, *ie* a separate measurement of density is not required, as would be necessary in the case of a flow meter, to determine the actual mass flow.

(viii) Transducers and other measuring devices in special configurations capable of reading or inferring flow rate from change of characteristic induced by the flow.

Mechanical flow meters are still widely used because they are usually complete in themselves and present the least problems in installation. Basically all that is required is that the meter may be installed in the pipeline at a suitable position. Ideally, this should be in a position where the flow is smooth and free from excessive pulsations (which, apart from causing reading errors, could result in damage to moving mechanical parts) and where there is sufficient back pressure to maintain the meter full of liquid at all times. The meter may be mounted directly in the line, or in a bypass loop incorporating isolating valves.

Differential flow meters have the advantage that no moving parts are immersed in the fluid and that only the tapping points require to be connected to the separate flow registering device. These tapping points are critical however, and are normally incorporated in the construction of the device. As a general rule, tappings are located horizontally for metering fluids, and vertically for metering gases. It is also important that the device is mounted the right way round. Venturi and Dall tubes normally have an arrow marked on the casings indicating the correct flow direction and orifices have similar identification markings on the plate carriers. More specific information may be necessary for mounting pivots when the individual manufacturers instructions should be followed closely. See Table 2.

TABLE 2 – CLASSIFICATION OF DIFFERENTIAL FLOW METERS

Detecting Element	Size Range	Discharge Coefficient	Average Pressure Drop (% of differential)	Remarks
Venturi	13 mm – 3 m (½ in – 10 ft)	0.95–0.99		Can be constructed in any suitable material.
Dall tube	13 mm (½ in) upwards	0.65–0.7	5	Higher pressure recovery than Venturi, but only suitable for use with clean fluids.
Orifice	Produced in standard forms and sizes	*circa* 0.61	60	Head loss greater than that of Venturi and more sensitive to service conditions. Suitable for use with all clean liquids – easy to install. Special orifice plates may be used for metering viscous fluids.
Dall orifice			20	Basically a truncated Dall tube. Only suitable for use with clean fluids.
Pitot	Restricted			Velocity measuring device sensitive to position. Must also be located in a straight run of pipe.
Nozzle	Standard designs and sizes	0.95–0.99	50–60	Mostly used for measuring gas flow rates discharging into atmosphere (*eg* compressor delivery).

The basic rule when considering monitoring and measuring instruments for centrifugal pumps is to avoid everything superfluous as additional devices by no means enhance reliability, on the contrary they clutter the installation and increase the number of possible trouble sources. Partial or full automation should be justifiable and economical. Minimum attendance and maintenance costs should always be aimed for.

For a complete understanding of types of flow meters and their applications see *Handbook of Fluid Flowmetering,* published by The Trade & Technical Press Limited, Crown House, Morden, Surrey, England.

Filters and Strainers

COARSE FILTERS or strainers may be employed on the suction side of a pump to guard against clogging or damage handling fluid which may be contaminated with solids. The degree of protection provided must essentially compromise between desirable cut-off rating for pump protection (which will also depend on the product involved) and the necessity for minimal pressure drop through the filter. A clogged suction filter will reduce the flow to the pump and may lead to cavitation and loss of performance (and even damage to the pump in certain cases).

As a general guide, adequate protection for a roto-dynamic pump is usually given by a perforated metal screen with holes of the order of 0·75 mm (0·063 in) diameter or a 10 mesh screen, provided no fibrous or stringy material is present. In the case of positive displacement pumps, suction filter requirements are more specific to the type, size and internal appearances of the individual pump. In all cases the manufacturer's recommendations should be followed.

Suction strainers are often placed on the end of the inlet pipe where they are continuously submerged and relatively inaccessible. In such cases it may be

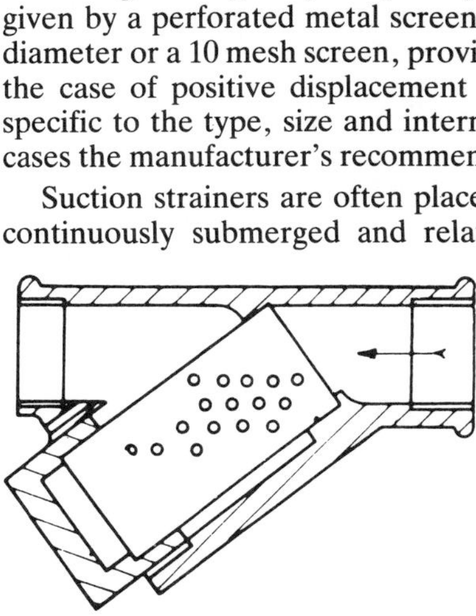

Figure 1
Y type simple pipeline strainer available with screwed or flanged couplings can be cleaned by removing the side plug and the element withdrawn.

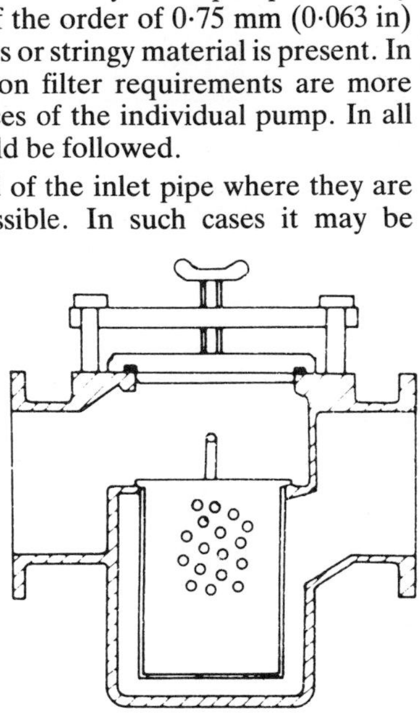

Figure 2
Basket-type pipeline strainer with detachable cover to enable the element to be withdrawn upwards for cleaning.

advisable to increase the size of the strainer, particularly if clogging material is present in the inflow, or even incorporate a warning device to indicate excessive back pressure and incipient starvation of the pump, *ie* that the strainer needs cleaning. In other cases the nature of the solids may be such that they fall away from the strainer when the pump is stopped when a normal size strainer may continue to provide satisfactory performance with little or no attention. Specific designs of inlet end strainer may also provide for simple cleaning, the main requirement in this case being simply that they are accessible and attended to at regular intervals as necessary. Typical application data for strainers are summarised in Table 1.

TABLE 1 – TYPICAL APPLICATION OF STRAINERS

Mesh*	Applications
Perforated screens (Holes up to 1.5 mm diameter)	Fibrous and stringy materials.
Wire cloths	
10	Dirty waters, river water, *etc.*
20	Dirty waters, water soluble paints.
30	Coarse filtration of water, pump inlet screens, *etc.* Glues, hot wax, size and viscous fluids.
40	Coolants, mill water supply, clarifiers.
60	Air conditioning, mill water supply, clarifiers.
100	Washing water and all fine mesh filtering duties.
150	Fine water filtering, fuel lines, *etc.*
200	Fine process filtering, fuel lines, iron oxide, fine grits, *etc.*
250	Food plant filtering and clarification, soft drink and beer filtering.
500 and up to 700	Very fine commercial process filtering, photographic solutions, chemicals, clarifiers for potable liquors.

*Wires per inch

Most pumps tend to be limited to handle dirt and solids of any size down to micro particles. Pump passageways (volutes, diffusers, impellers *etc*,) handle generally spherical objects up to a 'sticking size' but a severe problem may be caused by dust size particles which lodge in sleeve bearings, bushings and wearing rings and cause either rapid wear or rotation seizure.

Drum rotating strainers can handle solids down to approximately 250 microns (0·01 in) back-flushing is used to renew the strainer area. The addition of woven wire cloth to such strainers may remove materials down to 25 microns (0·1 in). Woven wire drum strainers used in conjunction with sand filters will reduce the amount of back flushing required for the sand filters.

For areas where wear can be extremely critical, such as bearings and stuffing boxes, additional filtering effort is necessary especially if the entrained silt is abrasive. A vortex filter using centrifugal flow action will remove particles down to a few microns. These filters have continuous sediment removal and should not require much maintenance.

If the fluid being pumped normally contains solids in suspension, then the pump must be selected accordingly *ie* it must be capable of handling the type of solids involved and have sufficient internal clearances to pass them. A suction filter may still be employed however, to ensure that larger solids which could clog the pump are now passed to the pump inlet. In this case the filtering action provided can be quite coarse. Alternative treatment is to introduce a chopping action into the inlet side via a comminuting device, which reduces larger solids to a size which can be handled and passed by the pump. No filter is used and so any chance of a filter blocking and starving the pump is avoided. Such treatment is usually reserved for specific applications *eg* certain sewage pumps or those handling fluids containing soft but stringy contaminants.

Delivery side filters

Filters on the delivery side of a pump may be used in various ways *eg*:

(i) One main filter in the delivery line for general system protection.

(ii) Individual filters in appropriate lines to protect individual system elements from clogging (*eg* valves with small clearances). The system may also incorporate a main filter in which case the main filter can be a relatively coarse type, with finer filters for the individual lines, as required.

The degree of protection likely to be required in a typical system is:

(i) Large valves – a 30 to 80 mesh screen or finer strainer.

(ii) Small valves – medium filter with 40 to 50 microns cut off.

(iii) Precision valves – ultra-fine filter or micron filter.

(iv) Large gears – a medium filter with 40 to 50 microns cut off.

(v) Medium size gears – a fine filter with 20 to 40 microns cut off.

(iv) Precision gears – ultra-fine filter.

(vii) Large bearings – a fine filter.

(viii) Medium size bearings – ultra-fine filter.

(ix) Small precision bearings – micron filter.

(x) Large rams – fine filter or ultra-fine filter.

(xi) Precision rams – ultra-fine or micron filter.

A general guide to filter performance is given in Table 2.

TABLE 2 – GENERAL FILTER PERFORMANCE

FILTER TYPE Parameter	Aperture filters	Edge-type	Absorption media	Adsorption media	Precoat filters	Filter presses
Moisture removal	No	Yes (paper)	Yes	Possibly	No	No
Removal of soluble contaminants	No	Yes (paper)	Possibly	Some	No	No
Removal of sub-micron particles	No	Yes (paper)	Possibly	Some	No	No
Suitability for: aqueous solutions	Excellent	Very good	Very good	Not generally suitable	Excellent	Excellent
Mild acids	Very good†	Very good	Some limitations	Not suitable	Very good†	Depends on cloth
Mild chemical solutions	Very good†	Very good	Some limitations	Not suitable suitable	Very good†	Depends on cloth
Synthetic fluids	Very good†	Very good	Some limitations	Not suitable	Very good	Very good

†With suitable choice of element or medium.

Traps and drainers

Traps or vent traps are components designed to vent collected air or gas from liquid systems automatically and continuously without loss of liquid. In this respect they are similar in function to air relief valves, but the description trap is specifically applied to such venting valves used on heat exchangers, surface condensers and hot water heating systems.

Drainers are the complement of traps. They are valves used to drain oil, water or condensate automatically and continuously from pressurised gas or vapour systems and also for interface control where continuous draining of the heavier liquid is required. Both traps and drainers are normally float operated valves, comprising a float chamber, float assembly and cover with a vent clock.

For complete information on all aspects of filters and filtration technology consult the *Filters and Filtration Handbook*, published by The Trade and Technical Press Limited, Crown House, Morden, Surrey, England.

SECTION 7

Pumping Duties, Services & Applications

Water Pumps

THE CENTRIFUGAL pump is normally the preferred type for handling water, provided the maximum suction lift required does not exceed about 4·5 to 6 m (15 to 20 ft). With suitable modification of impeller design centrifugal pumps can handle dirty liquids with high solids contents as well as clean water and provide a steady discharge flow. Both discharge pressure and capacity ranges available are very wide and multi-stage units can be employed where high heads are required. Efficiency tends to decrease with decreasing size, thus the most favourable application of centrifugal pumps is for medium to high deliveries. Small centrifugal pumps with simple impellers however, are widely produced for low demand requirements (normally handling only clean water), commonly in the form of submersible or immersible units with electric motor drive. An alternative in this particular size range is the flexible impeller pump.

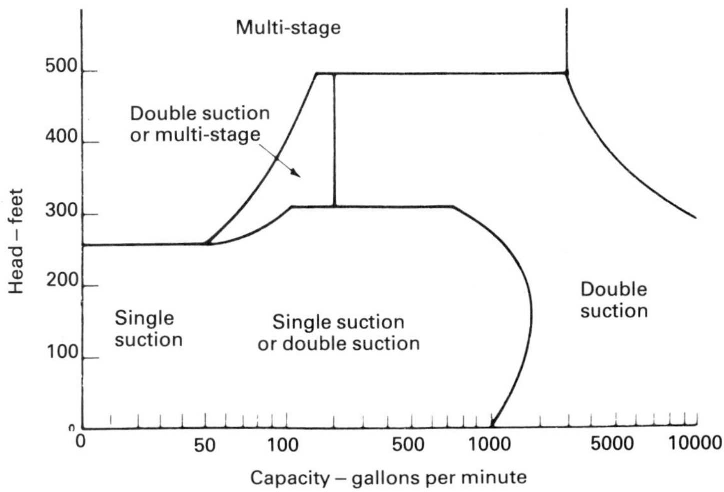

Figure 1
General guide to the normal operating envelopes of different types of centrifugal pumps in terms of head and capacity requirements.

With increasing capacity double suction is normally employed, although there is an intermediate range where either single or double suction is suitable. (Figure 1).

With increasing head, multi-stage constructions become necessary although, again, double suction is a method of increasing head over a single suction pump.

Single-stage pumps may provide heads of up to 30 m (100 ft) in the smaller sizes and up to 150 m (500 ft) in the larger sizes, the limitation being the practical one of casting large diameter very narrow impellers for small size pumps. Two-stage pumps are also readily available in this range offering lower initial cost than multi-stage pumps for heads of up to 250 m (800 ft). All pumps in these categories can be classified as general purpose types the majority being massed produced in standard ranges and sizes although some of the larger types may be produced specifically for certain applications, *eg* water works and bulk water supplies.

Single-stage inline pump shown left and single-stage end suction pump for water boosting transfer and circulation duties.

Multi-stage pumps usually incorporate a number of impellers on a common shaft in a multiple casing, each stage comprising an impeller, guide passage or diffuser and return passages within a chamber which discharges water to the next stage. Cellular construction is favoured in Europe whilst split casings are favoured in America for pressures up to 70 bar (1000 lb/in^2). For higher pressures, American manufacturers normally adopt cellular construction barrel-type casings.

Vertical pumps are often preferred to horizontal pumps not only because of the resultant reduction in floor space but also because priming can be easier to achieve and general purpose pumps of this type are more readily adapted to different duties. Horizontal pumps on the other hand, are normally better from the point of view of ease of maintenance and inspection and to a lesser extent for their resistance to corrosion and abrasion and (generally) more stable mounting.

Reciprocating pumps

Reciprocating pumps offer a certain advantage over centrifugal pumps in that the capacity is readily adjusted *eg* by varying the speed, and high efficiencies can be maintained over a wide range of heads. They are not generally competitive with centrifugal pumps, however where large deliveries are required and the traditional reciprocating pump for water supply duties has largely been replaced by roto-dynamic types.

Plunger pumps are better suited to developing high pressures than centrifugal pumps and thus more attractive for services involving modest deliveries. The positive displacement characteristics of reciprocating pumps also make them a preferred choice for metering and dosing. Thus plunger pumps are a normal choice for feeding chlorine or other chemical solutions in measured quantities for the treatment of water supply, swimming pools *etc*.

Diaphragm pumps are also suitable for metering or proportioning duties but their main application in water services is for the handling of toxic or corrosive fluids with a virtual absence of maintenance requirements. The ability of a diaphragm pump to handle water containing slurries or solids contaminants is governed by the valving system. Whilst such types may be employed for dewatering, pumping muddy water, *etc*, rubber covered ball valves may be required in order to combat the abrasive nature of the medium with valve designs aimed at providing a 'sulphur cleaning' action.

Rotary pumps
Rotary pumps are generally considered most suitable for handling fluids of a substantially higher viscosity than water, *eg* oils. This is not exactly true since the design of most types of rotary pump can be adapted to handle almost any liquid that is free of hard and abrasive solids (some can even accommodate solids in suspension). Thus the gear pump, which is the simplest type of rotary pump can handle water satisfactorily and is often used as an inexpensive solution where demand is small and head and pressure requirements are relatively low. Lobe rotor pumps, on the other hand, are less suited to handling water since the rotor form employed may have been developed to handle higher viscosity fluids efficiently. Efficiency as a water pump can, in consequence be low.

Sliding vane pumps are another type which can be produced inexpensively and work at high efficiency regardless of fluid viscosity. One of their main limitations in the handling of water is the lack of lubrication at the vane tips. This can be overcome by choice of suitable materials for parts in rubbing contact. Swinging vane pumps can handle solids and similar contaminants in water, although such pumps are normally only made in larger sizes for heavy duty applications.

The flexible impeller pump employs an elastomeric motor rotating concentrically inside a circular casing carrying a segmental insert to provide asymmetrical 'pocket' areas is particularly versatile and has a wide range of applications for small pump sizes. The flexible elastomeric impeller is self-priming and gives a constant discharge. Particular advantages are good sealing without the necessity of extremely accurate manufacture (as is required with a sliding vane pump), self-compensation for wear and an ability to handle and pass solid contaminants. Friction is however, higher than with other types of rotary pump and discharge pressure is normally limited to below 15 bar (50lb/in^2) if serious loss of efficiency is to be avoided. Nevertheless for small capacity duties such as bilge water pumping, it is an economic and highly attractive type. Numerous small pumps from fractional horse power sizes are now widespread use. The elementary impeller pump is attractive and inexpensive for small capacity duties, although basically this is the simplest form of centrifugal pump. The impeller comprises a simple moulding or a metal casting with a number of radial blades of high aspect ratio rotating in a circular chamber, the whole forming a simple pancake shaped unit which can be mounted directly onto the end of an electric motor to form a compact pump set. Efficiency may be low in small sizes but for simple dewatering services the low initial cost may more than justify its choice.

TABLE 1

Application or service	Type of pump used
Booster pumps	Single- or two-stage centrifugal (volute) Turbine Diffuser Rotary
Construction (site pumps)	Portable pump sets Portable centrifugal (close coupled) Reciprocating Rotary Diaphragm
Dewatering	Centrifugal (volute) Turbine Submersible motor Diffuser Reciprocating Rotary Diaphragm (heavily contaminated waters)
Fire protection	Centrifugal (generally preferred Rotary Reciprocating (limited) Portable pump sets
Hand pumps	Rotary Semi-rotary Peristaltic Diaphragm Piston (for infrequent or light duties)
Heating (hot water supply)	Single-stage centrifugal
Irrigation and drainage	Portable units Mixed flow (for large volumes) Axial flow (for large volumes)
Lawn sprinkling	(None, jet and sprinkler heads operated directly by mains water supply pressure Single-stage centrifugal (volute) for large demands and heads up to 30 m (100 ft) Two-stage or multi-stage centrifugal for large
demands up to	60 m (200 ft)
Portable pumps	Centrifugal Turbine Rotary Reciprocating Diaphragm

Application or service	Type of pump used
Sewage	Centrifugal (non-clogging) Mixed flow (for large volumes) Axial flow (for large volumes)
Shallow water supply	Reciprocating Turbine Centrifugal (volute) Mixed-flow (large volumes, moderate heads) Axial flow (large volumes, low heads) Flexible vane (low volumes, low heads)
Sludge	Single-stage vertical centrifugal (volute) Portable submersible pumps Diaphragm Pneumatic ejector
Spray heads	Centrifugal (see 'Sprinklers') with heads from 15 to 75 m (50 to 250 ft)
Sprinklers, *etc*	Single- or two-stage centrifugal (volute) Turbine Rotary
Surface water handling	Horizontal single-stage or two-stage Centrifugal Turbine Reciprocating
Swimming pools	Single-stage centrifugal (volute)
Water supply (surface water handling)	Centrifugal (moderate capacities, low heads) Mixed flow (high capacities, moderate heads) Axial flow (high capacities, low heads)
Water treatment	Proportioning or metering pumps
Water supply (water raising)	Reciprocating (for high heads) Centrifugal Deepwell Submersible Helical rotor Jet Air lift
Well water supply	Multi-stage diffuser Submersible motor Jet Helical rotor

The wide range of water services which require pumps is listed in alphabetical order in Table 1 together with the pumps normally used for such applications. Table 2 shows typical working ranges for various types of pump.

TABLE 2 – TYPICAL PUMP WORKING RANGES

Pump type	Capacity range litres/min	gal/min	Maximum head metres	feet
Centrifugal:				
Single-stage	25 to 225000	5 to 50000	30	100
	45 to 10000	10 to 2000	150	500
Two-stage	45 to 225000	10 to 5000	over 150	over 500
Multi-stage	450 to 225000	100 to 5000	over 300	over 1000
Peripheral	5 to 100	1 to 20	150	500
Mixed flow	1000 to 450000	250 to 100000	25 to 3	75 to 10
			decreasing with increasing capacity	
Axial flow	4500 to 900000	1000 to 200000	7·5 to 0	25 to 0
			decreasing with increasing capacity	
Reciprocating:				
Power driven	100 to 4500	20 to 1000	over 300	over 1000
Direct-acting	20 to 7000	5 to 1500	over 300	over 1000
Plunger	5 to 700	1 to 150	over 1500	over 5000
Diaphragm	up to 100	up to 20	6	20
Flexible vane	up to 350	up to 75	6	20
Rigid vane	up to 225	up to 50	125	400
Rolling vane	up to 225	up to 50	66	300
Screw, flexible stator	up to 1000	up to 200	50 to 15	175 to 50
			decreasing with increasing capacity (up to 1000 ft with multi-stage)	
Screw, rigid screws	45 to 225000	10 to 5000	60 to 25	200 to 80
			decreasing with increasing capacity	
Submersible (electric)	20 to 7000	5 to 1500	50	175

Hand pumps

Semi-rotary pumps are a common form of hand pump for water services, where the pumping action is provided by a semi-rotating wing mounted on the pump spindle and oscillated by to-and-fro movement of the pump handle. This wing is mounted in a circular pump casing, each side of the wing being fitted with a flat valve. A suction box at the bottom of the pump casing forms a V shaped chamber each side of which is fitted with a flat valve. Movement of the handle one way causes a depression in one chamber opening the flat valve in the wing to pass water already in the casing into the upper half of the casing. On the reverse stroke, fluid is forced out of the outlet as the half cycle of operation is repeated in reverse. Thus the pump is double-acting.

By the addition of a further valve box or outlet divider which rotates water in the delivery pipe and has flap valves opening into the chamber and no flap valve in the wing, a quadruple-acting pump can be produced. This will have an appreciably higher capacity than a double-acting pump of the same size but will require considerably more effort to operate continuously.

Other types of hand pump are diaphragm and peristaltic pumps, both of which are capable of handling contaminated waters without clogging. Deliveries available are somewhat limited, particularly with the latter type.

For greater capacities with hand pumps, it is generally preferable to employ a full rotary design where the handle can be turned continuously. Either type (semi-rotary or full-rotary) is generally to be preferred to hand operated piston pumps, except for the very lightest duties. Equally, in the field originally covered by hand pumps, modern motorised pump units of the impeller or flexible vane type are much to be preferred as these are suitable for operation of 6 or 12 volts as well as mains supplies. The cost of such units is often directly comparable with semi-rotary hand pumps of similar capacity.

Water supply

General water supply can involve the raising of water from natural sources such as limestone and sandstone beds beneath the earth's surface followed by transfer to a reservoir or similar storage and treatment basin. Further pumps may then be required to transfer the water from the main basin to individual storage towers or to feed ring mains. Both well pumps and surface pumps may, therefore be involved (see Table 3).

A well pump is obviously necessary where the lift involved is beyond the practical suction lift available from a conventional surface pump mounted at ground level. The basic method is to lower the pump to the bottom of a well or

TABLE 3 – PUMPS FOR WATER SUPPLY

Type of pump	Delivery range m^3/h	Maximum head m
1. Submersible motor	1 to 12500	1200
2. Vertical spindle (wet installation)	1 to 12300	160
3. Vertical, wet installation, multi-stage helical impeller	1000 to 6500	90
4. Single-stage, volute casing	4 to 36000	100
5. Single-stage, volute with diffuser	100 to 10000	400
6. Multi-stage, ring section	500 to 1200	575
7. Single-stage, double flow, volute casing	100 to 30000	200
8. Single-stage, double flow, volute casing with diffuser	1200 to 18000	500

Jet pumps for shallow well water supply.

borehole, when the necessary lift is obtained in the delivery side. The pump can then be driven either by a shaft from the driver mounted at ground level (or any convenient level above the pump), or the driver and pump can be directly coupled and assembled as an integral submersible unit. In the former case virtually any type of driver can be used and any type of pump (although, in practice, pump choice is limited by performance requirements). In the latter case electric motor drive is virtually standard although hydraulic drive is an alternative for shallower wells.

Centrifugal pumps are normally preferred for such a duty. Impellers are usually open- or semi-open with vertical configurations as many stages as necessary to realise the desired head economically. Thus in a deep well pump, heads of over 500 m (1500 ft) may be achieved in as many as 20 stages, although a much smaller number of stages is more usual. Typical diameter sizes for deep well pumps are from about 0·15 to 0·75 m (6 in to 30 in), with capacities ranging up to 13 5000 l/min (30 000 gal/min). Thus the range in size, head and capacity is considerable. The pump itself may be oil lubricated, in which case the driving shaft is usually surrounded by a tube, or lubricated by the water handled by the pump. The latter type is specified where oil-free delivery imperative, although for normal appliciations their is little, if anything to choose between the two.

In the case of submersible pumps, single- or multi-stage pumps may be employed, according to the performance requirements. Heads of up to 3500 m (12000 ft) have been achieved with such units, although capacity range is usually more restricted than that of shaft driven well pumps. As many as 30 stages have been used in larger pumps of this type, although again a very much smaller number is more usual. Once lowered, the only connection with the surface is the rising main and power cable to the motor. Extreme reliability is called for in the design of the motor as this must be capable of operating for long periods without servicing.

Reciprocating pumps continue to have a limited application for well surfaces, with the pump motor mounted above the water level and the head submerged and connected by a shaft. A double acting pump of this type is capable of realising heads of up to 210 to 240 m (700 to 800 ft) with capacities up to 1100 to 1350 l/min (240 to 300 gal/min). Alternative types for well pumping include the helical rotor pump which embodies a screw shaped rotor turning in an elastomeric stator and is suitable for deep well operation with heads of up to 300 m (1000 ft) with some saving in overall diameter. It is usually shaft driven rather than submersible, with some form of shock absorbing coupling to dampen the asymmetric forces generated by the rotor.

Borehole pumps

Borehole or deepwell pumps are of special design to enable the pump to be lowered to the bottom of the borehole or well until the suction side (or the hole pump) is immersed. The necessary lift to raise the water to surface level is then accomplished on the delivery side of the pump. Normally such pumps are one of two types:-

(i) Shaft driven

(ii) Submersible

Although other types of pump may be employed for such services.

With shaft driven pumps the driver is mounted at the surface of the borehole and connected to the pump via a length of vertical shafting. The shaft is normally protected by a sleeve, which can also act as the delivery pipe. Pump, sleeve and driver must be assembled as an integral unit (common with electric motor drives); or the driver may be separate and drive the upper end of the shaft through gearing (applicable where the driver is of a type which must be mounted horizontally, *eg* an i/c engine. Shaft and casing are assembled in sections to make up the total length required.

The shaft is normally supported at intervals along the length of casing, these bearings being of rubber or laminated thermoset plastic when water lubricated – *ie* by the pumped water flowing up through the casing. If the liquid being pumped is not suitable as a lubricant, then the shaft is further surrounded by an inner tube to isolate it from the liquid flow. This inner tube is then flooded separately with water or a suitable lubricant from a separate source.

A centrifugal pump is the usual choice although the diameter is necessarily restricted by the size of the bore hole available. Economic bore hole sizes may range from 150 mm (6 in) upwards, and bore hole pumps are produced to match standard bore hole sizes. This normally brings the specific speed of the pump within the mixed flow range covered by diagonal pumps where the maximum head available per stage is between 33 and 65 metres. The complete pump is then assembled as a multi-stage unit (usually with axial recuperators) the number of stages being chosen according to the head required. Very high head pumps may have 20 or more stages although with improvements in design yielding high heads per stage, modern bore hole pumps tend to have a smaller number of stages generating the required head.

With the considerable difference in 'borehole' size and the number of stages which may be employed, pumps of this type have a wide range of capacities (*eg* up to 135 m^3/min or more) and heads (*eg* up to 500 m). With unit construction a basic diameter size can be assembled in any number of stages, according to the head required.

The depth to which a shaft drive pump can be installed is, however, limited largely to the effect of shaft 'stretch'. This stretch depends not only on the weight of the parts and on the hydraulic down thrust imposed by the impellers when pumping, but also on the original length of the shaft. Once the stretch reaches the maximum permissible, the limitation of pump setting has been reached.

The pumping of water from below the ground involves additional losses in the frictional torque of the vertical shafting and in the power absorbed by the surface bearing on which this shafting is suspended. Additional head losses are incurred in the friction between the pump at water level and the discharge branch at ground level. These additional losses are taken into account in the guarantee for the pumping system as a whole.

Submersible pumps

Where a reliable source of mains electricity is available the submersible pump is now usually preferred. Both types are equally capable (in fact the only two types capable) of handling the output from larger wells. (See Figure 2). It is however usually possible to extract water at a slightly greater rate from the well of a given bore by using a shaft-driven pump once the inlet to the pump is not restricted by the presence of a submerged motor (Figure 3).

The submersible pump overcomes all the 'mechanical' troubles which can be encountered with shaft-driven pumps. Provided that one or two precautions are observed, they give very much better service than shaft driven pumps but they are also by no means immune to damage by sand in the water. They are more easily withdrawn and inserted since the pipe contains no shaft or bearings; maintenance is usually carried out at a central workshop and a few trained mechanics can

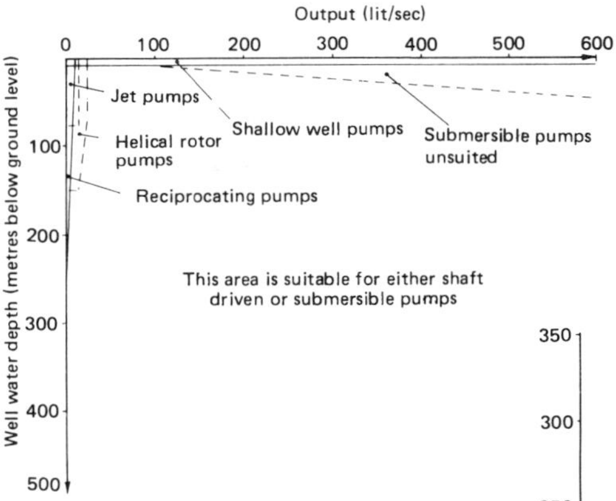

Figure 2
Range chart for different types of well pump.

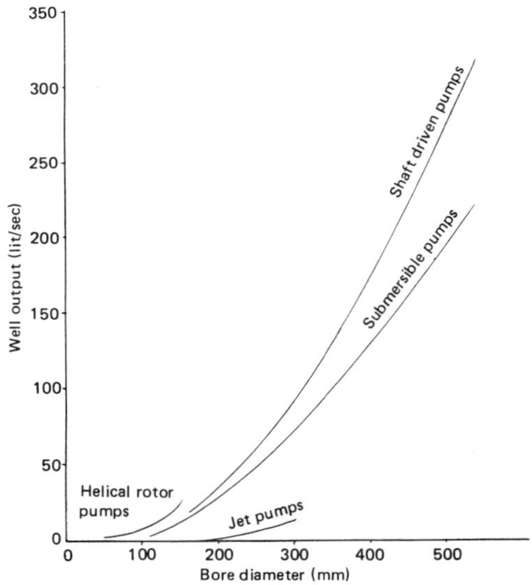

Figure 3
Well output versus bore diameter using various types of pump.

therefore overhaul, on the basis of repair by replacement, all the pumps for a large scheme. Reasonably reliable power supplies are of course essential; voltage variations can result in motor burn-outs due to the very low heat storage capacity of the motors unless close current protection is applied; this, however, can give rise to frequent tripping if the supply voltage is too inconsistent.

A basic disadvantage of a submersible pump, compared with a shaft-driven pump is that there is no way of varying the speed of a submersible except by varying the frequency of the a.c. power delivered to it. This always means having a local generator to drive the pump and a relatively large generator and expensive switchgear is needed to cope with pumps starting currents. It is possible to use the so-called 'frequency start' system in which the generator is connected directly to the pump before starting either, (through a closed circuit breaker) and the pump runs up simultaneously with the alternator. This largely overcomes the start up problem and enables a size of generating set to be selected which is more in keeping with the power required to run the pump. The system requires a special voltage regulator on the generator to regulate the output voltage according to the speed during the run up and this therefore renders the power output unsuitable for other constant voltage supplies such as lighting purposes.

Submersible pumps can suffer from deposits of calcium carbonate depending upon the carbon compound constituents in the water, especially on hard waters containing excess calcium, giving rise to flow passage choking and risks of seizure at rotational clearances. Corrosion can vary from almost negligible in benign waters to severe requiring all stainless construction of pumps and of motor end stampings with epoxy encapsulated windings. It is also essential to consider corrosion of the rising main and its fittings since a steel pipe is subject in its bore and outside to corrosion by the water for which a bitumen lining is helpful. The pipe, bolts and cable clips are subject to a dry atmosphere for the rest of the time to which mild steel is susceptable. In fact the wet and dry situation is much worse from a corrosion aspect than a situation of always dry or always wet. It has been found that chromising mild steel to a depth of 0·25 mm (0·01 in) has proved useful for rising main bolts, nuts and cable clips. Chromising is a similar process to case hardening using a bath of chromium salt.

Submersible pumping plant having motors operating in water has captured a large proportion of the bore hole pump field, but conventional shaft driven bore hole pumps are still attractive for the large quantity low and medium head duties.

Well straightners

Even with submersible pumps, well straightners can be important – not so much because of any particular difficulties in inserting submersible pumps but because in most makers' catalogues not nearly enough clearance is allowed between the pump or motor and the well casing to suit any but the straightest wells and the truest casings and joints. Often only about 10 mm on diameter is allowed over the largest diametral dimension of the pump motor and for pumps which can often be two or three metres long this is not sufficient. A good practical answer is to allow a diametral clearance of at least 10% of the largest diameter of the pump (with a minimum of 25 mm).

Efficiency

The operating efficiency of well pumps is usually regarded as very secondary to their suitability from other points of view. Fortunately, the types of pump for which higher power inputs are required *ie* the vertical turbine and submersible types, do have quite high efficiencies whereas the low efficiency types are those which usually, for different reasons are also low powered.

Other types such as jet pumps, helical rotor pumps, hydraulically driven submersible pumps and reciprocating pumps have efficiencies varying between 15% and 50% for the pumps alone, according to size and duty or, say, 10 to 40% for electric pumps and motors combined. All these types are basically inefficient; helical rotor pumps because of high mechanical losses and jet systems because of the inherent inefficiency of the jet energy conversion, the usual losses in the dry water pump and the fact that the pressure of the water delivered from a jet well pumping system is usually far in excess of the pressure required for water utilisation storage, since it is governed by some extent by the operating pressure needed for the jet drive water. Usually a reducing valve has to be inserted at the pump delivery branch to reduce the pressure of that proportion of the water delivered by the surface pump which constitutes the output from the well to a figure more suited to the method of utilisation. If, however, the pump has to deliver water under pressure to a water tower or tall building, this extra pressure can be effectively utilised. A further drawback to the use of the jet pump systems is that any given system is effective over only a very limited range of flows and water depths so that a system has to be supplied to suit conditions which are not only known in advance but unlikely to change during the service life of the system.

Domestic water from wells *etc.*

Where no mains water supply exists, domestic water supplies may have to be drawn from wells, boreholes or other sources. Modern systems of this type employ submersible electric borehole pumps, capable of providing a water supply equal to that of a mains supply.

The use of a pressure storage tank containing an air cushion (Figure 4) eliminates the need for separate storage tanks, the pump being turned on and off by the tank pressure. Thus, as water is drawn from the tap the pressure in the tank continues to fall to a level where a pressure switch cuts in the pump, recharges the tank and then automatically cuts out again when the tank is fully charged. A typical mean pressure realised by such a system is 2·1 to 2·25 bar (30 to 33 lb/in^2).

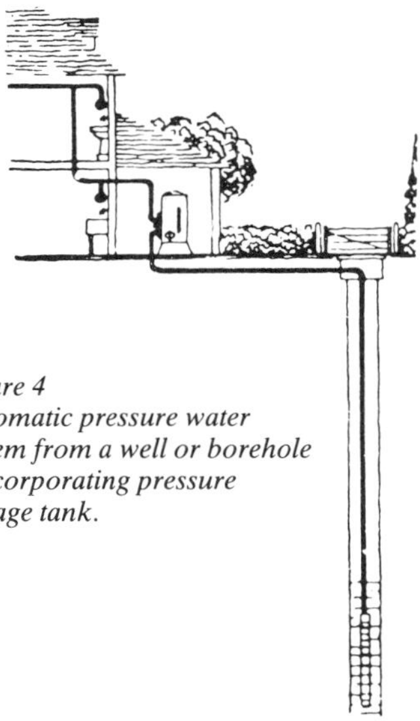

Figure 4
Automatic pressure water system from a well or borehole – incorporating pressure storage tank.

Figure 5
Gravity feed from an outdoor overhead storage tank – automatic float-switch control.

The gravity feed system utilising a large tank as shown in Figure 5, can supply heavy peak demands with only a small pump. The pump is automatically controlled by a float which cuts out the pump motor when the tank is full and cuts it in again whenever the level falls. Alternatively, a time switch control may be allied to a pressure switch control where a high delivery head is involved or where there is long delivery pipeline from the tank to the draw-off points.

Figure 6 shows a variation on an automatic pressure system, which is particularly suited to group feed applications where a single pump supplies a number of dwellings. The water supply in this case is delivered from a single-pressure storage tank through ball valves to separate roof-type storage tanks. Water is fed by gravity from these tanks to the individual dwelling systems.

Figure 7 shows a system commonly adopted for domestic supply where there is an existing roof-type storage tank. The pump delivers water directly into the roof tank which feeds the domestic points under gravity. The pump is automatically stopped and started at high and low water levels respectively by means of a float

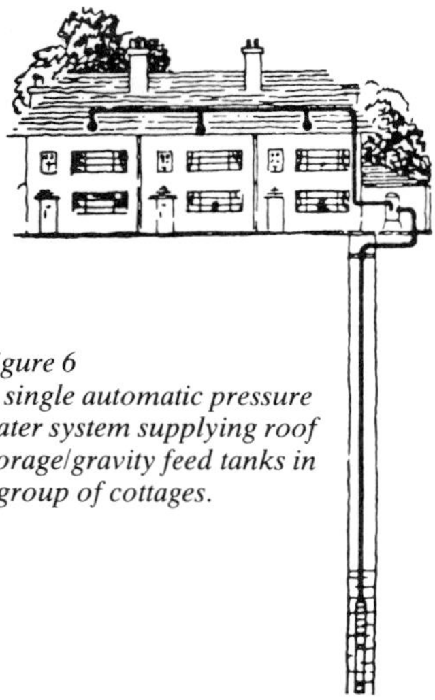

Figure 6
A single automatic pressure water system supplying roof storage/gravity feed tanks in a group of cottages.

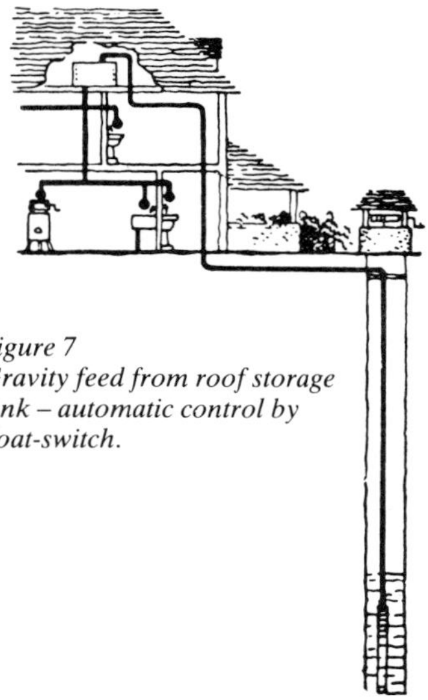

Figure 7
Gravity feed from roof storage tank – automatic control by float-switch.

switch installed in the tank. This is a particularly economical system, but the water pressure available is limited to the effective head at any draw off point, *ie* the height of the tank above that point.

Water supply in medium height buildings

With medium height buildings, mains pressure is generally adequate to supply domestic water to the lower floors at least. A pumped system may, however be needed to supply upper floors. A preferred system is shown in Figure 8. Water for general purposes is stored in one or more tanks with pumped drinking water stored in a closed header separate from the storage tank. The tank is fed direct from the mains or pumped water from the header. The header is normally fitted with an automatic air valve which allows air to enter the header to take the place of water drawn off and to allow air to be vented when the header fills up again with water.

Water authorities generally require a break tank to be provided in a building so that it effectively isolates the fittings on the building from the mains.

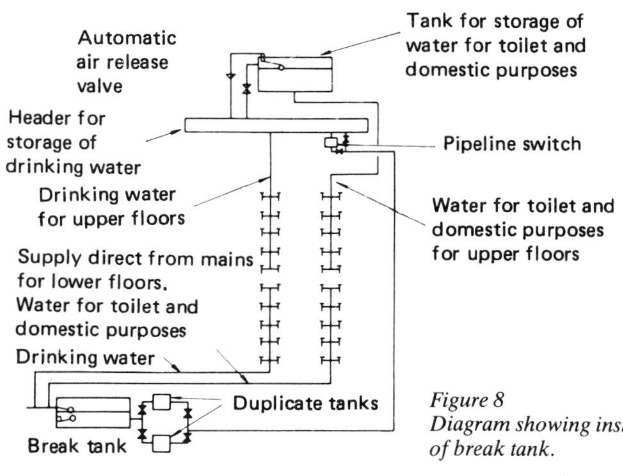

Figure 8
Diagram showing installation of break tank.

Water supply in high-rise buildings

An obvious method of supplying cold water services in high-rise buildings is to use large roof-level storage tanks fed from booster pumps situated in the basement of the building. This system has the facility of providing a large store of boosted water which will maintain supplies for a considerable period of time, should there be a failure in the electrical or water supplies. It is used in hospitals, where essential services must be maintained at all times, and in residential developments, where statutory requirements dictate a substantial storage volume per dwelling.

The pumps draw water from a covered break tank and supply the roof level storage tanks via a drinking water header, the drinking water for the lower floors being supplied directly from the main. The pumps are controlled either by float switches in the roof-level storage tank or by a pipeline float switch, situated just below the drinking water header (Figure 9). In the latter case, a time delay unit is fitted to provide a minimum running time of two minutes to prevent the pumps starting too frequently. In the event of the drinking water header refilling within this minimum time, the water flows into the roof-level storage tanks through the ball valve, which, when full will cause the pumps to run for a short period against closed valve conditions. In order to allow the water to flow out of the drinking water header under gravity, an automatic air vent must be fitted so that air can be drawn into the header as water is used.

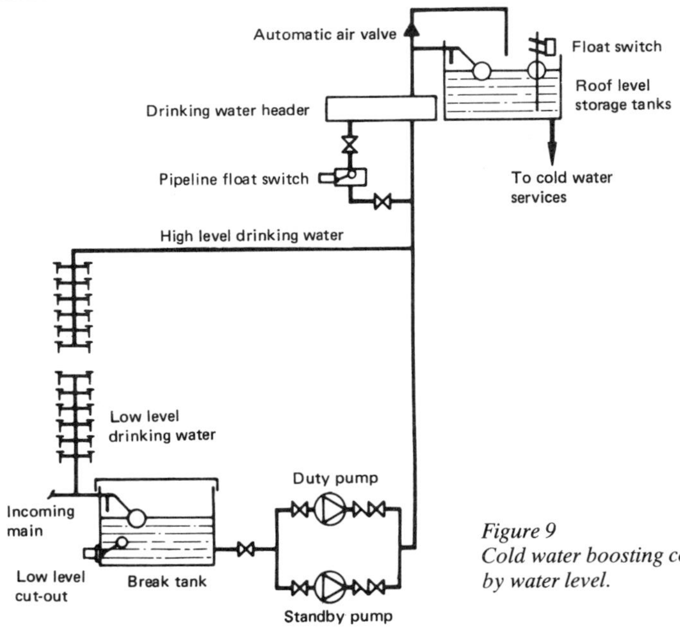

Figure 9
Cold water boosting controlled by water level.

If secondary hot water services for baths, washing machines, showers, dishwashers *etc*, are to be fed from this system, it is necessary for the duty pump to be run continuously (Figure 10), as opposed to being controlled by float switches and for a re-circulation line to be taken from the discharge of the pumps to avoid over-heating when no draw-off is taking place. A non-return valve, fitted into the feed line to the calorifier, prevents the hot water expanding into the cold main; this expansion can be taken up by diaphragm expansion tanks, sized to limit the pressure in the secondary hot water main to acceptable limits.

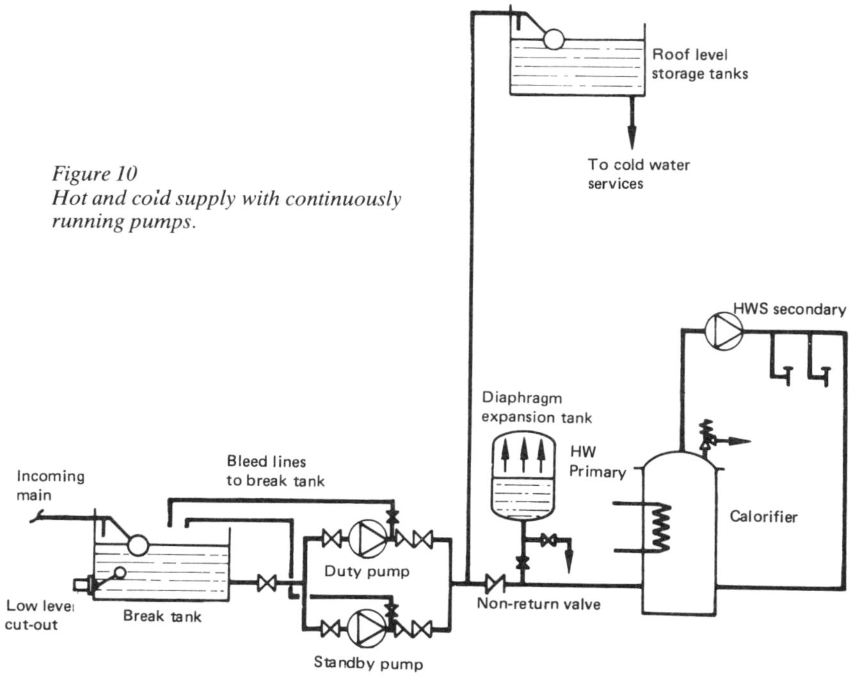

Figure 10
Hot and cold supply with continuously running pumps.

Two or more storage tanks are usually provided or the tank is sectioned so that one part can be isolated for cleaning and maintenance purposes. This means that a float switch, or pair of electrodes must be fitted in each tank or tank section for each pump.

The main disadvantage of roof tanks is that water storage at a high level adds substantially to roof loading which, in turn, increases building costs, as does the necessity for providing some form of weather protection. There is also the danger of flooding, due to fracture or overflow, which is much more serious if the tank is at the top of the building. Finally, large roof tanks break up the line of the building.

The principle of operation is that a compressed air cushion within the pressure vessel (Figure 11) supplies a reserve of pressurised water to the system. As this reserve is used, the volume of air in the vessel increases, thereby reducing the pressure. This reduction in pressure actuates the pressure switch, which automatically starts the duty pump. This supplies the system demand and at the same time replenishes the water in the vessel, thereby increasing the pressure and stopping the pump. The air within the vessel is gradually absorbed into the water, as will be detected by a rise in the water level to give the same pump cut-out pressure. This rise is sensed by air floats which in the upper half of the vessel which starts the air compressor. The compressor being automatically stopped by a pressure switch set slightly higher than the pump cut-out pressure.

In certain cases of high fluctuating demand, duty pumps may be used, the second pump being called into operation if the pressure in the vessel continues to reduce after the first pump has been started. The pumps are then stopped in sequence as the vessel is re-filled with water.

Figure 11
Cold water boosting using a pressure vessel.

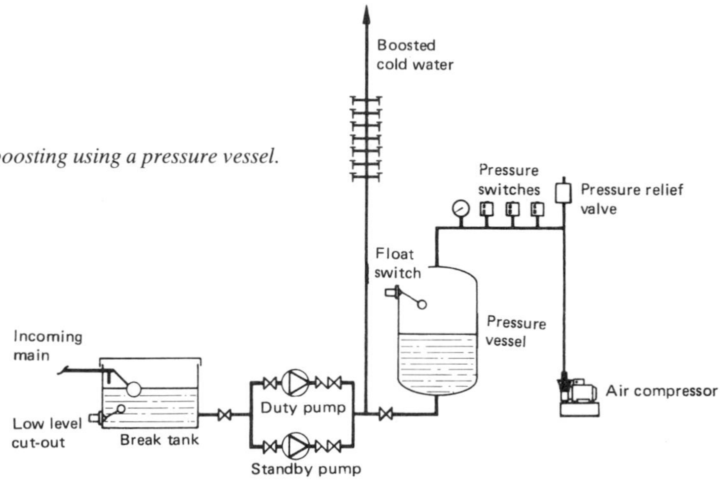

Figure 12
Cold water boosting plus hot water suppply using a diaphragm vessel.

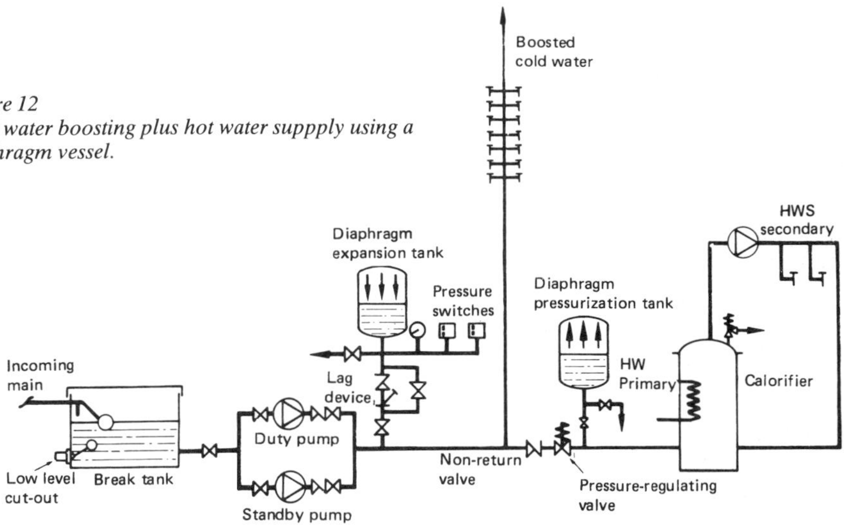

The system shown in Figure 12 uses a diaphragm vessel in place of the pressure vessel. The diaphragm separates the air from the water so that air cannot become absorbed into the system. This means that air compressor, together with associated electrical equipment and float switch, is no longer required thereby making a more economical unit. However, the stored capacity of the diaphragm vessel is normally less than that of the pressure vessel system described previously. The diaphragm vessel is used in similar applications to the previous system and is also suitable for certain factory developments. As previously explained pumps are controlled by pressure but as the pumps are sized to meet the maximum demand from the system, they are capable of recharging the vessel in a matter of seconds. This could cause a problem of too frequent motor starting but it is overcome by fitting a special lag device to the outlet of the vessel; this allows full flow out of the vessel but restricts the backflow in, thereby ensuring the pumps run for a period of two minutes.

Both the systems mentioned can be used to supply water for hot water services, but in this case as the control is by pressure variations in the cold main, it is advisable to fit a pressure regulating valve in the cold water feed to the calorifer, in addition to the non-return valve and expansion vessels normally used.

Booster sets for continuous duty

Booster sets for continuous operation embrace various systems, *eg*:

(i) Constant running pumps with bypass flow to the ground level storage tank.

(ii) Lead/lagged pumps where a small continuous pump meets demand up to a certain level when a larger or additional pump(s) automatically switches on.

(iii) Variable speed pumps.

In general (i) may prove uneconomic. Theoretically (iii) is best (and the most efficient), but there is the disadvantage of substantially higher costs and variable speed systems are not normally considered economical for sets under 18·5 to 22 kW. There are conditions in which the higher cost can be justified, such as on installations where close control of system pressure is required or on large schemes where there is substantial constant demand with variable high and low peaks or when the suction is being taken directly from the mains and there is wide variation in the mains pressure.

For reasons of economy the lead/lag system is often preferred – a typical system of this type is shown in Figure 13.

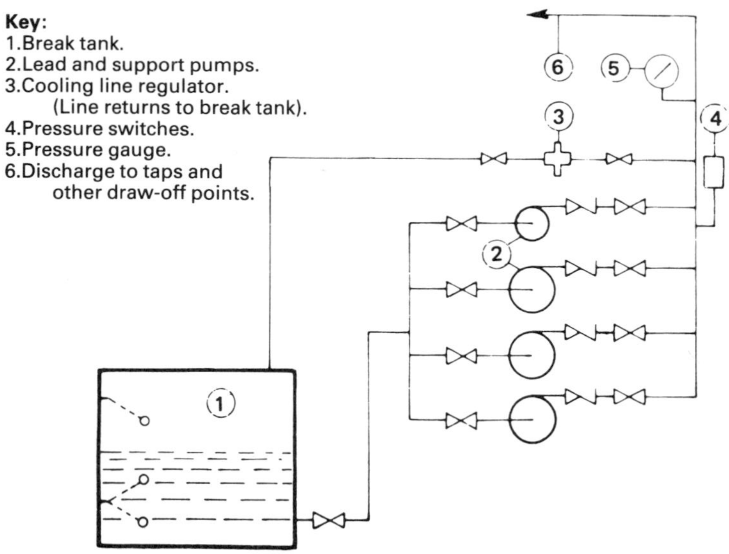

Figure 13
Continuously running set with one head pump and three support pumps.

Hot water systems

In office blocks, flats and high-rise buildings, hot water for the two systems – the primary system for space heating and the secondary system for domestic and toilet purposes – is usually supplied from one boiler situated in the basement (Figure 14).

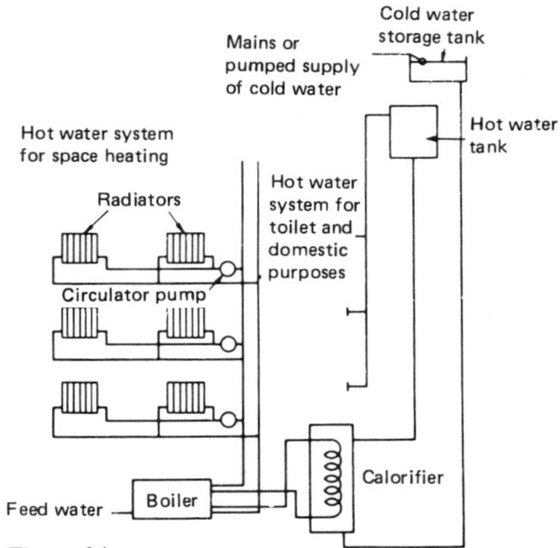

Figure 14
Hot water system for space heating and domestic/toilet purposes. There may be hot water tanks at various heights to serve the floors below them.

In the primary system the water heated to a temperature of 82 °C (180 °F), is pumped through the space heating loops, which consist of hot water radiators connected by piping, the whole forming a closed system, the water being returned to the boiler for re-heating and re-circulation.

Since in a large building the cost of large diameter piping would be very high small bore tubing is normally used. To carry the same amount of heat through the system, the water has to be heated to a higher temperature, by the boiler – higher than normal boiling point – and so is circulated through the closed system under pressure.

Pumps for large systems are often called circulators and those for smaller systems are known as accelerators.

A circulator typically has a capacity of up to 10 000 l/min (2250 gal/min) against a head of 32 m (105 ft) and pressures up to 7 bar (100 lb/in^2) the water temperature being up to 93 °C (200 °F).

An accelerator typically has a capacity of up to 900 l/min (200 gal/min) against a head of up to 6 m (20 ft) and pressures up to 7 bar (100 lb/in^2), the water temperature being up to 150 °C (300 °F) and such a pump is often of the in-line type.

District heating systems operate on a similar principle and are being installed more and more between groups of block of flats, hotels, old people's homes and so on since one boiler installed and piping system serving all blocks is more economical than separate systems to each group. Separate pumps may be required for the circulation of water in each block.

Pumps used on secondary systems are usually of all gun-metal construction so that the domestic hot water will not be tainted or discoloured.

In the secondary system, water at high temperature is taken from the boiler by a separate loop and passes through the coil or tubing in the calorifer so that it heats the surrounding water. This water is lifted to an expansion of storage tank in the roof and descends to the hot water taps by gravity.

Closed and open heating systems

In the closed system, the pump has only to be capable of overcoming the frictional resistance of the pipework fittings at the specified flow. A typical closed system is shown in Figure 15 where it will be see that there is only one possible working point at which the pump can perform.

A pump working on an open circuit system is required to overcome the static lift in the system in addition to the frictional resistance at the required flow rate. In this case, it is necessary to ensure that the pump head characteristic is suited to that of the particular system. This is clearly indicated in Figure 16 where it will be seen that pump 'A' has a head characteristic which will not overcome the static lift of the system at zero flow conditions, so that if the discharge pipework is fully primed, the pump will never lift any water. It is therefore, essential that a pump with a head characteristic of pump 'B' is selected. This situation only occurs when the static head is very high compared with the frictional resistance.

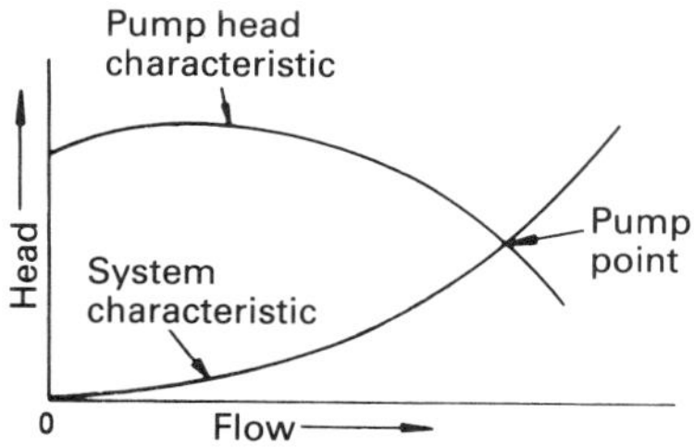

Figure 15
System characteristics of closed system.

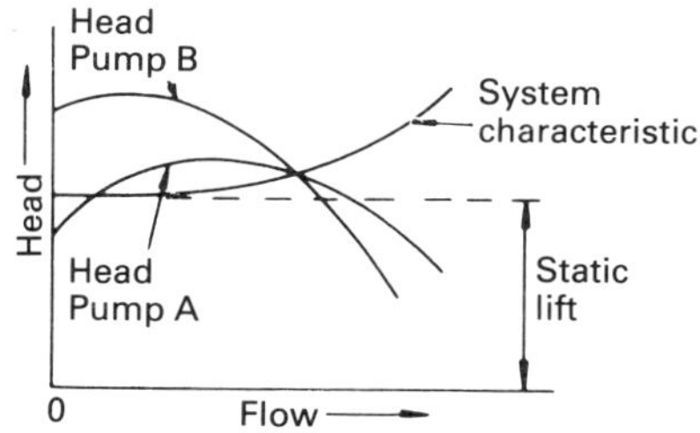

Figure 16
System characteristics of open circuit system.

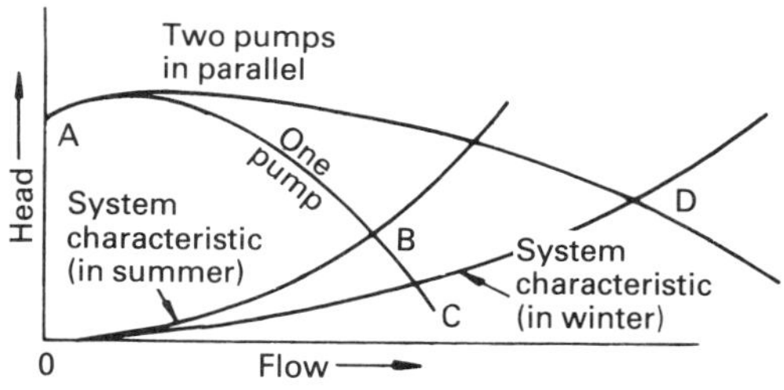

Figure 17
One and two pumps in parallel.

There are occasions when it is necessary to run two pumps in parallel. This could be the case when there are winter and summer duties and the second pump is run in parallel to cope with the extra winter demand on the heating system. It is necessary to provide a non-return valve on the discharge side of each pump so that when one pump is operating, it will not allow water to pass back through the other. Alternatively, a twin pump arrangement which contains its own non-return valve system can be used. The latter arrangement is often selected when duty and standby pumps are installed.

The head characteristics of pumps used for parallel operation must be taken into consideration. Figure 17 shows 1 and 2 pumps working on summer and winter duties. Here it will be seen that the first pump running on the summer system will operate at point 'B' whereas it will work at point 'C' on the winter system. When the second pump is run in parallel for winter operation the two pumps will deliver a flow equal to point 'D', this flow being shared equally between the two pumps. It is necessary for the closed valve head to be greater than the generated head at point 'C' to ensure that both non-return valves are open and that one pump is not running against a closed valve.

The other method of combining pump duties is to run the pumps in series. This is the principle of a multi stage pump, where the head generated by one stage is boosted by the next stage to produce a high head. Care must be taken when running pumps in series to ensure that the branch velocities do not become excessive as in this case it is the head which is shared between the two pumps, whereas each pump must pass the full flow of the system. This is illustrated in Figure 18 where it can be seen that one pump will work at flow rate 'A' and when two pumps are running each will operate at flow rate 'B'.

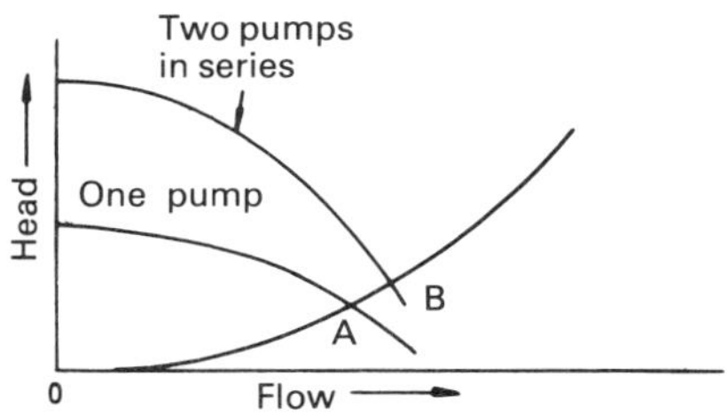

Figure 18
One and two pumps in series.

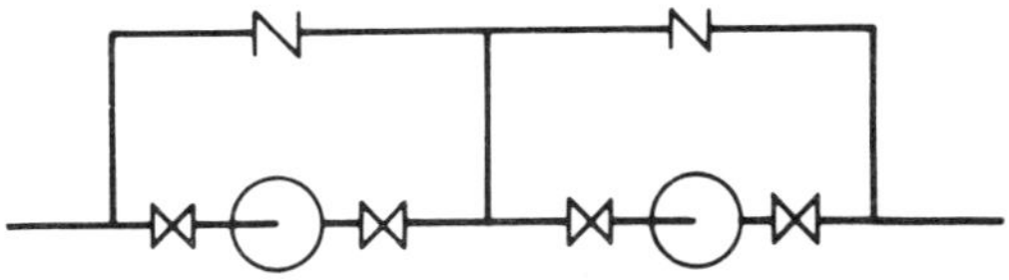

Figure 19
Bypass system for two pumps in series.

It is useful to have a bypass system such as that shown in Figure 19 arranged for series pumping; this will ensure that each pump can be run individually without having to discharge through the other and allows either pump to be isolated for inspection whilst the other is still in operation.

Pump selection
On principle, a circulating pump should be selected on the basis that the duty point will be in the middle section of or (provided it can be ensured that the maximum flow rate shown cannot be exceeded) in the lower third of the pump curve. When selected to operate in the upper third, uneconomic operation can be expected. If the duty point falls between two possible pump curves, it is always advisable to select the smaller pump.

The resultant reduction in volumes in heating systems normally is of such minor consequence that it can practically be neglected whilst the advantages such as more silent and more economic operation at lower velocity of the smaller pump with the reduced power motor are clearly predominant.

Water Transport

MAIN PUMPS for water transport (and water injection) may be divided into the following categories:

(i) Low pressure pumps (delivery heads up to 600 m).

(ii) Medium pressure pumps (delivery heads at about 600 m).

(iii) High pressure pumps (delivery heads above about 600 m).

In most cases a relatively small suction head (NPSH plant) is available for these pumps.

The general trend is to keep the pump dimensions as small as possible, *eg* by increasing the circumferential speed of the impeller and by raising the specific speed. Maximum pump speed is determined by the positive suction head available. Depending on the pump geometry (*eg* single- or double-entry) the suction behaviour of the impeller (NPSH) may be calculated from the formula for suction specific speed (SS).

$$SS = n \frac{\sqrt{Q}}{NPSH^{0 \cdot 75}}$$

where: $n = min^{-1}$
$Q = m^3/s$

For good suction impellers, the suction specific speed may be assumed constant over a wide range of specific speed. A typical value for suction specific speed is SS = 174 which can be achieved with centrifugal impellers of good manufacture having a flow angle of about 17 degrees and approximately 5 to 7 vanes. From this formula the maximum possible pump speed may be calculated from the flow rate for any specific pump type. For multi-stage pumps the stage head should be used in the aforementioned equation and for double-entry impellers the volumetric flow rate per impeller eye. Figure 1 shows a frequently used relationship of head as a function of specific speed and in addition the way in which impeller shaped coefficients change as a function of specific speed.

Suction capacity

The economical answer for the pumping unit can be found by employing double-entry pumps with one to three stages (the number of stages is limited by design

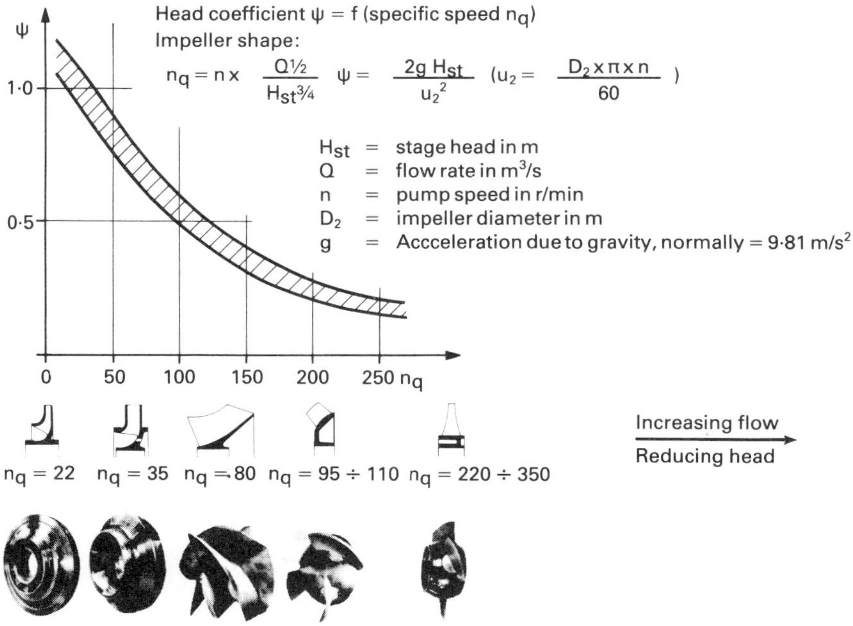

Figure 1
Impeller shapes and head coefficients.

criteria). In this way the absolute speeds may be raised about 40% above those of single-stage pumps with a given NPSH plant, without risk of cavitation damage. As a result, pumps with smaller dimensions are obtained, possessing advantages such as lower weight (lower purchase price and transport costs), lower costs for spare parts and repairs and lower construction costs for installation. These pump types are particularly suitable for the low and medium pressure range and are split at the centre line.

For high pressure pumps, casings split at the centre line are ruled out for design reasons above a certain size and (inlet) pressure. Deformation of the flanges on casings split along the centre line and the space needed for the studs dictate the adoption of vertically split casings. With moderate positive suction pressure, type of steel now commonly used and impeller diameters less than about 350 mm, the operating pressure limit is around 400 bar. At this pressure, satisfactory sealing can still be assured with acceptable flange dimensions. This limit is of course higher with smaller diameters.

Flow speed limit

Although water transport pumps are rarely engineered for stage heads exceeding 400 m, the cavitation risk is not to be under estimated. It is particularly high where salt water or heavily mineralised water is pumped, instead of fresh water. For such liquids the safety factors obtained from tests and operating experience with ordinary water must be corrected. The inter-relation between corrosion and cavitation certainly shifts the velocity limit at which loss of material begins down to lower values.

In order to move large quantities of sea water to the injection pumping stations, pumps capable of delivering 0·5 to 4 m^3/s over long distances are needed. The delivery head consists almost solely of line losses. Single- or multi-stage, single- or double-entry pumps are used here. Figure 2 shows a typical seawater transport pump.

Figure 2
Typical seawater transport pump.

If the pumped liquid contains solids as well, the velocity limit is lowered further, because the strength limit is exceeded by local stresses resulting from impact or sheering forces. Since however the water to be pumped is usually clean physically, but often aggressive chemically, sometimes very much so, the chief problem is choosing the right materials for the different pump components. Owing to the relatively high flow velocities, there are limits to the corrosion resistance of various materials. As laboratory tests have shown, with a given water, the corrosion behaviour of a material is characterised (in very simplified form) by three velocity ranges (Figure 3).

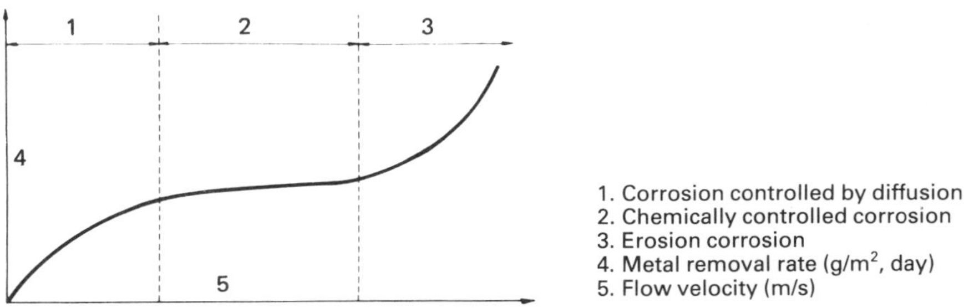

Figure 3
Effects of corrosion shown schematically.

Range 1
The material corrosion rate against the timescale is small and constitutes no danger.

Range 2
Due to the ability of the material to form a passivation layer and to keep renewing this, the loss of material through corrosion remains largely constant and is no danger to operation.

Range 3

The excessively high flow velocity destroys any passivation layer and prevents its re-appearance. Severe loss of material is the result.

Approximate material loss rates due to cavitation, and erosion are:

Cavitation $\frac{G}{T} \approx C^n$

Corrosion $\frac{G}{T} \approx C^i$

Erosion $\frac{G}{T} \approx C^m$

where:

$n = 6$ to 8

$m = 3$

i depends on the material and liquid properties

Critical pump shaft speed

With steadily increasing performances (raising the absolute and peripheral speeds) and owing to the adoption of multi-stage designs for very high pressures, more attention must also be given to the problem of critical speed in pump engineering. Shaft vibration results from external dynamic forces (unbalances) and self-excitation.

Self-excitation originates from the tangential forces in narrow clearances with axial flow, which may be further intensified by the peripheral velocity. Such clearances are the labyrinths of the impellers or balancing piston, which act as hydrodynamic bearings. Oil-lubricated radial bearings may also provide excitation.

Efficiency

The optimal efficiency of a pump is given in the first place by the relative disk friction losses. The ratio of these losses is approximately equal to:

$$\frac{k_1}{n_q^2}$$

and the relative leakage losses of the labyrinths which are approximately equal to:

$$\frac{k_1}{n_q^2}$$

Both losses drop steeply with increasing specific speed so that the optimal efficiencies for the various pump hydraulics considered all lie at relatively high specific speeds as shown in Figure 4. The drop in the efficiency at higher specific speeds is traceable in particular to increase losses at the impeller entry (steep increase in the relative entry owing to the rising volume flow generally, and especially in the case of multi-stage pumps because of the shaft dimensions needed to provide the necessary strength).

Once the pump performance stages are given, especially NPSH plant, it is possible to calculate the pump type having the highest efficiency with the help of the values from Figure 5 taking the efficiency formula into account. In this way a comparison of the economics can be made with other alternatives from the criterion of energy saving. Depending on the performance class and pump type, the energy

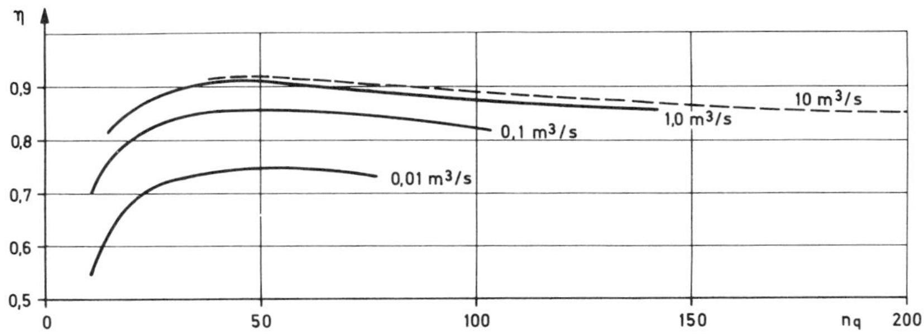

Figure 4
Optimum efficiencies as a function of specific speed and flow rate.

TABLE 1 – COMPARISON OF DIMENSIONS, SUCTION CAPACITIES AND EFFICIENCIES FOR VARIOUS POSSIBLE PUMP TYPES WITH CONSTANT DRIVE INPUT

Power input	MW	6	6	6	6	6	6	S	6	6	6	6
Delivery head	m	200	200	400	400	400	400	800	800	800	2000	2000
Discharge rate	l/s	2698	2600	1336	1330	1321	1288	658	648	640	256	256
Pump type		d	s	2d	s+s	d	s	3s	2d	s+s	4s+4s	8s
n_s (metric)		39	36	41	41	24	24	33	24	24	29	29
n_s (US)		3000	1880	2090	2090	1245	1685	1245	1245	1480	1480	
Speed	r/min	1780	1190	2645	1874	2660	1905	2665	3798	2701	3580	3580
at best point	%	88·2	86·9	87·3	86·9	83·6	84·2	86.0	84·7	83·7	86·3	83·2
NPSH-0%	m	25·9	23·8	27·5	27·5	27·5	27·5	27·5	27·5	27·5	21.7	21·6
D_2 impeller dia	mm	745	1102	506	714	650	908	557	455	640	392	392
Power loses	kW		89·7		27·6	69·5	220·9		92·1	164·8		28·9
Penalty	Sfr		89700		27600	69500	220900		92100	164800		28900
W_t/W_t 2d				1	1·29	1·37		1·54	1			

saving costs may weigh very heavily, arguing in favour of a more expensive pump operating with high efficiency. The optimal plant configuration can be arrived at only through collaboration between the pump maker and the installation planner. Table 1 gives the energy savings with various pumps for typical water transport duties.

Installation

In order to calculate the transient behaviour, the general characteristics of the pump must be known (its characteristic curves in the pumping, braking and turbining ranges, as well as the valve characteristic). These are established by means of model tests for all the components and hydraulics in question. With the help of the computer program, the water hammer calculations are performed; here the main problem is how to avoid inadmissible underpressure or vacuums with given plant configurations.

Depending on the size of the installation, the transients may be influenced by additional boundary conditions and controlled velocity changes in the suction and discharge lines. Additional boundary conditions are the attachment of a fly wheel mass to the pumping set, interposition of air receivers and surge tanks. Velocity is altered by the means of a bypass, air inlet valves and modified valve closing lag.

Pumps need protection against the overheating. If they are operated over the full flow range, especially against high heads at constant speed, the resulting

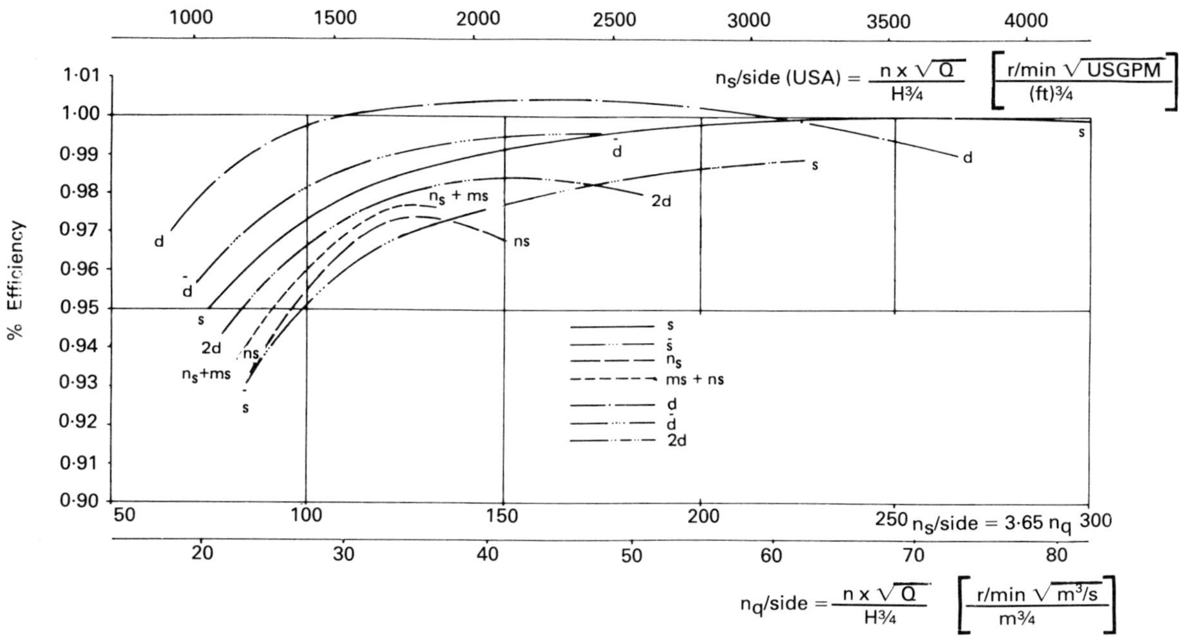

s	=	single entry + single-stage impeller + single volute
$\bar{s}$	=	single entry = single-stage impeller + double volute
ns	=	single entry = multi-stage impeller + return channels
ms + ns	=	single entry = multi-stage impeller arranged back-to-back
d	=	double entry = single-stage impeller + single volute
$\bar{d}$	=	double entry = single-stage impeller + double volute
2d	=	double entry = two-stage impeller + double volute
		Delivery head per stage 100 m (constant)
		Impeller diameter 0·5 m (with n_s = 250)

Figure 5
Hydraulic efficiency versus pump design and specific speed (for cold water only).

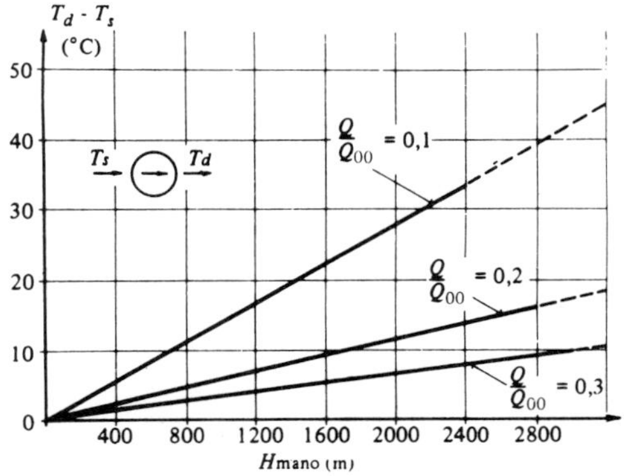

Key:
Due to loss of efficiency
Due to compression

T_s	=	temperature on suction side (°C)
T_d	=	temperature on discharge side (°C)
H_{mano}	=	pump delivery head (m)
η	=	efficiency (--)
Q	=	discharge rate (l/s)
Q_{00}	=	discharge rate at best point (l/s)
ß	=	coefficient of compressibility

Figure 6
Temperature rise in multi-stage pumps versus delivery head, leak-off capacity and minimum flow.

temperature rises in the pump must be taken into account. With the poorer hydraulic efficiency and pressure rise at diminishing loads, more and more of the power input is converted into heat. The temperature rise may be considerable (Figure 6). By installing a hot water valve a minimum flow must be led off at the pump outlet. This ensures that the admissible temperature increase does not give rise to a cavitation risk at the first impeller, nor evaporation leading possibly to dry running of the balancing part and over-stressing of material in the pump. In most cases, after throttling in the minimum flow valve, this flow is lead back into the suction line and mixed at a good distance from the pump. The risk of overheating is minimised if the water transport pump is speed-regulated.

Irrigation and Land Drainage

PUMPING WATER for land irrigation usually demands a large delivery at low to moderate heads, with the type and size of pump selected to suit the particular conditions of operation, mainly pumping conditions and type of power available. A basic requirement is that irrigation water should reach every part of the irrigated area at sufficient pressure for efficient dispersal on application.

The water source will have a major influence on the type of pump required. These can be classified as follows:-

(i) Free surface water supplies – *eg* water drawn from lakes, rivers or canals.

(ii) Shallow wells – *ie* drawing water from a depth of not more than 10 metres.

(iii) Deep wells or well points – where the water surface is below the suction capabilities of simple centrifugal pumps.

Roto-dynamic pumps are the usual choice and size may range from small, single-stage portable units to large axial flow pumps incorporated in a permanent station where the output from each pump may be as high as 900 m^3/min (200 000 gal/min). Submersible pumps also continue to find increasing application in both small and large irrigation schemes.

Free surface and shallow well supplies

Requirement here is for a low head pump with a radial impeller (centrifugal pump) for low to moderate deliveries. Larger pumps will have a Francis or mixed flow impeller. These would be suitable for floor or furrow irrigation. See Table 1.

TABLE 1

Pump Type	Impeller	Sizes (mm)	Mode
Self-priming (single-stage)	Open radial	50/100	Horizontal
End suction (single-stage volute)	Radial/Mixed flow	50/200	Horizontal
Split case (single-stage volute)	Radial/Mixed flow, single and double entry	100/1 000	Horizontal Vertical
Wet well turbine (diffuser) single- or multi-stage axial flow	Francis vane Mixed flow	100/1 000	Vertical

TABLE 2

Pump Type	Impeller	Sizes (mm)	Mode
End suction (single- and two-stage)	Radial	50/200	Horizontal
Split case (single- and two-stage)	Radial Francis vane	100/1 000	Horizontal
Wet well turbine (diffuser) multi-stage	Radial Francis vane	100/1 000	Vertical

For sprinkler or pressure irrigation a medium or high head pump is required either with a radial or Francis impeller. See Table 2.

Some very small items employ self-priming pumps. Horizontal shaft centrifugal pumps have the advantage of being efficient, of simple construction, reasonably trouble-free, easy to install and capable of high speeds. For this reason they are usually directly coupled to electric motors or diesel engines. One of the disadvantages is their limited suction and the need for priming. The practical suction lift will decrease with altitude, being not more than 6 m at sea level and decreasing to less than 4·5 m at a height of 1500 m.

Because of these limitations with horizontal centrifugal pumps, it is an advantage to locate them as near to the source and water surface as possible. It is important, however to protect them from any high water table that must arise to avoid flooding the river. Where such a possibility exists, a wet well pump should be installed.

A horizontal pump installation will comprise the suction pipe, foot valve and priming equipment. These items can in some instances, be costly and also prove troublesome, whereas with the wet well turbine pump, only the pump proper is required which is simpler and cheaper to install. Mention here should also be made of the virtues of the Archimedian screw pump for raising large quantities of water through small heights. The enclosed type is most efficient since slip is almost eliminated and can handle the types of water suitable for irrigation. Open screws are also used.

Water powered pumps

Water powered pumps use only the energy contained in a flowing stream. No fuel is used and thus there is neither cost nor pollution.

The method of operation is that water is allowed to flow with considerable force and speed down an inclined pipe to the pump (Figure 1). The water spills out through the waste valve until the pressure on the rubber disk in the valve causes it to close. Water flows on through the pump body – still with speed and force – through the delivery valve into the air vessel.

The air within the vessel – acting much like a spring – absorbs the momentum ot the water until the characteristic 'soft thump' noise of the pump is heard when the pressures reverse the form of a shock wave. This travels back through the water, out through the ram and drive pipe when the waste valve re-opens and the delivery valve closes. The water trapped in the air vessel is pushed out through the delivery pipe and into the storage tank. The complete cycle then repeats once again. The action being continuous, some of the water is always flowing through the delivery pipe.

Contractors' pump for continuous dewatering duties.

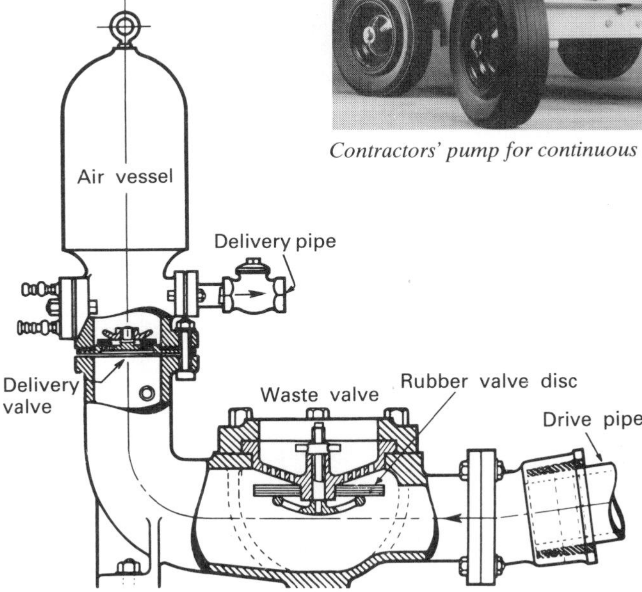

Figure 1
The Blake hydram water-powered pump.

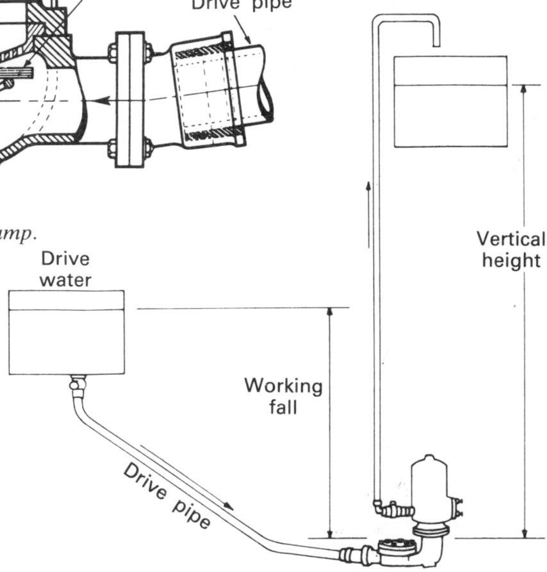

Figure 2
Operating principle of water-powered pump.

The performance of a water powered pump is determined by the working fall down which the driving water has to travel also by the vertical height to which the pumped water must be raised (Figure 2).

Water powered pumps have been successfully tested in continuous operation and in particular one unit has been tested over 1 million pulses and from a 5 metre fall on the drive pipe, has lifted 416 000 litres per 24 hours to a height of 50 metres.

Deepwell sources

Deepwell turbine pumps are used when the water surface is below the suction capability of the horizontal centrifugal pump or some other design concept favours its use. The impeller may be of the radial or mixed flow type, depending on the desired head to discharge relationship. Where open impellers are used, high efficiency is dependent on a close fit of the impeller against the pump housing. Many deepwell pump heads and electric motor drivers are equipped with a non-reversible ratchet to prevent reverse rotation due to the backflow of water when the power is turned off which can lead to damage of the unit.

The deepwell turbine pump can be driven by an internal combustion engine or an electric motor. Speed variation can be achieved by the use of a right-angled gear box situated at the well head. This conveniently converts the normally horizontal drive from the prime mover to the desired vertical drive of the pump. Where the pump speed matches the motor pole speed, a vertical hollow shaft may be fitted at the well head directly above the pump.

The pump is positioned in the well or borehole relative to the water level. This may be from 10 to 300 m below ground level although in some areas of the world it is not unknown to have boreholes as deep as 500 m. A drive shaft supported by intermediate bearings reaches from the driver at ground level to the pump. The size of the pump is related to the diameter of the borehole or well.

Submersible units

The submersible motor and pump provide an excellent means of extracting water from deepwell sources and the water can be supplied either to surface booster pumps or as is usually the case today, direct to the irrigators.

The downhole submersible pumping unit consists of a special squirrel cage induction motor designed to operate underwater, coupled to a multi-stage centrifugal pump developing sufficient head to lift the water from the strata level to the surface and in some cases to pump it direct to the irrigator spray nozzles. These units are generally small in diameter but to obtain the necessary power output, are quite long. This results in the pump having a number of stages, with water passing from one impeller to the next to generate the desired head.

The pumps generally fall into one of two categories; those developing high heads, but with low flow, generally using a radial impeller (Figure 3), or mixed flow pumps for high flow requirements (Figure 4). Both of these types generally use water-lubricated journal bearings to support the rotating assembly, the bearings being specially designed to handle a small proportion of solids such as sand. In most cases they consist of a stationary synthetic rubber bearing held in a housing, with the journal sleeve or shafts made of stainless steel. The pumps are fitted with inlets to allow water to the first stage impeller and a discharge assembly to provide connection to rising main. The inlet is also designed to allow direct coupling of the submersible motor, power to the pump being transmitted through a simple keyed or splined muff coupling.

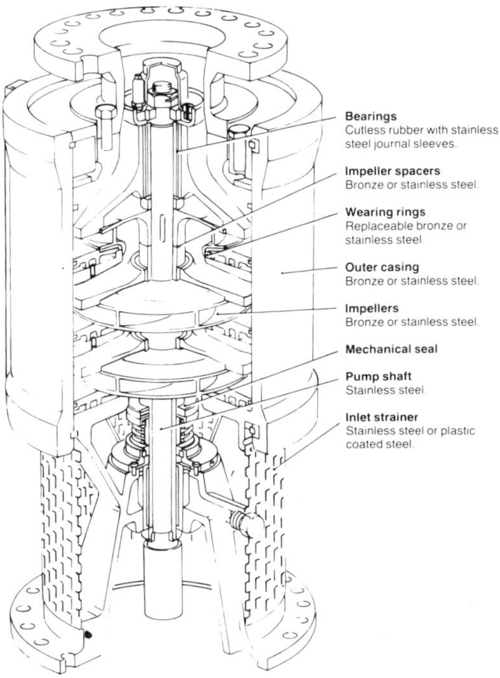

Figure 3
Radial pump.

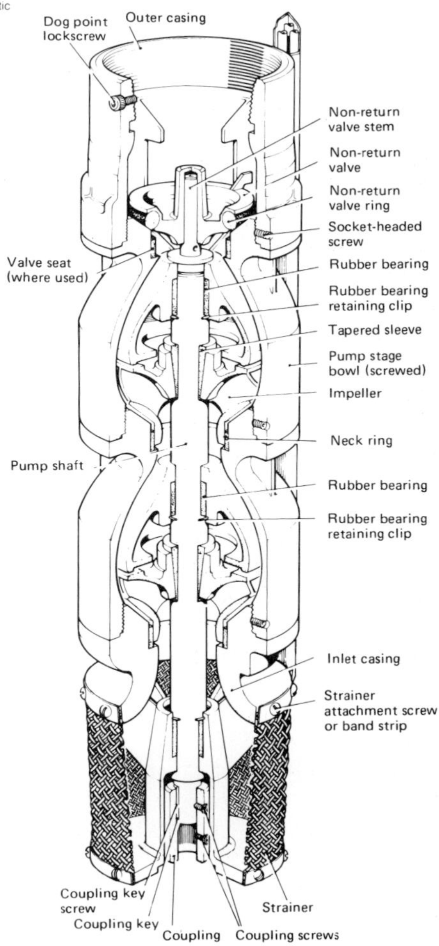

Figure 4
Mixed-flow submersible pump.

Long term plans need to be taken into consideration to ensure that water will be available for alternation of crop and worst weather conditions. Having determined the maximum likely water quantity, the pump head requirement can be decided from maximum well draw down conditions and pressure requirements at well head, taking into account pipeline friction losses and pump service wear. Although it is usual to fit a pressure control device at the well head to maintain the correct pressure for the discharge nozzles, the selection of excessive heads at the ground surface should be avoided, to limit losses in efficiency and the need to select higher-rated pipe flanges.

The below ground installation is similar in most submersible applications. The submersible unit is suspended from the rising main pipework, which must be of sufficient strength for the pressure requirements, the weight of the unit and any surging that may occur. It is normal to use water level electrodes or alternatively an air bubbling system to ensure that the unit is always submerged in water and that dry running cannot occur. In all applications if the borehole size permits, it is beneficial to fit a flow shroud, which ensures a flow of cooling water over the motor under all pumping conditions and becomes even more important when part duties, such as one irrigator out of a maximum of three or four are required. An integral non-return valve is sometimes fitted to the discharge of the submersible pump but if it is considered that a non-return valve should be fitted at the well head, or if the pressure control valve is fitted with a non-return valve, it may be desirable to delete the down hole one and replace it with an air relief valve at the well head surface. Two non-return valves in such close proximity can under some pumping conditions induce excessive surging on unit shutdown, although this situation does not always occur, as it depends upon the exact configuration of the system. If an air relief valve is used it must have sufficient capacity and be located where it will allow complete venting of the air; should any air be passed through into underground plastic mains, or worse into overground aluminium irrigation pipes, severe surging can occur with dangerous results.

Diesel-driven borehole pump providing water for small scale irrigation purposes.

The control systems are usually incorporated with the starter, which can be of direct on-line auto-transformer or star-delta type. In most cases some form of voltage reduction is required on rural applications, on starting, to limit in-rush currents and hence the size of the electrical network distribution system. Submersible pumps are also an advantage where flooding may occur at the pump house site where a structure above ground would be hazardous. They can also be used in wells which have been drilled eccentrically, making the successful installation of the shaft deepwell pump difficult.

Pumps for large deliveries

Axial and mixed flow pumps are used for low head, high discharge operation. By varying the vane pitch and curvature of the impeller, a wide range of head capacity requirements can be met without changing the impeller diameter. The pump should have sufficient submergence to avoid cavitation problems. The impeller must be sufficiently below the water surface to minimise the formation of vapour bubbles on the blades at the point of maximum local velocity. The characteristics of an axial flow pump make its use inadvisable where throttling of the discharge is required to provide a reduced delivery. It has a tendency to overload at increased heads and the selection of motor power must therefore by ample to cover all pumping conditions.

Vertical and horizontal spindle syphonic and open-flue type settings are popular, with automatic control of the rate or time of pumping by floats or electrode probes. Alternatively, flexibility of operation can be provided by variable pitch impellers. Coarse screen weed filters are usually installed on the inlet side of the pumps with a simple flat valve on the discharge side.

Where the water being handled contains sand or other solids in suspension rubber main shaft bearings are often preferred, lubricated by a through flow of water from the main pump flow. These are essentially similar to marine propeller shaft bearings and have a long and satisfactory life.

Specific types of pump such as ditch pumps and tail water pumps are also produced in a variety of sizes for general irrigation duties. Drainage pumps, or even pumps for general water services in all bronze, all iron or bronze fitted construction, may also be employed for temporary or semi permanent irrigation schemes.

Pressure boosting

Except in small irrigation systems and particularly when drawing water from bore-holes, it is not generally economic to select the primary pump to meet all pressure and capacity demands of the system. These are usually best met by a booster and/or additional pump(s) drawing from a service reservoir or the irrigation network. The following are typical types used for such purposes:

(i) Pressure boosting from a pipe system – horizontal centrifugal pump. The suction side of the pump can be directly attached to the supply pipe and its discharge side to the boosted pressure pipe system. It is, however, worth investigating the use of an electro-submersible pump as a booster. This pump may give a more suitable head capacity performance but the installation cost must be carefully scrutinised.

(ii) Supply from a service reservoir with an outlet pipe designed for surface irrigation – horizontal centrifugal pump or an inclined axial flow pump. Generally pumps can be attached directly to the outlet pipe downstream of a screening structure.

(iii) Pressure boosting from open water surfaces such as rivers, lakes and reservoirs – end suction, split case, horizontal and wet well turbine pumps. Generally the horizontal pump will provide the most economic arrangement, but the solution can only be determined after all alternatives have been analysed, taking into account operation and installation requirements.

(iv) Pressure boosting from an open canal system – vertical wet well pump. Generally a station of several pumps making up the total capacity for the requirement of a block area; the total area under irrigation being divided into equal block areas, making each station identical. The pumps are automatically controlled and brought on-stream, or closed down, by the varying demand.

(v) Supply from an surface source to a supplementary sprinkler system – horizontal centrifugal pump. The pump may be either or mobile and for small units a self-priming type can be employed. The mobile unit can be on a skid base, a pneumatic-tyred trolley or of the tractor-tow type; the last of these can be attached by a telescopic drive shaft to any standard tractor power take-off stubb. The advantages of portable pumps are that they can be moved along the river to wherever water is required, obviating the need for an extensive distribution system. The unit can be removed to a safe place during the winter or off-season period.

Water distribution

There are six common methods of irrigating the soil:

Sprinkler irrigation – where the water is sprayed onto the soil by mechanical sprinklers in the form of fine rain which effectively infiltrates into the soil.

Furrow irrigation – where the water is distributed to the irrigated land through ditches and furrows from which the water infiltrates into the soil.

Boarder strip irrigation – where the water flows in a shallow layer on a moderately sloped land which is then irrigated by infiltration.

Check-basin irrigation – where the land is occasionally flooded with water.

Drain irrigation – where the land is irrigated with water distributed through an underground pipe system.

Drip irrigation – this is normally used for larger plants and consists of a pipe run with a small drip feed to the base of each large plant.

Land drainage

The majority of large scale land drainage schemes employ mixed flow and axial flow pumps with flooded suction, although Archimedian screw pumps are also used.

Axial flow type pumps driven by electric motors are normally employed for large scale land drainage schemes. Such pumps are capable of generating very high capacities at lower heads – typically from 0·3 to 12 m (1 to 40 ft).

In many cases the pumping head can be kept to a minimum by employing a syphoned discharge system. The usual arrangement is for each pump to have its own syphon discharge pipe, the inlet at its highest point being slightly above flood level and the outlet always being drowned – see Figure 5. A vacuum breaker (*eg* a butterfly valve actuated by a paddle on which the water impinges to close the valve) is placed at the highest point in the pipeline. The valve is set to be slightly biased towards the open position so that as soon as water ceases to flow the valve will

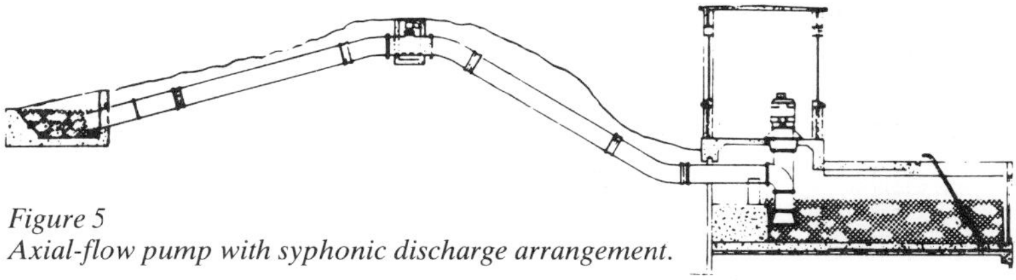

Figure 5
Axial-flow pump with syphonic discharge arrangement.

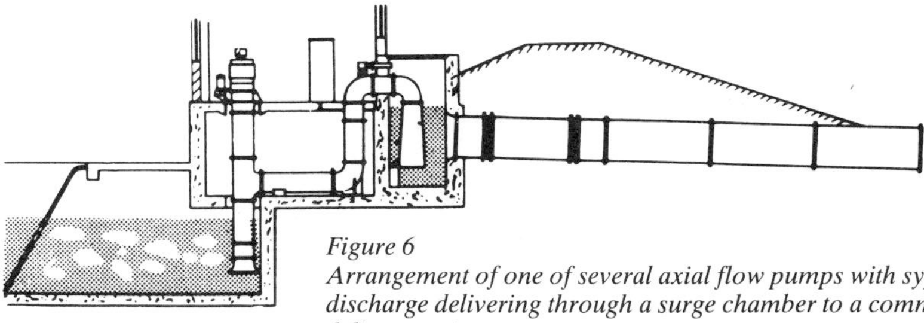

Figure 6
Arrangement of one of several axial flow pumps with syphonic discharge delivering through a surge chamber to a common delivery main.

automatically open and break the syphon. Where two or more pumps are involved, an alternative arrangement is to provide each individual pump with its own short syphon pipe discharging into a surge tower – see Figure 6. Flow is then taken from the surge tower by a common main to the river or higher drain.

Where smaller quantities are involved, *eg* for storm water systems, centrifugal pumps of smaller size may be employed. In the case of temporary or semi-permanent duties, portable pump sets may be employed as contractors' pumps or similar mobile units.

Water quality

Surface water to be drained generally has a pH value of around 8 and a positive Langelier Index indicating that the water is scale forming. The chemical analysis of the water must be taken into consideration in deciding the materials for pump construction with due regard to the calcium content if calcium carbonate deposits in the pump clearances or water lubricated bearings are likely to affect performance. Near coastal areas, the chloride content may be high and this should be taken into account.

In general, pumps of standard construction with casing and bellmouth in close grained cast iron and impellers in bronze are suitable for handling most surface waters. Most land drainage pumps are single-stage. Whilst two-stage axial flow pumps could be used, they are not recommended as they will tend to choke with weeds and other foreign matter.

Pumping plant layout

With roto-dynamic pumps for satisfactory performance good suction conditions must be ensured, particularly as the pumps are in the high specific speed range. Floating debris and weeds have to be dealt with. The pumping plant should be automatic in operation at predetermined levels and off-peak electricity tariff hours, the design should be as simple as possible for ease of operation and maintenance in an agricultural environment.

Examples of good sump design are shown in Figure 7.

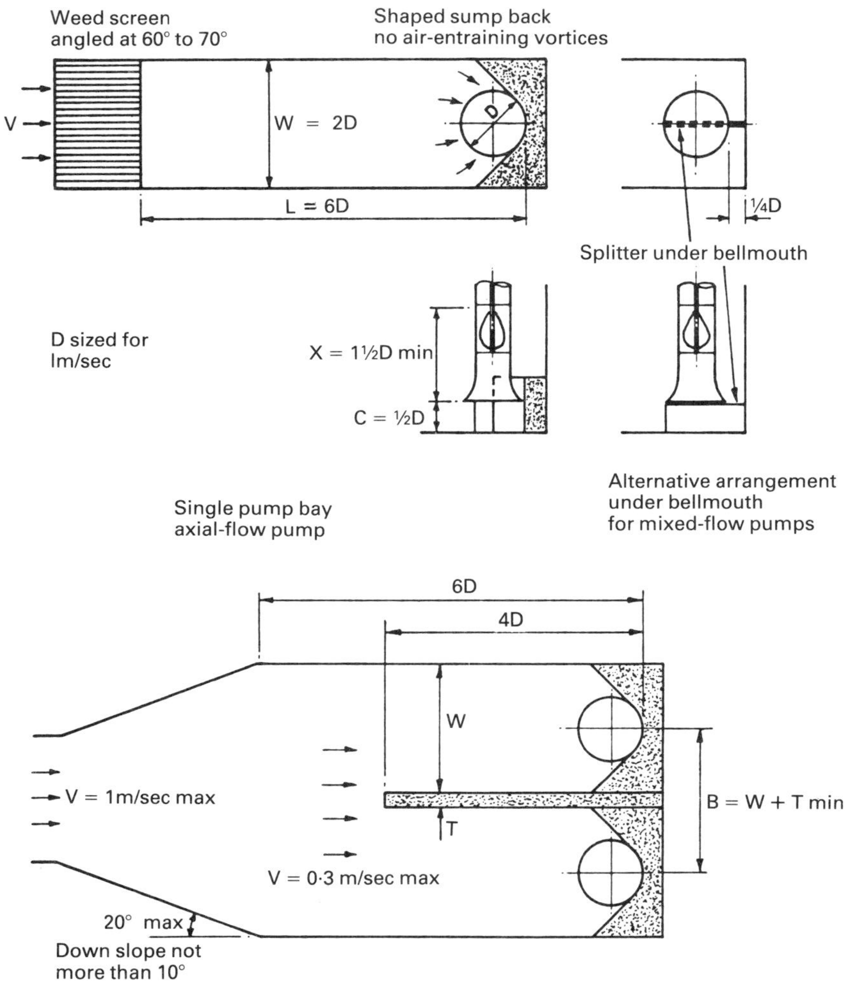

Figure 7
Example of good sump design.

The importance of smooth flow conditions to high specific speed pumps cannot be over emphasised for satisfactory performance and it should be borne in mind that from an approach flow of 0·3 m/sec through the short distance of the bellmouth to the eye of the impeller the velocity reaches approximately 4·9 m/sec or higher.

Examples of drainage pump configurations are shown in Figure 8.

Pit drainage

Fully submersible pump units are a usual choice for pit drainage although simple single-stage centrifugal pumps, shaft driven from a column mounted electric motor, are still widely employed. Automatic operation can be provided by float-operated controls which start the pump motor at a predetermined high level and switch it off when the water has been reduced to a selected low level. Installation involves little more than the provision of some form of sump into which the cellar water will drain,

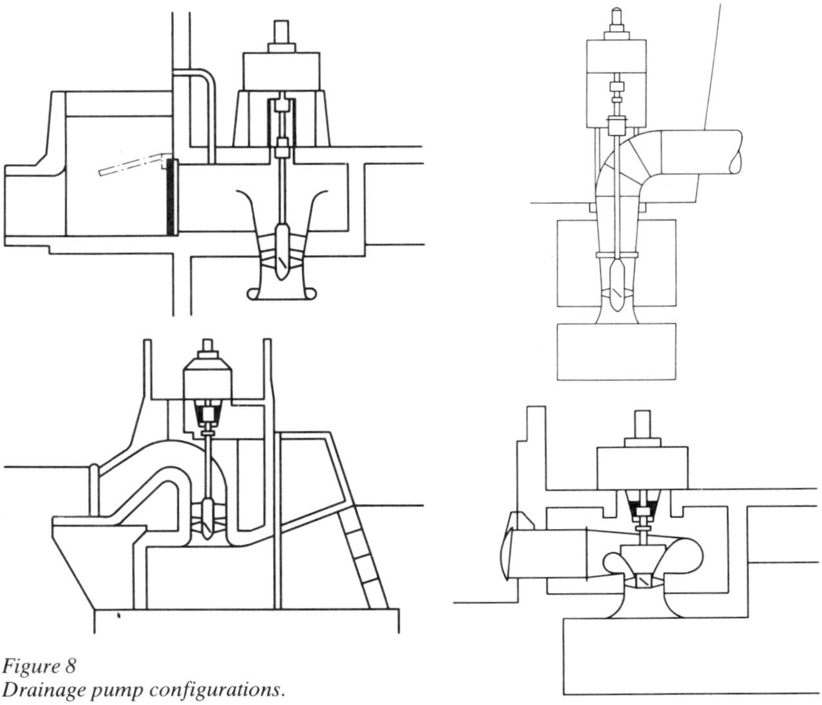

Figure 8
Drainage pump configurations.

mounting the unit in this sump and connecting up delivery and power lines. For a given size of pump motor unit, capacity will vary inversely with head.

Demand for handling seepage water in basements or pits for example may be represented by typical average figures such as 23 l/min (5 gal/min) per 93 m^2 (1000 ft^2) area in clay soils, increasing to 32 l/min (7 gal/min) in sandy soil. Actual figures which could be very much higher or very much less, will depend on the location of the site. Measurements taken to arrive at a realistic figure will enable the most economic size of pump to be selected.

To allow for variations, sump size (where applicable) will normally be proportioned to give twice the pump capacity in litres per minute assuming that pump start and stop is governed by low and high sump level respectively. The capacity referred to is the capacity between low and high levels. The actual capacity of the sump would normally be greater with the low level cut off above the level of the suction entry. Many of the submersible types of pumps however can be run indefinitely on 'snore' and are self-priming so that pumping the sump completely dry is practical if required.

The self-priming induced flow pump shown in Figure 9 can handle water containing abrasives as found on construction sites, oils and other viscous liquids. The exceptionally high air handling capacity makes it suitable for construction sites seepage control.

The pumping action is created by two horizontally posed reciprocating actuators. Each has annular valves arranged to give two stage compression. Integral pressure regulators are used to create volumetric efficiencies under low head conditions to 220%. These features overcome the problem of discontinuous output normally associated with reciprocating positive displacement pumps.

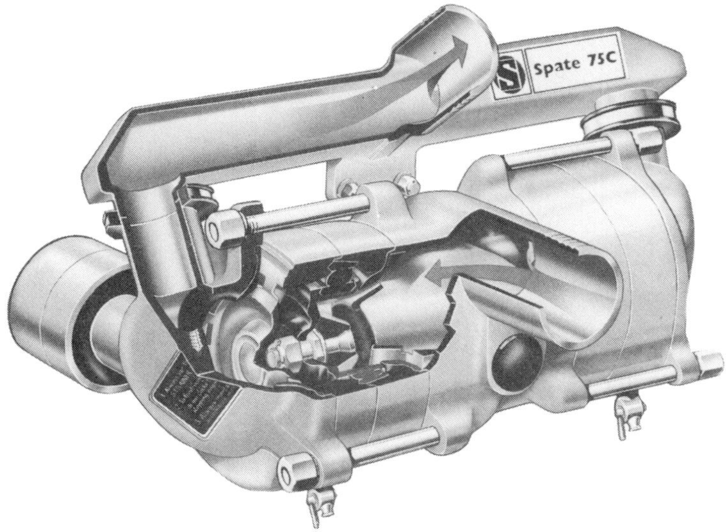

Figure 9
Positive displacement diaphragm pump with two horizontally-opposed cylinder stacks mounted on a central body unit.

Under most construction site conditions, pumped water often contains stones and other solid materials capable of damaging pumps of all types. Traditionally the problem has been tackled by fitting a strainer to the end of the suction hose immersed in the fluid. But, as strainers are easily damaged, lost or removed, they are not fully satisfactory devices.

A recent innovation that prevents all solids larger than 5 mm entering the suction branch of a pump is claimed to greatly improve pump reliability and utilisation. The unit as shown in Figure 10 is comprised of an aluminium alloy collection chamber

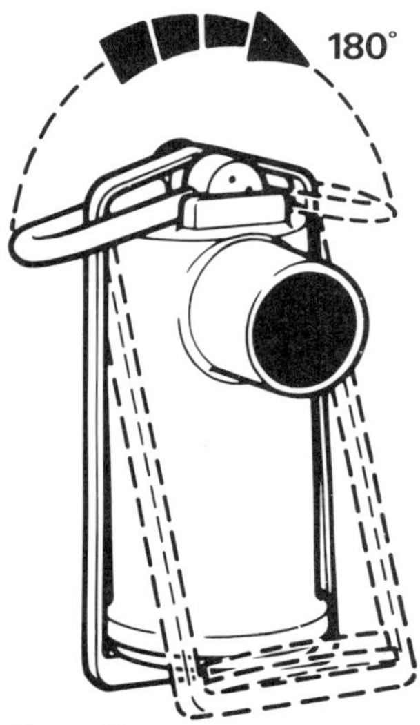

Figure 10
Stone collector.

General-purpose pump built to run 24 hours a day in rugged, hostile environments.

with an external attachment boss and two integral branches. A perforated steel screen is secured within the chamber in a position which ensures that all unacceptable solids are deflected downward and trapped. The lower end of the chamber is closed by a steel plug, which is raised and lowered by cam, operated by a self-locking lever.

Once installed, the pump is run until decreased output indicates that the collection chamber of the unit has become blocked with solids. With the pump running (if desired), the lever is rotated through 180°, lowering the plug and permitting it to be swung to one side. The contents will then be automatically discharged under gravity. Pumping will recommence immediately the plug is raised to its working position by means of the lever.

Well point dewatering

Duplex and occasionally triplex reciprocating plunger and piston pumps are used for high pressure applications *eg* long pipelines involving slurries and are particularly suited to well point dewatering applications. Horizontal-cylinder types with geared motor drive are used most frequently. Water, air or water mixtures are primed and discharged four times per crankshaft revolution. The pulsating mode of operation prevents clogging of the well point strainer thus water can be primed from greater depths. This type of pump (Figure 11) permits universal application and depending on soil conditions as many as 40 to 100 well points and 40 to 300 metres of header pipe section can be connected to one pump.

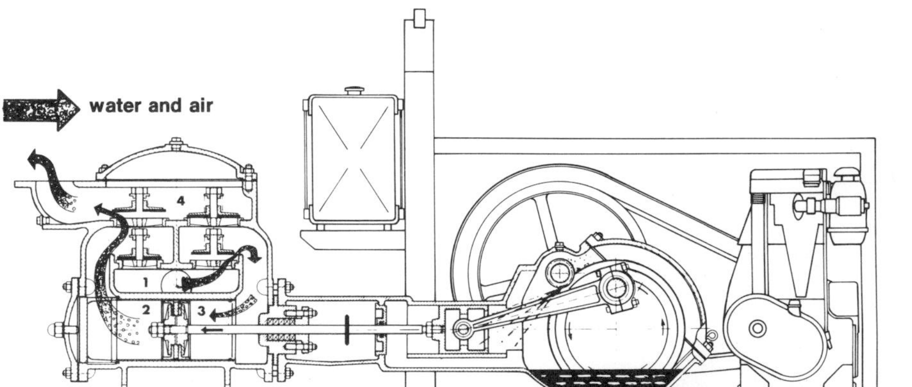

Figure 11
Quadruple-acting duplex piston pump for well point dewatering.

Heavy-duty self-priming contractor pumps are also extensively used for well point dewatering duties in fact particularly where heavily contaminated fluids containing solids such as sand sewage industrial waste water *etc*, must be pumped. (Figure 12).

The pump manufacturer is the main source of information and his experience in dealing with a wide range of customer requirements will enable him to advise on any special problems.

Mine Drainage

MINE DRAINAGE is the most significant role of pumping plant in the mining industry since the working of a mine and the safety of personnel and machinery depends on the availability and reliability of the pump sets, particularly as the mass flow of water from the mine often exceeds the tonnage of the product extracted. Because the pumping costs are obviously considerable the efficiency of the pump is also of major importance. In Europe mining is mainly associated with coal and here flow rates generally range upto 300 l/s with delivery heads from 500 to 1200 m. In African gold and copper mines and other mines throughout the world flows and heads may be appreciably higher than this.

Multi-stage centrifugal pumps predominate in mine dewatering and in very deep mines, it may be necessary to use a series of two or three pumping stations arranged one above the other.

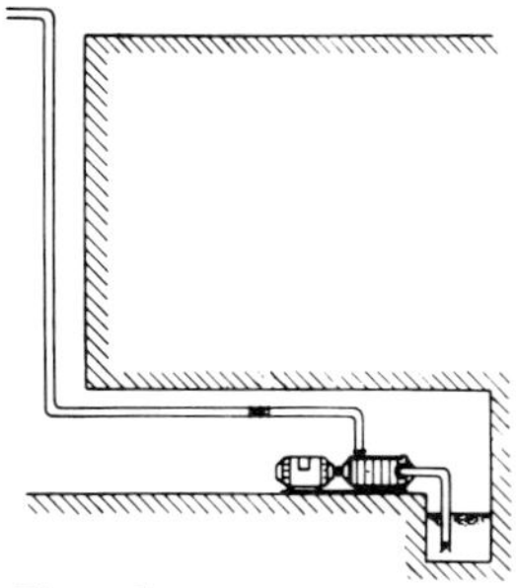

Figure 1
Horizontal multi-stage pump set in pump house at pit bottom.

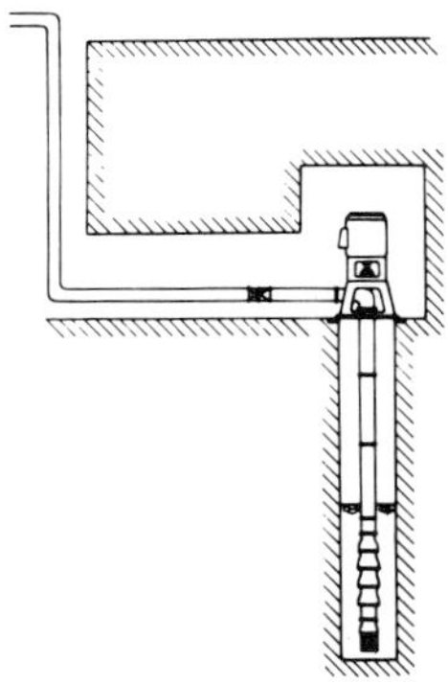

Figure 2
Vertical shaft driven borehole pump near pit bottom.

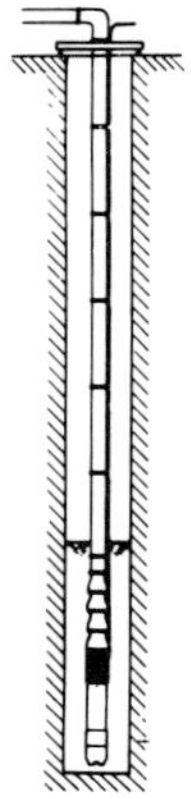

Figure 3
Fully submerged pump and motor suspended from surface.

The choice normally lies between the three arrangements shown in Figures 1, 2 and 3, namely:

(i) Horizontally mounted multi-stage centrifugal pump driven by an electric motor in a pump house at the mine bottom. (Figure 1).

(ii) Vertical multi-stage borehole pump submerged in water and suspended from the delivery pipework. (Figure 2).

(iii) Fully submersible electric motor and close-coupled pump suspended from the surface or an intermediate level by the rising main pipework through which the water is pumped to the surface (Figure 3).

Horizontal multi-stage pump set at pit bottom

The use of this type predominated in Britain for many years but although numbers are still in service, few new units are being installed. Placed in a suitable chamber at the pit bottom and operating on a suction lift or slight positive head, this unit involves high manning costs and is vulnerable if flooded, since the driving motor is then inoperable and the mine has no protection against total flooding.

In mines in the developing countries however, where labour costs are still relatively low, this type of unit is used in many instances.

Most pumps of this type run at four pole speed (1450 r/min) but operational experience on units handling 50 l/s at 1000 m head at two pole speed over a number of years has shown that high-speed operation is an entirely practicable and economic proposition where high heads are involved. It should be mentioned that when the pumping head exceeds 730 m (2400 ft) it is difficult to obtain satisfactory horizontally split-case multi-stage pumps and a decision should be made as to the viability of pumping in increments or moving to barrel pumps which are available for high pressures and developed for high pressure boiler feed pump service. Since most barrel pumps for mine service operate at high heads per stage with close clearances, the mine water must contain a minimum amount of abrasive particles in suspension.

Vertical multi-stage borehole pump set

With this arrangement the pump is submerged in water in a sump and suspended on an appropriate length or lengths of pipework within the centre of which is the driving shaft connecting the pump to the electric motor; the motor is mounted either at surface level or as shown in Figure 2, in a convenient dry situation underground where adequate headroom exists. This pump set arrangement is used to a limited extent, generally where there is customer preference based on the reliability of such units. Important advantages lie in the fact that no priming problems arise as the pump is always submerged and the balanced disc, the most vulnerable component in the conventional multi-stage pump can be eliminated. Instead, the pump thrust can be taken by an oil-lubricated tilting pad type thrust bearing housed in the pump head gear. Permanent sumps are seldom used in open-pit mines because the sump area generally moves as the mining operation progresses. Since mine water contains minute mineral particles the choice of materials is vitally important. Decisions should be taken not on the basis of the best available materials but on the basis of which material will best withstand the abrasive conditions during the intended life of the project. Care should be exercised when selecting alloys because many stainless steels do not have as great a strength as carbon steel.

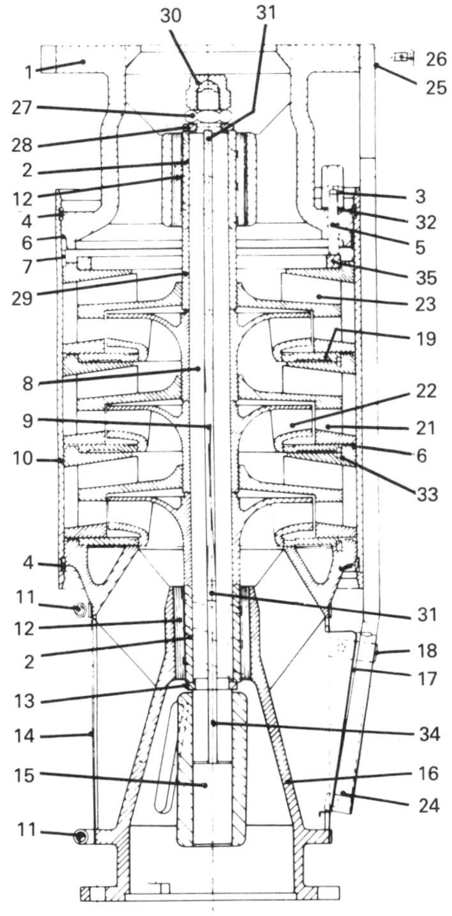

Key:
1. Delivery end
2. Journal sleeve
3. Cap nuts
4. Split ring (shell)
5. Clamping screws
6. O-ring seal
7. Support ring
8. Pump shaft
9. Key for pump shaft
10. Pump shell
11. 'Jubilee' clip
12. Bearing bush
13. Split ring (shaft)
14. Suction strainer
15. Coupling to motor
16. Suction piece
17. Strip for cable channel
18. Clip for cable sheath
19. Wear ring
20. O-ring
21. Guide vane
22. Impeller
23. Return vane
24. Cable sheath
25. Clip for cable sheath
26. Screws for cable sheath
27. Locknut
28. Washer for pump shaft
29. Distance sleeve
30. Cap nut
31. Pin key
32. Washer
33. Peg for return vane
34. Coupling key
35. Compression ring

Tubular casing mine pump.

Fully submersible electric motor-driven pump set
This arrangement in which the close-coupled submerged pump and motor are suspended from ground level or from a convenient position below ground by the rising main pipework through which the water is pumped to the surface, is the one that is most widely accepted in coal mines in Europe.

Particular advantages associated with submersible pumps are that no underground pump house is required, the pump set is smaller and cheaper to install and operate, there are no priming problems and failure of the power supply does not endanger the pumping plant.

Some typical submersible pump installations for mine drainage are shown in Figure 4.

For many years there was a tendency in mine drainage to use a small number of very large pumps in wells, with up to 800 mm diameter well piping, as far as the hydrogeological conditions would allow. These very large submersible pumps of up

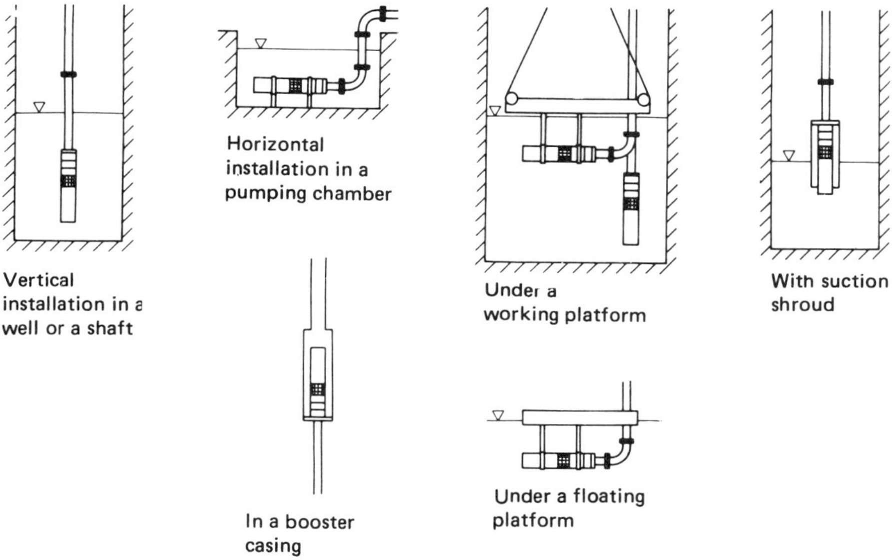

Figure 4
Submersible pump installations for mine drainage.

to more than 1500 kW rated power were normally double suction pumps running at 1450 r/min (50 Hz); for smaller pump sizes the mining industry preferred for a long time the double suction principle. Such pumps are well designed and reliable but the mining industry has started to use more and more single flow pumps running at 2900 r/min, first in the smaller sizes but more and more extending to the medium and large ones.

There are many reasons for this. Dimensions, weight and price can be reduced, the diameter of the well piping can be reduced, handling of the smaller units is easier, the repair work is less sophisticated and in many cases pump efficiency is better due to the higher specific speed of the single flow pumps. Also significant is the fact that in many mine drainage applications the duration of the maintenance-free intervals between overhauls is not limited by the wear of the structural parts of the pump, but by clogging with ochre and other deposits.

One method of combining the advantages of series production with individual requirements is to take a standard pump as the basis and add special packages to meet the particular requirements of the working conditions at the mine. Examples of these packages are a heavy-duty thrust bearing and a 'sand package' for very small units, with plastic impellers and diffusers consisting of replaceable polyurethane wear-rings on the impellers and stainless steel wear-rings in stage casings and diffusers. This 'sand package' increases the time between overhauls and allows quick reconditioning in case of wear. Further packages may include a tungsten carbide mechanical seal to protect the motor against deterioration and fire damp proofing in underground coal mines.

At the same time it must be appreciated that operating conditions for mine drainage pumps differ from mine to mine, so it is difficult to produce an economic 'standard' unit. A standard unit for water supply, for example, may be suitable in some cases but not in others.

Chemical Process and Refinery Duties

THE CONSIDERABLE development of seals of metals, plastics and ceramics in the last few years has provided the pump maker with the means to supply reliable plant for the most severe chemical duties.

In general, chemical duties include all liquids which present special problems on corrosion, erosion, high or low temperatures, vapourising, high viscosity and tendency to choking. The chief difference between a chemical pump and a water pump is the provision of special materials and the designs to resist corrosion. These features must protect not only the flow passages but also the bearings and most important of all, the personnel.

Many manufacturers do not make chemical pumps as such, but only process pumps suitable for chemical duties. Others continue to produce chemical and process pumps of different design – and in some cases the incorporation of modifications and refinements, application of special devices and the use of new materials can result in what is virtually a 'new and exclusive' pump.

There are good reasons for both approaches. The centrifugal process pump constructed in stainless steel will only remain commercially viable up to a certain size and may not be available with a capacity required for a particular chemical duty. Specific chemical fluids or processes may call for special considerations.

The cost of constructing such pumps in chemically resistant materials throughout can be extremely expensive for large pump sizes and the centrifugal pump, however, is simple in design so that castings can be utilised to a large extent in place of machining where the more 'difficult' materials – such as stainless steels, alloy steels, monel, hastelloy, durion, ceramics and glass are involved. Alternatively, wetted parts can be made in a cheaper material – *eg* iron, steel or bronze, subsequently lined or coated with rubber, plastic, lead, titanium, *etc*. The petrochemical industry bases its purchase of centrifugal pumps on the American Petroleum Institute Standard API 610, but for the remainder of the process industry companies there is no similar standard. The first problem facing a plant designer when charged with the responsibility for the specification, selection and procurement of pumps is to make a preliminary decision on the general type of pump which will fulfil each of a series of stated process duties. These pumps could be either centrifugal, positive displacement reciprocating or positive displacement rotary.

Not all pumping installations require the same degree of sophistication in the approach to selection. Clearly pumps required for duties involving high temperature, high pressure, handling fluids of high viscosity or with suspended solids require a much more sophisticated treatment than say a pump for a duty involving cold, clean water pumping from a large reservoir with a high inlet static head to a low pressure outlet.

Pumps for process duties should be integrated into the process systems in such a way as to obtain safe, efficient and reliable operation over long periods of time. In this regard installations having high availability are classified:

Class one

A class one installation achieves high availability by having a single machine of high intrinsic reliability and is characterised by:

(i) The machine being a single unspared unit upon which the process stream is wholly dependent.

(ii) The plant section having a single process stream with a long process recovery time after a shut down so that the loss of product owing to a machine stoppage is large even though the shutdown is for a short time.

(iii) A capability of continuous operation within given process performance tolerance is over a period of more than three years without enforced halts for inspection and adjustment.

(iv) Component life expectancies exceeding 100 000 hours operation.

Class two

As for class one, but where infrequent plant shutdowns of short duration are acceptable because the process recovery time is short. Consequently the period of continuous operation capability can be reduced and is taken as 4 000 hours for this classification.

Class three

As for class one or two but with a machine performance deterioration during the operating period accepted, or countered by adjustment of process conditions or by other action on the part of the plant operators.

Class four

A class four installation achieves high availability by redundancy and is characterised by having:

(i) One or more machines operating with one or more standby machines at instant readiness at all times to take over automatically upon malfunction of a running machine.

(ii) Operating and standby machine designed specifically for their functions so that they are not necessarily identical.

(iii) Component life expectancies exceeding 25 000 hours operation.

Class five

A class five installation follows the class four redundancy concept and is characterised by:

(i) One or more machines operating with one or more identical machines installed as spares to take over the process duty at the discretion of the plant operators.

(ii) One or more machines operating in plant sections where product storage is sufficient to give the plant operators adequate time to assess the malfunction and take remedial action. Alternatively, plant sections where a single machine stoppage does not cause a disproportionately large process upset.

Class six
Machines intended for batch or intermittent duty. Where high demand availability is essential the machines lie within class four.

Magnetic drive pump made in plastic for capacities below ISO 2858.

Pump types
Centrifugal pumps are the most extensively used type in the chemical and processing industries (over 80%). The majority are single-stage single- entry designs driven by two pole motors at 2900 r/min (3500 r/min in USA). Capacities may range up to 5 m^3/min (1 000 gal/min) and pressures up to 40 bar (600 lb/in^2).

Individual pumps of this type may have centre line lug mounting instead of foot or base mounts formed integral with the casing. This is to ensure support at the horizontal centre line at the pump to assist in maintaining correct alignment over a wide range of operating temperatures. With close coupled units however, the pump may be radially mounted on the end of the motor mount. A desirable design feature is generous spacing between the ball bearings carrying the pump shaft, particularly with an overhung impeller. Shaft diameter may have to be increased however, to avoid deflection and to enhance seal life. With a horizontally mounted pump the discharge nozzle is normally vertical but the inlet may be either horizontal or vertical. A horizontal inlet is the more common. The simplest solution for matched pump and driver units is to mount them radially on a stool or directly on the motor pedestal; or in the case of small units, directly on the motor. Where pumps are supplied separately for use with alternative drivers, centre line suspension of the pump on its own separate mount is generally to be preferred as this enables thermal expansion within the pump to be absorbed without affecting alignment. This is particularly important in the case of larger pumps which may be called upon to handle hot fluids or are worked as process transfer pumps.

The frame mounted pumps generally have a horizontal shaft carried in two bearings with axial inlet branch and radial upward discharge branch. The drive may be *via* a spacer coupling, thus permitting the withdrawal of the impeller shaft bearings and seal out of the pump towards the motor without disturbing motor or pipe joints. This is referred to as back pull-out and can also be arranged on vertical sets.

In-line pumps with L configuration are bolted into a straight run of pipeline which often takes the weight of the set. The U-configuration is similarly arranged, but in this case the inlet and outlet pipes are at the same side of the pump, hence the U designation. In-line pumps are generally combined with the motor to form a compact set, the pump impeller being on the motor shaft with the back pull-out but in this case the motor and the cabling must be disturbed.

Pumps known to be capable of class one operation are:

(i) Glandless canned motor or canned coupling pumps.
(ii) Glandless wet stator motor pumps.
(iii) Cantilever shaft vertical immersed pumps.
(iv) Special purpose pumps designed to meet the mechanical seal needs where the intrinsic L.10 life of the seal exceeds 20 000 hours.

Even these pumps will only achieve class one operation under favourable operation and maintenance routines.

Canned and wet motors

For freedom from gland leakage, a totally enclosed motor pump unit with the rotor in the pumped liquid (canned) or the whole motor in the pumped liquid (wet) may be used.

Cantilever pumps

The cantilever pump shown in Figure 1 is a variant of the more common sump pump shown in Figure 2. The external features are the same for both styles in that they are vertical pumps mounted to a vessel by a support plate with their pump ends submerged in the liquid to be pumped. Their drivers are fitted to the 'dry side' of the support plate and are thus external to the vessel. Usually these pumps are driven by directly coupled vertical electric motors but belt drives, again from vertical motors can be used. Less common although feasible are horizontal drivers but in this case right angle gear boxes are required.

Suction is taken directly into the pump *via* (usually) downward facing opening which may be fitted with an extension tail pipe and/or a suction strainer depending upon the application. The use of a tail pipe essentially extends the operating depth of the pump in that, provided the impeller and pump case are flooded for start up, the pump will continue to draw liquid until the end of the suction pipe is uncovered and air is drawn in, thereby causing the pump to loose prime. Pump discharge is taken by a separate pipe up to the pump support plate. Thus the pump only has one pipework connection; that of the discharge.

The cantilever pump (Figure 1) by virtue of its design does not have the bearing related problems associated with the traditional sump pump. As the name suggests, in this style of pump, the impeller is 'cantilevered' from conventional anti-friction bearings mounted away from the pumped liquid and the shaft is therefore unsupported at its lower end. In this way the need for immersed bearings is avoided and thus the problems encountered with dirty pumpage on conventional pump sumps do not occur.

Generally, any type of pump end can be incorporated into a cantilever pump but typically open impeller designs are used. Hydraulic designs from standard end-suction pumps can be used and often the same volutes, pump covers and impellers are utilised. However, when predicting the performance of cantilever pumps developed from standard end-suction machines, due regard must be paid to the

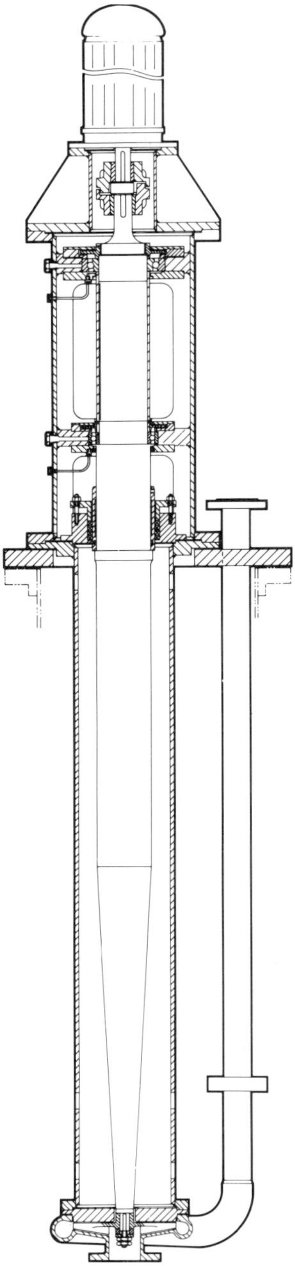

Figure 1
Cantilever pump.

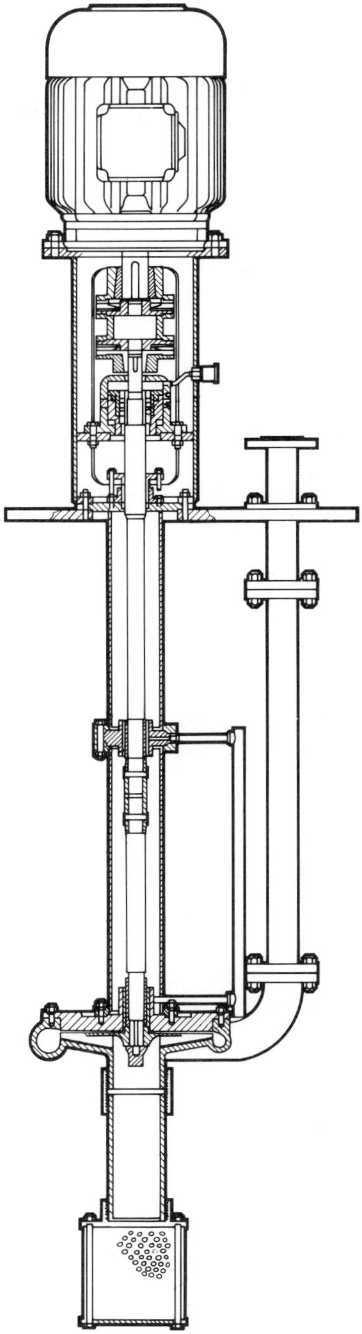

Figure 2
Sump pump.

likely efficiency to ensure the motor is adequately sized. Losses in efficiency occur due to leakage around the back of the impeller, through the pump cover where the shaft penetrates it and also due to the power absorbed in just rotating the pump shaft. Where shaft sealing is required, due to the diameter of shafts used, losses in packed glands and mechanical seals can be a significant proportion of the total losses and these must not be overlooked either.

Typical areas where pumps of this type have been successfully used are in the production of hydrofluoric acid and in pumping titanium tetrachloride containing highly abrasive solids.

Multi-stage pumps

For higher pressures, two-stage or multi-stage, horizontally mounted centrifugal pumps may be used, such types being generally suitable for pressures from 20 to 70 bar (300 to 1000 lb/in^2). Casings in this instance are split horizontally. For even higher pressures, barrel-type construction is normally favoured in view of the difficulty of maintaining a satisfactory seal on a horizontally split casing. Multi-stage pumps with barrel construction are used particularly for high-pressure feed pumps. Capacities of multi-stage centrifugal pumps for general process may range up to approximately 22·75 m^3/min (5000 gal/min). High head duties most frequently arise from a need to inject liquid into gas scrubbers or reactors operating at high gas pressures. Process requirements for exit gas purity or product quality often demand 100% availability. Then a standby pump on auto start for immediate readiness is required.

Vertical in-line centrifugal pumps come more and more into use for process duties, being cheaper than end-suction and split-casing designs on a total installation basis. Apart from occupying the minimum of floor space (smaller sizes without bed-plates), such pumps can usually be disassembled quickly and easily without disturbing the pipework. The whole motor-stool- impeller assembly can normally be withdrawn without disturbing the pump casing. One further practical advantage with the vertically-mounted in- line pump is that no alignment is necessary and thermal expansion within the pump will have no affect on alignment. The latter can be an attractive feature where the pump may be required to handle fluids over a wide range of temperatures.

Unit construction

Unit construction pumps offer maximum adaptability to requirements that may not be permanent or possibly cannot be predetermined with sufficient accuracy or surity to decide on a single pump size and specification. Unit pumps are assembled from a number of pre-machined construction parts which can be built up as multi-stage assemblies with the option of various glands seals, mechanical seals and bearing constructions. Additionally, pumps can be changed or converted, if necessary without any machining being necessary.

Due to their constructional adaptability and the fact that standard unit components are normally available in a number of different materials, but with common major dimensions to maintain interchangability without altering pump performance, such pumps are suitable for handling a very wide range of liquids. Units are produced for both horizontal and vertical pumps and other useful forms, such as container pumps. With horizontal pumps the design is usually symmetrical, in which case reversal of the direction of flow can be accomplished by dismantling and turning the shaft round end to end.

Positive displacement reciprocating pumps

Metering pumps account for a relatively small proportion of all pumps used on process plants. However, with the increasing trend towards more automation of process plants, the proportion of metering pumps must inevitably increase as the measurement of flow to fine tolerances by any other means is notoriously difficult.

The positive displacement reciprocating metering pump was first developed in the United States in 1936. Apart from the direct measurements of small flows, one of the main applications is for the injection of measured small quantities of fluid to high pressure process streams and they are used universally across the whole range of process industries. Fluids handled range from viscous slurries to solvents, corrosive fluids, radio active fluids and liquids that must be maintained at elevated temperatures.

The volume of liquid displaced per stroke – within limits – remains constant whatever the rate of stroking so that by varying the rate of stroking the rate of delivery can be changed, which is a great advantage. As the liquid is delivered only during the discharge stroke, the flow is pulsating which may be a disadvantage but it can be overcome in a number of ways by use of a double acting pump or the use of a duplex, triplex, quadruplex pump or by a pulsation dampener in the outlet line, consisting of a bell filled with air or gas which has a cushioning effect on the liquid being delivered.

Reciprocating metering pumps fall into reliability classes 4, 5 or 6. A standard arrangement is one running pump rated at a 100% duty with one identical pump as the spare either installed or available as a replacement. Where batch metering is required then a reciprocating metering pump with a stroke counting or time controlling device should be used. For rough flowmeter where accuracy worse than ±10% pump flow rate is acceptable, a sliding vane rotary pump with variable speed drive can be used. For accurate flowmetering a reciprocating variable stroke metering pump should be employed. All these requirements relate to small flows.

In large flows a centrifugal pump with a standard flowmetering system should be used or a multiplex plunger reciprocating pump or special purpose centrifugal pump providing the liquid is clean.

For accurate metering, pumps should have a flooded inlet and the gland subject to a pressure above atmospheric pressure to avoid inward air leakage. The pressure at the inlet should be greater than the pressure differential required to open both inlet and discharge valves against their spring forces.

Horizontal close-coupled end suction polypropylene chemical pump.

Special-purpose reciprocating pumps

Multiplex, crank driven, reciprocating plunger pumps can be used for delivering pressures exceeding 60 bar absolute and capacities exceeding 0·4 l/sec.

Reciprocating pumps comprise a very small proportion of all pumps used on process plants (certainly less than 5%). They are particularly suitable for small to medium flow at high pressure but because of high initial cost and greater maintenance requirements, tend only to be used when no other solution is available. Nevertheless, they perform many critical duties on process plants and there are a wide variety of different configurations to be considered.

A crucial decision is whether the process permits the injection of a lubricant. The mean time before failure (mtbf) of unlubricated glands seldom exceeds 1300 hours, consequently the pumps then fall into reliability classes 4, 5 or 6.

Because the mean time to repair (mttr) usually exceeds 20 hours, standard arrangements comprise:

(i) One 100% duty pump with an identical installed spare.

(ii) Two 50% duty pumps with an identical installed spare.

The mtbf of lubricated glands can exceed 4000 hours consequently the pumps can be used in reliability class 2 or 3. In principle class 1 operation is possible.

Other considerations are:

(a) Systems that cannot tolerate an interval of no-flow upon change over to a standby pump require two running pumps each rated at 50% duty together with a third identical pump as standby.

(b) Systems requiring approximately constant pressure should include an accumulator.

Diaphragm pumps should be considered when:

(i) Gland leakage cannot be tolerated on grounds of sterility, toxicity, corrosion, or expense of the loss.

(ii) The process fluid contains abrasive particles, or precipitates solids in gland, and a flushing medium compatible with the pumped fluid and acceptable to the process is not available.

(iii) A lubricant compatible with the pumped fluid and acceptable to the process is not available.

Rotary positive displacement pumps

This classification includes gear pumps, screw pumps, lobe pumps, sliding vane pumps, progressing cavity pumps, and peristaltic pumps.

Rotary positive displacement pumps comprise the largest proportion of pumps next to centrifugals, used on process plants, but even so, this amounts to less than 10% of all pumps used. Their great field of application is for pumping oils or other liquids having lubricating properties.

Rotary pumps fall into reliability classes 4, 5 or 6. The common arrangement is one running pump rated at 100% duty with one identical pump as the spare either installed or available as a replacement.

Gear pumps in all stainless steel constructions have wide application for handling non-abrasive chemical solutions where low to moderate flow rates are required although basically the type is most suitable for handling fluids which are effective lubricants. This latter limitation does not apply to flexible vane pumps where adequate lubrication is provided by aqueous solutions.

In the case of smaller pumps the scope for material selection is often wider since individual components may require comparatively low overall strength and the bulk (and costs) of material used is relatively small. Thus all-plastic construction may be a practical proposition, or wider use may be made of high duty plastics for wetted parts.

These lobe rotor pump contains no glands, valves or seals (except shaft seals). The wetted parts can be made throughout in PTFE and are only three number – the pump body with its cover plate, the lobe and the orbital converter. The design is such that the lobe effectively divides the pump chamber into two sections and its orbital motion progressively increases the volume of one creating suction so that the liquid is expelled. By using PTFE throughout this pump is suitable for any concentration of acids, bases, alkalines, solvents, oils and most other liquids.

Screw pumps in general, are rather less used for chemical duties although single screw types are extremely versatile and can handle a wide variety of fluids, including slurries and pastes. The combination of a stainless steel screw and a fluorocarbon rubber stator renders the type suitable for general chemical duties within a working temperature range of 5 to 95 °C (40 to 200 °F). Performance is generally limited to low heads and low flow velocities. Head can be increased by employing multi- stages, the maximum head obtainable from a single-stage being of the order of 50 m (150 ft). A particular advantage for handling chemically active fluids is that the bearings can be housed separately from the wetted section, with sealing provided by a single gland.

Diaphragm pumps have specific applications for handling chemically active fluids, their advantage being that the fluid is completely isolated in the diaphragm chamber so that both corrosion and leakage problems can be minimised.

The peristaltic pump also provides complete fluid isolation, this time in a flexible tube which is subject to a 'rolling squeeze' in order to develop a pumping action. Capacity is necessarily limited to the product of the effected displacement volume of the working length of the tube and the frequency of the squeeze cycle.

The peristaltic pump will handle practically all liquids, including those of high viscosity and those containing a high proportion of solids and slurries. The pumped fluid does not come into contact with any component except the interior of the tube, which can be of any suitable material. It is self-priming and the rate of flow can be varied without loss of head. The temperature at which liquids can be handled is only limited by the material of the tube.

Chemical pumps

To enable pumps to deal with the wide range of chemicals, the essentials are:

(i) They must be simple in design and permit easy and rapid maintenance.

(ii) The wetted parts must be of materials suited to the liquid being pumped and suitable for use together.

(iii) The possible points of leakage must be as few as possible or preferably there should be none at all.

These requirements apply to all types of pumps used for chemicals, be they centrifugal, reciprocating and rotary and modifications of those types.

Many of the difficulties associated with the corrosion of metals and alloys are now being eliminated to a great extent by making or lining the wetted parts with non-metals such as plastics or similar materials. Such a step may seem obvious, but until recently it has not been easy to do. One reason for this is that a suitably resistant material may not produce a pore-free coating, allowing the chemical to attack the underlying metal which is supposed to be protected. Thus nitrile, polychloroprene and polysulphide rubbers have less resistance to water penetration than natural, butyl and silicon rubbers and could retain sufficient salt solution to promote galvanic action on the underlying metal. Similarly, whilst PTFE is a material possessing exceptional chemical resistance, it is generally unsuitable as a coating or lining unless applied as a thick sheet. Normal coating methods do not produce pore-free coatings.

In all cases, a good design of chemical pump is easily stripped down (preferably without disturbing the pipeline) for regular inspection and replacement of components as necessary. The advisability of replacing a component by one of a different material (*ie* a more resistant material) can be determined by assessing respective costs and service lives; although certain components may be designed for limited service life and made in low cost materials. The design must allow for the passage of solids in suspension, where applicable, and ensure that as far as possible active chemical solutions cannot find their way into bearings, or become trapped in stagnant pockets or crevices. If the pump bearings are lubricated by the fluid being handled, then the bearing design and materials must be compatible both with the chemical activity of the fluid and the degree of lubrication it can provide. In both these respects, increasing use is being made of filled PTFE as a lining material for plain bearings – the basic material possessing extreme chemical resistance and the 'filler' providing the mechanical strength which PTFE lacks. Table 1 shows the suitability of linings for use with acids and Table 2 the suitability of linings used with some other chemicals.

High volume chemical dosing pump.

Pumps for volatile fluids

In the process and chemical industries, it is often necessary to pump liquids at or near their boiling point. To enable conventional centrifugal pumps to cope with such duties it is necessary to increase the NPSH by raising the feeder tank, which increases the cost; or by having a lower speed, which probably means a multi stage pump. The super cavitating pump is especially designed to enable cavitation to take place without erosion damage and to reduce loss of power. By combining a super cavitating impeller with a conventional impeller, NPSH values of one third of those of conventional pumps can be obtained, while maintaining the performance characteristics of the centrifugal pump.

TABLE 1 – SUITABILITY OF LININGS FOR USE WITH ACIDS

Lining	Natural Rubber	Butyl	Chloroprene (Neoprene)	Nitrile	CSM	Ebonites		
						Natural Rubber	SBR	Nitrile
Maximum Service Temperature	70-80°C	90-110°C	110°C	100°C	90°C	65-70°C	65-70°C	110°C
Acetic	X	L	S	L	S	S	S	S
Chromic (4%)	X	X	X	X	L	X	X	X
Hydrochloric	S	S	L	L	S	S	S	S
Hydrocyanic	S	S	S	S	S	S	S	S
Hydrofluoric	S	S	L	L	S	S	S	L
Nitric 8%	X	S	X	X	S	X	X	X
Nitric 20%	X	L	X	X	S	X	X	X
Nitric 40%	X	X	X	X	S	X	X	X
Phosphoric 80%	S	S	S	L	S	S	S	S
Sulphuric 20%	S	S	S	L	S	S	S	S
Sulphuric 35%	S	S	S	L	S	S	S	S
Sulphuric 50%	S	S	L	L	S	S	L	S

S = Suitable L = Limited suitability X = Unsuitable

TABLE 2 – SUITABILITY OF LININGS FOR USE WITH OTHER CHEMICALS

Lining	Natural Rubber	Butyl	Chloroprene (Neoprene)	Nitrile	CSM	Ebonites		
						Natural Rubber	SBR	Nitrile
Acetone	S	S	X	X	X	S	S	S
Alcohols	S	S	L	S	S	S	S	S
Ammonia (25%)	S	S	S	S	S	S	S	S
Ammonium hydroxide	S	S	L	S	S	S	S	S
Detergents	S	S	S	S	S	S	S	S
Ethers	X	L	L	S	S	X	X	X
Ethylene glycol	S	S	S	S	S	S	S	S
Ferric chloride	L	S	L	S	S	S	S	S
Methyl chloride	X	L	X	X	X	X	X	X
Phenol	L	L	X	X	X	S	S	S
Silver nitrate	L	S	S	L	S	S	S	S
Soaps	S	S	S	S	S	S	S	S
Vegetable oils	X	S	L	S	S	L	L	S
Zinc chloride	S	S	S	S	S	S	S	S

S = Suitable L = Limited suitability X = Unsuitable

Dosing Pumps

DOSING PUMPS are used throughout the world and range from pH control and treatment of waters to the control of liquid additives and/or quality in a large range of industries.The concept of the dosing pump itself is based on the metering and proportioning pump, but has largely evolved as a specialised type of double diaphragm design with magnetic instead of mechanical actuation. Piston (plunger) pumps incorporating a safety diaphragm behind the piston to contain leakage are used for higher pressures *eg* up to 100 bar; and standard metering and proportioning pumps are also used for dosing duties. Motor driven dosing pumps are also widely used for low cost metering, utilising variable stroke mechanisms.

An example of a magnetically operated dosing pump is shown in Figure 1. This is a double diaphragm type with the volume between the diaphragms filled with glycerine (a fluid with low compressibility). The electro- magnetic oscillating drive has the advantage of low inertia and faster, more precise response to control than mechanical drives, the control itself invariably being an electric system.

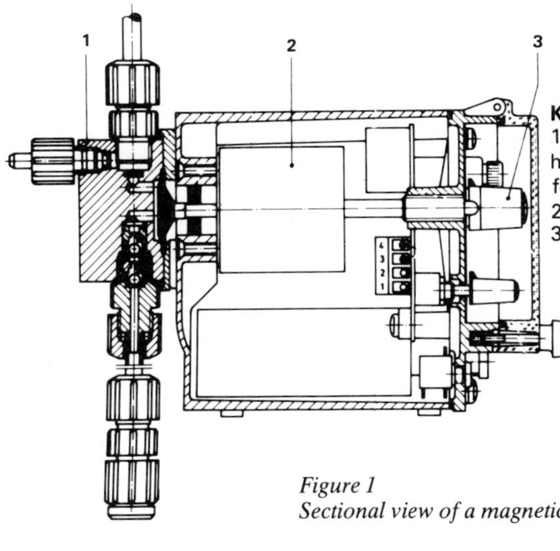

Key:
1.'Liquid dosing end' comprising dosing head, non-return valves, diaphragm and foot valve.
2.'Electro-magnet' diaphragm actuator.
3.Electronic control system.

Figure 1
Sectional view of a magnetically operated diaphragm pump.

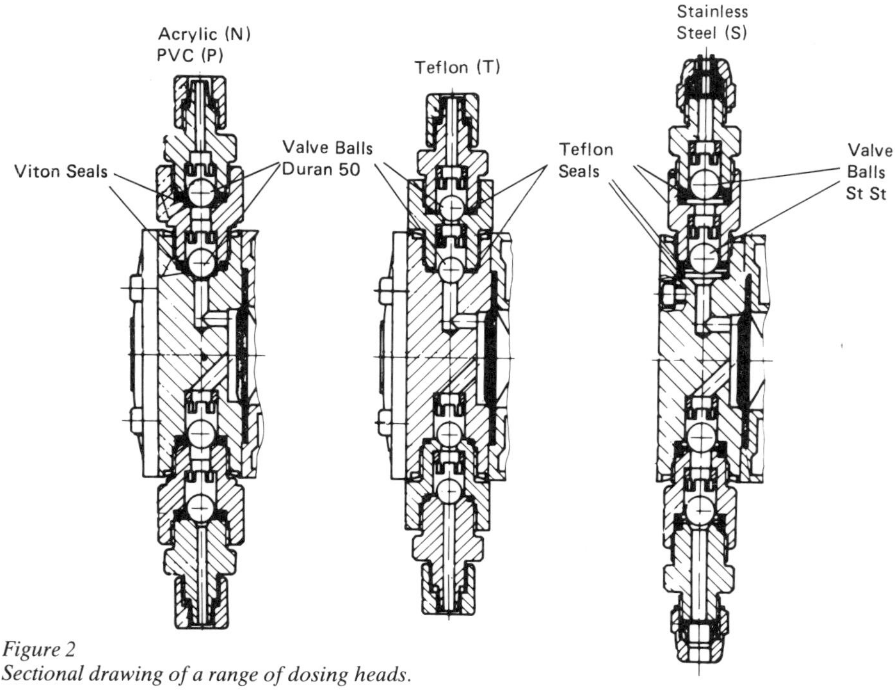

Figure 2
Sectional drawing of a range of dosing heads.

Examples of dosing heads are shown in Figure 2. This is the most important part of the entire pump since failure here negates all the advantages in the rest of the system. Composite diaphragms are commonly employed with metal (usually steel) core piece. The dosing head itself may be in stainless steel or plastic. Double non-return ball valves are normally used in stainless steel, titanium, PTFE or ceramic materials depending upon the product to be handled. Where liquids of high specific gravity or viscosity are to be dosed it is sometimes necessary to include valve springs to encourage the valve balls to seat correctly.

Valve assemblies are normally screwed securely onto the top and the bottom of the dosing head. Connection of the suction and dosing tube to be dosing head valves can be by compression fittings of flexible tube or by rigid plastic or metal pipes to suit the application. The dosing head assembly is secured to the pump body *via* equilaterally spaced screws which pass through the dosing head and the back plate. on some of the larger dosing heads manufactured from a plastic material, it is necessary to provide a reinforcing disk to withstand the pressure induced forces. To obtain varying dosed volumes a range of pumps will usually have a maximum diaphragm movement and the diameter of the working area of the diaphragm is calculated accordingly.

Thus it is possible to have accurate dosing from a few drops per stroke to several ml depending on the area of the diaphragm. The diaphragm itself is screwed directly onto the plunger of the electro magnet and this regulates the total diaphragm movement.

Electro-magnetic actuator

The electro-magnetic acutator operates against a spring return and is itself excited by electrical pulses. The energy of the electric impulse can be very high but since it is only applied over a very short period of time and the repetition rate is carefully calculated the actual power consumed by the system is very low, especially when compared with the rating of a motor to achieve the same efficiency of dosing.

Another important factor when calculating the electro-magnetic size is to ensure that the eventual temperature rise within the coil is kept as low as possible and that sufficient surface area is provided to dissipate efficiently any excess heat as rapidly as possible. Usually manufacturers provide several different electro-magnet sizes to cater for this and also to take account of the forces which will be required to allow the diaphragm to discharge the medium into a pressurised system.

Electronic control

Such dosing pumps are designed to operate with solid state electronic controls capable not only of governing the duration and magnitude of the 'on' signal pulses, but also their repetition rate. The pumps may therefore be operated in two modes.

1. Internally where the repetition rate of the electro-magnet 'on' impulse can be infinitely variable down to a very low percentage of the maximum (typically 4%).

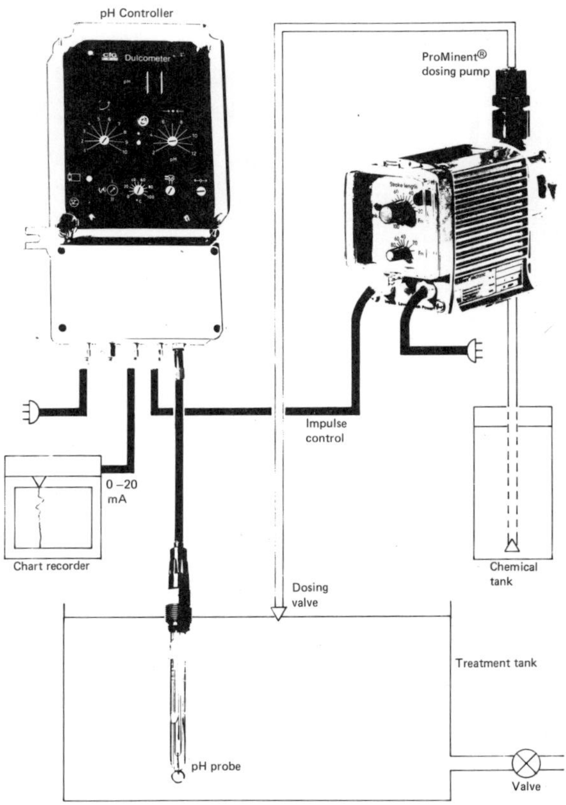

Figure 3(a)
Panel mounted analogue to impulse converter providing throughput proportional dosing related to the output from a zero to twenty milliamp flowmeter signal transmitter.

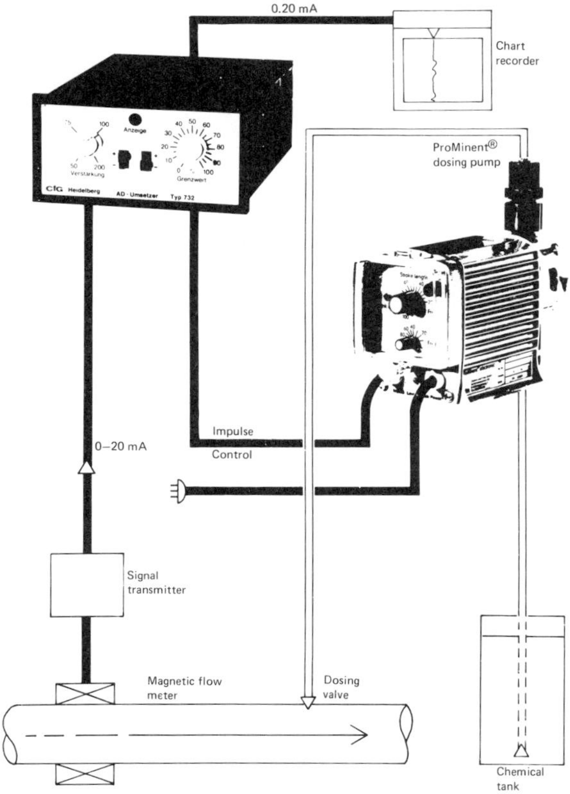

Figure 3(b)
Wall mounted pH pump control system for a neutralisation plant.

2. Externally where the repetition rate of the electro-magnet 'on' impulse can be a function of an externally measurable parameter *eg* flow *via* an impulse water meter; pH *via* a pH analogue/impulse converter; redox *via* a redox analogue/impulse converter; conductivity *via* a conductivity analogue/impulse converter *etc*.

Electronic controls also offer the possibility of including within the pump housing all the necessary external analogue signal conditioning amplifiers, comparators and analogue to impulse converters. This removes the problems which the pump user might experience in matching sophisticated equipment from different manufacturers. However, an integrally built in analogue control unit is not always convenient, particularly where a number of controlled pumps may be dispersed over an entire plant. In these cases, panel mounted units which can be assembled on to one control panel are preferred. These control externally connected magnetically actuated diaphragm dosing pumps. Two examples are shown in Figure 3.

Motor driven dosing pump with diaphragm head.

The uses to which dosing pumps are put today range from laboratory chromatography to the treatment of boilers and injection of chemicals into process plants. The field is so enormous that only a few can be mentioned:

Waste water treatment (pH controlled neutralisation);

Boiler water treatment (pH controlled, TDS controlled, make up water conditioning);

Drinking water treatment (pH controlled, chlorine controlled, approved additives *etc*);

Swimming pool water treatment (pH controlled, chlorine controlled, floccuant additives) Air conditioning treatment (pH controlled, hardness/softness stabiliser);

Chemical industry (controlling various additives);

Brewing industry (controlling various additives);

Phosphating industry (phosphate tanks quality control);

Plating industry (plating tanks quality control);

Dyestuffs industry (liquid additive control).

Oil and Gas Pumping

THE WINNING and refining of hydrocarbons and other products of the oil industry include some of the most arduous duties that pumps have to perform.

Oil and petroleum products represent the largest bulk of fluid handled by pumps after water. At the upper end of the scale bulk flow through pipelines up to 1 m (36 in) diameter may be involved, usually handled by longitudinal multi-stage centrifugal pumps. In the oil and petroleum industries too, the media handled may range from thick viscous fluids to light volatile hydrocarbons. At the other end of the scale, refined and processed lubricating oils are extensively used in circulatory systems where the pumping requirements can be met by small and simple positive displacement pumps.

The choice of the most suitable type of pump for handling oil fluids is mainly dictated by:

(i) Fluid viscosity – all pumps are affected by increase in viscosity of the fluid handled. In the case of roto-dynamic pumps, the main result is a marked loss of efficiency. With positive displacement pumps the main effect is an increase in the power input required and considerable heating of the fluid. This does not necessarily mean an inevitable loss of efficiency, for the efficiency figure can often be maintained by reducing the pump speed, although some internal modification of the design may be necessary to handle high viscosity fluids efficiently. The critical velocity level is of the order of 100 cSt, although centrifugal pumps are widely used up to viscosities of 600 to 700 cSt.

(ii) Capacity required – certain pump types, otherwise excellent for handling oil fluids, are inherently limited in size. Alternative types may thus necessarily be the logical choice where larger deliveries are required.

(iii) Pressure or head required – this can determine the working point in the case of centrifugal pumps.

(iv) Nature of the fluid – the presence of contaminants in the fluid may preclude the use of certain type of pump or alternatively call for special protection to be introduced *via* filters.

(i), (ii) and (iii) are inter-related to a certain extent. Thus the viscosity level can affect the size chosen. The following is a general outline of pump types listed in order of preference:

1. Where the capacity requirements are small, a gear pump will probably provide the simplest and most economic solution. A suitable size can then be selected on the basis of speed (and thus capacity) recommended with the oil viscosity concerned.
2. Where a rather high capacity is required, a lobe rotor pump will probably be the best choice. This type will also extend the capacity available outside the normal range of gear pumps.
3. If the capacity required is large (a) a centrifugal pump will probably be the optimum choice if the oil viscosity is not greater than 500 to 600 cSt. (b) If the fluid viscosity is greater than 100 cSt, choice may lie between a centrifugal, reciprocating or rigid screw pump. The respective merits of each must be assessed in detail and a final choice based on overall economics (unless other special requirements overule).
4. If a high pressure output is required, compare capacity requirements against type, *eg* (a) small moderate capacity – rotary plunger or rotary piston. (b) moderate or high capacity – reciprocating or rigid screw.
5. If the fluid is contaminated, possibilities are:-
   (a) Flexible vane pump for light duties.
   (b) Lobe rotor pump for medium duties.
   (c) Screw pump for large capacities (or possibly centrifugal for low viscosity oils).

Tables 1, 2 and 3 present details of pump selection based on the effect of fluid viscosity, size ranges and capacity.

Considerable developments have taken place over the past two decades in both onshore and offshore crude oil pipeline schemes. Onshore the trend has been towards the development of high speed pumping units to match the increasing availability of industrial derivatives of aero-engine gas turbine units. Offshore, two main trends are apparent: the use of high pressure oil pipelines and the use of water injection schemes.

Onshore, prime mover technology has progressed from low-speed gas/diesel engines or electric motors with four or more poles to high-speed gas turbines and two or four pole electric motors with speed increasing gear boxes and variable speed couplings.

Various aspects of this development are:

(i) Higher rotational speeds and higher heads per stage with the associated higher power levels induce higher stress levels so that, for example, a single 440 mm impeller is transmitting 11500 bhp with each vane transmitting approximately 2000 bhp. Thus the level of quality assurance has become of paramount importance, necessitating rigorous inspection standards and the use of sophisticated techniques of non-destructive testing such as X-radiography. Careful detailed design is necessary to minimise the stress raisers such as sharp changes in section and a high polish is

TABLE 1 – EFFECT OF FLUID VISCOSITY

Type of Pump	Significant* Viscosity Levels	Effect of Viscosity Level	Treatment and/or Remarks
Centrifugal	20		Performance maintained similar to water performance up to this level.
	20–100	Lowering of H-Q curve increase in input hp	General lowering of efficiency but may be acceptable.
	above 100	Marked loss of head	Considerable reduction in efficiency, but high efficiencies may still be attainable from larger pumps.
Regenerative	above 100	Marked loss of performance	Pumps of this type would not normally be considered for handling fluids with a viscosity greater than 100 centistokes.
Reciprocating	up to 100	Little	Performance generally maintained. Some reduction in speed may be advisable to reduce power input required.
	above 100	Performance maintained but power input increased	Speed is generally reduced to avoid excessive power inputs and fluid heating.
	above 1000	Flow through valves may become critical factor	Select larger pump size; run at reduced speed – *eg* 3 x size at 1000 centistokes running at one-third speed. Modification of valve design may be desirable for higher viscosities.
Plunger	–	–	For very high pressure deliveries only.
Sliding vane	above 100	Sliding action imparied; slip increased.	Not generally suitable for use with other than light viscosity fluids.
External gear	None	Power input and heat generated increase with increasing velocity.	May be suitable for handling viscosities up to 25000 centistokes without modification. For high viscosities:- (i) clearances may be increased, (ii) speed reduced, (iii) number of gear teeth reduced.
Internal gear	None	Power input and heat generated increase with increasing viscosity.	For higher viscosities:- (i) speed may be reduced, (ii) number of gear-teeth reduced, (iii) lobe-shaped gears employed.
Lobe rotor	250	None	
	above 250	Cavitation may occur.	(i) speed may have to be reduced, (ii) modified rotor form may be preferred.
Single-screw	None		Nitrile rubber stator used with oil fluids.
Twin- or multiple screw	up to 500	Little or none.	
	above 500	Increasing power input required.	Speed may be reduced to improve efficiency.

*Viscosity in centistokes

TABLE 2 – TYPICAL SIZE RANGES FOR OIL PUMPS

Type of Pump	Capacity		Maximum Head		Practical Suction Lift	
	gal/min*	lit/min*	Feet	Metres*	Feet	Metres*
Sliding vane	up to 10	up to 45	450	140	6	1.8
External vane	up to 150	up to 680	3000 to 4000	900 to 1200	5 to 25	1.5 to 7.5
Lobe rotor	10 to 50	45 to 227	200	60	–	–
Internal gear	5 to 500	23 to 2270	200	60	5	1.5
Single screw	up to 2000	up to 9100	150	45	15 to 25	4.5 to 7.5
Reciprocating	20 to 2000	91 to 9100	unlimited	unlimited	20 to 25	6.0 to 7.5
Rigid screw	10 to 5000	45 to 22700	200	60	15 to 20	4.5 to 6.0
Centrifugal	10 to 10000	45 to 45450	500 (single stage)	150	–	–

*approximate values

TABLE 3 – PUMP SELECTION BASED ON VISCOSITY AND CAPACITY

(Pumps normally listed in order of preference)

	Capacity Required			
	Low	Moderate	High	Very High
Viscosity below 100 centistokes	External gear Vane Internal gear	Lobe rotor Internal gear Reciprocating	Centrifugal Rigid screw Reciprocating	Centrifugal Rigid screw
Viscosity 100–500 centistokes	Gear Lobe rotor Diaphragm	Rigid screw Reciprocating Lobe rotor Gear Centrifugal	Rigid screw Centrifugal Reciprocating	Centrifugal Rigid screw
Viscosity above 500 centistokes	Heavy duty vane Gear	Lobe rotor Flexible screw Rigid screw Reciprocating	Rigid screw Reciprocating	

given to vane surfaces to eliminate potential crack propagation and minimise hydraulic losses.

(ii) Higher stress levels in impellers have lead to the use of high strength stainless steel such as 30% Cr, 4% Ni. High rotational speed and generated heads can lead to rapid erosion at both impeller inlet and outlet and thus the high resistance to erosion of 13% Cr, 4% Ni is also important.

(iii) Mechanical seals are now universally used for oil pipelines and pumps since the degree of reliability obtained more than compensates for the higher initial cost and permits pump sets to be remotely controlled and free from routine maintenance. Significant developments in pump sealing technology have recently taken place particularly in relation to pumping oils and gases. Dry running gas seals, formed metal bellows seals and high duty cartridge seals are making significant contributions towards added safety and cost effectiveness.

(iv) As speeds and power increase so the importance of ensuring low vibration level increases. Accurate alignment of internal hydraulic passages and a high degree of rotor dynamic balancing become vital factors in minimising exciting forces. It is now essential to consider the whole shaft system including bearings, couplings, mechanical seals and the hydro-dynamic support at the neck rings. Depending upon the value of clearances between the impeller and the casing neck rings, the rotor critical speed in water may increase by some three or four times that measured in air and at the same time, reduce the maximum amplitude at the critical speed.

(v) The use of pumps in series tends to predominate the parallel operation where pipeline schemes are concerned. It is now necessary to design axially split casing pumps which withstand working pressures up to 200 bar (3000 lb/in^2) with transient pressures considerably in excess of this figure.

Pipeline pumps are mainly used for conveying oil over longer distances. Delivery heads range from 400 to 1000 m. Up to about 800 m this can be managed with one stage. Flow rates vary between 80 and 1500 l/s. Single-stage double entry horizontally split pumps with double volute are chiefly used. For high pressures, vertically split casings are often specified.

Such requirements necessitate the careful design of casing splitting flanges and bolting arrangements supported by a precise knowledge of stress distribution within the complex shapes of a pump volute casing. Stress analysis research programs form an integral part of pressure casing design and form the link between theoretical analysis techniques and practical problems associated with casing distortion and non-uniform stress distribution.

Centrifugal pumps

Centrifugal pumps tend to suffer a marked loss of efficiency with increasing fluid viscosity, mainly loss of head and consequent lowering of the H-Q curve, together with increased power input required. This can only be offset by increasing the Reynolds Number of the flow through the pump. This implies increasing the pump size (diameter), speed or both. Thus, large centrifugal pumps running at high speed can maintain quite high efficiency, even for handling fluids with viscosities up to 5000 cSt. It is also possible to predict the performance when handling the viscous fluid, compared with the water performance by direct measurement of loss characteristics. The use of Stepanoff correction factors is probably the simplest and most straightforward method.

This procedure is based on the pump Reynolds Number calculated in terms of the capacity or discharge (Q).

$$R_p = \frac{Q}{vD^2}$$

where:

v is the fluid viscosity

D is the pump diameter

Head correction factors are determined from empirical data, related to the pump Reynolds Number and can be expressed graphically as in Figure 1. Efficiency is also shown in the same graph.

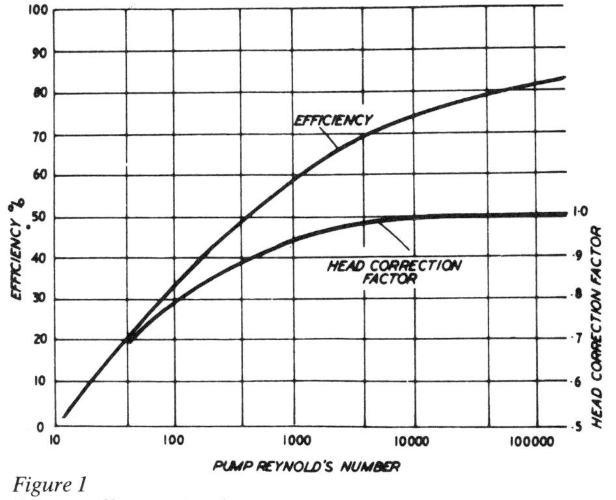

Figure 1
Steppanoff correction factors.

The capacity/head relation is independent of the specific speed, since this will not change for a constant speed and given power relationship. It can thus be expressed as:

$$\frac{Qw}{Qo} = \left(\frac{Hw}{Ho}\right)^{1\cdot 5}$$

where:

Q = capacity

H = head

suffix w refers to water performance and

suffix o refers to oil performance

Starting with the water performance of the pump as known:

(i) The pump Reynolds Number is calculated for nominal value of capacity (Q), the particularly pump size (D) and the viscosity of the oil to be pumped (v).

(ii) The head correction factor is read from the graph (Figure 1).

(iii) Corrected head value is calculated and plotted on water performance graph – Figure 2.

(iv) Using the water head figure and the corrected (oil) head figure, calculate the corrected capacity using:

$$Qo = \frac{Qw}{\left(\frac{Hw}{Ho}\right)^{1\cdot 5}}$$

(v) Establish the derated H-Q point on the pump performance graph. (Figure 2).

(vi) The procedure can then be repeated for different values of capacity to plot the oil performance H-Q curve.

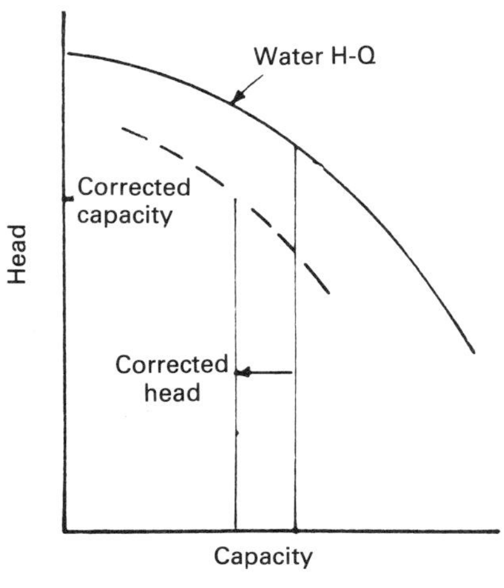

Figure 2
Water performance graph.

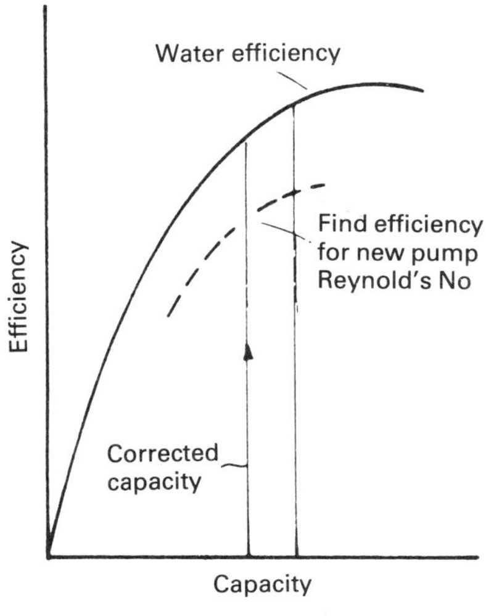

Figure 3
Derated efficiency curve.

The same procedure can be used to plot the derated efficiency curve for the pump – Figure 3. Efficiency figures are derived from Figure 1 for various calculated values of pump Reynolds Number. Note that the correction curves of Figure 1 can be related to specific groups of centrifugal pumps and are not necessarily restricted to the performance of individual designs.

Reciprocating pumps

Reciprocating pumps have a particular use in injection stations (forcing oil at higher pressures into a mainline intermediate station), chemical feeding, recirculating duties at refineries and specific process work. In the case of reciprocating pumps 'correction' for a high fluid viscosity can be applied by decreasing the speed. This means that a larger pump size is chosen initially to maintain a given output. Good efficiency is maintained because of the lower power required at the reduced speed of running. Conditions may still become critical if the fluid is so viscous that it channels or cavitates, in which case, rather than reduce the speed still further, it may be necessary to eliminate the suction valve from the design and modify the discharge valve and ports to ensure free flow.

Rotary pumps

Rotary pumps are used for handling both crude and refined products and particularly suitable for handling viscous fluids although, in the case of very viscous crudes, these pumps may be heated (steam jacketed). Favoured types are the gear and screw pumps. Gear pumps in particular can readily be adapted by modification of gear design to handle products ranging from low viscosity fluids like gas oil to the most viscous liquids and are produced in sizes ranging up to 200 tons/h capacity. For fuel oil or similar duties they can also develop pressures up to 35 bar (500 lb/in^2) or more; or for use as heat transfer pumps they can handle fluids at temperatures up to 300 °C. The positive displacement characteristics and reversable nature of the gear pump also make it attractive as a tanker cargo pump, as it can be used to reverse flow at the completion of loading so that delivery lines can be emptied back into the vehicle.

In the case of rotary pumps, correction for a high fluid viscosity by decreasing the speed is rather less than for reciprocating pumps. Initial speed reduction required is fairly high, but after that, speed reduction can taper off with further increase in fluid viscosities. (Figure 4). It may however, be necessary to increase clearances to

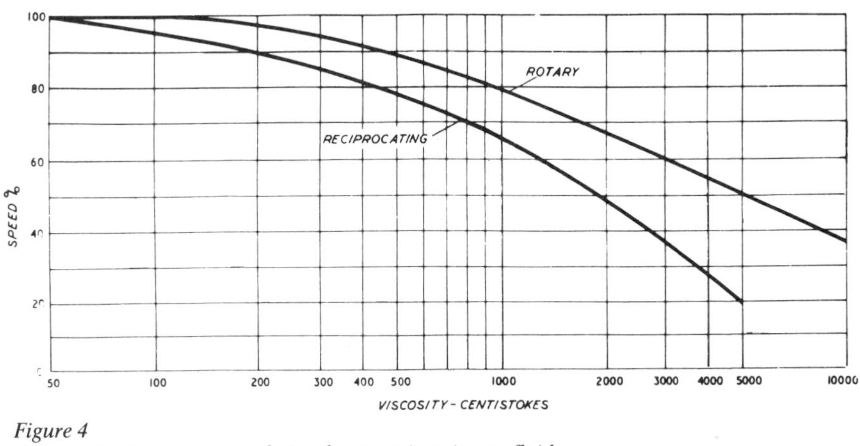

Figure 4
Speed reduction recommendation for pumping viscous fluids.

ensure satisfactory through flow without channeling, the potential loss of efficiency being largely offset by the better sealing given by the more viscous fluid, *ie* internal leakage or slip can remain very much the same or fall with increasing viscosity.

Many standard rotary pumps are capable of handling fluids with viscosities up to 10 000 cSt without modification (with speed reduction), and in some designs the figure may even be as high as 50 000 cSt.

With positive displacement pumps, viscosity effects are more specific. Higher fluid viscosity mainly represents higher internal resistance. Pump performance can be maintained by increasing the power input to overcome the increased resistance. This will necessarily reduce the efficiency but not to the same extent as in a centrifugal pump, which suffers both a performance loss and power input increase. Fluid heating will also be increased, but this may be favourable in tending to reduce the viscosity. Side effects may also be introduced, such as modifying sealing and slippage characteristics through clearances and ports.

Basically, where the fluid viscosity is less than 100 cSt the centrifugal pump appears the most versatile type, although its efficiency will tend to be low for moderate deliveries and generally too low to warrant consideration for small deliveries. With higher fluid viscosity it tends to be less competitive than other types, except where a large pump size can be used. It should be remembered that both the reciprocating pump and the rigid screw pump may also have to be oversized to handle high viscosities so that running speed can be reduced, although the critical velocity level will be higher.

Comparative performances of the gear and lobe rotor pumps are also interesting. The external gear pump is undoubtedly the simplest and cheapest type for handling low volumes of oil with high efficiency, almost regardless of viscosity. At quite moderate capacities, however, the internal gear and lobe rotor pumps are generally more attractive, the latter in particular offering higher specific outputs for a given size of pump. Special circumstances may also be present, such as head or pressure requirements and the ability to self prime over a positive suction lift.

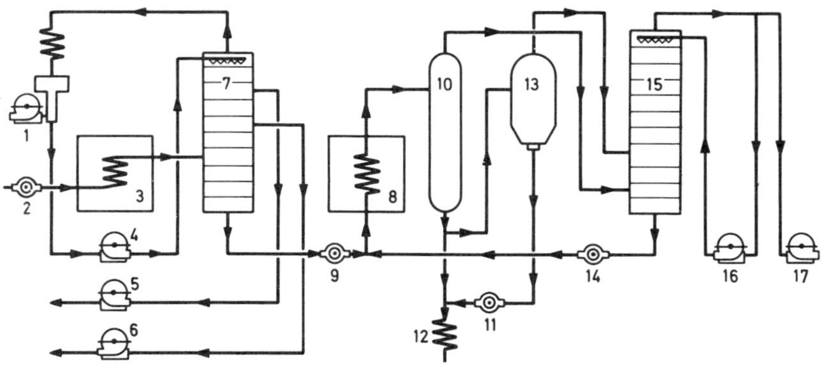

1 – Benzene pump	9 – High-pressure pump for hot, reduced crude oil
2 – Crude oil pump	10 – Reaction chamber
3.8 – Furnace reflux pump	11 – Pump for hot residual oil
4.16 – Recycling pump	12 – Residual oil
5 – Kerosene pump	13 – Flash chamber
6 – Gas oil pump	14 – High-pressure pump for recycled oil
7.15 – Fractioning column	17 – Pressure distillate pump

Pump arrangement in a petroleum refinery.

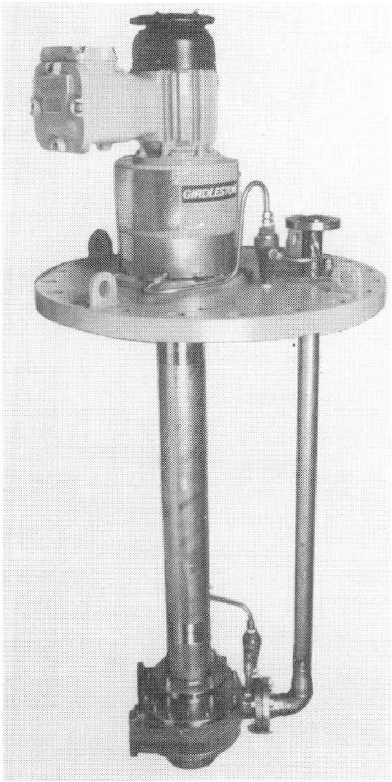

API 610 vertically suspended sump pump for hydrocarbon duties.

Cutaway view of rotary positive displacement pump showing the balanced vanes and the eccentric bore.

Volatile products

The handling of more volatile petroleum products presents specific problems, notably the requirement that the system NPSH must be greater than the required NPSH of the pump to prevent liquid flashing into vapour on the suction side of the pump. This is aggravated by the low boiling point of many such fluids. Various methods of cooling may be employed and particular attention may have to be paid to preventing volatile and flammable liquids from leaking past the gland and escaping. It is also essential that the glands of pumps handling flammable fluids should be made of non-sparking materials or be suitably smothered.

The general trend is to favour the use of mechanical seals rather than packed glands although they may still need to be smothered. The problem of gland design is essentially similar to that of chemical pumps, although the vapour pressure of the product handled may be unique. Also if fluid must be injected into the gland for cooling or smothering it will usually be oil.

Some typical pumps used in the oil industry are listed in Table 4.

Offshore developments

In offshore fields, reliability of pumping equipment is of major importance, even more than in land based systems, due to the relative inacceptability of the offshore platforms especially in the severe weather conditions of the North Sea and other hostile environments.

TABLE 4 – TYPICAL PUMPS

Performance range up to	Pump Types	Transfer	Blending
10 bar 250 m^3/h	**Rotary Lobe Pumps** Rotary lobe pumps usually fitted with bush bearings. Pumps can be supplied equipped with ball bearings if fluid to be handled has suitable lubricating properties. Jacketed versions are available to cover heating or cooling requirements.	An inexpensive, reliable and efficient type of pump suitable for the transfer of most industrial oils and similar substances in small to medium duty range.	With high volumetric efficiency, these pumps are ideal for use in small blending plants.
10 bar 250 m^3/h	Rotary lobe pumps with an arrangement of two stuffing boxes and with bearings housed outside the pumped liquid.	These pumps can handle contaminated fluids at high pressures and are suitable for fuel oils, *etc.*	
5 bar 90 m^3/h	Rotary lobe pumps of internal bearing design. Mainly of aluminium construction. Supplied for either reversing or non-reversing flow with drive shaft extension suitable for vehicle power-take-off connection.		
42 bar 2000 m^3/h	**Screw Pumps (Geared Type)** Internal bearing, geared screw pumps suitable for handling liquids having reasonable lubricating properties. Generally used for non-contaminating fluids.	Used for major transfer schemes. Pumps can be run at synchronous speeds.	For blending duties, these pumps can be driven by variable speed devices with accurate control and work usually in conjunction with centrifugal pumps.

When major maintenance is necessary, the pump outage must be minimised. Pumps employing axially split casings provide easier access to the pump internals and may be preferred for this reason. Also, due to the very high capital cost of offshore production platforms, it is vital to minimise space requirements, and here the axially split casing is advantageous since there is no need to provide axial withdrawal space as is required with radially split barrel type. However, where working pressure in excess of 200 bar (3000 lb/in^2) are concerned, or where a potentially corrosive fluid such as seawater is being pumped, a radially split double case pump, having replacable inner casing may be preferred.

USED IN THE OIL INDUSTRY

	INDUSTRIAL APPLICATIONS				
Rail Unloading	**Process**	**Petro-chemical**	**Road Tanker**	**Bitumen and Tar**	**Spirits and Light Hydrocarbons**
	These pumps can be supplied in a variety of materials to suit all fluids having reasonable lubricating properties.	For these duties pumps are usually supplied with bush bearings. Maximum pressure approximately 3.5 bar		Suitable for transfer duties etc, provided that the selected pump can be supplied in a jacketed version.	The pumps equipped with bush bearings can be used for handling varying grades of diesel and gas oils.
	For certain hot oil duties and handling similar fluids, pumps can be equipped with water cooled bearings and, if applicable, stuffing boxes.	Suitable for various aggressive fluids.		In high viscosity applications a bypass system is usually fitted. The pump can be jacketed and normally runs at low speed.	Suitable for certain applications pumping spirits having extremely low viscosity.
			For this duty a reversible or non-reversible pump can be used. Discharge lines can be purged as the pump can handle air up to approximately 1 bar.		
For this duty, pumps are supplied with automatic bypass devices controlled by either vacuum or pressure.	For certain process duties these pumps can be used at high pressure. A range of pumps with in-line-branches is specially designed for use up to about 10 bar.	A specifically designed range of in-line-branch pumps operating at about 7.0 bar	A special version of these pumps can be supplied for large capacity road tankers.		For pumping certain types of light oils (diesel and gas oil) against low pressures.

cont...

The traditional steel grouted-in-concrete bedplate is inappropriate for supporting pumping units in steel pumping modules used on production platforms, so that the skid type bedplate is normally employed. Although offshore platforms such as those located in the North Sea are designed to take into account 30 m (100 ft) waves, tilting of the whole platform and deflection of the supporting steel work still occur so the bedplate must be designed such that the accurate alignment of pump and driver is unaffected. Consequently, a three point semi-resilient mounting is normally employed in the design of the bedplate to isolate it from small movements of supporting structure.

TABLE 4 – TYPICAL PUMPS

Performance range up to	Pump Types	Transfer	Blending
20 bar 2000 m^3/h	**Screw Pumps (Geared Type)** External bearing, geared type screw pumps with bearings and gearing outside the pumped fluid. Suitable for heating or cooling as required.	For transfer duties handling con-taminated fluids including crude oil, fuel oils, *etc.*	
42 bar 1200 m^3/h	Internal seal, geared type screw pumps wth with bearings and gearing outside the pumped fluid.	Suitable for major transfer schemes such as pumping crude or other oils from refineries to power stations.	
7 bar 650 m^3/h	Variable capacity, geared type screw pumps. Depending on the properties of the fluid to be pumped, the pumps can be supplied with bearings and gears outside the pumped liquid. Suitable for semi- or fully-automatic operation with control by flow, pressure or vacuum.		For blending duties, the capacity of these pumps can be auto-matically controlled.
83 bar 90 m^3/h	**Screw Pumps (Non-Geared Type)** Three-spindle or five-spindle non-geared screw pumps of internal bearing design (bearings running in the pumped fluid).	High-speed pumps for small and medium transfer duties up to high pressures.	With very high volumetric efficiency, these pumps can be used for blending duties at high pressures.
7 bar 90 m^3/h	**Centrifugal Pumps** Vertical centrifugal pumps	Pumps for general transfer duties.	Suitable for blending duties
10 bar 140 m^3/h	**Vane Pumps** Horizontal external bearing fitted with mechanical seal sump heating or cooling as required.	An inexpensive and reliable unit for light industrial oils in small to medium range.	Suitable for use on small blending plants.

USED IN THE OIL INDUSTRY

INDUSTRIAL APPLICATIONS					
Rail Unloading	**Process**	**Petro-chemical**	**Road Tanker**	**Bitumen a and Tar**	**Spirits and Light Hydrocarbons**
Where fluid contact with bearings and gears is not advisable, this range of pumps is also very suitable for rail unloading.	Suitable for handling a wide variety of process fluids at high temperatures under medium range pressure	Pumps can be supplied in special materials for various petro-chemical processes.		An important application of this range is pumping tar and bitumen. Units can be supplied with jackets or electric heating devices.	Large capacity pump handling the lightest type of spirits and, where necessary, water.
	Pumps of this type can be supplied in stainless steel and other materials for handling aggressive liquids with high speed operation.	Large capacity unit for duties requiring high pressure.			
The classic pump for this application. Ensures optimum unloading rate for a very wide variety of fluids without noise or cavitation effects.	Where it is necessary to control the fluid pumped for certain process duties at variable capacity, these pumps can be used.				These pumps can handle light hydrocarbons against varying output conditions.
	Used in lubricating oil plants and dewaxing units at medium to high pressures.			This type of pump supplied in suitably heated version, can be used to pump bitumen and tar.	Pumps are suitable for low-pressure applications.
	For fluids at normal temperatures.	Where applicable pumps can be constructed in special materials.			Suitable for depot transfer and loading duties, can be equipped with self-priming device.
		Can be supplied in cast steel for certain medium duties.	Supplied in aluminium. Capable of pumping discharge lines.		Suitable for medium duties for light oils. Reliable external designs.

Due to the confined space available on offshore platforms it is necessary to limit the noise emission from machinery to provide an acceptable environment. In this respect noise can be transmitted *via* the bedplate through the supporting structure so the mounting arrangement has to be designed with this in mind. Insufficient knowledge is available on the noise generation process in relation to hydraulic machinery to permit reductions in the noise generated other than by minimising hydraulic losses. The use of acoustic enclosures and hoods over various individual items of machinery to limit noise emission is the most practical approach to this problem.

Injection pumps

As oil is extracted, the pressure on the oil reservoir (boreholes) tends to reduce and in certain cases leads to a very high gas/oil ratio. By injecting treated water (seawater, brackish water or formation water) at high pressure under the oil bearing formation, the pressure decline can be arrested and the optimum oil output maintained. Compared with the line losses, the delivery head is very high so that the resistance curve is practically a straight line with slight inclination. Consequently, stable characteristics are crucially important in parallel operation. Because the back pressure inevitably increases as the field is exploited, these pumps tend to have dummy stages (reduced number of stages) or the provision of speed control. It is important to be able to replace the rotor assembly of these pumps by a spare within one shift and special attention must be paid to the choice of materials used bearing in mind the severely corrosive water and high peripheral speeds necessitated by the high heads.

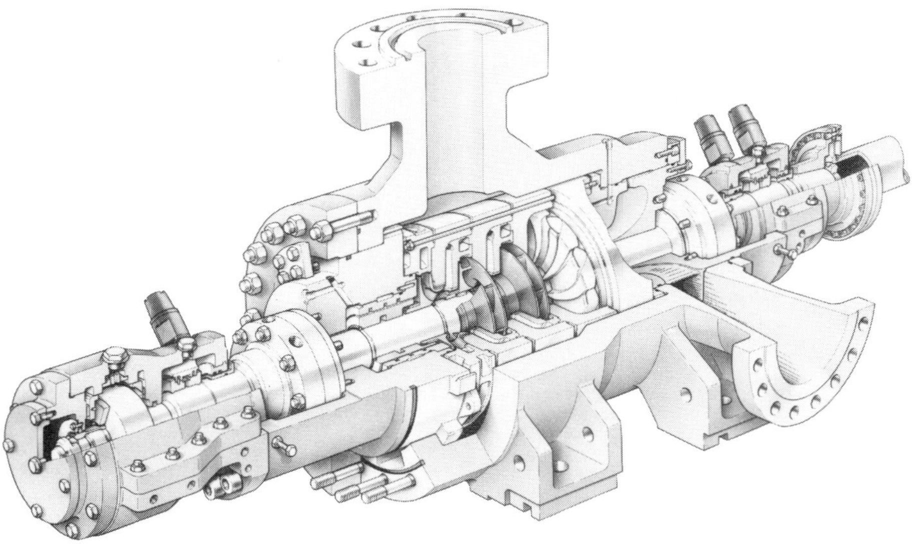

Injection pump for offshore duties with a locking and gear connection system for ease of maintenance.

Flow rates vary between 50 and 1000 l/s. Delivery heads range from 1000 to 3000 m depending upon the oil field.

Normally water injection pumps operate in parallel with each pump generating the required pressure. Thus with injection pressures above 200 bar (3000 lb/in^2) it is necessary to use a step up gearbox to give pump speeds of 5000 to 6000 r/min, thereby limiting the number of stages and also reducing the pump cost. For the more modest operating conditions up to 170 bar (2500 lb/in^2) discharge pressure, the axially-split casing arrangement tends to be simpler to produce, easier to maintain and of lower cost. However, for working pressures in excess of 170 bar (2500 lb/in^2), the case for a barrel casing arrangement becomes stronger from technical and economic considerations. Figure 5 shows a simplified layout of the pumps employed on an oil platform. In addition, the pumps must satisfy the API (American Petroleum Institute) requirements. Barrel-casing pumps with pull-out cartridge or horizontally split casings are employed.

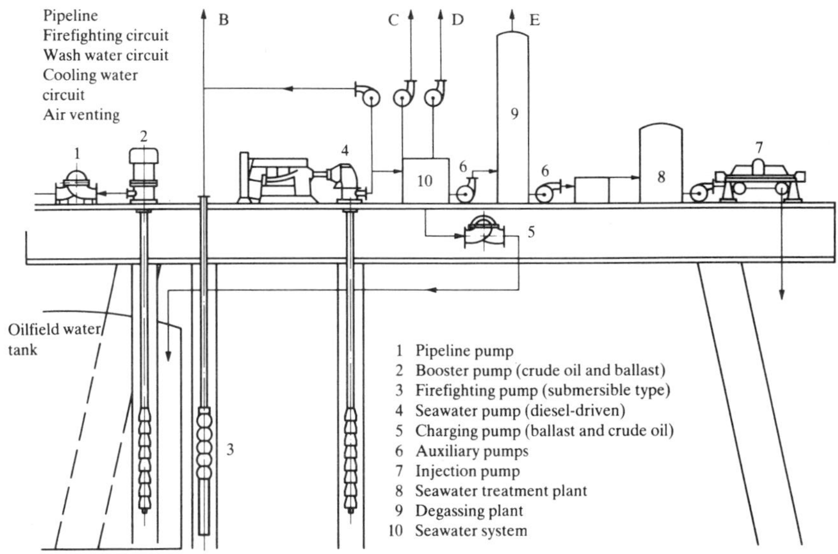

Figure 5
Simplified layout of pumps employed on an oil platform.

Liquified gases

Liquified gases are being increasingly used to cope with the requirements throughout the world. Submerged motor pumps are primarily used for handling liquified hydrocarbons and industrial gases such as LPG, LNG, ammonia, nitrogen *etc*. Areas of application include tank farms/terminals chemical plants, gas tankers, offshore installations, gas storage caverns and as drainage pumps filling/refilling pumps, booster pumps, spray pumps and circulating pumps. Figure 6 shows a sectional drawing of a three stage liquified gas pump to handle LPG or ammonia.

Submerged motor pumps are used to meet certain site requirements and three examples of installations are given here:

1. Permanent installation in tanks – the pumps is installed at the bottom of the tank.
2. Removable installation in sluice – the pump can be removed and refitted at any time even if the tank is filled. The liquified gas in the duct is forced back into the tank by means of an inert gas (nitrogen). The shut-off valve at the bottom of the duct operated from outside separates the sluice from the tank. (Figure 6).

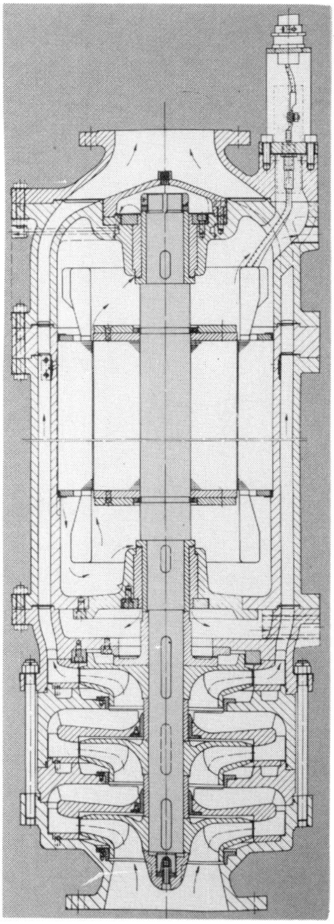

Figure 6
Three-stage liquified gas pumps.

Preferred installation – the pump with connected discharge pipe is suspended in the sluice. Alternative methods of installation are also possible, *eg* with a lowering mechanism in which case the sluice acts as discharge pipe at the same time.

3. Installation in suction container located next to the main tank – this method is preferred for plants in the chemical industry and also when one operating and one standby pump is used. Capacities of 0·5 to 2200 m^3/h and heads of 15 to 2500 m are achievable.

Power Generation

Boiler feed pumps

IN CONVENTIONAL (fossil) fired power stations using coal, oil or natural gas, boiler feed pumps are amongst the most critical items of plant which determine overall station availability. Feed pumps are amongst the most highly stressed, power intensive, rotating machines in any power station, often subject to rapidly changing operating regimes and they require special attention to detail, rotodynamic, hydraulic and component design if they are to provide the reliability required. A typical boiler feed water system for conventional power stations is shown in Figure 1.

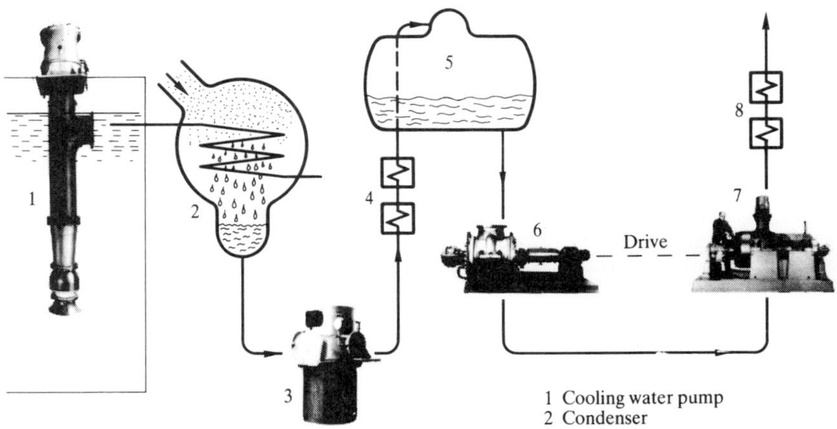

1 Cooling water pump
2 Condenser
3 Condensate pump
4 Low-pressure feedwater heater
5 Feedwater tank
6 Booster pumps
7 Feed pump
8 High-pressure feedwater heater

Figure 1
Boiler feed water system for a conventional power station.

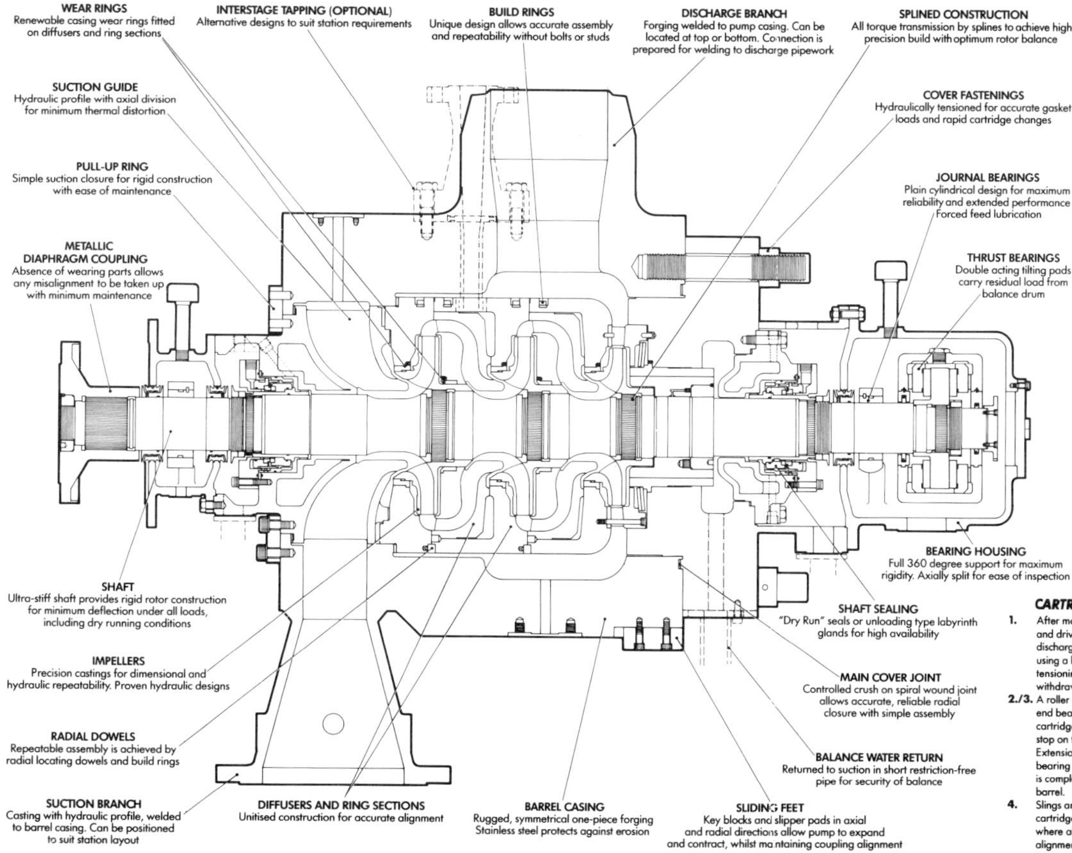

CARTRIDGE WITHDRAWAL

1. After moving the auxiliary pipework and drive coupling, the main discharge cover nuts are slackened using a lightweight hydraulic tensioning tool. The cartridge withdrawal cradle is installed.

2./3. A roller is set up under the drive end bearing housing, and the cartridge is rolled out to the first stop on the withdrawal cradle. Extension pieces are added to the bearing housing, and the cartridge is completely withdrawn from the barrel.

4. Slings are attached, and the cartridge removed to the workshop where all refurbishment and alignment can be carried out. Reassembly is the reverse of the above.

Figure 2
Advanced class boiler feed pump.

The total boiler feed pump capacity is established by adding to the maximum boiler flow a margin to cover boiler swings and the eventual reduction in effective capacity from wear. This margin varies from as much as 20% in small plants to as little as 5% in the larger central stations. The total required capacity must be either handled by a single pump or sub-divided between several duplicate pumps operating in parallel. Industrial power stations generally use several pumps. Central stations tend to use single full-capacity pumps to serve turbo-generators up to a rating of 100 or even 200 MW and two pumps in parallel for larger installations. There are obviously exceptions to this practice; some engineers prefer the use of multiple pumps even for small installations, whilst steam turbine driven boiler feed pumps designed for full capacity are being applied for units as large as 700 MW. A spare boiler feed pump is generally included in industrial plants. There is a trend however in central stations to eliminate spare pumps when two half-capacity pumps are used and in a few cases, even if a single full-capacity boiler feed pump is installed.

Depending on the boiler (sub critical less than 225 bar, super critical greater than 225 bar), feed pumps must provide heads from 1800 to 3800 m. The 100% flow rate in litres per second is 1 to 1·2 times the electrical output in megawatts. Depending on the availability demanded and the operating mode (base or peak load) the capacity is sub-divided into 100%, 50% or 33⅓%. The drive input of 100% boiler feed pumps claims some 3 to 4% of unit output. Segmental pumps are employed generally for lower final pressures and flow rates (up to a station output around 360 MW for a full-load pump). For high flow rates and pressures, barrel-casing pumps are mainly used.

Figure 2 shows an advanced class boiler feed pump particularly suitable for boiler feed duties in generating stations with turbine generator outputs in excess of 300 MW. Pumping units of this type are amongst the most advanced and reliable in the world and operate at speeds up to 8000 r/min with over 40 000 hours life achievable between overhauls.

The major factor in the mechanical design of the boiler feed pump is the thermal shock to which the pump may be subjected. In addition to the stresses imposed by pressure and by operation, consideration must also be given to the stresses due to differential thermal expansion during rapid changes of feed-water temperature. The bolts holding the casing elements together to form a pressure vessel are partially exposed to the air and consequently will change temperature less rapidly than the casing wall which is in contact with the feed water. When the pump is heated suddenly, the bolt stress is increased by the differential expansion between the hot casing and cool bolts. During this heating period, the stress in the bolts must not exceed a safe proportion of the yield stress of the materials from which they are made.

Conversely, when the casing is cooled suddenly to a temperature below that of the bolts, the resulting differential expansion will cause a reduction of bolt tension. It is essential that at their minimum stress conditions, the bolts contain a sufficient margin of tension to hold the main joints against risk of leakage.

The shell of the barrel is exposed to severe temperature fluctuations on its inner wall, whilst its outer wall exposed to atmosphere would tend to lag in temperature behind the inner walls during temperature changes. This gives rise to a temperature stress within the metal due to the differential expansion between the inner and outer walls. The temperature stress is integrated with the stresses resulting from pressure and operation give the total stress. Care must be taken to ensure that any local plastic yielding or autofrettaging under this total stress is under control and perfectly symmetrical. The thermal shock will also cause risk of misalignment of bearings and bushes internally and of pump and driver externally, if the elements of the pump are allowed to expand unequally with respect to the axis of the shaft.

Stress also causes risk to alignment if they are unsymmetrical around the shaft axis. To ensure correct alignment within a few hundreths of a millimetre under all operating conditions at present and future feed temperatures, it is therefore essential that all thermal flow during transient conditions and therefore all water flow, all pressure vessel sections and all stresses should be as nearly as possible perfectly symmetrical about the shaft axis.

The boiler drum has a similar general form and duty to that of the feed pump barrel, but has a lower pressure and a higher temperature. Considerable instrumentation and control equipment are provided to ensure that the boiler is free from rapid temperature changes. Minor deflections, however are not nearly so critical in the boiler as in the high speed pump, which must be designed for rigidity and for perfect alignment under all conditions.

For safe operation the boiler must have an uninterrupted supply of feed water which is within 50°C of its own temperature to avoid thermal shock and possible catastrophic failure of so vital a unit. Certain makers ensure that the feed pump is kept warm by leaking back full pressure water from the feed main through the standing pump. Suggesting that in the absence of such warming there is a risk of seizure on start up (the pumps are asymmetrical). Such warming procedure however, involves power loss, control equipment, orifices *etc*, with consequent erosion on the full pressure difference and more over does not take care of the thermal shocks of sudden reduction in temperature.

Pump characteristics

Typical characteristics of quantity, pressure, power and efficiency are shown in Figure 3. The upper pressure curve shows full speed operation whilst the lower curve shows operation corresponding to boiler demand at reduced pump speed.

Feed pump drives

Normally boiler feed pumps are driven by two pole a.c. motors and this has proved suitable for most duties. Where variable speed is considered desirable (that is to say on duties of 100 MW and over in Britain and 60 MW and over elsewhere), a hydraulic coupling between pump and motor is often provided. Alternatively, the motor may have a wound rotor with continuously rated slip rings. Such reduction of speed by slip-ring or hydraulic coupling reduces to one half the power loss consequent on operation at other than full speed and of course, almost eliminates the erosion of the boiler regulating valve.

For units below 500 MW it is generally practicable to run at higher speeds than 3000 r/min for which a gear drive or turbine drive would be provided. A reduction of efficiency of 1½ to 2% occurs in the gearbox, but this may be offset by the overall saving of capital costs, particularly as the introduction of a gear box to permit speeds higher than those corresponding to a 2-pole motor would, at no extra cost, permit a ratio of gears suitable for a slower motor which in certain circumstances, (*eg* with wound rotor) may be desirable.

Recent large turbo-generators have raised the consideration of a feed pump directly attached to the generator shaft, running at generator speed or, by gear box, at a higher speed.

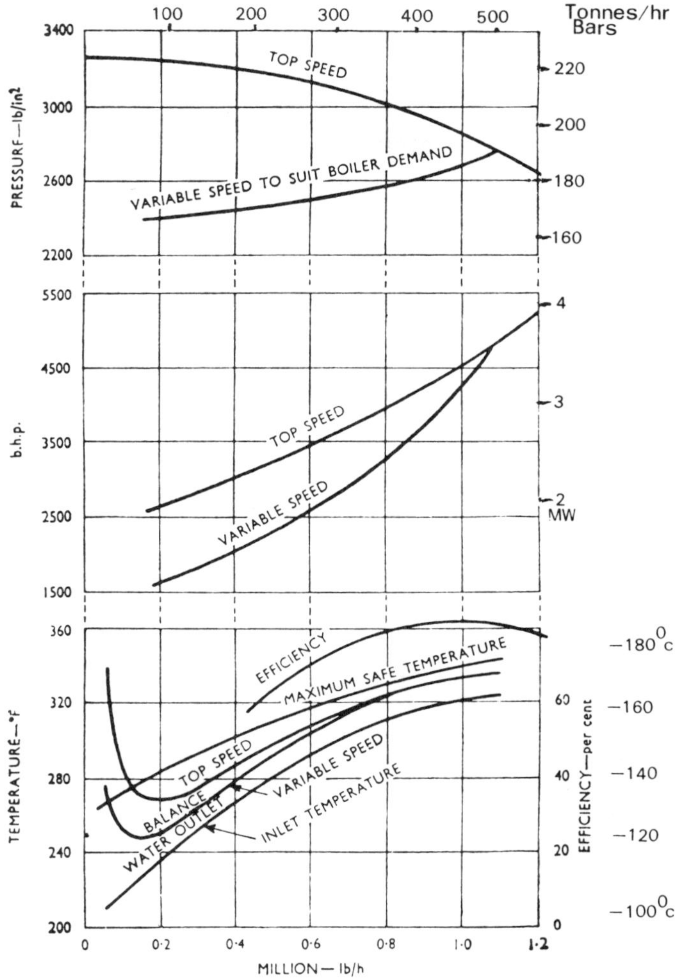

Figure 3
The 300 MW feed pump characteristics.

It would appear that the generator sizes are approaching the limit, at 50 cycles that can be manufactured and transported whilst the turbine limit has not yet been reached.

The use of electric feed pumps of say 20 MW would therefore subtract 20 MW from the total output of the generators, but a mechanical drive from the generator would only involve power in the steam turbine leaving the full generated output available for the grid. Here hydraulic couplings have the further advantage of isolating the pump during the run down time of the turbine. Alternatively, the feed pump may be driven by a bled steam turbine which gives speed variation very roughly comparable to load demand without the need for a hydraulic coupling and unlimited choice of a suitable operating speed for the pump duty.

Booster pumps for feed pumps

Booster pumps are placed before the main pump. They provide the necessary suction head for the feed pump, so that this does not cavitate in any operating range. For small deliveries single-stage overhung pumps are used; they must be designed for the high feed water temperatures. Normally double entry vertically split pumps are employed for high flow rates on account of the small suction heads available (depending on the height of the feed water tank above the pump centreline).

Condensate extraction pumps

Condensate pumps are used to collect condensed water and deliver it automatically to hot wells and boilers within their pressure range. For low pressure plant and de-aerator extraction duties, single or two stage double suction centrifugal pumps or regenerative (turbine) pumps are favoured with suction passages tapped on both sides of the impeller to vent any vapour present to a lower pressure area. For medium pressure plant, two-stage volute type horizontal centrifugal (with vented suction chamber) and multi-stage regenerative (turbine) pumps are widely used. Multi-stage pumps are the invariable choice for higher pressures and heads either horizontal or vertical (the latter offering advantages as regards siting, floor space occupied and ease of maintenance).

A 1300 hp glandless boiler circulating pump

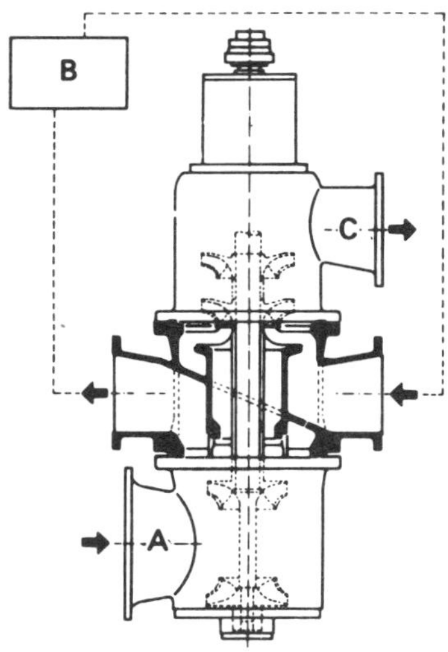

A Inlet from condenser
B Condensate polishing plant and auxiliary cooler
C Outlet to heater and feed pump

Figure 4
Re-entry condensate pump.

With re-entry condensate pumps, the full flow is branched off after one or two stages to the condensate polishing plant and the auxillary cooler. It is then lead back to the same pump and brought to its final pressure in the following stages. Some power station planners divide this duty between two separate pumps; a vertical slow running condensate pump and a horizontal, high speed condensate booster pump following, (Figure 4).

Boiler feed pumps and condensate pumps should not be operated at shutoff or even at certain reduced flows.

Heater drain pumps

The modern choice of drain pump for high pressure and low pressure services has been the vertical canned pump. This has evolved mainly as a result of lower first cost and a built in additional NPSH because the first stage impeller is lowered below floor level in the can. Heater drain pumps should be adequately vented to the steam space of the heater. Because heater drain pumps and especially those on low pressure surface may operate with suction pressures below atmosphere, it is necessary to provide a liquid supply to the sealed cages in the stuffing boxes. Low pressure heater drain pumps can use cast iron castings and bronze fittings if no evidence of corrosion erosion has been uncovered. On high pressure services, stainless steel fittings are generally demanded and 5% chrome stainless steel casings should preferably be used.

Cooling water pumps

Cooling water pumps for fossil fuel (conventional) power stations tend to be of the mixed flow bowl and axial flow, split casing or vertical bottom entry metal and concrete volute type. Cooling water pumps force water through the tube system of the condenser and depending on the vacuum required, 20 to 35 l/s of cooling water per MW electrical station output is needed. The necessary head is governed by the kind of cooling system. With river water cooling it is about 8 to 15 m depending on the station location; with cooling towers 15 to 28 m; and with air cooling 30 to 45 m. (See Figure 5).

Owing to the high flow rates and associated low heads of cooling water pumps, hydraulics with high specific speed are used exclusively. To assist maintenance, bigger cooling water pumps should be designed with pull out rotor assembly.

Glandless boiler circulating pumps

The basic concept of the glandless pump is that of a submersible motor and pump arranged inside a pressure tight enclosure without dynamic seals and with a minimum number of static seals (Figure 6).

The pressure encloser comprises essentially four continuously connected vessels. A pump casing which can accommodate fluids up to the highest boiler temperatures is separated thermally from the motor casing by a narrow 'neck'. This neck acts as a simple but effective thermal throttle which minimises the conduction of heat from the hot pump casing into the motor cavity. Typical heat flow across this barrier is only one or two kilowatts. The motor is maintained at a low temperature by a heat exchanger which is connected to the motor casing. The motor end cover completes the pressure vessel enclosure. An impeller incorporated into the motors rotating assembly circulates water through the motor cavity to the top of the heat exchanger and back to the lower part of the motor. This recirculation dissipates the heat generated by motor electrical losses (typically 10%) plus the 1 to 2 kilowatts from the thermal 'neck' and provides cool lubricants to the bearings. The relatively long annulus between pump shaft and motor neck forms a pressure connection with

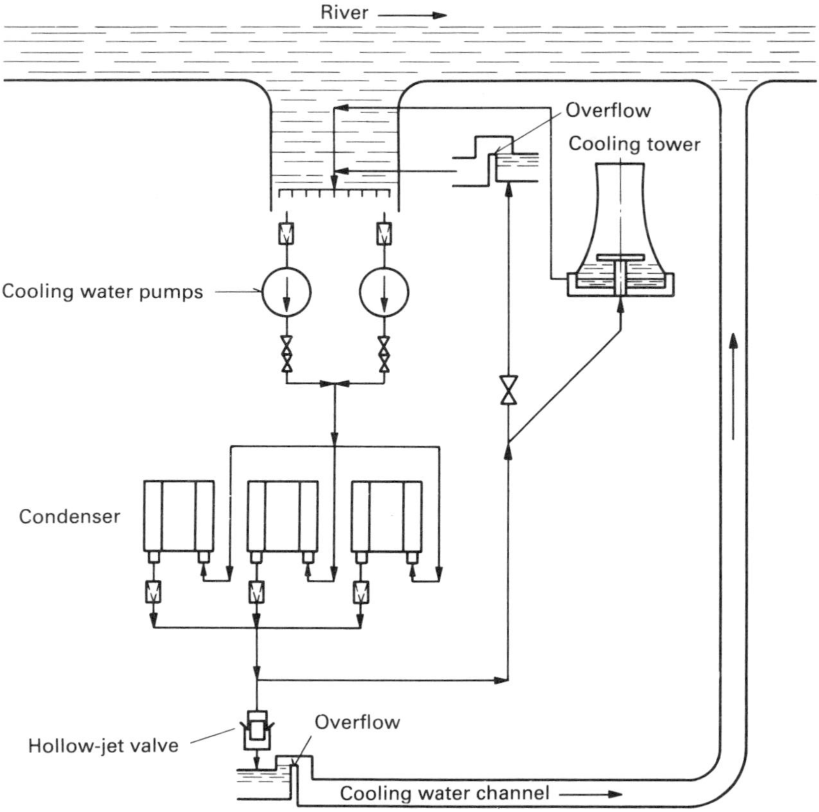

Figure 5
Layout of combined fresh water wet cooling tower cooling system.

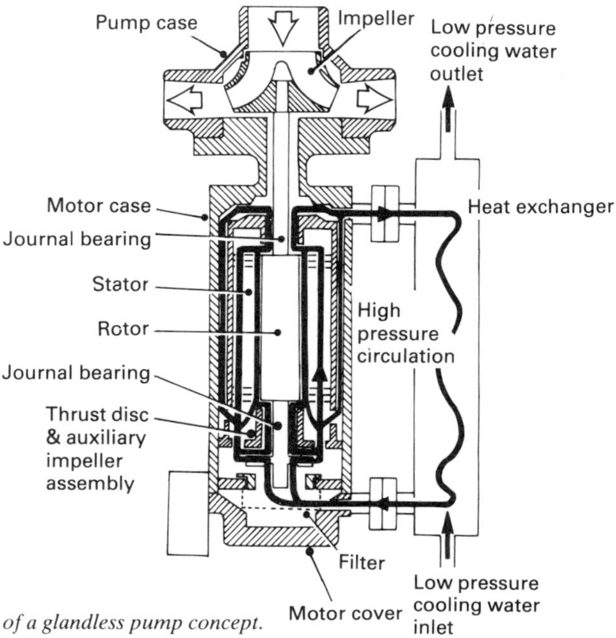

Figure 6
Schematic of a glandless pump concept.

the pump casing and reduces the diffusion of pump water into the motor cavity to a negligible level.

Wet stator pumps are now widely utilised for primary coolant recirculation and other critical pumping duties in fossil fuelled boilers and nuclear reactors. Their inherent pressure integrity is the main reason for the pumps worldwide acceptance, a consequence of the simplicity of their pressure containment design and zero leakage. Figure 7 shows a typical arrangement of a glandless unit suspended by the inlet and outlet nozzles of the pump casing which are permanently welded to the piping of the boiler circuit. Whilst motor above pump arrangement are also practical, and occasionally supplied, more normal practice is for the motor to be attached to the lower side of the pump casing. Clearly, this arrangement is thermally and hydraulically ideal with the hot end at the top and the inlet pipework feeding directly into the impeller eye. The unit simply hangs on the system pipework without further support and is free to move with the pipework under thermal expansion, with only differential movement of the inlet and outlet pipework causing loading on the pump branches.

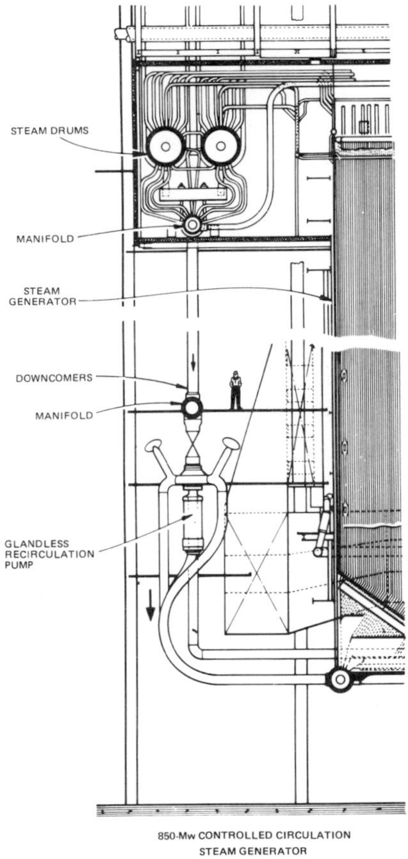

Figure 7
Glandless pump in a boiler circuit.

Nuclear Power Pumps

PARTICULAR REQUIREMENTS for new generation feed pumps for the largest thermal and all nuclear power stations are:

(i) Possibility of safe operation with disturbed feed and, specifically, in vapour phase to eliminate the causes of seizure at impeller seals.

(ii) Quick replacement (less than 1 day) of the internal hydraulic elements (motor and diffuser mechanism) since 125 to 700 MW thermal and 900 MW nuclear power stations do not normally have standby pumps.

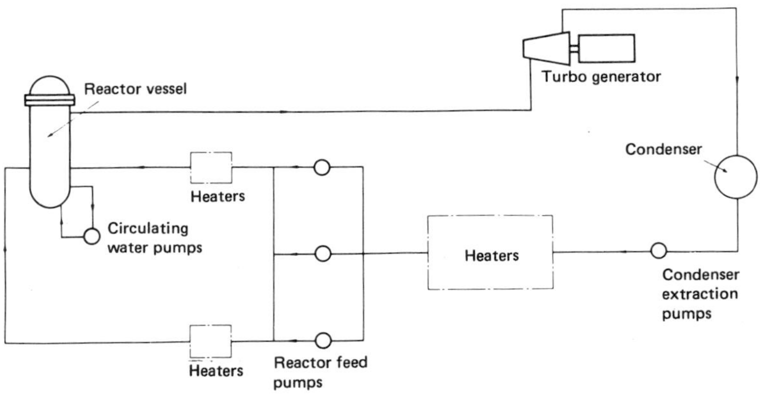

Figure 1
Simplified diagram of a reactor feed system.

Reactor feed systems

A simplified diagram of a reactor feed system is shown in Figure 1. Feed water enters the reactor and mixes with the forced circulation flow in the annulus beside the moderator tank. Approximately 10% of the combined flow passes through the reactor core between the fuel elements where fission energy release causes the water to boil. The steam generated passes through a series of steam separators to a collecting chamber at the top of the reactor vessel and thence to the turbo-generators and condenser. The feed system comprises three 50% feed pumps, two working and one standby being supplied with feedwater by three condensate extraction pumps *via* a series of pre-heaters. Control of the reactor power output is achieved by the use of core control rods and/or by variation of the moderator flow rate from the forced circulation pumps.

The liquid circuit is usually of stainless steel, possibly together with components in aluminium, zircaloy, *etc*.

The design of such systems is aimed at achieving the best possible compromise between hydraulic and mechanical considerations with the basic pump configuration and individual features required in the complete plant specification. Actual installations are thus largely individual and may vary appreciably in materials, pump design and detail design.

Secondary circuits

In general terms pumps for reactor secondary circuits handling uncontaminated water may be of conventional design. Certain services may also be met by standard centrifugal pumps adapted if necessary for controlled leakage (*eg* by the fitting of mechanical seals); or by glandless type. Canned motor pumps have also proved particularly suitable for circulating high pressure, high temperature water between a reactor and steam boiler and can be designed to handle other very high temperature fluids (including liquid metals). Other types of canned motor pumps include the gas filled motor pump which differed from the canned motor pump in that the motor section is pressurised by an inert gas (nitrogen or helium) so that the liquid being pumped is not allowed to enter the motor. it is capable of handling a brace of fluids (*eg* uranium slurry), whereas the canned motor pump can only handle clean fluids. It can also be constructed as a true zero leakage pump capable of handling ıhigh temperature fluids. It also has a higher efficiency than the canned motor pump although this is seldom a significant parameter in such services.

The oil-filled motor pump has rather more efficient motor cooling and good bearing lubrication. A major problem can be contamination of the seal separating the oil in the motor from the product being pumped. For zero leakage a mercury seal is used which can become contaminated both by the oil and the radio-active product.

The submersed motor pump has the complete motor unit, including shaft bearings in contact with the product being handled, requiring effective insulation of the stator windings. It is less suitable for nuclear energy services because of this latter requirement, which is difficult to meet when the product is radio active.

Where canned reactor pumps are used on circuits carrying radio-active fluids exclusion of radio-active material from the motor enclosure is essential if elaborate methods of decontamination are to be avoided prior to routine maintenance. Methods of ensuring this include injection of purged flows into the motor section and the use of baffles and weirs behind or under the impeller.

With the trend towards increased generator rating and feed flows, the overhung impeller configuration is approaching the limit of its usefulness. The problem of obtaining adequate rotor stability and sufficient NPSH to give an acceptable suction performance on the end suction, overhung design becomes uneconomic for generator ratings substantially greater than those considered. For larger generators it is likely that a double entry impeller pump will be employed. Any disadvantage inherent in this construction is offset by the reduced NPSH requirement and achievement of rotor stability with a more economic shaft arrangement.

Fast breeder reactors

With thermal reactors (BWR – Boiling Water Reactor or PWR – Pressurised Water Reactor) the high energy neutrons produced by fission are slowed down by the moderaters and coolant water to convert to thermal energy (produced by further fissions). In a fast breeder reactor the neutrons are not allowed to slow down but travel at high speed to the fissile material in which they produce fission and energy. At the same time neutrons captured by the non-fissile uranium atoms are converted into fissile plutonium atoms which can be used as a reactor fuel. This breeding effect is obtained by using steam, helium or liquid metal as a reactor coolant – sodium being a common choice.

With a liquid metal fast breeder reactor (LMFBR) the primary system may be of the pool type or a loop system. In the pool type the pump and intermediate heat exchanger are located in a single pool of liquid sodium within the main reactor vessel. In the loop system the reactor vessel contains only the core, with the pump and intermediate heat exchanger external and connected by pipes. In practice more than one loop is normally employed, both for considerations of component sizing and safety. Figure 2 is a diagramatic representation of a three loop LMFBR.

In PWR plants a component cooling water system is provided for cooling essential components and for supplying a variety of heat exchangers. Component cooling water pumps circulate clean water at low system pressures for the purposes of cooling primary water which is continuously bled for purification, main and auxillary pumps and auxillary pump bearings and seals, primary pump thermal barriers, larger motors, the containment vessel and the spent fuel pit water.

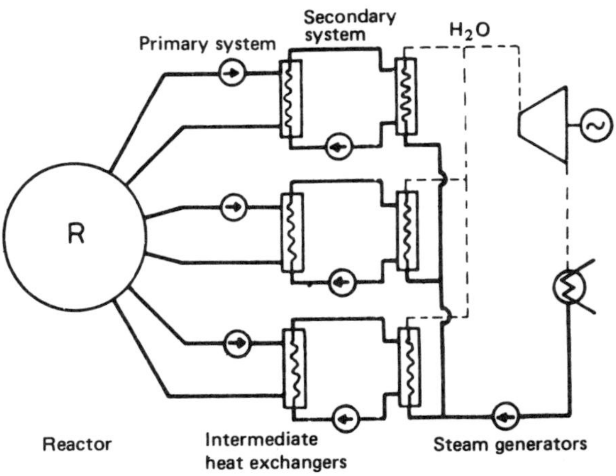

Figure 2
Simplified diagram of three loop LMFBR.

Sodium pumps

Both mechanical and electro-magnetic pumps may be used for handling liquid metals. At the present state of development special designs of centrifugal pumps are normally preferred, particularly where relatively large capacities are required.

Low blade lobes are typical for pumps of this type. The hollow impeller shaft is supported at its upper part by an oil lubricated roller bearing and at the lower by a hydrostatic groove bearing, which is lubricated by sodium. The hydrostatic

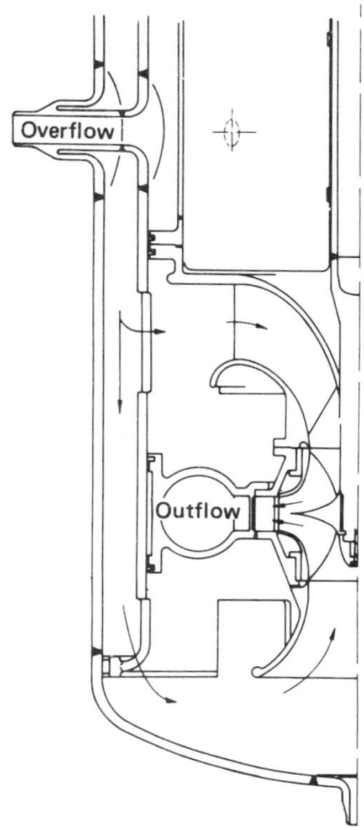

Figure 3
Sodium pump for future SNR operation (lower part).

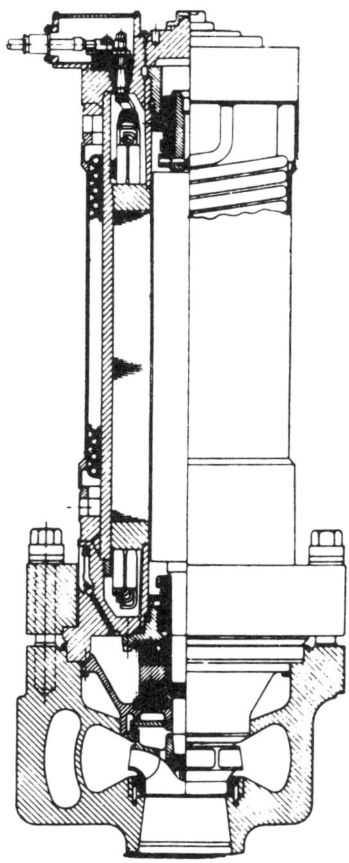

Figure 4
Nuclear reactor primary coolant pump 300 l/s 95m at 3550 r/min. (Wet rotor with can dry stator windings).

pressure on the bearing is supplied by the pump head and it varies with the speed of the pump. The design of the bearing is such that its speed may be lowered to 10% of its maximum without the risk of metallic contact between the shaft and the sleeve; and for specified times to between 5% and 10% of the maximum speed. The sleeve and the journal of the hydrostatic bearings are provided with a layer of hard facing material (stellite). There is a cushion of cover gas between the free sodium surface and the shield plug. This cover gas (argon) becomes radio-active, so that a 100% leaktight seal has to be provided. This sealing can be attained in two ways; either by using a mechanical seal or by a viscous seal. The advantage of a viscous seal is that there is no metallic contact between the rotary and the stationary parts of the pump and that, consequently, no wear will arise.

The temperature of the shield plug may not exceed a specified value (80 °C). Reducing the temperature at the top of the pump is achieved by arranging a number of anti-radiation baffles in the pump plenum. In order to prevent sodium from rotating in the cylindrical part of the pump, a number of anti-vortex baffles are also provided. For inspection and repair the complete pump interior can be retracted.

Since the pump passes through an opening in the shielding, provisions have to be made to limit the gamma dose rate of radio-active sodium, gas and corrosion products to an acceptable degree. This is accomplished by placing a shield plug between the pump plenum and the vessel cover; the plug consists of a stainless steel box filled with cast iron.

For larger plant where requirements may range up to 20 000 to 25 000 m^3/h, a pump with a single suction impeller is at a disadvantage because this demands a very low operating speed and very large impeller diameter. Thus in order to maintain reasonable dimensions for the pump a double suction impeller is preferred. (Figure 3).

Electro-magnetic pumps

The use of electro-magnetic pumps remains largely restricted to lower capacities (*eg* up to 1500 m^3/h) and thus appears more suited to secondary systems. Such pumps also have the disadvantage that their efficiency is relatively low. However, they have the advantage that they do not contain any moving parts so they are not subject to wear and reliability is generally high.

A pump may emit radio-activity at the rate of 2 to 50 rem/h after prolonged service in a nuclear plant. It is therefore paramount that provision for decontamination becomes an important design characteristic of the nuclear service pump. Not all nuclear pumps operate in highly radio-active environments; for these pumps, radio-activity levels may be low, but the equipment will usually require some degree of decontamination before it can be freely handled.

Pulp and Paper Pumping

THE NATURE of the fluid(s) to be handled in the paper and pulp industry may range from clean water to acidic and alkaline fluids and liquors. Centrifugal pumps are the type generally used, with the consistancy of the stock governing the optimum form of impeller. Screw-type positive displacement pumps have an advantage over centrifugal pumps in this respect since they are inherently capable of displacing gases as well as liquids. This can favour their selection for the pumping of stock over longer distances since the discharge is more uniform and free from fluctuations.

End-suction centrifugal pumps are widely used for stock concentrations up to about 6%. Normal closed impellers are suitable for handling concentrations below 1%. Concentrations above 1% usually require a semi-open impeller with back vanes. The hub of the impeller is often extended into the pump inlet to eliminate the formation air bubbles in the centre of the impeller.

For higher consistancies special designs of open or non-clogging impellers are called for. This and the greater clearances normally required to prevent clogging, inevitably results in some loss of efficiency, although overall efficiencies in excess of 50% are maintained by some designs handling stock up to about 5 to 6% consistency.

Back vanes of an impeller prevent fibres from entering the stuffing box and can eliminate the need for sophisticated shaft seals. A conventional stuffing box is adequate with this type of impeller. Many modern mills however particularly the larger ones, have installed separate water systems for mechanical seals and prefer to standardise on this type of seal to include stock pumps, the view being that this provides greater cleanliness and reduces daily maintenance. Both single and double mechanical seals have a good performance record. Sealing faces on the pump side are usually tungsten carbide. In the case of single mechanical seals it is necessary to isolate the seal chamber from the pump by means of a throttling bush. The clean water from the water seal system leaks out through this bush and counteracts fibre penetration.

Impeller design

The approach towards open or non-clog impeller design varies with individual manufacturers. The essential feature is an optimum compromise between non-clogging operation and the maintenance of hydraulic efficiency. A further problem arises in that all paper stuff contains entrained air, particularly in the higher consistancies and so both the impeller and volute on centrifugal pumps must be designed to prevent vapour locking. In the case of centrifugal pumps, alternative open impeller designs may be necessary to pass stringy solids which may be present in reclaimed pulp or stock containing rags or other fibrous materials. Generally, this ability to handle fibrous solids is only achieved at the expense of some further loss of efficiency. A recessed free passage impeller is rarely used because of its higher power requirements compared with a semi-open impeller (see Figure 1).

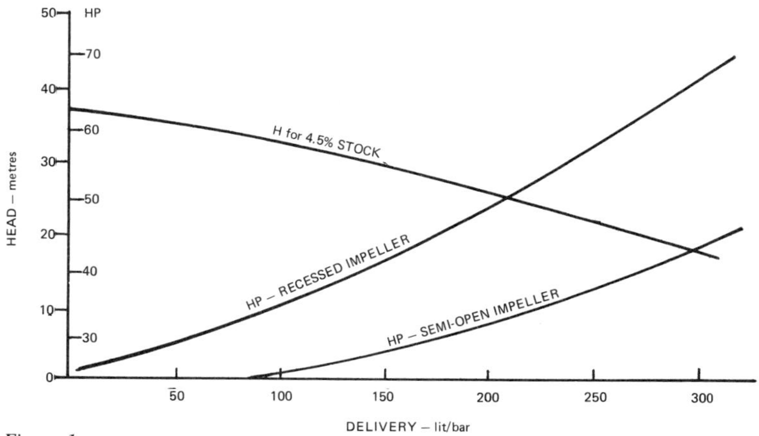

Figure 1
Comparison of power consumption between semi-open impeller and recessed impeller.

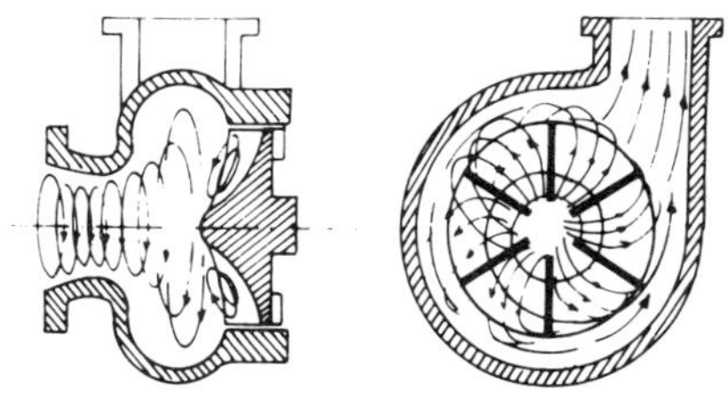

Figure 2
Vortex-type flow design.

Vortex-type flow design
A further approach with centrifugal pump design is the employment of an impeller form generating a vortex-type flow direct from the suction inlet to the discharge – Figure 2. Besides providing a more open through-passage for passing large solids, the impeller in such designs is largely excluded from contact with the solids and is in fact recessed as far as the main flow is concerned. Efficiencies of the order of 50% are obtained handling various classes of stock.

Ejector-type impellers
In a similar category come the ejector type impellers which have passages forming a low pressure region over the back face of the blade, making the impeller relatively insensitive to the presence of entrained air in the fluid being handled. Whilst these

are not basically non-clog types, they can show high efficiencies handling pulps and paper stock containing entrained gases. Notable examples are the Egger and Dress impellers. The former can show a particularly good performance, handling high consistencies, with perhaps less than one-half the derating suffered by a conventional open impeller at a consistency of around 10%.

Paper stock pumps must deliver virtually without pulsation, otherwise varying paper thickness will result. The schematic shown in Figure 3 shows the production of sulphite pulp (without chipping digesting acid preparation, thickening plant, bleaching and spirit plant).

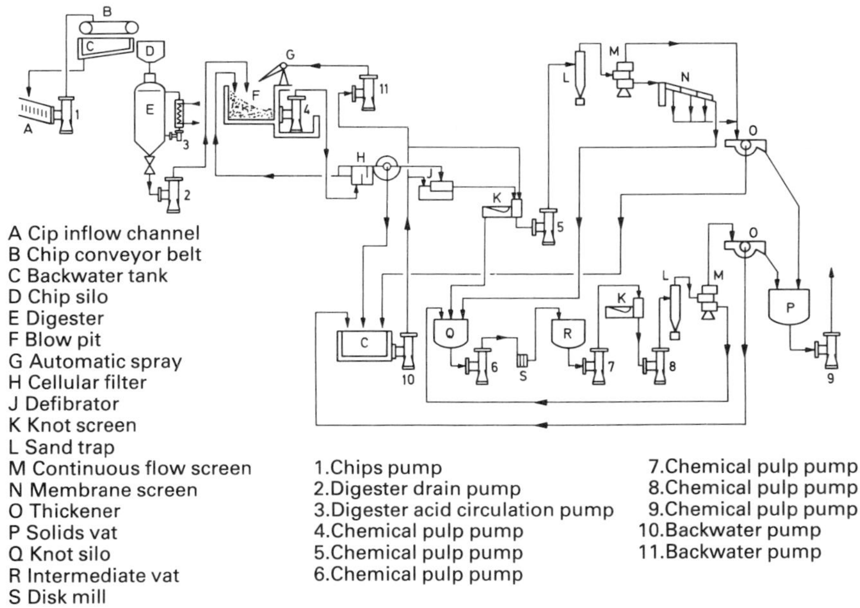

Figure 3
Production of sulphite pump shown schematically (without chipping, digesting acid preparation, thickening plant, bleaching and spirit plant).

Consistency

For every ton of paper produced, about 150 tons of water are needed. The consistency of a pulp and water suspension is the percent by weight of pulp in the mixture. Bone dry (BD) consistency is the amount of pulp left in a sample after drying in an oven at 100 °C or more. Air dry (AD) consistency is an arbitary convention used by papermakers and is the amount of pulp left in a sample after drying in atmosphere. Air dry stock contains 10% more moisture than bone dry stock, *ie* bone dry is 6·6% air dry. Air dry consistency is the term most commonly used and is employed here.

A centrifugal pump will deliver less head and capacity on paper stock than on water at the same impeller diameter and speed. The reduction of capacity increases sharply at high consistencies. Below 3% consistency, the pump performance will be approximately the same as water performance. Consistencies above 6% can be handled successfully, the upper limit not being any given percentage but rather one of fluidity and available suction head. Any consistency which can be freely delivered to the impeller can be pumped successfully with a properly applied centrifugal pump.

Pump performance

Centrifugal pumps are normally rated on water performance, corrected for the type of stock and stock consistency. Typical head-capacity correction factors are given in Figure 4. The correction factors are approximate for normally refined stock of 400 to 600 (Saybolt) SR seconds freeness, with short direct suction lines of ample size. Free or poorly agitated stocks and those with entrained air may require greater corrections. Slow stocks and stocks containing fillers and additives may require less correction.

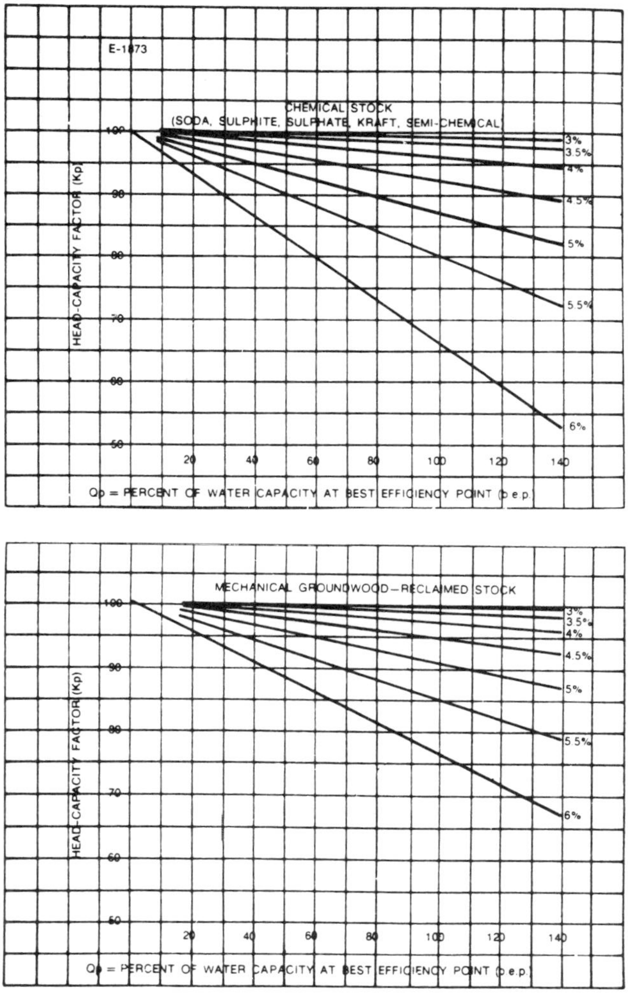

Figure 4
Approximate head-capacity correction factors for paper stock suspensions applied to water performance.

The required impeller diameter and running power will be those appropriate to this amended water rating. However, care must be taken to ensure that the motor power that is selected will be sufficient to deal with possible flow rate changes through the pump caused by consistency alterations. As the consistency falls the friction loss in the pipeline is reduced considerably, *eg* for 5% consistency in a 250 mm pipe HF is 30 m per 100 m for 5000 l/min flow, whereas for 3% stock the same flow rate in the same pipe size HF is 8 m per 100 m. If it is likely, therefore, that the consistency can change to an extent that will cause a large increase in flow through the pump and this can, of course very easily occur if the pump is used for pumping fresh water around the system, then the motor rating must be sufficient to deal with the highest flow condition anticipated. Alternatively, steps must be taken to restrict the maximum flow.

Over-selection of pumps on the basis of capacity and head usually results in the necessity for throttling the pump at the valve in the discharge line. Since the valve is normally located adjacent to the pump the restriction of the valve and the high velocity within the valve will result in some dehydration and cause vibration due to slugs of stock. This vibration will be transmitted to the pump and may reduce the life of the pump rotating element.

Centrifugal pumps operating at greatly reduced capacity also have more severe loading internally due to hydraulic radial thrust. Hence pumps which are greatly oversized in both the capacity and head have the combination of vibration due to throttling plus the greater internal radial load both acting to reduce the life of the rotating element. As a general rule, stock pumps should not be operated for extended periods at less than one-quarter of their capacity at maximum efficiency. When excessive throttling is required, reducing the impeller diameter to meet the maximum operating conditions can result in considerable power savings. Alternatively the installation of a bypass line could be considered, this line should include a valve for flow regulation.

Suction design

Inadequate suction design with under-sized pipe and excessive fittings can prevent the pump from delivering its rated capacity or even from operating at all on high consistency stocks. The stock must be delivered freely to the impeller for the pump to operate with the suction pipe as short and as direct as possible. The suction pipe and entrance from the stock chest should never be smaller than the suction connection and should be level with no air pockets. The direction of flow should always be kept in a straight line. Stock pumps will not operate when a vacuum is required to maintain flow into the pump. Thus there may be a static suction head sufficient to overcome suction line friction losses. Alternatively, a feed screw may be employed leading to the eye of the impeller to maintain positive feed.

Pump sizes

Sizes of centrifugal pumps may range up to 1200 mm and capacities of 200 000 l/min (1200 m^3/h). Larger pumps are usually of the horizontally split double suction type, speed controlled and driven by d.c. motors.

For handling large volumes, mixed flow and axial flow pumps are not excluded although their suitability is largely governed by the nature of the stock (particularly in so far as this governs the clearances required, which in turn will affect the hydraulic efficiency).

Positive displacement pumps

In addition to the screw pump – and the screw pump with elastomeric stator (progressing cavity pump) – other positive displacement types employed for handling stock include reciprocating, lobe rotor and diaphragm pumps. Reciprocating pumps which at one time were widely favoured have been almost completely replaced by centrifugal pumps for bulk handling although their use persists in metering and dosing duties. Lobe rotor pumps have a particular capacity for handling pulps, *etc*, where capacity requirements are modest and positive displacement characteristics are an advantage. Diaphragm pumps are mainly used for metering and dosing duties.

Liquor pumps

Liquor pumps span a wide range of capacities – from circulating service on digestors and evaporators with capacities of 40 000 l/min or more, to black liquor service with capacities as low as 1000 l/min. Temperatures of liquor service may range from 60 to 180 °C. Liquor pumps are usually of the end suction type mainly because of the lower capital outlay for stainless steel pumps of this type. other favourable features are the single stuffing box and the adaptability of this design to accommodate a cooling jacket.

Condensate pumps

Pumps for condensate are, generally, of the same basic design as liquor pumps, although the conventional stuffing box with soft packing is usually an adequate seal on these surfaces. Where mechanical seals are used they are most often the single type, provided that the condensate is clean. Polluted service would invariably dictate the use of double seals. Seal manufacturers can provide the best advice.

A standard chemical pump is widely preferred as a general-purpose pump for handling liquor or condensate in new mills or extensions and for handling all chemical fluids wherever the available sizes are suitable for the application.

Chemical pumps

With suitable choice of materials, standard chemical pumps generally prove adequate for most duties involving chemical products. Stainless steel is the usual choice but the service sometimes calls for more sophisticated materials such a titanium for hyprochlorite pumps in bleaching processes.

Plastic pumps are gaining considerable application in the industry and seem to have a reasonably good service record. Where the pumping temperature is below 60 to 80 °C and there are no abrasive solids present, plastic pumps can be expected to take over quite rapidly from alloy steel pumps mainly because of their lower cost. Plastic pumps usually have a solid impeller and a casing of polyethylene or polypropylene.

A special application for which heavy rubber-lined pumps are gaining wider use is the pumping of kaolin in paper mills. A centrifugal pump of this type can pump a kaolin suspension of up to 72% solids by weight and experience has shown that maintenance costs are relatively low. With a suitable quality of rubber and a lining about 10 mm thick, an impeller can be expected to last up to two years and the casing twice as long.

Food and Beverage Pumping

PUMPS THAT are used for handling foodstuffs and beverages must meet rigid hygiene standards with particular attention given to ease of cleaning – preferably cleaning in place (CIP). It is particularly important that wetted pump components are fully compatible with the product being handled and cannot contaminate it in any way. Where the product contains solids in suspension, these must not be harmed; and in many cases the product may need handling gently to avoid aeration or modification of entrained or dissolved gas content. Some delicate products may also be sensitive to shear and others may have fairly crystallizing tendencies.

Hygienic design and pump performance both contribute to the selection of pumps for the food industry. Externally, units should be smooth and free from crevices where dirt can lodge and insect infestation can occur. The internal design should be such that the flow path is smooth and no stagnant pockets are formed within the pumping chamber. Required flow rates may differ widely at different points in the process, calling for a variety of suction and pressure heads. Many operations may be inter-related, making it essential for flow rates to be controlled, whilst the actual volume handled at a particular stage may be very large or involve the admixture of two dissimilar flows.

Materials used for the manufacture of sanitary pumps are usually of stainless steel 316 grade, having good resistance to corrosion. However, stainless steels may be attacked by products with high chloride or chlorine content and by certain acids. Thus, if sterilisation agents containing halogens are allowed to remain in contact for long periods, corrosion of stainless steel pipes, valves and pumps may occur.

Plastics such as PTFE being chemically inert, are often used for gaskets and glands. PTFE itself has a structure which does not retain bacteria and therefore is not a source of contamination.

Choice of pump type

Choice of pump type depends on product viscosity, specific gravity, solids content (when present) and the other parameters outlined. Centrifugal, rotary and reciprocating pumps are used throughout the food and beverage industry.

Centrifugal pumps

Standard centrifugal pumps are widely used for handling free flowing clean liquids such as water, wines, beers and milk but are extensively used for auxiliary services

TABLE 1 – MATERIAL SUITABILITY

Stainless Steel	Copper Alloys (Bronze and Monel)	Elastomers	Glass and Sterile Materials
Suitable for: Apple butter Apple sauce Bakery ingredients Batters Brines Broths Candy creams Caramel Chocolate Cottage cheese Egg solutions Evaporative condensate Flavours and extracts Frostings Fruit juices and concentrates Gelatin Glazes Honey Hot pepper sauces Jams and jellies Ketchup Liquid sugar Mayonnaise Molasses Mustard. Peanut butter base Rum Salad dressings Tomato paste Tomato puree Tomato sauces Vegetable juices Vegetable oils Vegetable purees Vinegar Whisky Wine Yeast	**Suitable for:** Salt brines Note that copper-bearing alloys may discolour and taint other foodstuffs in salt brine, so suitability depends on product as well as basic liquid.	Sheet white rubber is a preferred choice for elastomeric diaphragms, seals, stator and rotor coatings or parts (where applicable). Hypalon is a favoured choice where greater mechanical strength is required.	**May be specified for:** Wetted pump parts valve had, valves, suction connections, delivery connections, mechanical shaft seals Note: glass and hard ceramics are particularly suitable for sterilization treatment.

Self-priming pump cowled.

Flooded suction pump cowled.

Compact stainless steel centrifugal pumps.

such as circulating, sterilisation, pasteurization services, disposal of waste products and unloading of road tankers.

In general the centrifugal pump can be used for most liquids of relatively low viscosity, however, specialised non-clogging pumps are available, capable of handling liquid suspensions containing pods and leaves, worts, mashes, sludges and slurries, providing of course that the partical size does not exceed the impeller channel size or input/output connection dimensions.

Generally speaking centrifugal pumps are unsuitable where one or more of the following requirements apply:

(i) Product viscosity above 2000 centipoise.
(ii) Relatively high proportion of entrained gases (above 5%).
(iii) The product is shear-sensitive or needs very gentle handling.
(iv) There are wide and frequent fluctuations in delivery head whilst a constant flow rate has to be maintained.
(v) Controlled volume or flow rate is required.
(vi) High pump efficiency is required with small flow rates.

Stainless steel centrifugal pumps for food processing.

Positive displacement rotary pumps
Rotary pumps of the gear, vane, flexible vane or impeller, spiral rotor, peristaltic and externally driven intermeshing lobe type are used extensively throughout most branches of the food and beverage production industry. The materials handled can range from water-like solutions to highly viscous fluids or solids. Gear and vane pumps are suitable for high temperature (up to approximately 200 °C) hot fats, oils, molasses and syrups.

Lobe rotor pumps
Lobe rotor pumps are widely used for food processing. They are suitable for CIP and are easily disassembled for cleaning without disconnecting pipework. For maximum hygiene, pumps with flushed mechanical seals or single externally mounted mechanical seals would be chosen. Counter ring flushing is also employed.

The versatility of the lobe rotor pump lies in the number of different rotor forms available, enabling the design to be 'tailored' to pump a wide variety of products. Rotors may be of stainless steel or food quality rubber covering, nylon, bronze or filled PTFE, when their advantages may even exceed those of stainless steel. For example, rubber covering has abrasion resistance, nylon is tough and so able to tolerate some forms of hard solids, bronzes are mechanically compatible with stainless steel so lessen damage from momentary overloads and filled PTFE combines abrasion resistance with chemical inertness. A typical rotor may have one to five lobes covered with an elastomer specially formulated for use with foods. The elastomer is resistent enough to effect a seal between the rotor and the casing and between the two rotors, yet hard enough to give prolonged trouble-free operation. Other covering materials include an alternative elastomer suitable for use with carbonated beverages and pickle juices and a plastics material for strong acids and alkalies. A single lobe rotor pump can be used for pumping such products as large curd cottage cheese, vegetable stews, whole kernal corn, fruit pie fillings, potato salad and other similar products, limited only by the particle size. Pump speeds and capacities may vary with the characteristics of the product being processed. For pumping products at high temperature, pumps with rotors slightly reduced in size can be used. The resilient covering of the rotor expands with increasing temperature at a faster rate than the stainless steel parts. The use of these rotors allows pumping at temperatures higher than are possible with standard rotors. For the handling of extremely viscous or sticky products such as dough and heavy sugar cream fillings, hopper fed pumps have been developed. These usually have rectangular entry ports with a greater area than the corresponding circular versions and the pumps are frequently mounted so that the hoppers are discharged – with the assistance of gravity – into the pumping chamber. Auger-fed pumps have also been developed, with one or two augers at the bottom of a hopper forcing the material to the pump.

Inter-meshing lobe pumps have considerable versatility. The rotors are gear driven and run with closely controlled clearances, thus enabling long life stainless steel rotors to be used without galling. They are capable of handling a wide variety of fluids ranging from free-flowing to highly viscous substances such as sausage meat, pressed yeast and bread dough. By virtue of their open flow path and low shear rate, they can handle large solids, such as meat chunks and easily damaged products such as whole strawberries, yogurt, curds and whey, with the minimum of damage. Many options of rotor designs are available for this type of pump, each rotor having been designed for a specific task. The most commonly specified rotor form is the tri-lobe however, twin-lobe rotor forms are common and can be used where products are non-flowing or have large solids, for example bread doughs, whole fruit jams, purees, meat and pie fillings.

The 'paddle pump' offers considerable scope within the food industry to handle large solids such as fish 'including bones or shell', fruit 'even with stones', jams, meat, pickles, salads, soups, vegetables *etc.*

The pump comprises a few relatively simple components and only has one moving part namely the paddle assembly which rotates within a circular split casing. The four paddles are mounted at 90 degrees to each other in a driving hub directly connected to the prime mover. Each paddle is free to swivel on its own axis as the hub revolves. Paddle angle is controlled by the narrow sealing channel between the suction and discharge branches. This type of pump is capable of safe dry running for sustained periods.

The 'signe' pump employs the concept of a sinusoidal rotor. The pump is used in the baking industry for toppings, fillings and batters, in canneries for aseptic packaging and sanitary transport, for process prepared food including sauces mixed entrees and condiments, in dairies for cottage cheese, whey products, yogurt and ice cream. It is also used for cooked and uncooked fruits and vegetables and meat and grain slurries.

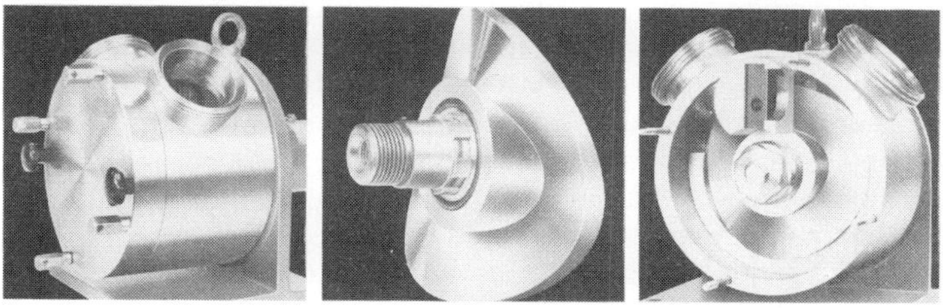

Positive displacement pump with sinusoidal rotor.

Gear pumps

Gear pumps are generally suitable for handling clean fluids which are lubricants, including highly viscous fluids such as syrups and molasses. They can also handle hot oils and fats at temperatures up to 200°C. A wide range of sizes is available with capacities up to 500 l/min and developing pressures up to 17 to 20 bar. Pumps are easily cleaned but are not suitable for handling fluids with a solids content.

Vane pumps

Vane pumps are suitable for handling clean fluids and highly viscous fluids at reduced speeds. Depending on the detailed design, they may or may not have a tolerance for solids content. The type is generally rather less easy to clean than a gear pump. In the sliding vane pump centrifugal force acting upon the vanes causes them to slide out and make contact with the case walls. As the rotor turns the volume between any two vanes increases and diminishes continuously during each revolution so that by arranging inlet and discharge ports at suitable points in the casing a continuous stream of liquid is drawn into and discharged from the pump.

The principle of operation of the flexible vane or impeller pump is very similar to that of the sliding vane, the difference being in the design of the vanes and casing wall. The pump casing is designed to compress the flexible vanes as they pass between the inlet and exhaust ports. The flexible vane rotors are self-priming and generally manufactured from a compound which is tasteless, odourless, non-toxic and has a high resilience to permanent deformation. One limitation of this type of pump is that the vanes are continuously in contact with the pump casing and are subject to wear.

Flexible vane or impeller pumps are suitable for handling a wide variety of fluids from water to those with medium viscosities and their gentle pumping action makes them suitable for handling products such as egg white, yogurt and curds. They can also handle small solids in suspension (*eg* pie and pastie fillings). Most flexible vane or impeller pumps are small, but capacities of up to 200 l/min are available.

Flexible stator screw pumps

Flexible stator screw pumps also known as progressing cavity pumps are versatile and widely used in the food industry. They are capable of handling a wide range of fluids varying from free-flowing to highly viscous. This type of pump gives pulsation-free flow, that is every type of fluid can be conveyed uniformly in the pump at a constant speed. In the case of media containing solids, the pump is capable, depending on its size of conveying solids of varying type and size without destroying them. They are of hygienic design, readily stripped for cleaning and can handle such foodstuffs as whole fruit jams and pulps containing pips and stones. About the only major requirements are that they should not be allowed to run dry or to run against a closed valve, otherwise damage to the stator will result.

Oversize barrels can be fitted for operating temperatures up to 100 °C. Stator sizes vary, depending on the aggressive nature and abrasiveness of the fluid. The particle size of solids which a pump of this type can handle is limited. However, generally speaking the cost of flexible stator screw pumps can be less than the lobe rotor pump and hence in many cases it is a preferred choice for a positive displacement pump. The flexible stator screw pump has a particular application in process work for handling slurries, liquids containing abrasive solids and very viscous liquids as well as chemically active liquids. Such pumps also have the characteristics of being able to operate at very low speeds so that very viscous fluids can be transported without shearing or noticeable temperature rise. They also have a powerful suction action which will pump against heads or pressures. The maximum operating temperature of the pump is limited by the type of elastomer selected for the material of the stator.

Reciprocating pumps

Reciprocating pumps have wide application since they can be made in a large variety of materials for handling chemically active fluids as well as a wide range of viscosities. Speed of pumping may have to be reduced when handling viscous fluids in order to prevent channelling or shear breakdown and leakage may also be a limitation for particularly 'clean' applications. In the case of piston pumps designed for accurate deliveries (metering pumps) design of the gland is particularly important since leakage at this point is likely to be a variable factor and will affect the accuracy of metering.

The twin piston pump is generally used for the transfer of high viscosity products and in some cases large particles in suspension. Types of product pumped include meat emulsions, spinach, mashed potato, cheese and puddings.

The use of two pistons ensures a continuous product flow *ie* while the first piston is pumping product the second is retracting and subsequently filling the pumping chamber ready for the return stroke. A reciprocating sleeve is used to trap the product within the pumping chamber prior to the compressive stroke of the piston.

Peristaltic pumps (hose pumps)

The peristaltic pump is versatile and useful for less demanding duties where complete isolation of the product within an interrupted tube is required. It is frequently used on pilot plant operation and for short, intermittent duties.

The fluid to be pumped is transported by means of cams, rollers or shoes acting directly upon the flexible hose containing the fluid. The cams or rollers squeeze the fluid along the hose. This type of pump by virtue of its design may be fitted with more than one hose and in some cases as many as thirty have been used together in a single machine.

Hose pump with specially developed hose can pump dry and run continuously without fluid.

The absolute control possible over pumping rate also makes this type of pump very suitable for handling fluids susceptible to shear breakdown under conventional pumping action. Delivery rate can be increased by increasing the tube diameter and squeeze cycle time, although as the tube diameter is increased, it may be necessary to lower the maximum cycling rate.

The principle of operation of the larger type of peristaltic pump (hose pump) is that of pushing a liquid in a hose forward by the use of a pressing shoe. This pressing shoe compresses the hose and pushes the product forward over 180 degrees. The tightening of the hose by the pressing shoe and its removal from the hose causes a change of volume. This change of volume causes a pulsating liquid flow in the line.

At the moment when the pressing shoe leaves the hose, an increase in volume in the hose and discharge line is created. This volume increase is equal to the volume of the pressing shoe. Due to the pressure in the line, the volume increase will be filled by the product. At the same time, however, the velocity in the line will come to a standstill for a short moment. Typical applications include tomato processing – semi-dry peel, edible oil processing – fats and tallow transfer, instant coffee production – abrasive slurry and fruit juice processing – pulpy filter media and abrasive particles. Other products include chocolate, caramel, jams, mayonnaise, milk products, meat products and jellies.

Diaphragm pumps

Diaphragm pumps are particularly suitable for handling fluids which are chemically active or must be kept completely free from contamination (or must not be allowed to contaminate other processed materials by leakage). Though diaphragm pumps are not suitable for pumping liquids at high pressures, this consideration does not normally affect liquids for the food and drink industries, where pressures usually are relatively low. An important advantage is that such pumps are very easy to clean by washing through with a sterilised solution or injecting hot steam. Diaphragm pumps of large size are frequently used in the brewing industry as well for pumping fats, flavourings and extracts.

Aseptic pumps

The basic difference between this type and the intermeshing lobe/piston pump lies in the design of the pump casing. The aseptic pump is designed to prevent bacteria or other micro-organisms entering the pump and contaminating the food product.

This is accomplished by a series of passageways in the pump casing through which live steam or a sterilising solution is circulated, allowing for a sterile condition at the ports, cover, and product seal areas.

Controlled volume pumps

Reciprocating type metering pumps are only suitable for handling clean fluids. Diaphragm pumps can handle most products, but are not suitable for working at high pressures. Plunger type (hydraulic diaphragm) pumps are preferred to mechanical diaphragm pumps for food processing.

Typical applications of controlled volume pumps in food processing are beverages – sherry blending, malt beer ingredient proportioning, dosing of filtration aids, preserving agents, sequestering chemicals for pipeline protection, *etc*. Bakery products – pumping basic swiss-roll mix, yeast and saline solution injection in continuous dough-making processes. Packaged meat dishes – blending animal stock, tomato puree, fats, extracts *etc*, to a predetermined and variable recipe. Cereal production – controlled addition of vitamins. Margarine manufacturing process – continuous controlled injection of oil, water, milk, vitamins, fats, *etc*.

Sugar and molasses

Sugar mills are concerned with converting sugar cane into crystal sugar; all the processes following the first stage where the cane is washed, chopped and crushed (macerated) are concerned with handling and processing sugar juice. The solid residue extracted after crushing is called bagasse and amounts to some 25% of the bulk of the original cane.

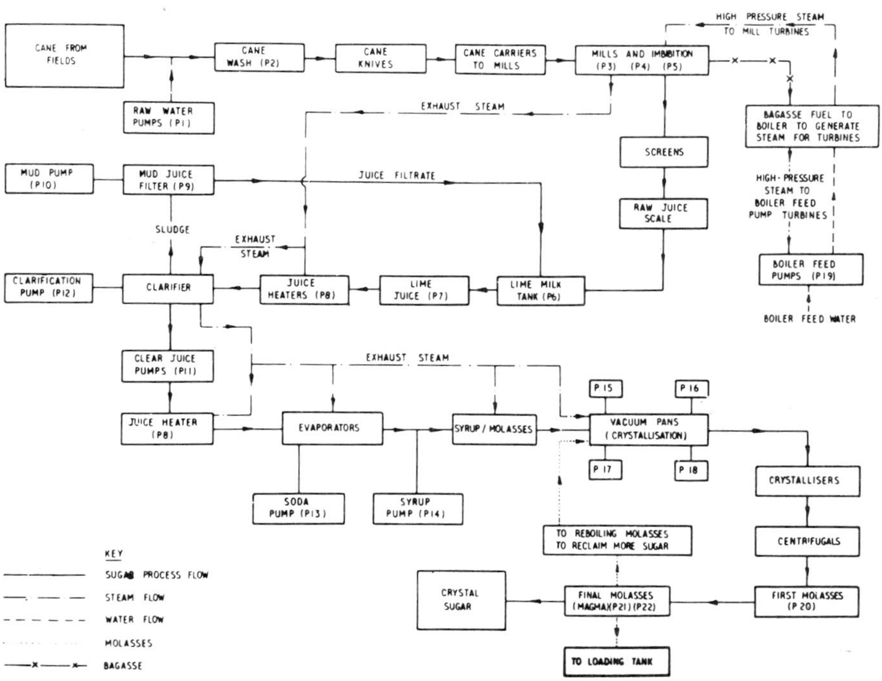

Simplified cane and sugar process diagram.

A wide variety of pumps are employed at the various stages of processing, pump types and materials of construction being influenced by capacity and pressure requirements and the properties of the fluid handled. The parameters in the latter case are fluid viscosity, specific gravity, temperature and chemical activity (*ie* pH value). Sugar mill handling capacities range from about 2000 to 10000 tons of crushed cane per hour.

Brewery industry

Pumps used in the processing stages of the brewery industry have of necessity to be of hygienic type. Whilst all-bronze or bronze fitted pumps may continue to be used at certain stages, normal construction is acid- resistant stainless steel to ensure product purity. The pumps themselves are also specially designed for the intended service, or are suitable modifications of a chemical process pump to meet individual brewery standards. Such modifications may include special polishing of the casing, special alterations to the rear cover plate, special casing drains and modifications to the casing flanges.

As a general guide, a standard centrifugal pump is suitable for use in virtually all the liquid handling applications in a brewery. Particular care should be taken in pump selection where CO_2 gas is injected or generated in the process. Centrifugal pumps are not designed to handle gases effectively. Liquid-gas separation in minor cases, causes the pump discharge pressure to surge and, in major cases, the pump will fail to operate because the liquid above the pump will trap the gas in the casing.

A small centrifugal pump will not generally handle more than 5% gas by volume, a medium centrifugal pump will not handle more than 10% gas by volume and a large centrifugal pump will not handle more than 15% gas by volume. Entrained gases also cause problems in the stuffing box at faces of mechanical seals where fitted.

For handling liquors with a high gas content, or to transport finished product without frothing, high speed screw pumps are favoured and in some cases low speed piston pumps. Portable screw-type rotary pumps are also commonly used in fermentation rousing. Equally portable centrifugal pumps with open impellers may be used to transfer mort from settling to fermentation tanks. In other examples rousing pump and fermentation tank are combined as an integral unit with permanent piping. The pump unit is then mounted externally at the base of the tank for easy access for inspection and cleaning.

Many breweries are selecting in-line pumps for brewery service because it is easier to keep the area around the pump clean. The in-line pump since it does not require a baseplate or foundation allows the area to be flushed without having to scrub around the foundations. Another important factor to be considered when selecting in-line pumps is that they do not require motor-to-pump alignment. This feature is available on in-line pumps that come equipped with a flexible coupling between the motor and the pump.

The in-line pump also requires much less floor space for installation. Saving in space is especially important in brewery service because many areas in breweries are tiled. Such pumps also allow easier piping design because the centre-line of the suction is in line with centre-line of the discharge. It should be noted that the in-line pump, with a flexible coupling between the motor and pump, can be maintained just like a centrifugal horizontal pump, *ie* the pump casing and the motor are not disturbed during normal maintenance.

Horizontal pumps selected for brewery service can be mounted on stilts. This also eliminates the need for foundations and allows for easy area washdown. Many breweries as well as chemical process plants are taking advantage of this option. The stilt bolts are designed to fit into cups that are placed directly on the floor. The cups do not need to be fastened to the floor in any way. The pump baseplate will normally be from 100 to 180 mm above the level of the floor. It should be noted that there are restrictions with respect to maximum motor size and coupling design when stilt mounted pumps are used.

There are several services in breweries where abrasive slurries are encountered. Slurries present special problems for pumps and require additional consideration. Normally, the pump should be run at the lowest r/min possible, operated at the best efficiency possible and utilise the full impeller diameter. Often the best way to pump slurries is to use a V- belt drive system which comes as close as possible to fulfilling these three requirements.

Another way to pump abrasive slurry is by using a recessed impeller pump. This design will usually show less wear than a standard pump because it does not have a close impeller-to-casing clearance. Recessed impeller pumps can be directly driven or V-belt driven.

Jet pumps

Jet pumps or injectors operate by the action of a jet of air, steam, gas, water or even the liquid to be pumped, directed into the material to be pumped without the assistance of moving mechanical components. Jet pumps are especially useful when it is necessary to mix the motive and pumped fluids, *eg* for transporting liquids which require simultaneous dilution.

Pump selection

Selecting a pump for a particular duty can be a complicated operation and it is advised that the final choice be made with the assistance of the pump manufacturer. Most pump manufacturers provide performance figures relating to liquid viscosities, output and total head (usually based on water) and, it is in the customer's interest to provide the pump manufacturer with the following information:

(i) Desired volume rate of flow, minimum, mean and maximum.

(ii) Annual period of operation.

(iii) Required delivery head, minimum, medium and maximum.

(iv) Properties of liquid – type of solids in suspension, variations in viscosity due to temperature changes and operating temperatures.

(v) The site where the pump is to be installed may determine the type of pump to be used – dry, wet, submersible, horizontal or vertical designs.

Variations in volume rate of flow will determine whether the flow should be shared by several pumps. Large variations in the viscosity of the liquid may mean that for example, a centrifugal pump should be used alternatively with a displacement pump in cases of low and high viscosity respectively.

Auxilary systems must also be taken into consideration, adequate space must be provided for installation. The pump may need to be water tight to prevent it from spillage. The environment of the site may also raise special demands with regard to the driving device for the pump.

TABLE 3 – TYPICAL FLUID VISCOSITIES

Fluid	Specific gravity	Viscosity CPS	Viscous type†
Bakery			
Batter	1·0	2200	T
Butter melted	0·98	18 at 140 °F	N
Egg whole	0·5	60 at 50 °F	N
Emulsifier		20	T
Frosting	1·0	10 000	T
Lecithiin		3250 at 125 °F	T
77% Sweetened condensed milk	1·3	10 000 at 77 °F	N
Yeast slurry 15%	1·0	180	T
Beer, wine			
Beer	1·0	1·1 at 40 °F	N
Brewers concentrated yeast 80% solids		16 000 at 40 °F	T
Wort			
Wine	1·0		
Confectionery			
Caramel	1·2	400 at 140 °F	
Chocolate	1·1	17 000 - 120 °F	T
Fudge, hot	1·1	36 000	T
Toffee	1·2	87 000	T
Dairy			
Cottage cheese	1·08	225	T
Cream	1·02	20 at 40 °F	N
Milk	1·03	1·2 at 60 °F	N
Cheese, processed		30 000 at 160 °F	T
Yogurt		1100	T
Fats and oils			
Corn oil	0·92	30	N
Lard	0·96	60 at 100 °F	N
Linseed oil	0·93	30 at 100 °F	N
Peanut oil	0·92	42 at 100 °F	N
Soya bean oil	0·95	36 at 100 °F	N
Vegetable oil	0·92	3 at 300 °F	N
Foods miscellaneous			
Black bean pase		10 000	T
Cream style corn		130 at 190 °F	T
Catsup	1·11	560 at 145 °F	T
Pablum		4500	T
Pear pulp		4000 at 160 °F	T
Potato, mashed	1·0	20 000	T
Potato skins		20 000 at 100 °F	T
Prune juice	1·0	60 at 120 °F	T
Orange juice conc.	1·1	5000 at 38 °F	T
Tapioca pudding	0·7	1000 at 235 °F	T
Mayonnaise	1·0	5000 at 75 °F	T
Tomato paste 33%	1·14	7000	T
Honey	1·5	1500 at 100 °F	T
Meat products			
Animal fat, melted	0·9	43 - 110 °F	N
Ground beef fat	0·9	11000 - 60 °F	T
Meat emulsions	1·0	22000 - 40 °F	T
Pet food	1·0	11000 - 40 °F	T
Pork fat slurry	1·0	650 - 40 °F	T
Sugar, syrups, molasses			
Corn syrup 41 Be	1·39	15000 at 60 °F	N
Corn syrup 45 Be	1·45	12000 at 130 °F	N
Glucose	1·42	1000 at 100 °F	
Molasses A	1·4 to 1·47	280 to 5000 at 100 °F	
Molasses B	1·43 to 1·48	1400 to 13000 at 100 °F	
Molasses C	1·46 to 1·49	2600 to 5500 at 100 °F	
Sugar syrups			
60 Brix	1·29	75 at 60 °F	N
68 Brix	1·34	360 at 60 °F	N
76 Brix	1·39	4000 at 60 °F	N

Note: Viscous behaviour type: N – Newtonian, T – Thixotropic

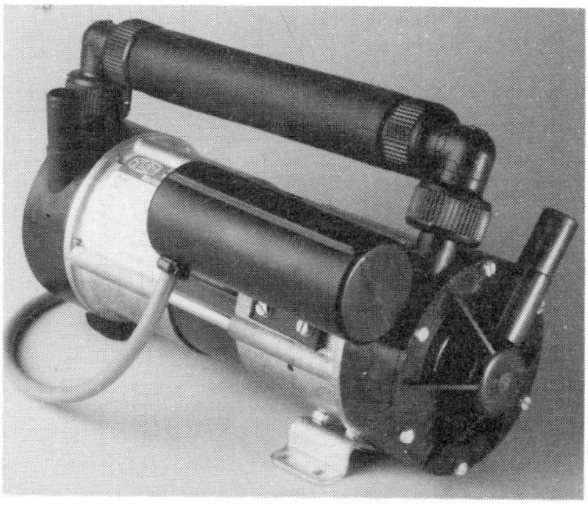

Magnetically-coupled pump for brewing applications.

Modern stainless steel hygenic pump with food grade impeller.

When choosing pumps for highly viscous liquids the design of the suction side must be considered with respect to the admixure of air, and other gases. Large pumps with large connection dimensions and low speeds may be considered more advantageous for the protection of solids in suspension. Those displacement pumps which can handle the maximum pumpable viscosities – approximately 1 000 000 mm^2/s are eccentric screw pumps, lobe rotor pumps and piston pumps.

For gentle pumping of foodstuffs a systematic choice of pump may not be available. In the case of centrifugal pumps, the delivery head per stage is an indication of the stirring of the liquid, while the speed of the pump should not exercise any influence on the liquid to be pumped. Among displacement pumps, lobe rotor pumps may be of special interest.

The most commonly used pumps in the food industry are spiral rotor and rotary lobe pumps, where a positive displacement of a highly viscous product is required. The peristaltic pump has successfully been used to pump solids in suspension, particle size being controlled by the internal diameter of the hose(s).

Viscous Products

VISCOUS LIQUIDS can be handled by many types of pump; but usually with reduced capacity. In the case of both reciprocating and rotary pumps this usually means a substantial reduction in speed with increasing viscosity over a specified limit depending on the design and size of the pump (see Table 1). Consideration should be given to the possibility of heat in the fluid so that it can be handled at an economic viscosity, *ie* without reducing the pump rating as this may well provide the cheapest solution.

Self-heating can be a problem when handling viscous fluids if the product is degraded by heat, although the corresponding lowering of viscosity is itself beneficial. Cooling of the pump may be necessary in extreme cases although a special pump such as screw and screw rotor pumps may be employed for sensitive

TABLE 1 – TYPICAL PUMP SPEED REDUCTIONS WHEN PUMPING VISCOUS FLUIDS

Fluid Viscosity Centistokes	TYPE OF PUMP		
	Reciprocating %	Lobe Rotor %	Other Rotary %
50	0	0	0
100	5	0	2
200	10	0	10
300	15	5	12
400	20	10	14
600	25	15	20
800	30	–	–
1000	35	–	–
1200	–	20	30
1600	–	40	40
2000	–	50	50
4000	–	–	55
6000	–	–	57
8000	–	–	60

or very viscous fluids difficult to handle satisfactorily with standard pumps. These subject the product to the minimum of shearing action thus avoiding shear breakdown, channelling and excessive self-heating and although pump speeds are generally low to moderate, high flow rates can be achieved by increasing the size of the pump.

Basically, centrifugal pumps have a limited capability to handle viscous fluids economically. As the fluid viscosity increases, positive displacement pumps become more and more attractive – *ie* gear or lobe rotor, vane and screw pumps. Different factors will influence which of the different positive displacement types is chosen for a particular application.

Screw pumps of the single-, two- or three-screw type are commonly used for viscous fluids. The single-screw type has one power rotor within a semi flexible stator and this unit can handle highly abrasive liquids and can also pump liquids containing fairly large solid particles. The two screw pump which has screws driven by external gears can handle liquids containing small amounts of abrasives. The three-screw pump has a central power rotor which drives two outer idler rotors; this unit is limited to liquids which have good lubricating properties. The three-screw pump is of particular interest however, as it can be supplied in element form; the actual pumping element can be mounted directly in the vessel containing the liquid to be handled, thus eliminating suction pipework and the ensuing losses.

Screw pumps of all types have an advantage over vane and lobe pumps in that they give a smooth flow free from pulsations and can generate high discharge pressures. The screw pump however, does tend to disturb the liquid as it is pumped and the large amount of shear in the passage from suction to discharge along the screw can give frictional losses.

Low speed heavy duty vane pumps are also used for viscous fluids. They will handle the liquid with the minimum of disturbance and relatively low shear is involved. The liquid is usually passed into one of a series of chambers in the suction side of the pump, the chamber is then transferred to the delivery side and emptied into the line. Heavy-duty vane pumps will pump any liquid that can be drawn into the suction chambers.

The major problem with all pumps handling viscous fluids is to ensure that the suction chamber of the pump is adequately fed. If the suction is starved then loss of output and cavitation will result. A positive suction head at the pump is usually essential and in some cases it may be necessary to mount the pump beneath the supply vessel. When drawing from a suction vessel care must be taken to ensure that air is not drawn into the pump. With very heavy liquids such as toothpaste, a loaded floating cover on the surface of the liquid may be necessary.

Drum and container pumps

Drum (barrel) and container pumps are used for handling a wide variety of viscous products. There are very few plants and manufacturing facilities that do not use fluids is some area of their production cycle. It could be finishing material, chemicals, food products or oil. Somehow, the fluids must be transferred from a shipping container to the point of use. A cost saving solution is a transfer and supply pumping system. Pumps transfer fluids and semi-solids from shipping containers to the point of use, faster, cheaper with less mess and more accurately than any other method available.

A pump mounted through the bung or open top of a drum with a spout or transfer hose is the simplest system. The drum is stationed near the work area.

There, low pressure transfer pumps are used to transfer oils, lubricants coolants, solvents and paint materials to the point of use. Compressed air operated pumps have gained considerable popularity in the automotive industry for paint spraying *etc.*, and for the transfer of heavy inks from vats in the printing industry. The horizontal plunger piston pump shown in Figure 1 has an unusually high suction capability enabling it to handle a wide variety of materials including heavy glues, asphalts, paints, resins, concrete and other chemical products.

Figure 1
Horizontal plunger piston pump for abrasive and highly viscous materials.

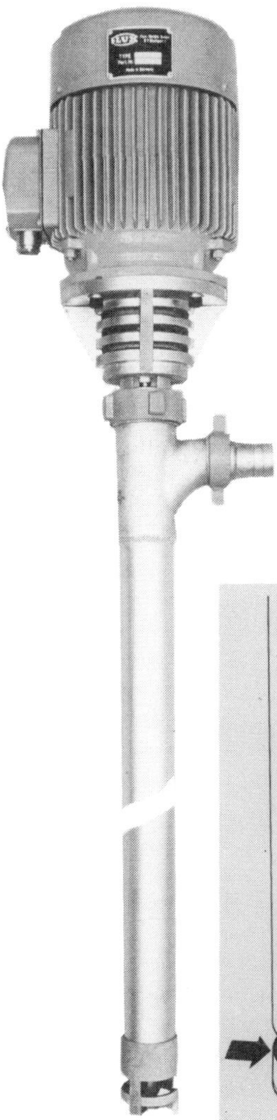

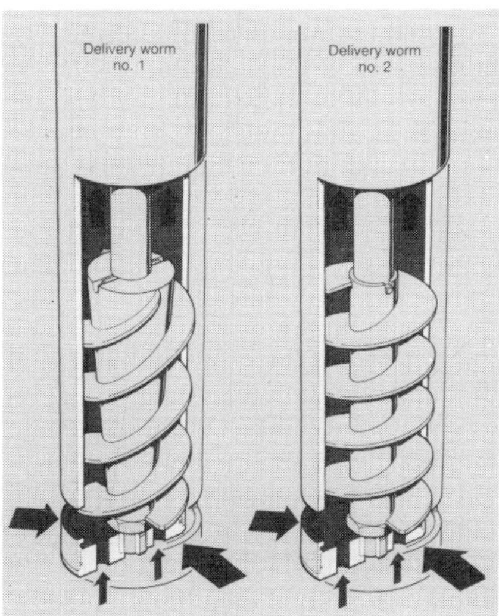

Figure 2
High viscosity liquid pump with three-phase gear motor showing delivery principle.

A typical example of a high viscosity liquid pump coupled to a three phase motor is shown in Figure 2. This unit is especially suitable for pumping motor oils, machine oils, gear oils and oils for super-heated steam cylinders as well as viscous liquids such as base constituents of liquid soap, plastic solutions, synthetic resin solutions, glues, softners, colloids, molasses, syrups, cocoa butter, liquid chocolate, plastic components *etc*.

In direct transfer systems, the drum containing the product is remote from the work area and the fluid is transferred directly to the point of use. Flow is controlled by the worker operating the dispensing device. The material is completely enclosed from the drum to the dispensing valve and the system is ideally suited for sanitary materials, oils, adhesives, industrial chemicals and food products.

Automatic direct transfer system

Using this method of transfer, an automatic dispenser valve removes the guesswork out of filling containers. The valve is triggered by either an operator using a mechanical switch or an automatic timer or electronic eye. Material is transferred and dispensed for a specific length of time. This system is adaptable to any measurable amount of material where volume is not critical, such as adding coolants to radiators or spraying insecticides on grain storage bins *etc*.

Circulating system

The most sophisticated transfer and supply arrangement is a circulating system. Material is transferred from the drum to the point of use, unused material is recirculated to the drum. Paint and finishing supply systems are usually of the circulating type. The continuous cycle keeps the fluid in suspension and provides instant material supply at the work station for colour control and uniform material consistency.

Where air-operated transfer pumps are concerned, it is important never to use more than the recommended maximum input air supply pressure. Material pressure developed by the pump is the pump ratio multiplied by the air pressure. The pressure ratio is the effective area of the air motor divided by the effective area of the fluid pump. As the pressure ratio increases the volume capability decreases. It is also important to ensure that any equipment, hoses and fittings used with the pump are rated for the fluid pressure to be used. Typical applications for drum (barrel) and transfer pumps include:

Acids – stainless steel transfer pumps for general transfer and for filling hoppers of packaging material.

Adhesives – stainless and non-stainless transfer equipment required for handling raw materials by adhesive manufacturers.

Antibiotic manufacture – stainless steel pumps for transferring raw materials from drums to mixing kettles and from processing equipment to packaging machinery and tablet-coating equipment.

Artists materials – transfer pumps for handling pigments, vehicles and solvents in the processing and manufacturing of artists paints and for the transfer of the finished material to packaging machinery.

Bag and box manufacture – transfer pumps are used for feeding adhesives to fountains on glueing machinery.

Bakeries – stainless steel pumps for handling butter, creams, corn syrups, trough grease spray, eggwash spray on to pies, sugar glaze on fruit cakes, transfer of frosting, jellies, various flavourings and additives as well as shortenings, margarine, butter and other viscous products used in quantity.

Beverage Plants – transfer pumps for moving concentrated flavourings and special coating pumps for can lining lacquers.

Sweets and chocolates – transfer pumps handle chocolate, cream fillings and flavourings. Pumps also apply the coatings to sweets, jelly-beans and other coated products.

Castings – transfer pumps handle core oils and silicon core release material.

Caulking material and equipment – transfer pumps handle raw materials used in the manufacture of these compounds.

Chemical manufacture – transfer equipment is required to move raw materials as well as finished products in manufacturing and packaging operations. Metering systems are used for low volume high viscosity blending and formulation.

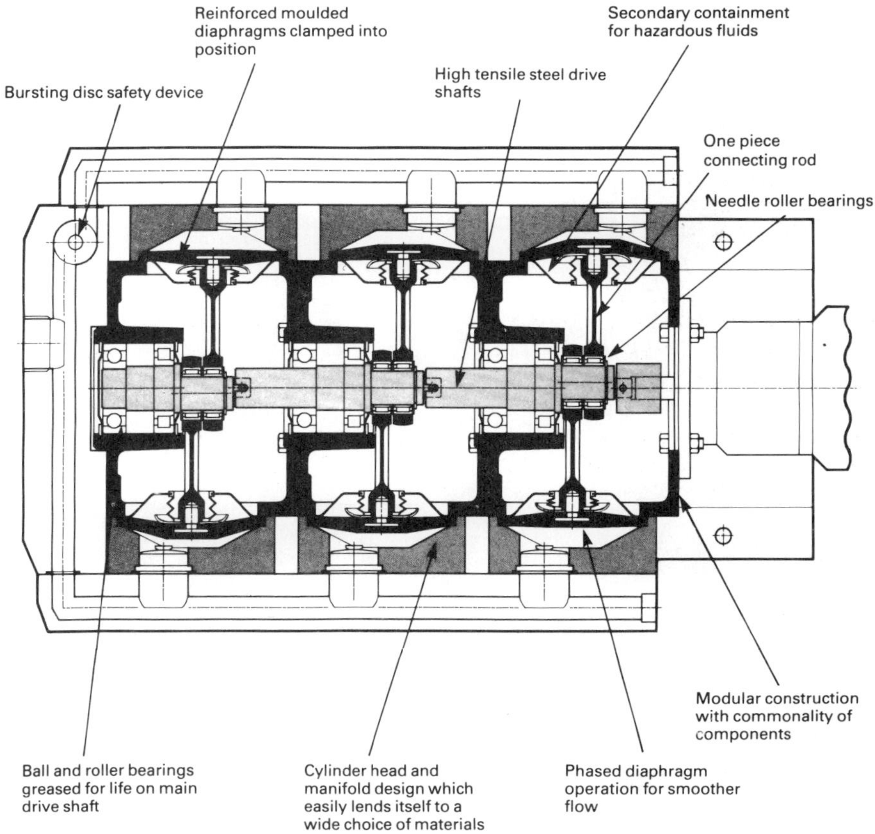

Diaphragm pump suitable for pumping viscous corrosive liquids.

Cosmetics – transfer pumps handle light fluids or extremely heavy pastes in manufacturing as well as packaging operations. This includes the handling of nail polishes, face creams and shampoos. Adhesive pumps are used for feeding adhesives to fountains on sealing and labelling machinery.

Food Products – this is a very large category using stainless steel pumps for handling flavourings, additives, food colouring, oils, tomato paste, batter, peanut butter, juices, fillings, jellies and literally hundred of other fluid to semi-solid products in the transfer, metering, flavouring extrusion processes and lubricants for maintenance.

Industrial ink – transfer pumps handle solvents and marking inks.

Paint manufacture – transfer pumps handle solvents, oils and pigments used in the manufacture of paints, varnishes and lacquers.

Pharmaceutical manufacture – stainless steel transfer pumps handle light fluids, ointments, salves and other compounds.

Pharmaceutical preparations – transfer pumps handle low and high viscosity materials. They are also used to feed hoppers on packaging machinery.

Printing industry – circulating systems for handling inks, colours and press-wash materials are found in this industry. Pumps are also required for handling heavier offset letter press inks, press-wash and lubrication materials.

Roofing materials – transfer pumps handle raw materials used in manufacturing these compounds.

Steel mills – lubrication equipment is required in large quantities for daily lubrication of heavy machinery.

Textile dyers – transfer and metering pumps handle textile dyes and other miscellaneous compounds.

Toy manufacture – transfer pumps move plastisols used in toy moulding.

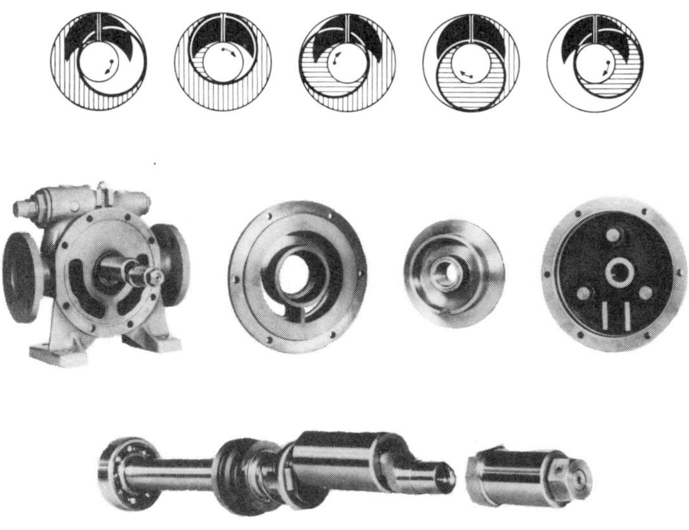

Rotating piston and shaft mounting for positive displacement pump for heavy and viscous products.

Solids Handling

THE DESCRIPTION 'solids handling' covers a wide range of duties involving the handling of solids in suspension. Products involved in solids handling may range from fluids containing a minimum proportion of solid contaminants (which may or may not be abrasive) to pure solids in powder form. Some solids handling applications may be performed satisfactorily by general-purpose or process pumps with or without detail design and/or material changes. Other applications are best (or can only be) met by special designs of pumps. These may be categorised as follows:

(i) Sludge pumps – particularly designed to handle soft solids and sludges. These can differ appreciably in detailed design to 'match' the solids being handled and may be separately categorised. For example, sewage pumps are one category of sludge pumps, designed specifically for the transport of sewage through sewage treatment works.

(ii) Slurry pumps – specifically designed to handle abrasive solids. Again these can differ appreciably in detailed design according to the classification of the solids to be handled. Thus whilst 'slurry pump' remains the main heading, individual designs may be more specifically described as sand pumps, gravel pumps *etc*.

(iii) Dredge pumps – basically still a slurry pump since it is designed to transport a mixture of soil (sand, gravel *etc*), in water, plus other debris. Its operating conditions, however, are such as to demand special designs and constructions in order to achieve optimum performance.

(iv) Special process pumps – designed to handle a particular class or type of solids, in which case the impeller form may be peculiar to the design.

(v) Dry solids pumps – these handle bulk solids rather than solids in suspension in a fluid and are essentially a separate class.

Pump performance

Solids which form an intimate mixture yield a homogenous fluid, in which case the pump performance is largely determined by the specific gravity and viscosity of the homogenous mixture, which behaves as a normal fluid. Solids in suspension however, form non-homogenous mixtures and flow is then heterogeneous, with particles tending to slide at the surface of a 'bed' of solids. This 'bed' is only carried fully suspended if the fluid velocity is greater than the settling velocity of the solids involved. At lower fluid velocity, there will be a corresponding degree of settlement producing a sliding rather than a suspended 'bed'. Typical minimum flow velocities for satisfactory solids in suspension are given in Table 1.

TABLE 1 – MINIMUM FLOW VELOCITIES FOR SOLIDS IN SUSPENSION

Particle classification	Minimum flow velocity† m/s	ft/s
Fines	0·9	3
Sands	1·5	5
Gravel	2·1	7
Sludge	3·35	11

†Based on a solids content of 30 to 35% by weight and solids of specific gravity 2·5 to 3·0

The overall effect will be to derate the water performance of the pump, due to the heterogeneous flow conditions. With low to moderate concentrations of solids, the loss may not be very great and only nominal corrections may be necessary for choosing the right size of general purpose pump with a suitable impeller and clearances (*ie* water performance test figures can be a satisfactory guide to selection.) With higher concentrations of solids and with all slurry pumps, performance can only be determined with any degree of accuracy by empirical tests handling equivalent sample fluids.

The efficiency figure realised can be very much lower than that of a similar sized centrifugal pump handling clear water. A further important factor is that internal leakage will increase (and thus efficiency decrease) with wear over the normal life of wear-resistant or replaceable parts. In other words, the 'end' performance of the slurry pump (where replacement of wear parts is to be undertaken) can be appreciably lower than the 'new' performance. This may have to be taken into account when deciding initially on the size of pump required.

The pump designer aims to reduce wear to a minimum or to lengthen the lives of parts to get the longest possible usage before parts must be replaced, in order to avoid considerable differences between 'new' and 'end' performance. This can be evaluated by straightforward pump tests or scale model wear tests and from accumulated field testing and operating results.

In practice the working range of the pump is limited at one end by the initial flow velocity of the mixture (lower limit); and at the other end by the flow rate corresponding to the continuous pressure on the suction side at which cavitation of the pump will occur (upper limit).

Sludge and sewage

Sludge is defined as a liquid (usually water) containing large solids with a particle size of 6 mm (¼ inch) or greater, the solids being soft rather than abrasive in nature. These solids may be further described as stringy, clogging *etc*, although a more useful classification would be 'soft' and 'hard' sludges, since if a sludge is defined by particle size, only the solids may be hard and abrasive in some cases. Sludges may also contain a high proportion of smaller solids or sand which could have an abrasive effect, affecting pump material choice, clearances, *etc*. Thus sludges may have some of the characteristics of slurries. Sewage, on the other hand, mostly involves soft solids.

Frictional losses involved in the transport of sludges and sewage are difficult to evaluate other than on empirical lines. However, where the mixture is reasonably homogenous friction factor may be calculated on the basis of a pseudo-Reynolds number. This takes the form:

$$R_e = \frac{AQ}{C^x d^y}$$

where:

Q is the flow rate

A is an empirical factor

C is the consistency of the mixture

d is the solids diameter

Values of the exponentials x y are determined empirically for different fluids. Typical values for pulps are $x = 1{\cdot}57$ and $y = 1{\cdot}795$.

The friction factor for insertion in standard function formulas, is then determined as:

$$fs = \frac{K}{(R_e^2)}$$

where:

K is a constant for a particular sludge

The value of the exponential z also varies with the type of sludge, but is typically of the order of 1·63.

Slurries

Slurries are defined as liquids (usually water) containing abrasive solids in suspension. They can be further categorised by the size of the solids *ie*:

Fines – particle size 75 micro-millimetres or less.

Sands – particle size 75 to 850 micro-millimetres.

Gravels or coarse – particle size 850 to 5000 micro-millimetres.

Particle size can have an appreciable effect on pump selection. Thus the requirements for pumping sands are different from those for handling gravels, not only from the point of view of differences in clearances required but also due to the different abraiding forces present.

Solids in suspension have the overall effect of increasing the apparent viscosity of the liquid being handled, with an inevitable loss of efficiency, compared with clean liquid or water performance, but the main parameter affecting the choice of pump is the nature and to a lesser extent the consistency of the solids present. It is thus more or less essential to consider different types of solids separately.

The specific gravity of the solids is usually of the order of 2·0 to 3·0 and typical solids contents by weight may be anything from 40% or 35% upwards. Table 2

TABLE 2 – SOME TYPICAL SLURRIES

Slurry	Proportion of Solids by Weight
Alumina	up to 50%
Crushed chalk	up to 68%
Clay	up to 60%
Coke fines	up to 55%
Gravel	up to 25%
Lime	up to 65%
Magnetite	up to 60%
Sand	up to 60%
Soda ash	up to 60%

shows some typical figures for slurries likely to be handled in large-scale process plants where something over 90% of such products are handled by centrifugal slurry pumps.

The quantity of water required to deliver a specific quantity of solids when pumping slurries can be determined as follows:

$$\text{Water quantity} = K \times T\left(\frac{W}{R} + \frac{1}{SG_D}\right)$$

where:

T = weight of dry solids per hour
W = percentage of water
R = percentage of dry solids
SG_D = specific gravity of dry solids

For water quantity in litres and T in metric tonnes $K = 1{\cdot}06$

For water quantity in imperial gallons and T in imperial tons $K = 3{\cdot}75$

For water quantity in US gallons and T in US tons $K = 4{\cdot}02$

Specific gravity figures for suspensions of solids in water are given in Table 3.

Abrasion, erosion and wear

A primary problem in solids handling pumps is in providing satisfactory resistance to wear. This favours the use of hard or very hard materials, or wear resistant liners. The problem however, is not purely one of material selection. Both the rotational speed of the pump and the hydraulic performance are additional abrasion parameters.

Theoretically, at least, a solids handling pump should have a low speed of rotation. As the pump rotor diameter is inversely proportional to speed for a required delivery, this leads to a large value of rotor diameter with considerable effect on the dimensions and cost of the pump. These characteristics are appropriate for pumps working under highly abrasive conditions. On the other hand, for comparable values of throughput and head the selection of a 'high' rotation speed results in wide motor outlets. A solids handling pump must have this special feature as by definition it must permit passage of all the solid particles contained in the supporting fluid.

TABLE 3 – SPECIFIC GRAVITY OF SUSPENSIONS OF SOLIDS IN WATER

Percentage by Weight of Solids	Ratio Water to Solids	Specific Gravity of Dry Solids																	
		2.0	2.1	2.2	2.3	2.4	2.5	2.6	2.7	2.8	2.9	3.0	3.1	3.2	3.3	3.5	4.0	4.5	5.0
		Specific Gravity of Solution																	
10	9:1	1.05	1.05	1.06	1.06	1.06	1.06	1.06	1.07	1.07	1.07	1.07	1.07	1.07	1.07	1.08	1.08	1.09	1.09
15	5.66:1	1.08	1.08	1.09	1.09	1.09	1.10	1.10	1.10	1.11	1.11	1.11	1.11	1.11	1.12	1.12	1.13	1.13	1.14
20	4:1	1.11	1.11	1.12	1.12	1.13	1.14	1.14	1.14	1.15	1.15	1.15	1.16	1.16	1.16	1.17	1.18	1.19	1.19
15	3:1	1.14	1.15	1.15	1.16	1.17	1.18	1.18	1.19	1.19	1.19	1.20	1.20	1.21	1.21	1.22	1.23	1.24	1.25
30	2.33:1	1.17	1.18	1.19	1.20	1.21	1.22	1.23	1.23	1.24	1.24	1.25	1.25	1.26	1.26	1.27	1.29	1.31	1.31
35	1.87:1	1.21	1.22	1.23	1.25	1.26	1.27	1.28	1.28	1.29	1.30	1.30	1.31	1.32	1.32	1.33	1.35	1.37	1.39
40	1.5:1	1.25	1.26	1.28	1.29	1.30	1.32	1.33	1.34	1.35	1.36	1.36	1.37	1.38	1.39	1.40	1.43	1.45	1.47
45	1.22:1	1.29	1.30	1.32	1.34	1.36	1.37	1.38	1.40	1.41	1.42	1.43	1.44	1.45	1.46	1.47	1.51	1.54	1.56
50	1:1	1.33	1.35	1.37	1.39	1.41	1.43	1.44	1.46	1.47	1.49	1.50	1.51	1.52	1.53	1.55	1.60	1.63	1.67
55	0.91:1	1.37	1.38	1.41	1.43	1.44	1.49	1.51	1.53	1.55	1.56	1.58	1.59	1.61	1.62	1.65	1.70	1.75	1.79
60	0.67:1	1.43	1.46	1.48	1.51	1.54	1.56	1.58	1.61	1.63	1.65	1.67	1.68	1.70	1.72	1.75	1.82	1.87	1.92
65	0.54:1	1.48	1.51	1.55	1.58	1.61	1.64	1.67	1.69	1.72	1.74	1.76	1.79	1.81	1.83	1.87	1.95	2.03	2.08
70	0.43:1	1.54	1.57	1.62	1.65	1.69	1.72	1.75	1.79	1.82	1.85	1.88	1.90	1.93	1.95	2.00	2.10	2.20	2.27
75	0.33:1	1.60	1.65	1.69	1.73	1.78	1.82	1.86	1.90	1.93	1.97	2.00	2.03	2.06	2.09	2.15	2.29	2.40	2.50

From an economic point of view, a solids handling pump should not have an excessively 'slow' speed and the quantity of noble materials used must be reduced to the greatest possible extent. As the diameter and width of the rotor directly condition the calculations and dimension of the mechanical assembly, the selection of a 'medium' speed will result in a pump design with optimum characteristics. In addition to the saving in energy costs, good hydraulic efficiency will result in reduced damage. In practice, hydraulic losses correspond in almost all cases to disturbance in the flow. On this point, however, it is important to note that the major factor is the care exercised in designing the installation into which the pump is to be incorporated, deciding the correct operating point and selecting the pump.

Pump types

Centrifugal pumps with chokeless impellers are generally favoured for high capacity, high head requirements. This necessarily implies a compromise between efficiency and the need for an open type impeller with maximum passage and satisfactory balanced flow. Ratings are thus generally reduced by a greater amount than would seem called for by the proportion of solids in suspension. By virtue of their simple design, uniform delivery, good ratio between delivery and size and low susceptibility to trouble, centrifugal pumps generally tend to be employed for handling solids. Where higher flow rates are concerned they are also cheaper than positive displacement pumps for comparable pumping data.

Sand, gravel, coal, flyash, iron ore, sewage, fish, sugar beet, wood pulp, paper stock and milk of lime can all be handled in slurry form by centrifugal pumps.

When centrifugal pumps are employed for solids handling the following conditions should be observed:

(i) The pumps must operated under sufficient inlet pressure.

(ii) The impeller channels and volute cross sections must be big enough to allow passage of the biggest solid particle expected. Clearances should be generous. Back shroud blades must keep abrasive particles away from the stuffing box.

(iii) Flow velocity through the impeller and volute must be kept low to minimise abrasion, which increases as the cubic number of the velocity. Generally heads of centrifugal pumps are presently limited to about 80 m. Admissible pipeline velocity depends on the density, particle size, form, concentration and strength of the solids involved.

(iv) Flow velocity through a pipeline may not drop below critical sinking velocity. Otherwise the solids will be precipitated from the suspension. The minimum flow velocity must be at least 0.3m/s above the critical sinking velocity.

(v) Pumps must have a steep characteristic. If the proportion of solids is changed, the resistance curve alters too. If the characteristic is steep, pump delivery will then drop only slightly and flow velocity variation in the lines is also only slight. Segregation of the solids is thus prevented.

(vi) Solids pumps are often operated in series in order to meet the demand for a steep characteristic.

(vii) When the pipeline is partly loaded with solids, the pump must generate sufficient pressure. The higher resistances encountered at start-up must be overcome, so that adequate flow velocity may be achieved to resume transportation process.

(viii) When pumping long fibres, open impellers should be used on account of the clogging risk. The inlet edges should be profiled and thickened so that fibres can slide off them more easily.

(ix) Solids pumps are subject to heavy wear. This is reflected in losses of head, flow rate and efficiency and must be taken into account when sizing the system and pumps.

(x) The pump materials must be matched accurately to the liquid involved. Depending on its abrasiveness and/or corrosiveness, interchangeable protective linings of rubber, plastic, ceramic, enamel or alloy steel must be provided. Shaft protection should be provided by interchangeable sleeves.

Vortex pump for handling fibres and large solids as well as delicate solids.

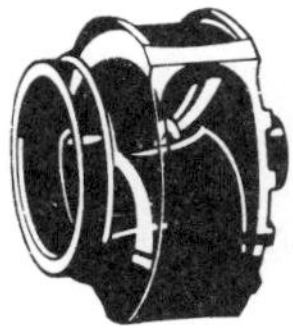

Closed non-clogging impeller.

For both clean and highly contaminated liquids without stringy, fibrous admixtures: spray water, flume water, waste water from the beet and cane washers, press water containing residues, raw juice, milk-of-lime, clear juice, thin juice, thick juice, remelt liquor.

Radial-flow impeller.

For clean fluids not containing gas inclusions: water, cleaned and treated flume water, thin juice, thick juice, oil, acid; condensate, boilerfeed water.

Single vane impeller.

Impeller not liable to clog, for stringy products such as bagasse, cossette water mixtures, waste water and raw waste water; also used for delicate handling of sugar beet.

Open multi-vane impeller.

For media containing gas and air, syrups, mixed juice and raw juice from sugar cane.

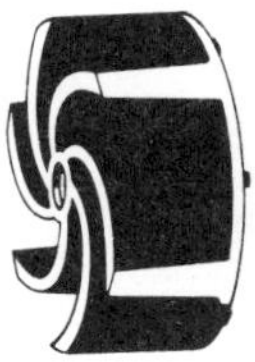

Free-flow impeller.

Suitable for liquids containing large quantities of air or stringy admixtures: diffuser juice, bagasse, waste water.

Closed mixed-flow impeller.

For clean and contaminated liquids with stringy admixtures, for high capacities and low heads: settled waste water, flume water, cossette water mixtures, recirculation juice.

Figure 1
Various impeller designs.

Single-stage electro-submersible pumps have also proved suitable for solids handling, particularly for pumping dirty liquids from below-ground pits and tanks. Conventional designs employ a fully recessed impeller of the vortex type, or a vane type with one or two vanes. Other impeller designs with improved performance have been developed, giving higher efficiencies whilst retaining the ability to pass large diameter solids and fibrous materials without blocking. (See Figure 1).

Reciprocating pumps are not excluded from handling solids in suspension, provided suitable clearances are present and the valve design can be adjusted to the task without loss of efficiency.

Rotary pumps as a rule are not generally suitable for handling solids, unless a particular design can accommodate solids without clearance spaces jamming or excessive wear. Particular exceptions are the swinging vane and heavy duty single vane pumps, both of which can handle a high proportion of solids. Heavily-constructed single-vane pumps in fact, working at very low speeds can handle semi-solids successfully and similarly almost 'unpumpable' media.

Chokeless pumps

Centrifugal pumps with non-clogging or chokeless impellers are known as chokeless pumps. there is no clear cut definition however, for 'chokeless' pumps may be produced for general service which can include sewage and sludge handling and a so called sewage pump may also be admirably suited for other duties involving some solids in suspension. Typically, in fact, these pumps can be expected to handle successfully the following media:

Chemical effluent;
Coal slurries and washing;
Corn and similar solids;
Cotton and wool waste;
Factory effluents;
Foodstuffs with solids content;
Fibrous materials;
Fish;
Fruit pulp;
Leaves, weeds, road and market sweepings;
Lime and similar slurries;
Thick oils;
Hot greases and lubricants;
Potatoes;
Peas;
Offals;
Seawater and bilge water;
Sewage, screened and unscreened;
Sludges;
Sugar, syrups, screened and unscreened;
Scale;
Swarf;
Spent hops;
Sugar beet whole and sliced;
Sump sludges of all kinds;
Tailings and many others.

Chokeless pumps normally embody a special design of impeller specifically developed by the individual manufacturer and to some extent modified by the actual service for which the pump is intended. A typical non-clogging 'chokeless' impeller is shown in Figure 2. Thus for a specific application a specially designed pump impeller may offer advantages compared with a 'general duty' chokeless pump but the latter may give equally satisfactory service over a wide range of applications involving the handling of solids, slurries and sludges. For example, the medium handled may have a tendancy to build up solids on the face of the impeller and entry side when a design of impeller with scraping action would obviate this. on the other hand a pump capable of handling sewage satisfactorily would also be capable of handling most other types of slurries, sludges and sediments.

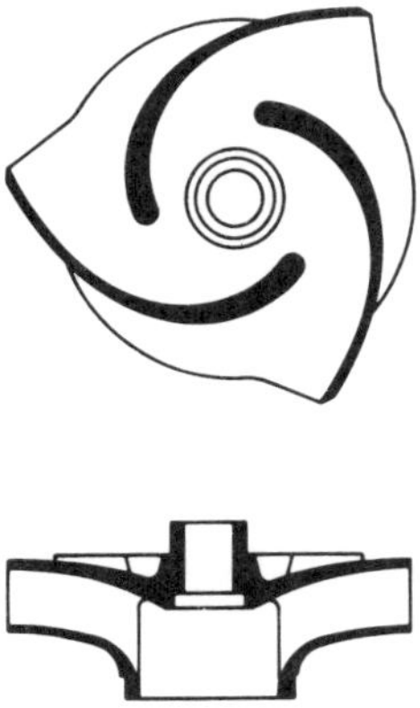

Figure 2
Closed non-clogging impeller.

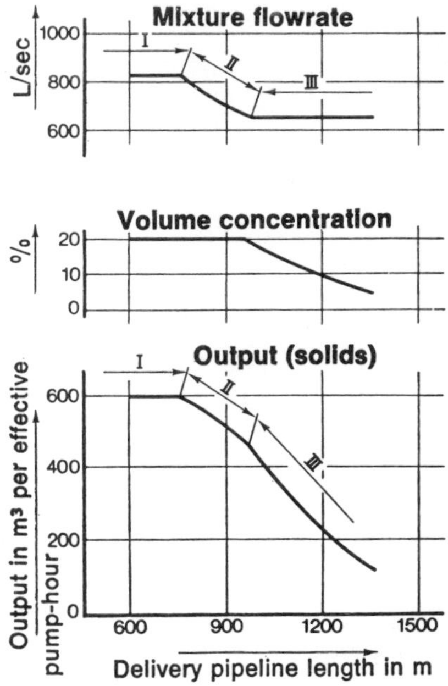

Figure 3
Typical output graph for a dredge pump installation.

Dredge pumps
Pumps that handle large amounts of solids material and develop high heads are called dredge pumps. There are many designs of pump on the market with large impeller diameters for operating at low rotational speeds to prolong the life of parts. Pumps of this type can be very expensive. A common factor linking all dredging operations is the need to achieve the highest possible production, not only in cubic meters of spoil per hour but also in terms of the return in the invested capital. Dredging requires relatively little labour but demands high investment.

The principle feature which distinguishes the dredge pump from the water pump is its much larger bore and the absence of restrictions. The bore is smallest on the inlet side of the impeller. Access to the housing is provided at this narrow point in order to enable debris which in spite of all precautions, still causes blockage to be removed easily. This is usually carried out by removing the inspection cover on the expansion piece situated on the suction side of the pump, immediately before the suction cover. Dredge pumps are designed with considerably larger volutes than water pumps. This is done chiefly to limit the peripheral velocities in the volute and thus to minimise wear on the housing, while ensuring that any wear which does take place is as uniform as possible. Viewed in the direction of rotation, the area of maximum wear in the housing is just beyond the cutwater. This is frequently of an intensely local nature and is manifested in vortex-shaped cavities caused by scouring. The shape of the cutwater is the principle factor which influences wear at this point; others are the outlet angle and the profile of the blades at the periphery of the impeller.

In order to cope with fluctuations in solids concentration, flow rate and changes in the pipeline arrangement, a dredge pump must have a fairly wide operating range. The efficiency curve must therefore be as flat as possible and where attainable, its highest point must coincide with the design point of the operating range in order that its efficiency throughout this range shall be high. In practice, this is difficult to achieve and the maximum efficiency of a dredge pump seldom exceeds 75 to 80%.

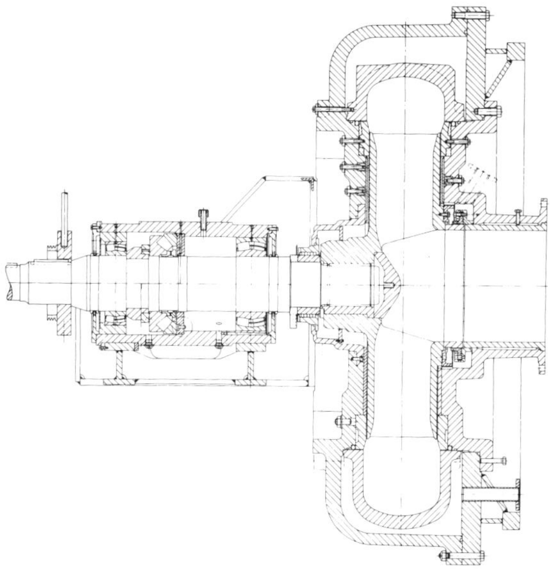

Double walled dredge pump.

Unlined dredge pumps

This type of pump incorporates an unlined casing made from a high chrome iron or similar material, with either open or closed impeller. It is commonly used in dredge pumps with wide impellers and casings to accommodate large particles to be passed through the pump. Due to the nature of the material of construction, it should be limited in application to maximum pressures of 100 kPa.

Double-walled dredge pumps consist of an outer housing of welded steel plate or cast steel which absorbs the stresses occuring within the pump and an inner housing made from a material which is resistant to the wear caused by the solids material to be transported. During operation, the space between the housing is pressurised to a level virtually equal to the delivery pressure. The inner housing is thus pressure-compensated. The double-wall principle and the pressure compensation together render it feasible to employ a highly wear-resistant material for the inner housing.

Such materials are usually so brittle that they cannot be used in a conventional pump housing without incurring serious risks. They can however be used for the inner housing of double-walled pumps. Pumps of this type are suitable for operations in which very high stresses have to be absorbed and very high resistance to wear is demanded.

In a complete installation, comprising dredge pump, prime mover (usually a diesel engine) and suction and delivery pipeline, the working point of the dredge pump is determined by the point at which the pump characteristic, as determined by the pump and its drive system and the pipeline characteristic intersect in their H-Q diagram. Where an installation is designed for a given pipeline layout and a given pit supply based on the nature of the soil and the operating circumstances, the only variable factor in calculating the output of solids is the length of the delivery pipeline.

Positive displacement pumps

Positive displacement pumps suitable for the transport of solids include:

(i) Duplex piston pumps.
(ii) Triplex piston pumps.
(iii) Plunger pumps.
(iv) Duplex piston diaphragm pumps.
(v) Triplex piston diaphragm pumps.

Duplex and triplex pumps

Duplex and triplex piston pumps as shown in Figure 4 can be economically used for pumping media with low or medium abrasiveness, such as chalk slurry, coal, flotation material, drilling mud and sludge. These pumps are directly actuated pumps, *ie* the piston and the packing are in direct contact with the medium. With the duplex piston pump, two flow lines are arranged so that the pump operates with a double action. The piston is surrounded by the flow medium at both sides. Triplex piston pumps have three flow lines, but are single-acting, *ie* the flow medium contacts the piston unilaterally. At its rear end, the cylinder liner is open.

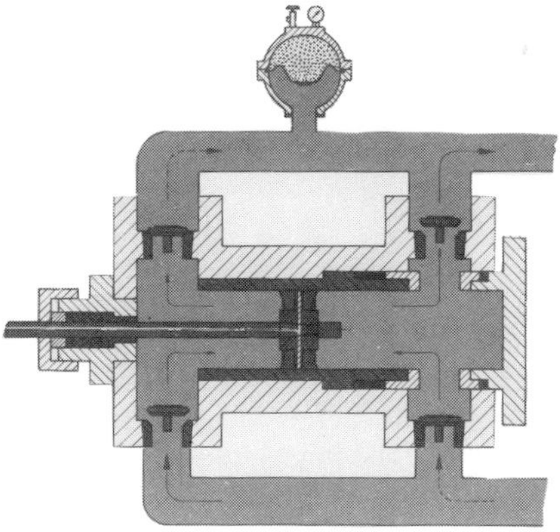

Figure 4(a)
Principle of duplex double-acting piston pump.

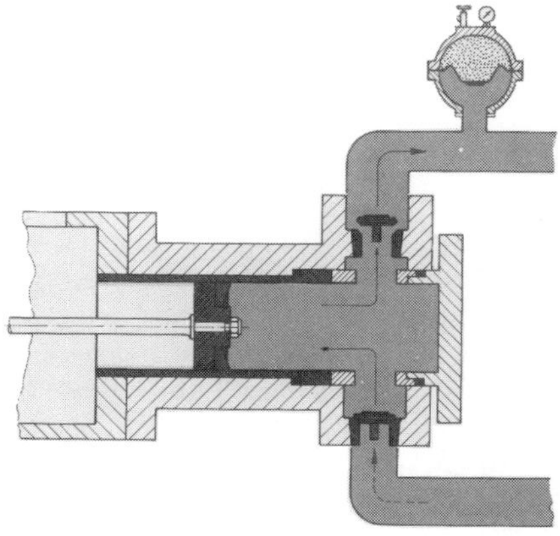

Figure 4(b)
Principle of triplex single-acting piston pump.

The duplex piston pump is a traditional pump, having been employed for several decades but with increasing lifting pressures, triplex piston pumps have become more prominent. Triplex piston pumps, however, have to be operated with a higher speed in order to achieve the same deliveries as duplex piston pumps. Due to the high number of strokes, the life time of the wearing parts is shorter. A comparison of the wearing parts of both pump types shows a considerable difference in the quantity of wear parts. Due to the bilateral effect, the duplex piston pump has more wear parts than the triplex piston pump.

Duplex double-acting piston pumps are in common use in the oil well drilling industry usually operated at approximately 65 strokes per minute. Triplex single-acting piston pumps are also used in the oil well drilling industry for operation at speeds of up to 170 strokes per minute. For long-distance coal slurry transportation systems triplex piston pumps are preferred to the duplex piston pump. However the speed of the pump should not normally exceed 70 strokes per minute.

Plunger pumps
Plunger pumps were originally developed for non-abrasive liquids in high pressure processes, water cleaning *etc*. They are however used for solids transport and operate at speeds of 100 to 140 strokes per minute. Consequently the rate of wear is extremely high causing very short valve life and a high valve opening and closing rate, very high operating costs and low availability.

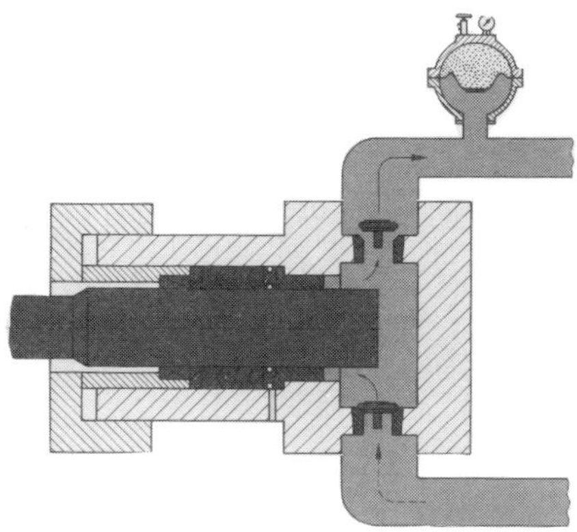

Figure 5
Principle of single-acting plunger pump.

The fluid end of a typical triplex single-acting plunger pump is shown in Figure 5. These pumps are used for pumping iron ore, phosphate ore *etc*. In order to protect the plungers of the pumps against the abrasive action of the slurry, the pumps are generally provided with a plunger water-flushing system. One of the disadvantages of these pumps is the dilution of the slurry due to the plunger water-flushing system. The rates of dilution increases with the rate of wear.

When pumping ore concentrates, valve life is normally only 300 to 500 hours.

For higher flow rates, quintuplex plunger pumps are available but these pumps possess a larger number of wearing parts. Operating costs therefore increase and the failure rate is higher.

TABLE 4 – COMPARISON TABLE FOR WEARING PARTS BETWEEN DUPLEX DOUBLE-ACTING AND TRIPLEX SINGLE-ACTING PISTON PUMPS†

Pump model	Triplex piston pumps				Duplex piston pumps			
Strokes p/min	50				50			
Wearing parts	A	B	C	D	A	B	C	D
Cylinder liners	3	6	45	180	2	4	45	180
Piston rod	–	–	–	–	2	2	30	240
Stuffing box packings	–	–	–	–	2	1	3	54
Piston bodies	3	4	10	60	2	1	10	160
Piston rubbers	3	2	5	60	4	1	5	160
Valve cones	6	4	4	48	8	4	4	64
Valve seats	6	4	5	60	8	4	5	80
Valve rubbers	6	2	1	24	8	2	1	32
Total cost factor				**432**				**970**
Mutual ratio	**1**				**1:2·25**			

†Table of comparison between the costs of wearing parts when pumping a certain liquid under continuous operating conditions, without allowance for fitting, waiting time and spare parts

Key:
A = number of wearing parts per pump.
B = comparison factor for parts life.
C = price factor for parts
D = cost factor at life factor 8

Table 4 shows a comparison between the individual wearing parts of a typical duplex double-acting and triplex single-acting piston pumps. the comparison is based on a pump speed of 50 strokes per minute both handling the same slurry *ie* coal. From the Table it can be seen that the cost of wearing parts on duplex pumps is more than double that of triplex pumps and the mutual ratio is as high as Figure 1:2·25.

Piston-diaphragm pumps
Piston-diaphragm pumps are used to transport very abrasive media, such as iron ore, copper ore, bauxite, red mud and sand. Figure 6 shows the fluid end of a typical

Triplex piston pump.

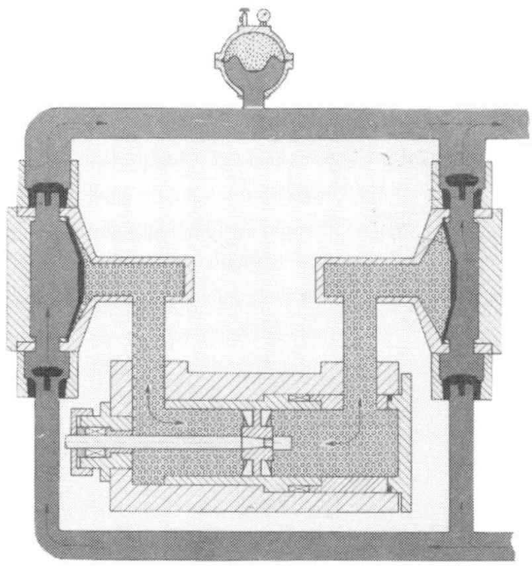

Figure 6
Fluid end of piston-diaphragm pump.

piston-diaphragm pump. The medium to be transported is not in direct contact with the pistons and packings, but is mechanically separated by a diaphragm and intermediate medium. The pistons, piston rods and cylinder liners are therefore not wear parts. Due to the mechanical separation between piston and media to be transported, the advantages of the piston pump are maintained. The different features between the duplex piston diaphragm pump and the triplex piston diaphragm pump correspond to those of the duplex and triplex piston pump.

Modern piston-diaphragm pumps are capable of transporting likely abrasive media with minimal wear. A diaphragm life of up to 12 000 hours is now quite common. The investment costs of diaphragm pumps are higher than those of plunger pumps. This advantage is however compensated within a few years due to the lower quantity of wearing parts and the lower expenditure in maintenance. The steady increase in the hydraulic transportation of solids has necessitated pumps with deliveries up to 700m^3/h (25 000 ft^3/h) to be manufactured.

In order to achieve long, disturbance-free operating times of the pumps, the lifting pressure should not normally exceed 100 bar. (1500 lb/in^2). Exceptions are the drilling mud pumps, operating with continuous operating pressures of more than 200 bar (3000 lb/in^2).

Duplex and triplex piston pumps are used for the hydraulic transportation of solids mixtures of medium abrasiveness such as coal, chalk, slurry, drilling mud and sludge. They are suitable for pumping solids mixtures of the highest abrasivity such as iron ore, copper ore, pyrites, sands, ashes, bauxite and red mud.

Table 5 shows a comparison between the individual wearing parts of typical triplex single-acting plunger and diaphragm pumps. The comparison is based on a pump speed of 100 strokes per minute for the plunger pumps and 50 strokes per minute for the diaphragm pumps, whereby it is assumed that both pumps are used for handling the same slurry *ie* iron ore. From the Table, it can be seen that the cost factor for wearing parts on plunger pumps is approximately six times that of diaphragm pumps and the neutral ratio is as high as Figure 1:6·3. If for example, wearing parts of a value of U.S.$100.00 are required for a diaphragm pump within a period of one year, the plunger pump will require (under exactly the same conditions), wearing parts of a value of U.S.$630.00.

TABLE 5 – COMPARISON TABLE FOR WEARING PARTS BETWEEN TRIPLEX SINGLE-ACTING DIAPHRAGM AND PLUNGER PUMPS†

Pump model	Triplex piston pumps				Duplex piston pumps			
Strokes p/min	**50**				**50**			
Wearing parts	**A**	**B**	**C**	**D**	**A**	**B**	**C**	**D**
Valve cones6	4	4	48	6	0·7	3	206	
Valve seats	6	4	5	60	6	0·7	4	274
Valve rubbers	6	2	1	24	6	0·35	1	137
Pumps diaphragms	3	8	7	21	–	–	–	–
Plungers	–	–	–	–	3	4	50	300
Plunger bushings	–	–	–	–	3	2	2	24
Plunger packings	–	–	–	–	3	2	2	24
Total cost factor				**153**				**965**
Mutual ratio		**1**				**1:6·3**		

†Table of comparison between the cost of wearing parts when pumping a certain liquid under continuous operaing conditions, without allowance for fitting, waiting time and spare parts.

Key:
A = number of wearing parts per pump.
B = comparison factor for parts life.
C = price factor for parts
D = cost factor at life factor 8

In the case of the plunger pump, the costs of wearing parts are much higher when expressed as a percentage of the capital investment. With a slurry pipeline involving a large number of pumps and the pipeline system designed for a service life of 25 years approximately the savings in maintenance costs are enormous.

Recently, larger sizes of peristaltic pumps with cycling speeds up to 30 r/min have also been developed for handling abrasive slurries at high concentrations (*ie* high specific gravity products).

Table 6 shows details of some typical pump types used for specialised services.

Mud pumps

The first positive displacement pumps were those used in the oil-well drilling industry. These pumps were popularly known as 'mud pumps', and were of the duplex double-acting type. They were developed for high pressure applications in the handling of relatively lightly abrasive drilling mud.

Thick slurries, pastes and semi-solid materials often cannot be handled by conventional designs of pump, even with modification, since the material is too thick to allow valves to operate or to pass the media. This has led to the modern development of the 'mud pump'. Basically the pump consists of a hydraulically operated power end and a mud end. The mud end comprises a hopper in the base of which are a cutting cylinder and a piston. At the beginning of the cycle of operation, the cutting cylinder is forced by a piston along inside the hopper, cutting through the material as it advances. At the end of its stroke it in effect forms a seal around the outlet. The ram, forced by another piston, then advances within the cylinder and forces the material through the outlet. The cylinder and ram together then retract, allowing more material to fall down inside the hopper. The material being forced out of the pump pushes that immediately in front of it along the pipe and so on. The material can be delivered along a pipe over almost any distance,

TABLE 6 – SOME TYPICAL SPECIAL-PURPOSE PUMPS

Description of Service	Pump Types	Remarks
Ash pumps	Single-stage centrifugal special designs – rubber lined	(i) Open suction entry and special impeller. (ii) Water-sealed glands usual.
Concrete pumps	Reciprocating – special design	Low speed piston pumps with hopper feed. Pipeline bore and pump delivery branch 3 to 4 times size of aggregate.
Dredging pumps	Single-stage centrifugal (usual)	Armoured construction and/or replaceable wear parts. Impeller design and casing clearances selected according to the nature of the ground.
Gravel pumps	(i) Centrifugal – chokeless impeller (usual) (ii) Diaphragm pumps (iii) Diaphragm pumps	Ni-Hard fitted. Impeller design and clearances must be selected with regard to the size of the solids to be handled. Contractors' type pumps.
Mud pumps	(i) Contractors' pumps (ii) Heavy-duty vane pumps (iii) Hydraulically-operated reciprocating pumps with cutting cylinder	For general applications. For handling very thick muds and semi-solids. True 'mud pump' for handling very stiff solids.
Muck pumps	(i) Contractors' pumps (ii) Choked impeller (iii) Diaphragm	For general applications. Lined or armoured. Limited capacity.
Sand pumps	(i) Reciprocating (ii) Centrifugal – chokeless impeller	Little used. Main type used, with lined or armoured casings and replaceable wear parts. Water-sealed glands or mechanical shaft seals.
Slip pumps (Ceramic slip)	(i) Single screw pumps (ii) Screw and platewheel pumps (iii) Rotary	Elastomeric stator. Less liable to clog than plain screw. Limited application because of high wear. **Note:** This duty specifically calls for the use of a positive displacement pump.

straight runs not being necessary. As the hopper can be connected directly to the point of production, such as the outlet from a filter press or the base of a thickening tank, the material can be conveyed in a completely closed system, without spillage, inconvenience, contamination of the material or the liberation of fumes.

Contractors' pumps may be suitable for handling lighter muds. Heavy duty vane pumps are also suitable for handling very thick mud and semi-solids. The progressing cavity pump can be successfully used for such duties. Abrasives that wear out other types of pumps are easily handled by this type of design. The elastomeric pump stator – within which rotates the pumps only moving part, the hardened plated steel rotor – is merely deformed by the passage of abrasive particles, resuming its original shape as the particles are flushed clear of the pump by the liquid flow.

Concrete pumps

Stationary concrete pumps have been in general use for over ten years and are probably among the most successful pumps to be developed in recent times. These pumps are equipped with a transfer tube valve system with outputs upto 200 m^3/h and concrete pressures up to 150 bar.

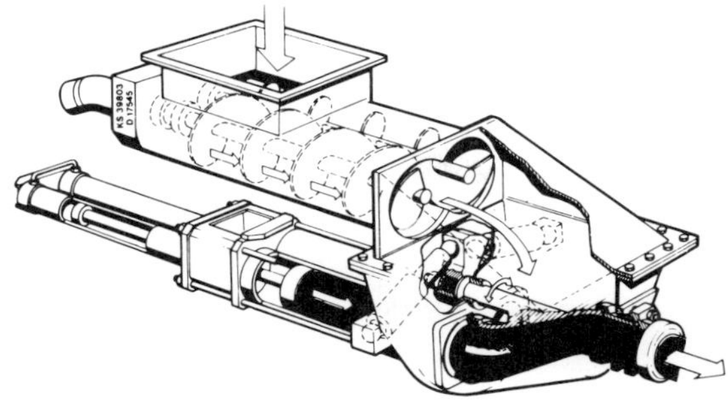

'S' transfer tube system for medium and compact stationary concrete pumps.

Dry solids

Special pumps are produced for handling powders, a typical example being the helical rotor/stator (progressing cavity) type of screw pump modified to suit the conditions of powder handling. A favourable feature with this type of pump is that the relatively low velocity of flow within the pumping chamber prevents much of the compaction which may cause powder handling problems and consequently, it can be used for conveying it through pipelines involving a number of changes in direction. The seal moves at a uniform velocity through the pumping chamber, producing a positive and uniform rate of displacement which smoothly generates the flow of the powder, ready for discharge through long lengths of pipeline. The continuously changing line of seal also ensures that wear caused by abrasion is kept to a minimum.

A specific advantage of the design in handling powders is that the pump rotor is the only moving part in contact with the powder and simplicity of construction offers easy dismantling for cleaning and maintenance. The gland seal and driving mechanism have also been designed to suit powder conditions and to isolate the powder from any contact with oil or grease.

Small volumes of fluidising air are injected into the intake chamber and discharge branch of the pump. In addition, the pressure of discharge from the pumping element reduces the amount of air needed for fluidisation at the delivery port, obviating the need to separate large amounts of excess air from the pocket.

Based on hydrated lime in a fluidised condition, with a powder density of 480 kg/m^3 (30 lb/ft^3). Maximum output is approximately 3060 kg/h (6750 lb/h).

Pumps of this type have been used successfully to pump up to 60 feet vertically and for horizontal distances of between 200 to 300 feet. PVC pipeline of up to 2 inch (50 mm) bore is used to discharge powder from the powder pump to the next stage of the system, which could be a mixing tank or supply hopper or a dosing unit.

Fluidisation with air

Powders and fine granular solids may be fluidised by low pressure air, in which form they may be transported by gravity or pumping. The basis of fluidisation is that if a suitable solid product is aerated by blowing with compressed air, there is an apparent swelling or inflation of the product. At a specific air velocity, the product will in fact remain effectively in suspension in the air, when it will behave and can be handled as a fluid. Under such conditions the product is said to be 'fluidised'.

See also Chapters on *Sewage and Sludge Pumping and Slurry Pumping.*

Sewage and Sludge

SEWAGE CONTAINS a large variety of solids which can differ with time and place. These may include fibrous materials, sand and miscellaneous waste products such as small plastic articles, fragments of other materials etc, – all of which the pump must be able to handle as well as water. Equally, whilst pumps in this category are used for the movement of untreated coarse screened or comminuted sewage, other duties involved may include sludge transfer and sludge circulation services and storm water pumping. Treated effluent and effluent hosing on the other hand can normally be handled by water pumps. It is understood that per inhabitant, 200 to 750 litres of effluent per day is the norm though this may trebled by rainfall.

Services

Untreated or coarse screened sewage has to be lifted from the incoming sewer to a level which will give gravity flow through the primary stages of sewage treatment. It may also be necessary to transfer waste from a remote district by direct pumping, or to lift it over intervening high ground before gravity flow can feed it to the treatment works.

Storm water may also be piped to the treatment works, usually by a separate sewage system, for retention or partial treatment or for direct discharge. The disposal of storm water assumes greater important in towns and cities where there is less opportunity for natural absorption of rainfall in open ground.

Sludges resulting from treatment processes vary from activated sludge and humus sludge with a solids content of 2% or less, to dewatered sludges and digested sludges where the solids content could be as high as 8%.

Pump types

Centrifugal mixed-flow and axial-flow pumps can all be considered for the handling of sludge, sewage and similar media, according to the capacity and requirements of the system. In practice, however, the axial flow pump is largely excluded from such duties, however attractive its performance for large capacity low-head services, because the passages between the impeller blades are small. Also, the leading edges of axial flow impellers are particularly prone to pick up stringy materials. Where large volumes are involved, therefore, the axial flow pump is most suitably

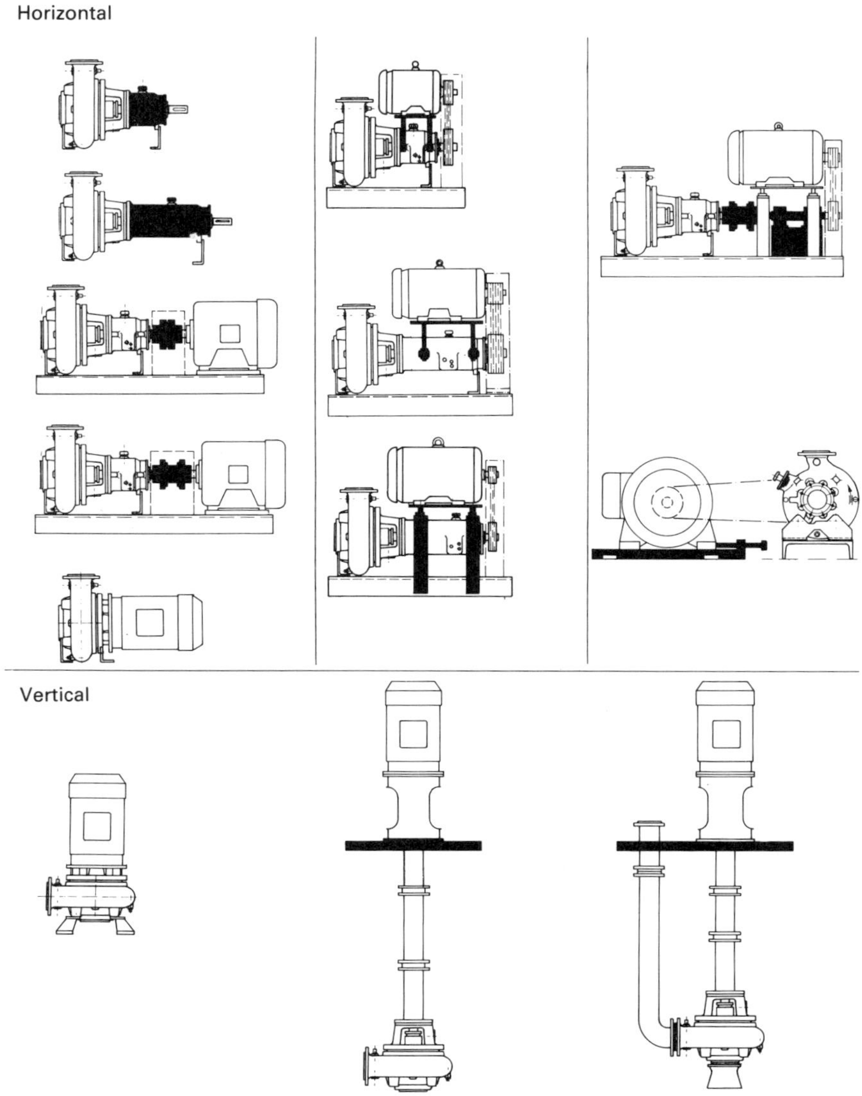

Effluent pump mounting arrangements.

employed in the handling of final effluent, digested sludge, or media which do not contain definite solids and are free from contaminants.

The centrifugal pump, on the other hand, can be designed to handle virtually any size of solid which can pass through the suction branch. This is largely a matter of suitable 'open' impellei design, although there is one problem to be considered when handling sludges with a low water content. This is the tendency for moisture to be extracted from the sludge with a possibility of building up a solid 'plug' in the suction bend. Where this is likely to occur the pump geometry can be modified as a preventative measure, although this may further reduce the hydraulic performance of the unit. An alternative solution is the use of a positive displacement pump in conjunction with a centrifugal pump for handling low water-content sludges, where the positive displacement pump can be used to clear any blockage which may develop in the roto-dynamic unit.

Reciprocating or other types of positive displacement pumps may be used in conjunction with or even as alternatives to, centrifugal pumps where the water content is known to be low and where high pressures may be needed to clear sludge plugs or blockages in the pipelines. Table 1 shows the various pump types that are used in sewage treatment plants.

TABLE 1 – PUMP TYPES FOR SEWAGE TREATMENT PLANT

Service	Radial Flow	Mixed Flow Volute	Mixed Flow Bowl	Axial Flow	Archimedean Screw	Clean Water	Vortex Flow
Crude rough screened sewage	X	X			X		X
Storm water (with sewage)	X	X	X		X		X
Storm water (surface water only)	X	X	X	X	X		X
Final screened/comminuted sewage	X	X	X		X		X
Settled storm water	X	X	X	X	X		X
Partially treated sewage	X	X	X	X	X	X	X
Final effluent	X	X	X	X	X	X	X
Crude sludge	X	X			X		X
Humus sludge	X	X	X	X	X		X
Activated sludge	X	X	X	X	X		X
Digested sludge	X	X	X	X			X
Grit	X	X					X
Supernatant liquid and drainings	X	X	X				X

Basic impeller design

In most cases the type and size of solids in the sewage call for the largest possible cross-sections. In border line cases, only one vane or one channel is provided and the free passage (spherical passage) is equal to the diameter of the suction and discharge connections. This design feature naturally results in a loss of efficiency. Consequently, impellers with a reduced spherical passage, or with two or three channels, are also used for appropriate applications or if suitable measures have been taken on the plant side.

Other points to be considered are:

(i) The leading edges of the vanes must be well rounded to prevent textiles and other long fibered fibre components from getting caught on them.

(ii) The gas content of the sewage calls for impeller forms or configurations which prevent an accumulation of gas bubbles in the negative pressure area of the vane threshold as this would cause the flow to break-off.

(iii) The destruction of sludge flakes, particularly with activated sludge can be reduced if shear forces that act on the flakes are minimised. This requires a reduction of the normal working speed of the impeller and the greatest possible restriction of the vortices.

Types of impellers

The single vane impeller (Figure 1) has only one vane or one channel with, in borderline cases, a free passage corresponding to the normal bore connection. Twisted formations of long fibrous components in the sewage does not interfere with its operation. the lateral spaces of the impeller are screened so that solids cannot get into its sealing surfaces.

The multi-channel impeller (Figure 2) has two or more vanes or channels with smaller passage cross-sections than the single vane impeller. This gives greater efficiency, but its applications are limited to non-gaseous, polluted fluids with solid admixtures which are not prone to twisting or bunching.

The open impeller (Figure 3) can have one or several vanes. Its properties make it especially suitable for conveying gaseous media.

The free flow impeller (Figure 4) fitted with radial vane, is set back into the drive side of the pump housing in such a way that a cross section corresponding at most, to the nominal diameter is available for the passage of solids. As a result of marked pre-rotation in front of the impeller, gas occlusions in the sewage are conveyed as well without the flow breaking.

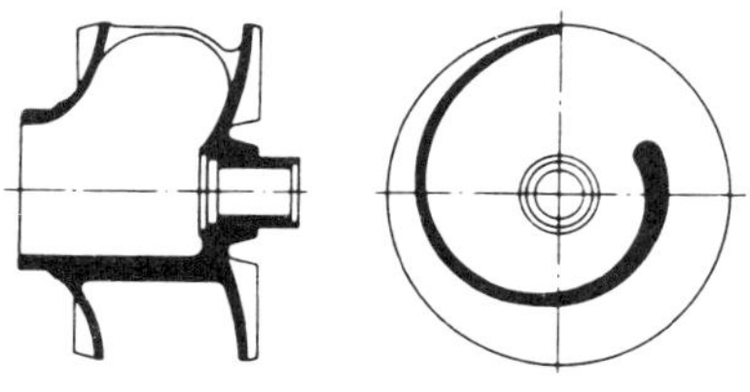

Figure 1
Single vane impeller.

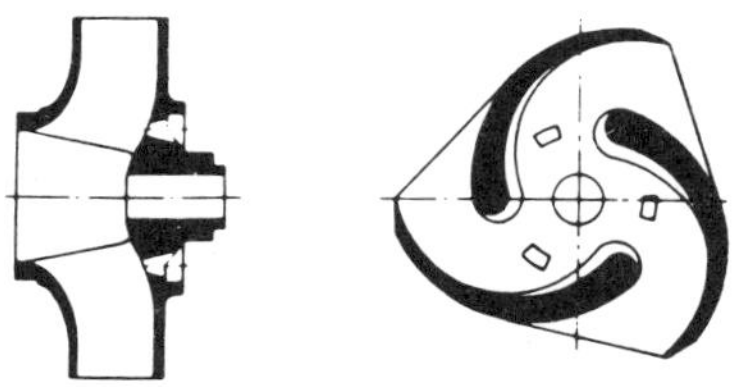

Figure 2
Multi-channel impeller.

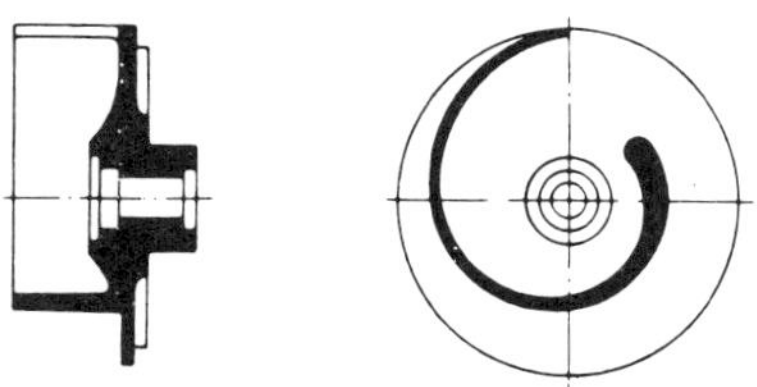

Figure 3
Open impeller.

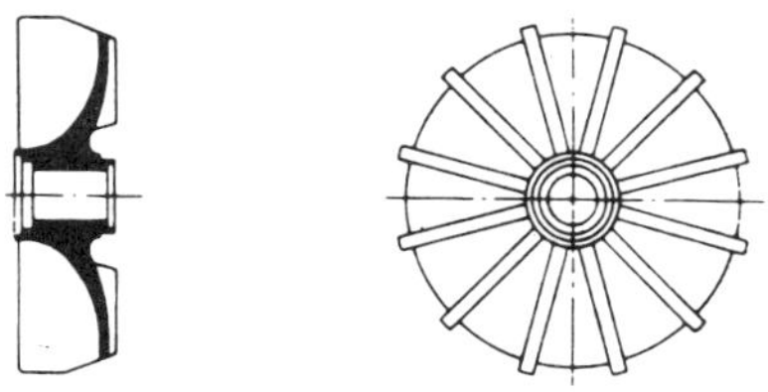

Figure 4
Free-flow impeller.

H-Q range

When sewage and sewage sludges are to be pumped, one of the general selection principles is that up to a nominal connection of approximately 150 mm, the size of the pump is determined more by the necessity for a free passage than by hydraulic factors. Thus these pumps usually work in the partial load region. The flows of sewage pumps are generally in the range of 500 to 1500 l/min, depending on their size. With single-vane and free flow impellers, the following maximum delivery head ranges may be defined:

Single vane impeller up to 40 m

Free flow impeller up to 100 m

The free flow impeller has the greater pressure coefficient and owing to its balanced radial forces, it permits higher peripheral speeds. This is why it is capable of higher delivery heads. Multi-channel impellers are designed so that the whole H-Q range in question is covered by pumps with high levels of efficiency.

Impeller characteristics

The characteristic H-Q curve shows the most marked rise in the case of a closed single vane impeller. The curve becomes flatter as the number of vanes increases and rises least sharply of all with the free-flow impeller. The risk of overloading grows as the curve flattens out because small divergence or fluctuations in the delivery head can result in a greatly increased flow. The closed impellers with two

TABLE 2 – COMPARISON OF DIFFERENT IMPELLER FORMS IN A 100 mm PUMP WITH NOMINAL IMPELLER DIAMETER OF 250 mm

Impeller form	Rise in characteristic curve H_o/H_{opt} H_o = zero delivery head H_{opt} = best delivery head	Efficiency at the best point when compared with radial impeller; normal vanes	$NPSH/NPSH_1$ (Fall in delivery head 3%, gas content 0.5%)	Remarks about the applications
 Radial impeller, normal vanes	1.28	1	1	For purified sludge.
  Multi-channel impeller closed	1.56	0.94–0.95	1.11	Channel impeller with big passage; danger of spinning and twisted formations in front of impeller inlet with unpurified sewage; for pre-purified and purified sewage, activated sludge; gentle conveyance; not for very gaseous fluids.
 Single vane impeller	1.64	0.75–0.88	1.37	Single vane impeller with a spherical passage corresponding to the nominal connection diameter; not susceptible to congestion; no spinning, no twisted formations; for unpurified sewage and all sludges; gentle con-
 Free flow impeller	1.14	0.56–0.66	2.89	Free flow impeller; free passage in pump up to size of nominal connection diameter; not susceptible to congestion; for unpurified sewage and sludges; for very gaseous fluids and sludges; not to be used when gentle handling of conveyed matter is required.

or three channels do not reach these levels of efficiency, since specific practical requirements do not permit the best hydraulic design. Values here lie around 75 to 85%.

The efficiency of the single vane impeller lies between 60 and 80%, and the free flow impeller between 45 and 60%. In certain cases requiring a greater delivery head, two single vane impeller pumps operating in tandem are used instead of the single-stage free flow impeller because they are more efficient.

Table 2 shows comparisons of different impeller forms in a 100 mm pump with nominal impeller diameter of 250 mm.

NPSH

By comparison, the minimum intake level (NPSH) is lowest with the normal vane closed radial impeller. The channel impeller and the single vane impeller needs somewhat greater minimum intake levels owing to the very rounded leading edges at the impellers inlet. The free flow impeller is markedly worse in this respect but, because of its ability to convey a relatively high proportion of gas, it is often preferred to closed impellers when there is a high delivery head.

Effects of solids

To reduce maintenance, pumping stations are built without screens wherever possible. Since the solids in sewage vary greatly in type, size and composition, the only impellers that can be used are single-vane or free flow impellers with a spherical passage corresponding, at least approximately to the nominal bore connection. In small pumping stations, experience has shown that the free spherical passage must measure at least 100 mm. With larger pumps the free-cross section can be slightly reduced relative to the nominal width in the interest of efficiency.

Of the sludges occuring in sewage works, raw sludge from preliminary purification and the circulation sludges from the septic tanks both contain large solids. As a result it is necessary to use the single vane impeller with full spherical passage. Thickened raw sludge and putrified sludge (*eg* from Imhoff tanks and full oxidation plants) often have a substantial gas content. Thus it is advisable here to use a free-flow impeller with full spherical passage.

Effect of gases

With the various sludges found in sewage purification plants and particularly, with the raw and putrified sludge, substantial quantities of methane sometimes arise through putrification. Owing to the drop in pressure which the flow entering the pump undergoes and which results in minimum pressure in the region of the impellers inlet, gas laden fluids make special demands on the design layouts and operation of the centrifugal pumps used. The fall in pressure levels leads not only to a considerable increase in the volume of undissolved gas mixed in with the fluid, but also to constant gas build-ups by the dissolved gas. Gas bubbles block the impeller inlet and cause a retardation on the feed side which, according to the proportion of gas and design of the impeller, can result in the decline in the flow and finally even in the flow breaking off. Susceptibility to gas is especially great in the partial-load region because of the backflows out of the impeller when partial admission occurs; these result in gas accumulations in front of the impeller inlet. Care must therefore be taken that pumps for gas-laden fluids are not designed too large.

To keep the fall in pressure on the inlet side as low as possible, pumps handling gas laden fluids may only be operated with a positive geodetic intake level. The

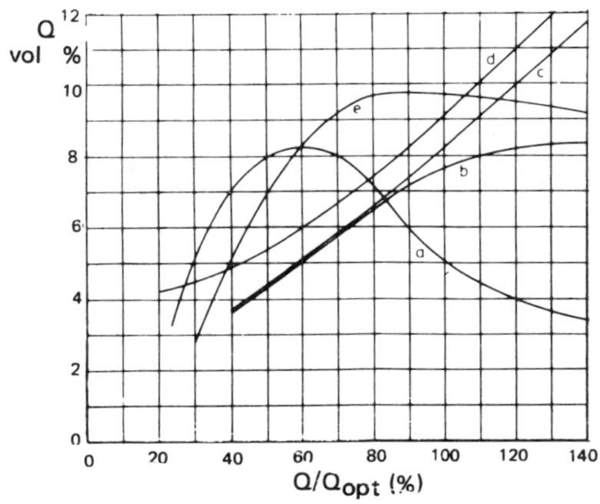

Proportion of gas Q_L as a function of
the flow with drop in delivery head,
$\Delta H/H = 5\%$.

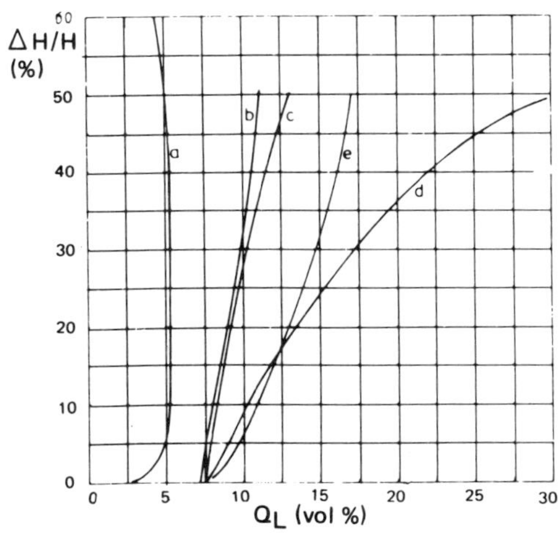

Drop in delivery head, $\Delta H/H$, as a
function of the proportion of gas,
Q_L, with Q_{opt}.

a — normal vane impeller, closed
b – channel impeller, closed
c – single-vane impeller, closed
d – free-flow impeller
e – single vane impeller, half-opened

Figure 5
Gas susceptibility of different impeller designs.

intake pipes must be of such a size that the flow resistances are kept as low as possible. In addition an impeller shape needs to be chosen which is largely unaffected by gas and works without congestion.

The gas susceptibility of different impeller designs is illustrated in Figure 5.

Effect of viscosity
Sewage plant sludges are generally non-Newtonian fluids with intrinsically viscous flow behaviour. The solid matter in these sludges can be up to 6%. All the impeller forms described previously which are suitable for conveying waste water and sludge, can cope with this percentage. In fact, if the pumps are well arranged in the plant, with a short intake pipe and an adequate positive geodetic intake level, these impeller designs can convey sludges with up to 10% solid matter, but the design must take account of the increased pipe resistances and the fall in the flow level due to gas content and viscosity.

Running clearance

The pressure level outside a closed impeller is higher than it is in the suction inlet. To reduce internal leakage losses a narrow suction clearance is formed between the impeller and the volute casing, the width of which is usually of the order 0·5 to 1 mm. The magnitude of this clearance affects the efficiency of the pump and the H-Q curve, for which reason the clearance should be kept as small as possible. When designing the suction clearance for sewage pumps, the following points should be taken into account:

(i) In sewage there are impurities which may penetrate into the suction clearance along with a leakage flow but which do not pass through it. Such impurities become wedged more and more tightly in the clearance space causing excess friction, this necessitates an increase in motor power to such an extent that in the end the pump may no longer be able to run. This is called jamming. Nowadays, suction clearance designs have been developed which are capable of eliminating jamming.

(ii) Abrasive particles carried into the suction clearance by leakage flows cause the clearance gap to widen, which increases internal leakage flows, thereby lowering the H-Q curve. Depending on the clearance design, this can be done either by replacing or adjusting the component parts. Often in such cases the condition of other pump parts has not become impaired as a result of wear in this section of the pump.

Alternative running clearance designs

Figure 6 shows a number of different kinds of radial clearance. Designs shown in 6(a) and 6(b) have been developed to avoid jamming in pumps with radial clearance. The hindmost shoulder in the volute casing at the suction clearance point has been removed, thereby facilitating the passage of impurities through the clearance. In Figure 6(c) slots have been made in both the impeller and the volute casing, the width of which, in the direction of the periphery can be about 15 to 20 mm. Impurities which have found their way into the clearance are removed *via* the slots. The slots do not cause any substantial increase in leakage losses, as they

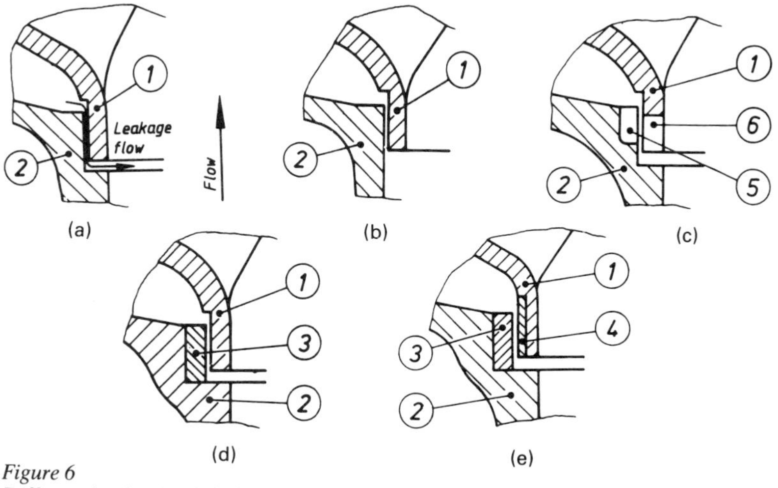

Figure 6
Different kinds of radial clearance.

are not quite as long as the length of the clearance and the time when the slots are against each other is so short that the quantity of water in them does not have time to increase.

This design has been patented in several countries. It is not possible by adjustment to reduce a radial clearance gap. If one wants to restore the original gap, the parts must be replaced. Different kinds of neckrings have been employed to make the replacement parts as cheap as possible. In Figure 6(d) the ring numbered 3 is located in the volute casing. In Figure 6(e) the rings numbered 3 and 4 are located in the volute casing and the impeller respectively. However rings can be made of more expensive but more wear-resisting material if one wants to extend their working life.

An example of axial clearance is given in Figure 7. This type of clearance has proved in practice to be less susceptible to jamming. This is probably due to the fact that fibrous particles, because of frictional forces, gravitate towards the centre and thus are removed from the clearance more easily. An axial clearance can be made adjustable. This is especially easy to do with submersible pumps because of their design and does not involve significant expense. Practice has shown a range of adjustment of about 10 mm to be quite sufficient. It is then possible to adjust the clearance about four times before the volute casing and impeller where out completely, due to wear in other component parts.

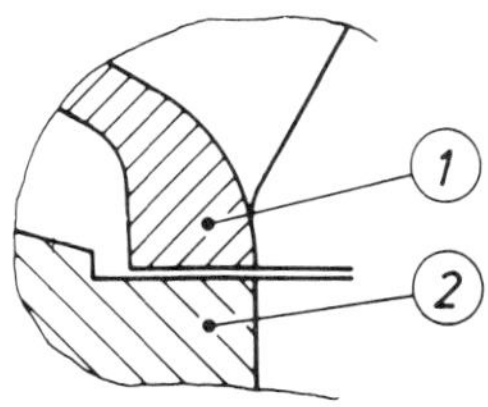

Figure 7
Example of axial clearance.

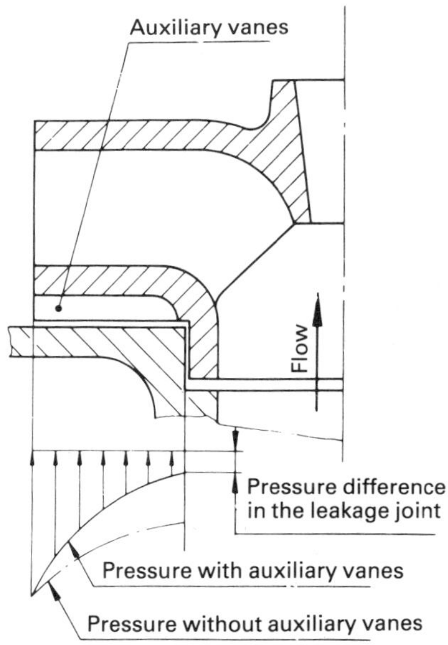

Figure 8
Auxilary vanes can reduce pressure difference.

Use of auxiliary vanes

Pressure difference can be reduced with the aid of auxiliary vanes, thereby minimising leakage flows. Because the water in the space between the impeller and the volute casing whirls more forcibly, a steeper pressure curve is achieved (Figure 8). A reduced leakage flow means fewer impurities getting into the suction clearance. Reducing in turn wear and tear and the danger of jamming. In addition wear in the clearance has a lessened effect on leakage flows, because the pressure difference is smaller.

Auxiliary vanes can only really be used effectively in the smallest sizes of pumps (10 kW), because in bigger pumps cavitation would occur at small head values and auxiliary vanes in any case cause a slight deterioration in efficiency. However, the need to counteract jamming in small pumps is greater because of their small motor torque.

Helical flow pumps

Helical flow pumps may be considered where relatively large discharges are involved. Here the impeller is normally of the open type, although the shrouded impeller is not excluded. A volute casing is standard. Once the delivery and head exceed the limit where the maximum cross section of the volute is less than that of the delivery branch, a constant section recouperator becomes necessary to carry the flow away from the impeller and the type is changed into a diagonal-flow pump. Possibly one of the main applications of the volute-casing helical flow pump is for storm-water pumping in dry well installations, with an ability to handle solids in suspension.

Diagonal flow pumps

Diagonal flow pumps feature a variety of impeller profiles, all characterised by being backward inclined with respect to the flow. For small deliveries, both open and closed blades of single curvature are employed, with double curvature for larger deliveries.

Closed impellers are generally considered more suitable for handling abrasive solids and contaminants such as sand. For sewage/sludge handling, however, a two-bladed open impeller is more usual, providing wide open passages for the through flow of solids. The impeller is followed by guide vanes disposed in an axial direction in a bowl-shaped casing and again these must be arranged with sufficiently wide passages to avoid clogging by solids. Apart from straightening the flow and converting kinetic energy into pressure energy, the fitting of guide vanes also makes it possible to employ a pump for a range of applications. Again, individual manufacturers should be consulted for specific recommendations when necessary.

The vertical-type diagonal pump is used for high deliveries. It is very economical in floor space and normally operates with flooded suction in a wet sump, thus avoiding the need for priming. Heads available are however more limited than with centrifugal pumps unless multi-stage units are employed. The main disadvantage of a vertical pump is usually difficulty of access to the impeller and bearings.

Axial flow pumps

Axial flow pumps may be used for pumping return sludge at medium to high flow rates with impeller shapes similar to or identical with water pumps as no large solids should be present at this stage. Clearance passages must however be large enough to prevent clogging by leaves or other debris (*ie* at least 50 mm wide). When used to handle fibrous material (present in activated sludge), axial flow pumps tend to 'matt up' at the inlet of the impeller.

Casing design

A sewage pump casing differs from a water pump casing in that generous clearances must be allowed; the smaller the pump the greater the importance of this factor. Access covers should be fitted at strategic points so that should there be any obstruction, (a possibility even in a well-designed pump), there is a chance of clearing it and subsequently inspecting the impeller without completely dismantling the pump.

It is difficult to prejudge the amount of wear which is likely to take place in sewage pumping as it varies widely with location and composition of the sewage, being greatest in industrial centres where there are increased amounts of trade wastes and grit. Most pumps are designed with easily renewable components at these points where wear is most likely to occur *eg* casing check plates, neckrings and shaft sleeves.

Pumping station

Station structure costs are reduced if the dry sump is dispensed with and either a submersible sewage pump or a trunk slung pump is used. The former has a close-coupled immersible electric motor and is lowered into the wet sump on guide rails, automatically engaging with its fixed delivery pipe when it reaches its operational level. Other submersible models use a flexible delivery hose and are lowered to stand freely on the sump floor. In either case, the submersible pump is easy to lift for inspection and if necessary, for clearing. The trunk slung pump is shaft driven from a surface mounted motor but, owing to its length and particularly if integrated intermediate bearings are fitted, it is much more difficult to remove for inspection and for this reason is less favoured for crude sewage pumping.

Other arrangements using only a wet sump employ a pump mounted at ground level either inherently self-priming or fitted with ancillary priming equipment. This arrangement restricts the volume to be pumped, the extent of the suction lift and the nature of the liquid pumped; and one must be prepared to accept that there are priming hazards which are not present in the previous arrangements. Figures 9(a), 9(b) and 9(c) show schematics of the aforementioned installations.

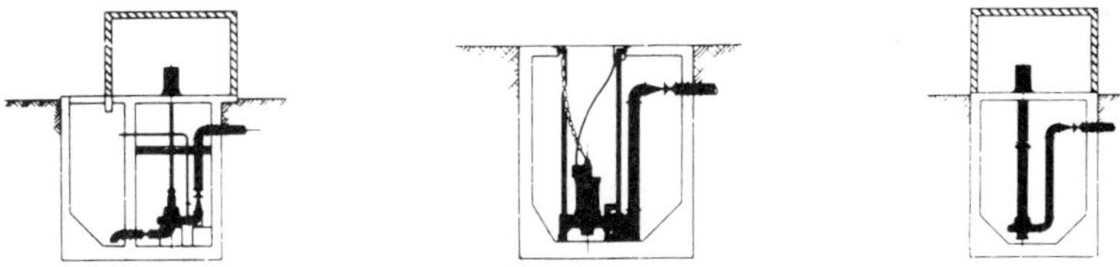

(a) Vertical dry sump installation.

(b) Wet sump submersible pump

(c) Wet sump trunk slung pump

Figure 9
Typical pumping station installations.

Packaged sewage pumps

Packaged sewage pumps of various types have been designed, some built around a receiving vessel to which the incoming sewer is directly connected and to which the externally arranged pumps are attached, complete with unit, switchboard and starters. Other types consists of prefabricated metal or reinforced plastic shells containing pumps of the dry sump type connected directly to the sewer or submersible pumps with the lower part of the shell forming a wet sump.

With electric motor drive now almost universally employed, most pumping stations incorporate automatic control, the pumps respond quickly to the change of inflow which occurs during the 24-hour cycle. The number, size and arrangement of pumps vary enormously according to the size of the district, town or city served.

A very small station may consist of only a duty pump and a standby, the latter either alternating in service with the duty set or taking over if the duty pump fails. Bigger and more complex stations may house as many as eight to ten large pumps of similar size, successive pumps coming on service as demand increases. Other arrangements have small pumps working on low rates of dry weather flow and pumps of increasing size take over and phase out the smaller sets as the inflow builds up. Variable speed motors are used to give addition flexibility in pumping.

Figure 10 shows a cutaway view of a modern well equipped pumping station arrangement.

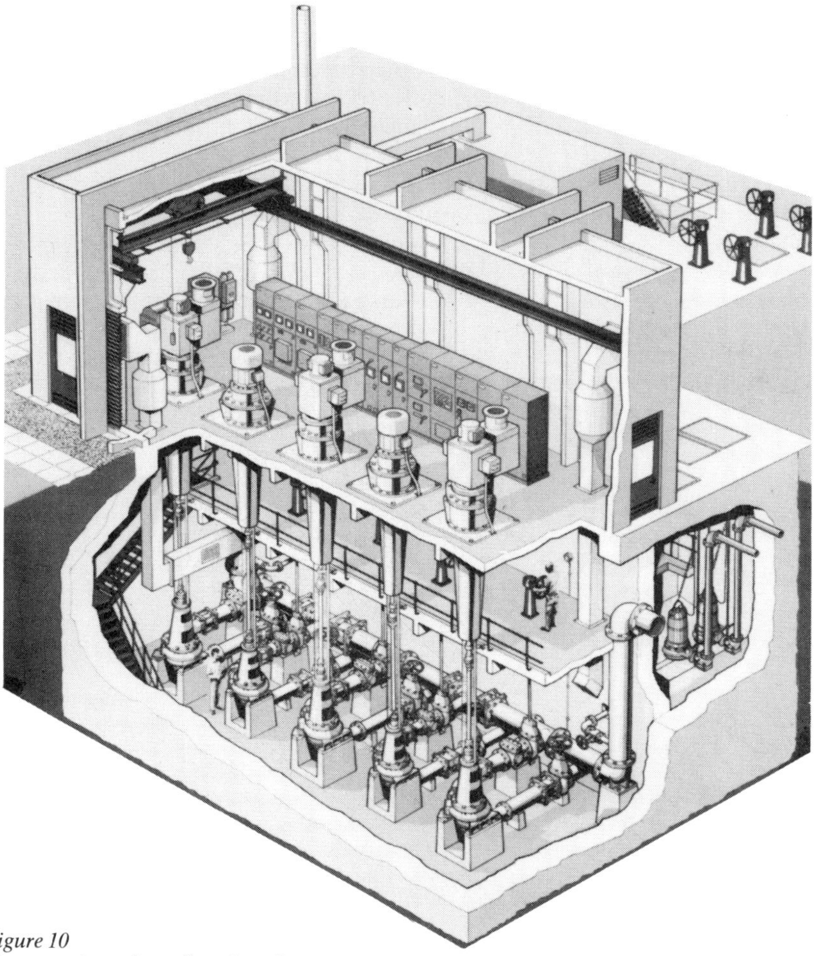

Figure 10
Cutaway view of a well equipped modern pumping station.

Piston pumps

Heavy viscous sludges encountered in sewage and industrial waste processes may also be handled by piston pumps of the type shown in Figure 11. Pumps of this type are usually high pressure units (up to 150 bar), and consist of a transfer tube with

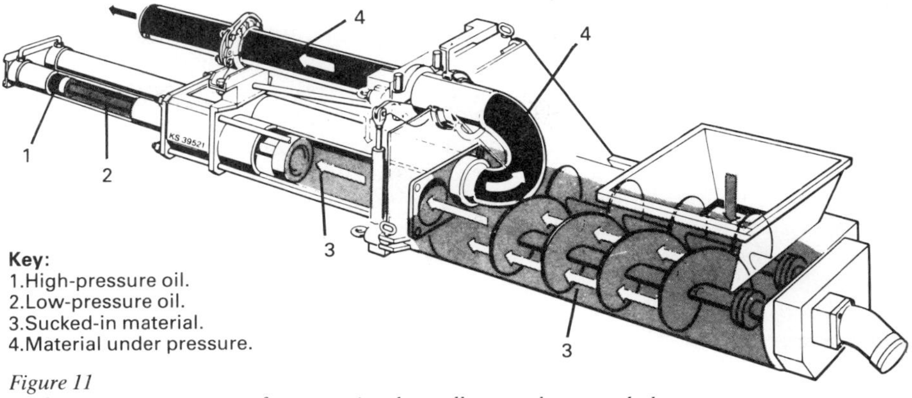

Figure 11
High pressure piston pump for conveying thermally-treated sewage sludge.

automatic sealing ring. The transfer tube is swung hydraulically from one cylinder opening to the other and synchronised with the piston strokes. The pump sucks material throgh the large suction opening into the free cylinder. After the transfer tube is switched over, the sucked-in sludge is pushed directly *via* the transfer tube into the delivery line.

The automatic ring is self-adjusting and seals under pressure. Internal pressure hydrostatically forces it to seal against the plate in front of the cylinder opening.

Materials which can be pumped include thermally treated sewage sludge, dehydrated by vacuum filters down to about 50% dry matter content. Very high consistency sludge *eg* paint sludge, dispersion paint residue with lumps up to 300 mm diameter. Other applications for similar pumps include carbonation sludge from vacuum filters in sugar factories (approximately 55% dry matter), coal sludge (70% dry matter content), sinter sludge and steel works waste, silt and floats to a particle size of 50 mm from mines and a variety of aggressive and abrasive materials. The double auger feed device presses nearly earth-dry material into the delivery cylinders. The interlacing action of the two augers automatically cleans both flights.

Piston/plunger pumps are powered by constant or variable speed motors through belt drive and reduction gearing. For sewage and sludge service they have several advantages over centrifugal pumps. For example high suction lifts can be handled efficiently without expensive manual or automatic priming devices. Also, each stroke delivers a positive metered volume, which permits an exact operating cycle to be established within the plant. Through stroke length adjustment, this volume can be changed to allow for seasonal changes in plant capacity. Another advantage is that sludge concentrations beyond the capability of centrifugal pumps can be handled by piston/plunger pumps since these are inherently more suitable for handling hard tramp solids with less chance of internal damage. Running dry in a treatment plant is possible owing to pipe blockages caused by waste materials and heavy sludges being pumped. Piston/plunger pumps are durable and can run dry for lengthy periods provided the packing has not been allowed to dry out.

Progressing cavity pumps

The positive displacement progressing cavity pump has achieved remarkable success in sewage and sludge applications. The pumping principle is based on a hard helical metal rotor revolving within a resilient rubber stator. The rotor makes an interference fit with the stator forming a cavity with a continuously forming seal behind it which progresses through the pump with the rotation. Particulate matter is contained within the cavity and is positively displaced to the discharge end. The pump is valveless, very simple to maintain and very abrasion resistant. Typical applications include pumping raw sewage in rural or remote areas, factories, industrial estates and office blocks, motorway service stations, residential leisure sites, on-board sewage from offshore rigs, ships and submersibles and of course small sewage treatment works. The positive pumping action affords high head capability and allows long runs of rising main (up to 5 km) without intermediate pumping stations. These pumps are normally coupled to a mutration/maceration device which is described in greater detail in the following paragraphs.

Pump macerators

The principle of maceration or reducing solids in water-borne waste has been widely used in both domestic and institutional locations since the mid-1960s. From these have developed macerator/mutrator units specifically designed for raw sewage handling. The expansion or establishment of sewage treatment in rural areas frequently involves the basic problem of distance between the community – new or established – and the strategically sited sewage treatment plant. Naturally, pipeline diameter is a major factor in the practicalities and economics of pumping sewage for this purpose.

Traditional systems employing centrifugal pumps and rising mains with a diameter of 100 mm or more, are dictated by size of solids in the sewage flow. Corresponding pump sizes are used to ensure adequate flow velocity even when the volume from a small community does not require such a high flow rate.

Excavation and pipe laying costs are high. Also, when the pumps run, they may deliver a high volume in a short time - a mode that is particularly bad for small biological treatment plants.

The problem worsens with long rising mains. The high volume held in the main can mean three days of retention, leading to possible septicity and resulting biological environmental hazards.

Installation of pump macerators involving many locations throughout the world has helped to minimise or remove these problems. Plant standardisation and rationalisation of spares use are further crucial factors in developing area installations, particularly where a single community project is involved.

Most pump macerators follow the principle of an impeller driven by a powerful motor, turning at high speed and creating a centrifugal force which throws the solid content of the effluent against a stationary cutter ring so disintegrating the solid content to a particle size small enough to pass through the radial slots in the impeller. Specifically, though it is necessary to match the performance of both the types and sizes of solid products involved. There are now macerators developed to deal with screaning, sludge or raw sewage – in the latter case normally a combined package incorporating a macerator with screening.

Development of such heavy-duty macerators have also enhanced lift and throughput capacity. If higher heads still are required a third pumping vane can be incorporated in the macerator. The relationship between the degree of maceration achieved and possible throughput and lift can be adjusted by designing the macerator for a particular application. Thus if particularly fine standard maceration is the paramount consideration over and above throughput and lift requirements,

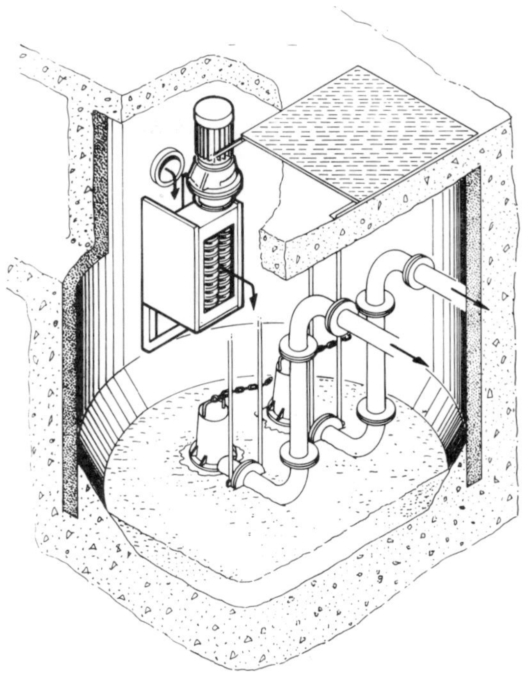

Sewage pump protection showing macerator installed on in-flow above submersible pump.

Pumping macerator designed to macerate and pump screenings sludge up to a total head of 7 metres through a nominal 50 mm discharge outlet.

a standard macerator configuration would be selected. On the other hand, if it was particularly important to be able to achieve a high head and velocity with only a coarser maceration, then a model including finger element and pump vane would be acceptable.

Units of this type are often installed in unmanned pumping stations, finely macerating domestic effluent from approximately 30 dwellings and pumping the liquor to the reclamation works some distance away. The macerating/pumping unit as shown in Figure 12 is usually situated above the sump which collects the raw sewage. The positive displacement action of the pump lifts the sewage from the sump into the cutting chamber, where textile, fibrous matter, paper *etc*, are held against the macerating impeller.

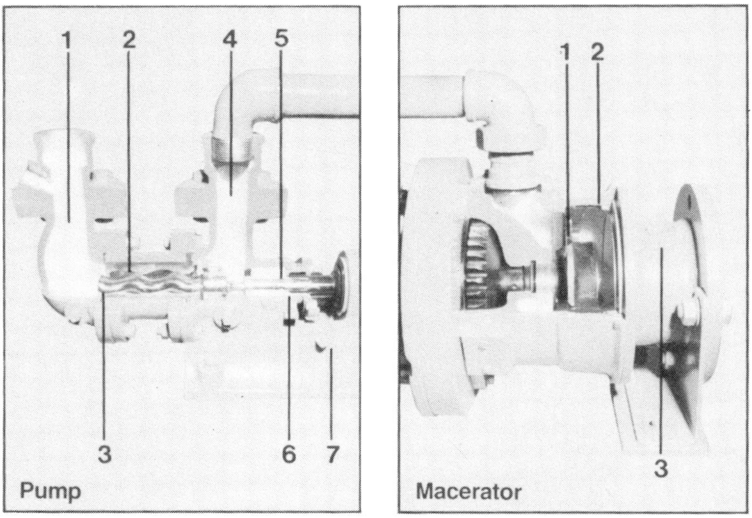

Figure 12
Macerating/pumping unit.

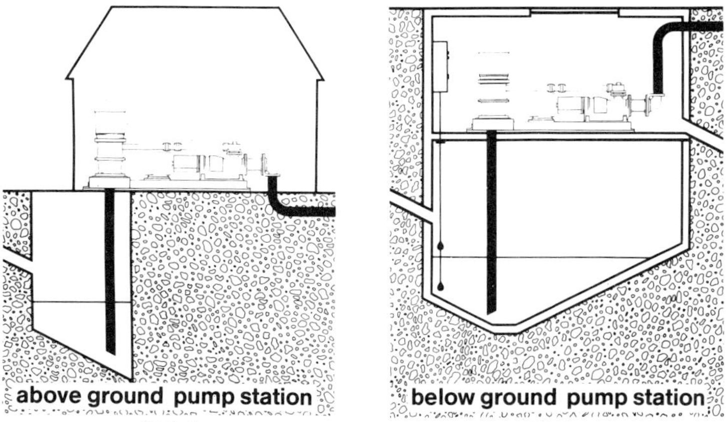

Figure 13
Typical unmanned installations.

As the liquid content acts as an elutriation agent, large solid objects such as metal, glass, stones *etc*, fall back out of suspension into the sump. When the pumping cycle ends, macerated material falls back into the cutting chamber, where textile, fibrous matter, paper *etc,* are held against the macerating impeller (Figure 13(a)).

As the liquid content acts as an elutriation agent, large solid objects such as metal, glass, stones, *etc* fall back out of suspension into the sump; clearing the suction pipe for the next duty run. (Figure 13 (b)).

Unlike pure pumping with a regular consistent homogeneous medium, no precise science has yet been evolved to measure performance of maceration and maceration/pumping. Since waste products in a liquid medium vary in consistency, percentage solid/liquid ratio, specific gravity, viscosity and temperature, each individual potential application has to be appraised on its own particular criteria.

Slurry Pumping

THE NEED to pump solid liquid mixtures is common to many process plants throughout the world. The centrifugal slurry pump provides, at the present time, the most efficient means of doing this. In order to select the best type of pump and materials of construction, it is necessary to know the following about the product to be pumped:

(i) Material hardness – generally speaking the harder the particles the higher the wear.

(ii) Particle shape – wear will be higher if the particles are sharp and angular, for example, from a crusher, rather than rounded, as from an alluvial deposit.

(iii) Particle size distribution - the size distribution curve of the solids is needed to determine both the derating factor which should be applied to the pump, if any, and also the critical settling velocity in the pipeline.

(iv) Solid concentration – this is expressed in terms of concentration in the mixture as % weight : CW or % volume : CV or gms/litre Cg. Figure 1 shows a simple nomograph giving these relationships.

(v) Particle specific gravity – see Figure 1.

(vi) Conveying liquid – viscosity, specific gravity (S1), temperature and chemical properties need to be known.

In a slurry pump, the major features which must be considered are:

Pump efficiency, which affects energy costs. Energy costs account for typically between 70 and 80% of the total operating costs of the pump. The efficiency is, that which is maintained through the life of the pump, (Figure 2).

Cost of maintenance, this includes, total downtime as well as cost of replacement parts.

Materials of construction

Due to the many variables in the properties of the media to be pumped, it will be apparent that alternative materials of construction of the pump are necessary to best meet these requirements. The major areas of concern are the impeller and

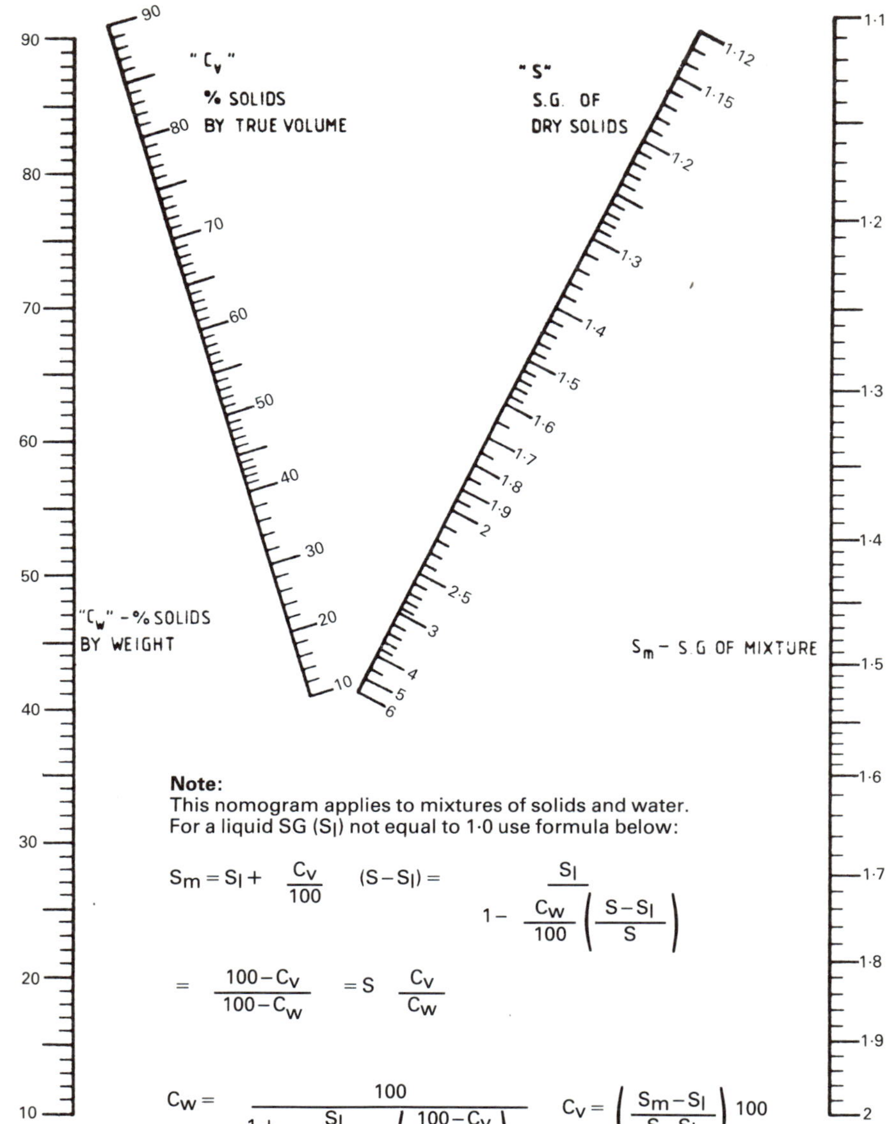

Note:
This nomogram applies to mixtures of solids and water.
For a liquid SG (S_l) not equal to 1·0 use formula below:

$$S_m = S_l + \frac{C_v}{100}(S - S_l) = \frac{S_l}{1 - \frac{C_w}{100}\left(\frac{S - S_l}{S}\right)}$$

$$= \frac{100 - C_v}{100 - C_w} = S\,\frac{C_v}{C_w}$$

$$C_w = \frac{100}{1 + \frac{S_l}{S}\left(\frac{100 - C_v}{C_v}\right)} \qquad C_v = \left(\frac{S_m - S_l}{S - S_l}\right) 100$$

$$C_w = \frac{C_g}{10\,S_m}$$ where:
C_g = grams of solids per litre of mixture

Figure 1
Density-concentration nomogram for solids-water mixtures.

casing. The differing mechanisms of wear that occur in slurry pumps can be briefly classified as follows:

Erosion – this involves a solid particle striking a solid surface and material being lost from that surface as a result of the impact. (See Figure 3).

Deformation – this involves high velocity impact on the solid surface at about 90 degrees to that surface. Wear occurs when the impact stress extends the local yield stress in the boundary material. (See Figure 4).

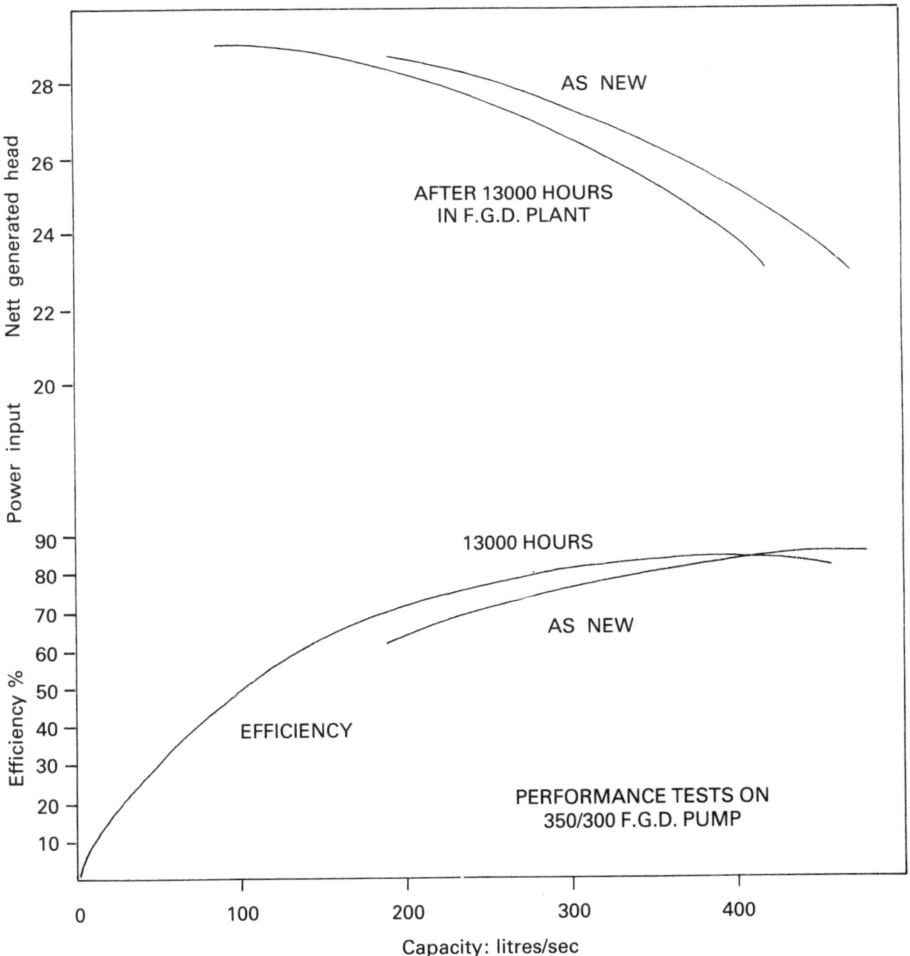

Figure 2

Grinding – this involves particles becoming trapped between two surfaces moving relative to each other. The concentrated stresses transmitted between the three bodies causes localised ductile or brittle failure. This is generally a sliding type of abrasion, but it can also cause further erosion due to scouring at low impingement angles. (See Figure 5).

Corrosion – this is the most complex of the wear mechanisms and typically will

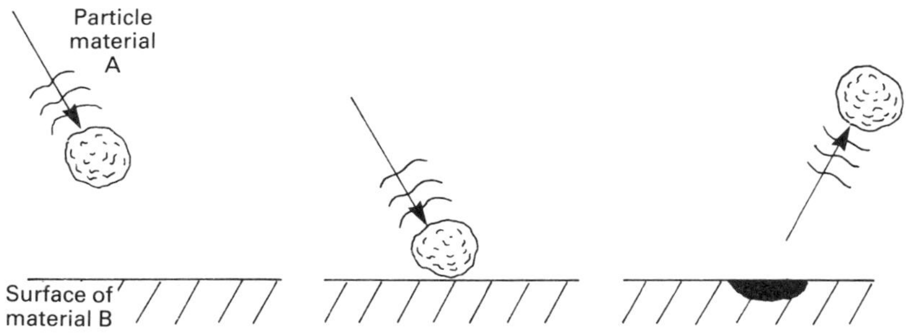

Figure 3
Erosion

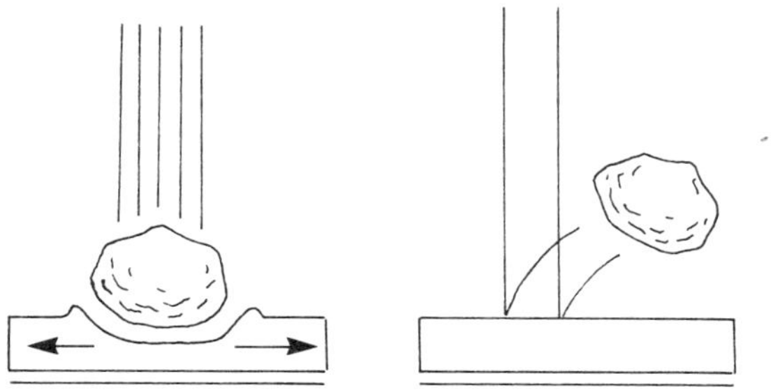

Figure 4
Deformations

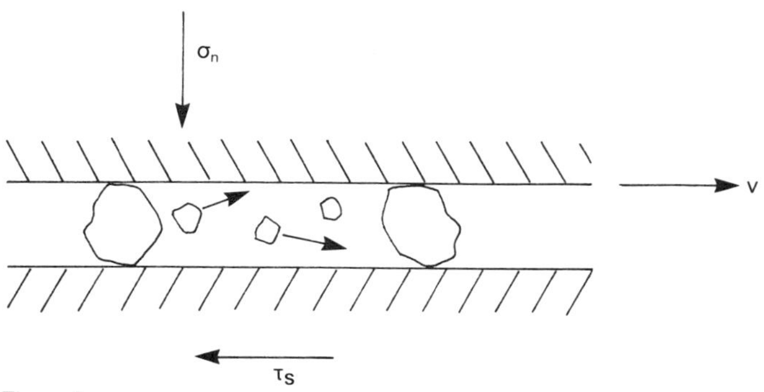

Figure 5
Grinding

act in addition to those previously mentioned. Corrosive media can vary from acid to alkalines, but typically acidic solutions with low pH values cause the greatest problems. A good example of corrosive wear, in addition to normal wear, is the Flue Gas Desulphurisation (F.G.D.) system, referred to later in this chapter.

The wear rate in ductile and brittle materials vary with the angle of impingement. Figure 6 shows the wear rate characteristics of various slurry pump materials, elastomers, hard metals and ceramics as a function of impingement angle.

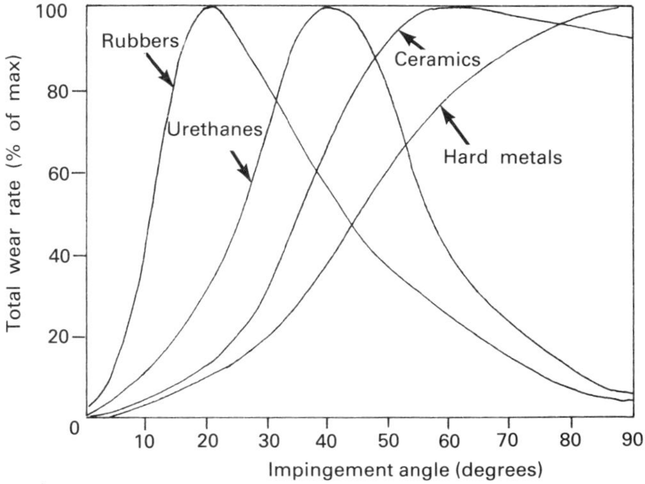

Figure 6
Effect of impingement angle.

Commonly used abrasive-resistant alloys
Nihard I – average Brinell hardness 550+
This is a relatively low-cost white iron suitable for handling coarse sharp particles due to the presence of an extremely hard carbide network in the martensitic matrix.

Nihard 4 – average Brinell hardness 525+
This is a slightly higher cost than Nihard I and its abrasive resistance is similar. However, its high strength and greater impact resistance make it more suitable for handling large particles such as gravel which are common in dredging applications.

High chrome iron – 27% chrome – average Brinell hardness 550+
This is now probably the most popular of the commonly used materials and offers extremely good wearing characteristics. It can be used in corrosive applications to pH values of 4.

15-3 chrome molybdenum alloy – average Brinell hardness 600

This gives similar results to 27% chrome but at increased cost due to the presence of molybdenum.

Elastomers
There are now available a large number of elastomers for use in slurry pumps, a few of the more commonly used are listed.

Natural rubber – Shore hardness A40-65
For small particles, below 5 mm, this is often the most economical solution, due to the fact that at high impact angles, the particles tend to bounce off the rubber surfaces. Large sharp particles tend to cut the rubber causing premature failure.

The properties can be varied by the addition of fillers, which can affect its vulnerability to cutting wear, and also chemical attack. Normal temperature limit 75 °C. Not suitable for oils or solvents.

Polychloroprene (neoprene)
This is inferior in abrasive wear to soft natural rubber in abrasive resistance, but can withstand higher operating temperatures and also a large number of chemicals, oils and solvents.

Polyurethane
The only advantage over natural rubber is an increased resistance to low angle impingement erosion, or sliding abrasion. It is resistant to a number of chemicals and hydrocarbons. In most highly abrasive applications, natural rubber is the preferred material.

Ceramics
This is a material whose use is expanding rapidly in abrasive condition. However, it is extremely brittle and is generally unsuitable for areas subjected to high impact loads. It does have high resistance to sliding abrasion.

Pump design
In general, for heavy abrasive applications, it is standard practice to use pumps of radial flow design of low specific speed. A range of values would be from about 18 to 45 (m^3/sec). Whilst low speed is preferable, for values below about 18, it becomes increasingly difficult to cast impellers with narrow passages with the relatively thick sections required for long life in a hostile environment.

Because the pump wet end parts are going to wear out, ease of maintenance is a prime design feature. For this reason, single end suction design of wet end with overhung impellers is the simplest form of construction. The design of the wet parts are such as to allow for the minimum of machining when made in hard metals.

The back pullout feature of many water and chemical pumps is not a significant advantage in a heavy-duty slurry pump. Quick-release couplings in the suction and discharge piping negates any possible advantage of a back pullout design. Tight wear ring clearances are of no use in an abrasive application as they will soon be opened up and efficiency will drop off.

Due to the difficulty of machining keyways in white iron impellers, impellers will normally be screwed to the shaft with a coarse pitch thread.

Lined pump – double casing
This type is normally of vertical split casing design to enable easy access to the replaceable liners. The liners will normally be available in a variety of elastomeric materials or hard metals. The outer casing itself acts as the pressure container by supporting the lining. In this manner, it is possible to have high pressure pumps with either elastomer or hard metal liners. It is standard practice to have high pressure units suitable for working pressures up to 6900 kPa.

The availability of either elastomer or hard metal wet ends, or a combination of both, make it relatively easy and inexpensive to enable the end user to find the best combination of wear components to best suit his actual slurry. This all makes for a commonality of pumps, which a plant may need for its process requirements, and lead to overall reduction in pumping costs. Figure 7 shows a cutaway view of an ultra-heavy-duty slurry pump with a rubber lining.

Impeller design
Open impellers are not normally used in the highly abrasive applications of the wear plate or throatbrush increases due to wear. As the pumping valves are generally relatively thick to allow for wear, there are normally between three and five. The width between shrouds is also dependent upon the size of solids that are required to be passed. Manufacturers of lined pumps also make near identical impellers in elastomer and hard metal, and this also restricts the freedom of the designer.

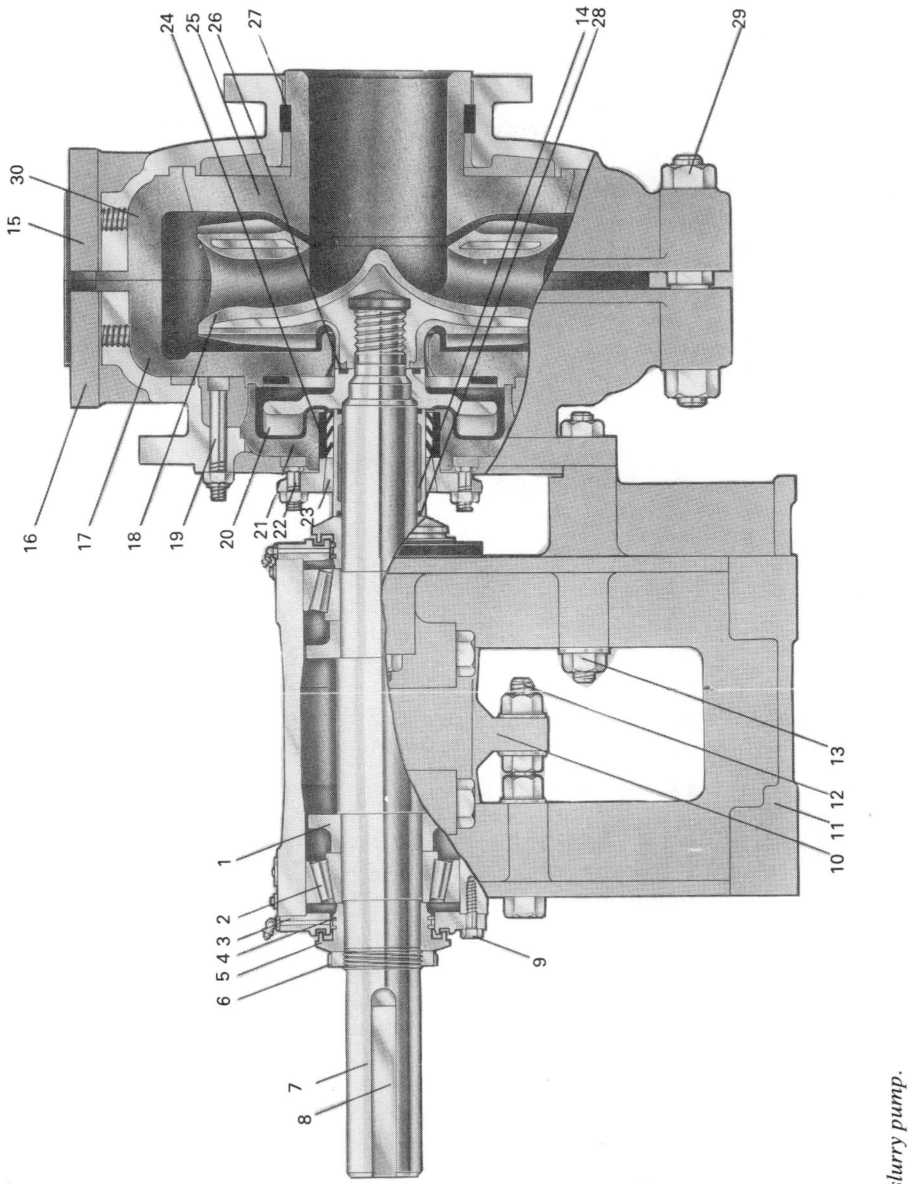

1. Grease retainer
2. Bearing
3. End cover
4. Piston ring
5. Labyrinth
6. Labyrinth locknut
7. Shaft
8. Shaft key
9. End cover set screw
10. Bearing housing
11. Base
12. Adjusting screw
13. Frame plate bolt
14. Shaft sleeve
15. Cover plate
16. Frame plate
17. Frame plater liner
18. Impeller
19. Frame plate liner stud
20. Expeller
21. Expeller ring
22. Gland stud
23. Lip seal gland
24. Lip seal
25. Throat bush
26. Impeller sealing O-ring
27. Cotter
28. Shaft sleeve O-ring
29. Cover plate bolt
30. Cover plane liner

Figure 7
Rubber-lined heavy-duty slurry pump.

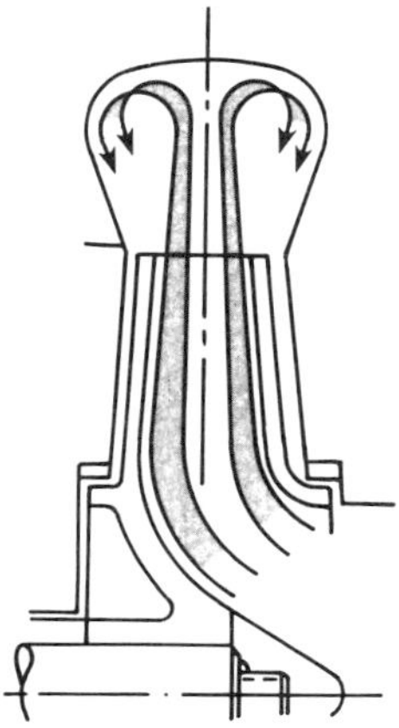

Figure 8(a)
Outward spiral of slurry in conventional pumps [8(a)] causes serious recirculation and consequent wear at the close impeller clearances.

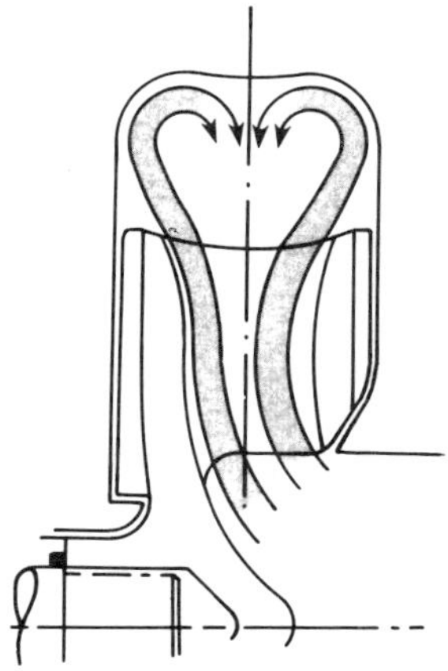

Figure 8(b)
The pump-out vanes and concave impeller vane of the pump [8(b)] force the slurry to form a double inward spiral. This results in uniform wear, a greater utilization of wearing parts, an increased shaft seal life and sustained high efficiency.

The hydraulic design of the impeller and casing is specifically designed to ensure minimum wear by inducing specific flow patterns. See Figures 8(a) and 8(b).

Pump out vanes will normally be provided on both the suction and drive side shrouds of the impeller. On the suction side, they have the effect of decreasing the amount of recirculation and hence wear. On the drive side, they decrease the pressure in the stuffing box area and also have the effect of keeping the particles out of that area. This helps to increase the life of the shaft seal.

Bearing frames

As previously discussed, the pump has an in-built wear allowance in it, and therefore, in order to maintain performance, the impeller must be adjustable to the suction liner. Many slurry pumps operate in dirty, dust-laden atmospheres, and therefore, heavy-duty sealing of the bearings is required. Ease of maintenance and adjustment is a prime requirement and therefore a separate bearing cartridge is normally mounted on a permanent frame. Bearings are normally grease lubricated for simplicity, but oil is also commonly used.

Double casing design, thick liners and thick section impeller all make for large overhangs. Also heavy impellers which are going to wear unevenly, all add to the loads on the shaft and bearings. Vee-belt drives are commonly used on these units and therefore these loads also need to be accommodated. Very heavy duty shaft and bearing assemblies will therefore be used often with B10 ratings in excess of 100 000 hours.

Wear areas

A high wear area is the cutwater or volute tongue and thus the clearance here is increased over normal designs to allow the flow to adjust to the casing. As slurry pumps are rarely used at or near B.P., it is essential to have a large cutwater gap. Another high wear area is the suction side wear plate, or throatbush, and this will normally be a separate replaceable item. It is quite normal to have to replace the suction wear plate without replacing the volute liner.

Most modern pumps now incorporate a volute of conventional design and also have specific features incorporated to ensure minimal wear.

Characteristic curve

The nett effect of a wide radial impeller inside a wide casing with large cutwater gap is a flat characteristic curve on a heavy-duty pump. Higher specific speeds will produce a steeper characteristic curve, but at the expense of wear performance.

Shaft sealing

This is probably the most severe problem area in a slurry pump. The three common options are:

(i) Flushed gland.

(ii) Expeller sealed, dry gland.

(iii) Mechanical seal.

Flushed gland

The full flow flushed gland is the most positive and widely accepted design for most applications where dilution of the product is permitted.

The flushing provides a two-fold function:

(i) It provides clean liquid lubrication of the packing.

(ii) It helps flush away particles from entering the stuffing box area.

The reduced flow design is used normally where there are less abrasive particles present and dilution of the product is a problem.

This option is commonly used on tailings pumps where there may be many pumps in series on a long pipeline.

Expeller seal

The purpose of this design is to keep the product away from the stuffing box whilst the pump is operating. The principle of operation is as follows:

The back vanes on the impeller generate a pressure which partially offsets the pressure generated by the main vanes in the impeller. An auxiliary impeller, commonly referred to as an expeller, operates in the expeller box cavity and generates additional pressure. The pressure in the pump casing is dependent upon the pump generated head plus the pump suction pressure. For this sealing system to operate satisfactorily, the pressure generated by the main impeller back vanes plus the impeller will balance the pump casing pressure.

The expeller seal will only operate with limited suction pressures and is only effective when the pump is operational. In process duties they can be very effective on 24 hour per day operation, but in stop/start application, this system is of doubtful benefit. The problem is that an effective seal is required when the pump is stationary.

From the foregoing, it will be apparent that no sealing water is required and then there is no dilution of the product. This system is very common in coal washing plants in the dense media circuit where the specific gravity of the product is closely controlled, and any dilution will affect the efficiency of the process.

Mechanical seals

Mechanical seals have only found limited acceptance in the slurry handling industry on abrasive applications. However, the availability of materials such as silicon carbide and tungsten carbide for seal faces has increased the usage of mechanical seals. In contrast to the chemical pump industry where the seal can be fitted into a standard stuffing box with a minimum of modifications, in the slurry market, a purpose designed seal operates typically in the main casing area. This design allows for good cooling of the seal faces and permits the seal to operate with no flushing water.

Sump Design

The majority of problems associated with slurry pumps could be eliminated if proper attention were paid to the sump and suction piping design. Major features are:

Pump should be as close as possible to the sump.

Sump should have 2 minutes pumping capacity between high and low levels.

Sump bottom should slope 30 degrees towards pump suction.

Easily removable length of pipe, incorporating flexible couplings,in the suction pipeline.

Bleed-off valve in suction line.

When handling settling type slurries a flushing connection should be incorporated.

Drives

The machining of hard metal impellers is extremely expensive. Elastomer impellers are manufactured in expensive moulds and cannot easily be reduced in diameter, as the metal frame will also have to be reduced prior to moulding. The flat characteristic curve requires that the pump is operated at the correct speed to give the required output and the simplest solution is to use Vee-belt drives. This gives a good degree of flexibility in that modifications to the process can be accommodated with a minimum of expense. Also all pumps of one size in a plant will use identical spares holdings. Vee-belt drives are commonly used up to 400 kW power ratings. Fluid drives are regularly used from 100 kW and above.

Pump performance when handling solid liquid mixtures

The principle of a centrifugal pump is to generate kinetic energy in the impeller and then convert this to potential energy, in the form of pressure, in the volute. This will occur in any fluid, liquid or gas, but not in a solid. Thus the solid particles will be given a certain kinetic energy within the impeller, but some of the energy will be lost within the mixture as the velocity of product decelerates within the volute. These losses are shown up as a head loss on the head quality curve, together with a decrease in efficiency. These are referred to as the Head Ratio (HR) and Efficiency Ratio (ER) and for all practical purposes are the same.

Example – refer to Figure 9.

The nomogram figure has been adopted for use with mixtures of solids and water in the estimation of HR and ER, known d_{50}, S and CW. The example illustrated represents a slurry of the following characteristics:

d_{50} = 0·88 mm
S = 2·0
CW = 35% yielding HR = ER = 0·85

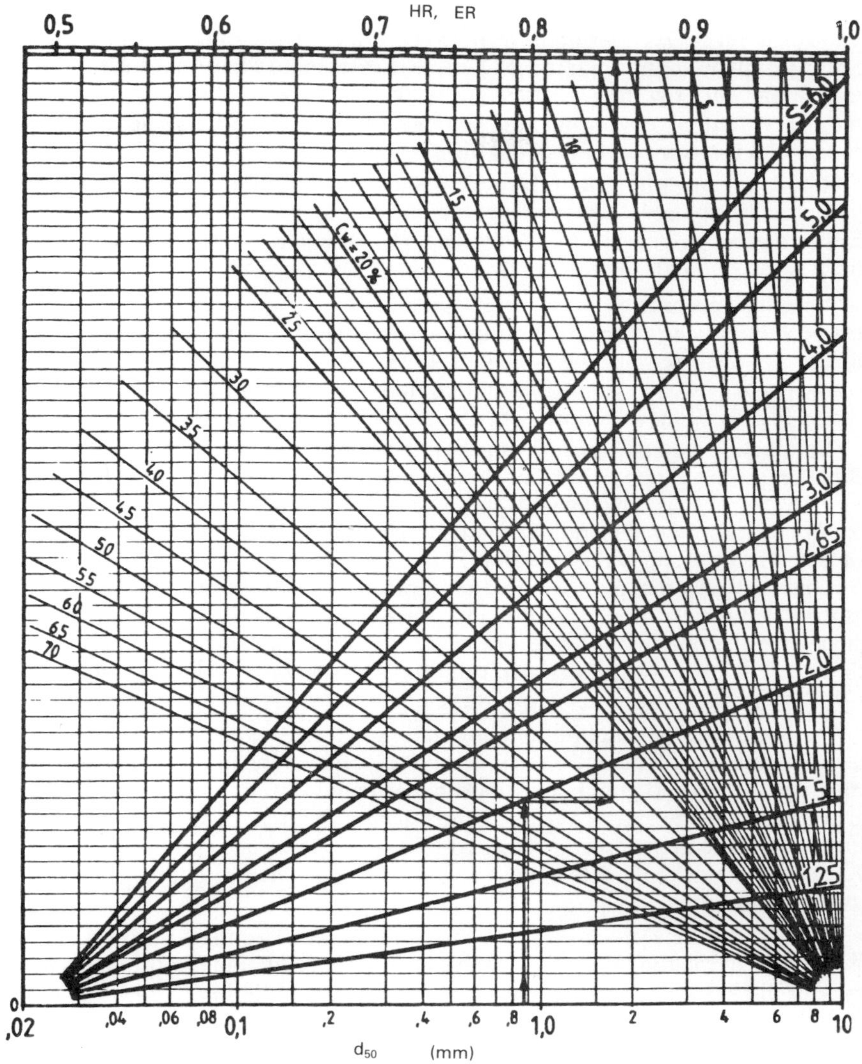

Note: This chart applies to simple mixtures of *solids and water only*. For mixtures of solids and *heavy media or liquids other than water,* refer to manufacturer.

$$HR = \frac{\text{Head on slurry}}{\text{Head on water}} \qquad ER = \frac{\text{Efficiency on slurry}}{\text{Efficiency on water}}$$

C_W = concentration by weight of solids in slurry – %
S = specific gravity of solids
d_{50} = average particle size (mm)

Figure 9
Circuitry of a boiling water reactor.

Flue gas desulphurisation (FGD)

The use of Flue Gas Desulphurisation (FGD) systems in electrical generating plants to control sulphur dioxide (SO_2) emission from fossil fuel power stations has had a significant growth in the 1970's and 80's. This is due to the growing concern over the extent of environmental damage caused by acid rain as a result of atmospheric moisture and SO_2 from burning coal.

Although many different FGD processes are available, only about ten have been commercially applied. The most common system presently in use is the wet limestone process, because of its low reagent cost and its successful application in a wide variety of high sulphur coals.

Wet limestone process

This process involves recirculation of limestone slurry to an absorber where the sulphur dioxide laden flue gas is treated. It consists of three major process sections namely (1) SO_2 Absorption, (2) Solid-liquid separation and (3) Alkaline additive system. Figure 10 shows a flowsheet of a basic wet limestone process.

The alkaline additive system consists of a limestone ball mill which converts pebble limestone to powdered limestone. Limestone ground to approximately 90% less than 200 mesh is mixed with water in an additive feed tank and then fed to the reaction tank through the additive feed pump as required to replenish the alkalinity lost in the process slurry during sulphur dioxide absorption. The fresh slurry in the reaction tank is then pumped to the spray tower by the recycle pump. This absorption slurry is sprayed against and contacted with the flue gas in the tower. It reacts with the sulphur dioxide in the gas stream to form calcium sulphite and sulphate. The process slurry is then returned and regenerated in the reaction tank by the addition of limestone before recycling to the spray tower.

The solid calcium sulphite and sulphate are removed continuously from the reaction tank by bleeding a portion of the process slurry to a thickener and centrifuge *via* a bleed pump. The thickened calcium salts precipitated at the lower part of the thickener are fed to the centrifuge by the underflow pump. The clean filtrate from the centrifuge is returned to the thickener for recycling. The clear overflow from thickener with make-up water are added to the additive feed tank for water replenishment.

The wet limestone process is proven to be economical for the large power plants. It is capable of meeting the current sulphur dioxide reduction requirements for all types of high sulphur coals. However, it has the potential disadvantages of equipment scaling, plugging, corrosion and erosion.

Limestone process with prescrubber

For the aforementioned process, a prescrubber may sometimes be needed to remove some soluble gases (in particular chlorides and fluorides) and fly ash in the flue gas before entering the sulphur dioxide absorber. This is shown in Figure 11 which is derived from the flowsheet of Figure 10. A prescrubber usually operates at low ph and wash water spray is used to purge chlorides and fluorides out of the system as dilute hydrochloric and hydrofluoric acids. After passing through a waste water treatment system, it is discharged to the sea or local water courses. However, an FGD system with prescrubber requires higher concentration and operating costs. Also more sludge is produced from the waste water treatment system. Prescrubbers are seldom used in the USA and West Germany. They are, however, used extensively in Japan for removing chlorides and keeping impurities out of the FGD system and the gypsum product. In the UK prescrubbers are required due to the very high level of chlorides in the local coals.

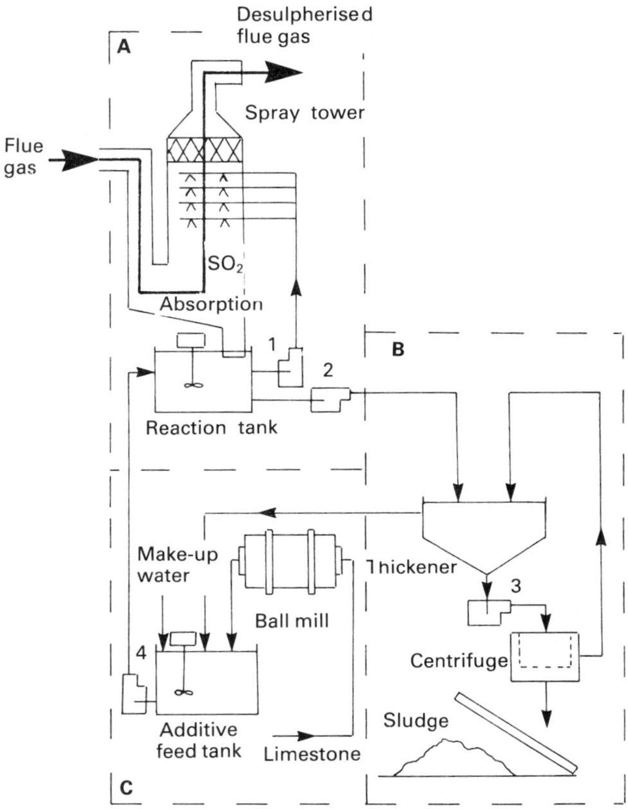

(a) Wet system – throwaway product process (sludge)
(b) For high sulphur fuel application with low level of chlorides and fluorides
(c) Low reagent cost
(d) Economical for large power plant

Process section:
A SO_2 absorption
B Solid-liquid separation
C Alkaline additive system

Pump duty:
1.Spray recycle pump
2.Slurry bleed pump
3.Thickener underflow pump
4.Additive feed pump

Figure 10
Wet limestone process without prescrubber.

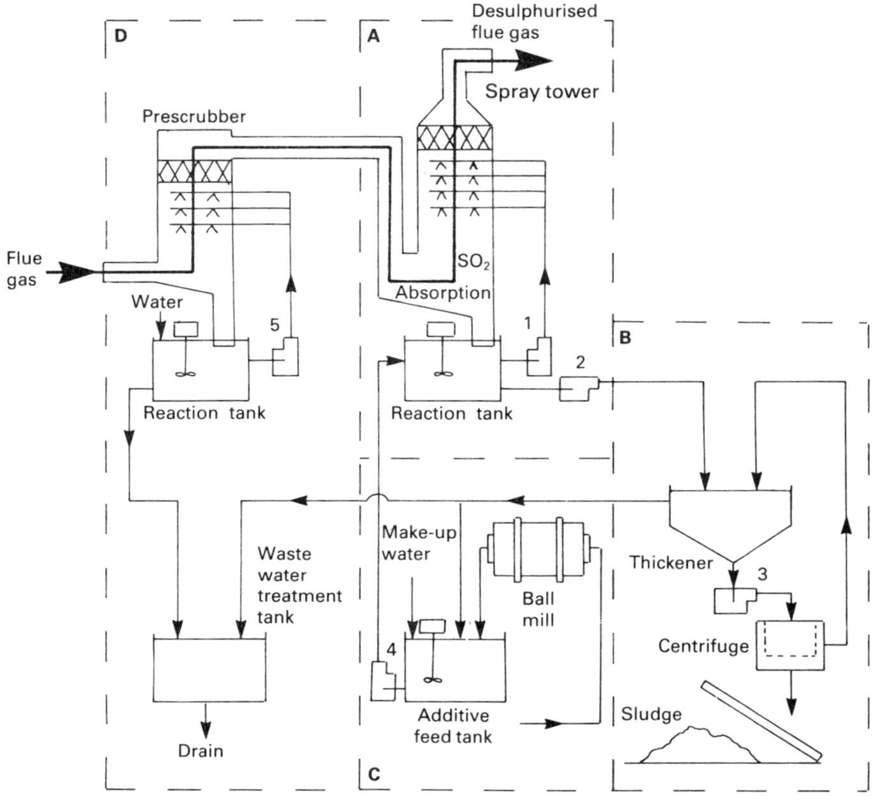

(a) Wet system – throwaway product process (sludge)
(b) For high sulphur fuel application with low level of chlorides and fluorides
(c) Low reagent cost
(d) Economical for large power plant

Process section:
A. SO_2 absorption
B Solid-liquid separation
C Alkaline additive system
D Prescrubbing

Pump duty:
1.Spray recycle pump
2.Slurry bleed pump
3.Thickener underflow pump
4.Additive feed pump
5.Prescrubber recycle pump

Figure 11
Wet limestone process with prescrubber.

Pump duties
The pump duties would be approximately as shown in Table 1.

TABLE 1 – RANGE OF SLURRY PUMP PERFORMANCE REQUIREMENTS FOR LIMESTONE PROCESS

PUMP CONDITIONS	(1) SPRAY RECYCLE PUMP	(2) SLURRY BLEED PUMP	(3) THICKENER UNDERFLOW PUMP	(4) ADDITIVE FEED PUMP	(5) PRESCRUBBER RECYCLE PUMP
Head. H (m)	20-35	20-35	10-30	30-40	20-35
Flow. Q (L/S)	400-1600	50-300	15-30	10-30	150-400
Specific Gravity (Sm)	1.05-1.15	1.05-1.15	1.15-1.30	1.15-1.25	1.00-1.05
Solids by Wt. (Cw)	8-15	10-15	20-40	15-40	2-5
Chloride Content (ppm)	300-500	300-500	500-1000	1000-10,000	10,000-40,000
Fluoride Content (ppm)					1,000-4,000
pH	4.5-6.5	4.5-6.5	4.0-7.0	6.5-14.0	0-2.0
Relative Abrasion	MODERATE	MODERATE	MODERATE	SEVERE	MODERATE
Relative Corrosion	MODERATE	MODERATE	MODERATE	MODERATE	SEVERE

FGD pumps – Materials of construction
As previously described, a pump for circulating limestone (typically) in the prescrubber and absorber will have to handle a light slurry, made up of fine particles with a variable pH between 4 to 6 absorber, and 0 to 2 prescrubber.

Most authorities specify a minimum period of maintenance free operation of 16 000 hours, or about two years continuous running. No dilution of the slurry is permitted, which in effect means that the pumps must be sealed with a mechanical seal with no flushing. Seals are normally of the cartridge type with faces of silicon carbide. In order to comply with the no flushing requirement, the seal is not mounted in a conventional stuffing box, but is set in the open area behind the impeller. Also the springs *etc*, are all stationary with the only rotating item being the hard face.

Air purging is necessary in the absorber to improve the chemical reaction, and together with the absorbed gases will get into the pump. Gases coming out of solution in the low pressure area of the impeller lead to shock loadings on the shaft and can cause major seal problems. Extra heavy-duty shafts are therefore the preferred standard.

For all systems where large particles can be kept out of the pump, lined pumps can be used, generally with all wetted parts in moulded natural rubber. Where it is impossible to keep large lumps from going through the pump, metal impellers can be used. With pH values down to 4, 27% chrome iron can be used, but, for the prescrubber a duplex stainless steel is preferred. Single casing pumps of either of the above materials, have been successfully employed, but they do not have the flexibility, nor the interchangeability of lined pumps, which can incorporate a wide mixture of materials with the minimum of cost.

Fire Pumps

IN BUILDINGS, a small fire can soon become a major disaster if it is not tackled swiftly and effectively. Primary protection in the case of fire is provided by fire extinguishers, installed hose reels and automatic sprinklers. Secondary protection can then take the form of a wet riser installation on automatic control whereby the fire brigade can reach areas of the building outside the range of its own pumping equipment.

Specifications for automatic sprinkler systems, drencher systems and water spray systems are set by various authorities and must also be approved by the insurance company covering the building.

It is essential that water is delivered to the fire at a predetermined flow rate and pressure based upon the hazard classification of the protected risk.

Industry and commerce has seen the growth of larger volume storage units utilising higher product stacking, the greater use of plastics and the continued development of high rise buildings. As a result, towns mains water supplies are no longer regarded as adequate for many fire protection installations.

In these cases, alternative water supply systems are necessary and would be provided by either one or a combination of the following:

(i) Permanent installed fire pumps.
(ii) Elevated private reservoirs.
(iii) Gravity tanks.
(iv) Pressure tanks.

To ensure maximum reliability of a fixed fire protection system under emergency conditions, wherever possible the system should be self- contained with 'in house' water supplies within the control of the occupier.

Fire pumps are used when towns mains water supplies are inadequate or unreliable and these would draw water from:

(i) A direct towns mains connection and would boost the system pressure to that required. The main must be capable of providing the necessary flow rate to meet the maximum demand. Direct connections, however, are not allowed in many areas due to local legislation designed to eliminate any source of possible contamination to the public water supply system.

(ii) A suction storage tank sized to hold the full capacity required for fire protection purposes. (A novel solution to meet the stored water requirements at some protected premises has been the installation of a swimming pool).

(iii) A reduced size storage tank designed to allow for an inflow of water from the towns mains supply over a given period of time.

(iv) A virtually inexhaustible source such as a river, canal or lake. A deep well, where the source of water is located below ground level, can also be used subject to the establishment of satisfactory aquifier characteristics.

Given adequate water supplies and knowing the fire fighting requirements of an installation the most suitable equipment available can then be selected within the parameters and design criteria of the fire protection rules to be applied.

Large vertical diesel-driven fire pump for protecting an offshore oil platform.

Pump types

Preferred types of fire pumps for fixed fire protection installations are end suction centrifugal pumps with horizontal split casing; or vertical multi-stage centrifugal (turbine) pumps. Horizontal pumps may have certain limitations – *eg* may not be permitted under certain regulations for operating on suction lift. All centrifugal pump installations should be fitted with protection against dry running. That is to say that horizontal centirfugal pumps should be installed under positive head conditions, where the minimum water level is above the centre-line of the pump.

When pumps are located above the water level of the supply source it is necessary to ensure that they are always maintained fully primed (*ie* full of water) ready for immediate use.

If the water supply is from a bore hole, then the vertical turbine type of pump is preferred.

Portable fire pumps are a standard part of fire brigade equipment, superseding the trailor mounted pump in a great number of cases. In general, these pumps are used in locations where an appliance cannot be brought to bear on the fire (*ie* there is no road access) and often must achieve high lifts from the water source. Because speed is essential the standards demand that these pumps should be able to prime to a height of 7·3 metres in under 24 seconds. This can be achieved by an exhaust gas ejector priming system which is manually operated.

Gear pumps are normally supplied for dosing foam concentrate into the main water stream on fire engines used at airports and refineries *etc*. Duties are not so demanding on other types of fire engine and a lower cost alternative may be used.

Air/water turbine-driven pumps are low capacity portable units used on offshore rigs where a gun metal-cased gear pump with bronze rotor and stainless steel shaft is driven by a geared water turbine or pelton wheel.

Portable lightweight fire pump giving 1600 l/min at 8 bar.

Pump selection

When selecting pumps for fire protection application, it is important not only to meet the duty point required but also consider the inter- relationship between pump and fire protection system characteristics.

These characteristics of a pump must be examined:

(i) The pump performance curve, which shows the pressure (head) generated by the pump against varying water flow rates. This should be a constantly falling curve (*ie* the greater the flow rate the less the pressure) to ensure satisfactory site operation when two or more pumps are working together or when high static heads are involved.

(ii) The suction lift curve, which shows lift capabilities of the pump at varying flow rates. Correct interpretation of this curve ensures that the pump will not cavitate and lose performance under site suction conditions. Rules relating to fire pumps state that the unit must be capable of a 4·5 m suction lift at the maximum anticipated flow rate.

(iii) The power curve which shows the power absorbed by the pump at varying flow rates. The power developed by the driver would normally be expected to be greater than that absorbed by the pump at the maximum anticipated flow rate.

The two primary fire protection system characteristics that have to be considered are:

(i) The water demand curve for the most remote (or highest) area of the installation.

(ii) The water demand curve for the most favourable (or lowest) area of the installation.

When considering the inter-relationship of pump and system curves, the design of the pump must be such as to provide water to the most remote area of the installation but assessment of the pump cavitation and driver power must be based on the intercept of the most favourable demand curve and the pump performance curve.

Hose reel systems

In a number of buildings, the first line of defence against a fire is a hose reel system. Secondary protection can take the form of a wet riser installation on automatic control with which the fire brigade can reach areas of the building outside the range of its own pumping equipment. In the case of sprinkler systems, specifications are governed by the Fire Officers' Committee and other bodies and must also be approved by the insurance company governing the building.

First-aid hose reels require a minimum water pressure of 2 bar at the nozzle and at this pressure will deliver 23 l/min (5 gal/min). Fire office regulations require that there should be sufficient pressure for up to three hoses at any one time with a 100% standby from the same pump, calling for a total of 136 l/min (30 gal/min). This can set particular problems in high-rise buildings in providing the required pressure at the top hose reels. In such cases a pressurised supply to the hose reels must be maintained at all times by the installations own pumping system.

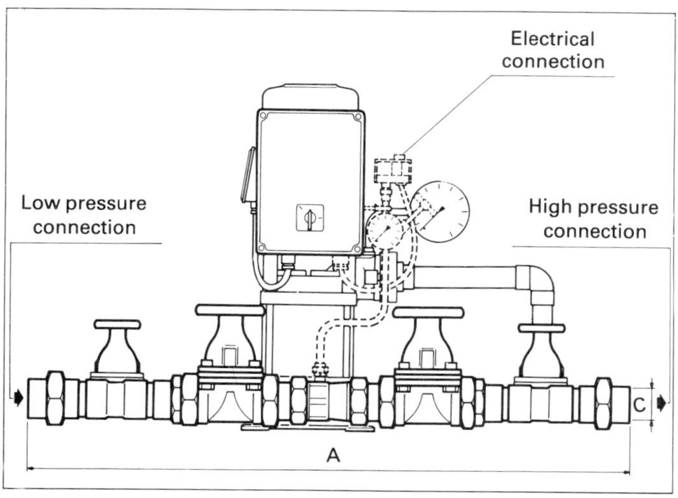

Fire-fighting booster sets.

Regulations vary from country to country and in the UK at least, from district to district but hydraulic hose reels are now standard fittings for office blocks, public buildings *etc*. When mains pressures are sufficient, some fire authorities allow the operation of hose reels from the main but normally pumps are necessary for buildings of three stories or more. Usually the duty pump is sized so that it can serve any three hose reels at once.

The hydro-pneumatic pump set is widely used in modern buildings for pumped water services and can also be adapted for fire fighting services by the addition of a flow switch to keep the pump running if there is a demand. Modern sets of this type are extremely compact using only a small accumulator.

High-rise buildings

In high-rise buildings, high pressure pumps are required to provide water to the fire protection system at the highest levels. To eliminate what would then otherwise be unacceptable high pressures at the lower floors if one common system were used, the building is divided into a number of zones at different levels, each fed by separate pumps.

Pumping methods in high rise buildings differ between the various countries but there are two commonly used arrangements:

(i) All the pumps are sited at or below the ground level. One set of pumps supplies water for fire fighting to all floors in zone 1. A second set of pumps supplies water to all floors in the higher zone two – and so on.

Pumps feeding the upper floors are generally of the multi-stage type. Alternatively, multi-stage pumps can be provided in a number of outlets, each at different pressure points along the pump in order that single units can be used to deliver water to the various zones at the lower and higher pressures required.

(ii) Pump sets are situated at intermediate levels within the building, each drawing water from an adjacent 'break' tank. The first set of pumps are sited at or below ground level and draw water from the main supply source. These pumps feed zone one fire fighting requirements and the first 'break' tank. The second set of pumps are sited at the base of zone two and draw water from the first 'break' tank. These pumps feed zone two and the next 'break' tank up the building and so on. This arrangement has the advantage that ordinary 'low pressure' pumps can be used and that no pipework is subjected to high pressure.

Operation

Where pumps form the sole source of water supply to the fire protection system, two units are normally installed, a duty pump and a standby pump. The duty pump is generally driven by an electric motor connected to an incoming power supply. The standby pump is driven by either a diesel engine or an electric motor powered from an in house generator.

On an automatically-controlled installation the inclusion of a small jockey pump ensures that any minor water leakage in the system is made up without starting the main fire pumps.

All the pumps are automatically brought into operation by pressure switches situated in the pressurised fire protection system. When the pressure in the system drops, the jockey pump operates, replenishes any small water loss and is then cut out. In the event of a fire, the jockey pump is unable to cope with the water demand and the pressure in the system continues to fall. The main duty fire pump is then called in *via* a pressure switch which transmits a signal to the electric motor starter. This pump satisfies the fire demand, increases the pressure in the system and continues to run until shutdown manually. If, due to electrical or mechanical failure, the electric motor driven pump set fails to function satisfactorily the pressure in the system will continue to fall. Another pressure switch, set at a lower pressure, then transmits a signal to the diesel engine automatic controller and the standby pump set is brought into operation. Once again this unit is designed to run until shutdown manually. The fire pumps are also fitted with separate auxiliary manual starting systems. When a remote alarm panel is installed in the building, conditions of operation and alarm signalled from the pump house equipment.

The pumping and associated electrical equipment should be installed in a pump room of ample size and located to permit properly arranged suction and discharge piping. The room should be well-heated and ventilated and together with the power sources should be protected from fire, frost, accidental damage and vandalism. Fire pumps should be operated each week to check the condition of all the equipment and should be well maintained.

High Pressure Pumping

A COMMON application of high pressure pumps is to feed a boiler, chemical reactor, or similar service. The pressure required is then that needed to feed the fluid into vessels, tubes or towers and the flow is that dictated by chemical reactor formulas, steam demand *etc*.

High pressure pumps are normally of the reciprocating type (plunger pump), where theoretically at least, the maximum pressure which can be generated is limited only by the mechanical strength of the components involved. Reciprocating pumps can handle both low and high viscosity fluids and with suitable design, can operate at both high and low temperatures. The critical part is the fluid block where extremely high forces are generated on the plungers. Also the complete fluid block and its components are subjected to fluctuating stresses.

A typical design of high pressure pump divides construction into two sections – the fluid head and the mechanical end which transforms the rotary motion of the driver into a reciprocating action to drive the fluid head plungers. To provide a seal for the high pressure chamber, a plunger seal chamber is fitted to the high pressure block in the fluid head. The plungers pass through this into the high pressure cylinders. Cooling and lubrication of these seals is important and can be done in numerous ways namely:-

(i) The pumped fluid can be allowed to weep along the plunger to perform this action on the seal.

(ii) Packing can be inpregnated with heat-conducting material and manufactured in low friction polymer and/or lubricated by greasing.

(iii) Sealed packings can either be held by an adjustable gland follow or maintained at constant pressure using spring loaded packings.

(iv) Pressure-energised seal sets (V-rings) are used which should require little or no adjustment for the majority of their life.

The plungers themselves have a significant effect on gland life. Any damage to the plungers will considerably reduce seal life. It is important that they are perfectly sized and have a smooth hard surface. It is also important in many applications that they can withstand maintenance by personnel who do not come into contact frequently with these items. In these circumstances the hardeners should not be associated with a brittle material.

Mechanical end

The action of the crankshaft is transmitted to the plunger *via* a crosshead. The crossheads are connected to the big ends by a connecting rod and bear a very close resemblance to internal combustion engine piston heads. Large diameter crossheads reciprocating a finely machined bore ensure movement of the plungers in one dimension only, *ie* backwards and forwards and further reduce packing or seal wear.

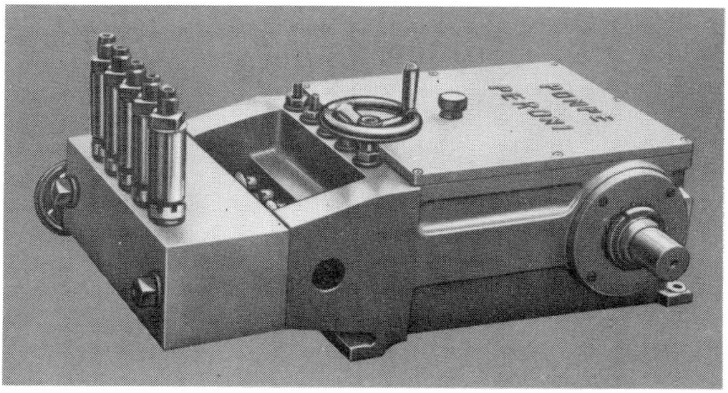

Quintuplex plunger pump with adjustable stroke.

Five-plunger pumps

To reduce the strain on all parts of many high powered pressure pumps the five-plunger pump has been developed in place of the conventional three-plunger or triplex pump. For a given crankshaft throw and speed to achieve the same flow and pressure, the plunger area can be reduced by a factor of three/five. This factor is in turn reflected in the forces on the crankshaft and all the sections of the pump between the crankshaft and the plunger. More generally, the benefits of the pump itself of obtaining the required displaced volume by using two additional plungers can be gained in any one of the following ways or by a combination of them. Comparing five- and three-plunger pumps with similar flow and pressure characteristics the five-plunger pump can have:

(i) Smaller diameter plunger and thereby reduced plunger, frame and bearing loads.

(ii) A shorter stroke, hence smaller crank flow and reduced movement about the crank axis.

(iii) A reduction in the fluctuating loads on the entire assembly.

This five-plunger design is particularly important when the pump is attached to a pulsation sensitive operation and in particular, to rigid high pressure pipework. The fluctuations in flow from a five-plunger pump are sufficiently low to allow feed direct from the pump to the pipework without generating vibrations harmful to the installation or personnel working near by. With three-plunger pumps particularly those with a high flow, there is a significant thud with each stroke that would severely disturb any installation not buffered by a pulsation dampener.

The complete system

The specification for the pump will be the flow required by the duty and the pressure required by the duty plus the pressure losses resulting from friction in the pipework. The detailed design on the pump will be a function of its requirement to withstand extremes of temperature and any special requirements of metallugy and sealing brought about the nature of the fluid.

Any high pressure pump system breaks down into three sections:

(i) The high pressure pump and pump suction feed.

(ii) High pressure pump discharge and high pressure pipe network.

(iii) Application and method of application.

It is the duty performed in the application section of the system which determines the pressure and flow of fluid required from the high pressure discharge of the system. The location and number of individual duties defines the overall layout of the network. The fluid flow will be constant from the pump to the final high pressure outlet. Fluid friction will cause the pressure available from the fluid to drop as it passes through the network. It is therefore the combination of the network and the application sections which define the pump characteristics. The pump itself will define the suction characteristics required.

The design parameters and complexity of some of these pumps is such that a minimum suction head of 3 bar (pressure) and suction filtration of 150 microns is required.

High pressure pipework

It is important in high pressure pipework design to ensure that there are no parts which, under the influence of pressure or the stresses and strains caused by pressure turned on and off can rupture in such a way as to generate projectiles. In general, the ideal pipework system will be flanged with a suitable high pressure alternative to a joint.

System start-up

In any high pressure pump system it is important to reduce the shock loads such as the severe pulsation which can occur during operation start up. it is important to ensure that all air is removed both from the pump cylinders and the pipe network. This is best done by running initially at low pressure to purge air. The pressure should then be applied steadily and in the case of a portable diesel pump, this can be done in two stages – the first is while the diesel is running slowly, by diverting the flow from either recycle or drain to the high pressure nozzle; once this has been done the speed of the diesel and hence the pump is increased until the full rate of flow is reached through the high pressure nozzle.

Typical fault finding and maintenance requirements for high pressure pumps are summarised in Table 1.

Applications

Reciprocating (plunger and piston) pumps are used extensively in the following industries:

Chemical, petrochemical and refinery industries – handling of chemicals hydrocarbons, heavy tails, slops, slurries, emulsions etc. High pressure washing of pipings, valves, tanks *etc*. Boiler feed applications.

Steel industry – hydraulic units for lubrication and cooling of rolling stands, high pressure hydraulic steel descaling, hydraulic pipe test presses.

Shipbuilding industry – boiler feed duties, high pressure water cleaning of ship tanks bottom, systems and shipyard facilities. Transfer of hydrocarbon and slurries.

TABLE 1 – FAULT-FINDING AND MAINTENANCE GUIDE FOR TYPICAL HIGH PRESSURE PISTON AND PLUNGER PUMPS

Problem	Probable Cause	Solution
Pulsation	Faulty Pulsation Dampener.	Check precharge, if low recharge it or install a new one.
Low pressure	Worn nozzle.	Replace nozzle, of proper size.
	Belt slippage.	Tighten or replace; use correct belt.
	Air leak in inlet plumbing.	Disassemble, reseal, and reassemble.
	Pressure gauge inoperative or not registering accurately.	Check with new gauge; replace worn or damaged gauge.
	Relief valve stuck, partially plugged or improperly adjusted; valve seat worn.	Clean, and adjust relief valve; check for worn and dirty valve seats.
	Inlet suction strainer clogged or improper size.	Clean. Use adequate size. Check more frequently.
	Worn piston assembly or packing. Abrasives in pumped fluid or severe cavitation. Inadequate water supply.	install proper filter. Suction at inlet manifold must be limited to lifting less than 20 feet of water.
	Fouled or dirty inlet or discharge valves.	Clean inlet and discharge valve assemblies.
	Worn inlet or discharge valves. Leaky discharge hose.	Replace worn valves, valve seats and/or discharge hose.
Pumps run extremely rough, pressure very low	Restricted inlet or air entering the inlet plumbing.	Proper size inlet plumbing; check for air tight seal.
	Inlet restrictions and/or air leaks. Damaged cup or stuck inlet or discharge valve.	Replace worn cup or cups, clean out foreign material, replace worn valves.
	Worn inlet manifold seals.	Replace worn seals.
	Worn inlet seals allow pump to draw air.	Install new inlet manifold seals.
Cylinder O-rings blown next to discharge manifold.	Pressures in excess of rated.	Check for plugged nozzle, closed valves or improperly adjusted bypass valve.
	Warped manifold.	Replace manifold.
Leakage at the cylinder O-rings at the discharge manifold and black, powdery substance in the area of the O-rings.	Loose cylinders. Cylinder motion caused by improper shimming of the discharge manifold.	Remove spacer shims on manifold studs. Do not remove too many shims or the ears of the manifold will be bowed when the manifold is retightened, causing looseness in the centre cylinder.
Water leakage from under the inlet manifold.	Worn inlet manifold seals. Leaking sleeve O-ring.	Install seals. If piston rod sleeves are scored, replace sleeves and sleeve O-rings.
Oil leak between crankcase and pumping section.	Worn crankcase piston rod seals.	Replace crankcase piston rod seals.
	Excess oil from wicks	Reduce quantity of oil per oiling.
Oil leaking in the area of crankshaft.	Worn crankshaft seal or improperly installed oil seal retainer packing, O-ring.	Remove oil seal retainer and replace damaged gasket and/or seals.
	Bad bearing.	Replace bearing.

cont...

TABLE 1 – FAULT-FINDING AND MAINTENANCE GUIDE FOR TYPICAL HIGH PRESSURE PISTON AND PLUNGER PUMPS (contd...)

Problem	Probable Cause	Solution
Excessive play in the end of the crankshaft pulley.	Worn main ball bearing from excessive tension on drive belt.	Replace ball bearing. Properly tension belt.
Water in crankcase.	May be caused by humid air condensing into water inside the crankcase.	Change oil.
	Leakage of manifold inlet seals and/or piston rod sleeve O-ring.	Replace seals, sleeve and O-rings.
Oil leaking from underside of crankcase.	Worn crankcase piston rod seals.	Replace seals, sleeve and O-rings.
Oil leaking at the rear portion of the crank-case.	Damaged or improperly installed oil gauge or crankcase rear cover O-ring, and drain plug O-ring.	Replace oil gauge or cover O-ring, and drain plug O-ring.
Oil leakage from drain plug.	Loose drain plug or worn drain plug seal.	Tighten drain plug or replace seal.
Loud knocking noise in pump.	Pulley loose on crankshaft.	Check key and tighten set screw.
	Broken or worn bearing.	Replace bearings.
Frequent or premature failure of the inlet mani-fold seals or the packing.	Scored rods or sleeves or plungers.	Replace rods and sleeves.
	Over-pressure to inlet manifold.	Reduce inlet pressure per instructions.
Short cup or packing life.	Damaged or worn chrome plating of the cylinders.	Replace cylinders.
	Damaged or worn plungers.	Replace plungers.
	Abrasive material in the fluid being pumped.	Install proper filtration on pump inlet plumbing.
	Excessive pressure and/or temperature of fluid being pumped.	Check pressures and fluid inlet temperature; be sure they are within specified range.
	Over-pressure of pumps.	Reduce pressure.
	Running pump dry.	Do not run pump without water.
	Front edge of piston sharp.	Replace with new piston.
	Chrome plating of cylinders damaged causing excessive wear of cups. May be caused by pumping acid solution.	Install new cups and cylinders. Pump only fluid compatible with chrome.
Strong surging at the inlet and low pressure on the discharge side.	Foreign particles in the inlet or discharge valve or worn inlet and/or discharge valves.	Check for smooth lap surfaces on inlet and discharge valve seats. Discharge valve seats and inlet valve seats may be lapped on a very fine oil stone; damaged cups and discharge valves cannot be lapped but must be replaced.

Pulp and paper industry – cleaning felts and general cleaning services, steam pumps for boiler feed.

Nuclear power industry – self-contained units for hydrostatic testing of reactors, pumps for boiler feed.

Civil engineering industry – air and electric motor driven for high pressure injection of liquid mortar and cement grout, for reinforcing and waterproofing tunnels, mines, dams, foundations, canals, bulkheads, walls *etc*. Pumps for aquaducts.

Pipeline industry – self-contained units for pipeline cleaning, filling and hydraulic yield testing.

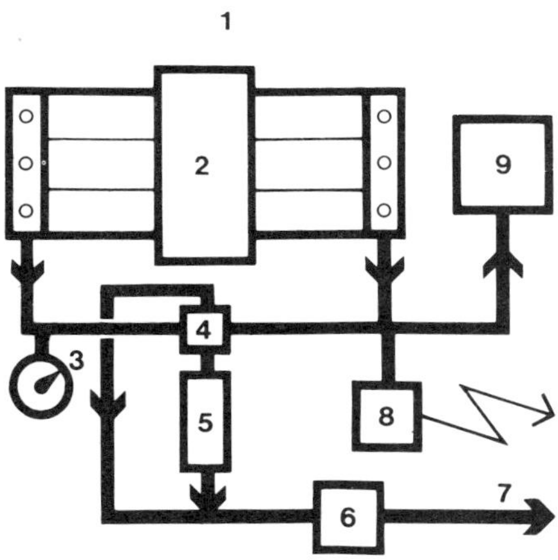

1. Water intake.
2. High pressure pump.
3. Pressure meter.
4. Bypass valve – ensures maximum pressure when operating on high pressure.
5. Injector – adds cleaning fluids.
6. Flow control – switches off the burner in case of failing water flow.
7. Water under pressure for the heating spiral.
8. Pressure switch – switches off the burner when the spray gun is closed.
9. Pressure release valve – opens when the spray gun is closed or if, for instance, the nozzle is fouled.

Figure 1
Typical high-pressure cleaner unit incorporating safety features.

High pressure water jetting

High pressure water jetting is another particular application of high pressure (water) pumps. This utilises pressures up to 1000 bar (14 500 lb/in^2) with jet speeds up to 400 m/sec (1300 ft/sec) and minimal usage of water.

It is now widely employed for a variety of cleaning operations in the marine, construction, process and manufacturing industries, as well as for other purposes. By correct selection of nozzles, accessories and power sources, the impact of fine high velocity water jets can remove deposits which defy mechanical cutting tools without any damage to underlying materials.

One of the more difficult applications to define is the removal of fouling, scale and dirt from surfaces ranging from boiler tubes, chemical reactors etc., to sluice gates and ships hulls using high pressure jetting. Unless there is previous experience, the flow and pressure required will have to be evaluated by trial. These two variables are considerably effected by the stand off distance of the high pressure jetting nozzle. The stand-off distance is the gap between the surface to be cleaned and the discharge nozzle. The temperature of the fluid is a further factor common to both chemical reactors and jet cleaning.

Editorial Index

D

E

N

O

P

R